J. Lytton

ANNUAL REVIEW OF
BIOPHYSICS AND
BIOMOLECULAR STRUCTURE

very sensitive, not only to diffusion, but also to relative interactions between colliding spin labels, including how they are influenced by their milieu (14, 50). Also, any nonideal mixing of the spin labels will influence the probability of bimolecular collisions (14, 50).

The basic idea underlying SS imaging methods is that the spatial dependence of the ESR spectral intensity can be represented as a pseudo-object in a space consisting of an intrinsic frequency coordinate (the spectral dimension) and one or more spatial dimensions. The imaging method used is the multiple stepped gradient (19, 45) algorithm. In this technique, one sweeps through the ESR spectrum repeatedly, each time with a different constant magnetic field gradient. At each field gradient, $B'(\alpha)$, the spectrum obtained is the projection of the pseudo-object after it is rotated through some angle α, given by $B'(\alpha)$ $= (\Delta I/\Delta x)\cot\alpha$ where ΔI is the spectral width and Δx is the size of the object. Once projections are collected for a set of rotation angles α, the image of the spectral-spatial object can be reconstructed using standard tomographic methods (19, 44, 77). In the diffusion experiment, the concentration distribution obtained by the multiple stepped gradient method was analyzed with Equation 6 for a Gaussian initial distribution given by Equation 8. The resultant Gaussian has a variance $\sigma^2(t) = \delta^2 + 2D_{\text{macro}}t$. Here t was 10 h, corresponding to an average molecular displacement, $\Delta x = (2Dt)^{1/2} \approx 400$ μm and $D_{\text{macro}} = (2.3 \pm 0.4) \times 10^{-8}$ cm^2 s^{-1} at 22°C in agreement with the result from DID-ESR (68).

The concentration-dependent ESR line broadening arises from HE and from electron-electron dipolar (EED) interactions between the electron spins on neighboring spin probe molecules. According to modern HE theory (50), the Heisenberg spin exchange contribution to the line width, assuming isotropic three-dimensional Brownian diffusion, is given for ^{14}N nitroxides by

$$T_2^{-1}(\text{HE}) = (8\pi/3) \, dD_{\text{micro}}N_A C f^*, \qquad\qquad 15.$$

where d is the encounter distance for two spins, D_{micro} is the microscopic spin-label self-diffusion coefficient, N_A is the Avogadro number, C is the molar concentration of spins, and f^* is a partition function given by $(f^*)^{-1} = d \int_d^\infty \exp[U(r)/kT]r^{-2} \, dr$, in which $U(r)$ is a mean-field pair interaction potential for the spin probe molecules. By contrast, the EED contribution to the linewidth for isotropic motion is (50):

$$T_2^{-1}(\text{EED}) \approx \hbar^2\gamma_e^4 \left(\frac{19\pi}{405}\right)\left(\frac{N_A C}{dD_{\text{micro}}}\right)\left[f^* \exp\frac{U(d)}{kT}\right]^{-1} \qquad 16.$$

Equations 15 and 16 express the fact that the linewidth contributions from both HE and EED are linear with concentration in the limit of ideal solutions.

To make Equations 15 and 16 applicable to labeled lipids in membranes, the value of C was doubled to account for collisions between spin labels on different sides of the bilayer, following Sachse et al, because the nitroxide moiety is attached close to the end of one of the 16-PC acyl chains. These equations were also corrected for lateral (two-dimensional) diffusion in membranes by replacing the D_{micro} with $(2/3)D_{micro}$ (2, 50). With the assumption of Arrhenius behavior for D_{micro} [i.e. $D_{micro} = D^0 \exp(-E_{act}/kT)$], the temperature dependence of the concentration-dependent linewidth was used to separate $T_2^{-1}(HE)$ and $T_2^{-1}(EED)$. This separation leads to $E_{act} = 6.8 \pm 0.4$ kcal/mol, and $U(d) = 1.6 \pm 0.1$ kcal/mol. The result for E_{act} compares favorably with the value of $E_{act} = 6.3$ kcal/mol from D_{macro} measured for this system with DID-ESR (68). At 22°C, $D_{\perp,micro} = (1.0 \pm 0.4) \times 10^{-7}$ cm^2 s^{-1}. By comparison, linewidth studies by Sachse et al (60) yielded $D_{micro} \approx 1.2 \times 10^{-7}$ cm^2 s^{-1} (from the HE contribution) at 30°C for 16-PC in DMPC.

These measurements of D_{macro} and D_{micro} show that D_{micro} is about four times greater than D_{macro}. This result is in agreement with previous observations that D measured with microscopic techniques is larger than D measured with macroscopic techniques (39, 55). Pfeiffer et al (55) found that D_{micro} measured by quasielastic neutron scattering is approximately twofold larger than D_{macro} measured using FRAP in dipalmitoylphosphatidylcholine (DPPC) model membranes. Saxton (61) postulated that such discrepancies could result from different sample preparation techniques that produce inhomogeneous defects in the model membrane. However, the spectral-spatial measurements of D_{micro} and D_{macro} were carried out on the same sample.

The discrepancy between D_{macro} and D_{micro} may reflect important details in the microscopic molecular dynamics. Shin et al (67) point out that: (a) The d corresponding to the rigid diameter of the lipid may require correction for chain wagging (79). (b) The more subtle effects of two-dimensional motions in a plane and details of membrane structure may need to be included in the analysis of HE and EED (37, 80). The role played by nonideal mixing in the dynamic structure can also be important. Vaz & Almeida (73) have also considered discrepancies between D_{macro} and D_{micro} in the context of the free volume model.

In summary, the SS method provides an unambiguous comparison between D_{macro} and D_{micro} that eliminates possible artifacts resulting from differences in probe molecules, sample preparation, hydration, etc, which are otherwise inevitable when D_{micro} and D_{macro} are measured using two different methods. We have suggested "such simultaneous measurements on various systems will provide an important tool to study the microscopic dynamic structure of membranes, and it will be extremely useful in the development of better models for molecular dynamics in membranes" (67, p. 955).

FOURIER TRANSFORM ESR IMAGING

Even though DID-ESR is now a well-developed technique, future developments are expected. For the most part, investigators have performed ESR imaging using cw methods. Researchers predominantly use the Fourier transform (FT) method in NMR imaging, but this method has been difficult to combine with ESR because of its higher frequencies, much shorter relaxation times, and much greater spectral bandwidths. FT-ESR imaging offers a number of advantages over cw methods, including faster data acquisition and more straightforward data analysis with fewer artifacts. A particulary nice feature of FT-ESR imaging applied to the DID-ESR experiment is that the Fourier-transformed spectra, $\hat{I}_g(\kappa,t)$ and $\hat{I}_0(\kappa)$ of Equations 2a and b are obtained directly by collecting the free induction decay (or else the echo decay). This permits one to obtain the Fourier-transformed concentration distribution $\hat{C}(\kappa,t)$ directly from the experiment, unlike in cw-DID-ESR where one must first Fourier transform $I_g(\xi,t)$ and $I_0(\xi)$ (17, 18, 47).

Spectral-spatial imaging, in particular, would benefit from FT imaging methods. FT imaging is much more flexible with respect to the possible combination of dimensions, both spectral and spatial, that can be presented in the final image. For example, one could perform two-(spectral) dimensional ESR in combination with one or more spatial dimensions. Thus modern two-dimensional Fourier transform (2D-FT)-ESR methods (28, 29, 53, 54) could enable ESR to measure molecular dynamics as a function of spatial coordinate.

Recent efforts in these laboratories have overcome the significant difficulties of FT-ESR imaging, and the method has been applied to spectral-spatial ESR imaging (17). In addition, we (18) have extended these techniques to spatially resolved two-dimensional electron-electron double resonance (2D-ELDOR). 2D-ELDOR is a form of two-dimensional exchange spectroscopy that is very sensitive to cross-relaxation processes such as HE (28, 29). Spatial resolution, would, for example, permit one to study microscopic molecular dynamics in inhomogeneous media. Most interesting is the potential application of

2D-ELDOR to the simultaneous study of both macroscopic and microscopic translational diffusion. This is likely to be an improvement over the cw method described above, in which the (inhomogeneously broadened) ESR linewidths are measured in the spectral dimension and the HE and EED are estimated from their concentration and temperature dependence to yield D_{micro} (30, 50). We have shown that 2D-ELDOR is a natural way to directly measure HE from the cross-peaks (28, 29). Thus, spatially resolved 2D-ELDOR could be the method of choice for comparative studies of microscopic vs macroscopic diffusion.

ACKNOWLEDGMENTS

I thank my coworkers, especially Drs. YK Shin and JK Moscicki for their considerable help and advice. This research was supported by NIH Grant GM25862 and NSF Grants CHE 9004552 and DMR 92-10638.

Literature Cited

1. Alecio MR, Golan DE, Veatch WR, Rando RR. 1982. Use of fluorescent cholesterol derivative to measure lateral mobility of cholesterol. *Proc. Natl. Acad. Sci. USA* 79:5171–74
2. Bales RL, Swenson JA, Schwartz RN. 1974. EPR studies of Heisenberg spin exchange in a nematic liquid crystal. *Mol. Cryst. Liq. Cryst.* 28:143–53
3. Berliner LJ, Fujii H. 1986. EPR imaging of diffusional processes in biologically relevant polymers. *J. Mag. Res.* 69:68–72
4. Berner B, Kivelson D. 1979. The electron spin resonance linewidth method for measuring diffusion. A critique. *J. Phys. Chem.* 83:1406–12
5. Cleary DA, Shin Y-K, Schneider DJ, Freed JH. 1988. Rapid determination of translational diffusion coefficients using ESR imaging. *J. Magn. Res.* 79:474–92
6. Cohen MH, Turnbull D. 1959. Molecular transport in liquids and glasses. *J. Chem. Phys.* 31:1164–69
7. Crank J. 1976. *The Mathematics of Diffusion.* Oxford: The Clarendon
8. Crawford MS, Gerstein BC, Kuo, A-
L, Wade CG. 1980. Diffusion in rigid bilayer membranes. Use of combined pulse and multiple pulse gradient techniques in nuclear magnetic resonance. *J. Am. Chem. Soc.* 102:3728–32
9. Demsar F, Cevc P, Schara M. 1986. Diffusion of spin probes in tissues measured by field-gradient EPR. *J. Mag. Res.* 69:258–63
10. Demsar F, Swartz HM, Schara M. 1988. Use of field gradient EPR to measure diffusion of nitroxides in tissues. *Mag. Res. Med. Biol.* 1:17–25
11. Demsar F, Walczak T, Morse PD II, Bacic G, Zolnai Z, et al. 1988. Detection of diffusion and distribution of oxygen by fast-scan EPR imaging. *J. Mag. Res.* 76:224–31
12. Devaux P, McConnell HM. 1972. Lateral diffusion in spin-labeled phosphatidylcholine multilayers. *J. Am. Chem. Soc.* 94:4475–81
13. Diogo AC, Martins AF. 1982. Order parameter and temperature dependence of the dynamic viscosity of nematic liquid crystals. *J. Phys.* 43:779–86
14. Eastman MP, Bruno GV, Freed JH.

ESR study. PhD thesis, Cornell Univ., Ithaca, NY. 170 pp.

66. Shin YK, Budil DE, Freed JH. 1993. Thermodynamics and dynamics of phosphatidylcholine-cholesterol mixed model membranes in the liquid crystalline state: effects of water. *Biophys. J.* 65:1283–94

67. Shin YK, Ewert U, Budil DE, Freed JH. 1991. Microscopic versus macroscopic diffusion in model membranes by ESR spectral-spatial imaging. *Biophys. J.* 59:950–57

68. Shin YK, Freed JH. 1989. Dynamic imaging of lateral diffusion by electron spin resonance and study of rotational dynamics in model membranes. Effect of cholesterol. *Biophys. J.* 55:537–50

69. Shin YK, Freed JH. 1989. Thermodynamics of phosphatidylcholine-cholesterol mixed model membranes in the liquid crystalline state studied by the orientational order parameter. *Biophys. J.* 56:1093–1100

70. Shin YK, Moscicki JK, Freed JH. 1990. Dynamics of phosphatidylcholine-cholesterol mixed model membranes in the liquid crystalline state. *Biophys. J.* 57:445–59

71. Stemp EDA, Eaton GR, Eaton SS, Maltempo MM. 1987. Spectral-spatial EPR imaging and transport of radicals in nonuniform media. *J. Phys. Chem.* 91:6467–69

72. Trauble H, Sackmann E. 1972. Phase transition of lipid model membranes. III. Structure of a steroid-lecithin system below and above the lipid-phase transition. *J. Am. Chem. Soc.* 94: 4499–4510

73. Vaz WLC, Almeida PF. 1991. Microscopic vs. macroscopic diffusion in one-component fluid phase lipid bilayer membranes. *Biophys. J.* 60: 1553–54

74. Vaz WLC, Clegg RM, Hallmann D. 1985. Translational diffusion of lipids in liquid crystalline phase phosphatidylcholine multilayers. A comparison of experiment with theory. *Biochemistry* 24:781–86

75. Wade CG. 1977. NMR relaxation in thermotropic liquid crystals. *Annu. Rev. Phys. Chem.* 28:47–73

76. Woods RK, Dobrucki JW, Glockner JF, Morse PD II, Swartz HM. 1989. Spectral-spatial ESR imaging as a method of noninvasive biological oximetry. *J. Magn. Reson.* 85:50–59

77. Woods RK, Hyslop WB, Marr RB, Lauterbur PC. 1991. Image reconstruction. See Ref 16, pp. 92–117

78. Wu ES, Jacobson K, Papahadjopoulous D. 1977. Lateral diffusion in phospholipid multilayers measured by fluorescence recovery after photobleaching. *Biochemistry* 16:3936–41

79. Yin JJ, Feix JB, Hyde JS. 1990. Mapping of collision frequencies for stearic acid spin labels by saturation-recovery EPR. *Biophys. J.* 58:713–20

80. Zientara GP, Freed JH. 1979. Chemically-induced dynamic spin polarization in two dimensional systems: theoretical predictions. *J. Chem. Phys.* 71: 3861–79

unsaturation in the fluid phase. *Biochim. Biophys. Acta* 854:307–17

41. Lee AG. 1977. Lipid phase transitions and phase diagrams I. Lipid phase diagrams. *Biochim. Biophys. Acta* 472: 237–81

42. Lindbloom GL, Johansson BA, Arvidson G. 1981. Effect of cholesterol in membranes. Pulsed nuclear magnetic resonance measurements of lipid lateral diffusion. *Biochemistry* 20:2204–7

43. Lis LJ, McAlister M, Fuller N, Rand RP, Parsegian VA. 1982. Interactions between neutral phospholipid bilayer membranes. *Biophys. J.* 37:657–65

44. Maltempo MM, Eaton SS, Eaton GR. 1987. Spectral-spatial two-dimensional EPR imaging. *J. Magn. Reson.* 72:449–55

45. Maltempo MM, Eaton SS, Eaton GR. 1988. Reconstruction of spectral-spatial two-dimensional EPR images from incomplete sets of projections without prior knowledge of the component spectra. *J. Magn. Res.* 77:75–83

46. Moscicki JK, Shin YK, Freed JH. 1989. Dynamic imaging of diffusion by ESR. *J. Mag. Res.* 84:554–72

47. Moscicki JK, Shin YK, Freed JH. 1991. The method of dynamic imaging of diffusion by EPR. See Ref. 16, pp. 189–219

48. Moscicki JK, Shin YK, Freed JH. 1993. Translational diffusion in a smectic-a phase by ESR imaging: the free-volume model. *J. Chem. Phys.* 99:643–59

49. Mueller HJ, Galla HJ. 1987. Chain length and pressure dependence of lipid translational diffusion. *Eur. Biophys. J.* 14:485–91

50. Nayeem A, Rananavare SR, Sastry VSS, Freed JH. 1989. Heisenberg spin exchange and molecular diffusion in liquid crystals. *J. Chem. Phys.* 91: 6887–6905

51. Noack F. 1984. NMR studies of self-diffusion in some homologous nematic liquid crystals. *Mol. Cryst. Liq. Cryst.* 113:247–68

52. Pali T, Ebert B, Horvath LI. 1992. Dynamic imaging and spatially localized ESR spectroscopy of oriented phospholipid multilayers. *J. Magn. Res.* 96:491–500

53. Patyal BR, Crepeau RH, Gamliel D, Freed JH. 1990. Two-dimensional fourier transform ESR in the slow-motional and rigid limits: SECSY-ESR. *Chem. Phys. Lett.* 175:445–52

54. Patyal BR, Crepeau RH, Gamliel D, Freed JH. 1990. Two-dimensional fourier transform ESR in the slow-motional and rigid limits: 2D-ELDOR. *Chem. Phys. Lett.* 175:453–60

55. Pfeiffer WG, Schlossbauer G, Knoll W, Farago B, Steyer A, et al. 1988. Ultracold neutron scattering study of local lipid mobility in bilayer membranes. *J. Phys. France* 49:1077–82

56. Popp CA, Hyde JS. 1982. Electron-electron double resonance and saturation-recovery studies of nitroxide electron and nuclear spin-lattice relaxation times and Heisenberg exchange rates: lateral diffusion in dimyristoyl phosphatidylcholine. *Proc. Natl. Acad. Sci. USA* 79:2559–63

57. Prausnitz JM, Lichtenthaler RN, Azevido EG. 1986. *Molecular Thermodynamics of Fluid-Phase Equilibria*. Englewood Cliffs: Prentice-Hall. 2nd ed.

58. Rananavare SB, Pisipati VGKM, Freed JH. 1987. Nematic ordering near a tricritical nematic-smectic A phase transition. *Chem. Phys. Lett.* 140:255–62

59. Rubenstein JLR, Smith BA, McConnell HM. 1979. Lateral diffusion in binary mixtures of cholesterol and phosphatidylcholines. *Proc. Natl. Acad. Sci. USA* 76:15–18

60. Sachse J, King DM, Marsh D. 1987. ESR determination of lipid translational diffusion coefficients at low spin-label concentrations in biological membranes, using exchange broadening, exchange narrowing, and dipole-dipole interactions. *J. Magn. Res.* 71: 385–404

61. Saxton MJ. 1989. Lateral diffusion in an archipelago. Distance dependence of the diffusion coefficient. *Biophys. J.* 516:615–22

62. Schneider DJ, Freed JH. 1989. Calculating slow motional magnetic resonance spectra: a user's guide. In *Biological Magnetic Resonance*, ed. LJ Berliner, J Reuben, 8:1–76. New York: Plenum

63. Seelig J. 1977. Deuterium magnetic resonance; theory and application to lipid membranes. *Q. Rev. Biophys.* 10: 353–418

64. Shimshik EJ, McConnell HM. 1973. Lateral phase separation in phospholipid membranes. *Biochemistry* 12: 2351–60

65. Shin YK. 1990. *Thermodynamics and dynamics of phosphatidylcholine-cholesterol mixed model membranes: an*

1970. ESR studies of Heisenberg spin exchange II. Effects of radical charge and size. *J. Chem. Phys.* 52:2511–22
15. Eastman MP, Kooser RG, Das MR, Freed JH. 1969. Studies of Heisenberg spin exchange in ESR I. Linewidth and saturation effects. *J. Chem. Phys.* 51: 2690–2709
16. Eaton GR, Eaton SS, Ohno K, eds. 1991. *EPR Imaging and in Vivo EPR.* Boca Raton: CRC Press. 321 pp.
17. Ewert U, Crepeau RH, Dunnam CR, Xu D, Lee S, Freed JH. 1991. Fourier transform electron spin resonance imaging. *Chem. Phys. Lett.* 184:25–33
18. Ewert U, Crepeau RH, Lee S, Dunnam CR, Xu D, Freed JH. 1991. Spatially resolved two-dimensional Fourier transform ESR. *Chem. Phys. Lett.* 184:34–40
19. Ewert U, Herrling T. 1986. Spectrally resolved EPR tomography with stationary gradient. *Chem. Phys. Lett.* 129:516–20
20. Fahey PF, Koppel DE, Barker LS, Wolf DE, Elson EL, et al. 1976. Lateral diffusion in planar lipid bilayers. *Nature* 195:305–06
21. Feigenson GW. 1989. Calcium ion binding between lipid bilayers; the 4-component system of phosphatidylserine, phosphatidylcholine, calcium chloride, and water. *Biochemistry* 28: 1270–78
22. Feix JB, Yin JJ, Hyde JS. 1987. Interactions of ^{14}N:^{15}N stearic acid spin-label pairs: effects of host lipid alkyl chain length and unsaturation. *Biochemistry* 26:3850–55
23. Ferrarini A, Nordio PL, Moro GJ, Crepeau RH, Freed JH. 1989. A theoretical model of phospholipid dynamics in membranes. *J. Chem. Phys.* 91: 5707–21
24. Freed JH. 1976. Theory of slow tumbling ESR spectra for nitroxides. In *Spin Labeling. Theory and Applications,* ed. LJ Berliner, pp. 53–132. New York: Academic
25. Galtseva EU, Yakimchenko YO, Lebedev YS. 1983. Diffusion of free radicals as studied by tomography. *Chem. Phys. Lett.* 99:301–4
26. Gennis RD. 1989. *Biomembranes, Molecular Structure and Function.* New York: Springer-Verlag. 533 pp.
27. Golan DE, Alecio MR, Veatch WR, Rando RR. 1984. Lateral mobility of phospholipid and cholesterol in the human erythrocyte membrane: effect of protein-lipid interactions. *Biochemistry* 23:332–39
28. Gorcester J, Freed JH. 1988. Two-dimensional Fourier transform ESR correlation spectroscopy. *J. Chem. Phys.* 88:4678–93
29. Gorcester J, Millhauser GL, Freed JH. 1990. Two-dimensional electron spin resonance. In *Modern Pulsed and Continuous-Wave ESR,* ed. L Kevan, MK Bowman, pp. 119–94. New York: Wiley
30. Gorcester J, Rananavare SB, Freed JH. 1989. Two-dimensional electron-electron double resonance and electron spin-echo study of solute dynamics in smectics. *J. Chem. Phys.* 90: 5764–86
31. Hawlicka E, Reimschuessel W. 1981. Component self-diffusion in liquid binary solutions. *Ber. Bunsenges. Phys. Chem.* 85:210–14
32. Hornak JP, Moscicki JM, Freed JH. 1984. *Translational diffusion coefficients by ESR imaging technique.* Presented at 7th Int. EPR Symp. Rocky Mountain Conference, Denver CO
33. Hornak JP, Moscicki JM, Schneider DJ, Freed JH. 1986. Diffusion coefficients in anisotropic fluids by ESR imaging of concentration profiles. *J. Chem. Phys.* 84:3387–95
34. Ipsen JH, Karlstrom GK, Mouritsen OE, Wennerstrom H, Zuckermann MJ. 1987. Phase equilibrium in the phosphatidylcholine-cholesterol system. *Biochim. Biophys. Acta* 905:162–72
35. Jan N, Lookman T, Pink DA. 1984. On computer simulation methods used to study models of two-component bilayers. *Biochemistry* 23:3227–32
36. Kar L, Ney-Igner E, Freed JH. 1985. ESR and electron-spin-echo studies of oriented multilayers of L_α-phosphatidylcholine water systems. *Biophys. J.* 48:569–93
37. Korb J, Ahadi PM, Zientara GP, Freed JH. 1987. Dynamic effects of pair correlation functions on spin relaxation by translational diffusion in two-dimensional fluids. *J. Chem. Phys.* 86: 1125–30
38. Krüger, GJ. 1982. Diffusion in thermotropic liquid crystals. Phys. Rep. 82:229–69
39. Kuo AL, Wade CG. 1979. Lipid lateral diffusion by pulsed nuclear magnetic resonance. *Biochemistry* 18:2300–8
40. Kusumi A, Subczynski WK, Pasenkiewicz-Gierula M, Hyde JH, Merkle H. 1986. Spin label studies on phosphatidylcholine-cholesterol membranes: effect of alkyl chain length and

ANNUAL REVIEW OF BIOPHYSICS AND BIOMOLECULAR STRUCTURE

VOLUME 23, 1994

ROBERT M. STROUD, *Editor*
University of California, San Francisco

CHARLES R. CANTOR, *Associate Editor*
Center for Advanced Biotechnology

THOMAS D. POLLARD, *Associate Editor*
The Johns Hopkins University School of Medicine

ANNUAL REVIEWS INC. 4139 EL CAMINO WAY P.O. BOX 10139 PALO ALTO, CALIFORNIA 94303-0139

ANNUAL REVIEWS INC.
Palo Alto, California, USA

International Standard Serial Number: 1056-8700
International Standard Book Number: 0-8243-1823-4
Library of Congress Catalog Card Number: 79-188446

Annual Review and publication titles are registered trademarks of Annual
Reviews Inc.

∞ The paper used in this publication meets the minimum requirements of
American National Standard for Information Sciences—Permanence of Paper
for Printed Library Materials, ANSI Z39.48-1984.

Annual Reviews Inc. and the Editors of its publications assume no responsibility for the statements expressed by the contributors to this *Review*.

TYPESET BY MARYLAND COMPOSITION CO., INC.
PRINTED AND BOUND IN THE UNITED STATES OF AMERICA

PREFACE

The *Annual Review of Biophysics and Biomolecular Structure* provides the forum for reviews that focus on the molecular-level understanding of biology, the most fundamental level at which we can comprehend biological phenomena. Annual Reviews in general place both historical and recent developments in perspective alongside a critical appraisal of the present status of the subject—reviews on a classic rather than popular level. Uniquely, the *Annual Review of Biophysics and Biomolecular Structure* emphasizes understanding of biological and cellular phenomena at levels that extend to the quantum mechanical, where the most exacting forefront science seeks definitive explanations for mechanisms in biology. For those interested in entering the field of biophysics, we hope the *Review's* articles provide an orientation. More established scientists will find that our chapters heighten their awareness of developments in fields close to their own. The Editorial Committee intends to retain this focus and represent these interests, and to maintain this Annual Review series as the most highly cited in its subject area.

On behalf of the Editorial Committee, I would like to thank the former Editor, Donald Engelman, and the out-going Associate Editors, Charles Cantor and Thomas Pollard, for their years of dedicated service to the *Review*. I also thank the authors for their contributions, as well as the Production Editor, Amanda Suver, and the staff of Maryland Composition Company for their efforts in the production of the volume.

Robert M. Stroud
Editor

Annual Review of Biophysics and Biomolecular Structure
Volume 23, 1994

CONTENTS

DYNAMICS

EMERGING TECHNIQUES

SOME RELATED ARTICLES IN OTHER *ANNUAL REVIEWS*

From the *Annual Review of Biochemistry,* Volume 63 (1994):

Quinoenzymes in Biology, J. P. Klinman and D. Mu

The Centrosome and Cellular Organization, D. R. Kellogg, M. Moritz, and B. M. Alberts

Homeodomain Proteins, W. J. Gehring, M. Affolter, and T. Bürglin

Control of RNA Initiation and Elongation at the HIV-1 Promoter, K. A. Jones and B. M. Peterlin

Structures and Functions of Multiligand and Lipoprotein Receptors: Macrophage Scavenger Receptors and LDL Receptor-Related Protein (LRP), M. Krieger and J. Herz

Function and Structure Relationships in DNA Polymerases, C. M. Joyce and T. A. Steitz

The Retroviral Enzymes, R. A. Katz and A. M. Skalka

Nitrogenase: A Nucleotide-Dependent Molecular Switch, J. B. Howard and D. C. Rees

Structure, Function, Regulation, and Assembly of D-Ribulose-1,5-Bisphosphate Carboxylase/Oxygenase, F. C. Hartman and M. R. Harpel

Intermediate Filaments: Structure, Dynamics, Function, and Disease, E. Fuchs and K. Weber

Structure and Function of G Protein–Coupled Receptors, C. D. Strader, T. M. Fong, M. R. Tota, D. Underwood, and R. A. F. Dixon

Role of Chromatin Structure in the Regulation of Transcription by RNA Polymerase II, S. M. Paranjape, R. T. Kamakaka, and J. T. Kadonaga

From the *Annual Review of Cell Biology,* Volume 9 (1993):

Peptide Binding to Major Histocompatibility Complex Molecules, L. D. Barber and P. Parham

Tumor Necrosis Factor, Other Cytokines, and Disease, K. J. Tracey and A. Cerami

Transcriptional Repression in Eukaryotes, B. M. Herschbach and A. D. Johnson

Role of the Major Heat Shock Proteins as Molecular Chaperones, C. Georgopoulos and W. J. Welch

From the *Annual Review of Microbiology,* Volume 48 (1994):

Biology and Genetics of Prion Diseases, S. B. Prusiner

Developing Marine Bacterial Resources: Ecological Perspectives, P. R. Jensen and W. Fenical

Genetics and Biochemistry of Dehalogenating Enzymes, D. B. Janssen, F. Pries, and J. R. van der Ploeg

(*continued*)

From the *Annual Review of Pharmacology and Toxicology*, Volume 34 (1994):

Putative Mechanisms of Toxicity of 3-Methylindole: From Free Radical to Pneumotoxicosis, T. M. Bray and K. S. Emmerson

DNA Topoisomerases: Essential Enzymes and Lethal Targets, A. Y. Chen and L. F. Liu

β-Amyloid Formation as a Potential Therapeutic Target for Alzheimer's Disease, B. Cordell

Permeation Properties of Neurotransmitter Transporters, H. A. Lester, S. Mager, M. W. Quick, and J. L. Corey

The Cholinesterases: From Genes to Proteins, P. Taylor and Z. Radić

α_1-Adrenergic Receptor Subtypes, K. P. Minneman and T. A. Esbenshade

From the *Annual Review of Physical Chemistry*, Volume 44 (1993):

Pressure Stability of Proteins, J. L. Silva and G. Weber

Scanning Tunneling Microscopy Studies of Low-Dimensional Materials: Charge Density Wave Pinning and Melting in Two Dimensions, H. Dai and C. M. Lieber

High-Resolution Spectroscopy of Solid Hydrogen, T. Oka

From the *Annual Review of Physiology*, Volume 56 (1994):

Ca^{2+}-Binding and Structural Dynamics in the Functions of Calmodulin, H. Weinstein and E. L. Mehler

Modulation of Ion Channels by Protein Phosphorylation and Dephosphorylation, I. B. Levitan

Structure and Function of Cyclic Nucleotide-Dependent Protein Kinases, S. H. Francis and J. D. Corbin

For the convenience of readers, a detachable order form/envelope is bound into the back of this volume.

Annu. Rev. Biophys. Biomol. Struct. 1994. 23:1–25

FIELD GRADIENT ESR AND MOLECULAR DIFFUSION IN MODEL MEMBRANES

J. H. Freed

Baker Laboratory of Chemistry, Cornell University,
Ithaca, New York 14853

KEY WORDS: phospholipids, cholesterol, order parameters, free
volume model, spectral-spatial imaging

CONTENTS

INTRODUCTION

The dynamic behavior of biomembranes occupies a central focus of modern membrane research (26). In particular, translational diffusion of lipids and proteins is essential for various biological processes (26). The techniques developed to measure the translational diffusion coefficients in model or biomembranes can be divided into two general categories according to their relevant distance scales. Modern macroscopic methods include NMR-spin echo (8, 39), fluorescence recov-

1

1056-8700/94/0610-0001$05.00

ery after photobleaching (FRAP) (59, 74) and dynamic imaging of diffusion by electron spin resonance (ESR) (5, 47, 65, 68, 70). These enable one to study how the bulk distribution of labeled molecules changes with time and they have resolution on the order of a few to several hundred micrometers. Microscopic methods allow one to observe diffusion over the order of molecular diameters, i.e. a few tens of Ångstroms. Such techniques typically reveal diffusion via encounters between labeled molecules through excimer formation (49), quasi-elastic neutron scattering (55), NMR T_1 relaxation measurements (75), or Heisenberg spin exchange (4, 15, 50, 56, 60, 72).

Macroscopic experiments are usually interpreted in terms of simple phenomenological descriptions of diffusion (e.g. Fick's law) to yield the diffusion coefficient. The pulsed field-gradient NMR technique has been utilized to study diffusional processes in model membranes and related systems (38, 39, 51, 75). Although this method can measure the self-diffusion coefficient of the actual solvent molecules, it is limited by the short T_2 for membranes (~ 10 μs to ~ 1 ms). To measure even fairly large diffusion coefficients, i.e. $D \approx 10^{-7}$ to $\sim 10^{-5}$ cm^2 s^{-1}, one needs at least several Teslas cm^{-1} field gradients (51). FRAP is by far the most commonly used technique to measure the lateral diffusion coefficient for lipids in membranes (59, 74) and enables the investigator to measure a wide range of diffusion coefficients (10^{-12} to 10^{-6} cm^2 s^{-1}). Despite the widespread applicability of the FRAP technique to the study of diffusion of macromolecular additives such as proteins and polypeptides, there is an intrinsic problem in using the technique for the study of diffusion of the basic components in mixed membranes such as phospholipids and cholesterol. The size of the photosensitive functional group attached to the parent molecules is usually quite substantial, allowing it to dominate the diffusional process; this can mask the subtle dynamic properties of the individual components (1, 27). More recently the technique of dynamic imaging of diffusion (DID)-ESR was introduced and applied to the study of lateral diffusion of spin-labeled molecules in lipid membranes. In general, one may use nitroxide spin-labeled lipids, cholesterol, peptides, and/or proteins. The nitroxyl functional group is relatively small and therefore will not introduce a large perturbation in most cases. This method and its recent applications are the principle subject of this review.

For microscopic methods, unlike macroscopic methods, the analysis leading to the relative diffusion coefficient depends heavily upon the choice of the microscopic molecular dynamic model; this stricture can result in considerable uncertainty in the estimated diffusion coefficient. Also, because such methods detect encounters between labeled molecules, how the labeled molecule mixes in the fluid is relevant. In magnetic resonance a further difficulty can arise from the complexity of interpreting the spin relaxation (4, 50, 75). Nevertheless, these methods are extremely important for investigating the microscopic dynamic molecular structure of membranes. Several groups have used microscopic ESR methods to measure translational diffusion over distances of molecular dimensions in model membranes (4, 22, 56, 60). Although ESR techniques can potentially be used to study the diffusion of components at a microscopic scale in mixed membranes, there have been no reports on this matter. The limits and drawbacks of the various macroscopic and microscopic methods necessitates the development of new techniques that are reliable and can accurately determine the diffusion coefficient in membranes.

ESR is very useful in the study of dynamic properties of membrane components (36) because of its high sensitivity and favorable time scale. In particular, the DID-ESR imaging method developed in these laboratories can be employed to accurately and conveniently measure macroscopic diffusion coefficients of spin probes in model membranes (68, 70). Moreover, the usual ESR spectra can be analyzed with ESR spectral simulation to simultaneously obtain orientational order parameters and rotational diffusion rates. Such a combined study can provide better insight into the dynamical properties of membranes (65, 69, 70).

The first experiments that used ESR imaging to measure diffusion coefficients (3, 9–11, 25, 32, 33) either required long experimental times (e.g. 10 days) (33) or assumed an idealized model for the analysis (9). However, developments such as the use of Fourier-space analysis of the data (5, 46, 47), along with narrow initial spin probe concentration profiles, reduced the experimental time by about four orders of magnitude (e.g. to 1 h for $D \approx 10^{-8}$ cm^2 s^{-1}), yet allowed a high degree of accuracy in studies of lateral diffusion in model membranes.

The DID-ESR method is based upon continuous wave (cw)-ESR experiments in the presence of field gradients to achieve spatial resolution (16). In principle, one can apply ESR experiments analogous to pulsed field-gradient NMR to measure diffusion. Unfortunately, because the ESR time scale is so much faster than that of NMR, the pulsed field gradient method cannot be applied to diffusion coefficients for which D is less than about 10^{-1} cm^2 s^{-1}. However, in fluids including membranes the molecules exhibit $D < 10^{-5}$ cm^2 s^{-1}. The cw-DID-ESR method is capable of measuring the latter values. Nevertheless, modern pulse and Fourier transform ESR methods do have their place in the study of molecular diffusion, as recent developments have indicated.

THE DID-ESR METHOD

The measurement of the diffusion coefficient, D, by DID-ESR involves two stages. After preparing the sample with an inhomogeneous distribution of spin probes along a given direction, the investigator uses the ESR imaging method to obtain the (one-dimensional) concentration profiles at several different times. Spatial resolution results from the magnetic field gradient, because spin probes at each spatial point experience a different resonant frequency. With time, this inhomogeneous distribution will move toward a homogeneous distribution via translational diffusion. The second stage is to fit the time-dependent concentration profiles to the diffusion equation in order to obtain D.

The ESR spectrum recorded in the presence of a magnetic field gradient B' (G cm^{-1}) is a convolution of the usual ESR spectrum (gradient-off spectrum), $I_o(\xi)$, with the concentration of spin probes $C(x,t)$ (33):

$$I_g(\xi,t) = \int_{-\infty}^{\infty} C(\xi',t)I_o(\xi - \xi') \, d\xi', \qquad 1.$$

where $\xi \equiv (B - B_o)$ measures the spectral position as the deviation of the magnetic field B from the field B_o at the nominal center of the spectrum, corresponding to the position $x = 0$, since B' maps x onto $\xi = B'x$. Thus the variable ξ is used in place of x and B in the development below. The concentration of spin probe at any position in the sample is kept low enough that the spectral shape does not vary from position to position owing to Heisenberg spin exchange.

The determination of $C(\xi,t)$ from the two spectra $I_g(\xi,t)$ and $I_o(\xi)$ is, in principle, a straightforward calculation. If the Fourier transform of the two spectra are represented as

$$\hat{I}_g(\kappa,t) = \int_{-\infty}^{\infty} I_g(\xi,t) \exp(-2\pi i\kappa\xi) \, d\xi \qquad 2a.$$

$$\hat{I}_o(\kappa) = \int_{-\infty}^{\infty} I_o(\xi) \exp(-2\pi i\kappa\xi) \, d\xi, \qquad 2b.$$

where κ is the inverse wavelength associated with ξ, then the Fourier transform of both sides of Equation 1 yields

$$\hat{I}_g(\kappa,t) = \hat{C}(\kappa,t)\hat{I}_o(\kappa), \qquad 3.$$

where $\hat{C}(\kappa,t)$ is the Fourier transform of $C(\xi,t)$. Therefore $C(\xi,t)$ is equal to

$$C(\xi,t) = \int_{-\infty}^{\infty} [\hat{I}_g(\kappa,t)/\hat{I}_o(\kappa)]W(\kappa) \exp(2\pi i\kappa\xi) \, d\kappa, \qquad 4.$$

where we have inserted $W(\kappa)$, a filter function necessary for the indicated division. An analysis that depends on $C(\xi,t)$ in real space will suffer from the accumulated errors of two forward Fourier transformations, one filtered division, and one back Fourier transformation (33). One can avoid the back transform step and the use of a filter function by analyzing the data in Fourier space. Also, only those Fourier components with sufficient sensitivity to the diffusion need be included, as noted below.

The usual one-dimensional diffusion equation is written in terms of the universal variable ξ as (7):

$$\frac{\partial C(\xi,t)}{\partial t} = D_\xi \frac{\partial^2 C(\xi,t)}{\partial \xi^2} , \qquad\qquad 5.$$

where $D_\xi \equiv D(B'^2)$ (i.e. the units of D_ξ are $G^2\ s^{-1}$). The ideal experiment would be the diffusion of spin probes from an instantaneous point source (δ-function). If the source is placed at $x = 0$ at $t = 0$, then the solution of Equation 5 is $C(\xi,t) = [C_o/(4\pi D_\xi t)^{1/2}]\ \exp[-(\xi^2/4D_\xi t)]$, which is a Gaussian concentration profile for all time. For an arbitrary initial distribution of spin probes, in the absence of boundary effects, the solution is a convolution of the initial distribution $C(\xi,t = 0)$ with the solution for the point source:

$$C(\xi,t) = [1/(4\pi D_\xi t)^{1/2}] \int_{-\infty}^{\infty} \exp[-(\xi - \xi')^2/4D_\xi t]C(\xi,t = 0)\ d\xi'.$$

$$6.$$

Taking the Fourier transform of both sides, one obtains $\hat{C}(\kappa,t) = \exp(-4\pi^2\kappa^2 D_\xi t)\hat{C}(\kappa,0)$ or alternatively,

$$\ln \hat{C}(\kappa,t) - \ln \hat{C}(\kappa,0) = -4\pi^2 D_\xi \kappa^2 t. \qquad\qquad 7.$$

Only the amplitude of $\hat{C}(\kappa,t)$ changes as a function of time as a result of the diffusion process (5, 46). Note that $\hat{C}(\kappa,t)$ is obtained from Equation 3.

If the initial spin probe distribution is well approximated by a Gaussian (68), then

$$C(\xi) = \frac{C_0}{\sqrt{2\pi}\ \delta_\xi} \exp\left[-\left(\frac{\xi^2}{2\delta_\xi^2}\right)\right], \qquad\qquad 8.$$

where δ_ξ is the variance and C_0 is a measure of the maximum value of $C(\xi)$. Very narrow initial distributions, even of irregular shape, quickly develop into a Gaussian because of diffusion (46). One can start the experiment at such a time; then Equations 7 and 8 apply, yielding

$\ln |\hat{C}(\kappa,t)| = -2\pi^2\sigma_\xi^2(t)\kappa^2 + \ln C_o$, where $\sigma_\xi^2(t) = \delta_\xi^2 + 2D_\xi t$. Thus, by plotting $\hat{C}(\kappa,t)$, with respect to κ^2 one obtains the slope $-2\pi^2\sigma_\xi^2(t)$. Then a plot of $\sigma_\xi^2(t)$ with respect to t yields $D = D_\xi B'^{-2}$ from the slope. Graphs of $\ln \hat{C}(\kappa,t)$ vs κ^2 for CSL spin probe in a POPC (see Table 1, below, for full names) model membrane were linear up to a maximum in κ^2, showing the concentration profile is well approximated by a Gaussian (5).

The diffusion constants of CSL in the POPC model membrane (5) at various temperatures derived from the ESR imaging technique are close in value to those of fluorescence probes as measured by FRAP (74). The small difference that was observed may result from the structural differences of the probe molecules used in those two techniques.

For samples that do not have a Gaussian spin probe distribution, one can perform the analysis by pairing the profiles at different times (5). Given two concentration profiles obtained at different times, t_i and t_j, Equations 3 and 7 shows that a plot of $\ln |I_g(\kappa,t_j)| - \ln |\hat{I}_g(\kappa,t_i)|$ vs $\kappa^2\Delta(t_i - t_j)$ yields a slope equal to $-4\pi^2 D_\xi$.

A practical consideration arises in locating the range of κ modes that provide accurate data on the diffusion coefficient. Whereas the high (or low) κ modes are the most (or least) sensitive to D, the κ^2 dependence in Equation 7 causes the modes' amplitudes to be low (or high). Thus, there is an optimum range of κ modes (see 46 for a useful procedure to locate this range). The accompanying analysis has led to the inequality $D_x t_D > (\Delta_B^2/B'^2 + \delta_\xi^2)\epsilon_\kappa^{-1} (1 + 1/\ln \epsilon_\kappa)$, where Δ_B^2 is the variance of the EPR line [i.e. the root mean square (rms) width of a Gaussian EPR line in the absence of a field gradient], ϵ_κ is the signal-to-noise ratio in the Fourier domain (assumed to obey $\epsilon_\kappa \gg 2.4$), and δ_ξ^2 is the variance of (a Gaussian) concentration profile at the beginning of the measurement. This expression sets the lower limit on the diffusion coefficient that can be estimated in a given time, t_D. For example, Shin et al (65) report an ϵ_κ of the order of 50. One can prepare dynamic model membrane samples or liquid crystal samples that have an initial spin probe distribution as narrow as $\delta_x = 2$ mm. The usual ESR line width varies from $2\Delta_B = 0.5$ G to 2 G. Therefore, for a 1-h measurement ($t_D = 4000$ s) with a 100 G cm^{-1} field gradient, one can measure a diffusion coefficient as slow as $2-4 \times 10^{-9}$ cm^2 s^{-1}.

One can also estimate the optimum gradient (46, 47). For example, under operating conditions of $\epsilon_\kappa = 50$, $t_D = 4000$ s, $D_x = 10^{-8}$ cm^2 s^{-1}, and $\delta_x^2 = 0.01$ cm^2, the optimum B'^2 approximately equals 40 cm^{-2} $\times \Delta_B^2$, which is in fairly good agreement with the gradients used in practice (80–100 G cm^{-1}).

Pali et al (52) recently described a variation of this technique. Instead of preparing samples with a thin strip containing labeled molecules, they produce a negative (i.e. a sample with a substantial uniform concentration of spins, except in a small strip). They also used a time-modulated magnetic-field gradient, which permits direct observation of spatial distributions without numerical Fourier transformation.

DID-ESR STUDIES ON MIXED MODEL MEMBRANES AND RELATED STUDIES

Lateral Diffusion of Cholesterol and Lipid

The applicability of DID-ESR to measurement of the lateral diffusion coefficient, D, in model membrane has been demonstrated by us in investigations of the effects of cholesterol on the dynamics of two different spin probes, the sterol type CSL (cf Table 1) and the phospholipid type 16-PC (cf Table 1) in phospholipid-cholesterol oriented multilayer model membranes (46, 68, 70). Furthermore, an analysis using EPR spectral simulation methods of the gradient-off spectra collected in the course of the DID-ESR experiment determined the order parameter, S, and the rotational diffusion coefficient, $R_\perp$, for the same sample (24, 62). The choice of spin probes that mimicked either cholesterol (CSL) or phospholipid (16-PC) behavior enabled in-depth considerations of the effects of the membrane composition and temperature on the dynamic molecular structure of the membranes.

Figure 1 shows results on D vs the cholesterol mole fraction, x, over a temperature range of 15–60°C for a binary lipid–cholesterol system. Quite different dependences of D_{CSL} and $D_{16\text{-PC}}$ upon x are evident. The presence of cholesterol influences the cholesterol diffusion more

Table 1   Fits of lateral diffusion coefficient to an activation energy dependent upon $S^{2\,a}$

System[b,c]	D° (cm^2 s^{-1})	a' [d] (K)	b' [d] (K^2)	β (K)
CSL in POPC/cholesterol[e]	9.18×10^{-6}	-3364	1.30×10^6	1303
CSL in DMPC/POPC/cholesterol	1.16×10^{-7}	-4363	1.55×10^6	~0
16-PC in POPC/cholesterol	1.06×10^{-4}	-2.60×10^4	8.56×10^6	2317

[a] From Ref. 68. See Equations 9 and 10.

[b] CSL, 3-doxyl derivative of cholestane-3-one; 16-PC, 1-palmitoyl-2-(16doxyl stearoyl) phosphatidylcholine; POPC, 1-palmitoyl-2-oleoyl-sn-glycero-phosphatidylcholine; DMPC, 1,2-dimyristoyl-sn-glycero-phosphatidylcholine.

[c] 17 wt% H$_2$O.

[d] $\alpha(T)$ of Equation 10 is given by $\alpha(T) = a' + b'/T$.

[e] A reanalysis of these data shows that $\alpha(T)$ fits better to the quadratic function $(-18.1 \times 10^3) + (1.07 \times 10^7/T) - (1.48 \times 10^9/T^2)$. The graph in Figure 3 is unaffected, since it utilized the experimental values of $\alpha(T)$ (cf 68).

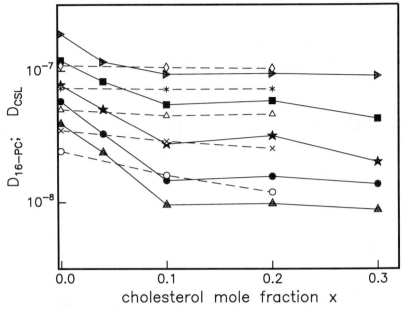

Figure 1 Plots of the variation of D_{CSL} *(solid lines)* and $D_{16\text{-}PC}$ *(dashed lines)* with cholesterol mole fraction x at different temperatures in POPC-cholesterol mixtures. Temperatures: for CSL 15 *(shaded triangles)*, 25 *(shaded circles)*, 35 *(shaded stars)*, 48 *(solid squares)*, and 60°C *(shaded arrowheads)*; for 16-PC 15 *(open circles)*, 24 *(×)*, 35 *(open triangles)*, 48 *(asterisks)*, and 60°C *(open diamonds)*. Data from Ref. 68.

than that of the phospholipid. Also, the observed nonlinear variations of the diffusion coefficients are characteristic of a nonideal solution, because in an ideal solution, the self-diffusion rate should be linear with composition (31). Related nonlinear variations (described below) appear in the order parameter, S (cf Figure 2), and in the rotational diffusion coefficient, $R_\perp$ obtained from the ESR spectral simulations. These studies showed a preferential association of cholesterol molecules with each other in the lipid solvent. In dilute solution, this tendency of the cholesterol (including CSL) molecules to aggregate means that the environment of CSL changes significantly as a function of x, from that of flexible lipid molecules to the more rigid cholesterol molecules. A cholesterol rich region would be more dense and compact than the pure lipid bilayer, thus providing less room for the molecules to diffuse. As a result, the self-diffusion of CSL in such a region should be slower than in the pure lipid bilayer. The tendency of cholesterol to aggregate means that the lipid-rich regions are less influenced by cholesterol molecules than would otherwise be expected. This obser-

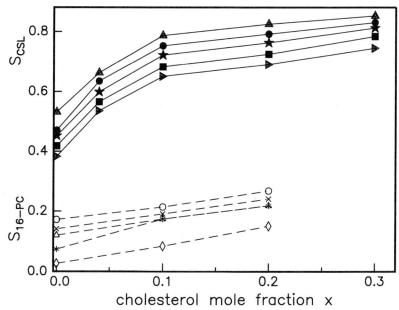

Figure 2 Plots of the $S(x,T)$ for CSL and for 16-PC vs cholesterol mole fraction x at different temperatures in POPC-cholesterol mixtures. See Figure 1 for labeling of points. Data from Ref. 68.

vation is consistent with the rather modest effect of cholesterol on the lateral diffusion of 16-PC.

Self-association, creating larger and more cholesterol-rich regions or clusters, possibly competes with the creation of new clusters in the nonideal solution. The observed saturation effect on D_{CSL} for $x > 0.1$ (cf Figure 1) suggests that the addition of more cholesterol merely increases the extent, but not the nature, of the cholesterol-rich clusters. This may be thought of as a preseparation regime of the nonideal solution. Experiments with CSL in DMPC-POPC-cholesterol ternary mixtures (cf Table 1) show a weaker effect of cholesterol on D_{CSL}, indicating that addition of the saturated lipid DMPC to the unsaturated lipid POPC enhances the mixing of cholesterol in phosphatidylcholine model membranes (70).

In general, the deviations of the D_{CSL} and $D_{16\text{-PC}}$ temperature dependences from Arrhenius behavior at each composition suggest a temperature-dependent activation energy. However, for large x (>0.3) and low temperatures ($\leq 32°C$), D_{CSL} for the DMPC-POPC-cholesterol system remained constant with the temperature. This constancy was attributed to a phase separation (70) that occurs at high cholesterol concentration (40, 64, 69).

Comparison with Other Techniques

Previous studies of lateral diffusion by other techniques (1, 27, 39, 42, 59, 78) have almost all focused upon phospholipid diffusion. The DID-ESR results for $D_{16\text{-PC}}$ do not exhibit significant cholesterol influence. A pulsed NMR study of the same system (42) also showed little effect of the cholesterol on the self-diffusion of the POPC molecules. Only FRAP studies of lateral diffusion in DMPC and egg-PC model membranes containing cholesterol (1, 27) investigated both fluorescence-labeled sterol and phospholipid. However, the results of these experiments significantly differed from the results of those DID-ESR studies in three respects. First, the diffusion rates of the fluorescence-labeled sterol and phospholipid probes were nearly equal under all conditions of cholesterol concentration and temperature in the liquid crystalline state. Second, the temperature dependence of the self-diffusion coefficient was very mild in all compositions. Finally, self-diffusion coefficients of both fluorescence probes were almost constant until the concentration of cholesterol reached $x = 0.1$; they then decreased by factors of three at $x = 0.2$ but did not change much from $x = 0.2$ to 0.4. In all likelihood, the two experiments yielded different results because the photosensitive functional group attached to the parent molecules used in the FRAP experiments is very substantial in size and hence could have a dominant influence on the diffusional process. This could result in identical diffusion coefficients that are different from those of cholesterol and lipid.

Correlation Between Lateral Diffusion and Orientational Order Parameter

The most pronounced and important feature of the liquid crystalline phase is the existence of significant orientational order of the long axis of the phospholipid chains. This orientational order results from the mean ordering potential experienced by each molecule, which is usually taken to be that calculated in the mean field approximation, $U(\theta) = \rho(p,T)bS\ [(3\cos^2\theta - 1)/2]$, where θ is the angle between the long axis of the molecule and the direction of the average orientation (the director), S is the order parameter defined as $S = \int [(3\cos^2\theta - 1)/2] \exp[-U(\theta)/\Re T]\ d(\cos\theta)$ while $\rho(p,T)$ is the number density, and b is the interaction constant. Figure 2 illustrates the results for S_{CSL} and $S_{16\text{-PC}}$ vs x for different temperatures in the binary POPC/cholesterol system. S_{CSL} increases sharply with x up to $x \approx 0.1$, but is not very sensitive to further addition of cholesterol. The results for $S_{16\text{-PC}}$ show a more modest and gradual increase vs x. A comparison with Figure 1 shows that S and D have very similar but opposite trends vs x for both the labeled lipid and the labeled sterol. Equivalent observations were made for the DMPC-POPC-cholesterol system (70). As a result, an empirical relationship between D and S was established, and this relationship served as the basis for a model that explains how the structural changes in the membrane associated with the increased ordering from addition of cholesterol will influence the membrane fluidity as measured by D. Second, given that the nonlinear dependence of D_{CSL} on x and the very different behavior of $D_{16\text{-PC}}$ vs D_{CSL} with x are manifestations of nonideal solution behavior, the related behavior of S_{CSL} and $S_{16\text{-PC}}$ with x should also be attributed to nonideal behavior. In fact, for an ideal ordered fluid, S should vary linearly with composition (58).

We first consider the relationship between D and S. The empirical relation is of an Arrhenius form (68):

$$D(S,T) = D^0 \exp[-E(S,T)/\mathscr{R}T], \qquad 9.$$

where D^0 is the preexponential factor, $\mathscr{R}$ is the universal gas constant, and the activation energy $E(S,T)$ is given by:

$$E(S,T)/\mathscr{R} = \alpha(T)S^2(x,T) + \beta, \qquad 10.$$

with $\alpha(T)$ and β empirically determined. Figure 3 illustrates this relationship for both D_{CSL} and $D_{16\text{-PC}}$, in POPC-cholesterol mixtures. An equivalent result was found for DMPC-POPC-cholesterol mixtures (70). The values of $\alpha(T)$ and β appear in Table 1. What is most interesting about Equations 9 and 10 is that the only way the mole fraction of cholesterol, x, affects D is through the dependence of E on S. Finally, it is important to stress that the spectral measurements from which D and S were obtained were performed on the same sample during the same time period.

Correlation Between Rotational Diffusion and Orientational Order Parameter

The rotational diffusion tensor also reflects directly on the membrane fluidity. A very similar relationship to Equations 9 and 10 has been found for $R_{\perp,\text{CSL}}$, the perpendicular component of the rotational diffusion tensor for CSL (66, 68, 70), which measures the rate of reorientation of the long axis of CSL. In particular:

$$R_{\perp} = R_{\perp}^0 \exp[-AS^2(x,T)/\mathscr{R}T]. \qquad 11.$$

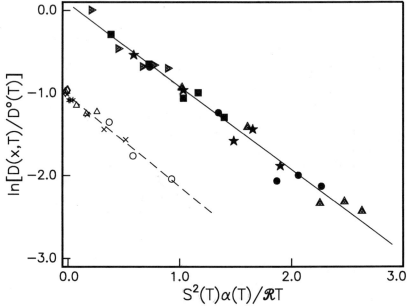

Figure 3 Plots of ln $D(x,T)$ − ln $D^0(T)$ vs $S^2(T)\alpha(T)/RT$ for CSL *(solid line)* and for 16-PC CSL *(dashed line)*, for the cholesterol mole fractions and temperatures shown in Figures 1 and 2. For 16-PC, ln $D(x,T)$ − ln $D^0(T)$ − 1 is plotted. Note $D^0(T) \equiv D^0$ exp($-\beta/RT$). Data from Ref. 68.

Figure 4 displays an example of the validity of this relationship. (Here $A = 4.02$ kcal mol^{-1} and $R_\perp^0 = 2.02 \times 10^8$ s^{-1}.) Thus the overall rotational dynamics is also affected by the cholesterol simply through the structural change induced in the membrane, which is directly related to the order parameter. Similar comments also apply to the role of water (66), consistent with the fact that the cross-sectional area per lipid molecule is nearly proportional to the water content (43). Furthermore, if we recognize that the DID-ESR measurement of D is a macroscopic one ($\Delta x \approx 100$ μm and $t \approx 1$ h), whereas those of S and $R_\perp$ are microscopic ones (i.e. $\Delta x \approx$ molecular dimensions and $t \approx \tau_R \approx 3$–200 ns) such correlations imply temporal and spatial uniformity in the effects of mixing on dynamics characteristic of a single simple fluid solution.

No simple relation between $R_\perp$ and S emerged for labeled lipids 16-PC (68) and 7,6-PC (66). Unlike CSL, the lipid chain is nonrigid, so one must consider the complex internal modes of motion of the chain, as well as the overall molecular reorientation in any interpretation of $R_\perp$ (23).

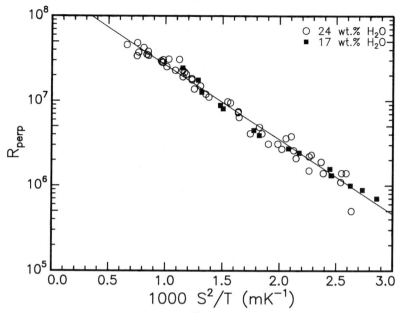

Figure 4   Semilog plot of $R_\perp$ for CSL vs S^2_{CSL}/T for a range of cholesterol mole fractions and temperatures in DMPC-cholesterol-H_2O mixtures. From Ref. 66.

FREE VOLUME MODEL

The S^2 dependence of the activation energy of lateral diffusion and of overall rotational reorientation can be interpreted within the context of the free volume model of Cohen & Turnbull (6). The principal concept of the free volume model is that each molecule of a system is confined to a cage by its neighbors. The molecule rattles inside this volume until fluctuations in density open a hole within the cage large enough to permit a substantial translation of the molecule.

If we introduce two characteristic free volumes, a critical free volume V^* that is large enough to permit a substantial displacement, and V^f, the average free volume per molecule, the diffusion coefficient can be expressed as (6): $D \approx D(V^*) \exp(-\lambda V^*/V^f)$, where $D(V^*)$ is the diffusion coefficient in a cage of volume $(V^* + \overline{V})$, $\overline{V}$ being the mean molecular volume. Because V^f can be assumed to arise from the isobaric thermal expansion, then

$$D = g(V^*)D^0(T) \exp[-\beta/(T - T_0)],\qquad\qquad 12.$$

where $\beta = \lambda\delta V/\alpha\overline{V}$, $\delta V = V^* - V^f$, α is the mean value of the thermal expansion coefficient, and T_0 is the temperature at which the volume per molecule would be reduced to the close-packing limit. $D^0(T)$ is the small-scale diffusion constant, and $g(V^*)$ is a numerical factor related to the cage size for V^*, such that $D(V^*) = g(V^*)D^0(T)$. λ is a numerical constant. Usually $g(V^*)D^0(T)$ is written as $g^D \exp(-E_D/\mathcal{R}T)$ where E_D is an activation energy associated with $D^0(T)$. Equation 12 explains the fluidity of numerous glass-forming substances (6). Vaz et al (74) applied it to PC model membranes, taking into account the drag forces at the membrane-water interfaces. Diogo & Martins (13) used an approach based upon the Cohen-Turnbull model to explain the twist viscosity in nematic liquid crystals, and Moscicki et al (48) used such a model to describe the translational diffusion in smectic liquid crystals. Also taking this approach, Shin et al (70) obtained a model explaining the composition and temperature dependence of lateral diffusion in mixed model membranes.

The ordering of the long molecular axis in membranes decreases the average free volume at the disposal of a molecule. Therefore, if the molecule is to gain the critical free volume, the cage must first expand by the amount that the orientational order has reduced it (ΔV^*), and second by the amount it would need in the fully disordered, or isotropic, fluid (i.e. δV). For phospholipid-cholesterol mixtures, one introduces the mean ordering potential experienced by a cholesterol molecule as: $U_{ch}(\theta) = -\rho_0[\xi b_{ch}S_{ch} + (1 - \xi)b_{lp}S_{lp}](3\cos^2\theta - 1)/2$, where ξ is the fractional average number of cholesterol molecules in the neighborhood of the CSL probe. Shin et al (70) show that for $T \gg T_0$ (cf Equation 11):

$$D_{ch}(T,S_{ch}) \approx g^D \exp\left(-\frac{E_D}{\mathcal{R}T}\right)$$

$$\times \exp\left[-\frac{\beta_{or} + \xi\theta_{ch}S_{ch}^2 + (1 - \xi)\theta_{lp}S_{lp}S_{ch}}{T}\right], \quad 13.$$

where β_{or}, θ_{ch} and θ_{lp} are constants of the cholesterol (ch) and lipid (lp) mixture. Expressions for the diffusion coefficient of the phospholipid molecules can be written in the same fashion.

When the concentration of cholesterol is significant, cholesterol molecules experience mostly the cholesterol environment ($\xi \to 1$) according to the experimental results. Thus, $\xi\theta_{ch}S_{ch}^2 \to \theta_{ch}S_{ch}^2$ and $(1 - \xi)\theta_{lp}S_{lp}S_{ch} \to 0$ in Equation 13. This is just the form observed experimentally, implying that ξ approaches 1 at low mole fractions, x—i.e. the cholesterol molecules are aggregating. It would also appear that $\theta_{ch} \gg \theta_{lp}$. This result is consistent with the idea that for the elongated and structurally rigid cholesterol molecule, the intermolecular interaction between cholesterol molecules is significantly larger than the interaction between the cholesterol probe and the phospholipid environment.

Shin et al (70) have shown that a very similar free volume approach may be applied to obtain an expression for $R_\perp$. For example, they obtain in the limit $\xi \to 1$, and $T \gg T_0$:

$$R_\perp(T,S_{ch}) \approx g_{ch}^R \exp\left(-\frac{E_R + \epsilon_{ch}S_{ch}}{\mathcal{R}T}\right) \exp\left(-\frac{\beta_{ch} + \theta_{ch}S_{ch}^2}{T}\right).$$

14.

The definition of terms is essentially the same as for Equation 13 except that the β_{ch} and θ_{ch} in Equation 14 are of different magnitude than in Equation 13. A comparison of Equation 14 with experiment shows that $\theta_{ch}S_{ch}^2$ is the dominant term in the effective activation energy for $R_\perp$. The observations are consistent with a θ_{ch} for D_{CSL} being less than that for $R_{\perp CSL}$, implying a more crucial dependence of the rotational diffusion on the free volume.

THE ORDER PARAMETER AND THERMODYNAMICS

Given the important relationships between the diffusion coefficients and the order parameter, some further discussion of S is appropriate. S, an important thermodynamic quantity, results from the statistical average of the orienting forces (or torques) from the surrounding molecules. Thus, S for the ith component in a multicomponent system should reflect the average local composition of surrounding molecules. The ordering of the rigid CSL spin probe is particularly important in this context, because it has no intramolecular modes of motion, and it reports the overall ordering in the solution (36). For a label on a flexible chain position, one must correct the observed order parameter for the additional effects of internal motional averaging (23, 63).

The order parameter of the ith component and its activity in solution should be connected. We have explored this possibility (65, 66, 68, 69) and have proposed a general method for obtaining the activity coefficients of the components of mixed model membranes from the composition dependence of their orientational order parameters. The basic approach has been tested on phospholipid-cholesterol-water systems, partly in conjunction with the DID-ESR experiments. The order parameter for the ith component, S_i, is an intensive thermodynamic property somewhat analogous to the partial pressure (57, 69). Thus, S_i should be a linear function of the composition variable(s) if the solution is ideal. When S_i varies nonlinearly with x_i (cf Figure 2), the replacement of x_i by the activity of the ith component should reestablish the linear nature of the functional dependence, just as it does other intensive thermodynamic properties of a solution. An analysis of the data on S_i for CSL and a labeled lipid (16-PC and 7,6-PC) vs cholesterol mole fraction showed that the activities obtained satisfied a necessary requirement of thermodynamics (i.e. the Gibbs-Duhem equation) (57).

Classical thermodynamics suggests that the most important thermodynamic quantity in the study of mixtures is the activity of each component. The activities of components in a binary mixture are related to each other by the Gibbs-Duhem equation. The variation of the activity (or equivalently the order parameter) of PC molecules can be predicted by integrating the Gibbs-Duhem equation once the activity of cholesterol is obtained. The good agreement of such predictions with the experimental results for PC-analog spin probes has three important implications: *(a)* the PC-cholesterol mixture forms a single phase solution, because the Gibbs-Duhem equation is only valid for components in single phase mixtures; *(b)* obtaining the thermodynamic activities from the order parameters is valid; and *(c)* one need only obtain the activity of one component as a function of all composition variables, because the activities of all other components can be calculated by integrating the Gibbs-Duhem equation (65, 66, 68, 69).

We also showed that the activities obtained from the order parameter can correctly predict the observed phase boundary between the single liquid crystalline phase for lower x_{ch} and the two-phase region for higher x_{ch}. Thermodynamic stability conditions for binary mixtures demonstrate that the chemical potential of a component should increase vs its mole fraction as long as the mixture is stable. However, the chemical potential, and hence the activity (or the order parameter), must reach its maximum at the phase boundary. Therefore, one can predict the phase boundary directly from the measured order parameter.

The obtained activities are consistent with the results of D_{CSL} and D_{16-PC} in that they show nonideal mixing between lipid and cholesterol that leads to aggregation of cholesterol. They also showed that acyl chain unsaturation leads to poorer mixing of cholesterol in the PC model membranes (for $T > 35°C$) in the liquid crystalline phase. However, in a mixed solvent consisting of two types of lipid (DMPC and POPC), the dissolved cholesterol deviates less from ideality than it does in either of the two binary lipid–cholesterol mixtures.

Almost all the mixing properties may be deduced from the thermodynamic activities of the components. However, in the case of mixed membranes a practical method has not been available for measuring the thermodynamic activities of the membrane components. Consequently, investigators could characterize the nonideal behavior of mixed membranes only indirectly, e.g. by comparing the phase diagram with that predicted using an appropriate theory (34, 35, 41). However, tractable theories are necessarily very approximate, and reliable data on thermodynamic activities in membranes would also enable one to accurately test and refine theoretical models. Feigenson (21) has developed a reliable experimental method based on solubility products. This method is, however, only applicable to systems containing phosphatidylserines. Thus a general method, such as that proposed by Shin & Freed, could be extremely valuable if it can be extended to a wide range of mixed membranes.

SPECTRAL-SPATIAL IMAGING: MACROSCOPIC VS MICROSCOPIC DIFFUSION

Spectral-spatial (SS) ESR imaging (19, 44, 45) is a promising technique for generalizing DID-ESR in order to study diffusion of spin probes in systems with substantial spin concentration. SS ESR imaging provides a way to resolve the concentration (or position)-dependent spectral variation in a two-dimensional fashion, as illustrated in Figure 5—i.e. along one axis (the spatial axis) it gives the spin concentration profile, whereas along the other axis it gives the ESR spectrum at that position (and spin concentration). This method had previously been illustrated for the investigation of transport in nonuniform media (71) and for studying O_2 distributions (76).

This technique was successfully applied to the simultaneous measurement of both the macroscopic and microscopic diffusion coefficients, D_{macro} and D_{micro}, respectively, of a spin-labeled phospholipid (16-PC) in oriented multilayers of POPC utilizing a substantial spin concentration (67) (larger than for DID-ESR). If the spin probe is initially concentrated in a small region of the sample, its distribution will tend over time to become homogeneous via translational diffusion. By measuring several SS images at different times, one can analyze the spread of the concentration profile as a function of time to obtain the macroscopic diffusion coefficient from the diffusion equation, by analogy with DID-ESR. In addition, such an experiment will be equivalent to the spectra obtained from many different homogeneous samples that must be prepared with different spin concentrations for conventional ESR studies of Heisenberg spin exchange (HE) (4, 50, 60). The ESR line broadening that results from spin relaxation induced by spin-spin

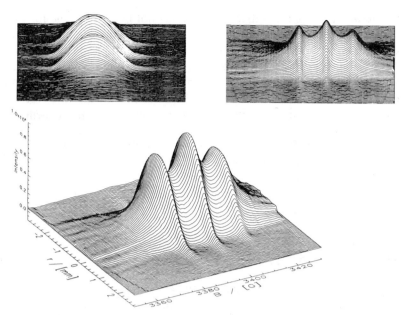

Figure 5 ESR spectral-spatial image of 16-PC diffusing in aligned multilayers of POPC viewed *(top left)* along the spectral axis to display the spatial distribution, *(top right)* along the spatial axis to display the spectral dependence on position, and *(bottom)* in perspective. From Ref. 67.

interactions such as HE can be analyzed to obtain the microscopic diffusion coefficient.

Devaux & McConnell (12) (prior to the development of ESR imaging) used the concentration dependence of the ESR spectra together with an inhomogeneous initial distribution of spin-labeled lipids to measure D_{macro}. The spatial distribution was deduced through a complicated simulation of the composite spectrum as a superposition of spectra from regions of different concentration. Spectral-spatial imaging effectively separates the spectra for each concentration, permitting a direct determination of D_{macro} from the time-dependent broadening of the concentration profile, as well as D_{micro} from the line broadening.

In comparing the results on macroscopic diffusion via ESR imaging vs microscopic diffusion via spin-spin interactions, one should remember that the former provides the macroscopic tracer diffusion coefficient of the spin label, which can be identified as the self-diffusion coefficient of the lipid when the two are very similar (68, 70). However, the latter provides a microscopic relative diffusion coefficient that is

Annu. Rev. Biophys. Biomol. Struct. 1994. 23:27–51

HYDRATION AND STERIC PRESSURES BETWEEN PHOSPHOLIPID BILAYERS

Thomas J. McIntosh

Department of Cell Biology, Duke University Medical Center, Durham, North Carolina 27710

Sidney A. Simon

Departments of Neurobiology and Anesthesiology, Duke University Medical Center, Durham, North Carolina 27710

KEY WORDS: water, entropic pressure, X-ray diffraction, membranes

CONTENTS

PERSPECTIVES AND OVERVIEW

Biological cells and extracellular matrices contain a variety of macromolecular structures separated by an aqueous phase. Both specific and nonspecific interactions between these hydrated macromolecules

27

1056–8700/94/0610–0027$05.00

determine the separation between their surfaces and play critical roles in a variety of biological processes in which these structures come close together. The short-range nonspecific interactions that are thought to occur between all surfaces in solvent are the focus of this review.

Numerous experimental and theoretical studies have been undertaken to understand the physical basis for the nonspecific interactions between surfaces in water. The classical DLVO theory (10, 84) explains the interactions between small, smooth, charged surfaces in terms of two relatively long-ranged interactions; electrostatic repulsion and van der Waals attraction. However, many types of physiologically important macromolecular assemblies are neither small nor smooth. For example, biological membranes (a) have relatively large surface areas and are very hydrophilic; (b) are rough at the molecular level because of protruding lipid head groups, proteins, and carbohydrate moieties; and (c) are flexible. These properties give rise to strong short-range repulsive hydration and steric pressures that are only beginning to be understood. In fact, the problem of determining the interactions be-

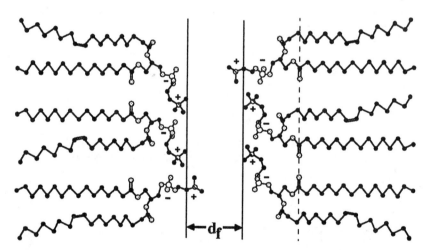

Figure 1 Schematic representation of two apposing monolayers of a multilamellar array of PC bilayers. Depicted are two extremes of lipid head group orientation (as taken from 21); four lipids are shown with the phosphocholine moiety parallel to the plane of the bilayer and two lipids with the phosphocholine moiety nearly perpendicular to the plane of the bilayer. The negatively charged phosphate and positively charged trimethylammonium moieties are labeled with $(-)$ and $(+)$ symbols, respectively. The solid line denotes our definition of the edge of the bilayer, where the phosphocholine moiety is parallel to the plane of the bilayer. The fluid space between adjacent bilayers is labeled d_f. Water penetrates into the head group region up to the dotted line, which denotes the approximate location of the hydrocarbon-water interface.

tween hydrated biological surfaces is so formidable that Ninham (64) stated, "The situation seems so complicated that one wonders if any unity can be inferred."

The total repulsive pressure as a function of surface separation has been measured for a variety of macromolecules, including lipid bilayers (47, 60, 65, 71), lipid hexagonal phases (16), DNA helices (72), polysaccharides (73), and amphiphilic polymers (19, 34). This review focuses on data from the electrically neutral, zwitterionic phospholipids phosphatidylcholine (PC) (shown schematically in Figure 1) and phosphatidylethanolamine (PE). We choose these phospholipid bilayers as our topic for several reasons. First, the composition, structure, cohesive properties, and electrostatic potential of these bilayers can be precisely controlled so that key physical parameters of the steric and hydration pressures can be investigated and models for their origin tested. Second, these lipids have been extensively investigated by a variety of methods and much is known about their properties. Third, these lipid bilayers are simple enough that theoretical models and computer simulations can describe inter- and intrabilayer interactions, and these can then be compared with experiment. Fourth, PC and PE are the most common phospholipids in biological membranes.

MODELS FOR SHORT-RANGE REPULSION BETWEEN BILAYERS

To understand the interactions between hydrated bilayers one should first consider the hydration properties of lipids and the location of the water molecules with respect to the bilayer. At low water contents both PCs and PEs form three-dimensional crystals consisting of stacks of crystalline bilayers with no intervening fluid space (24, 67). PC crystals have two water molecules per lipid molecule, and these waters reside in the polar head group, near the phosphate moiety (67). The water molecules form H-bonds with the oxygens on the phosphate and with each other, and may also interact with the choline on the trimethylammonium group (22). Upon the addition of more water molecules, structural changes occur in each bilayer. For water contents up to about 7–10 waters per lipid molecule, the waters distribute themselves in the polar head group regions and wedge the lipids apart, increasing the molecular area and decreasing the transition temperature (49). These waters are intercalated throughout the polar head group but do not, on average, penetrate past the deeper carbonyl group (75, 87), so that the hydrocarbon-water interface is on average at the level of the deeper carbonyl group (dotted line, Figure 1). The further addition of water will create fluid spaces between adjacent bilayers. The total amount of water imbibed by phospholipid bilayers at full hydration depends on the lipid head group and the physical phase of the lipid (reviewed in 52).

In general, PCs imbibe more water than do PEs, and liquid crystalline–phase bilayers (with fluid hydrocarbon chains) imbibe more water than do gel-phase bilayers (with more rigid hydrocarbon chains) (63). For example, at full hydration, PC bilayers imbibe about 25 and 14 waters, whereas PE bilayers imbibe about 10 and 7 waters, per lipid molecule in the liquid crystalline and get phases, respectively (59, 63). The fluid spaces between fully hydrated PC bilayers are about 15 and 12 Å wide in the liquid crystalline and gel phases, respectively (60), whereas PE bilayers have fluid separations of less than 5 Å in both phases (59). A water molecule has a diameter of 2.8 Å, so for these various types of bilayers, apposing bilayers are separated by fluid spacings only 2 to 5 water molecules wide. A complicating factor in understanding lipid hydration is that the lipid surface is neither flat nor static. Phospholipid head groups are mobile, and the lipids in the liquid-crystalline phase can undergo a variety of out-of-plane fluctuations, including thermally induced undulations, density fluctuations, and protrusions of individual molecules from the plane of the bilayer (5, 26, 68).

Thus, hydrated lipids exhibit water-water, lipid-water, and lipid-lipid interactions, and the energy of hydration includes all of these interactions. In its most general form, the hydration pressure (P_h) can be written $P_h = -\partial G(d_f)/\partial(d_f)$ where d_f is the fluid space between bilayers and $G(d_f)$ is the excess Gibbs free energy per-unit area (65). Thus, any work to remove water between surfaces at any fluid spacing could be considered to be the work of hydration. This general definition of P_h would include a variety of repulsive pressures arising from water-water interactions as well as from lipid-lipid (steric) interactions including polar head group overlap, thermally induced molecular protrusions, or elimination of bending modes. However, the term *hydration pressure* is now commonly defined to include only the repulsive pressure that arises from the changes in water orientation or the H-bonding pattern (water-water interactions) induced by the bilayer surface. That is, the short-range interactions between electrically neutral bilayers are often broken into two classes of interactions, a hydration pressure, resulting from partial water orientation by the bilayer, and steric pressures, resulting from physical contact between lipid molecules from apposing bilayers (12, 28). In this review, we use this somewhat arbitrary definition of hydration and steric pressures and try to provide information on the relative contributions of each mechanism to the total interaction energy.

We start by briefly reviewing some of the theoretical models of these short-range pressures. Additional details can be found elsewhere (28, 38).

Hydration Pressure

MODELS FOR STRUCTURELESS SURFACES Marcelja & Radic (45) proposed the first model, called the order parameter model, of the repulsive hydration pressure (P_h). In this model, water is confined between identical, infinitely thin structureless surfaces. The surface orders the water, and the degree of order is maximal at each surface and decreases with distance into the bulk fluid phase such that

$$P_h = P_0/\sinh(d_f/2\lambda),\qquad\qquad 1.$$

where d_f is the fluid space between adjacent bilayers and λ is the characteristic decay length associated only with the size of the solvent molecule. For $d_f \gg \lambda$, this expression becomes

$$P_h \approx 4P_0 \exp(-d_f/\lambda),\qquad\qquad 2.$$

thus predicting an exponential decay of the hydration pressure. Although Marcelja & Radic did not speculate on the physical basis of the gradient in the order parameter, or on the factors that affect P_0, it was evident that the factors could arise from either the polarization of water by surface charges or dipoles on the polar head groups, which in turn propagate into the bulk water phase, or by a rearrangement of the hydrogen-bonding pattern of water. Both these factors were incorporated explicitly into later models.

Gruen & Marcelja (18) extended this original order parameter theory to provide a molecular basis for the exponentially decaying P_h. They assumed that water was polarized by a spatially varying electric field from the bilayer. In developing their analysis they used a particular function to describe the relationship between the electric field and the polarization of the solvent (the dielectric dispersion). Attard et al (3) have questioned the use of this functional form for the dielectric dispersion as applied to polar fluids and have stated that other functional forms would not be likely to lead to a pressure that decayed exponentially with increasing fluid separation.

Cevc & Marsh (7) presented a nonlocal electrostatic model of the hydration pressure in which the polarizing electric field arose from the dipoles and multipoles of the lipids. They arrived at the expression (when $d_f \gg \lambda$),

$$P_h = 2\chi(\Psi h/\lambda)^2 \exp(-d_f/\lambda), \qquad\qquad 3.$$

where Ψ_h is the hydration potential, and χ is the orientational suscep-
tibility of the solvent, which is equal to $\epsilon_0 \cdot (\epsilon - 1)/\epsilon$, where ϵ and ϵ_0
are the bulk dielectric constant of the solvent and the permittivity of
free space, respectively. This model predicts that the magnitude of P_h
depends on the square of the polarizing electric field (Ψ_h/λ).

Attard & Batchelor (2) developed a very different model of the hydration pressure. In this model the solvent is considered as an H-bonding liquid containing various types of H-bond orientational defects that
is positioned between two infinitely thin structureless boundaries, and
the repulsive pressure arises from the ordering of water by the surfaces.
The primary water of hydration reduces the configurational entropy
for the remaining water molecules to form a tetrahedral network of
hydrogen bonds. To maximize the number of H-bonds, the water effects defects of various types that give rise to a hydration pressure (2).
This model predicts that the hydration pressure is a function of the
density of hydrogen-bond defects. Its drawbacks are that it can only
be tested using computer simulations and that the polar head group,
which in PC has a thickness of about 10 Å, can greatly influence the
type and number of defects.

MODELS WITH SURFACE STRUCTURE   To obtain more realistic models of
the hydration pressure, one must include some information about the
width and the distribution of dipole charges in the polar head group.
In the first approach to this problem, the interface was assumed to be
molecularly thin, but spatial periodicities between the charges comprising the dipoles in the plane of the bilayer were considered (36). In
this model for surfaces ordered with an in-plane periodicity a, another
repulsive term (P_h') was added to the hydration pressure:

$$P_h' = \beta\langle\sigma^2\rangle/\sinh^2(d_f/\lambda_{eff}), \qquad\qquad 4.$$

where β is a parameter inversely proportional to the dielectric constant,
σ is the excess charge density, and $\lambda_{eff} = [2(1/\lambda_w)^2 + (2\pi/a)^2]^{-1/2}$ is
the effective decay length (where λ_w is the intrinsic decay length of
water). This model predicts that the smaller the area per lipid molecule
(the more correlated the surface dipoles), the larger the magnitude and
the smaller the decay length of the hydration pressure. In the second
approach, Cevc (6) extended his original nonlocal electrostatic model
to include the fact that the polar headgroup has a finite thickness (d_p)
and that the decay length should should depend on the details of the

interface. When the charge density of the polar group decays as $\exp(-d_p/\lambda)$, one may write

$$P_h = \beta\sigma^2[C \exp(-d_f/\lambda) + D \exp(-d_f/\lambda) \exp(-d_f/d_p)$$
$$+ E \exp(-d_f/d_p)], \qquad\qquad 5.$$

where B, C, D, and E are constants. For other functional forms of the charge distribution (such as Gaussian), this model predicts that P_h does not decay exponentially (6).

Thus, most models for the hydration pressure involve the partial polarization or orientation of water by the bilayer surface. Molecular dynamic simulations designed to reveal such a polarization profile have given ambiguous results. Early studies (32, 33) could not connect a polarization profile with a hydration pressure, whereas more recent ones have made this connection (48, 89).

Steric (Entropic) Pressures

All the above models for the hydration pressure assume that the bilayer surface is smooth. However, as noted above, lipids in the liquid crystalline phase can exhibit a variety of out-of-plane motions that also must be considered in evaluating the interaction between bilayers. These include head group motions, molecular protrusions, and thermally induced bending and breathing modes. These motions will be markedly smaller in gel (solid)-phase bilayers compared with liquid crystalline (fluid)–phase bilayers.

UNDULATION PRESSURE   This pressure results from thermally induced bilayer undulations or fluctuations that arise because the fluidity and thinness of liquid crystalline bilayers makes them easy to bend (20). The approach of bilayers reduces such motions, but damping the undulations requires work, and hence this pressure is repulsive. In the presence of an underlying hydration pressure of magnitude P_0 and decay length λ, and for fluid spacings near the equilibrium fluid spacing, the undulation pressure, P_u, may be expressed as

$$P_u = (\pi kT/32\lambda)[(P_0/B\lambda)^{1/2} \exp(-d_f/2\lambda)], \qquad\qquad 6.$$

where B is the bilayer bending modulus, which is about 10^{-12} ergs for liquid crystalline–phase bilayers (12, 13). Thus, P_u has a decay length that is one half that of the underlying hydration pressure. For larger values of d_f, the formula derived by Harbich & Helfrich (20) is applicable

$$P_u \approx (kT)^2/2Bd_f^3. \qquad\qquad 7.$$

Both of these formulas (Equations 6 and 7) indicate that for gel phase bilayers, where B is very large, $P_u \approx 0$.

PROTRUSION PRESSURE   This pressure is thought to arise from individual molecules that protrude to various extents from the bilayer surface (30, 31). For amphiphiles, the length of the protrusion is limited by the work necessary to transfer a hydrocarbon from a fluid bilayer to the water phase. In this case,

$$P_p \approx (2.7 \, kT/A\lambda') \exp(-d_f/\lambda'), \qquad\qquad 8.$$

where $\lambda' = kT/\alpha$ and $\alpha \approx 1\text{–}5 \times 10^{-11}$ J/m, and A is the area per lipid molecule (30, 31). This pressure should be significantly larger for liquid crystalline bilayers than for gel-phase bilayers, as the energy to remove hydrocarbons from gel-phase bilayers includes the energy of fusion, which makes it prohibitively high. Although individual molecules in fluid bilayers undoubtedly undergo vertical fluctuations, the magnitude of these fluctuations is not well established. Furthermore, Parsegian & Rand (66) have questioned the role of molecular protrusions in producing an appreciable repulsive pressure.

HEAD GROUP OVERLAP PRESSURE   As two lipids approach each other, their headgroups eventually come into contact and reduce their configurational entropy, resulting in a short-range repulsive pressure (53). Assuming the polar headgroups act as very short polymers (a questionable assumption), Israelachvili (28) derived an equation describing this pressure as

$$P_{hg} \approx (100kT/A^{3/2}) \exp(-d_f/\lambda''), \qquad\qquad 9.$$

where $\lambda'' = d_{hg}/\pi$ and d_{hg} is the effective length of the polar head group. The range of this pressure is $2d_{hg}$.

Experimental tests of these theoretical models may encounter several problems. First, the definition of fluid space (d_f) that appears in all of these expressions might not have the same plane of origin (where $d_f = 0$) for each pressure and, in many theoretical analyses, the plane of origin of the pressure is ill-defined. Second, the repulsive pressures are either exponentially or power-law dependent on d_f. Because the range of fluid spaces over which most pressure-distance (d_f) data are obtained is quite small (0 Å $< d_f <$ 15Å), in many cases it is difficult to distinguish experimentally an exponential from a power law dependence.

METHODS

Two techniques, a surface force apparatus and X-ray diffraction analysis of osmotic stressed multilamellar liposomes, have been used to
measure pressure-distance data between opposing lipid bilayers. These
two techniques provide complementary data, because the surface force
apparatus can measure pressures at relatively large bilayer separations
(ten to thousands of Ångstroms) whereas the osmotic stress–X-ray
diffraction method provides information over a range that includes extremely small interbilayer spacings (0–200 Å). When appropriate corrections are made for the different geometries involved, the two techniques give similar pressure-distance data for distances of 10 to about
150 Å (25, 83).

Surface Force Apparatus

The most commonly used surface force apparatus contains two curved
molecularly smooth mica surfaces between which the interaction forces
are directly determined with interchangeable force-measuring springs
(8, 27, 29). The distance between apposing mica surfaces is ascertained
with an optical technique using multiple beam interference fringes.
Force-distance curves between lipids are measured with the mica surfaces coated with lipid bilayers.

  The surface force apparatus can measure both attractive and repulsive pressures—a unique advantage. Moreover, the surface apparatus
can measure relatively weak interactions at long interbilayer distances
(thousands of Ångstroms), so that it is ideal for the measurement of
electrostatic pressures between charged bilayers and van der Waals
pressures between amphiphiles. However, this method is limited in
that it cannot accurately measure short-range pressures, such as the
hydration pressure, at small interbilayer distances (<10 Å) (46). This
is because the presence of the strong repulsive pressures causes the
mica sheet supporting the bilayer to bend at very small interbilayer
spacings (46). In addition, since the bilayers are immobilized on a solid
support, undulation pressures between bilayers (12, 13, 20) should be
significantly suppressed (83) and thus cannot be measured directly with
the surface force apparatus. However, comparisons of pressure-distance data obtained with immobilized bilayers by the surface force
technique and with multilamellar liposomes by the osmotic stress technique have provided information on the magnitude of undulation pressure relative to the other short-range pressures (47, 83).

Osmotic Stress and X-Ray Diffraction

In the osmotic stress method, varying osmotic pressures are applied to lipid multilayers and the distance between adjacent bilayers at each applied pressure is measured using X-ray diffraction. The osmotic stress–X-ray diffraction method does not provide direct information on attractive pressures, but it can determine repulsive pressures at very small interbilayer spacings in the range of 0 (molecular contract) to about 200 Å. Thus, much of the data concerning short-range interactions have been obtained with the osmotic stress method. The basic principle behind the method is as follows: At a given applied pressure (P), the total repulsive pressure between bilayers (P_r) is balanced by the sum of the applied pressure and the van der Waals attractive pressure (P_v). However, for interbilayer separations a few Ångstroms less than that observed in the absence of applied pressure, P is greater than P_v (40). Under these circumstances $P \approx P_r$, and therefore the application of a known osmotic pressure can be used to obtain the total repulsive pressure between bilayers (40).

Known osmotic pressures can be applied in two ways: (*a*) by incubating multilamellar liposomes in aqueous solutions containing various concentrations of large, neutral polymers such as dextran or poly(vinylpyrrolidone) (39, 40, 65) and (*b*) by exposing oriented multilayers to constant relative humidity atmospheres (53, 65). The range of pressures that can be applied with these two techniques overlap, and it has been shown (53, 65) that the same bilayer separation is obtained with equivalent pressure applied by each method.

Lamellar X-ray diffraction patterns are recorded for each lipid system at each value of osmotic pressure and directly provide the lamellar repeat period as a function of applied pressure. However, the lamellar repeat period contains two components, the width of the bilayer and the width of the fluid space between adjacent bilayers. Two different methods have been used to analyze the X-ray data to obtain the distance between bilayers at each applied osmotic pressure.

GRAVIMETRIC ANALYSIS OF X-RAY DATA   Rand, Parsegian, and colleagues used the gravimetric method in their pioneering osmotic stress experiments (39, 40, 42, 65) as well as in their more recent studies (for recent reviews, see 38, 71). In this method, first developed by Luzzati (43), one assumes that the lamellar repeat period d can be divided into two distinct layers, a lipid layer with thickness d_l and a fluid layer with thickness d_w, so that $d = d_l + d_w$. If the volume fraction of water in the sample (ϕ_w) is known, then d_w can be calculated by $d_w = \phi_w d$. For the osmotic stress experiments, one measures ϕ_w gravimetrically in a separate series of X-ray experiments with lipid-water mixtures (39, 40, 42, 65).

Although accurately measuring ϕ_w can be difficult (35, 85), the gravimetric method is quite useful for analyzing long-range interactions. However, in the case of short-range interactions, the gravimetric method includes the problematical assumption that the specimen contains separate lipid and water layers. Thus, when applied to an analysis of pressure-distance data, this model of separate lipid and water layers implicitly assumes that no short-range steric interactions occur between apposing lipid layers until all of the water is removed from the system. In addition, because the lipid head group region contains a significant amount of water (17, 77, 88), the gravimetric method produces a fluid layer that in fact extends well into the lipid head group. For PC bilayers, where the polar head group has a thickness of about 10 Å, this has the effect of significantly increasing the range of the hydration pressure.

FOURIER (ELECTRON DENSITY PROFILE) ANALYSIS OF X-RAY DATA   Many investigators have used the Fourier method to determine the organization of lipid bilayers (15, 41, 50, 51, 82, 86) as well as to interpret osmotic stress data (53–55, 57, 60, 62, 74, 76, 78, 79). This method does not require separate gravimetric measurements of repeat period–water volume fraction (ϕ_w) relations, but instead uses measured X-ray intensities from each osmotic stress experiment to obtain one-dimensional electron density profiles across the bilayer and adjacent fluid space. Such profiles are used to estimate directly the width of the fluid space between bilayers for each applied osmotic pressure (60). Specifically, the positions of the high density peaks in the profiles, which correspond to the phospholipid head groups, are used to estimate the distance between apposing bilayers for each applied pressure (53, 54, 60).

The Fourier method requires that several orders of lamellar diffraction must be recorded from each osmotic stress experiment in order to obtain electron density profiles of reasonable resolution (about 6 Å). At this moderate resolution, modeling analyses in both real and reciprocal space have shown that changes in bilayer thickness on the order of 1–2 Å can be detected (60). Such moderate-resolution data cannot always be obtained for fluid bilayers with large interbilayer spacings. However, 6-Å resolution diffraction patterns can almost always be recorded for phospholipid bilayers with fluid spacing less than about 20 Å, so that the Fourier method is applicable for the measurement of short-range interactions such as hydration and steric pressures.

PRESSURE-DISTANCE DATA

Pressure-distance data have been obtained for several lipid bilayer systems using either the surface force apparatus or the osmotic stress method. In this review we focus on the short-range interactions measured using the osmotic stress method. To simplify the data comparison between different bilayer systems, all of the illustrations of pressure-distance relations presented below were obtained with the electron density profile method.

Phosphorylcholine-Containing Phospholipids: Phosphatidylcholine and Sphingomyelin

The most common phospholipid in biological membranes, phosphatidylcholine (PC) (Figure 1), is also the most extensively studied system. Much of the first pressure-distance data was obtained from PC derived from egg yolk (EPC). At room temperature, EPC is in the liquid crystalline bilayer phase, in which the lipid hydrocarbon chains have a similar organization to the lipids in biological membranes. Figure 1 shows our definition for the plane of origin (solid line) that we estimated from electron density profiles (53–55, 57, 60, 62, 76, 78). This estimation of d_f represents a maximum fluid spacing, because the lipids and head groups exhibit some out-of-plane motions.

Figure 2 shows a plot of $\log P$ versus d_f for EPC bilayers. As the applied pressure is increased from 0 dyn/cm^2 to about 1×10^5 dyn/cm^2 ($\log P \approx 5$), the fluid space decreases less than 2 Å from the equilibrium fluid separation in excess water of about 15 Å. As the applied pressure further increased from 1×10^5 dyn/cm^2 to 3×10^7 dyn/cm^2 ($\log P \approx 7.5$), d_f decreases from about 13 to about 4 Å. For this range of d_f the data points fit closely with the single straight line shown in Figure 2, so that $P = P_0 \exp(-d_f/\lambda)$, with $P_0 = 4 \times 10^8$ dyn/cm^2 and $\lambda = 1.7$ Å (60). Repulsive pressures that decay exponentially with similar decay constants and magnitudes have been determined for a variety of phosphatidylcholine bilayer systems (see Table 8 in 71). This exponential decaying pressure is commonly referred to as the hydration pressure (39, 40, 42, 54, 60, 65, 71), and one should note that the exponential dependence extends over a range of 2 to 3 log units and over a range of fluid spacings of about 10 Å.

A distinct upward break in the pressure-distance relation occurs at an applied pressure of $\log P \approx 7.5$ and $d_f \approx 4$–5 Å. We have argued that this upward break results from the onset of steric repulsion between the lipid head groups from apposing bilayers (53, 54). The rather bulky and mobile head groups can extend beyond the plane of origin into the fluid space between bilayers (Figure 1) owing to either head group motion or lipid protrusions. Figure 1 depicts the two extremes of head-group orientation as determined by structural analysis (21) and shows that head group motion should begin to cause steric hindrance between the PC head groups at fluid spacings of 4–6 Å. Consistent with this idea, NMR spectra of PC bilayers show that with decreasing hydration the N^+ end of the phosphocholine group moves closer to the hydrocarbon layer (4).

If the upward break at $d_f \approx 4$ Å in the pressure distance (Figure 2) indeed arises from the onset of steric hindrance between head groups from apposing bilayers, then the sharpness and magnitude of the break should be a function of the surface density of PC head groups at the interface. That is, decreasing the surface density should decrease this pressure. One can experimentally increase the area per PC head group in two ways: (a) by incorporating into the bilayer cholesterol, which acts as a spacer molecule between PC molecules in the plane of the bilayer (54), and (b) by forming an interdigitated gel phase in which lipid chains from apposing monolayers of the bilayer fully interdigitate, thereby increasing the area per lipid head group (58, 69).

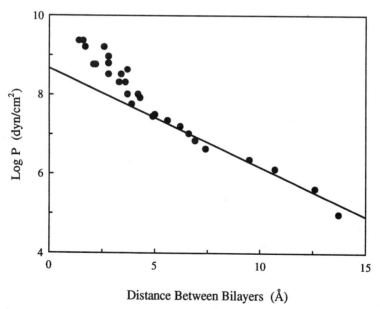

Figure 2   Plot of logarithm of applied pressure (log$P$) versus distance between bilayers (d_f) for egg phosphatidylcholine. The solid line is the least squares fit to the data points for 4 Å $< d_f <$ 15 Å. Data are from Refs. 53, 60.

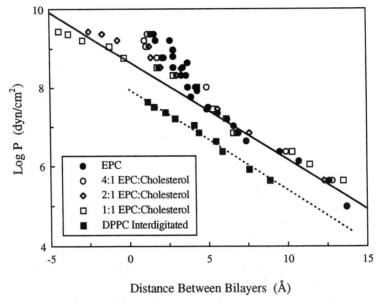

Figure 3 Plot of log*P* versus d_f for EPC (*solid circles*), 4:1 EPC:cholesterol (*open circles*), 2:1 EPC:cholesterol (*open diamonds*), equimolar EPC:cholesteral (*open squares*), and DPPC in the interdigitated phase (*solid squares*). The solid line is the least squares fit ot the EPC data points for 4 Å < d_f < 15 Å and the dotted line is the least squares fit to the DPPC data. Data are from Refs. 53, 54, 60, 78.

Figure 3 shows pressure-distance data from bilayers of EPC containing various concentrations of cholesterol and for dipalmitoyl phosphatidylcholine (DPPC) in the interdigitated phase. The areas per EPC
head group are 64 Å^2 for EPC, 69 Å^2 for 4:1 EPC:cholesterol, 74 Å^2
for 2:1 EPC:cholesterol, and 89 Å^2 for 1:1 EPC:cholesterol (37). The
area per molecule for DPPC in the interdigitated phase is about 78 Å^2
(78). The solid line in Figure 3 represents the fit for EPC and illustrates
that the decay length of the exponentially decaying pressure for d_f >
5 Å is not markedly changed by the incorporation of cholesterol. The
deviation of the data points from this line for d_f < 4 Å decreases with
increasing area per EPC head group. Note in particular that in the EPC:
cholesterol (1:1) pressure-distance relation the upward break for d_f <
4 Å is minimal. Calculations (54) show that incorporation of equimolar
cholesterol spreads the PC molecules apart in the plane of the bilayer
enough to allow the PC head groups from apposing bilayers to inter-
penetrate as the bilayers squeeze together. Thus, at high applied pressures (log*P* > 8.5) PC head groups from apposing bilayers interpene-

trate so that d_f becomes less than 0 Å, a conclusion supported by the merging of head group peaks from apposing bilayers in electron density profiles (54). Also, no detectable upward break occurs in the $\log P$-d_f relation for DPPC in the interdigitated phase for 1 Å $< d_f <$ 8 Å. Therefore, all of these data show that the upward break in the pressure-distance relation is a function of the surface density of PC head groups, providing strong evidence that this upward break results from steric hindrance between head groups from apposing bilayers.

For $\log P > 7.5$ for EPC, the $\log P$ versus d_f data can be fit with an exponential decay with a decay length of about 0.6 Å (53), a result not predicted by Equation 9, unless the effective length of the polar head group is 1.9 Å, a value too small to be reasonable. Clearly more detailed theoretical models of the interaction between polar head groups are required to describe these data.

We now consider the possible origins of the exponentially decaying repulsive pressures for $d_f > 5$ Å. A series of experiments with different physical phases of PC bilayers provided information on the relative roles played by hydration and entropic (steric) pressures in the total short-range pressure between bilayers. We (61) compared pressure-distance values for bilayers in the liquid crystalline and subgel phases because in the liquid crystalline phase the lipid hydrocarbon chains and head groups are mobile (Figure 1), whereas in the subgel phase the acyl chains are crystallized in the plane of the bilayer and the polar head group motion is severely restricted (1). Therefore, entropic pressures resulting from bilayer undulations or molecular protrusions should be much smaller in the subgel phase than in the liquid crystalline phase. Figure 4 shows measured $\log P$-d_f relations for EPC in the liquid crystalline phase and for DPPC in the subgel phase. For the range 4 Å $< d_f <$ 8 Å, the data points for the two bilayers are very similar, which suggests that for this small range the mechanism(s) underlying the repulsive pressure is the same. We argue that, since entropic steric pressures must be small for the subgel phase over this range, this pressure is probably a hydration pressure due to removal of water oriented by the polar head groups. Also, because the decay lengths for the hydration pressure are similar for bilayers in the liquid crystalline phase, interdigitated phase, and subgel phases, surface correlations as predicted from Equation 4 (36) do not contribute significantly to the measured hydration pressure.

The differences between the two pressure-distance relations (Figure 4) for $d_f < 4$ Å and $d_f > 8$ Å can be explained by differences in the steric interactions for the two phases. Specifically, for $d_f < 4$ Å, the upward break in the pressure-distance relation is much sharper for the

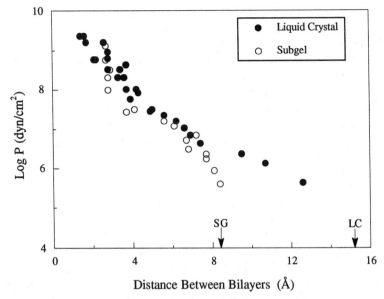

Figure 4 Plot of logarithm of applied pressure versus distance between bilayers for EPC in the liquid crystalline phase (*solid circles*) and for DPPC in the subgel phase (*open circles*). Arrows indicate fluid separations in the absence of applied pressure for the liquid crystalline (LC) and subgel (SG) phases. Data are from Refs. 53, 61.

subgel phase than for the liquid crystalline phase or for the gel phase of sphingomyelin (SM) (see below). This observation is consistent with the upward break resulting from steric hindrance between head groups from apposing bilayers (61). The observation that the total repulsive pressure extends to larger fluid spaces so that the equilibrium fluid separation is significantly larger in the liquid-crystalline than in the subgel phase (Figure 4) can be explained (61) by the presence of an additional pressure in the liquid crystalline phase caused by thermally driven bilayer undulations (11, 13, 23). Theoretical treatments (11, 13, 23) have indicated that the undulation pressure should extend the range of the underlying repulsive pressure (in this case the hydration pressure), as shown experimentally in Figure 4. This behavior is also observed between monoglycerides whose bending moduli differ greatly (56). However, because the data for liquid crystalline bilayers such as EPC (Figure 2) can be fit to a single exponential of $d_f > 5$ Å, extracting information about the undulation pressure from a single data set is very difficult.

Experiments were also performed to test various models outlined above for the short-range pressure for $d_f > 5$ Å. Specifically, we tested whether the measured pressure depends on disruption of the H-bond distribution in the solvent (2), interfacial structure of the polar surface (6), molecular protrusions (30, 31), and the magnitude of the polarizing electric field (7). To address these points, we studied three types of bilayers. (a) The first contained 6-ketocholestanol, a steroid molecule with a large dipole moment located at the hydrocarbon-water interface (14, 79). (b) The second type was composed of sphingomyelin (SM). This molecule has the same polar head group as PC but a different backbone, which may influence water structure differently. In addition, SM exists in a gel phase at 20°C, so that the protrusion pressure should be small. (c) The final type consisted of bilayers formed in nonaqueous solvents of widely different sizes, dielectric constants, and surface tensions (55). In all cases we measured the resulting changes in both the hydration pressure (or, more acurately in the case of nonaqueous solvents, the solvation pressure) and the electric (dipole) potential (44). To test explicitly the hypothesis that the hydration pressure depends on electric fields produced by the bilayer, we (76) equated the measured value of the dipole potential (V) to the hydration potential (Ψ_h) in Equation 3. With this substitution, Equation 3 predicts that the magnitude of the hydration pressure can be written (76)

$$P_0 = 2\chi(V/\lambda)^2. \hspace{4cm} 10.$$

The $\log P$ versus d_f data for bilayers composed of EPC, EPC:ketocholestanol, and SM (Figure 5) show that for $d_f > 5$ Å the repulsive pressure for each of these systems decays exponentially with approximately the same decay constant. This result indicates that the decay length does not depend greatly on the details of the surface topology or distributions of dipoles in the interface. Thus, these data are inconsistent with models of the hydration pressure involving: (a) H-bond distributions influencing the decay length, because the H-bond distribution could not be the same in these three bilayers, and (b) implicit contributions of the charge density of the head group (Equation 5). Also, for EPC and SM bilayers, the $\log P$ versus d_f data are nearly the same for 2 Å $< d_f < 12$ Å, and both data sets show an upward break at $d_f \approx 4$ Å. Since SM is in the gel phase and EPC is in the fluid phase, these data indicate that molecular protrusions are not likely to contribute much to the magnitude of the repulsive pressures for this range of d_f. Furthermore, comparisons of the dotted and solid lines in Figure 5 show that the magnitude of the hydration pressure (P_0), but not the

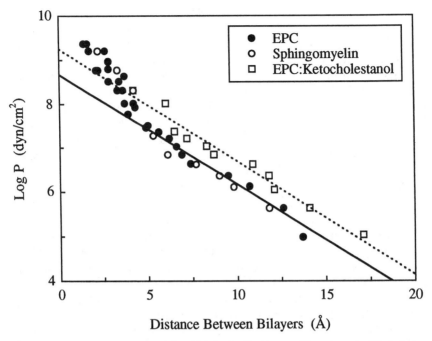

Figure 5 Plot of log*P* versus d_f for EPC in the liquid crystalline phase (*solid circles*), sphingomyelin in the gel phase (*open circles*), and equimolar EPC:ketocholestanol bilayers (*open squares*). The solid line is the least squares fit to the EPC data points for 4 Å < d_f < 15 Å, and the dotted line is the least squares fit to the EPC:ketocholestanol data. Data are from Refs. 53, 60, 79.

decay length, increases with the incorporation of equimolar ketocholestanol to EPC (79). Moreover, the incorporation of equimolar ketocholestanol into EPC monolayers increases V from 415 to 703 mV, a change that correctly predicts the increase in P_0 from Equation 10 (79). In the experiments where EPC and EPC:cholesterol bilayers were formed in two nonaqueous solvents, formamide and 1,3-propanediol, the measured values of V and P_0 for lipids in these solvents decrease by corresponding amounts (55). In addition, decay length (λ) increases by an amount related to the size of the solvent molecule (61).

Figure 6 shows the results of all of our experiments with phospholipid bilayers relating the magnitude of the hydration pressure (P_0) to the dipole potential (V). This figure includes data obtained with liquid crystalline and gel-phase PC bilayers (60, 74), bilayers containing cholesterol (54) and ketocholestanol (79), SM bilayers (62), and bilayers in nonaqueous solvents (55). The plot in Figure 6 shows that P_0 increases with increasing $(V/\lambda)^2$. Because V arises from the dipoles (and multi-poles) of both the lipid polar head groups and the associated solvent molecules (80, 89), we argue that the correlation shown in Figure 6 indicates that (a) the repulsive pressure for $d_f > 5$ Å (Figure 2) involves oriented solvent molecules, so it must be, at least in part, a true hydration pressure, and (b) electric fields are at least a factor in orienting interlamellar water molecules and in causing P_h (74, 76, 79). The experiments with ketocholestanol are particularly significant in showing the importance of dipole fields, because the location of this molecule deep in the bilayer would preclude direct hydrogen bond formation between ketocholestanol and interlamellar water (79). The fact that the correlation between P_0 and $(V/\lambda)^2$ is not perfect can be rationalized by several factors. First, there is a large uncertainty in the determination of P_0 by extrapolating to $d_f = 0$ from the observed pressure-distance data points (Figures 2–5). Second, as discussed elsewhere (53–55, 60, 76, 79), there is uncertainty in the location of the plane of origin, where $d_f = 0$.

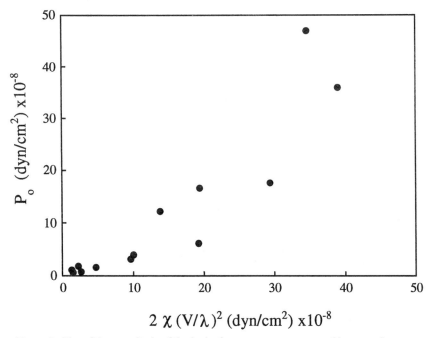

Figure 6 Plot of the magnitude of the hydration pressure as measured by osmotic stress experiments (P_0) and the quantity $2\chi(V/\lambda)^2$, where χ is the orientational susceptibility of water and V is the measured dipole potential. Data are taken from Refs. 54, 55, 60, 62, 74, 76, 79.

Taken together, the results of all the experiments with PC and SM systems indicate that both hydration pressure and steric pressures contribute to the total repulsive pressures between bilayers. The major pieces of evidence for the presence of the hydration pressure are: (a) the similarity of $\log P$ versus d_f data for liquid crystalline–phase EPC and gel-phase SM data (Figure 5), (b) the similarity of $\log P$ versus d_f data for liquid crystalline–phase EPC and subgel-phase DPPC for 4 Å $< d_f < 8$ Å (Figure 4), and (c) the correlation between P_0 and the polarizing electric field as given by $(V/\lambda)^2$ (Figure 6). The upward breaks in the $\log P$ versus d_f data suggest the presence of a very short-range steric pressure due to head group overlap; the sharpness of these breaks depends on the surface density and mobility of PC head groups (Figures 2–5). Evidence for the presence of longer range steric pressure(s), probably primarily caused by bilayer undulations, is the extended range of the $\log P$ versus d_f data for liquid crystalline bilayers as compared with subgel bilayers (Figure 4).

Phosphatidylethanolamine

Data obtained with both the surface force apparatus (47) and with the osmotic stress technique (60, 70) clearly show that the total interbilayer pressure is very different for PE and PC bilayers. Figure 7 compares the pressure-distance data from EPC and bacterial PE (BPE), both naturally occurring lipids that form liquid crystalline bilayers at 20°C. At full hydration the fluid space between adjacent BPE bilayers is about 5 Å, compared with 15 Å for EPC, and at each applied pressure the interbilayer space is smaller for BPE than for EPC bilayers. Rand et al (70) have collected pressure-distance data for a variety of PEs and PE analogs. They find that the addition of relatively small amounts of PC to PE bilayers causes a large increase in the interbilayer fluid space and that a single methylation of the amine in PE almost completely converts the hydration properties to those of PC. They also found that successive methylations produce little further hydration.

Several possible explanations for the differences in the pressure-distance behavior for PC and PE bilayers have been proposed, including H-bond water bridges between PE bilayers (59), the presence of an attractive hydration pressure between PE bilayers (70), the presence of head group correlations (38), and the formation of H-bonds between the ammonium hydrogens on one lipid with the phosphate group on a lipid in the apposing bilayer (9). Because the equilibrium distance between adjacent PE bilayers in excess water is so small, the magnitude of the van der Waals pressure is large compared with the repulsive pressure over the entire observed pressure-distance range.

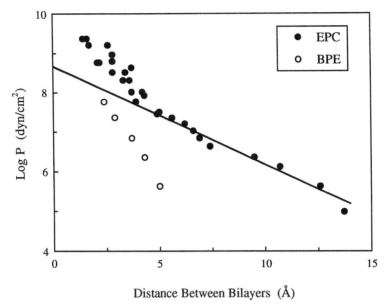

Figure 7   Plot of logarithm of applied pressure versus distance between bilayers for EPC (*solid circles*) and bacterial PE (*open circles*). The solid line is the least squares fit to the EPC data points for 4 Å < d_f < 15 Å. Data are from Refs. 53, 60.

This makes it extremely difficult to extract the repulsive pressure for PE from the total pressure-distance relation. Thus, at present there is no definitive evidence for the reasons that the two major phospholipids in biological membranes have such different hydration properties.

CONCLUSIONS

The total repulsive pressure between electrically neutral liquid crystalline phosphatidylcholine bilayers contains contributions from both the hydration pressure, resulting from partially oriented water molecules, and steric pressures, resulting from lipid motion and bilayer undulations. Experiments with gel and subgel PC bilayers indicate that the range of the hydration pressure is on the order of 4–10 Å, or one or two water molecules from each bilayer surface. For liquid crystalline PC bilayers, steric interactions increase the range of the total repulsive pressure to about 15 Å.

ACKNOWLEDGMENTS

We thank Dr. Alan Magid for his many contributions to the work described in this review. This research was supported by NIH grant GM-27278.

Literature Cited

1. Akutsu H, Ikematsu M, Kyogoku Y. 1981. Molecular structure and interaction of dipalmitoylphosphatidylcholine in multilayers. Comparative study with phosphatidylethanolamine. *Chem. Phys. Lipids* 28:149–58

2. Attard P, Batchelor MT. 1988. A mechanism for the hydration force demonstrated in a model system. *Chem. Phys. Lett.* 149:206–11

3. Attard P, Wei D, Patey GN. 1990. Critical comments on the nonlocal dielectric function employed in recent theories of the hydration force. *Chem. Phys. Lett.* 172:69–72

4. Bechinger B, Seelig J. 1991. Conformational changes of the phosphatidylcholine headgroup due to membrane dehydration. A 2H-NMR study. *Chem. Phys. Lipids* 58:1–5

5. Bloom M, Evans E, Mouritsen OG. 1991. Physical properties of the fluid-bilayer component of cell membranes: a perspective. *Q. Rev. Biophys.* 24:293–397

6. Cevc G. 1991. Hydration force and the interfacial structure of the polar surface. *J. Chem. Soc. Faraday Trans.* 87:2333–79

7. Cevc G, Marsh D. 1985. Hydration of noncharged lipid bilayer membranes. Theory and experiments with phosphatidylethanolamine. *Biophys. J.* 47:21–32

8. Christenson HK, Horn RG. 1985. Forces between mica surfaces in ethylene glycol. *J. Colloid Interface Sci.* 103:50–55

9. Damodaran KV, Merz KM. 1993. Headgroup-water interactions in lipid bilayers: a comparison between DMPC- and DLPE-based lipid bilayers. *Langmuir* 9:1179–83

10. Derjaguin BV, Landau L. 1941. *Acta Physiochim. USSR* 14:633–62

11. Evans E, Ipsen J. 1991. Entropy-driven extension of electric double-layer repulsion between highly flexible membranes. *Electrochim. Acta* 36:1735–41

12. Evans E, Needham D. 1987. Physical properties of surfactant bilayer membranes: thermal transitions, elasticity, rigidity, cohesion, and colloidal interactions. *J. Phys. Chem.* 91:4219–28

13. Evans EA, Parsegian VA. 1986. Thermal-mechanical fluctuations enhance repulsion between bimolecular layers. *Proc. Natl. Acad. Sci. USA* 83:7132–36

14. Franklin JC, Cafiso DS. 1993. Internal electrostatic potentials in bilayers: measuring and controlling dipole potentials in lipid vesicles. *Biophys. J.* 65:289–99

15. Franks NP. 1976. Structural analysis of hydrated egg lecithin and cholesterol bilayers. I. X- ray diffraction. *J. Mol. Biol.* 100:345–58

16. Gawrisch K, Parsegian VA, Hajduk DA, Tate MW, Gruner SM, et al. 1992. Energetics of a hexagonal-lamellar-hexagonal-phase transition sequence in DOPE membranes. *Biochemistry* 31:2856–64

17. Griffith OH, Dehlinger PJ, Van SP. 1974. Shape of the hydrophobic barrier of phospholipid bilayers: evidence for water penetration in biological membranes. *J. Membr. Biol.* 15:159–92

18. Gruen DWR, Marcelja S. 1983. Spatially varying polarization in water. *J. Chem. Soc. Faraday Trans. 2* 79:225–42

19. Hadziioannou G, Patel S, Granick S, Tirrell M. 1986. Forces between surfaces of block copolymers adsorbed on mica. *J. Am. Chem. Soc.* 108:2869–76

20. Harbich W, Helfrich W. 1984. The swelling of egg lecithin in water. *Chem. Phys. Lipids* 36:39–63

21. Hauser H. 1981. The polar group con-

formation of 1,2-dialkyl phosphatidyl-cholines. An NMR study. *Biochim. Biophys. Acta* 646:203–10

22. Hauser H, Pascher I, Pearson RH, Sundell S. 1981. Preferred conformation and molecular packing of phosphatidylethanolamine and phosphatidylcholine. *Biochim. Biophys. Acta* 650:21–51

23. Helfrich W. 1973. Elastic properties of lipid bilayers: theory and possible experiments. *Z. Naturforsch.* 28C:693–703

24. Hitchcock PB, Mason R, Thomas KM, Shipley GG. 1974. Structural chemistry of 1,2 dilauroyl-DL-phosphatidylethanolamine: molecular conformation and intermolecular packing of phospholipids. *Proc. Natl. Acad. Sci. USA* 71:3036–40

25. Horn RG, Israelachvili JN, Marra J, Parsegian VA, Rand RP. 1988. Comparison of forces measured between phosphatidylcholine bilayers. *Biophys. J.* 54:1185–86

26. Ipsen JH, Mouritsen OG, Bloom M. 1990. Relationships between lipid membrane area, hydrophobic thickness, and acyl-chain orientational order. The effects of cholesterol. *Biophys. J.* 57:405–12

27. Israelachvili J. 1987. Direct measurements of forces between surfaces in liquids at the molecular level. *Proc. Natl. Acad. Sci. USA* 84:4722–24

28. Israelachvili JN. 1991. *Intermolecular and Surface Forces*. London: Academic

29. Israelachvili JN, Adams GE. 1976. Direct measurement of long range forces between two mica surfaces in aqueous KNO_3 solutions. *Nature* 262:774–76

30. Israelachvili JN, Wennerstrom H. 1990. Hydration or steric forces between amphiphilic surfaces? *Langmuir* 6:873–76

31. Israelachvili JN, Wennerstrom H. 1992. Entropic forces between amphiphilic surfaces in liquids. *J. Phys. Chem.* 96:520–31

32. Kjellander R, Marcelja S. 1985. Inhomogeneous Coulomb fluids with image interactions between planar surfaces. *J. Chem. Phys.* 82:2122–35

33. Kjellander R, Marcelja S. 1985. Interactions between ionic surface layers. *Chem. Scr.* 25:112–16

34. Klein J, Luckham P. 1982. Forces between two adsorbed polyethylene oxide layers immersed in a good aqueous solvent. *Nature* 300:429–30

35. Klose G, Konig B, Meyer HW, Schulze G, Degovics G. 1988. Small-angle x-ray scattering and electron microscopy of crude dispersions of swelling lipids and the influence of the morphology on the repeat distance. *Chem. Phys. Lipids* 47:225–34

36. Kornyshev AA, Leikin S. 1989. Fluctuation theory of hydration forces: the dramatic effect of inhomogeneous boundary conditions. *Phys. Rev. A* 40:6431–37

37. Lecuyer H, Dervichian DG. 1969. Structure of aqueous mixtures of lecithin and cholesterol. *J. Mol. Biol.* 45:39–57

38. Leikin S, Parsegian VA, Rau DC. 1993. Hydration forces. *Annu. Rev. Phys. Chem.* 44:367–95

39. LeNeveu DM, Rand RP, Parsegian VA. 1976. Measurement of forces between lecithin bilayers. *Nature* 259:601–3

40. LeNeveu DM, Rand RP, Parsegian VA, Gingell D. 1977. Measurement and modification of forces between lecithin bilayers. *Biophys. J.* 18:209–30

41. Lesslauer W, Cain JE, Blasie JK. 1972. X-ray diffraction studies of lecithin bimolecular leaflets with incorporated fluorescent probes. *Proc. Natl. Acad. Sci. USA* 69:1499–1503

42. Lis LJ, McAlister M, Fuller N, Rand RP, Parsegian VA. 1982. Interactions between neutral phospholipid bilayer membranes. *Biophys. J.* 37:657–66

43. Luzzati, V. 1968. X-ray diffraction studies of lipid-water systems. In *Biological Membranes*, ed. D Chapman, pp. 71–125. New York: Academic

44. MacDonald RC, Simon SA. 1987. Lipid monolayer states and their relationship to bilayers. *Proc. Natl. Acad. Sci. USA* 84:4089–94

45. Marcelja S, Radic N. 1976. Repulsion of interfaces due to boundary water. *Chem. Phys. Lett.* 42:129–30

46. Marra J. 1986. Direct measurement of the interaction between phosphatidylglycerol bilayers in aqueous electrolyte solutions. *Biophys. J.* 50:815–25

47. Marra J, Israelachvili J. 1985. Direct measurements of forces between phosphatidylcholine and phosphatidylethanolamine bilayers in aqueous electrolyte solutions. *Biochemistry* 24:4608–18

48. Marrink S-J, Berkowitz M, Berendsen HJC. 1993. Molecular dynamics simulation of a membrane/water interface: origin of the hydration force. *Langmuir*. In press

49. Marsh D. 1990. *CRC Handbook of Lipid Bilayers*, p. 156. Boca Raton, FL: CRC Press

50. Mattai J, Sripada PK, Shipley GG. 1987. Mixed-chain phosphatidylcholine bilayers: structure and properties. *Biochemistry* 26:3287–97

51. McIntosh TJ. 1978. The effect of cholesterol on the structure of phosphatidylcholine bilayers. *Biochim. Biophys. Acta* 513:43–58

52. McIntosh TJ, Magid AD. 1993. Phospholipid hydration. In *Phospholipid Handbook*, ed. G Cevc, pp. 553–77. New York: Marcel Dekker

53. McIntosh TJ, Magid AD, Simon SA. 1987. Steric repulsion between phosphatidylcholine bilayers. *Biochemistry* 26:7325–32

54. McIntosh TJ, Magid AD, Simon SA. 1989. Cholesterol modifies the short-range repulsive interactions between phosphatidylcholine membranes. *Biochemistry* 28:17–25

55. McIntosh TJ, Magid AD, Simon SA. 1989. Range of the solvation pressure between lipid membranes: dependence on the packing density of solvent molecules. *Biochemistry* 28: 7904–12

56. McIntosh TJ, Magid AD, Simon SA. 1989. Repulsive interactions between uncharged bilayers. Hydration and fluctuation pressures for monoglycerides. *Biophys. J.* 55:897–904

57. McIntosh TJ, Magid AD, Simon SA. 1990. Interactions between charged, uncharged, and zwitterionic bilayers containing phosphatidylglycerol. *Biophys. J.* 57:1187–97

58. McIntosh TJ, McDaniel RV, Simon SA. 1983. Induction of an interdigitated gel phase in fully hydrated lecithin bilayers. *Biochim. Biophys. Acta* 731:109–14

59. McIntosh TJ, Simon SA. 1986. Area per molecule and distribution of water in fully hydrated dilauroylphosphatidylethanolamine bilayers. *Biochemistry* 25:4948–52

60. McIntosh TJ, Simon SA. 1986. The hydration force and bilayer deformation: a reevaluation. *Biochemistry* 25:4058–66

61. McIntosh TJ, Simon SA. 1993. Contribution of hydration and steric (entropic) pressures to the interaction between phosphatidylcholine bilayers: Experiments with the subgel phase. *Biochemistry* 32:8374–84

62. McIntosh TJ, Simon SA, Needham D, Huang C-h. 1992. Interbilayer interactions between sphingomyelin and sphingomyelin:cholesterol bilayers. *Biochemistry* 31:2020–24

63. Nagle JF, Wiener MC. 1988. Structure of fully hydrated bilayer dispersions. *Biochim. Biophys. Acta* 942:1–10

64. Ninham BW. 1989. Hydration forces—real and imagined. *Chem. Scr.* 29A:15–21

65. Parsegian, VA, Fuller, N, Rand, RP. 1979. Measured work of deformation and repulsion of lecithin bilayers. *Proc. Natl. Acad. Sci. USA* 76:2750–54

66. Parsegian VA, Rand RP. 1991. On molecular protrusion as the source of hydration forces. *Langmuir* 7:1299–1301

67. Pearson RH, Pascher I. 1979. The molecular structure of lecithin dihydrate. *Nature* 281:499–501

68. Pfeiffer W, Henke T, Sackmann E, Knoll W, Richter D. 1989. Local dynamics of lipid bilayers studied by incoherent quasi-elastic neutron scattering. *Europhys. Lett.* 8:201–6

69. Ranck JL, Keira T, Luzzati V. 1977. A novel packing of the hydrocarbon chains in lipids. The low temperature phase of DPPG. *Biochim. Biophys. Acta* 488:432–41

70. Rand RP, Fuller N, Parsegian VA, Rau DC. 1988. Variation in hydration forces between neutral phospholipid bilayers: evidence for hydration attraction. *Biochemistry* 27:7711–22

71. Rand RP, Parsegian VA. 1989. Hydration forces between phospholipid bilayers. *Biochim. Biophys. Acta* 988: 351–76

72. Rau DC, Lee B, Parsegian VA. 1984. Measurement of the repulsive force between polyelectrolyte molecules in ionic solution: hydration forces between parallel DNA double helices. *Proc. Natl. Acad. Sci. USA* 81:2612–25

73. Rau DC, Parsegian VA. 1990. Direct measurement of forces between linear polysaccharides xanthan and schizophyllan. *Science* 249:1278–81

74. Simon SA, Fink CA, Kenworthy AK, McIntosh TJ. 1991. The hydration pressure between lipid bilayers: a comparison of measurements using x-ray diffraction and calorimetry. *Biophys. J.* 59:538–46

75. Simon SA, McIntosh TJ. 1986. The depth of water penetration into lipid bilayers. *Methods Enzymol.* 127:511–21

76. Simon SA, McIntosh TJ. 1989. Magnitude of the solvation pressure depends on dipole potential. *Proc. Natl. Acad. USA* 86:9263–67

77. Simon SA, McIntosh TJ, Latorre R. 1982. Influence of cholesterol on water penetration into bilayers. *Science* 216:65–67

78. Simon SA, McIntosh TJ, Magid AD. 1988. Magnitude and range of the hydration pressure between lecithin bilayers as a function of head group density. *J. Colloid Interface Sci.* 126:74–83

79. Simon SA, McIntosh TJ, Magid AD, Needham D. 1992. Modulation of the interbilayer hydration pressure by the addition of dipoles at the hydrocarbon/water interface. *Biophys. J.* 61:786–99

80. Smaby JM, Brockman HL. 1990. Surface dipole moments of lipids at the argon-water interface. Similarities among glycerol-ester-based lipids. *Biophys. J.* 58:195–204

81. Smith GS, Sirota EB, Safinya CR, Plano RJ, Clark NA. 1990. X-ray structural studies of freely suspended ordered hydrated DMPC multimembrane films. *J. Chem. Phy.* 92:4519–29

82. Torbet J, Wilkins MHF. 1976. X-ray diffraction studies of lecithin bilayers. *J. Mol. Biol.* 62:447–58

83. Tsao Y-h, Evans DF, Rand RP, Parsegian VA. 1993. Osmotic stress measurements of dihexadecyldimethylammonium acetate bilayers as a function of temperature and added salt. *Langmuir* 9:233–41

84. Verwey EJW, Overbeek JTG. 1948. *Theory of the Stability of Lyophobic Colloids*. Amsterdam: Elsevier

85. Wiener MC, Suter RM, Nagle JF. 1989. Structure of the fully hydrated gel phase of dipalmitoylphosphatidylcholine. *Biophys. J.* 55:315–25

86. Wiener MC, White SH. 1991. Fluid bilayer structure determination by the combined use of x-ray and neutron diffraction. II. "Composition-space" refinement method. *Biophys. J.* 59:174–85

87. Wong PTT, Mantsch HH. 1988. High-pressure infrared spectroscopic evidence of water binding sites in 1,2-diacyl phospholipids. *Chem. Phys. Lipids* 46:213–24

88. Worcester DL, Franks NP. 1976. Structural analysis of hydrated egg lecithin and cholesterol bilayers. II. Neutron diffraction. *J. Mol. Biol.* 100:359–78

89. Zheng C, Vanderkooi G. 1992. Molecular origin of the internal dipole potential in lipid bilayers: calculation of the electrostatic potential. *Biophys. J.* 63:935–41

Annu. Rev. Biophys. Biomol. Struct. 1994. 23:53–86

DNA BRANCHED JUNCTIONS

Nadrian C. Seeman and Neville R. Kallenbach

Department of Chemistry, New York University, New York, NY 10003

KEY WORDS: Holliday junctions, genetic recombination,
              macromolecular structure, molecular design,
              nanotechnology

CONTENTS

PERSPECTIVES AND OVERVIEW

Genetic recombination entails the interaction of two molecules of DNA to yield new genetic material that may include insertions, dele-

1056–8700/94/0610–0053$05.00

tions, changes in sequence, rearrangements, or exchanges of flanking markers. The best-known molecular paradigm in recombination is the Holliday junction (40). This branched DNA structure is known to be an intermediate in site-specific recombination (39, 42, 52, 79) and is thought to be involved in homologous recombination (18). As shown in Figure 1, the Holliday junction may be formed by the exchange of homologous strands; the joint in this structure, or the branch point, is free to migrate throughout the entire region of homology. Branch migration is a direct consequence of homologous, or two-fold, sequence symmetry. This isomerization (49, 53) makes studying naturally occurring Holliday junctions and the way they interact with recombination enzymes difficult because the branch points of individual junctions in a population of junctions may be at different positions. Molecules with stable branch points are necessary to study many of the structural, dynamic, and thermodynamic features of this system.

One can use synthetic oligonucleotides to construct model systems, termed immobile junctions, that fix the branch point precisely (46, 96, 103); in a related class of constructs, partially mobile junctions, migration is limited to a specific number of steps (1, 9, 35, 42, 95). The term immobile here refers only to the ability of the junction to branch migrate and is not meant to suggest any other limitations on its degrees of freedom. The development of immobile and partially mobile junctions has opened a window on the structure and properties of Holliday junctions. Nevertheless, one must realize that immobile junctions are low-symmetry analogues of the Holliday structure; this low symmetry may introduce structural features that differ from those of true Holliday junctions. The secondary structure of branched junctions is formally equivalent to that of cruciform structures extruded from underwound circular DNA molecules (33, 56). Likewise, cruciforms may be an inappropriate system to model the properties of Holliday junctions, because of possible residual torsional stress in the supercoiled arms. The branching discussed here lies at the level of secondary structure. Other branched nucleic acid systems (which are beyond the scope of this review) include primary structure branches from 2′ hydroxyls (43, 80) or from bases (41) and tertiary structure branches involving triple helices (17).

Work in this area depends upon the convenient availability of synthetic oligodeoxynucleotides (7). Early attempts to make partially mobile branched junctions (1, 42, 72) relied on large molecules that could be isolated from natural sources. Small synthetic immobile junctions, tractable to physical and chemical probes, have proved to be of greatest utility. The advantage of synthetic branched molecules is that their sequences can be tailored easily to include features of interest, such

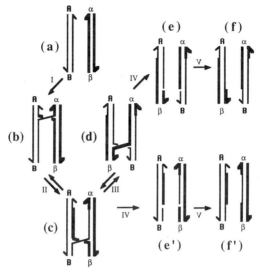

Figure 1 The Holliday junction in recombination. Letters in parentheses show the stages of recombination, while Roman numerals identify the processes that produce them. (*a*) Two homologous double helices of DNA align with each other. The two strands of each duplex are indicated by the two pairs of lines terminated by half arrows, which indicate the 3' ends of the strands. Strands are distinguished by their thickness. Each of these two homologous regions carries a flanking marker, A and B in the case of the strands on the left, and α and β on the right. (*b*) The homologous pairs have formed a Holliday intermediate by exchanging strands. Note that the two crossover strands are composite strands with both a thick and a thin portion formed through any of several possibilities for process I. The two-fold sequence symmetry of this structure permits it to undergo the iterative isomerization process, branch migration (process II); movement in the direction indicated would result in *c*. The Holliday intermediate may or may not undergo isomerization process III to produce *d*, in which the strands are switched (98). This process only has meaning if the Holliday intermediate is two-fold symmetric, rather than four-fold symmetric. If process III occurs an odd number of times, cleavage (process IV) of the crossover strands yields *e*, although *e'* results if III occurs an even number of times before cleavage. Ligation (process V) of *e'* generates a pair of linear duplex DNA molecules that contain heteroduplex DNA because of branch migration, but that have retained the same flanking markers (*f'*). Ligation of *e* yields molecules that have exchanged flanking markers (*f*). Note that a parallel motif has been used for the structure of the junctions.

as minimized sequence symmetry (95, 99), specific nucleotides placed near the branch point (9, 62), restriction sites (10, 25), and hairpin or other loops attached to the ends of double helices (51, 75, 76).

Most structural studies on branched junctions to date have centered on analogues of the four-arm Holliday intermediate. Lilley & Clegg (57) recently reviewed the structural features of the Holliday junction in solution, and West (121) has reviewed the enzymes known to interact with Holliday junctions. In this chapter, we examine the structural features of Holliday junctions to introduce the wider context of their dynamic, thermodynamic, and resolution properties, as well as their interactions with small molecules and protein ligands.

Four-arm junctions are not the only branched DNA molecules that have been explored. Three-arm junctions have been studied in great detail (22, 36, 44, 54, 55, 59, 67, 93, 94), and five- and six-arm structures have also been constructed and characterized (116). In addition, studies have focused on three- (127) and four-arm (23, 128) junctions containing specific mismatches at the branch point. Furthermore, structurally constrained tethered junctions (51) and double-crossover molecules (32) have been analyzed in order to isolate particular conformers of junctions. Here, we discuss these molecules and their uses in explaining the properties of unconstrained junctions.

The unusual topology of the branched junction leads directly to other unusual DNA arrangements. The attachment of sticky ends to branched DNA molecules permits them to be used as the components of stick figures, in which the edges are double helical DNA and the vertices are branch points (95, 100). With this idea in mind, branched junctions have served as the source of vertices in the construction of geometrical objects, such as a quadrilateral and a cube (8, 10). The rationale of this work is the utilization of branched DNA molecules as a means to directed structural assembly, with the ultimate goals of constructing nanoscale devices and periodic matter (92, 100, 101). A consequence of the plectonemic nature of DNA is that the stick figures are complex catenanes that are intimately related to knots (122). Exploration of this aspect of DNA topology has shown that branched junctions can serve as basic units in the construction of single-stranded DNA knots (20, 102), and analysis of knotting structures has shown that branched junctions represent a special case of those multistranded structures in which each strand is associated with two different double helices (102). Other arrangements, called antijunctions and mesojunctions, have also been constructed and compared with branched junctions (21). Hence, branched junctions are related to many aspects of nucleic acid structure. We attempt to impart a sense of the richness of the subject by describing these unconventional aspects of branched junctions, as well the structural features that impinge on recombination.

THE DESIGN OF BRANCHED DNA STRUCTURES

The construction of nucleic acid molecules containing stable branches entails an exercise in molecular design. Under nondenaturing conditions, complementary strands of DNA form linear duplex molecules. Sequences that deviate from simple collinear Watson-Crick complementarity are not guaranteed to form particular target structures. Thus, one must ensure that the target secondary structure containing the branch is indeed the favored form of the molecule. This is particularly true if the molecule is to be very small. Many of the applications to date have used DNA designed by a sequence-symmetry minimization procedure (e.g. 8, 46, 116). Figure 2 illustrates the features of this

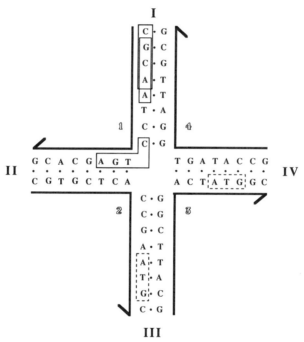

Figure 2 A stable DNA branched junction. The junction shown, J1, is composed of four strands of DNA, labeled with Arabic numerals. Half-arrows indicate the 3′ end of each strand. Each strand is paired with two other strands to form a double helical arm, each numbered with a Roman numeral. Dots between the bases show the hydrogen-bonded base paring that forms the double helices. The sequence of this junction has been optimized to minimize symmetry and non-Watson-Crick base pairing. No homologous two-fold sequence symmetry flanks the central branch point, thereby stabilizing the junction. At the upper part of arm I, two of the 52 unique tetrameric elements in this complex are boxed—CGCA and GCAA. At the corner of strand 1, the boxed sequence CTGA is one of twelve sequences in the complex (three on each strand) that span a junction. The complements to each of these 12 sequences are absent. Whereas tetrameric elements have been used to assign the sequence of this molecule, some of the trimers in the molecule, such as the ATG sequences shown in dotted boxes, are redundant.

procedure, showing the well-characterized four-arm junction J1 (103). Each of the four strands of this molecule is a 16-mer, which is involved in forming two double helical segments termed arms. Each 16-mer is divided into a set of 13 overlapping tetramers; two of these tetramers on strand 1 are shown boxed at the 5' end, CGCA and GCAA.

Symmetry minimization entails making sure that each of the 52 tetramers in the structure is unique. In addition, the complement to any tetramer that spans a bend is forbidden; thus, the sequence TCAG has been disallowed, because it is complementary to the boxed bend sequence CTGA on strand 1. This exclusion removes the linear complement of a bent sequence, providing it with no favorable alternative to pairing with segments on two separate arms. In four-arm junctions, two-fold symmetry is eliminated around the junction site to prevent branch migration. By adhering to this procedure, the only linear structures in J1 that are competitive with the target molecule are repetitive trimers, such as the ATG sequences in dotted boxes. Using tetramers as the basis for parsing the structure provides a set of 240 (4^4 − 16 self complementary sequences) elements from which the 52 sequences can be selected. Larger structures require elements five or six nucleotides in length (8, 116). Large geometrical objects designed from branched structures often require restriction endonuclease sites, proto-Z sequences, oligo-dT hairpins, or other symmetric sequences; these features are usually incorporated into the sequence first, and then the best sequence symmetry minimization possible is attempted around them (99).

THE SOLUTION STRUCTURES OF BRANCHED JUNCTIONS

Among the known nucleic acid structures that contain more than a single duplex unit, the ends of the duplexes tend to form intramolecular stacks if it is feasible for them to do so. This stacking behavior was first seen crystallographically in the 1970s in the structure of yeast tRNA[phe] (50). At about the same time, Sigal & Alberts proposed a structure for the Holliday junction that incorporates this feature (107). They suggested a model like that shown on the right of Figure 3a, in which each pair of two helical arms forms a stacking structure that constitutes a single helical domain.

Investigators have tackled the structure of the four-arm junction experimentally in several ways. Churchill et al (13) showed that hydroxyl radicals generated by Fe(II)EDTA^{2-} [iron(II) ethylenediaminetetraacetic acid] cleave J1 in a two-fold symmetric pattern consistent with

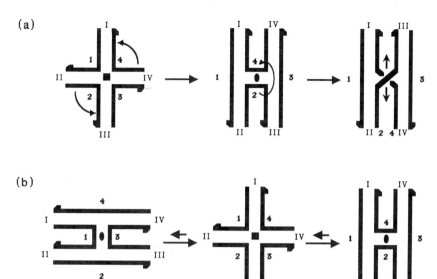

Figure 3 Holliday structure representations. (*a*) Possible conformers of the Holliday structure. An Arabic numeral and a Roman numeral number each arm and strand, respectively. The 3' ends of the strands are indicated by half-arrowheads, and double helical regions by parallel lines. In the structure implicit from the sequence (*left*), the possible four-fold symmetry is indicated by the square in the center of the figure. If the arms stack as indicated by the curved arrows, an antiparallel structure (*middle*) would result. Note that this structure is two-fold symmetric, as indicated by the lens-shaped object, and that the helical (straight) strands are antiparallel. This structure may be transformed into a parallel structure (*far right*) by rotating the domain on the right. Now, the helical strands are parallel. The two-fold axis (*double-headed arrows*) lies in the plane of the page. (*b*) The crossover preferences of the four-arm immobile junction J1. The implicit symmetry of the structure appears in the middle; the square represents a potential four-fold symmetric structure. The lens-shaped object at the center of the two structures that flank the central structure indicates the dyad symmetry of the structure of J1. The dominant structure is on the right, in which arm I stacks on arm II, and arm III stacks on arm IV. No experiments have detected the presence of the structure on the left.

two stacking domains. In this autofootprinting experiment, the cleavage pattern of a strand in the branched molecule is compared with its pattern in linear duplex DNA. Strands 1 and 3 of J1 have similar patterns suggestive of a helical structure in both environments, whereas strands 2 and 4 show marked protection at the branch point, consistent with a structure that crosses over between helical domains. A two-domain stacking structure contains two strands that cross over between domains (the crossover strands) and a strand in each domain (the helical strand) that is similar in structure to a strand in an ordinary double helix. If the Holliday structure is two-fold symmetric, and not four-fold symmetric, it can exist as two different crossover isomers, as illustrated in Figure 3b. The difference between these isomers is the pair of strands that assumes the role of the crossover strands, and, conversely, the pair that assumes the role of helical strands. Chen et al (9) have used the autofootprinting experiment with two monomobile junctions to demonstrate that changing the mobile bases alters the preferred crossover isomer. The crossover preference and extent of this preference in immobile junctions is sequence dependent (37), and Lilley's group has reported similar results (25), noting that the penultimate base pair is not involved. Unequal crossover preference is a consequence of a more general phenomenon, stacking dominance, in which one set of stacking interactions is more stable than its competitors (116).

Cooper & Hagerman have attached long reporter arms to J1 pairwise and have shown that the gel electrophoretic mobilities are consistent with an antiparallel stacking arrangement of two helical domains (14). The term *antiparallel* means that the helical strands of each domain have their $5' \rightarrow 3'$ polarities pointing in opposite directions in space. Whereas exact parallelism or antiparallelism is unlikely, the term *parallel* applies to junctions with their helical domains oriented to each other in the range $0° \pm 90°$, and the term antiparallel applies to junctions with their helical domains oriented to each other within the range $180° \pm 90°$. Duckett et al (25) have performed similar mobility experiments on different junctions and have confirmed the structural findings of Cooper & Hagerman, as well as the dependence of the crossover isomer on the bases flanking the junction.

In additional work, Cooper & Hagerman used transient electric birefringence to measure the angles between each of the pairs of arms (15). Their data are consistent with an antiparallel two-domain structure. The six pairwise angles they have determined define four spherical triangles whose spherical excess must sum to $720°$ (84), much as the contiguous angles about a point in a plane must sum to $360°$. In fact, the spherical triangles corresponding to Cooper & Hagerman's native structure sum to an upper bound of $774°$, within 7.5% of the expected sum. Murchie et al (77) have reached similar conclusions by means of fluorescence resonance energy transfer experiments. They interpret their data to suggest that the helical domains form a right-handed X-like structure with an angle of about $60°$ between them. Thus, the helical domains in the object on the right of Figure 3b would be tilted into and out of the page in opposite directions by $30°$; the direction of this tilt would be about a horizontal axis contained within the plane of the page. The ends of arms II and IV would be closer to the reader and the ends of arms I and III would be farther from the reader than in the planar representation shown. Time-resolved fluorescent measurements by Eis & Millar (27) also support this structure, but the measurements suggest a large dispersion (of perhaps as much as 30°) about the 60° favored angle. In summary, the right-handed X model satisfies a variety of experimental criteria, yet raises three crucial questions concerning immobile four-arm junctions: (*a*) Do the helix axes of the arms deviate from linearity in the vicinity of the branch? (*b*) What isomeric substates contribute to the ensemble of conformations representing a junction, and what are their populations and life times? (*c*) How do these substates vary with environmental variables? No crystal structure or detailed NMR structure of a four-arm junction has yet appeared.

One dimensional (1D) ^{1}H NMR experiments by Wemmer et al have shown that the bases all seem to pair in J1 (120). Two-dimensional (2D) NMR experiments by Chen et al (11, 12) have verified this finding and have found evidence for the stacking domains. Murchie et al (78) have attempted to address the issue of linearity of the helical domains by using a restriction enzyme, *Mbo*II, whose recognition site is on one side of the branch and whose cleavage site is on the other. Cleavage does occur in this experiment, but the enzyme may enforce a linear helix axis on the domain. von Kitzing et al have modeled a three-dimensional (3D) structure of the junction, basing it on theory (114); Timsit & Moras (111) have done likewise, basing their model on the packing of DNA dodecamers within a trigonal crystal. Their proposed structural model for the four-arm junction involves a ridge of phosphates from one duplex stack entering the major groove of the second.

All the structural studies discussed above have depended on the presence of Mg^{2+} or other multivalent cations to stabilize the junction structure. Junctions with 25 or more nucleotides per arm assume a less well-defined structure in the absence of such stabilization (15, 26), and small junctions, such as J1, actually fall apart (104). This observation is not surprising, because all models of the two-domain structure place the negatively charged phosphates of the crossover strands in close proximity to each other. Their repulsive interaction apparently must be neutralized for the structure to remain intact. Autofootprinting (66) detected a selective interaction with Fe^{2+} at the branch site in a four-arm immobile junction; when Fe^{2+} was used as a radical source, scission at the branch site of the two crossover strands was enhanced, relative to neutral Fe(EDDA) (ethylenediamine-N,N'-diacetic acid) or negatively charged Fe(EDTA)$^{2-}$ controls that are protected at these positions. This was the first evidence for the selective interaction of metal ions at the branch (66).

STRUCTURAL CONFORMERS OF HOLLIDAY JUNCTIONS

The characterization of Holliday junction analogues as antiparallel two-domain structures raises questions about the nature of the Holliday structure within the cell. An important question is whether the features of the structures seen to date reflect the behavior of the Holliday junction in its role as a recombination intermediate. Two unexpected aspects of the structure should be pointed out. First, junctions strongly tend to adopt a particular crossover isomer in all the immobile structures studied to date (13–15, 25, 61). Second, the structure is antiparallel, rather than parallel, as proposed by Sigal & Alberts (107).

Tethered Junctions

Does a particular two-domain structure represent a deep thermodynamic minimum? In principle, any two-domain junction can assume four overall canonical conformations by combining two opposite crossover isomers with parallel or antiparallel domain orientations. Kimball et al (51) have built all four conformers of a junction derived from J1, by using a covalent oligo-dT linker to tether selected arms together. They find that all four structures can be formed without altering the $Fe(II)EDTA^{2-}$ autofootprinting pattern in the vicinity of the junction. Thus, a covalent linkage can impose an unfavorable conformation on the junction, without leading to detectable structural distortions within the helical domains.

Ligation Studies

Petrillo et al (85) have performed a series of sticky-ended ligation experiments about all six angles between the four arms of J1. In each experiment, two arms of J1 have been extended with a single-stranded overhang, so that the ligated structure contains 20 nucleotide pairs from branch point to branch point. A series of macrocyclic oligolaterals forms in each case. The series always begins with the cyclic trimer, and progresses through higher macrocycles. Were the arm-to-arm stacking interactions within the domains of J1 as persistent as those in linear duplex DNA, one would not expect significant cyclization for those pairs of arms (I and II, III and IV) that stack to form domains until the lengths of the duplexes exceed a minimum cyclization length of DNA, around 240 nucleotide pairs (106) Thus, either the stacking interactions between arms within the domains of J1 are weaker than those of linear duplex DNA, or the opposite stacking interactions (I and IV, II and III) provide stacking alternatives that are more favorable than those available to linear duplex DNA. The picture that emerges is a flexurally pliable structure over the time course of this experiment (> 10 h). By using incompatible twists (16 nucleotide pairs between branch points), Petrillo et al showed that junction torsional stiffness is substantial (85).

Symmetric Immobile Junctions

Another key question about transferring data from immobile junctions to Holliday junctions is how asymmetry influences the stacking dominance of particular crossover isomers. Some of the structure-probing experiments described above, such as gel retardation, are likely to detect another structural isomer present as a 10–20% component. Nevertheless, none has been reported. Does the asymmetric sequence generate the asymmetric stacking structure? Recently, symmetric immobile junctions were constructed from double crossover molecules (see below) containing one symmetric junction and one immobile junction (124). Experiments measuring the crossover preferences of symmetric immobile junctions suggest that indeed asymmetric sequences generate asymmetric crossover preferences: measurements of the crossover preferences of symmetric junctions show that they are 600 calories/mol or less at 4°C (S Zhang & NC Seeman, in preparation).

Stacking Dominance in Five- and Six-Arm Junctions

Stacking dominance is not limited to four-arm junctions. Wang et al (116) have constructed five- and six-arm branched junctions whose arms contain 16 nucleotide pairs. No dominant stacking motif is seen in the five-arm junction, but one pair of adjacent arms of the six-arm junction appears to form a dominant stacking domain. The sequence flanking the stacking site (dGpdA on the helical strand) is the same as that in the arm III–arm IV stack in J1. Comparison of the relative friction constants determined from Ferguson plots for three-, four-, five-, and six-arm junctions shows that the friction constant of the four-arm junction is anomalously low, possibly because its two domains occlude each other.

Double Crossover Molecules and Antiparallel Bias

Models of recombination involving double strand breaks invoke double crossover Holliday junction molecules (108, 109). Recent models of these structures (32) reveal five qualitatively different structural isomer classes in this system (Figure 4). Double crossover molecules are an extreme version of tethered junctions. Thus, molecules in which the helical domains are parallel or antiparallel correspond to different iso-

DAE   DAO

DPE   DPOW   DPON

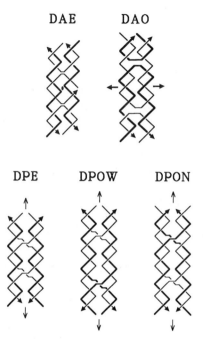

Figure 4   Schematic drawings of the five isomers of double crossover structures. The structures shown are named by the acronym describing their basic characteristics. All names begin with D for double crossover. The second character refers to the relative orientations of their two double helical domains, A for antiparallel and P for parallel. The third character refers to the number (modulus 2) of helical half-turns between crossovers, E for an even number and O for an odd number. A fourth character describes parallel double crossover molecules with an odd number of helical half-turns between crossovers. The extra half-turn can correspond to a major (wide) groove separation, designated by W, or an extra minor (narrow) groove separation, designated by N. The strands are drawn as zig-zag helical structures, in which two consecutive, perpendicular lines correspond to a full helical turn for a strand. The arrowheads at the ends of the strands designate their 3' ends. The structures contain implicit symmetry, indicated by the conventional markings. The differing thickness of the strands aids in symmetry visualization. In the case of the parallel molecules, the dark strands are related to the other dark strands by the two-fold axes vertical on the page; similarly, the light strands are symmetrically related to each other. In DAE, the two-fold axis perpendicular to the page relates the two dark helical strands to each other, and the two light outer crossover strands to each other. The 5' end of the central double crossover strand is related to the 3' end by the same dyad element. With DAO, the dark strands are related to the light strands by the dyad axis lying horizontal on the page.

mers, as do molecules containing even or odd numbers of double-helical half-turns between crossovers. As shown in Figure 4, in antiparallel molecules an even number of half-turns (DAE) requires a fifth cyclic strand in the center, which is unnecessary in molecules with an odd number of half-turns (DAO). The same strands are involved in both crossovers in parallel molecules with an even number of half-turns (DPE), but different strands are involved in the crossovers if the number of strands is odd (DAO). The parallel-odd class is subdivided between those molecules with an extra minor (narrow) groove spacing between crossovers (DPON), and those with an extra major (wide) groove spacing (DPOW). The preference for antiparallel domains is amplified in these molecules: at high concentrations, parallel molecules with greater than a single turn between crossovers form multimeric structures, which may permit the phosphates to be separated from each other in oligolateral structures. Decreased protection between crossovers in autofootprinting experiments suggests that parallel structures with greater than 1.5 turns between crossovers may bow to accommodate charge accumulation near the central axis. Antiparallel molecules appear to form linear antiparallel helices, with no evident distortions to their helix axes.

Double crossover molecules clarify the structural basis of the antiparallel bias of Holliday junctions. In parallel structures (Figure 4), the backbone strands are directly opposite each other. Phosphate-phosphate repulsion between strands is likely to be much greater in this configuration than in the antiparallel structure, in which the strands are displaced from each other along the domain interface. As discussed below, hydration, as well as polyelectrolyte effects, may be involved here. The antiparallel structure is inconsistent with many features of recombination; however, a branch can be modeled to be locally antiparallel, but within a globally parallel context (105).

Thermodynamics of Antiparallel Bias

A comparative thermodynamic analysis has been carried out on two junctions that differ in the orientation of the two duplex arms (65). As pointed out above, in all four-arm junctions investigated to date, the duplex arms tend to lie antiparallel rather than parallel, although the strength of this preference probably varies with sequence (37). The basis for the thermodynamic analysis was the observation noted above by Kimball et al (51) that oligo-dT sequences can be used as tethers to constrain the orientations of junction domains to be antiparallel or parallel, without distorting the duplex arms of the junction. The thermodynamic study involves a competition assay, in which a small quantity of a labeled strand is allowed to partition between its complement and the two strands needed to complete either junction. Figure 5 shows the scheme involved in this experiment. The results reveal only a small free energy difference in stability between the two complexes, JA and JP; the antiparallel model is more stable by 1.4 ± 0.5 kcal/mol junction at 25°C.

Branch Migration

The homologous two-fold sequence symmetry of the naturally occurring Holliday junction permits the position of the branch point to migrate spontaneously. This important phenomenon has been studied intermittently for almost a quarter century (49, 53). An early model proposed by Meselson (70) assumes that rotary diffusion of a Sigal-Alberts structure is rate limiting. However, this model predicts migratory rates that are much faster than those measured in experiments that monitor the disappearance of junctions derived from figure-8 replicative intermediates in phage G4 (110, 118) or from cruciform disappearance in linearized cyclic molecules (16, 34).

Panyutin & Hsieh (81) recently refined this measurement, allowing a short cold duplex to invade a homologous labeled sequence residing on a much longer single strand carrier. The design of their assay enabled them to show that in the presence of Mg^{2+}, a single-base mismatch is sufficient to inhibit branch migration, as predicted by a kinetic model of Robinson & Seeman (91). Interestingly, in the absence of Mg^{2+}, the block presented by a base mismatch is overcome. In a different system, Panyutin & Hsieh (82) estimated the step rates of branch migration in semisynthetic junctions that can only resolve in one direction. These rates are 270–300 ms/step at 37°C in the presence of Mg^{2+}, but 0.3–0.4 ms/step when the cationic environment is exclusively Na^+. This large difference in estimated step rate opens the possibility that the two-domain structures requiring multivalent cations may not be key intermediates in the cellular process of branch migration, whose rate is known to be at least as fast as the magnesium-free rate (110). These experiments contribute fundamentally to our understanding of the dynamics of branch migration, but one should note that the average step rate is inferred rather than determined directly.

The discovery that RuvAB (112) and RecG (58) can drive branch migration with their ATPase activities has inspired renewed interest in this topic. Johnson & Symington (45) recently constructed a convenient migratory system, similar to the G4 system, from phagemid vectors, allowing a comparison of the rates of spontaneous branch migration in

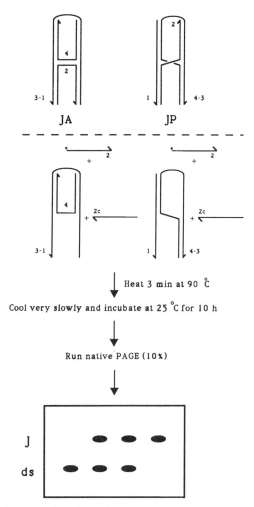

Figure 5 The scheme used to determine parallel-antiparallel relationships. The two tethered junctions are shown above the dashed line. The tethered junction on the left, JA, is constrained to be antiparallel, and the tethered junction on the right, JP, is constrained to be parallel. The half-arrows indicate the 3' ends of the strands, where the strands are numbered. The tether in JA constrains the 5' end of strand 1 to be close to the 3' end of strand 3 (of the untethered junction) by uniting them with a short oligodeoxythymidine linker to form strand 3-1. Similarly, the 3' end of strand 4 is tethered to the 5' end of strand 3 in JP, to form strand 4-3. Note that strand 2 is identical in both junctions. The electrophoretic equilibrium assay is shown below the dashed line. A small quantity of the labeled strand 2 is allowed to partition between two complexes: the duplex (ds) formed by the labeled strand pairing with its complement, 2c, and the junction (J) formed by pairing the strands with an excess of the remaining set of strands. After the annealing reaction and allowing 10 h for equilibration at 25°C, the two samples, corresponding to JA and JP, respectively, are run on polyacrylamide gel electrophoresis (PAGE) under native conditions, and the bands corresponding to duplex and junction are excised and counted.

vitro. This system aims to ascertain the roles of protein factors in the migration process.

Partially mobile junctions contain a limited amount of homologous sequence symmetry around the branch point. Characterization of monomobile (9) and bimobile junctions (62) has shown that each possible migratory conformer appears to be present, but this finding has not been quantitated. In addition, stacking dominance has been noted in monomobile junctions (9), but not in junctions with more migratory degrees of freedom. A key assumption in the analysis of branch migration is that all migratory positions are equally probable, but this remains to be demonstrated.

THERMODYNAMICS OF DNA BRANCHING

The energetic cost of forming a branch in a DNA molecule was initially evaluated by Mizuuchi et al (73), who analyzed the interconversion between supercoiled and cruciform states in a plasmid construct containing a fully palindromic sequence. Later efforts by several groups refined these values, using short palindromic sequences embedded in circular duplexes rather than a palindromic plasmid. The free energy of forming a branch in a linear duplex is estimated to be $+13$ to $+18$ kcal/mol of branch from extrusion experiments in supercoiled DNA. Similarly, analysis of the thermal unfolding of the four-arm junction J1 compared with a set of four octamer duplexes (corresponding to the individual arms) shows that the thermal stability of the junction is roughly equivalent to that of these octamers (68), which are much less stable than a 16-mer duplex. By using a set of eight 16-mer strands that can associate to form two four-arm junctions, J1 and J1c, with complementary sequences, or four fully complementary duplexes, D1, D2, D3, and D4, one can evaluate the free energy for forming junctions from duplexes and determine the associated $\Delta H°$ and $\Delta S°$ values (61). The single strands are S1, S2, S3, S4, S1c, S2c, S3c, and S4c. S1 + S1c forms D1; S2 + S2c forms D2; S3 + S3c forms D3; and S4 + S4c forms D4. Likewise, S1 + S2 + S3 + S4 forms J1, and S1c + S2c + S3c + S4c forms J1c. The net conversion reaction is:

$$D1 + D2 + D3 + D4 \leftrightarrow J1 + J1c. \qquad 1.$$

The set of eight single strands is allowed to equilibrate between two junctions or four duplexes. One can control the products by introducing an excess of some strands into the mixture. At low temperature, the products at equilibrium include both duplexes and junctions, with a greater amount of duplexes. In contrast, at higher temperatures, the system is expected to favor exclusively formation of duplexes, in light of the above free energy estimates. Two methods have been used to characterize the system. First, titration microcalorimetry allows direct measurement of the enthalpy of forming duplexes or junctions from the appropriate mixtures of strands. For example, an equimolar solution of strands S1 + S3 can be added to a similar solution of S2 + S4 to form J1, or S1c + S3c to form D1 + D3. In the second approach, a labeled strand is allowed to partition between the cold strands required to form a duplex and a junction. By allowing the system to reach equilibrium, and assaying the products by electrophoresis under quenching conditions, the ratio of duplex to junction can be determined, yielding the free energy difference. Together, these measurements afford a complete thermodynamic description of Reaction 1, in which two four-arm junctions are formed from four duplexes, apart from effects of hydration.

The resulting thermodynamic profile for forming a single junction from two duplexes, rather than Reaction 1, is as follows: $\Delta G^\circ = +1.1$ (± 0.4) kcal/mol; $\Delta H^\circ = +27.1$ (± 1.3) kcal/mol; $T\Delta S^\circ$ (at 18°C) = $+26.1$ (± 9.0) kcal/mol; $\Delta Cp = +0.97$ (± 0.05) kcal/deg per mol. Several features of these numbers merit comment. First, the free energy difference between two duplexes and a junction is surprisingly small at low temperature. A mixture of strands at 18°C shows that both duplexes and junctions can be detected using a stain, rather than autoradiography, in polyacrylamide gels, confirming that the free energy difference is small. At higher temperatures, however, the free energy increases because of the large positive heat capacity involved. Creating a branch by bringing two duplexes together is accompanied by an unfavorable enthalpy change, compensated by a favorable $T\Delta S$ term.

Any reaction in which two molecules associate to form a single species should have an unfavorable entropy change. However, for solution processes involving nucleic acids, changes in counterion binding and solvation can be very large. The fact that Mg^{2+} or similar multivalent cations are essential to junction-structure stabilization suggests that metal binding is important at the branch. A densimetric experiment by LA Marky & DW Kupke (in preparation) indicates a very large positive change in volume (~2.0 liters/mol junction) that accompanies Reaction 1. This corresponds to a release of water(s) of hydration on forming the branch from duplexes, a process that occurs in the direction of the entropy change determined. Dramatic ion binding effects can be anticipated as well. Timset-Moras type groove-phosphate interactions (111), noted above, can reasonably be imagined to be associated with a major loss in hydration of the backbone.

A complete description of a process such as Reaction 1 must include changes in ions and water as reactants and products. When a junction forms from two duplexes, these changes are large enough to lead to the favorable $T\Delta S$ term that apparently drives the reaction. The large apparent ΔCp value accompanying branch formation is unusual in nucleic acids, but familiar in proteins when buried hydrophobic side chains are exposed to solvent on unfolding. In the case of junctions, the effect is unlikely to represent exposure of hydrophobic surfaces upon branch formation. For example, release of bound water upon netropsin binding to the minor groove of a duplex is associated with both a large positive ΔV for the reaction and a positive ΔH (69).

Measurements of the interstrand spacing in condensed DNA as a function of osmotic pressure by Parsegian and his coworkers show that powerful repulsive forces are at work between adjacent DNA molecules whose surfaces are separated by several Ångstroms in solution (89, 90). This repulsion is attributed to hydration and not to polyelectrolyte effects, because the force is independent of salt concentration, yet sensitive to the nature of the ions present. Intersection of two duplexes at a branch point, and their subsequent separation, places parts of the arms in just this range of spacing. Thus, hydration forces probably play an important role. The underlying mechanism presumably involves interactions between orientationally ordered water dipoles within the hydration shells of each duplex. These effects may need to be considered in order to explain the geometry of junctions and thermodynamic results in detail.

INTERACTIONS OF DNA BRANCHED JUNCTIONS WITH OTHER MOLECULES

Ligand Interactions

In the course of the Warner group's experiments to measure the step rate of branch migration (118), they observed that low concentrations of the intercalating dye used to prepare the DNA, ethidium bromide, had an inhibitory effect on the rate. Intercalation of the dye might stiffen the arms, or ethidium might interact preferentially with the branch; either of these actions could inhibit the migration rate. Using the reactive ethidium analogue MPE·Fe(II), synthesized by Dervan's group (113), and an oligomeric four-arm junction, Guo et al found that ethidium interacts preferentially at or near the branch point (38, reviewed in 60). Enhancement in MPE·Fe(II) reactivity at bases flanking the branch is measured relative to duplex controls, and this effect is sensitive to competition by addition of ethidium or similar DNA-binding agents. Various ligands interact preferentially at the branch, including porphyrins (63) and other intercalators such as quinacrine and the thiocarbacyanin dye Stains-All (64). The interaction has several unusual properties. Estimates of the affinity of ethidium for the preferred site in J1 suggest that it is 10–100 times tighter than for normal intercalation into a 16-mer duplex. The stoichiometry of ethidium binding is difficult to establish, given the excess of weaker sites that are present in the duplex arms. Nevertheless, titration calorimetry results are consistent with the presence of two classes of binding site, a tight class with an affinity above 10^7, involving about 3–4 ethidium molecules, and a weaker class with an affinity around 10^5, involving 15–16 drug molecules. One could associate the second class of sites with intercalative sites in the duplex arms, which contain 28 potential sites, of which about 16 would be available for occupancy if subject to next-neighbor site exclusion. The tight sites would then correspond to interactions at the branch.

Junction-Binding Proteins

Nonenzymatic proteins have been isolated and identified that bind selectively to DNA junctions. Bianchi and his coworkers have shown that HMG1, a nuclear protein found in the nucleus of eukaryotes, binds selectively to junctions (3–6, 28, 87). HMG proteins are a major class of acid-soluble proteins extractable from chromatin by salt or dyes, such as ethidium bromide (4). HMG1 proteins also contain two N-terminal regions rich in basic and aromatic residues, designated HMG boxes, to which their DNA interacting ability is attributed. Experiments by Bianchi's group demonstrate that intact HMG1 associates tightly with a four-arm junction, but not with normal duplex DNA or single-stranded DNA. The function of HMG1 is not known, but several transcription factors contain HMG boxes. The primary target for HMG box proteins may be a perturbed form of DNA, including bent or kinked (28, 87) forms in addition to branches per se. Recent investigations showed that the bacterial protein HU interacts with branched DNA; the proposed role for HU is in initiation of bacterial DNA replication at *oriC*, which contains a number of palindromic sequences (87). Interestingly, HU stimulates the resolving activity of endonuclease VII (endoVII).

A different approach to obtaining junction-binding proteins involves the isolation of monoclonal antibodies directed against branched DNA. These antibodies were first described in 1987 (29); subsequent study has shown that the antibodies interact at or near the base of cruciforms (30). These proteins have been used as reagents in identifying structures that contain origins of replication in eukaryotic DNA and to determine the phenotypic consequences of introducing these antibodies into permeabilized cells (117).

Cleavage of Junctions by Resolvases

Numerous enzymes have been described that cleave junctions in the vicinity of their branch points (reviewed in 24, 57, 121). The most extensively studied of these proteins is endonuclease VII (endo VII), the product of gene 49 of bacteriophage T4. This enzyme has been shown to cleave partially mobile branched junctions, cruciforms, and immobile three- and four-arm branched junctions, as well as a variety of other DNA molecules whose structures are less well defined (reviewed in 48). Endo VII also cleaves the crossover strands of the branched junction three nucleotides 3' to the branch point (75). To function, endo VII requires the presence of nine nucleotide pairs in at least one arm of the junction (76). In antiparallel junctions, the opposite surfaces of the junction are distinct; the side containing the two minor grooves at the junction is the site of cleavage (2, 76). Pottmeyer & Kemper (88) have suggested that this enzyme cleaves by individual nicks. Despite its strong structural preference, Picksley et al (86) demonstrated sequence specificity 3' to thymidines. These authors used a highly mobile junction to assess cleavage preferences for both endo VII and bacteriophage T7's endo I, which they find cleaves between pyrimidines. This latter enzyme cleaves the helical pair of strands in J1, with a lower size requirement.

Bhattacharayya et al (2) have compared the cleavage sites of several resolvase enzymes. Some of these cleave on the helical strands, but all cut on the same minor-groove side of the junction. They have used tethered antiparallel junctions to demonstrate that structure is the primary determinant of cleavage specificity, and suggest that these enzymes require a 120° relationship between the helical domains. In contrast to this suggestion, DAO-type double crossover molecules, which are unlikely to contain such bends (32), are readily cleaved by endo VII in a fashion similar to single-crossover junctions (T-J Fu, B Kemper & NC Seeman, in preparation). Endo VII cleaves DPON (see Figure 4) isomers of double crossover molecules symmetrically between the crossover points, but asymmetrically beyond the crossover.

THREE-ARM JUNCTIONS

Structural Models and Thermodynamics

Although four-arm junctions are models for intermediates that arise in recombination between two duplexes, in certain cases three-arm junctions can also arise in vivo. For example, inhibition of DNA replication in phage T4 leads to the accumulation of three-arm branched DNA structures visible in electron micrographs (71). Three-arm DNA junctions provide useful benchmarks for the properties of branches in RNA, which are important structurally and mechanistically in splicing. In addition, three-arm junctions have found use as elements in the assembly of more complex structures from branched DNA (8, 10).

What does a three-arm junction look like? Unlike four-arm junctions, model building suggests that stacking two arms distorts ideal double helical pairing and base stacking in the third arm near the branch point. Hybridization of three 16-mer strands with eight nucleotide pairs per arm can lead to the formation of a complex, termed JL, that migrates as a single species in native polyacrylamide gels (36). Appending pairs of long reporter arms to JL gives rise to structures with distinct mobilities in the presence of Mg^{2+}, implying that the geometry of JL is not symmetric. Instead, one combination of pairs has a mobility close to that of a linear duplex, while the other two behave as if they are bent or otherwise distorted (36, 59). Our current interpretation of the role of sequence is that different combinations of bases have distinct stacking contributions and bending probabilities. Stacking alone seems incapable of accounting for the preferences observed thus far.

The structure of a three-arm junction depends on the bases flanking the branch, as well as on the identity of the pairs adjacent to the flanking ones (59), as seen in mobility experiments with junctions containing pairs of extended arms. An initial report by Lilley's group (22) suggested that three-arm junctions are symmetric structures, based on analogous mobility measurements on three-arm junctions with extended arms. However, correct interpretation of mobility effects in gels also requires consideration of the length of the appended arms relative to the composition of the gel (36, 59). Asymmetry in three-arm junctions disappears without Mg^{2+} or a similar counterion (22, 36).

Autofootprinting experiments using single strand–specific reagents reveal that the branch in three-arm junctions behaves as a relatively open structure, in contrast to the branch in a four-arm junction. Bases flanking the branch in three-arm junctions are reactive to osmium tetroxide or diethyl pyrocarbonate (36, 59). In the cases studied, these experiments reveal an asymmetric pattern of reactivity consistent with the mobility results. Further clues to the properties of three-arm junctions come from experiments in which short duplex sequences (necks) are allowed progressively to grow from a parent duplex (Figure 6). As the number of potential pairs in the neck increases from one to three, the properties of the complexes change in unexpected ways if Mg^{2+} is present (126). The apparent perturbation in geometry increases in-

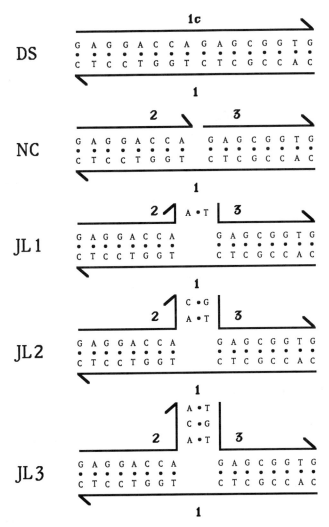

Figure 6   Five molecules that form a progression from linear duplex to a three-arm neck. These molecules are derived from the three-arm junction JL. The individual strands are numbered, and the half arrowheads indicate the 3' ends of the strands. Each molecule consists of a common 16-mer (strand 1) and one or two complementary strands with different lengths.

crementally with the number of possible pairs, judged from gel elec-trophoretic mobility experiments on complexes with long reporter arms. On the other hand, reactivity to a single strand-reactive probe becomes evident when only a single potential base pair is present, and the reactivity increases only slightly as additional potential pairs are added. Surprisingly, calorimetric experiments indicate progressive loss in enthalpy of formation as the neck extends (126). A survey of the region of the ^{1}H NMR spectrum where H-bonded ring NH protons resonate clearly shows that base pairing in the duplex is disrupted by the presence of one or more neck bases or potential pairs. Thus bases of the neck interact with the duplex from which they extend.

In the absence of Mg^{2+}, however, gel mobility experiments show that the structure of the complexes containing necks exhibits no asym-metry. The interactions between neck bases and the duplex thus seem to require screening of charge repulsions between phosphates in the vicinity of the branch. A possible analogy with duplexes containing an unpaired base suggests itself: An excess base in an otherwise comple-mentary duplex can remain extrahelical (83) or stack into the duplex (47, 123). The actual event depends on the identity of the base itself, the neighboring base sequence, and salt conditions.

If we imagine that this process persists in three-arm junctions con-taining arms of equal length, we can offer a simple explanation of sev-eral properties of three-arm junctions. Rather than forming a well-de-fined structure that is lower in free energy than the available isomeric alternatives, as the four-arm junctions appear to do, the three-arm junc-tion represents an ensemble of flip-flopping states; in each (at least) one base pair flanking the branch breaks transiently, freeing one (or more) bases to interact with the remaining duplex. The actual number of bases involved in the flip-flop is unknown. If only the flanking base pair breaks, the dependence of the conformation of the three-arm junc-tion on the sequence of both the base pairs flanking the branch and the next pair in each arm (59) can be rationalized. The probability of breaking the terminal pair presumably depends on next-neighbor stack-ing interactions involving the adjacent pair. The fact that the hydroxyl radical autofootprint of a three-arm junction extends to these next-neighboring bases is consistent with this idea (22). The thymidines spanning a full turn of helix surrounding the branch become labile to osmium tetroxide (59), suggesting that the perturbation in a three-arm junction is delocalized over a considerable distance. The susceptibility of three-arm junctions to single strand–specific endonucleases supports this idea: Several bases surrounding the branch are sensitive to cleav-age by single strand–specific *Neurospora crassa* endonuclease (31).

Finally, two noteworthy experiments show that three-arm junctions are inherently flexible with respect to the valence angle at the branch. First, oligomerization of sticky-ended three-arm junctions by T4 DNA ligase produces closed rings corresponding to trimers, tetramers, and higher macrocycles (67). This is unlikely to occur unless the valence angle is effectively variable. Second, Jensch & Kemper (44) constructed a three-arm junction containing the *Eco*RI restriction site spanning the branch on all three arms and observed that the enzyme cleaves each arm with roughly identical rates. The flip-flop model readily accounts for these observations, whereas static models do not.

The Effect of Mismatched and Pendant Bases at the Branch

The picture developed above describes a fundamentally dynamic three-arm junction, the properties of which are determined by the flip-flop among an ensemble of isomers. It is interesting to test this picture against further data, in which base mismatches or noncomplementing pendant bases are introduced into three-arm junctions. The patterns of single-strand reactivity of three-arm junctions containing single or double T-T mismatches at the branch are consistent with a dynamic equilibrium between isomers (127). Depending on the sequence of the mismatch, the overall geometry of the original junction can be retained or switched to another one (127).

Noting that unpaired nucleotides occur frequently in the junction regions of RNA, Leontis and his coworkers have investigated the effect of unpaired nucleotides at the branch of a three-arm DNA junction (54). They concluded that two pendant As or Ts stabilize the three-arm junction, relative to three or more, or to the junction alone. A recent NMR study from this group provides a detailed structural explanation for this effect (55). The complex investigated contains two pendant thymidines, or a thymidine-cytosine unit, at the branch, which form a stack that allows the branch to assume a T-like shape. The role of these thymidines can be interpreted as altering the distribution of isomers in the tight form of the junction, permitting one state or set of states to dominate. Similarly, the extra thymidines can be regarded as adding an 18-bond backbone at the joint, instead of a six-bond backbone, thereby alleviating the strain associated with stacking two arms. An NMR study of three-arm junctions containing pendant CC bases independently arrived at a conclusion similar to Leontis's (94). The effect of these pendant bases at the branch is believed to relieve strain in the tight junction discussed above although no tight junctions were investigated in this study. In agreement with this idea, electrophoretic reporter-arm experiments with three-arm junctions containing pendant bases show marked shifts in mobility relative to a tight junction control as bases are added (M Zhong, L Liang & NR Kallenbach, unpublished data).

EXTENDED STRUCTURES

Antijunctions and Mesojunctions

If the ends of the duplex arms of a DNA branched junction are converted to hairpin loops, the resulting structure is a cyclic single-stranded molecule. However, connecting the 3' and 5' ends of different arms of a branched junction can result in knots or catenanes (102). This characteristic was used recently to construct a DNA knot from a branched-junction motif (20). Investigations into the possible role of junctions in single-stranded knotted DNA structures have shown that branched junctions are a subset of a more general class of structures in which, as in junctions, each strand is involved in two duplex segments (20, 102). The differences between branched junctions and these close relatives are worth noting.

If each arm contains a half-turn of DNA, one can represent a four-arm branched junction structure as flanking a square; the object labeled 4_4 at the top center of Figure 7 illustrates this point. Each edge of the square corresponds to a strand in the complex, has polarity, and is drawn to extend past the vertices. The vicinity of each vertex is thus flanked by four regions, two between parallel strands, and two between antiparallel strands. The helix axes of the junction arms pass through the antiparallel regions, because they are normal to the base pairs. The local dyad axis of each helical arm is perpendicular to it and is oriented in a circumferential direction. Thus, the diagonals of the large square are coincident with the helix axes. Rotating pairs of domains 90° causes the diagonals of the square to coincide with some or all of the dyad axes. These new structures, with circumferential helix axes, are called antijunctions (in which all helix axes are circumferential) or mesojunctions (in which some helix axes are circumferential). They can serve as components of complex knots (102) and catenanes (10).

The three-strand and four-strand structures in which each double helical domain contains 1.5 turns have been characterized and found to be of varying levels of stability (21): Closure into discrete structures, noted with branched junctions at micromolar concentrations (46), is often competitive with stacking interactions that promote the sort of oligomerization seen with parallel double-crossover molecules. Anti-

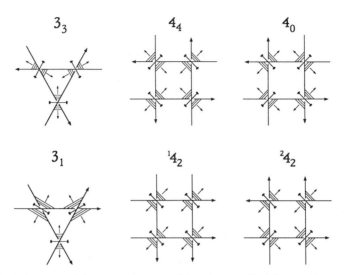

Figure 7 Schematics of three- and four-strand junctions, antijunctions, and mesojunctions. Each polygon is flanked by strands of DNA that extend beyond the vertices in each direction. The arrowheads indicate the 3' ends of the strands. The vertices correspond to the nodes formed by approximately a half-turn of double-helical DNA. Base pairs are represented by lines between antiparallel strands. Thin lines perpendicular to the base pairs represent the axis of each helix. Normal to the helix axes are the central dyad axes of each half-turn. The large number labeling each figure indicates the number of strands; the subscript indicates the number of helix axes that point to the centers of the polygons formed by the strands; and a presuperscript (if necessary) enumerates different members of a class otherwise undifferentiated by the first two numbers. The complexes 3_3 and 4_4 correspond to conventional branched junctions. Their helix axes are all pointing towards the center of the triangle or square along the bisectors of the angles of the polygons (radial). The complex 4_0 is a four-strand antijunction, in which each helix axis ideally is perpendicular to the angular bisectors (circumferential). The mesojunction complexes on the bottom row contain a mix of the two orientations of helix axes.

junctions and mesojunctions form cleanly only at 100 nM concentrations, which are too low for oligomerization to occur. Conventional branched junctions melt at higher temperatures than the other structures in this broader class, even though they contain the same sequences in their helical structures.

Geometrical Objects Built From Branched Junctions

In addition to their role in recombination, branched junctions offer a unique window on nanotechnology, whose goals include the controlled assembly of nanometer-scale molecular fragments. The covalent assembly of linear double-helical DNA molecules by sticky-ended ligation is well known. The ligation of duplex molecules with linear helix axes is the structural equivalent of concatenating line segments, which can yield only longer lines, circles, or perhaps knots. However, the addition of sticky ends to branched DNA molecules enables the construction of stick figures, in which the edges are double helical DNA and the vertices correspond to branch points. Figure 8 illustrates this principle. A key concept associated here is *connectedness* (119), or the number of other vertices to which a given vertex is connected by edges of the figure.

As noted above, in the first experiments that attempted this type of assembly, three- (67) and four-arm (85) branched junctions containing a single pair of complementary sticky ends were oligomerized to form longer linear molecules, and a series of macrocycles, beginning with the trimer. The ability to form a series of macrocycles indicates that branched DNA is not structurally rigid over the long time periods of the ligation reactions.

One can exert greater control on the products of DNA assembly by replacing oligomerization with directed synthesis. In this type of construction, specific sticky ends are associated with each edge of the object to be formed. In a quadrilateral constructed by assembly of four three-arm junctions containing a unique set of complementary sticky ends (10), each of the exocyclic arms is closed into a hairpin loop, which can contain a unique restriction site used to demonstrate synthesis. More recently, a three-connected DNA object whose helix axes

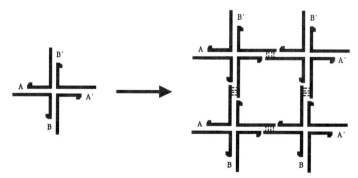

Figure 8 Formation of a 2D lattice from an immobile junction with sticky ends. A is a sticky end and A' is its complement. B and B' have the same relationship. Four of the monomeric junctions on the left are complexed in parallel orientation to yield the structure on the right. Note that A and B are different from each other, as indicated by the pairing in the complex. DNA ligase can close the gaps left in the complex. Note that the complex has maintained open valences, so that it could be extended by the addition of more monomers.

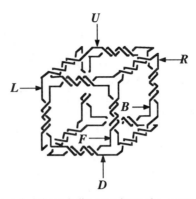

Figure 9 A DNA molecule whose helix axes have the connectivity of a cube. The molecule shown consists of six cyclic strands that have been catenated together in this particular arrangement. They are labeled by the first letters of their positional designations, up, down, front, back, left, and right. The structure is drawn with the major groove portions of the helices on the outside at the vertices, but whether they are inside or outside has not been determined. Since each edge contains 20 nucleotide pairs of DNA, we expect that their lengths will be about 68 Å. Model building (98) indicates that the axis-to-axis distance across a square face is about 100 Å, with a volume (in a cubic configuration) of approximately 1760 nm^3, when the cube is folded as shown, so that major grooves form the outsides of the corners. The molecule is markedly smaller when the corners are formed from minor grooves.

are arranged like the edges of a cube was constructed (Figure 9). The molecule contains two double-helical turns between branch points, so that each face corresponds to a cyclic single strand of DNA (96, 97). Another way to think of the cube-like molecule is that it is a hexacatenane, with each strand doubly linked to its four nearest neighbors. The correct assembly of this molecule has been demonstrated by specific cleavage of particular edges of the figure, each of which contains a unique restriction site. An improved solid-support-based synthetic methodology developed recently (125) was utilized to construct a DNA 14-catenane, whose helix axes are arranged like the 36 edges of a truncated octahedron (Y Zhang & NC Seeman, in preparation).

CONCLUDING REMARKS

Branched DNA molecules have been implicit in the biological functioning of DNA since the original proposal of semiconservative replication, which involves the formation of a disjoint three-arm Y-junction. Likewise, the four-arm Holliday junction is a central intermediate in genetic recombination. Immobile junction analogues have enabled the characterization of the dynamics, structure, thermodynamics, binding, and resolution properties of junctions in detail. Specific structural proposals have been advanced for the four-arm junction, which make predictions about the interactions responsible for their folding (111, 114). The ability of branched DNA to associate preferentially with a variety of small molecules and proteins opens new routes to the control of branch migration and DNA integration events in vivo (60). We hope that the recent advent of immobile symmetric junctions (124) will allow the characterization of other properties of the Holliday junction that have been veiled by the asymmetry of the immobile junction.

In addition, research on branched junctions has led to other DNA applications, from topological synthesis to nanotechnology. The assembly of DNA molecules into geometric objects has the ultimate goal of constructing periodic matter deliberately; use of DNA to direct the assembly of other molecules (92) is a key part of the nanotechnological goals of this effort. Nevertheless, these objects are also complex catenanes, closely related to DNA knots (19, 74, 115, 122). Thus, the branching of DNA helix axes impinges directly on unusual features involving the wrapping of single-stranded DNA into complex linking topologies.

The next generation of experiments analyzing DNA branched junctions will clearly involve techniques of higher resolution, such as multidimensional NMR and X-ray crystallography. The *sine qua non* of crystallography, high-resolution crystals, have not been reported to date. More complex structures, such as double crossovers that isolate individual conformers, may hold the key to the detailed structural and dynamic questions that remain about the molecular features of DNA branched junctions. In particular, we remain profoundly ignorant about the high-resolution structural details of branched junctions, as well as the mechanistic details of branch migration and crossover isomerization. Hopefully, the next few years will provide insight into these key aspects of DNA branched junctions.

ACKNOWLEDGMENTS

This research has been supported by grants CA-24101 (NRK) and GM-29554 (NCS) from the National Institutes of Health and by grant N00014-89-J-3078 from the Office of Naval Research (NCS). We are grateful to the WM Keck Foundation for their support of biomolecular imaging on the NYU campus. We thank Marco Bianchi, Walter Chazin, Peggy Hsieh, Börries Kemper, Richard Kolodner, Neocles Leontis, David Lilley, David Millar, Wilma Olson, Stephen West, and Maria Zannis-Hadjopoulus for reprints and prepublication materials. We also thank Paul Hagerman for a helpful discussion. Finally, we appreciate the efforts of Rong-Ine Ma, Mary Petrillo, Colin Newton, Junghuei Chen, John E Mueller, Min Lu, Qiu Guo, Tsu-Ju Fu, Yuwen Zhang, Yinli Wang, Shou Ming Du, Min Zhong, and Siwei Zhang, who have performed experiments in our laboratories that enabled us to write this article.

Any *Annual Review* chapter, as well as any article cited in an *Annual Review* chapter, may be purchased from the Annual Reviews Preprints and Reprints service.
1-800-347-8007; 415-259-5017; email: arpr@class.org

Literature Cited

1. Bell LR, Byers B. 1979. Occurrence of crossed strand-exchange forms in yeast DNA during meiosis. *Proc. Natl. Acad. Sci. USA* 76:3445–49
2. Bhattacharyya A, Murchie AIH, von Kitzing E, Diekmann S, Kemper B, Lilley DMJ. 1991. Model for the interaction of DNA junctions and resolving enzymes. *J. Mol. Biol.* 221:1191–1207
3. Bianchi ME. 1988. Interaction of a protein from rat liver with cruciform DNA. *EMBO J.* 7:843–49
4. Bianchi ME, Beltrame M, Falciola L. 1992. The HMG box motif. *Nucleic Acids and Molecular Biology,* ed. F Eckstein, DMJ Lilley, 6:112–28. Berlin/Heidelberg: Springer Verlag
5. Bianchi ME, Beltrame M, Paonessa G. 1989. Specific recognition of cruciform DNA by nuclear protein HMG1. *Science* 243:1056–59
6. Bianchi ME, Falciola L, Ferrari S, Lilley DMJ. 1992. The DNA binding site of HMG1 protein is composed of two similar segments (HMG boxes) both of which have counterparts in other eukaryotic regulatory proteins. *EMBO J.* 11:1055–63
7. Caruthers MH. 1985. Gene synthesis machines: DNA chemistry and its uses. *Science* 230:281–85
8. Chen J, Seeman NC. 1991. The synthesis from DNA of a molecule with the connectivity of a cube. *Nature (London)* 350:631–33
9. Chen JH, Churchill MEA, Tullius TD, Kallenbach NR, Seeman NC. 1988. Construction and analysis of monomobile DNA junctions. *Biochemistry* 85:6032–38
10. Chen JH, Kallenbach NR, Seeman NC. 1989. A specific quadrilateral synthesized from DNA branched junctions. *J. Am. Chem. Soc.* 111:6402–7

11. Chen SM, Heffron F, Chazin WJ. 1993. Two-dimensional ^{1}H NMR studies of 32-base-pair synthetic immobile Holliday junctions. *Biochemistry* 32:319–26
12. Chen SM, Heffron F, Leupin W, Chazin WJ. 1991. Two-dimensional ^{1}H NMR studies of synthetic immobile Holliday junctions. *Biochemistry* 30:766–71
13. Churchill MEA, Tullius TD, Kallenbach NR, Seeman NC. 1988. A Holliday recombination intermediate is twofold symmetric. *Proc. Natl. Acad. Sci. USA* 85:4653–56
14. Cooper JP, Hagerman PJ. 1987. Gel electrophoretic analysis of the geometry of a DNA four-way junction. *J. Mol. Biol.* 198:711–19
15. Cooper JP, Hagerman PJ. 1989. Geometry of a branched DNA structure in solution. *Proc. Natl. Acad. Sci USA* 86:7336–40
16. Courey AJ, Wang J. 1983. Cruciform formation in a negatively supercoiled DNA may be kinetically forbidden under physiological conditions. *Cell* 33:817–29
17. Distefano MD, Dervan PB. 1992. Ligand promoted dimerization of oligonucleotides binding cooperatively to DNA. *J. Am. Chem. Soc.* 114:11006–7
18. Dressler D, Potter H. 1982. Molecular mechanisms in genetic recombination. *Annu. Rev. Biochem.* 51:727–61
19. Du SM, Seeman NC. 1992. Synthesis of a DNA knot containing both positive and negative nodes. *J. Am. Chem. Soc.* 114:9652–55
20. Du SM, Seeman NC. 1993. The construction of a trefoil knot from a DNA branched junction motif. *Biopolymers.* In press

21. Du SM, Zhang S, Seeman NC. 1992. DNA junctions, antijunctions and mesojunctions. *Biochemistry* 31:10955–63
22. Duckett DR, Lilley DMJ. 1990. The three-way DNA junction is a Y shaped molecule in which there is no helix-helix stacking. *EMBO J.* 9:1659–64
23. Duckett DR, Lilley DMJ. 1991. Effects of base mismatches on the structure of the four-way DNA junction. *J. Mol. Biol.* 221:147–61
24. Duckett DR, Murchie AIH, Bhattacharyya A, Clegg RM, Diekmann S, et al. 1992. The structure of DNA junctions and their interaction with enzymes. *Eur. J. Biochem.* 207:285–95
25. Duckett DR, Murchie AIH, Diekmann S, Von Kitzing E, Kemper B, Lilley DMJ. 1988. The structure of the Holliday junction and its resolution. *Cell* 55:79–89
26. Duckett DR, Murchie AIH, Lilley, DMJ. 1990. The role of metal ions in the conformation of the four way DNA junction. *EMBO J.* 9:583–90
27. Eis PS, Millar DP. 1993. Interarm flexibility in a DNA four-way junction revealed by time-resolved fluorescence resonance energy transfer. *Biochemistry*. Submitted
28. Ferrari S, Harley VR, Pontiggia A, Goodfellow PN, Lovell-Badge R, Bianchi ME. 1992. SRY, like HMG1, recognizes sharp angles in DNA. *EMBO J.* 11:4497–4506
29. Frappier L, Price GB, Martin RG, Zannis-Hadjopoulos M. 1987. Monoclonal antibodies to cruciform DNA structures. *J. Mol. Biol.* 193:751–58
30. Frappier L, Price GB, Martin RG, Zannis-Hadjopoulos M. 1989. Characterization of the binding affinity of two anticruciform DNA monoclonal antibodies. *J. Biol. Chem.* 264:334–41
31. Fraser MJ. 1980. Purification and properties of *Neurospora crassa* endo-exonuclease, an enzyme which can be converted to a single-strand specific endonuclease. *Methods Enzymol.* 65:255–76
32. Fu TJ, Seeman NC. 1993. DNA double crossover molecules. *Biochemistry* 32:3211–20
33. Gellert M, Mizuuchi K, O'Dea MH, Ohmori H, Tomizawa J. 1978. DNA gyrase and DNA supercoiling. *Cold Spring Harbor Symp. Quant. Biol.* 43:35–40
34. Gellert MM, O'Dea MH, Mizuuchi K. 1983. Slow cruciform transitions in palindromic DNA. *Proc. Natl. Acad. Sci. USA* 780:5545–49
35. Gough GW, Lilley DMJ. 1985. DNA bending induced by cruciform formation. *Nature (London)* 313:154–56
36. Guo Q, Lu M, Churchill MEA, Tullius TD, Kallenbach NR. 1990. Asymmetric structure of a three-arm junction. *Biochemistry* 29:10927–34
37. Guo Q, Lu M, Kallenbach NR. 1991. Conformational preference and ligand binding properties of DNA junctions are determined by sequence at the branch. *Biopolymers* 31:359–72
38. Guo Q, Lu M, Seeman NC, Kallenbach NR. 1990. Drug binding by branched DNA molecules: analysis by chemical footprinting of intercalation into an immobile junction. *Biochemistry* 29:570–78
39. Hoess R, Wierzbicki A, Abremski K. 1987. Characterization of intermediates in site-specific recombination. *Proc. Natl. Acad. Sci. USA* 84:6840–44
40. Holliday R. 1964. A mechanism for gene conversion in fungi. *Genet. Res.* 5:282–304
41. Horn T, Urdea MS. 1989. Forks and combs and DNA. *Nucleic Acids Res.* 17:6959–67
42. Hsu PL, Landy A. 1984. Resolution of synthetic ATT-site Holliday structures by the integrase function of bacteriophage lambda. *Nature (London)* 311:721–26
43. Hudson RHE, Damha MJ. 1993. Nucleic acid dendrimers: novel biopolymer structures. *J. Am. Chem. Soc.* 115:2119–24
44. Jensch F, Kemper B. 1986. Endonuclease VII resolves Y-junctions in branched DNA in vitro. *EMBO J.* 5:181–89
45. Johnson RD, Symington LS. 1993. Crossed-stranded DNA structures for investigating the molecular dynamics of the Holliday junction. *J. Mol.Biol.* 229:812–20
46. Kallenbach NR, Ma RI, Seeman NC. 1983. An immobile nucleic acid junction constructed from oligonucleotides. *Nature (London)* 305:829–31
47. Kalnik MW, Norman DG, Swann PF, Patel DJ. 1989. Conformation of adenosine bulge-containing deoxytridecanucleotide duplexes in solution. *J. Biol. Chem.* 264:3702–12
48. Kemper B, Pottmeyer S, Solaro P, Kosak H. 1991. Resolution of DNA-secondary structures by endonuclease VII. See Ref. 94a, pp. 215–30
49. Kim JS, Sharp P, Davidson N. 1972. Electron microscope studies of heter-

oduplex DNA from a deletion mutant of bacteriophage fX-174. *Proc. Natl. Acad. Sci. USA* 69:1948–52

50. Kim SH, Quigley GJ, Suddath FL, McPherson A, Sneden D, et al. 1973. Three-dimensional structure of yeast phenylalanine transfer RNA. *Science* 179:285–88

51. Kimball A, Guo Q, Lu M, Kallenbach NR, Cunningham RP, et al. 1990. Conformational isomers of Holliday junctions. *J. Biol. Chem.* 265:6544–47

52. Kitts PA, Nash HA. 1987. Homology dependent interactions in phage lambda site-specific recombination. *Nature (London)* 329:346–48

53. Lee CS, Davis RW, Davidson N. 1970. A physical study by electron microscopy of the terminally repetitious, circularly permuted DNA from coliphage particles of *Escherichia coli* 15. *J. Mol. Biol.* 48:1–22

54. Leontis NB, Kwok W, Newman JS. 1991. Stability and structure of three way DNA junctions containing unpaired nucleotides. *Nucleic Acids Res.* 19:759–66

55. Leontis NB, Hills MT, Piotto M, Malmotra A, Nussbaum J, Sorenstein D. 1993. A model for the solution structure of a branched, three-stranded DNA complex. *J. Biomol. Struct. Dyn.* 11:215–23

56. Lilley DMJ. 1980. The inverted repeat as a recognizable structural feature in supercoiled DNA molecules. *Proc. Natl. Acad. Sci. USA* 77:6468–72

57. Lilley DMJ, Clegg RM. 1993. The structure of the four-way junction in DNA. *Annu. Rev. Biophys. Biomol. Struct.* 22:299–328

58. Lloyd RG, Sharples GJ. 1993. Dissociation of synthetic Holliday junctions by *E. coli* RecG protein. *EMBO J.* 12:17–22

59. Lu M, Guo Q, Kallenbach NR. 1991. Effect of sequence on the structure of three-arm DNA junctions. *Biochemistry* 30:5815–20

60. Lu M, Guo Q, Kallenbach NR. 1992. Interaction of drugs with branched DNA structures. *Crit. Rev. Biochem. Mol. Biol.* 27:157–90

61. Lu M, Guo Q, Marky LA, Seeman NC, Kallenbach NR. 1992. Thermodynamics of DNA branching. *J. Mol. Biol.* 223:781–89

62. Lu M, Guo Q, Mueller JE, Kemper B, Studier FW, et al. 1990. Characterization of a bimobile DNA junction. *J. Biol. Chem.* 265:16778–85

63. Lu M, Guo Q, Pasternack RF, Wink DJ, Seeman NC, Kallenbach NR. 1990. Drug binding by branched DNA: selective interaction of tetrapyridyl porphyrins with an immobile junction. *Biochemistry* 29:1614–24

64. Lu M, Guo Q, Seeman NC, Kallenbach NR. 1990. Drug binding by branched DNA: selective interaction of the dye stains—all with an immobile junction. *Biochemistry* 29:3407–12

65. Lu M, Guo Q, Seeman NC, Kallenbach NR. 1991. Parallel and antiparallel Holliday junctions differ in structure and stability. *J. Mol. Biol.* 221:1419–32

66. Lu M, Guo Q, Wink DJ, Kallenbach NR. 1990. Charge dependence of Fe(II) catalyzed DNA cleavage. *Nucleic Acids Res.* 18:3333–37

67. Ma RI, Kallenbach NR, Sheardy RD, Petrillo ML, Seeman NC. 1986. Three arm nucleic acid junctions are flexible. *Nucleic Acids Res.* 14:9745–53

68. Marky LA, Kallenbach NR, McDonough KA, Seeman NC, Breslauer KJ. 1987. The melting behavior of a DNA junction structure: a calorimetric and spectroscopic study. *Biopolymers* 26:1621–34

69. Marky LA, Kupke DW. 1989. Probing the hydration of the minor groove of AT synthetic DNA polymers by volume and heat changes. *Biochemistry* 28:9982–88

70. Meselson M. 1972. Formation of hybrid DNA by rotary diffusion during genetic recombination. *J. Mol. Biol.* 71:795–98

71. Minagawa T, Murakami A, Ryo Y, Yamagishi H. 1983. Structural features of very fast sedimenting DNA formed by gene 49 defective T4. *Virology* 126:183–93

72. Mizuuchi K, Kemper B, Hays J, Weisberg R. 1982. T4 endonuclease VII cleaves Holliday structures. *Cell* 29:347–65

73. Mizuuchi K, Mizuuchi M, Gellert M. 1982. Cruciform structures in palindromic DNA are favored by DNA supercoiling. *J. Mol. Biol.* 156:229–43

74. Mueller JE, Du SM, Seeman NC. 1991. Design and synthesis of a knot from single-stranded DNA. *J. Am. Chem. Soc.* 113:6306–8

75. Mueller JE, Kemper B, Cunningham RP, Kallenbach NR, Seeman NC. 1988. T4 endonuclease VII cleaves the crossover strands of Holliday junction analogs. *Proc. Natl. Acad. Sci. USA* 85:9441–45

76. Mueller JE, Newton CJ, Jensch F,

Kemper B, Cunningham RP, et al. 1990. Resolution of Holliday junction analogs by T4 endonuclease VII can be directed by substrate structure. *J. Biol. Chem.* 265:13918–24

77. Murchie AIH, Clegg RM, von Kitzing E, Duckett DR, Diekmann S, Lilley DMJ. 1989. Fluorescence energy transfer shows that the four-way DNA junction is a right-handed cross of antiparallel molecules. *Nature (London)* 341:763–66

78. Murchie AIH, Portugal J, Lilley DMJ. 1991. Cleavage of a four-way DNA junction by a restriction enzyme spanning the point of strand exchange. *EMBO J.* 10:713–18

79. Nunes-Duby SE, Matsumoto L, Landy A. 1987. Site-specific recombination intermediates trapped with suicide substrates. *Cell* 50:779–88

80. Padgett RA, Konarska MM, Grabowski PJ, Hardy SF, Sharp PA. 1984. Lariat RNA's as intermediates and products in the splicing of messenger RNA precursors. *Science* 225:898–903

81. Panyutin IG, Hsieh P. 1993. Formation of a single base mismatch impedes spontaneous DNA branch migration. *J. Mol. Biol.* 230:413–24

82. Panyutin IG, Hsieh P. 1993. A dynamic study of spontaneous DNA branch migration. *J. Biomol. Struct. Dyn.* 10: a147

83. Patel DJ, Kozlowski SA, Marky LA, Rice JA, Broka C, et al. 1982. Extra adenosine stacks into the self-complementary d(CGCAGATTCGCG) duplex in solution. *Biochemistry* 21:445–51

84. Patterson AL. 1972. *Int. Tables X-Ray Crystallogr.* 2:41

85. Petrillo ML, Newton CJ, Cunningham RP, Ma RI, Kallenbach NR, Seeman NC. 1988. Ligation and flexibility of four-arm DNA junctions. *Biopolymers* 27:1337–52

86. Picksley SM, Parsons CA, Kemper B, West SC. 1990. Cleavage specificity of bacteriophage T4 endonuclease VII and bacteriophage T7 endonuclease I on synthetic branch migratable Holliday junctions. *J. Mol. Biol.* 212:723–35

87. Pontiggia A, Negri A, Beltrame M, Bianchi ME. 1993. Protein HU binds specifically to kinked DNA. *Mol. Microbiol.* 7:343–50

88. Pottmeyer S, Kemper B. 1992. T4 endonuclease VII resolves cruciform DNA with nick and counter-nick and its activity is directed by local nucleo-tide sequences. *J. Mol. Biol.* 223:607–15

89. Rau DC, Lee B, Parsegian VA. 1984. Measurement of the repulsive force between polyelectrolyte molecules in ionic solution: hydration forces between parallel DNA double helices. *Proc. Natl. Acad. Sci. USA* 81:2621–25

90. Rau DC, Parsegian A. 1992. Direct measurement of temperature dependent solvation forces between DNA double helices. *Biophys. J.* 61:260–71

91. Robinson BH, Seeman NC. 1987. Simulation of double stranded branch point migration. *Biophys. J.* 51:611–26

92. Robinson BH, Seeman NC. 1987. The design of a biochip. *Protein Eng.* 1: 295–300

93. Rosen MA, Patel DJ. 1993. Conformational differences between bulged pyrimidines (C-C) and purines (A-A, I-I) at the branch point of three stranded DNA junctions. *Biochemistry* 32: 6563–75

94. Rosen MA, Patel DJ. 1993. Structural features of a three stranded DNA junction containing a C-C junctional bulge. *Biochemistry* 32:6576–87

94a. Sarma RH, Sarma MH, eds. 1991. *Structure & Methods*, Vol. 1. New York: Adenine. 251 pp.

95. Seeman NC. 1982. Nucleic acid junctions and lattices. *J. Theor. Biol.* 99: 237–47

96. Seeman NC. 1985. Macromolecular design, nucleic acid junctions and crystal formation. *J. Biomol. Struct. Dyn.* 3:11–34

97. Seeman NC. 1985. Interactive design and manipulation of macromolecular architecture utilizing nucleic acid junctions. *J. Mol. Graph.* 3:34–39

98. Seeman NC. 1988. Physical models for exploring DNA topology. *J. Biomol. Struct. Dyn.* 5:997–1004

99. Seeman NC. 1990. *De novo* design of sequences for nucleic acid structural engineering. *J. Biomol. Struct. Dyn.* 8: 573–81

100. Seeman NC. 1991. Construction of three dimensional stick figures from branched DNA. *DNA Cell Biol.* 10: 475–86

101. Seeman NC. 1991. DNA for nanoscale fabrication. *Nanotechnology* 2:149–59

102. Seeman NC. 1992. The design of single-stranded nucleic acid knots. *Mol. Eng.* 2:297–307

103. Seeman NC, Kallenbach NR. 1983. Design of immobile nucleic acid junctions. *Biophys. J.* 44:201–9

104. Seeman NC, Maestre MF, Ma RI, Kallenbach NR. 1985. Physical characterization of a nucleic acid junction. In *Progress in Clinical & Biological Research: Thermonuclear Bases of Cancer*, ed. R Rein, 172A:99–108. New York: Alan Liss. 576 pp.

105. Seeman NC, Mueller JE, Chen JH, Churchill MEA, Kimball A, et al. 1990. Immobile junctions suggest new features of the structural chemistry of recombination. See Ref. 94a, pp. 137–47

106. Shore D, Langowski J, Baldwin RL. 1981. DNA flexibility studied by covalent closure of short fragments into circles. *Proc. Natl. Acad. Sci. USA* 78: 4833–37

107. Sigal N, Alberts B. 1972. Genetic recombination: the nature of a crossed strand-exchange between two homologous DNA molecules. *J. Mol. Biol.* 71:789–93

108. Sun H, Treco D, Szostak JW. 1991. Extensive 3'-overhanging, single-stranded DNA associated with the meiosis-specific double strand breaks at the *ARG4* recombination intitation site. *Cell* 64:1155–61

109. Thaler DS, Stahl FW. 1988. DNA double-chain breaks in recombination of phage 1 and of yeast. *Annu. Rev. Genet.* 22:167–97

110. Thompson BJ, Camien MN, Warner RC. 1976. Kinetics of branch migration in double stranded DNA. *Proc. Natl. Acad. Sci. USA* 73:2299–2303

111. Timsit Y, Moras D. 1991. Groove-backbone interaction in B-DNA. Implication for DNA condensation and recombination. *J. Mol. Biol.* 221:919–40

112. Tsaneva IR, Müller B, West SC. 1992. ATP-dependent branch migration of Holliday junctions promoted by the RuvA and RuvB proteins of E. coli. *Cell* 69:1171–80

113. van Dyke MW, Dervan PB. 1983. Methidiumpropyl-EDTA·Fe(II) and DNase I footprinting report different small molecule binding site sizes on DNA. *Nucleic Acids Res.* 11:5555–67

114. von Kitzing E, Lilley DMJ, Diekmann S. 1990. The stereochemistry of DNA four-way junctions, a theoretical study. *Nucleic Acids Res.* 18:2671–83

115. Wang H, Du SM, Seeman NC. 1993. Tight DNA knots. *J. Biomol. Struct. Dyn.* 10:853–63

116. Wang Y, Muller JE, Kemper B, Seeman NC. 1991. The assembly and characterization of 5-arm and 6-arm DNA branched junctions. *Biochemistry* 30: 5667–74

117. Ward GK, Shihab-el-Deen A, Zannis-Hadjopoulos M, Price GB. 1991. DNA cruciforms and the nuclear supporting structure. *Exp. Cell Res.* 195:92–98

118. Warner RC, Fishel RA, Wheeler FC. 1978. Branch migration in recombination. *Cold Spring Harbor Symp. Quant. Biol.* 43:957–68

119. Wells AF. 1977. *Three-Dimensional Nets and Polyhedra*. New York: Wiley & Sons. 268 pp.

120. Wemmer DE, Wand AJ, Seeman NC, Kallenbach NR. 1985. NMR analysis of DNA junctions. *Biochemistry* 24: 5745–49

121. West SC. 1992. Enzymes and molecular mechanisms of genetic recombination. *Annu. Rev. Biochem.* 61:603–40

122. White JH, Millett KC, Cozzarelli NR. 1987. Description of the topological entanglement of DNA catenanes and knots. *J. Mol. Biol.* 197:585–603

123. Woodson SA, Crothers DM. 1989. Conformation of a bulge-containing oligomer from a hot-spot sequence by NMR and energy minimization. *Biopolymers* 28:1149–77

124. Zhang S, Fu TJ, Seeman NC. 1993. Construction of symmetric, immobile DNA branched junctions. *Biochemistry* 32:8062–67

125. Zhang Y, Seeman NC. 1992. A solid-support methodology for the construction of geometrical objects from DNA. *J. Am. Chem. Soc.* 114:2656–63

126. Zhong M, Kallenbach NR. 1993. Conformation and thermodynamics of DNA 'necks.' *J. Mol. Biol.* 230:766–78

127. Zhong M, Rashes MS, Kallenbach NR. 1993. Effect of T-T mismatches on three arm DNA junctions. *Biochemistry* 32: In press

128. Zhong M, Rashes MS, Marky LA, Kallenbach NR. 1992. T-T mismatches enhance drug binding at the branch site in a four arm DNA junction. *Biochemistry* 31:8064–71

Annu. Rev. Biophys. Biomol. Struct. 1994. 23:87–113
Copyright © 1994 by Annual Reviews Inc. All rights reserved

THE LIGHT-ADDRESSABLE POTENTIOMETRIC SENSOR: Principles and Biological Applications

John C. Owicki, Luc J. Bousse, Dean G. Hafeman, Gregory L. Kirk, John D. Olson, H. Garrett Wada, and J. Wallace Parce

Molecular Devices Corporation, Menlo Park, California 94025

KEY WORDS: LAPS, sensor, immunoassay, bioassay, receptor

CONTENTS

87

INTRODUCTION

Semiconductor technology and biotechnology are two major technical disciplines that have large practical ramifications. This review describes the fruits of a research and development project that combines the two fields: the light-addressable potentiometric sensor (LAPS) and its bioanalytical applications.

Our focus on this particular device prevents us from describing in detail other noteworthy work at the interface (both intellectual and physical!) between semiconductor technology and biology. Such studies include the work of Fromherz et al on using field-effect transistors to sense action potentials (25) and others on the fabrication of microelectrodes (18, 21, 57). Several groups have used photolithography to pattern the chemical or physical properties of cell-culture substrates to control the patterns of adhesion or migration of cells (17, 20, 32, 66). The work of Fodor et al combining photolithographic chemical synthesis with optical sensing (24) is also worth reading about.

Here, we first present the principles of operation of the LAPS without relying too heavily on solid-state physics. Next we indicate how the LAPS can be integrated into sensitive analytical systems, stressing the sensor's usefulness for microvolume applications. Finally, we survey the two primary applications of the LAPS to date: an enzyme-linked immunosorbent assay (ELISA) system and a system for performing bioassays on living cells, the microphysiometer.

PRINCIPLES OF THE LIGHT-ADDRESSABLE POTENTIOMETRIC SENSOR

The LAPS, as currently used in analytical instrumentation, consists of lightly doped silicon with a thin silicon nitride insulator that contacts an aqueous solution (Figure 1). The accompanying electronic equipment serves two purposes. It controls the potential (Ψ) applied from the noninsulated side of the silicon to the solution and measures an alternating photocurrent (I_p) generated when a light source, such as one of the light-emitting diodes (LEDs) pictured in Figure 1, flashes rapidly. Both chemical sensing and signal transduction occur immediately adjacent to the insulator layer, at the solution-insulator interface, and the silicon-insulator interface respectively.

Figure 2 is a schematic of the LAPS showing the changes in potential that occur as the circuit is traced from solution through the sensor and back through the electronics to the solution again. Ground potential is chosen as the potential of the noninsulated side of the silicon chip.

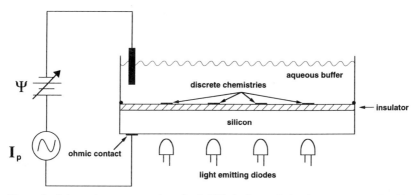

Figure 1 Schematic representation of a LAPS device and circuit components. In this case, the electrode placed in the aqueous buffer serves both as a controlling and a reference electrode. See text for details.

Beginning at the left side of the figure, this potential is changed by a potentiostat, depicted here as a variable potential, Ψ, such that the solution is negative with respect to the potential of bulk silicon. Scanning through solution toward the right, the potential remains essentially constant up to within a few nanometers of the insulator surface.

Measurement of pH

The silicon nitride surface contains primarily silanol groups with a small percentage of silamine groups (9, 10). The silanol groups titrate with

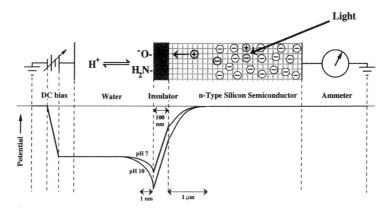

Figure 2 Physical principles of LAPS operation. This is a schematic view of the change in potential around the circuit depicted in Figure 1. Circled minuses and pluses represent electrons and holes, respectively, in the silicon. The bold-outlined circles represent electron-hole pairs created by the absorption of light. Note that the lateral dimensions are not to scale.

protons from solution and exist as either negatively charged SiO^- or neutrally charged SiOH functions. Likewise the silamine groups can exist as neutral or positively charged functions. The surface is neutrally charged at a pH of ~3.5 (point of zero charge). Therefore at neutral pH the surface is negatively charged as depicted in the figure, and the potential of solution becomes more negative as the surface is approached. The distance over which the solution potential deviates from that of the bulk is determined by the ionic strength of solution. At physiologic ionic strength, ~150 mM, the $1/e$ distance for the exponential decay of the surface potential is approximately 1 nm. Also as depicted in the figure, the difference in potential between bulk solution and the insulator surface is pH dependent, and therefore the potential at the surface is more negative at pH 10 than at pH 7. The pH dependence of the surface potential is Nernstian, ~59 mV/pH unit at room temperature (5, 27). This is the attribute of the sensor that enables measurement of solution pH. Nernstian responses require a high density of titratable groups on the sensor surface. Based on the relatively short shielding distance in physiologic saline in relation to the size of a typical globular protein, one would predict that adsorbed proteins would have little influence on sensor performance. In fact, the LAPS has been used to measure the pII of whole blood without experiencing any fouling problems (D Hafeman, personal communication).

Progressing through the insulator, the potential rises back toward that of the bulk silicon. In the silicon adjacent to the insulator, a depletion layer (space-charge region) may be formed owing to the electrostatic repulsion of majority charge carriers (electrons in n-type silicon). This region, in which the potential decays to that of the bulk silicon, is ~1 μm thick for the densities of phosphorus dopant used in the LAPS (~10 Ωcm silicon). It is the electric field (voltage gradient) in this region that is sensed electronically to determine changes in the surface potential and therefore changes in the solution pH. Completing the circuit on the right hand side is an ammeter used to measure alternating current.

As can be seen, the LAPS belongs to the family of electrolyte-insulator–silicon field–effect sensors. This family also includes the ion–selective field–effect transistors, sometimes called ChemFETs (4, 30). The differences between these devices result from the different mechanisms used to detect changes in the potential at the silicon-insulator interface.

The Photoeffect

The presence of a depletion layer in the sensor can be determined by shining light on the silicon and measuring the current in the ammeter.

When silicon absorbs light of the appropriate wavelength, hole-electron pairs are generated. These pairs become separated in the electric field in the depletion layer. Electrons move toward the silicon bulk, and holes accumulate at the silicon-insulator interface. This charge separation results in a compensatory capacitatively coupled movement of charge in the external circuit that the ammeter can detect. Figure 3*a* shows the current generated in the external circuit by illuminating a sensor with an LED as depicted in Figure 1. When the light is turned on, the current rises as holes diffuse from their point of generation near the back of the sensor and are separated in the electric field in the depletion layer (drift current). Holes accumulate at the silicon-insulator interface until a steady state is reached at which the rate of diffusion of holes back toward the bulk silicon (diffusion current) equals the drift current. At that point, the current in the external circuit has decayed to zero. When the LED is turned off, the diffusion current now predominates, and current flows transiently in the opposite direction as the light-induced charge separation is reversed. Because there is no flow of direct current through the insulator, the areas under the charg-

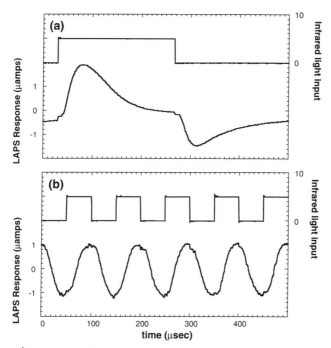

Figure 3   Photocurrents in the LAPS. (*a, lower trace*) Transient photocurrents resulting from initiating and ceasing sensor illumination (*upper trace,* in arbitrary units). (*b*) The continuous response to a 10-kHz square-wave modulation of the light intensity.

ing and discharging curves in Figure 3a are equal. To generate a more useful signal, in practice the LED is flashed rapidly with respect to the decay processes, resulting in the signal shown in Figure 3b. This signal is rectified to give to give a root mean square (rms) amplitude for the AC photocurrent (I_p).

The photocurrent described above only exists when a depletion layer is present in the silicon. If the potential applied to the solution becomes sufficiently positive, the depletion layer collapses and no photocurrent is generated. This effect appears in Figure 4, where I_p is plotted versus the applied potential (Ψ). Note that the three photoresponse curves shown for three different solution pH values are identical except for shifts on the potential axis. This is because the potential sensed in the silicon is the sum of any fixed potentials in the series circuit, Ψ, and the surface potential at the insulator-aqueous interface. As mentioned previously, the surface potential depends on the solution pH. Change in pH can be measured by determining the shift in the photoresponse curve from its position at any starting pH value. The value of Ψ at which the inflection point ($d^2I_p/d\Psi^2 = 0$) occurs in the photoresponse curve is called Ψ_{pip} and is used to monitor the shift on the potential axis.

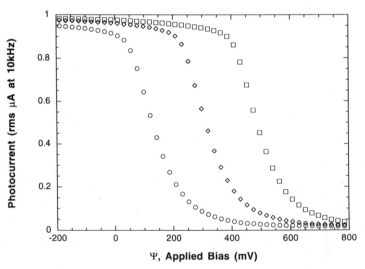

Figure 4 Photocurrent-voltage curves in LAPS and the effects of pH. The potential from solution to the silicon bulk, as determined by a Ag/AgCl reference electrode, was swept from −200 mV to +800 mV while the light intensity was modulated at 10 kHz and the photocurrent was recorded. The curves represent pH 4.0 (*circles*), pH 7.0 (*diamonds*), and pH 10.0 (*squares*).

Light Addressability

As shown in Figure 1, the pH of solution is only measured where the sensor is illuminated. Thus the four LEDs can be energized one at a time and used to measure local changes in pH due to the discrete chemistries adjacent to the sensor surface. By multiplexing the LEDs, one can use this light addressability to perform many measurements practically simultaneously with a single sensor and a single set of accompanying electronics.

Measurement of Other Chemical Species

Our discussion so far has focused on sensing pH. However, the LAPS is a generic potentiometric sensor, and as such can be configured to sense a variety of species (27). Figure 5 shows near Nernstian responses of the LAPS for the sensing of pH, redox potential, and potassium ions. The redox potential of a solution of ferri- and ferrocyanide was determined using a LAPS with a thin gold spot evaporated onto the solution side of the insulator. For determining $[K^+]$, a polyvinyl chlo-

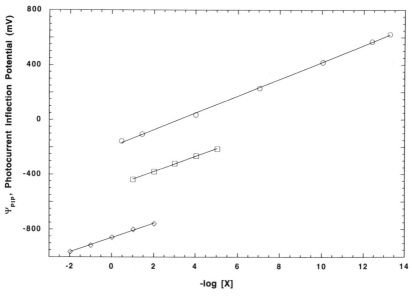

Figure 5 Detection of pH, redox potential, and $[K^+]$ with LAPS. Three different LAPS devices were used to perform these measurements: for pH measurements (*circles*), the silicon nitride insulator contacted solution; for determination of redox potential (*diamonds*), a thin layer of gold was evaporated on the insulator surface; for measurements of potassium (*squares*), a thin membrane of polyvinylchloride containing valinomycin was pressed onto the LAPS insulator surface by means of an o-ring.

ride membrane containing the potassium ionophore valinomycin was deposited on the surface of the sensor.

THE LAPS AS A SENSOR IN AN ANALYTICAL SYSTEM

As discussed above, the LAPS displays a variety of novel attributes. From an analytical point of view, a sensor is only as good as the system in which it is incorporated. The remainder of this article focuses on measurement systems designed to take advantage of the LAPS's capabilities.

Electrical Measurements of Phospholipid Membranes

An early use of the LAPS was to measure the electrical properties of phospholipid bilayer membranes. Transmembrane potentials, as well as membrane capacitance and conductance, were all determined using a black-lipid membrane (BLM) configuration (65). Although this configuration has not been pursued further, it should be possible to combine phospholipid membranes with micromachined structures on LAPS to construct novel sensor systems. Membrane stability is of paramount importance.

Discrete Sensor Arrays

One of the first analytical applications of the LAPS, proposed originally by Hafeman et al (27), was an array of sensors for different analytes, fabricated by placing an ion-selective membrane at the solution-insulator interface over each sensing spot. Investigators have explored this type of LAPS application in several systems to measure potentiometric responses of arrays of different chemical sensors. Examples include the recent work of Kanai et al (31) on taste sensors and of Sato et al (63) on gas sensing. As we discuss later, an array of sensing sites has also been used to increase the parallelism in a LAPS-based immunoassay system.

LAPS as an Imaging Sensor

Several research groups have used LAPS devices to make potentiometric images of the front surface by scanning light from an LED or a laser on the backside of the silicon chip or wafer. This amounts to an extension of the discrete sensor arrays, in which the number of sensor spots becomes very large. This concept was first demonstrated by Lundstrom et al in 1991 using arrays of gas-sensitive materials (37), and it is being further developed to generate artificial olfactory images

(38, 72). Another type of recently demonstrated imaging involves enzyme reactions (64). Here, different enzymes are immobilized on the surface of the LAPS to measure concentrations of the enzyme substrates (glucose and urea). Iwasaki et al (45), investigating the spatial resolution of such imaging LAPS systems, concluded that with backside illumination, resolution is approximately equal to the wafer thickness. Clearly, this whole area is still in its infancy and is being actively developed.

Microvolume Systems

The most important applications of LAPS devices to date have been to measure time-varying chemical concentrations in very small volumes (11). A LAPS device especially suits this application because the silicon front surface is extremely flat, and it has no metallization leads or bond wires with their required encapsulation. The microvolumes used are typically on the order of 1 mm by 1 mm by 100 μm, or 100 nl. However, even thinner chambers are relatively easy to make, and a goal of 10 nl could be met if needed. In most work so far, the chemical quantity monitored has been either pH or redox potential.

Molecular Devices Corporation has pursued two families of microvolume applications in which different agents cause a pH change. One application is an ELISA based on a pH-changing enzyme. In the other, the excretion of acidic metabolites by living cells provides a means to measure metabolic activity. Both cases are discussed in more detail below, but here we note that the measured quantity is the rate of pH change, not pH itself. Clearly, for a given number of protons or hydroxyl ions added to the system, the resulting rate of pH change will be larger if the total volume is smaller. A general expression for the rate of pH change in a microvolume is

$$\frac{dpH}{dt} = \frac{R}{V\beta_V + S\beta_S} , \qquad\qquad 1.$$

where R is the rate at which H^+ or OH^- ions are generated (positive for OH^- ions and negative for H^+ ions); V and S are the volume and surface area of the reaction chamber, and β_V and β_S are volumetric and surface buffer capacities (11). Rapid equilibration of the pH in an unstirred microvolume chamber requires that the chamber be thin, customarily 100–200 μm thick, and that most of the buffer capacity be contributed by diffusing species rather than by bound species. Thus $V\beta_V$ should be at least a factor of 10 greater than $S\beta_S$. The volumetric buffer capacity β_V is determined by the concentration of buffer present; at a pH equal to the pK of the buffer, $\beta_V(\text{max}) = 0.576c$ for monovalent buffers, where c is the buffer concentration. When pH is different from pK, β_V decreases from this maximal value. The term in Equation 1 corresponding to surface buffering is very important in the immuno-assay applications, in which a membrane is used to capture and immobilize the immunocomplexes. This membrane has a large surface area, and because of its own composition as well as adsorbed protein, it can contribute significantly to the total buffer capacity. A 100-μm-thick nitrocellulose membrane coated with biotinylated bovine serum albumin has a surface buffer capacity equivalent to the buffer capacity of ~2–3 mM sodium phosphate near its pK_a in the same volume (6).

The principles for measuring rate of redox potential change are exactly the same as for pH except that the sensing area on the LAPS has a noble metal surface for sensing redox potential rather than a pH-sensing surface (27). An equation analogous to Equation 1 can be defined for redox measurements. For useful membrane materials and in biological systems, the buffer capacity for redox is usually much lower than that for pH (J Song, personal communication), which renders redox detection much more sensitive than pH detection as long as the detection limits are set by the size of the potentiometric signal.

The Sensor as a Structural Element of Analytical Systems

The front side of a LAPS device has no metallizations or transistor structures. Photocurrent is measured from the device through a single electrode in the conductive solution, with a single wire lead from the backside of the device. The requirements of electronic and micromachining steps in the fabrication of chemical sensors often conflict. Therefore, the relatively minor electronic constraints on LAPS fabrication make this device quite useful for applications requiring micromachining. Micromachining has been used in some microphysiometer applications to make $50 \times 50 \times 50$ μm wells in which nonadherent cells can be sedimented (12, 53) and to etch flow channels for multichannel microphysiometer chips (7, 8).

Data Analysis in LAPS Systems

When examining data obtained in a system using a LAPS device, one should understand the hierarchy of the different data levels. The first level consists of the measured photocurrent as a function of bias voltage, as shown in Figures 4 and 6a. The exact relationship between photocurrent and bias voltage is complex and has been used to study the presence of fixed charges and electron-accepting or -donating states at the silicon-insulator interface (26). Several efforts to model LAPS photocurrent/bias-voltage curves have been published (11, 39, 61, 62).

The details of this structure are unimportant for potentiometric sensing applications; as described earlier, potentiometric measurements usually only quantify the shift in this relationship along the bias-potential axis, typically in the form of the photocurrent inflection potential (Ψ_{pip}), as shown in Figure 6a. Adami et al (1) have described another

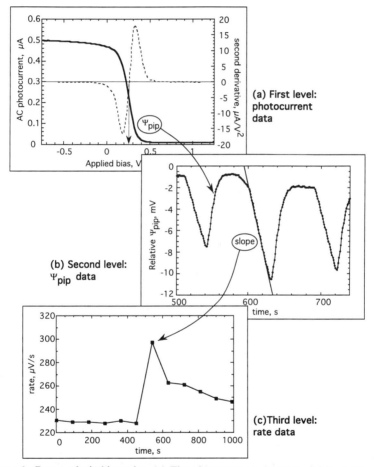

Figure 6   Data-analysis hierarchy. (*a*) The photoresponse curve (*solid line*). The inflection point of the photoresponse curve (Ψ_{pip}) is determined by finding the zero crossing of the second derivative (*dashed line*). (*b*) A typical experiment in which the voltage (Ψ_{pip}) is plotted versus time as some change in surface potential shifts its value. (*c*) The rate of change in the surface potential is determined by a least-squares fit of the χ_{pip} data. The data shown are from a microphysiometer, and the change in pH is caused by the build-up of excreted acidic substances during a brief halt in the flow of culture medium past the cells; the increase in acidification rate results from the addition of an agonist for muscarinic receptors on the cells in the microphysiometer chamber.

method for measuring this shift using a dual LAPS device. In commercially available sensor systems, this first level of data analysis is made invisible to the user, and the Ψ_{pip} data are shown as sensor-output data. The Ψ_{pip} data (Figure 6b) constitute the second level of data, which are equivalent to the voltages that would be measured by a pH-sensitive glass electrode. Where the rate of pH change is desired, these Ψ_{pip} data over time are fit by linear regression, giving the rate of potential change (Figure 6c). With a Nernstian response of 60 mV/pH unit, 1 μV/s corresponds to a rate of pH change of about 1 milli-pH unit per min.

APPLICATIONS FOR BIOCHEMICAL ASSAYS

Measurement of Enzyme Substrates and Inhibitors

To measure various compounds in a solution, LAPS devices have been coupled with enzymes that produce either pH or redox potential changes. Enzymes have been immobilized directly onto the surface of the LAPS to measure the concentration of enzyme substrates, urea and glucose, via pH changes (64). In this particular application, the sensor response depends on the pH buffer capacity of the medium in which it is immersed (16). These devices can be used in cases where a constant buffer capacity is expected, such as in a fermentation tank, and the pH response can be calibrated to the concentration of substrate. Enzymes have also been used in conjunction with the LAPS to measure specific enzymatic inhibitors such as anticholinesterase insecticides (23).

The major use of enzymes with LAPS has been in enzyme-linked immunoassays, as detailed below. Urease has been used most often as an enyme label; the catalyzed hydrolysis of urea increases pH at a rate proportional to enzymatic activity. Enzymes that catalyze reactions that change redox potential have also been used. For example, Wada et al have coupled the horseradish peroxidase-catalyzed oxidation of tetramethyl benzidine and the alkaline phosphatase-catalyzed hydrolysis of 5-bromo-4-chloro-3-indolylphosphate to the redox potential mediators hexacyanoferrate or ruthenium pentamine pyridine (71).

Enzyme-Linked Immunoassays

Most immunoassays involve the binding of enzyme-linked antibodies to ligands and separation of bound and free enzymes. These assays can be set up in two formats. First, multiepitopic ligands can be sandwiched between two antibodies (or other binding proteins): one to attach the ligand to the solid surface, and one to attach it to the enzyme label. Second, small haptens can be attached to the solid surface to compete with haptens in solution for binding sites on enzyme-labeled antibodies.

The surface of the sensor itself can be used as the solid phase for separation, or an alternative support can cause the separation and then be transferred to the sensor. Because solid phases can dramatically affect the performance of enzyme immunoassays (54), one should use a solid phase and assay protocol that minimally perturb the binding reaction and the signal detection.

Microporous membranes such as nitrocellulose are ideal solid supports for use with the LAPS. The monolithic nature of the sensor allows presentation of membranes to the LAPS surface under conditions that maintain a precise microvolume for measurement. The act of capturing the enzyme complex on a membrane also concentrates the complex into a small volume (47). The nitrocellulose filter membrane (0.45 μm pore size) is ~120 μm thick and ~30% solid. Capture by filtration through a spot 3 mm in diameter defines a solution volume of approximately 0.64 μl in which the enzyme changes the pH or redox potential.

Microporous capture membranes also have the advantage that reactants can be filtered rapidly with efficient, high-capacity capture because of the large surface area of the membrane (~150 cm^2 per 1 cm^2 of planar surface). This high surface area has its drawbacks, however. Proteins tend to adsorb to surfaces, and unwanted (nonspecific) binding of the enzyme to the solid phase can reduce assay sensitivity (22). Furthermore, high surface-buffer capacity reduces the signal obtained per enzyme molecule.

A commercial application of the LAPS for immunoassays (Threshold®) uses a biotinylated nitrocellulose capture membrane and streptavidin to capture specific binders and urease (41). The binding reactions involving the antibodies are performed in solution, followed by filtration through the membrane for rapid separation (Figure 7a). The sensor chamber, or reader, is designed to accept the membrane mounted across an aperture on a plastic stick, align the filtration spots with the light-interrogated areas of the LAPS, and create a microvolume by pressing the membrane against the sensor (Figure 7b). Eight samples are assayed in parallel on a membrane stick, taking advantage of the light addressability of the sensor.

Table 1 lists several ligands that have been detected with the LAPS and membrane capture. The analytes in the various assays were bound by specific antibodies (for protein antigens and haptens), DNA-binding proteins (for total DNA), or DNA probes (for specific-sequence DNA).

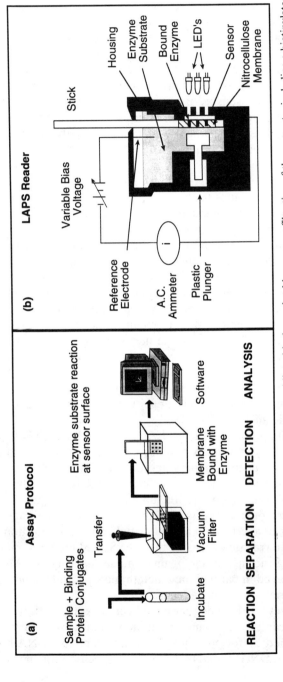

Figure 7 Solution-phase binding of enzyme conjugate and ligand is determined by vacuum filtration of the reagents, including a biotinylated component with streptavidin, through multiple spots on a biotinylated capture membrane. (*a*) The membrane is transferred to a LAPS reader (*b*), which aligns the filtration spots with the LEDs. A plunger presses the membrane against the sensor, creating individual microvolumes at each filtration spot for the captured enzyme complexes. Either pH or redox changes are sensed in the microvolumes.

Table 1 Lower limit of detection and assay time for various analytes in a LAPS-based immunoassay

Analyte	Sensitivity	Assay time	Reference
Total DNA	2 pg	2 h	14
Specific-sequence DNA	2×10^7 molecules	1 h	48
Tick anticoagulant protein	2.5 pg	2.5 h	58
Protein A	10 pg	4 h	41
Human chorionic gonadotropin	10 pg	20 min	47
Anti-PreS2 antibody	750 pg	overnight	29
Nicotinic acetylcholine receptor	1 ng	<10 min	59
Chlamydia trachomatis	600 cells	30 min	70
Neisseria meningitidis	800 cells	30 min	35
Yersinia pestis	4000 cells	30 min	35
Newcastle disease virus	130 pg	6 min	33a
	40 ng	65 min	
T-2 mycotoxin	1.0 ng	3 min	36
Saxitoxin	1.5 ng	3 min	73

In the case of the nicotinic acetylcholine receptor, biotinylated bungarotoxin was used to capture the receptor on the membrane (59). The incubation time and binding affinity of the reactants affect assay sensitivity. Assays listed in the table were optimized either for sensitivity or speed (or, in the case of the anti-PreS2 antibody assay, were run in parallel with an overnight radioimmunoassay).

Affinity constants for binding pairs have been determined using this assay configuration (K Dill & D Hafeman, personal communication). The rapid-filtration system allows equilibration to take place in the solution phase and minimizes the time of binder-receptor exposure to the solid phase. The affinity constants are thus unperturbed by the presence of the solid phase. In some other solid-phase measurement systems, as in most microplate determinations, equilibrium is established on the solid phase, or the time of contact between solution and solid phases is long enough for binding to the solid phase to perturb the solution-phase equilibrium and lower the measured affinity constant (28).

Other instruments have been developed that use the filtration/sensor system described above to run enzyme-linked assays. One such system applies the attributes of the Threshold® system in an automated form (36, 51). Here, the membrane is mounted on a continuous tape that is automatically transferred from a chemistry station, where regents have been automatically metered and filtered, to a reader. This system is designed for unattended continuous monitoring, for example in environmental applications.

APPLICATIONS FOR CELL-BASED BIOASSAYS: THE MICROPHYSIOMETER

Biological Basis

The hydrolysis of an ATP molecule in a cell liberates about 0.7 H^+ ions, whereas the synthesis of an ATP may produce or consume H^+, depending on the carbon source and catabolic pathway, but it usually does so in smaller amounts. ATP synthesis and hydrolysis must be balanced in the long term (typically minutes), and so the net effect of energy metabolism is to produce acid. This typically appears as the excretion of lactic acid or CO_2, through glycolysis or respiration. Hence, the rate of extracellular acidification is a measure of catabolic activity that is similar in principle to the rate of glucose or O_2 consumption, or to the rate of lactate, CO_2, or heat production. Extracellular acidification has, however, some instrumental advantages.

An additional component of extracellular acidification is independent of energy metabolism. Intracellular pH (pH_i) is altered during a variety of physiological processes, including the activation of many growth-factor receptors. The transition from one steady-state pH_i to a higher steady-state pH_i involves the transfer of protons from the cytoplasmic buffer to the environment as a pulse during the transition.

We summarize the relationships of some of the biological processes in Figure 8 and have discussed them in more detail elsewhere (49). Monitoring the extracellular acidification rate can in principle be used as a relatively generic method of detecting physiological changes, because many such changes alter pH_i, and most alter the use or generation of metabolic (free) energy. A LAPS-based instrument called a microphysiometer provides a practical means for doing so.

Instrumental Characteristics

Figure 9 indicates how the LAPS can be placed within proton-diffusion distance of living cells to sense extracellular pH changes in a microvolume flow chamber. Acidification rates are determined by measuring the rate of pH change during periodic brief halts in the flow of culture medium through the flow chamber, as in Figure 6, during which the pH drops transiently by ~0.1 unit. To reduce buffering, typical media buffers such as $NaHCO_3$ and HEPES are omitted from the medium;

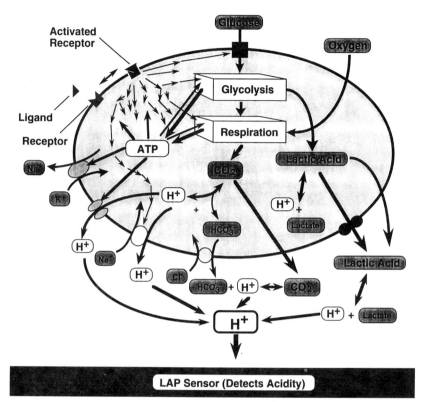

Figure 8   Relationships between cell physiology and extracellular acidification. Cellular energy metabolism is the principal ongoing source of protons; changes in intracellular pH can modify this flux transiently. The activation of cellular receptors can alter extracellular acidification by acting directly on energy metabolism, by changing the demand for ATP, and by changing the regulation of intracellular pH.

the remaining buffers (phosphate, amino acids) typically contribute ~ 1 mM/pH unit to the buffer capacity. The rms noise on individual pH measurements (one per second) is 5×10^{-4} to 1×10^{-3} pH units. The standard deviation of successive acidification-rate measurements is typically $\sim 2\%$. The best time resolution of this version of the microphysiometer is about 30 s, which is approximately the minimum time between acidification-rate data points and is also about the time it takes for the concentration of a test substance to stabilize within the chamber after the fluid-selection valve is switched. Vertical diffusional equilibration of protons and buffer species within the chamber is not kinetically limiting.

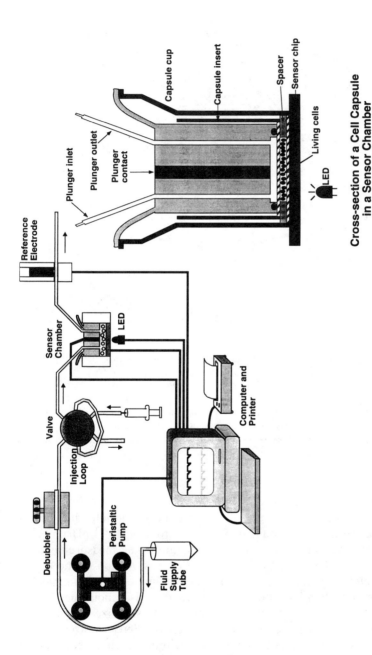

Cross-section of a Cell Capsule in a Sensor Chamber

Figure 9 Schematic diagram of the Cytosensor® microphysiometer. Culture medium is pumped by a peristaltic pump through a debubbling/degassing device, through a fluid-switching valve, into the cell-containing flow chamber, and then out past a reference electrode to waste. The valve selects one of two fluid streams or, as is shown, controls an injection loop. Cells are retained in the flow chamber between two track-etched polycarbonate membranes, either by natural adherence to one of the membranes or by immobilization, e.g. in a fibrin clot. The LAPS device forms the floor of the flow chamber. The superfused volume is a disk-shaped region 135 μm high and 6 mm in diameter (4 μl), and culture medium typically flows at ~100 μl/min. A microcomputer controls fluidics and data acquisition. A complete instrument has four or eight chambers operating in parallel.

Applications of Microphysiometry

MEASURING METABOLIC ACTIVITY   Extracellular acidification rate depends on carbon source (e.g. glucose or pyruvate) and on metabolic inhibitors (40, 52), and this finding is consistent with elementary considerations of intermediary metabolism (49). The microphysiometer has also been used to record the recovery of metabolic activity in cells recently thawed from cryopreservation (33).

Sapolsky and coauthors have used the microphysiometer to study how 24-h exposure to glucocorticoids affects fibroblast metabolism. Pretreatment with 1 nM corticosterone, but not 1 μM estradiol, progesterone, or testosterone, significantly decreased the acidification rate (56). These authors concluded that this inhibition was caused by decreased rates of glucose transport and protein synthesis in the cells, which are well established effects of glucocorticoids on fibroblasts. In another study that included microphysiometry, this group discovered that virally transformed fibroblasts were resistant to such metabolic inhibition (60). The authors proposed that stress, which causes the secretion of glucocorticoids, accelerates the growth of some types of tumors by this mechanism.

The Na^+/K^+-ATPase, or sodium pump, is a major user of ATP in many cell types. The acidification rate of TE671 rhabdomyosarcoma cells was decreased by 9% when this pump was inhibited either with ouabain or the removal of extracellular K^+ (42). In the same work, stimulation of the Na^+/K^+-ATPase by activation of a muscarinic receptor was shown to be mediated by an increase in intracellular $[Na^+]$.

PHARMACOLOGY   A surprising observation, now established for most major classes of plasma-membrane receptors and transduction mechanisms, is that receptor activation typically changes the extracellular acidification rate by 10–100% (40). We next describe how this phenomenon can be used to construct a relatively generic assay for receptor activation, temporarily deferring questions about the mechanisms of these acidification-rate changes.

Most pharmacological assays measure either the binding of a drug to a macromolecule or some functional consequence of that binding. The latter category includes extracellular acidification measured by microphysiometry, which is often similar in sensitivity and information content to other functional assays for receptor activation such as cAMP, protein phosphorylation, or mitogenesis. An important difference is that most assays are restricted in application to a limited range of receptors operating by the mechanism being probed; microphysiometry can be applied to a wider range of receptors because the cellular proton economy operates at a very high level of physiological integration.

Among the receptors whose activation has been detected under pharmacologically relevant conditions are protein tyrosine kinases such as epidermal growth factor (50, 53), ligand-gated ion channels such as the kainate glutamate receptor (55), hematopoietin-family receptors such as that for granulocyte-macrophage colony-stimulating factor (GM-CSF) (69), the T-cell receptor (43, 44), and receptors that are linked to G proteins, including β_2-adrenergic receptor through G_s (50), the D_2 dopamine receptor through G_i (13, 46), and the m_1 muscarinic receptor through G_q (40, 50). Figure 10 shows an example of the concentration-response data that can be obtained.

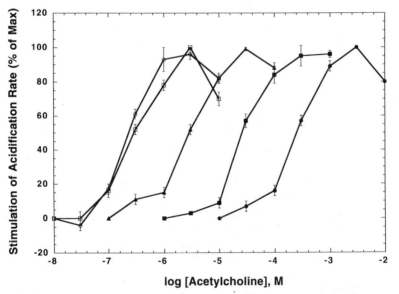

Figure 10 Concentration-response curves for the cholinergic stimulation of mouse pancreatic acinar cells as detected in the microphysiometer (19). Cells in a microphysiometer chamber were exposed to successively higher concentrations of acetylcholine, generating a sigmoid concentration-response curve as shown in the figure (*open circles* and *open squares* for two experiments, normalized to the highest stimulation of acidification rate). Fifty percent of maximum response was elicited by 0.20 ± 0.04 μM acetylcholine. When the experiment was repeated in the presence the muscarinic cholinergic antagonist atropine, the curve was shifted to the right to an extent depending on the concentration of atropine (10 nM, *filled triangles;* 100 nM, *filled squares;* 1 μM, *filled circles*). Schild analysis gave a pA_2 of 9.2, which is the negative logarithm of the concentration of antagonist sufficient to shift the curve rightward by a factor of two. Error bars indicate the standard error of the mean (SEM) based on $n = 4$–6.

When receptor activation is not strongly coupled to cell physiology, changes in extracellular acidification rate may not be observed. Changing the host cell or its physiology may induce responsiveness. Thus the responses seen by microphysiometry are characteristic of the combination of receptor and host cell, not of the receptor alone.

SIGNAL TRANSDUCTION   The metabolic pathways by which receptor activation alters extracellular acidification can be identified by observing the effects of modulating their activity on acidification rate. To date this has been done primarily by using specific inhibitors. Figure 11 shows, for example, that a component of the acidification response to GM-CSF in TF-1 erythroleukemia cells depends on the presence of extracellular sodium, implicating the Na^+/H^+ exchanger. Further studies demonstrated that the response is initiated by protein kinase activity and results from increased rates of glycolysis as well as activation of the Na^+/H^+ exchanger (69). In the same system antisense oligonucleotides were used to show that the ϵ isoform of protein kinase C is involved in the acidification response (3).

TOXICOLOGY   Extracellular acidification rate, as a measure of overall metabolic activity, lends itself naturally to in vitro toxicology. A close

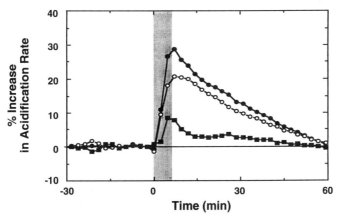

Figure 11   Demonstration that the Na^+/H^+ antiporter causes part of the acidification-rate increase observed when TF-1 erythroleukemia cells are stimulated with GM-CSF (69). The cells in the microphysiometer are stimulated with 10 ng/ml GM-CSF during the shaded period either under normal conditions (*filled circles*) or with sodium in the extracellular medium replaced by choline (*open circles*), which is not transported by the antiporter. The difference (*filled squares*) represents the contribution of the antiporter; when the experiment is repeated in the presence of amiloride, an inhibitor of the antiporter, the difference disappears (data not shown).

correlation has been established between the severity of ocular irritants, such as detergents and organic solvents, and the concentrations at which brief exposure to these compounds inhibits the acidification rates of fibroblasts or keratinocytes in the microphysiometer by 50% (2, 15, 53). In some cases the cells recover from the toxic insult (15). The ability to monitor recovery indicates that the microphysiometer measures a metabolic disturbance more subtle than cell death.

Medically relevant results for pharmacological toxicology are more difficult to obtain in vitro, because here the toxic compound acts by a tissue-specific mechanism. This case minimally requires a match between the toxic compound and type of responding cell. The only study of this type yet based on microphysiometry demonstrated excitotoxicity of a glutamate analogue in cocultures of hippocampal rat neurons and glia (55).

OTHER CELLULAR PREPARATIONS   Nearly all published microphysiometry results have used cultured mammalian cells. The metabolism of intact tissue, for example gastric glands (67) or organ slices (R Kuo & A Harris, personal communication) also may be monitored. Immobilized microbial cells can also be studied, as has been shown for bacteria and yeasts (34; J Libby & K Hahnenberger, personal communication). Free-swimming ciliates such as *Tetrahymena thermophila* can be studied (J Libby, personal communication), as can the slime mold *Dictyostelium discoideum* (R Metzger, personal communication). Finally, the cytopathic effects of viruses on mammalian cells have been demonstrated in the microphysiometer, both with fast-acting viruses such as vesicular stomatitis virus (~8 h) (53), and with slow-acting viruses such as HIV-1 (~4 days during 6 days of continuous culture in the microphysiometer) (40).

Prospects

The microphysiometer has been established as a useful tool in the cell-biology and pharmacology laboratory, providing functional information with a combination of promptness, convenience, and generality of application. It has applications in screening for drug discovery, though its throughput is not sufficient for truly large-scale screening. In some cases it should be possible to achieve $\sim 10^4$ tests per year with an eight-channel instrument (R Metzger, personal communication). The microphysiometer should be particularly useful for identifying ligands for so-called orphan receptors, proteins of unknown function that are presumed to be receptors, based on loose sequence homology to known receptors.

Clinical applications are as yet essentially unexplored. Some nonclinical data suggest that microphysiometry may be useful for detecting patterns of resistance of patients' tumors to chemotherapeutic agents (53). Given the published results for T-cell activation (43, 44), microphysiometry might be useful in monitoring the immune status of immunosuppressed patients. Finally, the ability of the microphysiometer to detect cellular metabolic activity sensitively and in real time may make it suitable for clinical microbiology.

Many of these additional applications will require substantial improvements in instrumentation. In particular, we are constructing research prototypes based on LAPS chips that have been extensively micromachined and include a microfluidics system. The benefits of miniaturization include reduced sample consumption and increased time resolution. They also include higher throughput via an increase in the number of parallel measurements, which will facilitate applications such as screening for new therapeutic drugs.

CONCLUDING PERSPECTIVE

The LAPS is a chemical sensor that, when used for biological applications, may be called a biosensor. It has been noted correctly that this field has had its share of hyperbole and unfulfilled expectations (68); one test of a technology's significance is the extent to which it migrates outside the laboratory of its creators, and the number of biosensors that pass that test has been disappointingly small. An important root of the problem is the highly interdisciplinary nature required of the research and development effort: biology, physical science, and engineering must be thoroughly intertwined. How to construct an atmosphere that nurtures this synthesis is an important question, but one beyond the scope of this review. We have, however, tried to convey the spirit of the endeavor by emphasizing the LAPS as a component of an analytical system, rather than the LAPS as a device.

ACKNOWLEDGMENTS

Much of the work on the immunological and cellular applications of LAPS would not have been possible without the support of ARPA, Contracts DAAL03-86-C-0009 (with USA/CRDEC) and MDA972-92-C-0005. We thank P Lam and S Mostarshed for help with the illustra-

110   OWICKI ET AL

tions, and J Denyer for the data in Figure 10 (from the study reported in Ref. 19).

Any *Annual Review* chapter, as well as any article cited in an *Annual Review* chapter, may be purchased from the Annual Reviews Preprints and Reprints service. 1-800-347-8007; 415-259-5017; email: arpr@class.org

Literature Cited

1. Adami M, Sartore M, Baldini E, Rossi A, Nicolini C. 1992. New measuring principle for LAPS devices. *Sens. Actuators B* 9:25–31
2. Bagley DM, Bruner LH, de Silva O, Cottin M, O'Brien KAF, et al. 1992. An evaluation of five potential alternatives in vitro to the rabbit eye irritation test in vivo. *Toxicol. Vitro* 6:275–84
3. Baxter GT, Miller DL, Kuo RC, Wada HG, Owicki JC. 1992. PKCε is involved in GM-CSF signal transduction. Evidence from microphysiometry and antisense oligonucleotide experiments. *Biochemistry* 31:10950–54
4. Bergveld P, Sibbald A. 1988. *Analytical and Biomedical Applications of Ion-Selective Field-Effect Transistors.* Amsterdam: Elsevier
5. Bousse L, Hafeman D, Tran N. 1990. Time dependence of the chemical response of silicon nitride surfaces. *Sens. Actuators B* 1:361–67
6. Bousse L, Kirk G, Sigal G. 1990. Biosensors for detection of enzymes immobilized in microvolume reaction chambers. *Sens. Actuators B* 1:555–60
7. Bousse L, McReynolds RJ, Kirk G, Dawes T, Lam P, et al. 1993. Micromachined multichannel systems for the measurement of cellular metabolism. In *Proceedings of Transducers 93, 7th Int. Conf. on Solid-State Sensors and Actuators.* pp. 916–20. Yokohama, Japan: Inst. Electr. Eng. Japan
8. Bousse L, McReynolds RJ, Kirk G, Lam P, Parce JW. 1993. Integrated fluidics for biosensors used to measure cellular metabolism. In *Proceedings of the Symposium on Chemical Sensors II, Proceedings of the Electrochemical Society Hawaii,* pp. 742–45. Pennington, NJ: Electrochem. Soc.
9. Bousse L, Mostarshed S. 1991. The zeta potential of silicon nitride thin films. *J. Electroanal. Chem.* 302:269–74
10. Bousse L, Mostarshed S, Hafeman D. 1992. Combined measurement of surface potential and zeta potential at insulator/electrolyte interfaces. *Sens. Actuators B* 10:67–71
11. Bousse L, Owicki JC, Parce JW. 1992. Biosensors with microvolume reaction chambers. In *Chemical Sensor Technology,* ed. S Yamauchi, 4:145–66. Amsterdam: Elsevier; Tokyo: Kodansha
12. Bousse L, Parce JW, Owicki JC, Kercso KM. 1990. Silicon micromachining in the fabrication of biosensors using living cells. In *Technical Digest, IEEE Solid State Sens. Actuator Workshop,* pp. 173–76. Piscataway, NJ: Inst. Electr. Electron. Eng.
13. Bouvier C, Salon JA, Johnson RA, Civelli O. 1993. Dopaminergic activity measured in D_1- and D_2-transfected fibroblasts by silicon-microphysiometry. *J. Receptor Res.* 13:559–71
14. Briggs J, Panfili PR. 1991. Quantitation of DNA and protein impurities in biopharmaceuticals. *Anal. Chem.* 63:850–59
15. Bruner LH, Miller KR, Owicki JC, Parce JW, Muir VC. 1991. Testing ocular irritancy in vitro with the silicon microphysiometer. *Toxicol. Vitro* 5:277–84
16. Caras SD, Janata J, Saupe D, Schmitt K. 1985. pH-Based enzyme potentiometric sensors. Part I. Theory. *Anal. Chem.* 57:1917–20
17. Chehroudi B, Gould TR, Brunette DM. 1990. Titanium-coated micromachined grooves of different dimensions affect epithelial and connective-tissue cells differently in vivo. *J. Biomed. Mater. Res.* 24:1203–19
18. Connolly P, Clark P, Curtis AS, Dow JA, Wilkinson CD. 1990. An extracellular microelectrode array for monitoring electrogenic cells in culture. *Biosens. Bioelectr.* 5:223–34
19. Denyer JC, Thorn P, Bountra C, Jordan CC. 1993. Acetylcholine and cholecystokinin induced acid extrusion in mouse isolated pancreatic acinar cells as measured by the microphysiometer. *J. Physiol. (London)* 459:390P

20. Dulcey CS, Georger JH Jr, Krauthamer V, Stenger DA, Fare TL, Calvert JM. 1991. Deep UV photochemistry of chemisorbed monolayers: patterned coplanar molecular assemblies. *Science* 252:551–54

21. Edell DJ, Toi VV, McNeil VM, Clark LD. 1992. Factors influencing the biocompatibility of insertable silicon microshafts in cerebral cortex. *IEEE Trans. Biomed. Eng.* 39:635–43

22. Ekins R. 1990. Immunoassay design and optimisation. In *Principles and Practice of Immunoassay*, ed. CP Price, DJ Newman, pp. 96–153. New York: Stockton

23. Fernando JC, Rogers KR, Anis NA, Valdes JJ, Thompson RG, et al. 1993. Rapid detection of anticholinesterase insecticides by a reusable light addressable potentiometric biosensor. *J. Agric. Food Chem.* 41:511–16

24. Fodor S, Read JL, Pirrung MC, Stryer L, Lu AT, Solas D. 1991. Light-directed, spatially addressable parallel chemical synthesis. *Science* 251:767–73

25. Fromherz P, Offenhäusser A, Vetter T, Weis J. 1991. A neuron-silicon junction: a retzius cell of the leech on an insulated-gate field-effect transistor. *Science* 252:1290–93

26. Hafeman DG. 1988. Method of analyzing semiconductor systems. *US Patent No. 4,758,786*

27. Hafeman DG, Parce JW, McConnell HM. 1988. Light-addressable potentiometric sensor for biochemical systems. *Science* 240:1182–85

28. Hetherington S. 1990. Solid phase disruption of fluid phase equilibrium in affinity assays with ELISA. *J. Immunol. Methods* 131:195–202

29. Hurni WM, Miller WJ, Zuk RF, Kung VT. 1991. Detection of antibody to the PreS2 sequence of the hepatitis B virus envelope protein using an immuno-ligand assay with a silicon sensor detection system. *J. Immunol. Methods* 145: 19–26

30. Janata J. 1989. *Principles of Chemical Sensors*. New York: Plenum

31. Kanai Y, Shimizu M, Uchida H, Maekawa H, Nakahara H, Zhou CG, Katsube T. 1993. Integrated taste sensor with surface photovoltage technique. In *Proc. Transducers 93, 7th Int. Conf. Solid-State Sensors and Actuators*, pp. 407. Yokohama, Japan: Inst. Electr. Eng. Japan

32. Kleinfeld D, Kahler KH, Hockberger PE. 1988. Controlled outgrowth of dissociated neurons on patterned substrates. *J. Neurosci.* 8:4098–4120

33. Kuo RC, Baxter GT, Alajoki L, Miller DL, Libby JM, Owicki JC. 1993. A metabolic view of receptor activation in cultured cells following cryopreservation. *Cryobiology* 30:386–95

33a. Lee WE, Thompson HG, Hall JG, Fulton RE, Wong JP. 1993. Rapid immunofiltration assay of Newcastle disease virus using a silicon sensor. *J. Immunol. Methods* 166:123–31

34. Libby JM, Miller DL, Humphries GM. 1989. Determination of metabolic activity and antibiotic sensitivity of *E. coli* with a silicon-based biosensor. *Natl. Meeting Am. Soc. Microbiol., New Orleans, LA.* Abstr. C-385

35. Libby JM, Wada HG. 1989. Detection of *Neisseria meningitidis* and *Yersinia pestis* with a novel silicon based sensor. *J. Clin. Microbiol.* 27:1456–59

36. Lucas ME, Huntington MF, Regina FJ, Bolts JM, Alter SC, et al. 1990. Rapid, filtration-based immunoassays performed with a silicon biosensor. In *Biosensor Technology, Fundamentals and Applications*, ed. RP Buck, WE Hatfield, M Umana, EF Bowden, pp. 351–65. New York:Marcel Dekker

37. Lundstrom I, Erlandsson R, Frykman U, Hedborg E, Spetz A, et al. 1991. Artifical 'olfactory' images from a chemical sensor using a light-pulse technique. *Nature* 352:47–50

38. Lundstrom I, Sundgren H, Winquist F. 1993. Physics of artificial olfactory images produced by catalytic sensing surfaces. *Proc. Transducers 93, 7th Int. Conf. Solid-State Sensors and Actuators*, pp. 416–19. Yokohama, Japan: Inst. Electr. Eng. Japan

39. Massobrio G, Martinoia S, Grattarola M. 1992. Light-addressable chemical sensors: modelling and computer simulations. *Sens. Actuators B* 7:484–87

40. McConnell HM, Owicki JC, Parce JW, Miller DL, Baxter GT, et al. 1992. The Cytosensor microphysiometer: biological applications of silicon technology. *Science* 257:1906–12

41. Merrick H, Hawlitschek G. 1992. Threshold™—a complete system for quantitative analysis of total DNA, protein impurities and relevant proteins. *Biotech. Forum Eur.* 6/92:398–403

42. Miller DL, Olson JC, Parce JW, Owicki JC. 1993. Cholinergic stimulation of the Na^+/K^+ ATPase as revealed by microphysiometry. *Biophys. J.* 64:813–23

43. Nag B, Wada HG, Deshpande SV, Pass-

112   OWICKI ET AL

more D, Kendrick T, et al. 1993. Stimulation of T cells by antigenic peptide complexed with isolated chains of major histocompatibility complex class II molecules. *Proc. Natl. Acad. Sci. USA* 90: 1604–8

44. Nag B, Wada HG, Fok KS, Green DJ, Sharma SD, et al. 1992. Antigen-specific stimulation of T cell extracellular acidification by MHC class II–peptide complexes. *J. Immunol.* 148:2040–44

45. Nakao M, Yoshinobu T, Iwasaki H. 1993. Scanning-laser-beam semiconductor pH-imaging sensor. In *Proc. Transducers 93, 7th Int. Conf. Solid-State Sensors and Actuators (late news papers).* pp. 52–53. Yokohama, Japan: Inst. Electr. Eng. Japan

46. Neve KA, Kozlowski MR, Rosser MP. 1992. Dopamine D_2 receptor stimulation of Na^+/H^+ exchange assessed by quantification of extracellular acidification. *J. Biol. Chem.* 267:25748–53

47. Olson JD, Panfili PR, Armenta R, Femmel MB, Merrick H, et al. 1990. A silicon sensor-based filtration immunoassay using biotin-mediated capture. *J. Immunol. Methods* 134:71–79

48. Olson JD, Panfili PR, Zuk RF, Sheldon EL. 1991. Quantitation of DNA hybridization in a silicon-based system: application to PCR. *Mol. Cell. Probes* 5:351–58

49. Owicki JC, Parce JW. 1992. Biosensors based on the energy metabolism of living cells: the physical chemistry and cell biology of extracellular acidification. *Biosens. Bioelectr.* 7:255–72

50. Owicki JC, Parce JW, Kercso KM, Sigal GB, Muir VC, et al. 1990. Continuous monitoring of receptor-mediated changes in the metabolic rates of living cells. *Proc. Natl. Acad. Sci. USA* 87: 4007–11

51. Parce JW, Kirk GL. 1989. High sensitivity silicon biosensors designed for continuous environmental monitoring. *Int. Chemical Congr. Pacific Basin Soc. Honolulu, Hawaii.* Section 01, Abstract #150

52. Parce JW, Owicki JC, Kercso KM. 1990. Biosensors for directly measuring cell-affecting agents. *Ann. Biol. Clin.* 48: 639–41

53. Parce JW, Owicki JC, Kercso KM, Sigal GB, Wada HG, et al. 1989. Detection of cell affecting agents with a silicon biosensor. *Science* 246:243–47

54. Pesce AJ, Michael JG. 1992. Artifacts and limitations of enzyme immunoassay. *J. Immunol. Methods* 150:111–19

55. Raley-Susman KM, Miller KR, Owicki JC, Sapolsky RM. 1992. Effects of excitotoxin exposure on metabolic rate of primary hippocampal cultures: application of silicon microphysiometry to neurobiology. *J. Neurosci.* 12:773–80

56. Redish DM, Raley-Susman KM, Sapolsky RM. 1993. Inhibition of acidification rate in cultured fibroblasts by glucocorticoids: application of silicon microphysiometry to endocrinology. *Hormone Metabol. Res.* 25:262–65

57. Regehr WG, Pine J, Rutledge DB. 1988. A long-term in vitro silicon-based microelectrode-neuron connection. *IEEE Trans. Biomed. Eng.* 35:1023–32

58. Robinett RSR, Herber WK. 1993. Nanogram quantitation of secreted protein in a recombinant yeast fermentation using an immuno-ligand assay. *J. Immunol. Methods* 159:229–34

59. Rogers KR, Fernando JC, Thompson RG, Valdes JJ, Eldefrawi ME. 1992. Detection of nicotinic receptor ligands with a light addressable potentiometric sensor. *Anal. Biochem.* 202:111–16

60. Romero LM, Raley-Susman KM, Redish DM, Brooke SM, Horner HC, Sapolsky RM. 1992. Possible mechanism by which stress accelerates growth of virally derived tumors. *Proc. Natl. Acad. Sci. USA* 89:11084–87

61. Sartore M, Adami M, Nicolini C. 1992. Computer simulation and optimization of a light addressable potentiometric sensor. *Biosens. Bioelectr.* 7:57–64

62. Sartore M, Adami M, Nicolini C, Bousse L, Mostarshed S, Hafeman D. 1992. Minority carrier diffusion length effects on light-addressable potentiometric sensor (LAPS) devices. *Sens. Actuators A* 32:431–36

63. Sato T, Shimizu M, Uchida H, Maekawa H, Katsube T. 1993. Light addressable suspended gate gas sensor. In *Proc. Transducers 93, 7th Int. Conf. Solid-State Sensors and Actuators,* pp. 438–41. Yokohama, Japan: Inst. Electr. Eng. Japan

64. Shimizu M, Uchida H, Zhou CG, Maekawa H, Matsuda I, Katsube T. 1993. Integrated biosensor employing a surface photovoltage technique. In *Proc. Transducers 93, 7th Int. Conf. Solid-State Sensors and Actuators,* pp. 495–98. Yokohama, Japan: Inst. Electr. Eng. Japan

65. Sigal GB, Hafeman DH, Parce JW, McConnell HM. 1989. Electrical properties of phospholipid bilayer membranes measured with a light addressa-

ble potentiometric sensor. In *Chemical Sensors and Microinstrumentation, ACS Symposium Series 403*, ed. RW Murray, RE Dessy, WR Heineman, J Janata, WR Seitz, pp. 46–64. Washington, DC: Am. Chem. Soc.

66. Ternaux JP, Wilson R, Dow J, Curtis AS, Clark P, et al. 1992. Dendritic processing: using microstructures to solve a hitherto intractable neurobiological problem. *Med. Biol. Eng. Comput.* 30: CE37–41

67. Thibodeau A, Kuo RC, Yao X, Owicki JC, Forte JG. 1993. Real-time measurement of extracellular acidification rate in isolated gastric glands using a microphysiometer. *FASEB J.* 7:A576

68. Vadgama P. 1993. Biosensors in clinical biochemistry. *Ann. Clin. Biochem.* 30: 337–40

69. Wada HG, Indelicato SR, Meyer L, Kitamura T, Miyajima A, et al. 1993. GM-CSF triggers a rapid, glucose dependent extracellular acidification by TF-1 cells: evidence for sodium/proton antiporter

and PKC mediated activation of acid production. *J. Cell. Physiol.* 154:129–38

70. Wada HG, Libby JM, Rice LS, Masino RS, Kasper KC, et al. 1989. Detection of *C. trachomatis* in clinical specimens using a silicon-based sensor. *Annu. Meeting of Am. Soc. Microbiol., 89th, New Orleans, LA.* Abstr. C-122

71. Wada HG, McConnell HM, Hafeman DG. 1990. Polyredox couples in analyte determinations. *US Patent No. 4,942,127*

72. Winquist F, Sundgren H, Hedborg E, Spetz A, Lundstrom I. 1992. Visual images of gas mixtures produced with field-effect structures. *Sens. Actuators B* 6:157–61

73. Dill K, Lin M, Poteras C, Fraser C, Hafeman DG, et al. 1994. Antibody-antigen binding constants determined in solution phase with the Threshold® membrane-capture system. Binding constants for anti-fluorescein, anti-saxitoxin, and anti-ricin antibodies. *Anal. Biochem.* In press

Annu. Rev. Biophys. Biomol. Struct. 1994. 23:115–39

BIOMOLECULAR IMAGING WITH THE ATOMIC FORCE MICROSCOPE[1]

Helen G. Hansma and Jan H. Hoh

Department of Physics, University of California, Santa Barbara, California 93106

KEY WORDS: scanning force microscope, membranes, DNA, proteins, structure

CONTENTS

[1] This article is dedicated to Albrecht Weisenhorn (March 24, 1961–August 18, 1993) in memory of his outstanding contributions to the development of biomolecular imaging with the AFM. We admire his work in many areas, including molecular resolution of lipid films, DNA, and proteins, and his early insights into the importance of force curves. Two of his images are at the top and bottom of the color plate.

1056–8700/94/0610–0115$05.00

PERSPECTIVES AND OVERVIEW

Atomic force microscopy of biological materials is a rapidly growing new field. In 1991, the *Annual Review of Biophysics and Biophysical Chemistry* reviewed the biological applications of the atomic force microscope (AFM) and other scanning probe microscopes (32). To thoroughly cover this field at that time, the author needed only two pages with nine references to work done in two or three laboratories. Now over 200 references in this area come from nearly three dozen laboratories, and the quality and usefulness of the work is increasing rapidly as the field expands. In the earliest years, just obtaining an image was an accomplishment, but now the AFM is becoming a reliable tool for biological use.

The field of atomic force microscopy was born with the invention of the atomic force microscope in 1986 by Binnig, Quate & Gerber (7). This microscope, an offspring of the scanning tunneling microscope (STM) (9), provides detailed topographic maps of sample surfaces. The AFM maps surfaces by raster scanning a fine tip gently over the surface, resulting in a three-dimensional profile of the surface that can reach atomic resolution on hard flat surfaces (6, 80, 107).

This review focuses on molecular-resolution AFM imaging of biological macromolecules and cells, particularly emphasizing early work in each area and the highlights of the recent experiments. Space limitations prevent us from covering all of the research, but other reviews are available (10, 18, 56, 125). In addition, several reviews cover STM of biological materials (e.g. 14, 40, 50, 90, 128).

The AFM is also known as the scanning force microscope (SFM). In addition, numerous other microscopes image by scanning surfaces. These microscopes as a class are called scanning probe microscopes (SPMs) and include not only the STM and AFM but also a couple dozen other microscopes such as the magnetic force microscope, the scanning near-field optical microscope, the scanning ion-conductance microscope, and the scanning electrochemical microscope (118, 119).

INSTRUMENTATION: THE ATOMIC FORCE MICROSCOPE

The AFM (5, 97, 99) is a small instrument; current designs weigh approximately 3 kg, excluding the accompanying computer and controller. The heart of the microscope is the tip, which raster-scans across

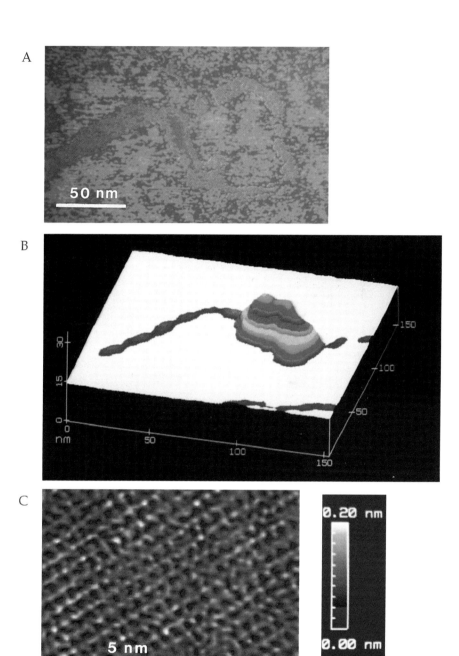

Figure 2 Color can enhance height information in AFM images. (*A*) A loop of plasmid DNA shows negative supercoiling, because the downward arm of the loop clearly lies on top of the upward arm (98). (*B*) Colored bands each 1.5 nm high facilitate comparisons of large T antigen molecules on SV-40 DNA (75a). (*C*) Early molecular-resolution image of a Langmuir-Blodgett film of dioctadecyldimethylammonium bromide in water (112).

the sample and is positioned at the end of a cantilever. As the tip encounters elevation changes on the surface, the cantilever deflects. An optical lever is typically used to detect and amplify this deflection (2, 77), i.e. a laser reflects off the cantilever onto a segmented photo diode that detects the changes in cantilever deflection as changes in the ratio of laser light in the photo diode segments. Usually one wants to maintain a small cantilever deflection in order to image the sample gently; a feedback loop that adjusts the height of the sample will keep the cantilever deflection, and thus the force, at a small value. The height changes and raster scanning in the x and y directions are all accomplished with a piezoelectric crystal (for an AFM schematic, see 27).

Imaging Modes

The most common imaging mode is the constant force mode, sometimes referred to as the height mode, which displays the changes in sample height during scanning. This mode gives calibrated height information about the sample surface. Images taken in this mode are generally displayed in shades of gray, such that the highest areas are lightest and the lowest areas are darkest.

Alternatively, one can monitor the small changes in cantilever deflection that signal the feedback loop to make the height adjustments; this imaging mode is called the error-signal mode (86) or deflection mode. Images taken in this mode resemble a derivative of the height image. Thus they accentuate edges on the sample surface but do not give height information. One can also record the cantilever deflections without feedback to obtain images that do contain height information; this mode has the disadvantage that the force varies with the deflection and can damage the sample.

In addition to raster scanning the surface, the cantilever can oscillate at high frequency (e.g. 300 kHz). When the tip encounters elevation changes on the surface, the amplitude of the oscillation changes. Here, the feedback system responds to keep the amplitude of cantilever oscillation at a constant level. This mode of operation reduces the lateral forces that can push the sample around. Two imaging types of this kind have been reported: noncontact (sometimes called attractive mode) (75, 120) and, more recently, tapping (31, 45), in which the amplitude of the oscillation is larger. In noncontact mode, forces between the tip and the sample likely affect the oscillation, while in tapping mode the tip actually touches the surface at the bottom of the oscillation. At present these modes are used only in air or other gases such as helium, because fluids damp the cantilever oscillation.

Imaging Environment

The AFM can image under diverse conditions, including in air, vacuum, or a variety of fluids. The operating temperatures vary from room temperature or above to liquid-nitrogen temperature or below, but room-temperature operation is the easiest.

Substrates

Because the AFM images the surface of a sample, the sample must usually be supported on a substrate, such as mica or glass. Mica is an atomically flat, cleavable aluminum silicate crystal, which is useful for imaging molecules less than a few nanometers high. Although glass, with a typical surface roughness of 1–2 nm, is generally not used for imaging thin molecules such as DNA at high resolution, it serves as a good substrate for imaging thicker biological samples such as cells. Both glass and mica have a negative surface charge, which must be taken into account when developing conditions for binding the sample to the substrate. For some samples, such as Langmuir-Blodgett films, silicon oxide has also proved to be a useful substrate (76, 91, 92).

Unlike the STM, the AFM can image surfaces that are either electrical insulators or conductors. This is especially advantageous in biological applications, because most biological materials are not conductors.

New Combination Microscopes

Now that biologists use AFMs more frequently, these microscopes are being optimized for biological applications. Most AFMs now have a low-power optical microscope that helps locate specific areas on a sample and is useful for adjusting the laser spot on the cantilever. Combined AFM-fluorescence microscopes have been useful for imaging cells (55) and polymerized lipid films (37, 89).

APPLICATIONS

Nucleic Acids

DNA AND RNA Excitement has surrounded scanning probe microscopy of DNA since Binnig published an STM image of DNA in 1984 (8). The early AFM images, first achieved by Lindsay et al (68), came from microscopes in which the tips consisted of diamond fragments glued onto the cantilevers. Many of the early AFM images of DNA were not stable, although their resolution appeared to be sufficient to show individual nucleotides (49, 112, 113).

AFM of DNA greatly advanced when Vesenka and colleagues suc-
ceeded in reproducibly imaging plasmid DNA attached to mica (15,
109). With this method, dry air (40% relative humidity or less) is the
key to keeping the DNA bound to the mica under the force of the
scanning AFM tip and for getting good contrast (Figure 1, bottom right).
Another advance came with imaging in fluid. Propanol or butanol result
in higher resolution than possible when imaging in air (44, 47) (Figure
1, top left), and water and some buffers allow for imaging under more
nearly physiological conditions, though at a lower resolution (43, 72)
(Figure 1, bottom left). Imaging in buffer can also allow one to observe
processes involving DNA, such as DNA-enzyme interactions, occurring in real time. The imaging of single-stranded DNA continues to be
a challenge, although stable images of partially extended single-
stranded DNA have appeared (46, 106, 124).

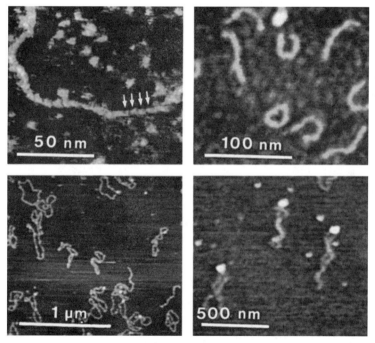

Figure 1   AFM of DNA. (*Top left*) Resolution is best in butanol (44), as shown here,
or in propanol, in which substructure the size of helix turns is sometimes visible (*arrows*).
(*Top right*) Tapping mode is the most convenient. These images of kinetoplast DNA were
taken in dry helium (45). (*Bottom left*) Imaging in water is more nearly physiological (43)
(image courtesy of M Bezanilla). (*Bottom right*) Biotinylated DNA labeled with streptavidin gold shows the potential for AFM-mapping of DNA sequences at a resolution of
several dozen bases (102).

Even though the resolution of DNA and RNA by AFM remains far below that needed for sequencing (44), investigators now routinely use AFM to obtain biological information. Taking advantage of the height information provided by AFM, Samori et al (98) have ascertained the chirality or handedness of supercoiling in plasmids (Figure 2A, color plate). Several groups have shown that DNA can be dissected at a selected location with the AFM (47, 53, 109). Lyubchenko et al have measured the lengths of double-stranded reovirus RNA ranging in size between 0.2 and 1.8 μm (70) and have imaged entire 17-μm λ DNA molecules (72).

DNA-protein complexes imaged in the AFM include DNA complexed with *Escherichia coli* RNA polymerase (43, 96, 131), with DNA polymerase (124), with the *EcoR*1 restriction enzyme (79), and with the large T-antigen of SV-40 (Figure 2B, color plate). When complexed with RNA polymerase, DNA bending angles are different for open promoter complexes and elongation complexes (96). AFM images have been combined with masses derived from scanning transmission electron microscopy to yield a partial specific volume for the large T-antigen from SV-40 complexed to DNA of 440 Daltons nm^{-3} (Figure 2B) (75a).

The length of DNA in a nucleosome has been estimated by plotting the length of 3780–base pair DNA vs the number of nucleosomes assembled on it (3) (Figure 3, top). The experimental results agreed well with the theoretical prediction. This work used glass as a substrate, which is flat enough to show the nucleosomes and the DNA along most of its length.

Biotinylated DNA labeled with streptavidin complexes holds promise for high-resolution gene mapping (78, 102). Streptavidin bound to 5-nm gold balls can be readily visualized on biotinylated DNA and can facilitate the orientation of DNA by air flow (102) (Figure 1, bottom right). The streptavidin gold balls stick firmly to mica, and the DNA stretches out behind them when the sample is blown with compressed air.

The most common substrate for AFM of DNA is freshly cleaved mica, sometimes pretreated with a magnesium salt or the salt of some other di- or trivalent cation (15, 43, 102, 105, 109, 130). The presence of a multivalent cation helps spread the DNA (105) and bind it to the mica; samples as small as 200 pg DNA can give good coverage over a surface area of 10 mm^2 (45). Other substrates used for AFM of DNA include mica treated with aminopropyltrimethoxy silane (70–72), carbon-coated mica (124), and self-assembled monolayers of thiols on gold (LA Bottomley, T Allison, T Warmack & T Thundat, personal com-

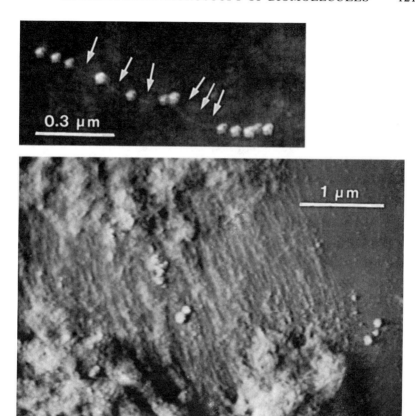

Figure 3 AFM of nucleosomes and chromosomes. (*Top*) Nucleosomes assembled on DNA containing 18 tandem repeats of a nucleosome-organizing sequence show spaces where 6 other nucleosomes could form (*arrows*) (3). The 18 tandem repeats, each 208 base pairs long, were prepared from a gene for ribosomal DNA. (*Bottom*) Detail of a polytene chromosome from *Drosophila melanogaster* shows condensed bands and an elongated interband with nucleosomes barely visible along the DNA strands. Fixed chromosome from a squash preparation (see 85) (image by C Putman). Both images were taken in air.

munication). Potentiostatic deposition of DNA on gold has been described for AFM, but currently researchers use this method mostly for STM (69). A novel method for anchoring DNA is to coat DNA on mica with carbon, remove the mica, and image the carbon-DNA surface (19).

AFM of DNA should not be confused with STM of DNA; the description of graphite artifacts that resembled DNA gave the latter a bad reputation (24, 51). It turns out that graphite dramatically affects the appearance in the STM of molecules adsorbed to it (e.g. 52) because of its nearly two-dimensional electronic states.

CHROMOSOMES AND CHROMATIN   Nucleosomes imaged in isolated chromatin (3, 110) and in polytene chromosomes (85) (Figure 3, bottom) appear as 25- to 30-nm particles. In the case of chromosomes, AFM has shown in situ hybridized probes and bands on stained, trypsinized chromosomes with a resolution comparable to electron microscopy and superior to light microscopy (88, 95). Furthermore, AFM combined with light microscopy and Raman spectroscopy has been used to compare substructure and DNA content of bands and interbands of chromosomes (85).

Biological Membranes

LIPID BILAYERS   The title of a 1992 paper, "Does the scanning force microscope [AFM] resolve individual lipid molecules?" (94), summarizes the urgent question concerning early images of LB (Langmuir-Blodgett) films in aqueous solutions. The level of optimism rose and fell daily as the images were alternately believed to be either lipid molecules or the underlying mica lattice. Finally, Weisenhorn resolved the question when he distinguished between the lattice parameters of the lipid molecules imaged at low force and the underlying mica at high force (112).

One can produce models of biological membranes, with a hydrophilic head group exposed, in several ways. The model membranes can form spontaneously when lipids are present on various surfaces, or as lipid vesicles, or by LB deposition, for example. Several studies have reported supported bilayer membranes imaged in aqueous solutions, primarily on mica, with approximately the expected thickness (48, 103). Such bilayers have also been seen to heal when defects are introduced with the AFM tip (12). Furthermore, Egger and coworkers have reported periodic surface structure on the surface of a dimyristoyl-phosphatidylglycerol (DMPG) monolayer deposited on alkylated mica and imaged in buffer (30). This orthorhombic lattice has a unit cell size of $a = 0.62$ nm and $b = 0.79$ nm, and occupies an area of 0.45 nm^2. These values are consistent with those expected for individual phospholipid head groups, suggesting that molecular resolution was achieved. Similarly a periodic surface structure with a unit cell size of $a = 0.5$ nm and $b = 0.8$ nm on the surfaces of dimyristoyl-phosphatidylethanolamine (DMPE) has been reported (129).

Other LB films imaged in aqueous solution at molecular resolution include polymerized lipids and fatty acids (37, 48, 91, 101, 123) (Figure 2c). Interestingly, the degree of surface order increases along with the number of layers in LB films of cadmium arachidate (101). Streptavidin binding to biotinylated LB films has also been observed with the AFM (117).

In addition to this work on bilayers of lipids and fatty acids in aqueous solution, much work has been done on hydrophobic monolayers or multilayers (for reviews see 36, 125). While these studies are of great importance in many fields, they are beyond the scope of this review.

2D PROTEIN ARRAYS   Several membrane proteins occur in nature as regular arrays in lipid membranes, and many others can be reconstituted into two-dimensional (2D) crystals. Such samples have features that make them suitable for structural analysis by atomic force microscopy: the large flat membrane sheets are relatively easy to attach to a substrate; the orientation of the molecules relative to the substrate is controlled; the tight packing in the array stabilizes lateral movement during imaging; and signal averaging methods such as correlation averaging and Fourier filtering are more easily applied.

Halobacterium halobium's purple membrane, a compact 2D hexagonal array of bacteriorhodopsin, was the first membrane protein array examined with atomic force microscopy, in both air (122) and water (17). Images clearly revealed a hexagonal periodic structure with a spacing of 6.2 nm between the unit cells, consistent with the spacing of rhodopsin trimers. The power spectra from Fourier transforms of the best images showed diffraction spots out to 1.1 nm (17), though comparable morphology was not visible. The measured thickness of the membranes varied from 11.1 nm when supported on silanized glass to 5.2 nm when supported on a lipid membrane. This phenomenon has not yet been fully explained, though it may be related to the problem of friction described below. These studies demonstrated that fully hydrated biological membranes could withstand the interactions with the AFM probe, something not obvious a priori. This fundamental observation prompted suggestions that structure-function relationships might someday be examined directly and led others to attempt a variety of different systems.

Hoh et al (57, 58) examined gap junctions, which are specialized eukaryotic plasma membranes with an array of channels that connect the cytoplasms of adjacent cells. These membranes, which are composed of two bilayers, adsorb well to both glass and mica. By varying the imaging force, they manipulated the membranes on the scale of a few hundred nanometers to remove one of the two bilayers and provide experimental access to the extracellular surface of the remaining membrane (57). Initial images revealed a periodic surface structure of 9.4 nm, consistent with the spacing of the individual channels. The gap junction images have now been extended to a lateral resolution of 2.5 nm (58), based on the spectral signal-to-noise ratio criterion of Unser (108). These images show channels extending 1.4 nm above the lipid bilayer (Figure 4, bottom left) and a well delineated pore with a maximum diameter of 3.8 nm (Figure 4, bottom right) and represent the first time an individual ion channel in aqueous solution has been visualized.

Bacterial S-layers from *Sulfolobus acidocaldarius* supported on graphite and coated with a thin film of titanium have been imaged in air (26). Comparison of the AFM images with electron micrographs strikingly demonstrated the high signal-to-noise ratio in the AFM images. The AFM images allowed for direct identification of defective structures in the array, which could not clearly be seen with electron microscopy. The problem of noise in images from the electron microscope is particularly acute for unstained samples, because most biological material is relatively electron translucent.

Yang et al (126) have stabilized artificial membranes by lateral cross-linking using the polymerizable lipid 1,2-dipentacosa-10,12-diynoyl-phosphatidylcholine mixed with a ganglioside. The ganglioside in turn binds cholera toxin that can be visualized with the AFM. Many of these structures appear to have a pentameric symmetry, indicating that the contribution of individual B subunits to the shape of the complex has been resolved (Figure 4, top right). The authors estimate the point-to-point resolution in the images to be near 2 nm. Furthermore, preparations in which the A subunit, which binds to the complex of B subunits, was added prior to imaging show a distinctly different morphology. The A subunit is apparently bound to the center of the complex, demonstrating that this receptor-ligand pair is stable under the imaging forces used.

The hexagonally packed intermediate (HPI) layer from *Deinococcus radiodurans,* a regular array of protein on the outer membrane of this bacterium, is one of the few membranes imaged with noncontact AFM (120). These images reveal a hexagonal surface periodicity corresponding to the unit cell size ($a = b = 18$ nm), though there is little fine structure. Similar images of air-dried HPI layers achieved in the contact mode have also appeared (100). More recent images acquired by contact mode imaging in aqueous solution show exceptional fine structure of the HPI layer (Figure 4, top left), with a lateral resolution of better than 1.5 nm based on the radial correlation function (S Karrasch, R

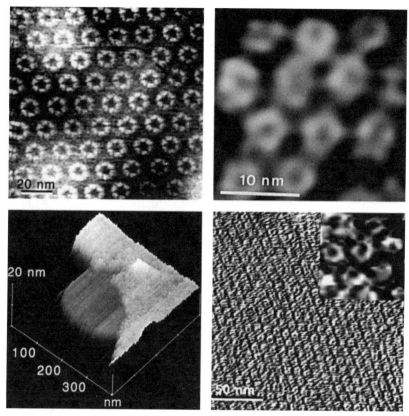

Figure 4 AFM images of 2D membrane protein arrays. (*Top, left*) The hexagonally packed intermediate (HPI) layer is a regular protein layer with a unit cell size $a = b = 18$ nm. Note the missing subunit in one of the hexameric unit cells (*arrow*). The sample was covalently bound to a glass surface and imaged in a buffer solution (60). The high signal-to-noise ratio in the AFM allows for direct identification of individual defects like this (image courtesy Frank Schabert). (*Top, right*) Oligomers of the cholera toxin B–subunit show pentameric structures. Individual B subunits are ~2 nm wide. (*Bottom, left*) Surface view of a gap junction showing the border between the extracellular surface of the protein array (*right*) and lipid membrane (*left*). The channels in the membrane protrude 1.4 nm above the lipid. (*Bottom, right*) The hexagonal array of channels in the gap junction membrane seen from the extracellular surface, with higher magnification of a few channels (*inset*) (58).

Hegerl, JH Hoh, W Baumeister & A Engel, submitted). A careful comparison of these images with a three-dimensional (3D) model of HPI generated by electron diffraction reveals an average root mean square (rms) difference of less than 0.5 nm between the surfaces. This remarkable agreement provides quantitative support for the idea that

AFM images are faithful representations of the structures being imaged.

LB films of a pore-forming peptide have been imaged at molecular resolution, which yielded 1-nm repeat distances (116). These distances indicated that the molecules were oriented perpendicular to the substrate. Acetylcholine receptors expressed in *Xenopus laevis* oocytes (67) and bacterial porin channels (66) have also been imaged.

OTHER MEMBRANES   The recent report of images of the nuclear pores in *X. laevis* nuclear envelopes (82) represents one of the few examples of a supported nonperiodic natural membrane. These images clearly show the asymmetry between the cytoplasmic and nucleoplasmic faces of the pore (Figure 5). However, staining methods for the AFM have not yet been developed, so identifying specific structures is often difficult. This may in part account for the general lack of progress on nonperiodic natural membranes.

Cell Surfaces

The earliest AFMs had a maximum scan range of less than 1 μm and were therefore not useful for imaging cells. Within hours after a prototype AFM with a several-micrometer scan range was built in 1989, finger blood was used to obtain images of a dry smear of red blood cells. White blood cells, red blood cells in saline, plant cells, and bacteria were imaged soon afterward (11, 21, 38, 39, 41).

The resolution of AFM images of cells remains less than molecular; the smallest visible substructures are typically 30–50 nm in size. The

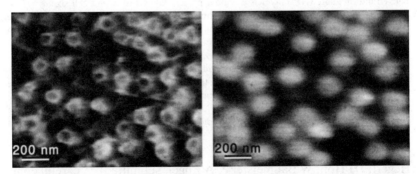

Figure 5   AFM images of nuclear pore complexes in a nuclear envelope, from *Xenopus laevis,* supported on carbon-coated glass and imaged in an aqueous buffer (82). (*Left*) The cytoplasmic side shows doughnut-like structures with interconnections. (*Right*) On the nucleoplasmic side, the pore is covered by a basket-like structure, i.e. there is no hole (image courtesy of Kenneth Goldie).

low resolution probably results from tip-induced deformation of the cell surface. Using a solid surface to support membranes enhances the resolution. In intact cells such as living glial cells and platelets, AFM has revealed actin and other cytoskeletal filaments (22, 54, 61; MF Fritz, M Radmacher & HE Gaub, submitted). The filamentous actin in glial cells can be resolved even though it is covered by the cell surface membrane. However, whether the AFM is scanning above the cell membrane or the tip is probing and scanning through the membrane, which is sealing behind itself, is not known. Immunochemistry and sensitivity to the actin-depolymerizing drug, cytochalasin B, did confirm that the filaments were actin (54).

In patients with hereditary spherocytosis, abnormal pseudopodia project 50–80 nm from the surface of the red blood cells. After removal of the spleen, the red cells return to normal, as imaged in the AFM. Use of the AFM is an easy, fast, reproducible method for evaluating these cells (127). AFM images of the cuticle cells of hairs show more pores in cancer patients' cells compared with controls (F Ruzicka, A Hofer, J Kraus & G Friedbacher, submitted). Another application of AFM of cells is the imaging of immuno-gold labels on the lymphocyte surface, which could lead to high-resolution surface mapping of antigens (87).

Currently, several processes in cells are being observed with the AFM. One of these involves AFM movies of an individual virus particle emerging from a cell (42). In this impressive technical feat, the cell was held with a micropipette while being scanned. Imaging of platelet activation with the AFM has revealed new information about the movement of granules in these cells (35; MF Fritz, M Radmacher & HE Gaub, submitted). Platelet elasticity and viscosity have also been measured (92). In addition, investigators have studied adhesion of living cells to substrates by increasing the imaging force progressively (83).

Nonmembrane Proteins

AFM of nonmembrane proteins is frequently difficult. Isolated protein molecules often adhere poorly to the substrate, and even in stable images substructures smaller than about 20 nm are usually hard to resolve. This is not surprising given the highly mobile nature of protein surfaces (34). The most successful imaging of individual protein molecules or of protein substructure has been done on large proteins [e.g. fibrinogen (27, 121) and RNA polymerase (64)], fibrous proteins [actin (111) and collagen (23; K Fisher & J Clarke, unpublished)] and protein arrays [hair (F Ruzicka, A Hofer, J Kraus & G Friedbacher, submitted), and ferritin on LB films (81)]. Other proteins imaged include immunoglobulins (48, 59, 111), phosphorylase kinase complexes (29), and α-macroglobulin (4). A number of the images, especially the early ones, show only a few molecules. A novel technique for binding proteins to a surface, used with an immunoglobulin, is to clone a metal-chelating peptide into it and bind it to nickel-coated mica (59).

Some of the highest-resolution images were taken with the early glued diamond tips. For example, 5-nm lumps the size of actin monomers were imaged on actin filaments (111), and diamond tips revealed substructure on polyalanine molecules (27). The 36-nm helix periodicity of actin (63) represents the best resolution from more recent actin images achieved with integrated tips. The tapping mode of imaging has improved resolution on collagen fibrils: in addition to the 70-nm D-bands, subbands also appear (EAG Chernoff & D Chernoff, unpublished data). With collagen monomers, the best resolution has been obtained in liquid pentane (K Fisher & J Clarke, unpublished data).

One of the earliest biological applications of the AFM was the filming of the process of fibrin polymerization (27). This video answered a question asked by blood-clotting researchers about whether short fibrin polymers can join together or whether growth occurs only at the ends of polymers. One of the most exciting sequences in the video occurs when two isolated molecules, with the two- and three-bump substructures seen with electron microscopy (EM), jump onto the growing polymer. Researchers have also viewed actin polymerization using the AFM (111), but the observation of molecular processes with the AFM remains relatively unexplored.

PROTEIN CRYSTALS   Some 3D protein crystals have been imaged, including Ca-ATPase crystals (65) and the process of lysozyme crystal growth (28), but molecular-resolution images have not been published. Kinetics of lysozyme crystal growth and the nature of defects and nucleation centers have been observed.

With Ca-ATPase, steps on the crystals had the thickness of the unit cell, but no molecular periodicity was seen on the surface (65). This result was expected in air, because transmission electron microscopy (TEM) has shown that drying destroys the surface periodicity. In buffer, the inability to see molecules was attributed to the flexibility of the surface. Two-dimensional arrays of proteins have given better resolution than 3D protein crystals, as described in the section on 2D protein arrays. These observations can be explained in terms of surface rigidity: the surface of a two-dimensional array of membrane proteins on a hard substrate is more rigid than the surface of a three-dimensional protein crystal. In contrast, with lipids in Langmuir-Blodgett films, obtaining molecular resolution is more difficult on monolayers than on multilayers, especially on the hydrophobic surface (101). In lipid films, the presence of lipid layers under the surface layer increases the degree of order of the surface layer (104).

FORCES DURING IMAGING

Initially the AFM was operated only in air, where condensed water forms a bridge between the tip and sample in contact mode imaging. The resulting capillary force produces a large interaction force that can damage the tip or sample. The success of Drake and coworkers (27) in imaging in liquids eliminated the water bridge and allowed routine imaging in the nanonewton range (114). In addition, this advance allowed the imaging of native biological material in aqueous solution, which is one of the most important capabilities of the AFM.

AFM imaging forces are generally reported as the force applied perpendicular to the cantilever, as determined from force curves (13, 14, 115). Two major caveats to these reports are that the calculations do not take into account the lateral forces involved and that the pressure at the contact site is not known, because of the extreme difficulty in determining the contact area between tip and sample, which probably varies from place to place over the sample. The lateral forces during imaging cause the cantilever to torque or bow parallel to the scan direction, in addition to eliciting the up and down deflections from the topography. This torquing of the cantilever can be used to examine frictional properties of surfaces as described below, but also causes anomalies in the height signal.

The force curves used for determining imaging forces are produced by monitoring the cantilever deflection as the sample is approached or withdrawn, without scanning in x and y. These curves can be used to examine interactions between the tip and sample that depend on the intermolecular forces between the two surfaces (13, 115). The curves are sensitive to complex attractive and repulsive interactions, including electrostatic repulsion and van der Waals attraction. Butt has used the AFM to measure the surface charge of purple membranes in aqueous solution by examining the electrostatic double layer repulsion for a series of salt and pH conditions, and calibrating this against the known surface charge of aluminum oxide (16). He finds a surface charge of -0.06 C m^{-2} (about 1 electron charge per 2.7 nm^2) for this membrane and estimates the lateral resolution of the measurement to be approximately 40 nm. Because all forces detected in the AFM result from a bending of the cantilever in some way, an accurate knowledge of spring constants is essential. The reported theoretical calculations of spring constants for several different cantilevers range between 0.01 and 1.00 N m^{-1} for those most commonly used in repulsive (contact) mode imaging (1). Cantilevers used for noncontact and tapping imaging usually have spring constants ranging from 2 to 50 N m^{-1}. Direct measurements of the bending spring constant for some microfabricated cantilever geometries have deviationed from predicted values by more than a factor of two. For example, Butt et al reported a value of 0.03 N m^{-1} for the common 200-μm and 40-μm V-shaped cantilevers (20), and Cleveland et al measured 0.04 N m^{-1} for the same geometry (25), while the theoretical value is 0.06. Much of the disparity in cantilever spring constants probably results from the thickness of the cantilever, which often varies by 100–200 nm in cantilevers that are estimated to be 500 nm thick. Since the bending spring constant scales with the cube of the thickness, even these small variations produce significant effects. The torquing spring constant, which is used to estimate lateral forces, has not yet been measured.

IMAGE INTERPRETATION

Factors that Contribute to Images

Many factors contribute to an AFM image in addition to the topography of the sample surface. These include the size and shape of the tip, properties of the feedback loop, and the mechanical and chemical properties of the sample and imaging environment.

The finite size of the tip limits the lateral resolution, and the shape of the tip contributes significantly to many images. The part of the tip that interacts with structures on the sample surface is often larger than the structures themselves, especially for small structures such as protein molecules and macromolecular assemblies with a radius of curvature 5–20 nm, where the image is in fact more a representation of the tip than the macromolecules (Figure 6, right). A constant orientation over an entire image characterizes the contribution of tip structure to the image for samples, such as adsorbed protein molecules, that would generally be rotationally disordered (Figure 6, right). Multiple tipping produces the most dramatic tip structure effects, when more than one tip is on the same scale as the features being examined (Figure 6, left). Such tipping can cause shadowing of the image and even produce an artifactual structure in some images. One cannot exclude tip structure effects by simply electronically rotating the scan direction, because this conserves the geometry of the tip-sample interaction. One

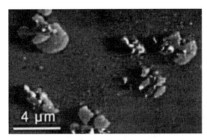 

Figure 6   Example of AFM images dominated by tip structure. (*Left*) Double tipping, here seen on isolated gap junction membranes in saline, produces multiplication or shadowing of structures. Looking at the membrane patch on the bottom edge of the image, one can see that the two tips producing this image are separated by almost 2 μm and are oriented such that the lower image of the membrane is to the right of the upper image. (*Right*) For small particles with a high radius of curvature, such as the ribosomes in propanol shown here, the shape is often dominated by tip structure. In this image the fact that all the particles are aligned in the same direction, with a small lump on the right side of the large lump, whereas they ought to be rotationally disordered, is the most immediate indication of the problem (image courtesy of E Henderson).

can gain information about the effects of tip structure, however, by physically rotating the sample in the AFM.

The scan speed affects image quality. If the scan speed is too fast, the cantilever cannot respond faithfully to features on the sample surface, especially in liquid (20). The response time of the feedback loop also affects the faithfulness of the imaging, especially in the constant force mode, where the feedback loop controls height changes of the sample that provide height information in the image. The feedback loop performance is generally controlled by a set of gain parameters that produce the output to the z piezo from the incoming deflection signal. A typical time constant (i.e. the amount of time needed for the feedback loop to adjust for half of a z offset) in the commercial microscope we use is on the order of milliseconds under normal operating conditions. Therefore, a full adjustment in height can take 10 ms or more, which significantly limits the scan rate at which faithful imaging can be performed. In practical terms, the gains should be adjusted slightly below the level at which oscillation or other gain-induced periodic artifacts occur. Also, one usually images at a speed that yields images with fine detail but is fast enough for collecting data in a reasonable time. The scan must be fast enough that the drift to high or low force during a single scan is not large enough for either sample damage or tip lift-off.

Drift and creep can greatly affect the apparent dimensions in the slow scan direction (*creep* is a slow movement of the piezo to its final position after being offset from the center of the scan range). Therefore one should measure features on sequential up and down traces, especially for measurements in the slow scan direction (usually y). Drift and creep decrease with time. Measurements with an accuracy better than about 10% require frequent calibration with a known sample under the exact experimental conditions used.

The lateral forces occurring during AFM imaging can be a major component of images. Friction between the tip and sample causes the cantilever to torque parallel to the scan direction in addition to the up/down deflection (74). This torquing can significantly influence the information in an image, and in fact can result in complete contrast reversal (131). Most beam deflection AFMs now utilize a four-segment photodiode, which allows frictional effects to be recorded simultaneously with the topography. For instruments with two segment photodiodes, a comparison of the forward and backward traces illustrates the effect of friction; if the images are the same, friction effects are probably minimal. Furthermore, one can minimize the frictional contribution to the image by rotating the scan direction, since the cantilever can torque more easily in some directions than others. For a V-shaped cantilever scanning the V sideways usually results in the lowest frictional contribution to the height signal. Rotating the scan direction is also useful to see whether the horizontal scan lines are affecting data interpretation.

The properties of the sample are, of course, important to the understanding of an image. A long-standing suggestion is that, beyond the repulsive van der Waals interaction used in contact mode imaging, the chemical nature of the tip and sample contributes to image formation. The recent work of Ohnesorge & Binnig on imaging calcium carbonate crystals in solution clearly demonstrates that this is the case (80). In addition, the measurements of Butt on electrostatic forces suggest that the magnitude of these forces could contribute to contrast (16). The mechanical properties of the sample often lead to deformation effects during imaging, which are still poorly understood. The extreme case of deformation is sample damage. Still, although AFM's ability to deform samples is often a problem, investigators can take advantage of this capacity to map elastic and viscous properties of soft samples with high resolution (73, 93).

Resolution Assessment

A major difference between electron micrographs and AFM topographs is that the AFM data has much less inherent noise. This means that the point-to-point resolution on relatively smooth surfaces is generally better in the AFM image. (Rough surfaces are typically dominated by the tip structure.) A common standard for the performance of an AFM is the ability to detect individual unit cells in a hexagonal lattice with spacing of 0.5 nm on the surface of mica. Also, the size of the smallest features, or the minimum distance between features seen in the AFM images, is often used to judge resolution. However, most quantitative methods for assessing resolution are based on the average properties of images. Criteria such as the spectral signal-to-noise ratio (SSNR) (108), radial correlation function (RCF), and cross-correlation function (107) measure the resolution over an entire image. The SSNR and RCF only provide a radially averaged resolution value, while the true resolution is often asymmetric because of tip structure effects and the scanning process (there is a fast and a slow scan direction). Furthermore, the resolution value per se can be very deceptive, since it does not distinguish information about the sample from information about the tip. Butt et al (18) offer a more extensive discussion of resolution in scanning probe microscopes.

Image Reconstruction

The fact that many AFM images are dominated by tip structure has led to attempts to reconstruct images (33, 62). With the current approaches, the investigator must know the structure of the tip; hence these methods are most useful for relatively large structures, on a scale at which the tip structure can be characterized. A more fundamental problem with attempts to correct images for tip structure effects are double contacts. In regions where the tip makes simultaneous contact with more than one position on a surface, the information about the surface between the double contacts is lost. Finally, despite the fact that most AFM images are taken in constant force mode by displaying the z piezo movement, we are not aware of any attempts to deconvolve the feedback loop characteristics from AFM images. As new methods are developed, reconstruction of AFM images should improve their accuracy and be a significant aid in interpretation.

CONCLUSION

For many applications, the AFM combines the convenience and versatility of optical microscopy with a resolution comparable to electron microscopy. In the early years, physicists performed most AFM imaging of biological materials, but now biologists are beginning to use the AFM on samples whose biology they understand well. As evident from this review, use of the AFM for biological applications is now routine. For the Human Genome Project, AFM-mapping of DNA is clearly feasible at sites separated by a few dozen bases or more. Furthermore, the ability of the AFM to image macromolecular structures in aqueous solutions may allow direct visualization of structural changes in functioning molecules. New microscopes have brought about many of the greatest advances in biology, from the cork cells first seen and named by Robert Hooke to the filterable viruses first seen with the electron microscope and the many discoveries with fluorescence microscopy, confocal microscopy, and other microscopies. The AFM is a new member of this distinguished family, and it will again advance our understanding of biology. Hence, the question posed by the 1987 paper, "The Atomic Force Microscope: Can It Be Used to Study Biological Molecules?" (84), can now be answered with an emphatic yes.

ACKNOWLEDGMENTS

We thank Paul Hansma, Manfred Radmacher, Ratnesh Lal, Srin Manne, Paul Hillner, Jason Cleveland, Magdalena Bezanilla, RL Sinsheimer, Hans Butt, and Eric Henderson for helpful advice. This work was supported by NSF DIR 9018846 (HH), Digital Instruments (HH), and the HFSP (LT-438/92) (JHH).

Literature Cited

1. Albrecht TR, Akamine S, Carver TE, Quate CF. 1990. Microfabrication of cantilever styli for the atomic force microscope. *J. Vac Sci. Technol. A* 8: 3386–96
2. Alexander S, Hellemans L, Marti O, Schneir J, Elings V, et al. 1989. An atomic-resolution atomic-force microscope implemented using an optical lever. *J. Appl. Phys.* 65:164–67
3. Allen MJ, Dong X-F, O'Neill TE, Yau P, Kowalczykowski SC, et al. 1993. Atomic force microscope measurements of nucleosome cores assembled along defined DNA sequences. *Biochemistry.* 32:8390–96
4. Arakawa H, Umemura K, Ikai A.

1992. Protein images obtained by STM, AFM and TEM. *Nature* 358: 171–73
5. Binnig G. 1992. Force microscopy. *Ultramicroscopy* 42–44:7–15
6. Binnig G, Gerber C, Stoll E, Albrecht RT, Quate CF. 1987. Atomic resolution with atomic force microscope. *Europhys. Lett.* 3:1281–86
7. Binnig G, Quate CF, Gerber C. 1986. Atomic force microscope. *Phys. Rev. Lett.* 56:930–33
8. Binnig G, Rohrer H. 1984. Scanning tunneling microscopy. In *Trends in Physics,* ed. J Janta, J Pantoflicek, pp. 38–46. The Hague: Eur. Phys. Soc.
9. Binnig G, Rohrer H, Gerber C, Weibel

E. 1982. Surface studies by scanning tunneling microscopy. *Phys. Rev. Lett.* 49:57–61

10. Blackford BL, Jericho MH, Mulhern PJ. 1991. A review of scanning tunneling microscope and atomic force microscope imaging of large biological structures: problems and prospects. *Scanning Microsc.* 5:907–18

11. Blackford BL, Jericho MH, Mulhern PJ, Frame C, Southam G, Beveridge TJ. 1991. Scanning tunneling microscope imaging of hoops from the cell sheath of the bacteria methanospirillum hungatei and atomic force microscope imaging of complete sheaths. *J. Vac. Technol. B. Microelectron. Process. Phenom.* 9:1242–47

12. Brandow SL, Turner DC, Ratna BR, Gaber BP. 1993. Modification of supported lipid membranes by atomic force microscopy. *Biophys. J.* 64:898–902

13. Burnham NA, Colton RJ. 1989. Measuring the nanomechnical properties and surface forces of materials using an atomic force microscope. *J. Vac. Sci. Technol. A* 7:2906-2913

14. Bustamante C, Dunlap D. 1991. Application of scanning tunneling microscopy to structural biology. *Semin. Cell Biol.* 2:179–85

15. Bustamante C, Vesenka J, Tang CL, Rees W, Guthold M, Keller R. 1992. Circular DNA molecules imaged in air by scanning force microscopy. *Biochemistry* 31:22–26

16. Butt H-J. 1992. Measuring local surface charge densities in electrolyte solutions with a scanning force microscope. *Biophys. J.* 63:578–82

17. Butt HJ, Downing KH, Hansma PK. 1990. Imaging the membrane protein bacteriorhodopsin with the atomic force microscope. *Biophys J.* 58:1473–80

18. Butt H-J, Guckenberger R, Rabe JP. 1992. Quantitative scanning tunneling and scanning force microscopy of organic materials. *Ultramicroscopy* 46:375–93

19. Butt H-J, Muller T, Gross H. 1993. Immobilizing biomolecules for scanning force microscopy by embedding in carbon. *J. Struct. Biol.* 110:127–32

20. Butt H-J, Siedle P, Seifert K, Fendler K, Seeger T, et al. 1993. Scan speed limit in atomic force microscopy. *J. Microsc.* 169(1):75–84

21. Butt HJ, Wolff EK, Gould SA, Dixon NB, Peterson CM, Hansma PK. 1990. Imaging cells with the atomic force microscope. *J. Struct. Biol.* 105:54–61

22. Chang L, Kious T, Yorgancioglu M, Keller D, Pfeifer J. 1993. Cytoskeleton of living, unstained cells imaged by scanning force microscopy. *Biophys. J.* 64:1282–86

23. Chernoff EAG, Chernoff DA. 1992. Atomic force microscope images of collagen fibers. *J. Vac. Sci. Technol. A* 10:596–99

24. Clemmer CR, Beebe TP. 1991. Graphite—a mimic for DNA and other biomolecules in scanning tunnel microscopy studies. *Science* 251:640–42

25. Cleveland JP, Manne S, Bocek D, Hansma PK. 1993. A nondestructive method for determining the spring constant of cantilevers for scanning force microscopy. *Rev. Sci. Instr.* 64:403–5

26. Devaud G, Furcinitti PS, Fleming JC, Lyon MK, Douglas K. 1992. Direct observation of defect structure in protein crystals by atomic force and transmission electron microscopy. *Biophys. J.* 63:630–38

27. Drake B, Prater CB, Weisenhorn AL, Gould SA, Albrecht TR, et al. 1989. Imaging crystals, polymers, and processes in water with the atomic force microscope. *Science* 243:1586–89

28. Durbin SD, Carlson WE. 1992. Lysozyme crystal growth studied by atomic force microscopy. *J. Crystal Growth* 122:71–79

29. Edstrom RD, Meinke MH, Yang XR, Yang R, Elings V, Evans DF. 1990. Direct visualization of phosphorylase-phosphorylase kinase complexes by scanning tunneling and atomic force microscopy. *Biophys J.* 58:1437–48

30. Egger M, Ohnesorge F, Weisenhorn AL, Heyn SP, Drake B, et al. 1990. Wet lipid-protein membranes imaged at submolecular resolution by atomic force microscopy. *J. Struct. Biol.* 103:89–94

31. Elings V, Kjoller K. 1993. A new AFM mode for improved imaging of soft samples. *Workshop on STM-AFM and Standard Biological "Objects," 1992,* p. 2. Niosy le Grand, France: Fondation Fourmentin-Guilbert

32. Engel A. 1991. Biological applications of scanning probe microscopes. *Annu. Rev. Biophys. Biophys. Chem.* 20:79–108

33. Franke F, Keller D. 1993. Toward high resolution imaging of DNA. *Proc. SPiE Int. Soc. Opt. Eng.* 1891:78–84

34. Frauenfelder H, Petsko GA, Tsernog-

136   HANSMA & HOH

lou D. 1979. Temperature-dependent
X-ray diffraction as a probe of protein
structural dynamics. *Nature* 280:588–
63
35. Fritz M, Radmacher M, Gaub HE.
1993. In vitro activation of human
platelets triggered and probed by
atomic force microscopy. *Exp. Cell
Res.* 205:187–90
36. Frommer J. 1992. Scanning tunneling
microscopy and atomic force microscopy in organic chemistry. *Angew.
Chem. Int. Ed. Engl.* 31:1298–1328
37. Goettgens BM, Tillmann RW, Radmacher M, Gaub HE. 1992. Molecular
order in polymerizable Langmuir-
Blodgett films probed by microflu-
orescence and scanning force microscopy. *Langmuir* 8:1768–74
38. Gould SAC, Drake B, Prater CB, Weisenhorn AL, Manne S, et al. 1990. The
atomic force microscope: a tool for science and industry. *Ultramicroscopy*
33:93–98
39. Gould SAC, Drake B, Prater CB,
Weisshorn AL, Manne S, et al. 1990.
From atoms to integrated circuit chips,
blood cells, and bacteria with the
atomic force microscope. *J. Vac. Sci.
Technol. A* 8:369–73
40. Guckenberger R, Hartmann T, Wiegrabe W, Baumeister W. 1992. The
scanning tunneling microscope in biology. In *Springer Series in Surface
Sciences*, ed. H-J Guntherodt, R Wie-
sendanger, 28:51-98. Heidelberg:
Springer-Verlag.
41. Haeberle W, Hoerber JKH, Binnig G.
1991. Force microscopy on living cells.
J. Vac. Sci. Technol. B 9:1210–13
42. Haeberle W, Hoerber JKH, Ohnesorge F, Smith DP, Binnig G. 1992. In
situ investigations of single living cells
infected by viruses. *Ultramicroscopy*
42–44:1161–67
43. Hansma HG, Bezanilla M, Zenhausern
F, Adrian M, Sinsheimer RL. 1993.
Atomic force microscopy of DNA in
aqueous solutions. *Nucleic Acids Res.*
21:505–12
44. Hansma HG, Hansma PK. 1993. Potential applications of atomic force microscopy of DNA to the human genome project. *Proc. SPIE Int. Soc.
Opt. Eng.* 1891:66–70
45. Hansma HG, Sinsheimer RL, Groppe
J, Bruice TC, Elings V, et al. 1993. Recent advances in atomic force microscopy of DNA. *Scanning* 15:296–99
46. Hansma HG, Sinsheimer RL, Li MQ,
Hansma PK. 1992. Atomic force microscopy of single- and double-
stranded DNA. *Nucleic Acids Res.* 20:
3585–90
47. Hansma HG, Vesenka J, Siegerist C,
Kelderman G, Morrett H, et al. 1992.
Reproducible imaging and dissection
of plasmid DNA under liquid with the
atomic force microscope. *Science* 256:
1180–84
48. Hansma HG, Weisenhorn AL, Edmundson AB, Gaub HE, Hansma PK.
1991. Atomic force microscopy: seeing
molecules of lipid and immunoglobulin. *Clin. Chem.* 37:1497–1501
49. Hansma HG, Weisenhorn AL, Gould
SAC, Sinsheimer RL, Gaub HE, et al.
1991. Progress in sequencing deoxyribonucleic acid with an atomic force microscope. *J. Vac. Sci. Technol. B* 9:
1282–84
50. Hansma PK, Elings VB, Marti O,
Bracker CE. 1988. Scanning tunneling
microscopy and atomic force microscopy: application to biology and technology. *Science* 242:209–16
51. Heckl WM, Binnig G. 1992. Domain
walls on graphite mimic DNA. *Ultramicroscopy* 42–44:1073–76
52. Heckl WM, Smith DPE, Binnig G,
Klagges H, Hansch TW, Maddocks J.
1991. Two-dimensional ordering of the
DNA base guanine observed by scanning tunneling microscopy. *Proc. Natl.
Acad. Sci. USA* 88:8003–5
53. Henderson E. 1992. Imaging and nan-
odissection of individual supercoiled
plasmids by atomic force microscopy.
Nucleic Acids Res. 20:445–47
54. Henderson E, Haydon PG, Sakaguchi
DS. 1992. Actin filament dynamics in
living glial cells imaged by atomic force
microscopy. *Science* 257:1944–46
55. Henderson E, Sakaguchi DS. 1993. Imaging F-actin in fixed glial cells with a
combined optical fluorescence/atomic
force microscope (OFAFM). *Neuro-
Image* In press
56. Hoh JH, Hansma PK. 1992. Atomic
force microscopy for high resolution
imaging in cell biology. *Trends Cell
Biol.* 7:208–213
57. Hoh JH, Lal R, John SA, Revel JP,
Arnsdorf MF. 1991. Atomic force microscopy and dissection of gap junctions. *Science* 253:1405–8
58. Hoh JH, Sosinsky G, Revel JP,
Hansma PK. 1993. Structure of the extracellular surface of the gap junction
by atomic force microscopy. *Biophys.
J.* 65:149–63
59. Ill CR, Keivens VM, Hale JE, Nakamura KK, Jue RA, et al. 1993. A
COOH-terminal peptide confers re-

giospecific orientation and facilitates atomic force microscopy of an IgG_1. *Biophys. J.* 64:919–24

60. Karrasch S, Dolder M, Schabert F, Ramsden J, Engel A. 1993. Covalent binding of biological samples to solid supports for scanning probe microscopy in buffer solution. *Biophys. J.* In press

61. Kasas S, Gotzos V, Celio MR. 1993. Observation of living cells using the atomic force microscope. *Biophys. J.* 64:539–44

62. Keller D, Chih-Chung C. 1991. Reconstruction of STM and AFM images distorted by finite-size tips. *Surf. Sci.* 253: 353–64

63. Keller D, Hoh J, Delaine E, Marchese-Ragona SP, Boland T. 1993. Actin reports. *Workshop on STM-AFM and Standard Biological "Objects," 1992,* pp. 38–46. Niosy le Grand, France: Fondation Fourmentin-Guilbert

64. Keller RW, Keller DJ, Bear D, Vasenka J, Bustamante C. 1992. Electrodeposition procedure of *E. coli* RNA polymerase onto gold and deposition of *E. coli* RNA polymerase onto mica for observation with scanning force microscopy. *Ultramicroscopy* 42–44(B): 1173–80

65. Lacapere J-J, Stokes DL, Chatenay D. 1992. Atomic force microscopy of three-dimensional membrane protein crystals. Ca-ATPase of sarcoplasmic reticulum. *Biophys. J.* 63:303–8

66. Lal R, Kim H, Garavito RM, Arnsdorf MF. 1993. Imaging reconstituted biological channels at molecular resolution using atomic force microscopy. *Am. J. Physiol.* In press

67. Lal R, Yu L. 1993. Atomic force microscopy of cloned nicotinic acetylcholine receptor expressed in *Xenopus* oocytes. *Proc. Natl. Acad. Sci. USA* 90:7280–84

68. Lindsay SM, Nagahara LA, Thundat T, Knipping U, Rill RL, et al. 1989. STM and AFM images of nucleosome DNA under water. *J. Biomol. Struct. Dyn.* 7:279–87

69. Lindsay SM, Tao NJ, DeRose JA, Oden PI, Lyubchenko Y, et al. 1992. Potentiostatic deposition of DNA for scanning probe microscopy. *Biophys. J.* 61:1570–84

70. Lyubchenko YL, Jacobs BL, Lindsay SM. 1992. Atomic force microscopy of reovirus dsRNA: a routine technique for length measurements. *Nucleic Acids Res.* 20:3983–86

71. Lyubchenko YL, Oden PI, Lampner D, Lindsay SM, Dunker KA. 1993. Atomic force microscopy of DNA and bacteriophage in air, water and propanol: the role of adhesion forces. *Nucleic Acids Res.* 21:1117–23

72. Lyubchenko YL, Shlyakhtenko LS, Harrington RE, Oden PI, Lindsay SM. 1993. Atomic force microscopy of long DNA: imaging in air and under water. *Proc. Natl. Acad. Sci. USA* 90:2137–40

73. Maivald P, Butt HJ, Gould SAC, Prater CB, Drake B, et al. 1991. Using force modulation to image surface elasticities with the atomic force microscope. *Nanotechnology* 2:103–6

74. Marti O, Colchero J, Mlynek J. 1990. Combined scanning force and friction microscopy of mica. *Nanotechnology* 1:141–44

75. Martin Y, Williams CC, Wickramasinghe HK. 1987. Atomic force microscope-force mapping and profiling on a sub-100 angstrom scale. *J. Appl. Phys.* 61:4723–29

75a. Mastrangelo IA, Bezanilla M, Hansma PK, Hough PVC, Hansma HG. 1993. Structures of large T antigen at the origin of SV40 DNA replication by atomic force microscopy. *Biophys. J.* In press

76. Meyer E, Howald L, Overney RM, Heinzelman H, Frommer J, et al. 1991. Molecular-resolution images of Langmuir-Blodgett films using atomic force microscopy. *Nature* 349:398–400

77. Meyer G, Amer NM. 1988. Novel optical approach to atomic force microscopy. *Appl. Phys. Lett.* 53:1045–47

78. Murray MN, Hansma HG, Bezanilla M, Sano T, Ogletree DF, et al. 1993. Atomic force microscopy of biochemically tagged DNA. *Proc. Natl. Acad. Sci. USA* 90:3811–14

79. Niu L, Shaiu W-L, Vesenka J, Larson DD, Henderson E. 1993. Atomic force microscopy of DNA-colloidal gold and DNA-protein interactions. *Proc. SPIE Int. Soc. Opt. Eng.* 1891:71–77

80. Ohnesorge F, Binnig G. 1993. True atomic-resolution by atomic force microscopy through repulsive and attractive forces. *Science* 260:1451–56

81. Ohnishi S, Hara M, Furuno T, Sasabe H. 1992. Imaging the ordered arrays of water-soluble protein ferritin with the atomic force microscope. *Biophys. J.* 63:1425–31

82. Pante N, Aebi U. 1993. The nuclear pore complex. *J. Cell Biol.* 122:977–84

83. Parpura V, Haydon PG, Sakaguchi DS, Henderson E. 1993. Atomic force

microscopy and manipulation of living glial cells. *J. Vac. Sci. Technol.* 11: 773–75

84. Persson BNJ. 1987. The atomic force microscope: can it be used to study biological materials? *Chem. Phys. Lett.* 141:366–68

85. Puppels GJ, Putman CAJ, de Grooth BG, Greve J. 1992. Raman microspectroscopy and atomic force microscopy of chromosomal banding patterns. *Proc. SPIE Int. Soc. Opt. Eng.* 1922: 145–55

86. Putman CA, van der Werf KO, de Grooth BG, van Hulst NF, Greve J. 1992. New imaging mode in atomic-force microscopy based on the error signal. *Proc. SPIE Int. Soc. Opt. Eng.* 1639:198–204

87. Putman CAJ, de Grooth BG, Hansma PK, van Hulst NF. 1993. Immunogold labels: cell-surface markers in atomic force microscopy. *Ultramicroscopy* 48:177–82

88. Putman CAJ, de Grooth BG, Wiegant J, Raap AK. 1993. Detection of in situ hybridization to human chromosomes with the atomic force microscope. *Cytometry* 14:356–61

89. Putman CAJ, Hansma HG, Gaub HE, Hansma PK. 1992. Polymerized LB films imaged with a combined atomic force microscope-fluorescence microscope. *Langmuir* 8:3014–19

90. Rabe JP. 1992. Molecules at interfaces: STM in materials and life sciences. *Ultramicroscopy* 42–44:41–54

91. Radmacher M, Goettgens BM, Tillmann RW, Hansma HG, Hansma PK, Gaub HE. 1992. Morphology of polymerized membranes on an amorphous substrate at molecular resolution by AFM. See Ref. 119a, 241:144–53

92. Radmacher M, Tillmann RW, Fritz M, Gaub HE. 1992. From molecules to cells: imaging soft samples with the atomic force microscope. *Science* 257: 1900–5

93. Radmacher M, Tillmann RW, Gaub HE. 1993. Imaging viscoelasticity by force modulation with the atomic force microscope. *Biophys. J.* 64:735–42

94. Radmacher M, Zimmerman RM, Gaub HE. 1992. Does the scanning force microscope resolve individual lipid molecules? In *The Structure and Conformation of Amphiphilic Membranes,* ed. R Zipowsky, D Richter, K Kremer, pp. 24–29. Berlin: Springer

95. Rasch P, Wiedemann U, Wienberg J, Heckl WM. 1993. Analysis of banded human chromosomes, in situ hybridi-

zation patterns by scanning force microscopy. *Proc. Natl. Acad. Sci. USA* 90:2509–11

96. Rees WA, Keller RW, Vesenka JP, Yang C, Bustamante C. 1993. Scanning force microscopy imaging of transcription complexes: evidence for DNA bending in open promoter and elongation complexes. *Science* 260: 1646–49

97. Rugar D, Hansma PK. 1990. Atomic force microscopy. *Phys. Today* 43:23–30

98. Samori B, Siligardi G, Quagliariello C, Weisenhorn AL, Vesenka J, Bustamante CJ. 1993. Chirality of DNA supercoiling assigned by scanning force microscopy. *Proc. Natl. Acad. Sci. USA* 90:3598–3601

99. Sarid D, Elings V. 1991. Review of scanning force microscopy. *J. Vac. Sci. Technol. B* 9:431–37

100. Schabert F, Hefti A, Goldie K, Stemmer A, Engel A, et al. 1992. Ambient-pressure scanning probe microscopy of 2D regular protein arrays. *Ultramicroscopy* 42–44:1118–24

101. Schwartz DK, Garnaes J, Viswanathan R, Zasadinski JAN. 1992. Surface order and stability of Langmuir-Blodgett films. *Science* 257:508–11

102. Shaiu W-L, Larson DD, Vesenka J, Henderson E. 1993. Atomic force microscopy of oriented linear DNA molecules labeled with 5 nm gold spheres. *Nucleic Acids Res.* 21:99–103

103. Singh S, Keller DJ. 1991. Atomic force microscopy of supported planar membrane bilayers. *Biophys. J.* 60:1401–10

104. Sitka V, Filipkowski M, Garito AF, Blasie JK. 1986. Profile structures of very thin multilayers by x-ray diffraction using direct and refinement methods of analysis. *Phys. Rev. B* 34:5826–37

105. Thundat T, Allison DP, Warmack RJ, Brown GM, Jacobson KB, et al. 1992. Atomic force microscopy of DNA on mica and chemically modified mica. *Scanning Microsc.* 6:911–18

106. Thundat T, Allison DP, Warmack RJ, Doktycz MJ, Jacobson KB, Brown GM. 1993. Atomic force microscopy of single- and double-stranded deoxyribonucleic acid. *J. Vac. Sci. Technol. A.* 11:824–28

107. Tillmann R, Radmacher M, Gaub HE. 1992. Hydrated amorphous silicon oxide surface at 3 angstrom resolution by scanning force microscopy. *Appl. Phys. Lett.* 60:3111–13

108. Unser M, Trus BL, Steven AC. 1987.

A new resolution criterion based on spectral signal-to-noise ratios. *Ultramicroscopy* 23:39–52
109. Vesenka J, Guthold M, Tang CL, Keller D, Delaine E, Bustamante C. 1992. A substrate preparation for reliable imaging of DNA molecules with the scanning force microscope. *Ultramicroscopy* 42–44:1243–49
110. Vesenka J, Hansma H, Siegerist C, Siligardi G, Schabtach E, Bustamante C. 1992. Scanning force microscopy of circular DNA and chromatin in air and propanol. *Proc. SPIE Int. Soc. Opt. Eng.* 1639:127–37
111. Weisenhorn AL, Drake B, Prater CB, Gould SA, Hansma PK, et al. 1990. Immobilized proteins in buffer imaged at molecular resolution by atomic force microscopy. *Biophys J.* 58:1251–58
112. Weisenhorn AL, Egger M, Ohnesorge F, Gould SAC, Heyn S-P, et al. 1991. Molecular-resolution images of Langmuir-Blodgett films, DNA by atomic force microscopy. *Langmuir* 7:8–12
113. Weisenhorn AL, Gaub HE, Hansma HG, Sinsheimer RL, Kelderman GL, Hansma PK. 1990. Imaging single-stranded DNA, antigen-antibody reaction and polymerized Langmuir-Blodgett films with an atomic force microscope. *Scanning Microsc.* 4:511–16
114. Weisenhorn AL, Hansma PK, Albrecht TR, Quate CF. 1989. Forces in atomic force microscopy in air and water. *Appl. Phys. Lett.* 54:2651–53
115. Weisenhorn AL, Maivald P, Butt H-J, Hansma PK. 1992. Measuring adhesion, attraction, and repulsion between surfaces in liquids with an atomic force microscope. *Phys. Rev. Lett. B* 45:11226–32
116. Weisenhorn AL, Roemer DU, Lorenzi GP. 1992. An atomic force microscope study of Langmuir-Blodgett films of a beta-4.4-helical pentadecavaline. *Langmuir* 8:3145–49
117. Weisenhorn AL, Schmitt FJ, Knoll W, Hansma PK. 1992. Streptavidin binding observed with an atomic force microscope. *Ultramicroscopy* 42–44:1125–32
118. Wickramasinghe HK. 1989. Scanned-probe microscopes. *Sci. Am.* Oct.:98–105
119. Wickramasinghe HK. 1992. Scanned probes old and new. See Ref. 119a, 241:9–22.
119a. Wickramasinghe HK, ed. 1992. *Scanned Probe Microscopy.* New York: Am. Inst. Phys.
120. Wiegrabe W, Nonnenmacher M, Guckenberger R, Wolter O. 1991. Atomic force microscopy of a hydrated bacterial surface protein. *J. Microsc.* 163:79–84
121. Wigren R, Elwing H, Erlandson R, Welin S, Lundstrom I. 1991. Structure of fibrinogen obtained by scanning force microscopy. *FEBS Lett.* 280:225–28
122. Worcester DL, Kim HS, Miller RG, Bryant PJ. 1990. Imaging bacteriorhodopsin lattices in purple membranes with atomic force microscopy. *J. Vac. Sci. Technol. A* 8:403–5
123. Yamada H, Akamine S, Quate CF. 1992. Imaging of organic molecular films with the atomic force microscope. *Ultramicroscopy* 42–44(B):1044–48
124. Yang J, Takeyasu K, Shao Z. 1992. Atomic force microscopy of DNA molecules. *FEBS Lett.* 301:173–76
125. Yang J, Tamm LK, Somlyo AP, Shao Z. 1993. Promises and problems of biological atomic force microscopy. *J. Microsc.* 171:183–98
126. Yang J, Tamm LK, Tillack TW, Shao Z. 1993. New approach for atomic force microscopy of membrane proteins—the imaging of cholera toxin. *J. Mol. Biol.* 229:286–90
127. Zachee P, Boogaerts MA, Hellamans L, Snauwaert J. 1992. Adverse role of the spleen in hereditary spherocytosis: evidence by the use of the atomic force microscope [letter]. *Br. J. Haematol.* 80:264–65
128. Zasadzinski JA. 1989. Scanning tunneling microscopy with applications to biological surfaces. *Biotechniques* 7:174–87
129. Zasadzinski JA, Helm CA, Longo ML, Weisenhorn AL, Gould SA, Hansma PK. 1991. Atomic force microscopy of hydrated phosphatidylethanolamine bilayers. *Biophys. J.* 59:755–60
130. Zenhausern F, Adrian M, ten Heggeler-Bordier B, Emch R, Jobin M, et al. 1992. Imaging of DNA by scanning force microscopy. *J. Struct. Biol.* 108:69–73
131. Zenhausern F, Adrian M, ten Heggeler-Bordier B, Eng LM, Descouts P. 1992. DNA and RNA polymerase/DNA complexes imaged by scanning force microscopy: influence of molecular-scale friction. *Scanning* 14:212–17

Annu. Rev. Biophys. Biomol. Struct. 1994. 23:141–65
Copyright © 1994 by Annual Reviews Inc. All rights reserved

ALAMETHICIN: A Peptide Model for Voltage Gating and Protein-Membrane Interactions

D. S. Cafiso

Department of Chemistry, University of Virginia, Charlottesville, Virginia 22901

KEY WORDS: ion channels, membrane electrostatics, lipid bilayers, peptide structure, membrane excitability

CONTENTS

PERSPECTIVES AND OVERVIEW

Characterizing the molecular structure and function of membrane proteins represents one of the greatest challenges in the field of structural biology. Membrane proteins arguably comprise some of the most important and fascinating proteins in biological systems; unfortunately, techniques that provide structural information on water-soluble pro-

1056–8700/94/0610–0141$05.00

teins, such as X-ray crystallography and high-resolution NMR, fail when applied to most membrane protein systems. Voltage-gated ion channels such as the sodium and potassium channels of nerves represent a particularly intriguing class of membrane proteins. These large ion channels provide a specific, low-energy pathway for the transport of ions. In addition, their conformational states depend upon the membrane electric field and are necessarily a consequence of the displacement or movement of protein charges or dipoles within the membrane interior. Site-directed mutagenesis has provided evidence for the involvement of charged segments of the sodium channel in the gating event; however, as with most membrane proteins, the molecular events have not been resolved. As a result, new approaches to resolve the structures and functions of this class of proteins are urgently needed.

One approach to obtain information regarding the structure and behavior of large intrinsic ion channels is to examine smaller channel systems. Alamethicin is a 20–amino acid peptide from the fungus *Trichoderma viride* that produces voltage-dependent conductance in lipid bilayers. This voltage dependence and its tractable size make alamethicin an attractive model for studying voltage-dependent gating. Although such small peptides may ultimately prove to be poor models for the sodium channel (indeed, the dynamics and membrane interactions of a small peptide could be very different from those of a larger membrane protein), the structural changes that accompany the gating of alamethicin will provide valuable information on the types of electrically active structural changes that are likely to occur for other peptides and proteins within membranes.

In addition to alamethicin serving as a model for channel gating, studies on this peptide lend insight into the activities of other interesting membrane-active peptides. The activities of numerous small channel-forming peptides, such as melittin, the magainins, and the mammalian defensins, are not resolved at the molecular level (8, 40, 61). Some of these peptides have antibiotic activity and function in immune responses. The membrane association of peptides derived from protein presequences is currently an active area of investigation (53).

Protein presequences or signal sequences direct the insertion, folding, and targeting of membrane and excreted proteins; however, the interactions that lead to this targeting and insertion have not been clarified. In the case of certain mitochondrial proteins, membrane electric fields appear to drive the transport and insertion of the protein presequence (41). Thus, studies on alamethicin should provide information relevant to several fascinating and critically important membrane active peptides, including the structural features that control the free energy of binding or membrane insertion of peptides, the molecular interactions that determine the rate of transmembrane migration of peptides, and the basis for membrane electric field interactions with peptide structures.

This chapter reviews some of the key electrical and structural data that have been obtained on alamethicin. The energetics of ion transport are discussed along with models for the channel structure and its gating. I evaluate these models in the context of these data and present additional alternative models.

ENERGETIC REQUIREMENTS FOR ION TRANSPORT

Ions have a low permeability in lipid bilayers primarily because of the high energy for placing charge in a low dielectric domain. Other interactions, such as steric interactions with the lipid chains, are of secondary importance. The energy cost for transferring an ion from a medium of dielectric ϵ_1 to a medium of dielectric ϵ_2 is given by the Born energy, Equation 1:

$$W_B = \left(\frac{q^2}{4\pi\varepsilon_0}\right) \frac{1}{2r} \left(\frac{1}{\varepsilon_2} - \frac{1}{\varepsilon_1}\right). \qquad 1.$$

Here q is the charge on the ion, r is the radius and ϵ_0 is the permittivity of free space. Biological membranes are thin, and the exact expression for W_B includes an image term, which takes into account the interactions of the ion with the lipid interface (21). Equation 1 clearly indicates that increasing the size of the ion, or the dielectric of the membrane, decreases the Born energy, W_B. Because the transport rate constants are exponentially dependent on the energy barrier, relatively small changes in r or the dielectric constant can dramatically affect ion permeation.

Organic ions such as tetraphenylborate or tetraphenylphosphonium are membrane permeable as a result of their large size and hydrophobicity. Figure 1A shows energy profiles of these ions across the lipid bilayer predicted by simple theories and experiment. The dramatic differences between a positive phosphonium and negative borate result from oriented dipolar groups in the membrane that give rise to an electrostatic field through the interface. Because of these dipole moments, structurally similar cations and anions differ by as much as 10^6 in their translocation rate constants (21, 23).

The electrostatic fields from a dipole layer can also dramatically affect the translocation rates of simple inorganic ions. For example,

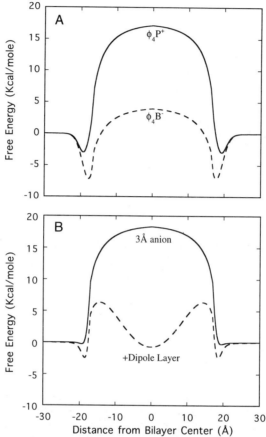

Figure 1 (*A*) Free energy profiles for tetraphenylborate (*dashed line*) and tetraphenyl-phosphonium (*solid line*) using a model and parameters described previously (21). (*B*) The energy profile for a 3-Å anion with (*dashed line*) and without (*solid line*) an additional dipole layer located $+10$ and -10 Å from the bilayer center. This additional dipole layer is present at a frequency of 1 in 10 lipids, is 35 Debye and has its negative end inward. This approximates the effect of an α-helix inserted halfway across the bilayer.

Flewelling & Hubbell (21) demonstrated that the appropriate placement of a dipole layer can virtually eliminate the energy barrier within the membrane for small ions. Figure 1*B* shows energy profiles for 3-Å anions, calculated using a simple dielectric model, when a dipole layer is placed in the membrane interior (21). This simple example illustrates that electrostatic barriers can be dramatically altered even in a low dielectric domain. In addition to lowering the magnitude of the Born energy, the appropriate positioning of dipoles can also dramatically reduce the effect of transport barriers, even in a nonpolar domain.

The current paradigm for an ion channel is an aggregate or bundle of amphipathic α-helices. In terms of the Born energy and steric interactions, this is a highly favorable configuration; however, two points are worth noting regarding such structures. First, highly amphipathic helices are probably not required to produce ion permeation. Indeed, calculations show that bundles of peptides formed from nonpolar amino acids can provide an effective pathway for ions (27). While alamethicin has an amphipathic character, it is also relatively nonpolar, especially when compared with other structures that are thought to form conductive pathways. Eisenman & Alvarez (19) have raised a second concern regarding helix bundles. In a parallel aggregate of α-helices, large electrostatic fields can be present along the axis of the channel; although the channel looks open, electrostatic forces can completely block ion transport. In the case of the acetylcholine receptor, ionizable groups located at the ends of the proposed channel can compensate for the electrostatic effects of the helix dipole, but this would not be the case for electrically neutral analogues of alamethicin. Most models for the alamethicin channel include parallel helix bundles, but this electrostatic problem has not been addressed. Presumably, compensation for the helix dipole could come from head-group dipoles or other structures in the lipid interface.

GENERAL FEATURES AND SEQUENCE OF ALAMETHICIN

Alamethicin is the best-studied of a class of membrane-active peptides of fungal origin rich in aminoisobutyric acid (Aib). Alamethicin I has the sequence Ac-Aib-Pro-Aib-Ala-Aib-Ala-Gln-Aib-Val-Aib-Gly-Leu-Aib-Pro-V al-Aib-Aib-Glu-Gln-Phol. The hypelcins (43), trichorzianins (18), and zervamicins (4) are related peptides, sometimes called peptaibols, that are also known to have channel activity. A complete discussion of these related peptides can be found in a review by Sansom (49).

Several features in alamethicin's sequence are worth noting and may have relevance to its channel activity. Aib residues generally restrict the possible conformers of peptides so that α and 3_{10} helical conformations are favored (54); this tendency is confirmed by the presence of a predominantly helical structure in alamethicin (see below). Alamethicin may contain a large 3_{10} helical content. In the crystal form, the maximum length for a 3_{10} peptide is about eight residues, unless over 50% of the residues are Aib. However, the maximum length may be much longer for peptides in solution or in membranes. In a membrane, the 3_{10} configuration will reduce the free-energy loss associated with unsatisfied hydrogen bonds at the peptide termini. In addition, recent work using spin labels indicates that alanine containing 16-residue peptides are in fact 3_{10} helices (45). Alamethicin and its related peptaibols are N-acetylated and have a reduced C terminus, which may assist in their membrane insertion. In fact, alamethicin appears to be ideally constructed for N-terminal insertion into a low dielectric domain. In a 3_{10} configuration, the acetylated N terminus and proline at position 2 would result in only one unsatisfied hydrogen bond upon insertion of the N terminus into the membrane interior. Typically alamethicin and its related peptides contain centrally located prolines with glutamine residues near both ends of the peptide. Prolines occur at a higher than normal frequency in putative membrane–spanning α-helices, influence both the static structure and dynamics of proteins, and may figure prominently into the function of channels (58). Also of note is the carbonyl group of the centrally located glycine in alamethicin, which often hydrogen bonds to solvent (22). Overall, alamethicin and its related peptides are very hydrophobic, but they can form laterally amphipathic helices. Unlike other membrane-active, channel-forming peptides such as melittin and magainin, alamethicin and its related peptides are not highly charged, and several active derivatives of alamethicin are uncharged.

CHANNEL ACTIVITY OF ALAMETHICIN

Macroscopic Conductances in Planar Bilayers

Macroscopic measurements of alamethicin induced conductances can be made in planar bilayers and provide information on the simultaneous activity of many channels. Several fascinating observations made in this way regarding the voltage-dependence yield clues to the likely structure of the conductive pore. Comprehensive descriptions of the electrical activity of alamethicin can be found in several earlier articles (11, 38).

Alamethicin produces a macroscopic conductance in planar bilayer systems that is highly voltage dependent. The steady-state conductance, G, induced by the peptide can be described by the empirical expression:

$$G = \Gamma C^n \exp(V/V_e), \qquad\qquad 2.$$

where C is the concentration of the peptide, V is the applied voltage, and V_e is the voltage that produces an e-fold change in conductance (31). The parameter G varies with the lipid type, ionic strength, and other experimental conditions. The conductance strongly depends on peptide concentration, described by n, and changes in peptide concentration shift the current-voltage curve by ΔV according to $\Delta V = -V_a\Delta(\ln C)$, where V_a is the voltage shift in the I-V curve for an e-fold change in concentration. Typical values for n are in the range of 8 to 12 and the values for V_e are approximately 5 mV. This behavior has been modeled in terms of a gating charge, α, where $V_e = kT/en\alpha$, and e is the electronic charge. For alamethicin, α is approximately 0.5 electronic charges (31). Note that this gating charge is model dependent and presumes that n monomers participate in the gating event. The parameter α appears to be relatively independent of lipid composition, while the values of n increase with the lipid chain length.

An important observation regarding the macroscopic currents is that they are often asymmetric. Currents are largest when the side of the bilayer to which alamethicin is added (the *cis* side) is made positive (55). When the opposite or *trans* side is made positive, little or no conductance is produced. This asymmetry varies with the lipid composition and vanishes when alamethicin is added to both sides of the bilayer. The current voltage asymmetry has been taken as evidence that the transmembrane migration rate for the peptide is slow relative to its membrane dissociation rate.

Single Channel Conductance Measurements

Alamethicin channel activity occurs in bursts composed of discrete, multilevel conductances (29). Relatively long periods of channel inactivity separate the bursts, and this inactive period varies with voltage. Apparently the voltage activation seen in the macroscopic conductances results from a decrease in the duration between bursts. Within each burst of channel activity, the conductance levels increase or decrease only in unit steps; furthermore, at higher conductance levels, the unit increases in the conductance also get larger. These data support a barrel-stave model for the channel structure in which the discrete conductance steps result from different multimeric forms of the channel (see below).

Conductance Measurements in Vesicles

Planar bilayers provide a facile means to electrically access a model membrane; however, direct structural measurements and binding measurements on peptides are difficult to carry out in these systems. Vesicle systems are amenable to several structural techniques including magnetic resonance and optical spectroscopies, but measurements of electrical activity in these systems can be much more challenging. Nonetheless, investigators have characterized the macroscopic conductance behavior of alamethicin in vesicle systems. Work by Lau & Chan (39) demonstrated that europium ions could be released when membrane potentials were applied across lipid vesicles containing alamethicin. More recently both fluorescence and EPR were used to examine the conductance properties of alamethicin in vesicles (2, 59). With spin-labeled probes of membrane potentials, one can evaluate the ion currents in a highly quantitative fashion and obtain data that are analogous with some of the data obtained in planar bilayer experiments. For more information on these techniques, the interested reader should consult other reviews (13, 24).

Figure 2 shows current-voltage data obtained for alamethicin in extruded egg phosphatidylcholine (PC) vesicles using spin-labeled probes (2), along with several data points from Vodyanoy et al (55) obtained in planar bilayers of phosphatidylethanolamine (PE)-squalene. The current-voltage behavior in vesicles resembles that found in planar bilayers, and the magnitudes of the currents are not inconsistent with those

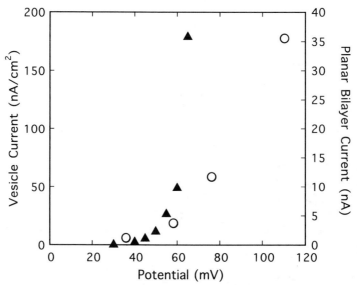

Figure 2   Current voltage-curves obtained for alamethicin in planar bilayers (*solid triangles*) formed from PE (data from 55) and in lipid vesicles (*open circles*) formed of egg PC (data taken from 1).

found in planar bilayers. The vesicle data can be fit to Equation 2; the conductances strongly depend upon alamethicin concentration; and the I-V curves shift to lower voltages at higher peptide concentrations. In fact, the values of V_a and α are close to those obtained for planar bilayers. However, the values of n are between 3 and 4 and the value of V_e is approximately 20 mV. Thus, the concentration and voltage dependence in vesicles is not as steep as in planar bilayer systems. This comparison should be viewed cautiously because of the dramatic differences in the systems and the measurements. Unlike the bilayer data, the vesicle data are not obtained in the steady state, and vesicle measurements are made over a much narrower range of peptide concentrations. Interestingly, planar bilayer measurements in shorter chain length lipids also yield smaller values of n, similar to those obtained in vesicles (31). In addition, a conductance of weaker voltage and concentration dependence resembling that in vesicles has been reported in planar bilayers (11, 15).

The Activity of Alamethicin Analogues

The gating of alamethicin is believed to result from the membrane insertion or movement of the N-terminal end of the alamethicin helix (31). In planar bilayers, *cis* positive potentials produce greater currents than *cis* negative potentials, an observation indicating that reverse gating or insertion of the C-terminus is unfavorable. Presumably the absence of reverse gating as well as the slow crossing rate of alamethicin in some lipids is a result of the negatively charged side chain of Glu18. Hall et al (31) measured currents for a neutral analogue of alamethicin, in which Glu18 was blocked by a benzyl-protecting group, and obtained a symmetric current-voltage curve. Thus, blocking this side chain resulted in enhanced membrane crossing and/or some reverse gating. When currents were measured for an analogue with a positively charged N terminus, an asymmetric current-voltage curve was again obtained. However, this analogue was back gated and conducted only when the applied potentials were *trans* positive.

This work suggests that a charge on either end of alamethicin can prevent it from crossing the membrane and that gating of the channel can occur by the movement of either end of the peptide. Interestingly, zervamicin IIB (a related but shorter peptaibol) exhibits a strongly asymmetric current-voltage curve even though it is uncharged (4). Even more surprising is the observation that zervamicin IC, in which a Glu replaces Gln3, is activated by *cis* negative potentials. In this manner it resembles the positively charged back-gated analogue of alamethicin. Although the mechanisms of gating by zervamicin may be different, these observations caution against a quick interpretation of the asymmetric conductance. Clearly, more direct physical information on the location and crossing rates for alamethicin and its analogues would be helpful in resolving the origins of the current-voltage asymmetry.

Peptides containing Aib are more difficult to synthesize than non-Aib–containing peptides because of their slow coupling rates. To explore the activity of non-Aib–containing analogues, and to determine the requirement for Aib, analogues were prepared that contained either Ala or Leu in place of Aib (46). Interestingly, the Ala-substituted analogue of alamethicin failed to produce multistate alamethicin-like channel activity, while the Leu analogue produced conductances similar to that of native alamethicin. Also, the Leu analogue appeared to be largely helical, while the Ala analogue's secondary structure varied considerably.

In more recently prepared derivatives of this leucine analogue, alanine replaced prolines at positions 2 and 14 (17). These analogues had the same strong voltage dependence as alamethicin, but the value of n (see Equation 2) was reduced when Pro14 was substituted. These analogues, particularly the Pro14 substituted peptide, also exhibited shorter open channel lifetimes and generally faster current fluctuations than native alamethicin. Thus, while proline is not required for channel activity, its absence does change the channel behavior.

Alamethicin has many natural channel forming analogues, and the electrical properties of a number of these have been characterized (49). While some of these analogues may differ in channel activity, in general it is difficult to draw definitive conclusions regarding the role of specific residues or domains.

STRUCTURE AND DYNAMICS OF ALAMETHICIN

Crystal Structure

Figure 3 shows one of the crystal structures for alamethicin determined by Fox & Richards (22). Three similar molecules occupy the unit cell of crystals formed from acetonitrile-methanol, and several relevant features of the peptide appear in this structure. The peptide assumes a helical structure that is bent about Pro14, and as illustrated in Figure 3, the peptide is laterally amphipathic, with both Gln7 and Glu18 residing on one face. The carbonyl oxygens of Aib10 and Gly11 are hydrogen bonded with solvent and are presumably highly accessible, although this is not apparent in the illustration. Aib10 and Gly11 also reside on this more polar face of the helix. The hydrogen bond pattern

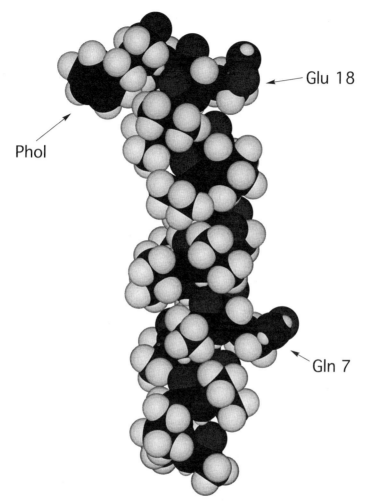

Phol

Glu 18

Gln 7

Figure 3   One of the crystal structures determined by Fox & Richards for alamethicin (22).

is α-helical in the N-terminal domain; however, the middle of the peptide and the C terminus possess H-bonding patterns characteristic of a 3_{10} helix.

Crystal structures are available for several shorter Aib-containing peptides and the related peptaibols. In general, these peptides also assume helical structures that are either α or 3_{10} (34), although in the zervamicins the helical structure contains a β-bend ribbon that includes Pro and Hyp residues (35).

Structure Derived from Spectroscopic Studies

The structure of alamethicin has been examined in solvents, micelles, and membranes using several spectroscopic techniques. Alamethicin has limited solubility in water, and it aggregates above concentrations of 10–20 μM (3). However, it is highly soluble in methanol, and as a result, a number of studies have been carried out in this solvent. Early NMR studies indicated that the N terminus was helical with β structure at the C terminus (5), but more recent studies are consistent with a helical structure similar to the crystal form (20, 36, 60). In these investigations, the peptide appears to be less well defined in the C-terminal domain than in the N-terminal domain, an observation that is consistent with the structural heterogeneity seen in the crystal forms of alamethicin.

The results of circular dichroism (CD), infrared, and raman measurements also indicate a significant helical content for alamethicin in organic solution (32, 56). Most of the CD measurements place this content between 30 and 40%. However, reports on the amount of β strand obtained by these techniques vary, as do conclusions on the differences between solution and membrane conformations. One study reported that the structure of alamethicin is similar between membranes and methanol when the lipid is in the liquid crystalline state (56). Interestingly, the level of helical content was found to increase below the membrane transition temperature. In another study, β structure decreases and helical structure increased for alamethicin in membranes compared with organic solvents (14).

Recently, the structure of alamethicin in SDS micelles was obtained in my laboratory using multidimensional NMR (25). This structure (see Figure 4) appears to be helical in the N-terminal domain up to residue 11 and weakly helical in the region from residues 14–18. A region in the middle of the peptide beginning at Gly11 appears capable of significant conformational heterogeneity, and several conformations consistent with the NMR data can be found. The poor alignment seen in the C-terminal domain in Figure 4 results from configurational heterogeneity primarily in residues 11–14.

Several NMR studies provide evidence for conformational flexibility in the C-terminal domain of alamethicin, and this observation has implications for the mechanisms of voltage-dependent gating (see below). Although more work is needed to define the dynamics of this system, evidence for conformational flexibility is found in measurements of amide exchange rates (16), coupling constants, and the lack of NOEs in the C-terminal portion of the structure (20, 60).

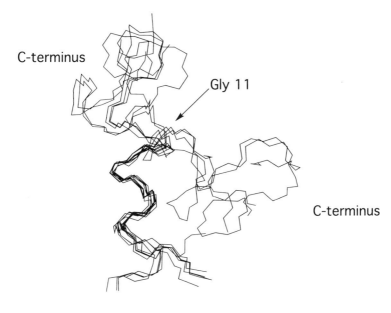

C-terminus

Gly 11

C-terminus

N-terminus

Figure 4   Structures obtained with high resolution NMR for alamethicin in SDS micelles that have been superimposed in the N-terminal domain (25). These structures represent the 10 lowest energy structures determined using NMR restraints in a simulated annealing procedure (47).

If the C-terminus has conformational flexibility, high-amplitude bending motions for the peptide backbone do not appear to occur in solution. One study examined the dynamics of alamethicin in methanol by using ^{13}C T_1 and ^1H-^{13}C nuclear Overhauser effects (36). These measurements were made at two magnetic field strengths, and the relaxation-rate data were fit to models for molecular motion that included an overall anisotropic tumbling, and rapid internal motions for the peptide. In methanol, the peptide backbone appears to be rigid, with the ends of the peptide showing slightly more motion. Rapid, large-amplitude bending motions of the backbone were not seen. This general picture is also consistent with the magnitude of the paramagnetic effects for a C-terminal spin-labeled analogue of alamethicin (1). Here the measured distances are close to those obtained in a molecular dynamics simulation when the entire peptide is held rigid except for the C-terminal residue and the proxyl nitroxide.

Membrane Binding and Aggregation of Alamethicin

Several spectroscopic studies have been directed at examining the binding, aggregation, and membrane orientation of alamethicin. Schwarz et al used CD to measure the binding of alamethicin to lipid vesicles (48, 51, 52). This binding is lipid and ionic-strength dependent and shows a cooperative behavior. The cooperative behavior evinced the aggregation of alamethicin in the membrane, and the data were analyzed in an elegant fashion to obtain critical concentrations for the peptide aggregation (51). Similar binding measurements were also made using a spin-labeled analogue of alamethicin, in which the C-terminus of alamethicin is derivatized with a proxyl nitroxide (3). Figure 5 depicts binding curves obtained for alamethicin in lipid vesicles. Interestingly, phosphatidylethanolamines show a diminished binding relative to PCs as do agents such as phloretin that depress the dipole potential.

To determine whether the cooperative binding of alamethicin was a result of aggregation, Archer et al (3) measured the EPR lineshapes of membrane bound spin-labeled alamethicin under conditions in which the peptide is predicted to be monomeric and extensively aggregated.

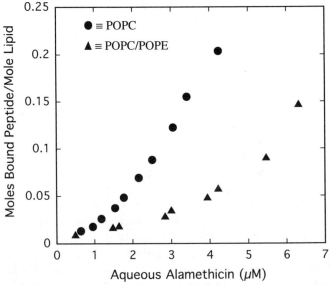

Figure 5 Binding curves for alamethicin to lipid vesicles formed from palmitoyloleoyl-phosphatidylcholine (POPC) or 30 mol% palmitoyloleoylphosphatidylethanolamine (POPE) in POPC (1). The binding was determined using a spin-labeled alamethicin derivative (3).

These measurements indicated that alamethicin was essentially monomeric in PC membranes over a wide range of concentrations and provided no evidence for aggregation in the membrane. Thus, the cooperative behavior seen in the binding curve for alamethicin is not a result of aggregation. The changes in free energy associated with varied slopes in the binding curve are quite small (about 0.8 kcal/mol) and the modulation of any number of steric or enthalpic peptide-membrane interactions could explain the shape of the binding curve.

Information on the orientation of membrane-bound alamethicin will be critical to define the mechanism of channel gating; unfortunately, few data are available on its membrane-bound state. Most studies suggest that alamethicin is incorporated into the lipid hydrocarbon rather than being associated with the membrane surface (26), a finding that is not surprising given the hydrophobicity of this peptide. Amide proton exchange experiments carried out on membrane-bound alamethicin indicate that the peptide is largely protected from exchange by the membrane except at penultimate and C-terminal residues (LP Kelsh & DS Cafiso, unpublished data). We would expect such protection if alamethicin is buried within the hydrocarbon with its C-terminus localized at the membrane interface. This position for the C-terminus is also consistent with the paramagnetic effects of a spin-labeled alamethicin analogue on lipid ^{13}C relaxation rates (3). CD measurements on the orientation of alamethicin have shown that the peptide is oriented along the bilayer normal under conditions of full hydration, but oriented in the plane of the membrane when the lipid was placed in the gel state (56). In a recent CD experiment, both the level of hydration and the peptide-lipid ratio were found to be critical determinants of the peptide orientation (33). At full hydration or low peptide-to-lipid ratios, these authors found that the peptide lies along the bilayer normal. At low water activities, or high peptide-lipid ratios, the peptide appeared to be oriented on the membrane surface.

Relatively few investigations of voltage-induced structural changes in alamethicin have been reported, but evidence indicates that such changes occur. In one study, polyanions were used to create potentials across membrane vesicles in the presence of alamethicin, and the peptide conformation was monitored using CD (12). An increase in the β content of the peptide was detected when vesicle potentials were inside positive, while an increase in the α-helical content was detected with inside-negative potentials. An examination of the spectrum of a spin-labeled analogue of alamethicin in thylakoid membranes revealed that a decrease in the rotational correlation time for the label accompanied energization of the thylakoid and an opening of the channel (57). Although several interpretations of these experiments are possible, both experiments are consistent with the insertion of the peptide deeper into the membrane interior upon the application of a membrane potential.

MODELS FOR THE ALAMETHICIN CHANNEL

The proposed models for alamethicin channel generally attempt to explain several striking features in the electrical data. These features include the high concentration dependence, the multilevel conductances, and the magnitude of the apparent gating charge. As a result, all the models share common features. However, the proposed mechanisms of voltage gating often differ substantially, and these differences generally reflect the poor level of understanding regarding the membrane-associated structures.

Structure of the Ion Channel

THE BARREL-STAVE MODEL   The high concentration dependence of the conduction is most easily interpreted in terms of a multimeric channel structure, which seems reasonable given the amphipathic nature of the peptide. The multistep conductances seen in single-channel recordings can be interpreted in terms of a barrel-stave model for the channel pore. In this model (see Figure 6), monomers can join or dissociate from the aggregate, which leads to changes in the conductance level of the channel. Further support for this model again comes from single-channel recordings, in which the conductance difference between levels increases at higher levels. The size of a pore formed from this type of aggregate should increase with the number of monomers in the aggregate, and general agreement between the increase in pore size and increase in conductance is taken as evidence for this model (49).

THE MULTIPORE CLUSTER MODEL   A recent study with polymers indicates that the size of the pore remains essentially unchanged as the conductance levels increase (9). This leads to a quite different picture for the channel, in which alamethicin aggregates to form a multipore cluster such as that depicted in Figure 6. Presumably multistep conductances in this model result from the binding and dissociation of alamethicin monomers (or nonconductive aggregates) from the cluster. Clearly, direct structural information regarding the alamethicin aggregate would be extremely valuable in determining the nature of the association between alamethicin monomers.

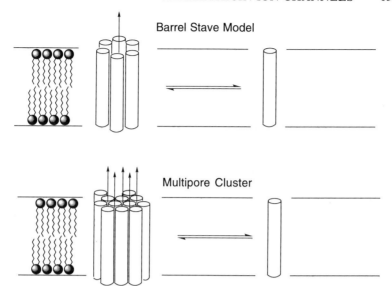

Figure 6   Models for the conductive pore of alamethicin. In the barrel-stave model (*top*), monomers can bind to or dissociate from the conductive channel aggregate, leading to altered conductance levels. In the multipore cluster (*bottom*), monomers (or noncon-ductive aggregates) bind to or dissociate from the cluster. Unlike the barrel-stave model, the pore size remains unchanged.

Models for Voltage-Dependent Gating

The proposed models for the voltage-dependent gating of alamethicin fall into several different classes, pictured in terms of a barrel-stave structure in Figure 7. For all the proposed mechanisms, the interaction leading to gating is the interaction of a helix dipole with the membrane electric field. The dipole moment of alamethicin in solution is about 67 Debye (50), which is consistent with the expected magnitude of the helix dipole and is large enough to account for the magnitude of the gating charge. In addition, the sign of the gating charge can be easily reconciled with a helix dipole–membrane interaction.

VOLTAGE-DEPENDENT STRUCTURAL CHANGE   The model shown in Figure 7A is based on the X-ray crystal structure of alamethicin (22). The peptide is preaggregated and bent about Pro14, and gating occurs as a result of a voltage-dependent conformational change that reorients the C terminus about this bend. An insertion of the aggregate into the bilayer accompanies the reorientation of the C terminus, leading to the conductive form of the channel. At present, no strong evidence refutes

A) Voltage-Dependent Conformational Change

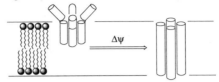

B) Voltage-Dependent Dipole Reorientation

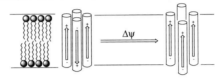

C) Voltage-Dependent Partitioning

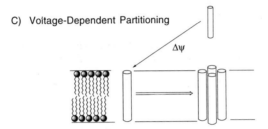

D) Voltage-Dependent Insertion

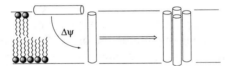

Figure 7   Several proposed models for the voltage-dependent gating of alamethicin (see text). A conductive channel may have many monomers (8 to12), but these channels are depicted here as tetramers for clarity.

this basic model; however, amide exchange data indicate that large portions of the C terminus are not exposed to the aqueous solution.

Hall et al (31) proposed a related model incorporating a voltage-dependent conformational change. . Here, preaggregated monomers are folded into a hairpin about a β-bend. Gating involves the unfolding of the molecule to insert an N-terminal α-helix across the bilayer. This model is based in part on earlier NMR work that indicated the presence of β-structure in the C terminus.

VOLTAGE-DEPENDENT HELIX REORIENTATION   In a second type of model (Figure 7B), gating involves the reorientation of the entire alamethicin helix (10, 42). Here, an aggregate in the nonconductive state is configured so that peptide monomers are in an antiparallel arrangement. Channel gatng is initiated by a change in the orientation of one of the monomers to produce a parallel alignment of several alamethicin monomers. The resulting electrostatic repulsion expands the aggregate to an open channel configuration.

This model raises several interesting questions. Helix reorientation in the bilayer may seem like an unlikely event; nonetheless, evidence supports it. Alamethicin monomers appear to move across the membrane in an autocatalytic fashion, and they also catalyze the flip-flop of lipids in a voltage-dependent fashion (30). For this mechanism to be effective, modulation of the channel structure with helix-helix electrostatic interactions must be energetically feasible. In addition, the interaction energy must be large relative to kT and the noncovalent interactions that hold the bundle together. These interactions are not expected to be large, but their magnitude will depend upon the position of the helix ends in the membrane (28).

One feature not easily explained by the helix reorientation model is the source of the asymmetry in the current-voltage curve. To be consistent with the data, this model must possess some asymmetry, but where this asymmetry comes from is not immediately apparent.

VOLTAGE-DEPENDENT PHASE PARTITIONING   Figure 7C shows a simple but elegant model for explaining the voltage dependence of alamethicin. Here, the voltage-dependent event involves a voltage-dependent change in the partitioning of alamethicin between the membrane and aqueous phases, with subsequent aggregation leading to pore formation (48).

This model is reasonable for several reasons. Given the large aqueous volumes in planar bilayer experiments and the partition coefficients of alamethicin, a significant fraction of peptide may be localized in the aqueous phase. Alamethicin appears to be buried in the membrane and a strong interaction between the helix dipole and the membrane field is expected. However, several experimental results argue against this model. The voltage-dependent phase partitioning of alamethicin was examined directly in thylakoid membranes (57). Although this is a complicated system, no evidence for a change in the partitioning of alamethicin with voltage was found. In addition, the voltage-dependent conduction for alamethicin in vesicles described above can be obtained under conditions in which all the alamethicin is membrane bound (2).

In this experiment, a voltage-dependent partitioning cannot contribute to the current-voltage behavior. Finally, analogues of alamethicin in which Aib residues are replaced with Leu are considerably more hydrophobic than alamethicin and exhibit virtually no solubility in the aqueous phase (3). Still, these analogues produce a strong current-voltage behavior that is similar to that of alamethicin.

That alamethicin does not exhibit a voltage-dependent binding is somewhat surprising. If the peptide is monomeric in the membrane and is inserted across the bilayer, the helix dipole and membrane electric fields should strongly interact. Given the magnitude of the helix dipole, an 80-mV transmembrane potential should shift the binding of the peptide by about 1 kcal/mol.

VOLTAGE-DEPENDENT INSERTION   In the much-discussed model described by Baumann & Mueller (7) (Figure 7D), a voltage-dependent change in the orientation of the peptide, from a surface to a transmembrane orientation, leads to its gating. Following insertion, the peptide aggregates to form a conductive pore.

Most of the data obtained regarding alamethicin indicate that it is not surface associated, arguing strongly against this model. However, recent CD data (33) provide evidence that the peptide can be oriented either parallel or perpendicular to the membrane surface, depending on experimental conditions. This result indicates that the energy difference between surface and transmembrane orientations is small. Although these measurements have not yet been confirmed using other experimental techniques, such as magnetic resonance, they argue that this model should not yet be discounted.

Additional Mechanisms and Structural Considerations

The above models do not represent a comprehensive list of the proposed mechanisms, only those most frequently discussed in the literature. Other mechanisms for the voltage gating of alamethicin are plausible. For example, a large amount of alamethicin appears to be monomeric in the membrane. If the channel structure is an aggregate, a monomer-aggregate equilibrium must exist, and the gating step could involve a voltage-dependent aggregation of the peptide. The C-terminal domain of alamethicin has significant conformational heterogeneity, and a voltage-dependent reorganization in the C-terminal half of the peptide could lead to favorable helix-helix interactions.

All the models discussed thus far involve voltage-dependent structural changes and rearrangements in the alamethicin peptide. The lipid bilayer in these models is poorly represented and is pictured simply as a passive matrix into which the peptide is dissolved. Bilayers are of course highly deformable with molecular dynamics similar to that of liquid hydrocarbons. Bilayers are also not the only stable configuration that lipids can assume. Alamethicin may promote structural changes in the lipid that lead to ion conduction. Indeed, alamethicin produces structural changes in lipid bilayers (6, 44), and the fact that alamethicin promotes a voltage-dependent flip-flop of lipids could easily be accounted for if the channel involved local changes in bilayer structure. However, how such a model would account for the detailed electrical behavior of alamethicin is not immediately obvious. Such behavior is also not easy to picture, as it would likely involve highly dynamic transient structures that could be difficult to study. Still, this possibility deserves consideration.

THE MULTIMERIC STATE OF THE ALAMETHICIN CHANNEL   The electrical data described above are interpreted rigorously in terms of an aggregation number for the alamethicin channel, and clearly the concentration dependence of the conduction provides strong evidence for a high aggregation number of alamethicin in its conductive form. However, the value of n might not directly reflect the molecularity of the channel. For example, diffusion-controlled reactions that occur on surfaces supporting clusters or islands can give rise to anomalous kinetics (37). For bimolecular reactions, these types of heterogeneous systems exhibit a strong concentration dependence. If the channel-forming events for alamethicin are diffusion limited, and the lipid systems used possess any surface heterogeneity, anomalous kinetics might occur.

The fact that alamethicin appears to be largely monomeric in membranes indicates that the energy of its aggregated form is not significantly lower than that of the monomer. In a helix-bundle, such as that described in the barrel-stave model, the energy barriers to bundle formation are likely to be small, because relatively little rearrangement of the peptide monomers would be required to form the aggregate. As a result, an alamethicin aggregate should be in relatively rapid equilibrium with the monomer, and channel-forming events might well be diffusion limited.

FUTURE DIRECTIONS

The electrical data on alamethicin point to an interesting and rich channel behavior that clearly suggests specific channel mechanisms. Yet, it has been difficult to resolve the mechanism from this electrical data alone. Several of the models described above appear viable, and additional information will be needed to resolve the gating mechanism. Studies on the membrane-associated structure of alamethicin, particularly its aggregated form, will be extremely important in determining the mechanisms of gating.

As indicated above, the majority of alamethicin appears to be in a monomeric state in vesicle membranes even under conditions of channel activity. The currents measured in vesicles could arise from a minor population of the peptide (2), and the monomers could be in equilibrium with a small population of aggregated peptide that is spectroscopically undetectable. Assuming that the active form is an aggregate, obtaining structural information regarding the active state of alamethicin may be very difficult. As a result, an important task for researchers is to find conditions that will increase the population of aggregated or active peptide. In the absence of these conditions, electrical measurements provide the only information on the active form of the peptide.

Clearly alamethicin serves as an interesting and complex model for channel activity. In addition, the fundamental questions raised by studies on this peptide are relevant to our general understanding of peptide-membrane interactions. For example, alamethicin exhibits significant differences in its binding to membranes as a function of the lipid headgroup and chain composition, and understanding the interactions that modulate this binding is an obvious goal. Another intriguing observation is the slow speed of alamethicin's transmembrane migration. This peptide is very hydrophobic and contains only one negative charge. Peptides such as the signal sequence of cytochrome oxidase IV (CoxIV) contain several positively charged residues, are overall much less hydrophobic than alamethicin, and transit model membranes on a time scale of minutes (41). This suggests that very different mechanisms facilitate the membrane translocation of these two peptides.

ACKNOWLEDGMENTS

I thank Drs. Craig Franklin, Laurie Kelsh, and Jeff Ellena for helpful discussions during the writing of this manuscript. Studies on alamethicin from our laboratory were supported by NIH grant GM-35215.

Literature Cited

1. Archer SJ. 1990. *Elucidation of the structure and activity of the peptide alamethicin in phospholipid vesicles.* PhD thesis. Univ. Virginia, Charlottesville, VA. 249 pp.
2. Archer SJ, Cafiso DS. 1991. Voltage-dependent conductance for alamethicin in phospholipid vesicles. *Biophys. J.* 60: 380–88
3. Archer SJ, Ellena JF, Cafiso DS. 1991. Dynamics and aggregation of the peptide ion channel alamethicin. *Biophys. J.* 60:389–98
4. Balaram P, Krishna K, Sukumar M, Mellor IR, Sansom MSP. 1992. The properties of ion channels formed by zervamicins. *Eur. Biophys. J.* 21:117–28
5. Banerjee U, Chan SI. 1983. Structure of alamethicin in solution: nuclear magnetic resonance studies. *Biochemistry* 22:3709–13
6. Banerjee U, Zidovetzki R, Birge RR, Chan SI. 1985. Interaction of alamethicin with lipid bilayers: A ^{31}P and ^{2}H NMR study. *Biochemistry* 24:7621–27
7. Baumann G, Mueller P. 1974. A molecular model of membrane excitability. *J. Supramol. Struct.* 2:538–57
8. Bernheimer AW, Rudy B. 1986. Interactions between membranes and cytolytic peptides. *Biochim. Biophys. Acta* 864:123–41
9. Bezrukov SM, Vodyanoy I. 1993. Probing alamethicin channels with water-soluble polymers. *Biophys. J.* 64:16–25
10. Boheim G, Hanke W, Jung G. 1983. Alamethicin pore formation: voltage-dependent flip-flop of α-helical dipoles. *Biophys. Struct. Mech.* 9:181–91
11. Boheim G, Kolb HA. 1978. Analysis of the multipore system of alamethicin in a lipid membrane. *J. Membr. Biol.* 38: 99–150
12. Brumfeld V, Miller IR. 1990. Electric field dependence of alamethicin channels. *Biochim. Biophys. Acta* 1024:49–53
13. Cafiso DS, Hubbell WL. 1981. EPR determination of membrane potentials. *Annu. Rev. Biophys. Bioeng.* 10:217–44
14. Cascio M, Wallace BA. 1988. Conformation of alamethicin in phospholipid vesicles: implications for insertion models. *Proteins* 4:89–98
15. Cherry RJ, Chapman D, Graham DE. 1972. Studies of the conductance changes induced by alamethicin in biomolecular membranes by alamethicin. *J. Membr. Biol.* 7:325–44

16. Davis DG, Gisin BF. 1981. 600MHz proton magnetic resonance studies of natural and synthetic alamethicin. *FEBS Lett.* 133:247–51
17. Duclohier H, Molle G, Dugast JY, Spach G. 1992. Prolines are not essential in the "barrel-stave" model for ion channels induced by alamethicin analogues. *Biophys. J.* 63:868–73
18. Duclohier H, Molle G, Spach G. 1989. The influence of trichorzianin C-terminal residues on the ion conductance in lipid bilayers. *Biochim. Biophys. Acta* 987:133–36
19. Eisenman G, Alvarez O. 1991. Structure and function of channels and channelogs as studied by computational chemistry. *J. Membr. Biol.* 119:109–32
20. Esposito G, Carver JA, Boyd J, Campbell ID. 1987. High-resolution ^{1}H NMR study of the solution structure of alamethicin. *Biochemistry* 26:1043–50
21. Flewelling RF, Hubbell WL, 1986. The membrane dipole potential in a total membrane potential model. Applications to hydrophobic ion interactions with membranes. *Biophys. J.* 49:541–52
22. Fox RO, Richards FM. 1982. A voltage-gated ion channel inferred from the crystal structure of alamethicin at 1.5Å resolution. *Nature* 300:325–30
23. Franklin JC, Cafiso DS. 1993. Internal electrostatic potentials in membranes: measuring and controlling dipole potentials in lipid vesicles. *Biophys. J.* 65: 289–99
24. Franklin JC, Cafiso DS, Flewelling RF, Hubbell WL. 1993. Probes of membrane electrostatics. Synthesis and voltage-dependent partitioning of negative hydrophobic ion spin-labels in lipid vesicles. *Biophys. J.* 64:642–53
25. Franklin JC, Kelsh LP, Ellena JF, Cafiso DS. 1993. The structure of alamethicin in sodium dodecylsulfate micelles. *Biophys. J.* 64:A376 (Abstr.)
26. Fringeli UP, Fringeli M. 1979. Pore formation in lipid membranes by alamethicin. *Proc. Natl. Acad. Sci. USA* 76: 3852–56
27. Furois-Corbin S, Pullman A. 1989. Energy profiles in the acetylcholine receptor channel. The MII helix and the role of the remaining helices. *FEBS Lett.* 252:63–68
28. Gilson MK, Honig B. Destabilization of an α-helix bundle protein by helix dipoles. 1989. *Proc. Natl. Acad. Sci. USA* 86:1524–28

29. Gordon LGM, Haydon DA. 1975. Potential-dependent conductances in lipid membranes containing alamethicin. *Philos. Trans. R. Soc. London Ser. B* 270: 433–47
30. Hall JE. 1981. Voltage-dependent lipid flip-flop induced by alamethicin. *Biophys. J.* 33:373–81
31. Hall JE, Vodyanoy I, Balasubramanian TM, Marshall GR. 1984. Alamethicin: a rich model for channel behavior. *Biophys. J.* 45:233–47
32. Haris PI, Chapman D. 1988. Fourier transform infrared spectra of the polypeptide alamethicin and a possible structural similarity with bacteriorhodopsin. *Biochim. Biophys. Acta* 943: 375–80
33. Huang HW, Wu Y. 1991. Lipid-alamethicin interactions influence alamethicin orientation. *Biophys. J.* 60:1079–87
34. Karle IL, Balaram P. 1990. Structural characteristics of α-helical peptide models containing Aib residues. *Biochemistry* 29:6747–56
35. Karle IL, Flippen-Anderson J, Sukumar M, Balaram P. 1987. Conformation of a 16 residue zervamicin IIA analog peptide containing 3 different structural features: 3_{10} helix, α-helix and β bend ribbon. *Proc. Natl. Acad. Sci. USA* 84: 5087–91
36. Kelsh LP, Ellena JF, Cafiso DS. 1992. Determination of the molecular dynamics of alamethicin using ^{13}C NMR: implications for the mechanism of gating of a voltage-dependent channel. *Biochemistry* 31:5136–44
37. Kopelman R. 1988. Fractal reaction kinetics. *Science* 241:1620–26
38. Lattore R, Alvarez O. 1981. Voltage-dependent channels in planar lipid bilayer membranes. *Physiol. Rev.* 61:78–150
39. Lau ALY, Chan SI. 1976. Voltage-induced formation of alamethicin pores in lecithin bilayer vesicles. *Biochemistry* 15: 2551–55
40. Lehrer RI, Lichtenstein AK, Ganz T. 1993. Defensins: antimicrobial and cytotoxic peptides of mammalian cells. *Annu. Rev. Immunol.* 11:105–28
41. Maduke M, Roise D. 1993. Import of a mitochondrial presequence into protein-free phospholipid vesicles. *Science* 260: 364–67
42. Mathew MK, Balaram P. 1983. A helix dipole model for alamethicin and related transmembrane channels. *FEBS Lett.* 157:1–5
43. Matsuzaki K, Nakai S, Handa T, Takaishi Y, Fujita T, Miyajima K. 1989. Hypelcin A, an α-aminoisobutyric acid containing antibiotic peptide, induced permeability change of phosphatidylcholine bilayers. *Biochemistry* 28:9392–98
44. McIntosh TJ, Ting-Beall HP, Zampighi H. 1982. Alamethicin induced changes in lipid bilayer morphology. *Biochim. Biophys. Acta* 685:51–60
45. Miick SM, Martinez GV, Fiori WR, Todd AP, Millhauser GL. 1992. Short alanine-based peptides may form 3_{10} helices and not α-helices in aqueous solution. *Nature* 359:653–55
46. Molle G, Duclohier H, Dugast JY, Spach G. 1989. Design and conformation of non-Aib synthetic peptides enjoying alamethicin-like ionophore activity. *Biopolymers* 28:273–83
47. Nilges M, Clore GM, Gronenborn AM. 1988. Determination of the three-dimensional structures of proteins from interproton distance data by dynamical simulated annealing from a random array of atoms. *FEBS Lett.* 239:129–36
48. Rizzo V, Stankowski S, Schwarz G. 1987. Alamethicin incorporation in lipid bilayers: a thermodynamic analysis. *Biochemistry* 26:2751–59
49. Sansom MP. 1991. The biophysics of peptide models of ion channels. *Prog. Biophys. Mol. Biol.* 55:139–235
50. Schwarz G, Savko P. 1982. Structural and dipolar properties of the voltage-dependent pore former alamethicin in octanol/dioxane. *Biophys. J.* 39:211–19
51. Schwarz G, Stankowski S, Rizzo V. 1986. Thermodynamic analysis of incorporation and aggregation in a membrane: application to the pore-forming peptide alamethicin. *Biochim. Biophys. Acta* 861:141–51
52. Stankowski S, Schwarz G. 1989. Lipid dependence of peptide-membrane interactions. Bilayer affinity and aggregation of the peptide alamethicin. *FEBS Lett.* 250:556–60
53. Tamm LK. 1991. Membrane insertion and lateral mobility of synthetic amphiphilic signal peptides in lipid model membranes. *Biochim. Biophys. Acta* 1071:123–48
54. Toniolo C, Benedetti E. 1991. The polypeptide 3_{10} helix. *Trends Biochem. Sci.* 16:350–53
55. Vodyanoy I, Hall JE, Balasubramanian TM. 1983. Alamethicin-induced current-voltage curve asymmetry in lipid bilayers. *Biophys. J.* 42:71–82
56. Vogel H. 1987. Comparison of the conformation and orientation of alamethicin

and melittin in lipid membranes. *Biochemistry* 26:4562–72

57. Wille B, Franz B, Jung G. 1989. Location and dynamics of alamethicin in unilamellar vesicles and thylakoids as model systems. A spin-labeled study. *Biochim. Biophys. Acta* 986:47–60

58. Williams KA, Deber CM. 1991. Proline residues in transmembrane helices: structural or dynamic role? *Biochemistry* 30:8919–23

59. Woolley GA, Deber CM. 1988. A lipid vesicle system for probing voltage-dependent peptide-lipid interactions. *Biopolymers* 28:267–72

60. Yee AA, O'Neil JDJ. 1992. Uniform ^{15}N labeling of a fungal peptide: the structure and dynamics of an alamethicin by ^{15}N and ^{1}H NMR spectroscopy. *Biochemistry* 31:3135–43

61. Zasloff M. 1987. Magainins, a class of antimicrobial peptides from *Xenopus* skin: isolation, characterization of two active forms, and a partial cDNA sequence of a precursor. *Proc. Natl. Acad. Sci. USA* 84:5449–53

Annu. Rev. Biophys. Biomol. Struct. 1994. 23:167–92

MEMBRANE PROTEINS:
From Sequence to Structure

Gunnar von Heijne

Department of Molecular Biology, Karolinska Institute Center for Structural Biochemistry, NOVUM S-141 57 Huddinge, Sweden

KEY WORDS: protein folding, protein translocation, structure prediction, protein topology

CONTENTS

PERSPECTIVES AND OVERVIEW

To understand the rules relating amino acid sequence to three-dimensional (3D) protein structure is a major goal of contemporary structural biochemistry. Interest in this area is mainly focused on globular proteins while membrane-embedded proteins receive less attention. Yet, despite the small number of 3D structures known for integral membrane

1056–8700/94/0610–0167$05.00

proteins, the field has advanced rapidly during the past few years, and we are well on the way to understanding the relation between sequence and structure for this class of proteins.

Here, I trace the steps from sequence to structure for the most abundant kind of membrane protein, the so-called helix bundle proteins. In these proteins, a bundle of transmembrane α-helices is oriented more or less perpendicular to the plane of the membrane. Their biosynthesis and membrane assembly depend critically on the cellular mechanisms responsible for translocating polypeptides across membranes. Reliable structure prediction is thus only possible once these processes are properly understood (for previous reviews, see 12, 26, 59, 81, 123).

The other major kind of integral membrane protein is the so-called β-barrel class, in which the membrane domain is formed by a large antiparallel β-sheet barrel (20, 117). These proteins are typically found in the outer membrane of gram-negative bacteria and in the mitochondrial outer membrane. Not much is know about their mode of membrane insertion, and they receive correspondingly less attention in this review.

3D STRUCTURE OF INTEGRAL MEMBRANE PROTEINS

Helix-Bundle Proteins

To date, the resolution of the 3D structures of only two helix-bundle proteins is sufficiently high for individual side-chains to be resolved. The classic example is bacteriorhodopsin, for which electron microscopy techniques were used to derive the structure (44, 45). The first, and so far only, high-resolution X-ray structure of a helix-bundle membrane protein is the bacterial photosynthetic reaction center (1, 24, 127). A number of proteins have been solved to a lower resolution at which individual helices start to become discernible, but at which amino acid side chains cannot be resolved (55, 56, 93, 99, 100, 104).

Several generalizations have emerged from the analysis of the reaction center structure (85, 86). Overall, the transmembrane helices have a very high average hydrophobicity. Residues buried between the transmembrane helices have an average polarity similar to that found in the interior of soluble proteins, whereas the lipid-facing residues are more hydrophobic. Buried residues also tend to be more conserved than the lipid-facing ones, again similar to the situation in globular proteins in which the core residues are often highly conserved. Helices apparently tend to pack against each other at preferred angles remi-

niscent of the well-known ridges-into-grooves packing that characterizes many helix-helix interactions in soluble proteins (16). These observations seem to imply that tight packing between the transmembrane
helices is important for protein stability, just as for soluble proteins.
Indeed, crude theoretical calculations indicate that van der Waals interactions between apolar transmembrane helices may be enough to
drive the formation of helix bundles in a lipid environment (116), and
some experimental results support this view (51). Thus, the formation
of transmembrane helix bundles in a lipid bilayer seems in many respects analogous to the formation of helical bundles in soluble proteins,
and methods that have been developed to predict helix-helix packings
in the latter case may also be applied to the former with suitable modifications.

As a result of the tendency for the buried residues to be more polar
than the lipid-exposed ones, many transmembrane helices are slightly
amphiphilic. Recent studies have also found a distinct center-to-end
heterogeneity in the distribution of apolar amino acids, with the aromatic residues Phe, Tyr, and Trp concentrated at the ends and the
aliphatic residues (Leu, Ile, Val) more often found near the center (60,
98) (Figure 1). Prolines, normally considered as strong helix-breakers,
are often found in the transmembrane segments of multispanning (but

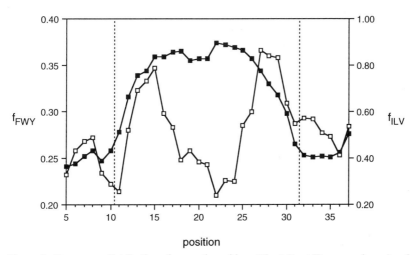

Figure 1 Frequency distribution of aromatic residues (Phe + Trp + Tyr, *open boxes*) and
aliphatic residues (Ile + Leu + Val, *closed boxes*) as a function of position in 222 transmembrane segments from 35 bacterial inner membrane proteins of known topology. The
curves have been smoothed by a three-point running average. Dotted lines indicate the
approximate extent of the membrane. The cytoplasmic side is to the left.

not single-spanning) proteins (14, 23) where they probably induce the formation of a kink in the helix (107, 111, 126).

β-Barrel Proteins

Porins in the outer membrane of gram-negative bacteria form rather large pores that allow the passive diffusion of small solutes across the bilayer. Their amino acid sequences do not contain long stretches of apolar amino acids and hence cannot form typical transmembrane helices. Instead, a continuous apolar surface develops only upon formation of the full 3D structure—a large, antiparallel β-barrel in which every second residue in each strand is hydrophobic and faces out towards the surrounding lipid (20, 117, 118).

This type of membrane-embedded structure probably evolved in part to allow the nascent chain passage across the inner membrane (where a long apolar stretch of amino acids would act as a stop-transfer sequence, see below) while still allowing the protein to form a structure with a largely apolar surface that can integrate into the outer membrane. The outer mitochondrial membrane contains both β-barrel proteins and proteins anchored in the bilayer by a hydrophobic transmembrane segment (most likely a helix); in this case, the proteins are made in the cytoplasm and thus need not pass through another membrane to reach their destination.

The concentration of aromatic residues in those parts of the membrane-embedded domain that are close to the lipid headgroup region is even more conspicuous in the β-barrel structures than it is the helix-bundle proteins. Two veritable life belts of aromatic residues surround the upper and lower ends of the barrel (20, 117) and possibly provide some extra stability to the molecule.

Finally, a recent proposition, based on electron microscopy data, suggests that the acetylcholine receptor heterooligomer has a structure consisting of a central transmembrane helix bundle surrounded by a large β-barrel (104). Possible mechanisms leading to the formation of such hybrid structures—if they exist—are not discussed further here.

MEMBRANE PROTEIN TOPOLOGY

The topology of a membrane protein is defined by the way it weaves back and forth across the membrane, i.e. by the location of the transmembrane segments in the amino acid sequence and the overall orientation of the molecule in the membrane. The topology represents the secondary structure of the membrane-embedded domain and may in fact, at least for the helix-bundle proteins, be thought of as a folding intermediate in which the transmembrane helices have formed but have not yet assembled into the final structure (80). The topology is thus a fundamental characteristic of the protein and is the obvious starting point for all attempts to predict the 3D structure.

Experimental Approaches

Several experimental approaches to the determination of membrane protein topology have been developed. The two basic ideas are (a) to modify specific sites in the molecule by membrane-impenetrable reagents (49) and (b) to make fusion proteins for which one can use the location of a reporter domain inside or outside the membrane to infer the topology of the protein of interest (67, 101).

One commonly used technique for studying the topology of eukaryotic proteins is chemical modification (see 36, 98, 113 for examples), which has the obvious drawback that large amounts of protein are often needed and that showing that the reagent cannot penetrate to the wrong side of the membrane is often difficult. Proteolysis of domains exposed outside the membrane sometimes gives good results, though many membrane proteins are surprisingly resistant to proteases. Antibodies raised against specific peptides can also be used as impenetrable labeling reagents, but again it is sometimes hard to unambiguously interpret antibody-binding data.

One kind of modification that seems to give a safer indication of topology is N-linked glycosylation, which normally takes place only on the lumenal side of the endoplasmic reticulum membrane (119). New glycosylation sites may be introduced by site-specific mutagenesis, and the resulting mutant protein can then be analyzed by in vitro translation in the presence of translocation- and glycosylation-competent microsomes (76). Sites located too close to a membrane-spanning segment may not be glycosylated even though they reside in the lumen (73).

The fusion-protein approach has so far found its widest applicability in the analysis of prokaryotic membrane proteins (15, 68, 101), although a few studies on eukaryotic proteins also used this technique (96). The most commonly used reporter proteins are alkaline phosphatase (PhoA), β-lactamase (Bla), and β-galactosidase (LacZ). PhoA and Bla are both active when located in the periplasm of *Escherichia coli* but are inactive in the cytoplasm, whereas LacZ is active in the cytoplasm but inactive when transported through the inner membrane. Thus, when PhoA or Bla is fused to a periplasmic part of an inner membrane protein, they are in most cases exported to the periplasm and display high activity, whereas fusions to cytoplasmic domains often have a low activity (the converse is true for LacZ fusions), and the topology can be derived from the activity pattern observed for a family of fusions placed throughout the protein. The topology of many inner membrane proteins have been successfully analyzed in this way (see 112 for a list of examples); in some cases, dual PhoA/LacZ fusions have provided an even more clear-cut picture (67). As with all other methods, one must be aware of the technical complications, e.g. the need to normalize measured PhoA activities to the relative expression levels of the different fusions (89) and variations in activity stemming from the precise positioning of the fusion joint (13).

The Positive Inside Rule

Some years ago, the number of bacterial inner membrane proteins with known topology was already sufficient to do meaningful statistical studies on the relative amino acid composition of cytoplasmic versus periplasmic loops. A major finding was that the positively charged amino acids, Lys and Arg, are extremely rare in periplasmic loops (~5%) but very abundant in cytoplasmic loops (~15%). Subsequent studies found a similar bias in eukaryotic plasma membrane proteins (113), thylakoid membrane proteins (35), and mitochondrial inner membrane proteins (36) (though in the latter case the bias was only clearly present in mitochondrially but not in nuclearly encoded proteins). In all cases, the more highly charged loops remain nontranslocated; i.e. they face the cytoplasm in the plasma membrane proteins, the chloroplast stroma in the thylakoid proteins, and the matrix in the mitochondrial proteins. Thus, a universal positive inside rule seems to apply to the helix-bundle proteins, irrespective of the particular membrane in which they reside.

Another aspect of the positive inside rule is that it is obeyed only by rather short translocated loops (up to ~60 residues in length), and likewise that the frequency of Arg and Lys in cytoplasmic loops decreases with loop-length over this interval (Figure 2). Long cytoplasmic and periplasmic loops have an amino acid composition that does not differ appreciably from that of soluble proteins. This observation led to the proposal that the mechanisms of membrane translocation are different for long and short loops, and that this places more restrictions on the amino acid content of short than of long loops (113). As shown below, we now know that the length of a translocated loop is intimately related to its dependence on the bacterial protein secretion machinery for translocation. Also, the great majority of periplasmic loops are short (≤20 residues; Figure 2), possibly because intermediate-length loops may be more difficult to translocate (7).

Finally, for bacterial inner membrane proteins, the bias in Arg + Lys content is independent of the position of the loop in the topology (112)

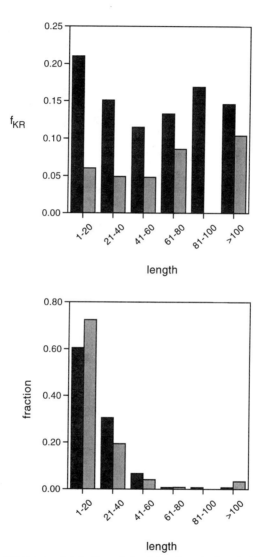

Figure 2   (*Top*) Frequency distribution of Arg + Lys in cytoplasmic (*dark shade*) and periplasmic (*light shade*) loops as a function of loop length from a sample of 35 bacterial inner membrane proteins of known topology. (*Bottom*) Frequency distribution of cytoplasmic (*dark shade*) and periplasmic (*light shade*) loop lengths in the same sample.

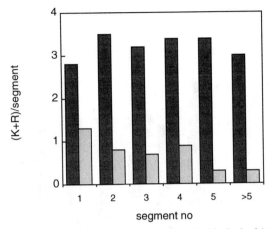

Figure 3 Average number of Arg + Lys in cytoplasmic (*dark shade*) and periplasmic (*light shade*) loops as a function of the position of the loop in the topology (first cytoplasmic and periplasmic segments, second cytoplasmic and periplasmic segments, etc, counting from the N terminus) in a sample of 24 bacterial inner membrane proteins with known topology (112).

(Figure 3), suggesting that individual loops are translocated independently of their neighbors, perhaps as parts of helical hairpins (33) composed of two transmembrane segments and the connecting periplasmic loop. In contrast, for eukaryotic plasma membrane proteins, the charge bias is maximal for the most N-terminal loop and then tapers off for the more C-terminal ones (98), possibly reflecting a different mode of membrane insertion.

MEMBRANE TRANSLOCATION AND INSERTION

Membrane protein insertion has much in common with protein secretion; in fact a transmembrane protein can be regarded as an incompletely secreted protein. In this section, I briefly review the biochemistry of protein translocation across different membrane systems and show how these systems function in membrane-protein assembly.

Bacterial Proteins: the Sec Machinery

Components of the *E. coli* protein translocation machinery have been extensively characterized, both genetically and biochemically (92, 124). The pathway involves both cytoplasmic (SecB, Ffh), peripheral inner membrane (SecA), and integral inner membrane (SecD, SecE, SecF, SecY) components. In addition, the final folding of a periplasmic protein may require the participation of disulfide-formation catalysts (DsbA, DsbB) (9, 10, 52). Further export of proteins across the outer membrane requires an even more extended set of components (82).

The cytoplasmic components are chaperones and help keep the pre-protein in a translocation-competent conformation (66, 83). SecA, SecY, and SecE form the central translocase complex in the inner membrane and require ATP, the proton-motive force, and acidic phospholipids for full activity (124). The SecD and SecF components probably act at a late stage of the translocation process (69) and have not been studied much. Precisely how the nascent polypeptide is driven through the membrane is unknown (see 94 for the latest model).

Secretory proteins are made with an N-terminal signal peptide that is removed once translocation is under way. The signal peptide is thought to interact in succession with the cytoplasmic Ffh protein [the *E. coli* homologue of the 54-kDa subunit of the signal-recognition particle (SRP), a ribonucleoprotein complex], SecA, and SecY, and is finally cleaved from the rest of the protein by the leader peptidase (Lep) enzyme located in the inner membrane. The signal peptide also may interact with phospholipids at some stage (27, 53).

Signal peptides look much like transmembrane segments, with a positively charged N-terminal cytoplasmic end, a central hydrophobic stretch (usually shorter than the typical transmembrane segment), and a C-terminal cleavage region with a leader peptidase recognition site (37, 110). Upon interaction with SecA, the signal peptide inserts into the inner membrane and probably pulls the immediate downstream region into the translocase complex, thus forming a loop with the N-terminus of the signal peptide tethered to the cytoplasmic face of the membrane (57, 97). An early step in the translocation reaction—possibly the formation of the initial loop structure—is very sensitive to the presence of positively charged amino acids in a region encompassing the first ~20 residues downstream of the signal peptide (5, 6, 12). This is consistent with an old statistical finding that this region has a markedly lower frequency of Arg + Lys than other parts of bacterial secretory proteins (108).

Although few inner membrane proteins have cleavable signal peptides, many still rely on the Sec machinery for the translocation of periplasmic domains. A case in point is leader peptidase, Figure 4*a* (left), which has a large, C-terminal periplasmic domain (P2) that absolutely depends on SecA, SecY, and the membrane potential for translocation (125). The second transmembrane segment (H2) acts as an uncleaved signal peptide (21) and can be converted to a cleavable signal peptide by insertion of a leader peptidase recognition site near its C-terminal end (75). In contrast, the first transmembrane segment (H1) can insert into the membrane even when the Sec machinery is non-functional (63). Membrane insertion of the phage M13 procoat protein—a small protein composed of a cleavable signal peptide, a short periplasmic region, and a C-terminal transmembrane anchor—is also Sec independent (123), as is the insertion of an inverted leader peptidase mutant (109) (Figure 4a, right).

Short periplasmic loops tend to contain few positively charged residues, whereas longer ones have an average content of Arg + Lys close to that observed for loops in soluble periplasmic proteins. The transition from low to normal Arg + Lys content occurs at loop lengths of approximately 60 residues (Figure 2). This observation prompted us to test the idea that the mechanism of translocation may be different for short and long loops. Indeed, when the length of the periplasmic loop in an inverted leader peptidase construct is increased gradually from 25 to 65 residues, its dependence on the Sec machinery for translocation correspondingly increases (7). Similarly, when the periplasmic domain in the M13 procoat protein is lengthened from 20 to 118 residues, its translocation becomes Sec dependent (58). Therefore the length of a periplasmic domain and its Sec dependence seem to be correlated [although one conflicting report has been published (70)], and the low frequency of Arg + Lys in short periplasmic loops would thus reflect the inability of the cell to translocate highly charged domains when the Sec machinery cannot be used. Why short loops cannot efficiently use the Sec pathway is unknown, but this arrangement is fortunate, because prediction of the topology of a membrane protein would be much more difficult if we did not have the positive inside rule to guide us.

The fact that all loops in a polytopic inner membrane protein conform to the positive inside rule suggests that membrane insertion is a local process in which individual helical hairpins (33) insert independently from the rest of the molecule (32). This is in contrast to a sequential process in which insertion would always be in an N-to-C–terminal direction and where the more N-terminal parts would influence the insertion of the downstream transmembrane segments. We recently tried to distinguish between these two models by constructing molecules with four transmembrane segments and two periplasmic loops (the overall topology is thus N_{in}-C_{in}). The periplasmic loops were either long (~90 residues) and Sec dependent or short (~25 residues) and Sec independent. The critical finding was that the short loop always inserts across the membrane even when translocation of the long loop is prevented by blocking the Sec machinery, and that this does not depend

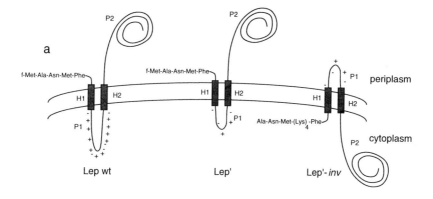

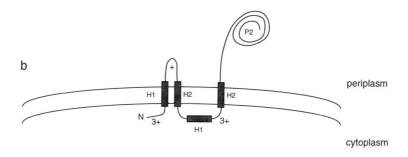

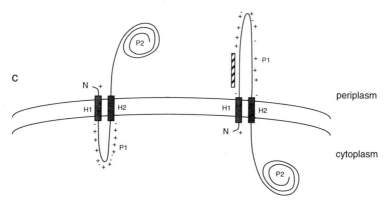

Figure 4 (*a*) Topology of wild-type leader peptidase (Lep; *left*), and of two mutants that differ only by four N-terminal lysines (*middle, right*). (*b*) Topology of a Lep-derived construct with four hydrophobic segments and an internally inconsistent distribution of Arg + Lys. (*c*) Topology of two Lep-derived contructs that differ only by the length of the P1 loop. The striped bar indicates the position of the inserted residues.

on the relative positions of the two loops (G von Heijne & G Gafvelin, unpublished data). Thus, insertion of the short loop is independent of whether or not the long loop has been translocated even when the long loop is N terminal to the short one, arguing against a strictly sequential model.

We thus favor the idea that bacterial inner membrane proteins are composed of two different kinds of independently inserting structural elements: (a) helical hairpins composed of two hydrophobic segments and a short connecting loop containing few positively charged residues that insert en bloc independently of the Sec machinery, and (b) Sec-dependent elements composed of an N-terminal hydrophobic segment preceded by a positively charged region and followed by a long (>60–70 residues) polar segment (and then possibly by a second hydrophobic stop-transfer segment).

Insertion into the ER Membrane

Although the mechanisms of protein translocation across the ER membrane and across the inner membrane of *E. coli* clearly differ, recent work suggests that the basic processes are nevertheless similar (84). Not only do signal peptides of prokaryotic and eukaryotic origin look the same (and often work the same when expressed in the heterologous system), but sequence similarities have also been detected between certain components of the two machineries. The *E. coli* Ffh protein forms a complex with a 4.5S RNA to make a particle with properties related to the eukaryotic signal recognition particle (SRP) (87); the SecY protein is homologous to the eukaryotic SEC61p protein found in the ER membrane (39); and the bacterial leader peptidase enzyme and subunits of the eukaryotic signal peptidase complex share weak sequence similarities (22).

An important difference between the two systems is that translocation is normally cotranslational in eukaryotes, but is often posttranslational in bacteria (34a, 83a). A strictly cotranslational, sequential process would conceivably thread the nascent chain into the membrane starting with the most N-terminal transmembrane segment and proceed towards the C terminus, always inserting the next transmembrane segment in the opposite orientation to the previous one. According to this scheme, the topology of the whole molecule would be determined by the orientation of the first transmembrane segment; the following segments would simply act alternately as either stop-transfer segments or uncleaved signal peptides.

Some support for this model comes from studies in which a single-spanning protein has been duplicated one or more times to make molecules with up to four transmembrane segments (65, 120). Here, the same hydrophobic segment acts either as an uncleaved signal peptide or as a stop-transfer sequence during membrane insertion depending on its position in the molecule. However, in these studies the translocated loops were all longer than the Sec-dependence cutoff discussed in the previous section; different results might have been obtained had the loops been short.

Statistical analysis of eukaryotic membrane proteins has revealed a transition between a low frequency of Arg + Lys in translocated loops to a normal frequency at loop lengths >60–80 residues (98), suggesting that in eukaryotes short loops are also translocated by a somewhat different mechanism.

Other Membrane Systems

According to the endosymbiont theory, chloroplasts and mitochondria trace their ancestry to once free-living prokaryotes (40). This hypothesis implies that mechanisms of organellar protein translocation and membrane insertion have much in common with the corresponding bacterial processes, at least for those proteins that are still encoded in the organellar genome and made inside the organelle. In fact, even nuclearly encoded, imported proteins may follow a conservative sorting pathway, in which they are first delivered to the organellar equivalent of the bacterial cytoplasm (i.e. the mitochondrial matrix or the chloroplast stroma) and then further transported to their final location by the ancestral sorting machinery (42). In line with these ideas, homologues of the bacterial SecA and SecY proteins have been found in plastid genomes (30, 90, 91).

The positive inside rule has been observed to hold for all proteins of the thylakoid membrane (35) and for mitochondrially encoded proteins of the inner mitochondrial membrane (36); the more highly positively charged domains of these proteins remain nontranslocated and thus face the stroma or the matrix. Some but not all imported mitochondrial inner membrane proteins also follow the rule, suggesting that membrane insertion may not always proceed along the conservative sorting pathway (see 38). With these exceptions, the mechanism of membrane protein assembly should be similar in bacteria and organelles.

ENGINEERING MEMBRANE PROTEIN TOPOLOGY

The positive inside rule suggests that one should be able to control the topology of membrane proteins by redistributing positively charged amino acids relative to the transmembrane segments. This has now been accomplished both for prokaryotic and eukaryotic proteins (12, 114); indeed, we can more or less envision what the sequence determinants for membrane protein topology are like, at least for bacterial proteins.

In our lab, these ideas have been tested using the *E. coli* inner membrane protein leader peptidase (Lep). As noted above, this protein has two transmembrane segments H1 and H2, and both its N terminus and its large C-terminal domain reside in the periplasm (Figure 4*a*, left). The distribution of positively charged residues in the wild-type protein is as expected from the positive inside rule: no charge on the periplasmic N terminus, 9 positively charged residues in the cytoplasmic P1 domain (residues 23–61), and 10% Arg + Lys in the large periplasmic P2 domain (residues 77–326). The topology of this molecule can be inverted by redistributing the positively charged residues such that the N terminus has a higher number than the P1 domain (74, 109) (Figure 4*a*, middle and right). Both arginines and lysines can initiate the topological switch, and even histidines can affect the topology, but only when the cytoplasmic pH is low enough to protonate them efficiently (4). Negatively charged amino acids do not normally affect the topology (4, 74), but we have recently found that they can partly neutralize the topological effects of nearby positively charged residues in a position-dependent manner (6).

To extend these studies to a more complex system, we have constructed molecules with four transmembrane segments by duplicating the H1-H2 region of Lep. These constructs generally insert into the inner membrane as predicted by the distribution of positively charged residues, except when different parts of the molecule have conflicting topological information. Figure 4*b* shows an example; in this case, our data indicate that the molecule solves the problem of conforming to the positive inside rule by only inserting three of the four hydrophobic segments across the membrane (G von Heijne & G Gafvelin, unpublished data).

One can also exploit the difference in sensitivity to positively charged residues between Sec-dependent and Sec-independent translocation to effect a topological switch. The P1 domain of wild-type Lep is only ~40 residues long and is thus not expected to be able to use the Sec machinery for translocation. Indeed, addition of a lysine to the N terminus of H1 does not lead to an inverted topology, although the H1 region (with an N-terminal lysine) can by itself promote Sec-dependent translocation of downstream domains in other contexts (115). However, when the length of the P1 domain is increased to ~70 residues, insertion becomes Sec dependent and the P1 domain rather than the P2 domain is translocated to the periplasm (7) (Figure 4c).

In eukaryotic systems, the topological determinants have so far only been studied in single spanning membrane proteins, and again positively charged residues seem to play an important role (11, 41, 78). As noted above, multispanning proteins have been made by fusing multiple copies of a gene encoding a single spanning protein in tandem, and molecules with up to four transmembrane segments have been constructed (65, 120).

FORMATION OF TRANSMEMBRANE DOMAINS: HELIX PACKING IN A LIPID BILAYER

Compared with what is known about the initial insertion of a polypeptide into a biological membrane, the next step on the folding pathway— the formation of the helix bundle—is only poorly understood. Studies of the reassociation of different fragments of bacteriorhodopsin containing various combinations of the seven transmembrane helices found in the intact protein have demonstrated that stable helices are formed prior to the formation of the bundle, and that their association is driven to a large extent by helix-helix interactions in the lipid environment (50, 81). The helix-helix interfaces known from high-resolution structural analysis are limited to those formed in the bacterial photosynthetic reaction center (24) and bacteriorhodopsin (44). As noted above, the interior residues in the reaction center tend to be slightly more polar than the residues facing the lipid (86), but no specific packing rules have emerged so far from studies of these two structures.

Faced with the lack of high-resolution structural information, molecular genetics techniques have been used to map helix-helix interfaces in a few cases. Glycophorin A has a single transmembrane anchor that mediates the formation of dimers that are stable even in SDS and that hence can be resolved by SDS-PAGE. Saturation mutagenesis of the transmembrane segment led to the identification of residues that are critical for dimer formation and that all map to one side of the transmembrane helix (64). Surprisingly, the interface is rich in hydrophobic amino acids and does not coincide with the most polar side of the helix.

Similar results have been obtained using disulfide mapping techniques to identify interface residues. The Tar receptor is a dimeric inner membrane protein from *E. coli*, and each monomer has two transmembrane helices. Cysteine residues were introduced by site-specific mutagenesis throughout the two helices, and the formation of either inter- or intramolecular disulfides were assayed by first isolating the membrane fraction and then oxidizing the cysteine residues chemically (77). The observed pattern of disulfides could be interpreted in terms of a four-helix bundle model; again, the interface residues were found to be largely apolar.

We (121) recently completed a disulfide mapping of the H1-H2 interface in Lep (Figure 5), providing yet another example of an interface formed from hydrophobic amino acids. In this case, the disulfides form spontaneously in vivo and do not adversely affect the catalytic activity of the enzyme. Interestingly, the formation of the H1-H2 disulfides is not facilitated by the DsbA and DsbB proteins that strongly affect disulfide formation in periplasmic proteins (122).

Charge-pairing between oppositely charged residues drives the as-

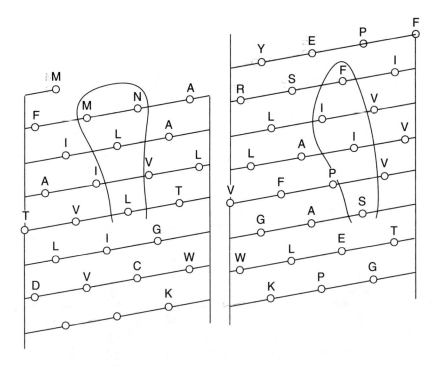

H1   H2

Figure 5   The interface between the H1 and H2 transmembrane helices in Lep. The encircled residues bury more than 50% of their surface area in the interface.

sociation between transmembrane helices in different subunits of the T-cell receptor complex (19, 61). The charge-charge interaction seems to be strong enough to induce a reorientation of the helices when the position of one of the charged residues is changed, suggesting that dimerization is driven not by the formation of a large interacting surface but simply by electrostatic interactions. Indirect evidence for the formation of interhelical salt bridges has been obtained in other systems as well (47, 62, 88).

Other methods that allow the mapping of buried and lipid-exposed residues in individual helices, but that provide little or no information on neighboring residues in other helices, include quenching of spin-labeled residues by aqueous or membrane-penetrating quenchers (2, 3), mutational analysis of presumed functionally important residues (17), and isolation of second-site revertants of nonfunctional mutant proteins (28, 47, 54, 62, 72).

PREDICTING THE TOPOLOGY AND STRUCTURE OF MEMBRANE PROTEINS

Helix-Bundle Proteins

How close are we to the goal of predicting the structure of membrane proteins directly from their sequence? A general conclusion from the previous discussion is that we seem to know a good deal about the topological information present in a nascent polypeptide (although we still do not fully understand how the cell reads this information) but much less about how the amino acid sequence of a transmembrane helix dictates its association with other helices. Therefore, we should be able to predict the topology fairly well but should be less successful in predicting the structure of helix bundles.

This is indeed the case: with the method described below, we can predict the correct topology—i.e. the correct number of transmembrane segments and the correct orientation of the molecule in the membrane—for about 90% of bacterial inner membrane proteins. The topology of eukaryotic plasma membrane proteins is, however, more difficult to predict.

Our own attempts at topology prediction start from the following premises: (a) transmembrane helices are formed from long stretches of predominantly hydrophobic amino acids; (b) short loops and tails not embedded in the membrane follow the positive inside rule; (c) in eukaryotic [but not prokaryotic (98)] membrane proteins, there is a strong correlation between the orientation of the most N-terminal trans-

membrane helix and the net charge difference across this segment
(counting both positively and negatively charged residues and including
15 flanking residues on either end) (43); and (d) the average amino acid
composition is different for long (>60 residues) cytoplasmic and exoplasmic domains in eukaryotic membrane proteins (71).

These premises form the basis of a strategy for predicting the topology of a bacterial membrane protein (112) (Figure 6). Candidate
transmembrane segments are first identified using a standard hydrophobicity analysis method [in our current implementation we use a 21-
residue trapezoid sliding window and the Goldman-Engelman-Steitz
(GES) scale (34), but many of the available hydrophobicity scales (18)
would presumably work equally well]. With suitably defined cutoffs,
this initial step will produce one set of certain (i.e. very hydrophobic)

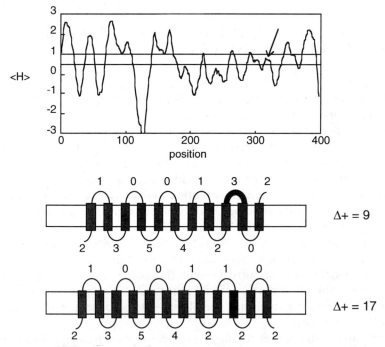

Figure 6   Prediction of the LacY topology. (*Top*) Hydrophobicity plot. All peaks above
the upper cutoff line are classified as certain transmembrane segments, and the peak
between the two cutoffs is classified as a possible transmembrane segments (*arrow*).
(*Bottom*) the two possible topologies and the distribution of Arg + Lys residues in their
respective loops. The lower topology has a higher Arg + Lys bias and is chosen as the
best prediction. It is also the experimentally observed topology (15a).

transmembrane segments and one set of possible (i.e. less hydrophobic) candidates. In the next step, one generates all possible topologies that include all of the certain candidates and either include or exclude the possible candidates. Thus, if there are N possible candidates, the number of different topologies is 2^N. These topologies are then ranked on the basis of decreasing bias in the overall distribution of Arg + Lys residues in the short loops (<60 residues) between the two sides of the structure, and the top-ranking topology is chosen as the best prediction. This analysis, as carried out automatically by the TOP-PRED program (available in a Macintosh version from G von Heijne), has so far proved highly reliable (112).

A similar strategy was recently applied to eukaryotic plasma membrane proteins (98). The positive inside rule helps also in this case, but to a lesser extent because the charge bias is generally less strong in eukaryotic compared with prokaryotic proteins and also tapers off towards the more C-terminal loops. However, as noted above, a net charge difference rule applies to the most N-terminal transmembrane segment in eukaryotic proteins (the more positively charged end tends to face the cytoplasm), and in addition, long polar segments tend to have different amino acid compositions depending on their intra- or extracellular location. At present, the best approach seems to be to predict the orientation of the N-terminal helix from the net charge difference rule and then proceed to build the remaining topology by trying to optimize the fit to the positive inside and compositional bias rules.

How might one improve these prediction schemes? Several of the parameters used are known only from statistical estimates and have not been rigorously checked experimentally. Thus, hydrophobicity scales are still based on rather scant experimental data, and it is not known to what extent charge-pairing between residues located one turn away from each other in a transmembrane α-helix can compensate for the free-energy loss upon membrane insertion (46). Other parameters that require better definition include: the minimum and maximum lengths of transmembrane helices (e.g. how long can one make a hydrophobic segment before it breaks up into two neighboring transmembrane helices?); the precise number of residues on either side of an N-terminal transmembrane segment that should be included in the net charge difference calculation; and any restrictions (length, composition, etc) on polar N-terminal tails located upstream of an N-terminal transmembrane segment with the N_{out} orientation. Finally, other, more difficult-to-predict features of the nascent chain, such as the formation of stably folded domains, may also play a role (11).

In spite of these remaining questions, it is probably fair to state that the basic problems of topology predictions have been solved and that the time is ripe for an attack on the full 3D structure-prediction problem. Not much progress has been reported in this area so far, though certain rules of thumb have been established. The best available predictor of helix-helix interfaces seems to be the pattern of sequence variability in aligned transmembrane segments from homologous proteins (29, 85, 86). This kind of information was recently used to model the 3D structure of the G-coupled receptor family of proteins (8), apparently with some success (93).

Molecular dynamics has been used to predict the known helix-helix interface in the glycophorin A dimer (102). A structure compatible with the experimentally observed interface was among the best candidates, but other structures of comparable energy were found as well. Some results have also appeared from simulations of the bacteriorhodopsin structure (48). Finally, a couple of methods that try to optimize side chain–side chain interactions across the helix-helix interface without recourse to a full molecular dynamics simulation have been presented recently (31, 103), but it is unclear how well they perform on a large sample of proteins and whether they are computationally efficient enough to analyze all possible rotational and translational helix-helix orientations in a multispanning protein.

Thus what the best prediction strategy will be is unclear, but with the increasing number of helix-helix interfaces being mapped experimentally, this field should progress rather rapidly.

β-Barrel Proteins

The recent publication of high-resolution X-ray structures of several bacterial outer membrane porins (20, 117) has made the prediction of the secondary and tertiary structures of related molecules possible. Investigators had attempted such prediction on several earlier occasions (79, 105, 106) using various kinds of input data such as the location of antigenic epitopes, phage-binding sites, location of conserved residues, predicted turns, and possible amphiphilic β-strands, and these models turned out to be fairly good when compared with the X-ray structure. However, one feature of the 3D structure that was not sufficiently appreciated in the early prediction schemes is the very high abundance of aromatic residues at the ends of the transmembrane β-strands, and inclusion of this pattern results in a considerably better prediction algorithm (95).

CONCLUSION

What then are the immediate challenges in the membrane protein field? Obviously, the paucity of known 3D structures or even of roughly mapped helix-helix interfaces makes approaching the structure prediction problem in a rational way very difficult. We may have to wait for more in-depth experimental and theoretical studies of the residue-residue interactions responsible for the formation of helix bundles before we can hope to come up with good prediction methods. On the other hand, we seem to have more or less solved the secondary structure prediction problem: we can reliably identify all the transmembrane helices and predict their orientations directly from the amino acid sequence (at least for bacterial proteins), and we have the necessary experimental tools at hand to validate the predictions rather easily (mainly the fusion protein technique; again, this applies in the first instance to bacterial proteins).

However, in one sense our understanding even of the membrane insertion step remains rather superficial. We know a fair bit about the how the topological information is encoded in the substrates—the nascent polypeptide chains—but we still have many gaps in our knowledge of how the cell decodes this information. Basic questions such as whether Sec-independent proteins insert directly into the lipid bilayer or whether they somehow interact with a component(s) of the secretory machinery remain unanswered. The actions of the protein-translocating machineries of bacterial and eukaryotic cells are also far from fully understood, and our interest in membrane protein biogenesis thus merges with more general problems of cell biology and biochemistry. Ultimately, we may come full circle and note that membrane proteins are the most important players in these machineries and hence that our abilities to predict membrane protein structure will be immediately relevant for our understanding of membrane protein biogenesis.

Literature Cited

1. Allen J, Feher G, Yeates T, Komiya H, Rees D. 1987. Structure of the reaction center from *Rhodobacter* *sphaeroides* R-26: The protein subunits. *Proc. Natl. Acad. Sci. USA* 84: 6162

2. Altenbach C, Flitsch S, Khorana H, Hubbell W. 1989. Structural studies in transmembrane proteins. 2. Spin labeling of bacteriorhodopsin mutants at unique cysteines. *Biochemistry* 28: 7806

3. Altenbach C, Marti T, Khorana HG, Hubbell WL. 1990. Transmembrane protein structure—spin labeling of bacteriorhodopsin mutants. *Science* 248:1088

4. Andersson H, Bakker E, von Heijne G. 1992. Different positively charged amino acids have similar effects on the topology of a polytopic transmembrane protein in *Escherichia coli*. *J. Biol. Chem.* 267:1491

5. Andersson H, von Heijne G. 1991. A 30-residue-long "export initiation domain" adjacent to the signal sequence is critical for protein translocation across the inner membrane of *Escherichia coli*. *Proc. Natl. Acad. Sci. USA* 88:9751

6. Andersson H, von Heijne G. 1993. Position-specific Asp-Lys pairing can affect signal sequence function and membrane protein topology. *J. Biol. Chem.* 268:21398

7. Andersson H, von Heijne G. 1993. *Sec*-dependent and *sec*-Independent assembly of *E. coli* inner membrane proteins—the topological rules depend on chain length. *EMBO J.* 12:683

8. Baldwin JM. 1993. The probable arrangement of the helices in G protein-coupled receptors. *EMBO J.* 12:1693

9. Bardwell JCA, Lee JO, Jander G, Martin N, Belin D, Beckwith J. 1993. A pathway for disulfide bond formation in vivo. *Proc. Natl. Acad. Sci. USA* 90:1038

10. Bardwell JCA, McGovern K, Beckwith J. 1991. Identification of a protein required for disulfide bond formation in vivo. *Cell* 67:581

11. Beltzer JP, Fiedler K, Fuhrer C, Geffen I, Handschin C, et al. 1991. Charged residues are major determinants of the transmembrane orientation of a signal-anchor sequence. *J. Biol. Chem.* 266:973

12. Boyd D, Beckwith J. 1990. The role of charged amino acids in the localization of secreted and membrane proteins. *Cell* 62:1031

13. Boyd D, Traxler B, Beckwith J. 1993. Analysis of the topology of a membrane protein by using a minimum number of alkaline phosphatase fusions. *J. Bacteriol.* 175:553

14. Brandl CJ, Deber CM. 1986. Hypothesis about the function of membrane-buried proline residues in transport proteins. *Proc. Natl. Acad. Sci. USA* 83:917

15. Broome-Smith JK, Tadayyon M, Zhang Y. 1990. Beta-lactamase as a probe of membrane protein assembly and protein export. *Mol. Microbiol.* 4: 1637

15a. Calamia J, Manoil C. 1990. Lac permease of *Escherichia coli*—topology and sequence elements promoting membrane insertion. *Proc. Natl. Acad. Sci. USA* 87:4937

16. Chothia C. 1984. Principles that determine the structure of proteins. *Annu. Rev. Biochem.* 53:537

17. Collins JC, Permuth SF, Brooker RJ. 1989. Isolation and characterization of lactose permease mutants with an enhanced recognition of maltose and diminished recognition of cellobiose. *J. Biol. Chem.* 264:14698

18. Cornette JL, Cease KB, Margalit H, Spouge JL, Berzofsky JA, De Lisi C. 1987. Hydrophobicity scales and computational techniques for detecting amphipathic structures in proteins. *J. Mol. Biol.* 195:659

19. Cosson P, Lankford SP, Bonifacino JS, Klausner RD. 1991. Membrane protein association by potential intramembrane charge pairs. *Nature* 351: 414

20. Cowan SW, Schirmer T, Rummel G, Steiert M, Ghosh R, et al. 1992. Crystal structures explain functional properties of two *E. coli* porins. *Nature* 358: 727

21. Dalbey RE, Kuhn A, Wickner W. 1987. The internal signal sequence of *Escherichia coli* leader peptidase is necessary, but not sufficient, for its rapid membrane assembly. *J. Biol. Chem.* 262:13241

22. Dalbey RE, von Heijne G. 1992. Signal peptidases in prokaryotes and eukaryotes—a new protease family. *Trends Biochem. Sci.* 17:474

23. Deber CM, Brandl CJ, Deber RB, Hsu LC, Young XK. 1986. Amino acid composition of the membrane and aqueous domains of integral membrane proteins. *Arch. Biochem. Biophys.* 251:68

24. Deisenhofer J, Epp O, Miki K, Huber R, Michel H. 1985. Structure of the protein subunits in the photosynthetic reaction centre of *Rhodopseudomonas viridis* at 3Å resolution. *Nature* 318:618

25. Deisenhofer J, Michel H. 1991. High-resolution structures of photosynthetic reaction centers. *Annu. Rev. Biophys. Biophys. Chem.* 20:247

26. Deisenhofer J, Michel H. 1991. Structures of bacterial photosynthetic reaction centers. *Annu. Rev. Cell Biol.* 7:1
27. de Vrije T, de Swart R, Dowhan W, Tommassen J, de Kruijff B. 1988. Phosphatidylglycerol is involved in protein translocation across *Escherichia coli* inner membranes. *Nature* 334:173
28. di Rago JP, Netter P, Slonimski PP. 1990. Intragenic suppressors reveal long distance interactions between inactivating and reactivating amino acid replacements generating three-dimensional constraints in the structure of mitochondrial cytochrome b. *J. Biol. Chem.* 265:15750
29. Donnelly D, Overington JP, Ruffle SV, Nugent JH, Blundell TL. 1993. Modeling alpha-helical transmembrane domains: the calculation and use of substitution tables for lipid-facing residues. *Protein Sci.* 2:55
30. Douglas SE. 1992. A *secY* homologue is found in the plastid genome of *Cryptomonas Φ. FEBS Lett.* 298:93
31. Efremov RG, Gulyaev DI, Modyanov NN. 1993. Application of 3-dimensional molecular hydrophobicity potential to the analysis of spatial organization of membrane domains in proteins. 3. Modeling of intramembrane moiety of Na⁺, K⁺-ATPase. *J. Protein Chem.* 12:143
32. Ehrmann M, Beckwith J. 1991. Proper insertion of a complex membrane protein in the absence of its amino-terminal export signal. *J. Biol. Chem.* 266:16530
33. Engelman DM, Steitz TA. 1981. The spontaneous insertion of proteins into and across membranes: the helical hairpin hypothesis. *Cell* 23:411
34. Engelman DM, Steitz TA, Goldman A. 1986. Identifying nonpolar transbilayer helices in amino acid sequences of membrane proteins. *Annu. Rev. Biophys. Biophys. Chem.* 15:321
34a. Garcia PD, Walter P. 1988. Full-length prepro-α-factor can be translocated across the mammalian microsomal membrane only if translation has not terminated. *J. Cell. Biol.* 106:1043
35. Gavel Y, Steppuhn J, Herrmann R, von Heijne G. 1991. The positive-inside rule applies to thylakoid membrane proteins. *FEBS Lett.* 282:41
36. Gavel Y, von Heijne G. 1992. The distribution of charged amino acids in mitochondrial inner membrane proteins suggests different modes of membrane integration for nuclearly and mitochondrially encoded proteins. *Eur. J. Biochem.* 205:1207
37. Gierasch LM. 1989. Signal sequences. *Biochemistry* 28:923
38. Glick BS, Beasley EM, Schatz G. 1992. Protein sorting in mitochondria. *Trends Biochem. Sci.* 17:453
39. Görlich D, Prehn S, Hartmann E, Kalies KU, Rapoport TA. 1992. A mammalian homolog of SEC61p and SECYp is associated with ribosomes and nascent polypeptides during translocation. *Cell* 71:489
40. Gray MW. 1989. The evolutionary origins of organelles. *Trends Genet.* 5:294
41. Haeuptle MT, Flint N, Gough NM, Dobberstein B. 1989. A tripartite structure of the signals that determine protein insertion into the endoplasmic reticulum membrane. *J. Cell Biol.* 108:1227
42. Hartl FU, Neupert W. 1990. Protein sorting to mitochondria—evolutionary conservations of folding and assembly. *Science* 247:930
43. Hartmann E, Rapoport TA, Lodish HF. 1989. Predicting the orientation of eukaryotic membrane proteins. *Proc. Natl. Acad. Sci. USA* 86:5786
44. Henderson R, Baldwin JM, Ceska TA, Zemlin F, Beckmann E, Downing KH. 1990. A model for the structure of bacteriorhodopsin based on high resolution electron cryo-microscopy. *J. Mol. Biol.* 213:899
45. Henderson R, Unwin PNT. 1975. Three-dimensional model of purple membrane obtained by electron microscopy. *Nature* 257:28
46. Honig BH, Hubbell WL. 1984. Stability of "salt bridges" in membrane proteins. *Proc. Natl. Acad. Sci. USA* 81:5412
47. Howitt SM, Cox GB. 1992. Second-site revertants of an arginine-210 to lysine mutation in the α-subunit of the F₀-F₁-ATPase from *Escherichia coli*: implications for structure. *Proc. Natl. Acad. Sci. USA* 89:9799
48. Jähnig F, Edholm O. 1992. Modeling the structure of bacteriorhodopsin. A molecular dynamics study. *J. Mol. Biol.* 226:837
49. Jennings ML. 1989. Topography of membrane proteins. *Annu. Rev. Biochem.* 58:999
50. Kahn TW, Engelman D. 1992. Bacteriorhodopsin can be refolded from two independently stable transmembrane helices and the complementary five-helix fragment. *Biochemistry* 31:6144
51. Kahn TW, Sturtevant JM, Engelman

DM. 1992. Thermodynamic measurements of the contributions of helix-connecting loops and of retinal to the stability of bacteriorhodopsin. *Biochemistry* 31:8829

52. Kamitani S, Akiyama Y, Ito K. 1992. Identification and characterization of an *Escherichia coli* gene required for the formation of correctly folded alkaline phosphatase, a periplasmic enzyme. *EMBO J.* 11:57

53. Keller RCA, Killian JA, de Kruijff B. 1992. Anionic phospholipids are essential for α-helix formation of the signal peptide of prePhoE upon interaction with phospholipid vesicles. *Biochemistry* 31:1672

54. King SC, Hansen CL, Wilson TH. 1991. The interaction between aspartic acid 237 and lysine 358 in the lactose carrier of *Escherichia coli*. *Biochim. Biophys. Acta* 1062:177

55. Krauss N, Hinrichs W, Witt I, Fromme P, Pritzkow W, et al. 1993. Three-dimensional structure of system I of photosynthesis at 6Å resolution. *Nature* 361:326

56. Kühlbrandt W, Wang DN. 1991. Three-dimensional structure of plant light-harvesting complex determined by electron crystallography. *Nature* 350:130

57. Kuhn A. 1987. Bacteriophage M13 procoat protein inserts into the plasma membrane as a loop structure. *Science* 238:1413

58. Kuhn A. 1988. Alterations in the extracellular domain of M13 procoat protein make its membrane insertion dependent on *secA* and *secY*. *Eur. J. Biochem.* 177:267

59. Kuhn A, Rohrer J, Gallusser A. 1990. Bacteriophages M13 and Pf3 tell us how proteins insert into the membrane. *J. Struct Biol.* 104:38

60. Landolt-Marticorena C, Williams KA, Deber CM, Reithmeier RAF. 1993. Non-random distribution of amino acids in the transmembrane segments of human type-I single span membrane proteins. *J. Mol. Biol.* 229:602

61. Lankford SP, Cosson P, Bonifacino JS, Klausner RD. 1993. Transmembrane domain length affects charge-mediated retention and degradation of proteins within the endoplasmic reticulum. *J. Biol. Chem.* 268:4814

62. Lee J-I, Hwang PP, Hansen C, Wilson TH. 1992. Possible salt bridges between transmembrane α-helices of the lactose carrier of *Escherichia coli*. *J. Biol. Chem.* 267:20758

63. Lee J-I, Kuhn A, Dalbey RE. 1992. Distinct domains of an oligotopic membrane protein are *sec*-dependent and *sec*-independent for membrane insertion. *J. Biol. Chem.* 267:938

64. Lemmon MA, Flanagan JM, Treutlein HR, Zhang J, Engelman DM. 1992. Sequence specificity in the dimerization of transmembrane alpha-helices. *Biochemistry* 31:12719

65. Lipp J, Flint N, Haeuptle M-T, Dobberstein B. 1989. Structural requirements for membrane assembly of proteins spanning the membrane several times. *J. Cell Biol.* 109:2013

66. Luirink J, High S, Wood H, Giner A, Tollervey D, Dobberstein B. 1992. Signal-sequence recognition by an *Escherichia coli* ribonucleoprotein complex. *Nature* 359:741

67. Manoil C. 1991. Analysis of membrane protein topology using alkaline phosphatase and β-galactosidase gene fusions. *Methods Cell Biol.* 34:61

68. Manoil C, Mekalanos JJ, Beckwith J. 1990. Alkaline phosphatase fusions—sensors of subcellular location. *J. Bacteriol.* 172:515

69. Matsuyama S, Fujita Y, Mizushima S. 1993. SecD is involved in the release of translocated secretory proteins from the cytoplasmic membrane of *Escherichia coli*. *EMBO J.* 12:265

70. McGovern K, Beckwith J. 1991. Membrane insertion of the *Escherichia coli* MalF protein in cells with impaired secretion machinery. *J. Biol. Chem.* 266: 20870

71. Nakashima H, Nishikawa K. 1992. The amino acid composition is different between the cytoplasmic and extracellular sides in membrane proteins. *FEBS Lett.* 303:141

72. Nelson DR, Douglas MG. 1993. Function-based mapping of the yeast mitochondrial ADP/ATP translocator by selection for second site revertants. *J. Mol. Biol.* 230:1171

73. Nilsson I, von Heijne G. 1993. Determination of the distance between the oligosaccharyltransferase active site and the endoplasmic reticulum membrane. *J. Biol. Chem.* 268:5798

74. Nilsson IM, von Heijne G. 1990. Fine-tuning the topology of a polytopic membrane protein. Role of positively and negatively charged residues. *Cell* 62:1135

75. Nilsson IM, von Heijne G. 1991. A de novo designed signal peptide cleavage cassette functions in vivo. *J. Biol. Chem.* 266:3408

76. Olender EH, Simoni RD. 1992. The intracellular targeting and membrane to-

pology of 3-hydroxy-3-methylglutaryl-CoA reductase. *J. Biol. Chem.* 267:4223

77. Pakula AA, Simon MI. 1992. Determination of transmembrane protein structure by disulfide cross-linking—the *Escherichia coli* Tar receptor. *Proc. Natl. Acad. Sci. USA* 89:4144

78. Parks GD, Lamb RA. 1991. Topology of eukaryotic type-II membrane proteins—importance of N-terminal positively charged residues flanking the hydrophobic domain. *Cell* 64:777

79. Paul C, Rosenbusch JP. 1985. Folding patterns of porin and bacteriorhodopsin. *EMBO J.* 4:1593

80. Popot J-L, Engelman DM. 1990. Membrane protein folding and oligomerization —the 2-stage model. *Biochemistry* 29:4031

81. Popot J-L, Gerchman S-E, Engelman DM. 1987. Refolding of bacteriorhodopsin in lipid bilayers. A thermodynamically controlled two-stage process. *J. Mol. Biol.* 198:655

82. Pugsley AP. 1993. The complete general secretory pathway in gram-negative bacteria. *Microbiol. Rev.* 57:50

83. Randall LL. 1992. Peptide binding by chaperone SecB—implications for recognition of nonnative structure. *Science* 257:241

83a. Randall LL, Hardy SJ. 1986. Correlation of competence for export with lack of tertiary structure of the mature species: a study in vivo of maltose-binding protein in E. coli. *Cell* 46:921

84. Rapoport TA. 1992. Transport of proteins across the endoplasmic reticulum membrane. *Science* 258:931

85. Rees DC, DeAntonio L, Eisenberg D. 1989. Hydrophobic organization of membrane proteins. *Science* 245:510

86. Rees DC, Komiya H, Yeates TO, Allen JP, Feher G. 1989. The bacterial photosynthetic reaction center as a model for membrane proteins. *Annu. Rev. Biochem.* 58:607

87. Ribes V, Romisch K, Giner A, Dobberstein B, Tollervey D. 1990. *E. coli* 4.5S RNA is part of a ribonucleoprotein particle that has properties related to signal recognition particle. *Cell* 63:591

88. Sahin-Tóth M, Dunten RL, Gonzales A, Kaback HR. 1992. Functional interactions between putative intramembrane charged residues in the lactose permease of *Escherichia coli*. *Proc. Natl. Acad. Sci. USA* 89:10547

89. San Millan JL, Boyd D, Dalbey R, Wickner W, Beckwith J. 1989. Use of PhoA fusions to study the topology of the *Escherichia coli* inner membrane protein leader peptidase. *J. Bacteriol.* 171:5536

90. Scaramuzzi CD, Hiller RG, Stokes HW. 1992. Identification of a chloroplast-encoded *secA* gene homologue in a chromophytic alga—possible role in chloroplast protein translocation. *Curr. Genet.* 22:421

91. Scaramuzzi CD, Stokes HW, Hiller RG. 1992. Characterisation of a chloroplast-encoded *sec-Y* homologue and *atpH* from a chromophytic alga—evidence for a novel chloroplast genome organisation. *FEBS Lett.* 304:119

92. Schatz PJ, Beckwith J. 1990. Genetic analysis of protein export in *Escherichia coli*. *Annu. Rev. Genet.* 24:215

93. Schertler GFX, Villa C, Henderson R. 1993. Projection structure of rhodopsin. *Nature* 362:770

94. Schiebel E, Driessen AJM, Hartl F-U, Wickner W. 1991. $\Delta\mu H^+$ and ATP function at different steps of the catalytic cycle of preprotein translocase. *Cell* 64:927

95. Schirmer T, Cowan SW. 1993. Prediction of membrane-spanning β-strands and its application to maltoporin. *Protein Sci.* 2:1361

96. Sengstag C, Stirling C, Schekman R, Rine J. 1990. Genetic and biochemical evaluation of eucaryotic membrane protein topology—multiple transmembrane domains of *Saccharomyces cerevisiae* 3-hydroxy-3-methylglutaryl coenzyme-A reductase. *Mol. Cell Biol.* 10:672

97. Shaw AS, Rottier PJ, Rose JK. 1988. Evidence for the loop model of signal-sequence insertion into the endoplasmic reticulum. *Proc. Natl. Acad. Sci. USA* 85:7592

98. Sipos L, von Heijne G. 1993. Predicting the topology of eukaryotic membrane proteins. *Eur. J. Biochem.* 213:1333

99. Toyoshima C, Sasabe H, Stokes DL. 1993. 3-Dimensional cryo-electron microscopy of the calcium ion pump in the sarcoplasmic reticulum membrane. *Nature* 362:469

100. Toyoshima C, Unwin N. 1990. Three-dimensional structure of the acetylcholine receptor by cryoelectron microscopy and helical image reconstruction. *J. Cell Biol.* 111:2623

101. Traxler B, Boyd D, Beckwith J. 1993. The topological analysis of integral cytoplasmic membrane proteins. *J. Membr. Biol.* 132:1

102. Treutlein HR, Lemmon MA, Engelman DM, Brunger AT. 1992. The gly-

cophorin A transmembrane domain dimer: sequence-specific propensity for a right-handed supercoil of helices. *Biochemistry* 31:12726

103. Tuffery P, Lavery R. 1993. Packing and recognition of protein structural elements—a new approach applied to the 4-helix bundle of myohemerythrin. *Proteins Struct. Funct. Genet.* 15:413

104. Unwin N. 1993. Nicotinic acetylcholine receptor at 9 Å resolution. *J. Mol. Biol.* 229:1101

105. van der Ley P, Tommassen J. 1987. PhoE protein structure and function. In *Phosphate Metabolism and Cellular Regulation in Microorganisms*, ed. A Torriani-Gorini, FG Rothman, S Silver, A Wright, E Yagil, pp 159–63. Washington: Am. Soc. Microbiol.

106. Vogel H, Jähnig F. 1986. Models for the structure of outer-membrane proteins of *Escherichia coli* derived from Raman spectroscopy and prediction methods. *J. Mol. Biol.* 190:191

107. Vogel H, Nilsson L, Rigler R, Meder S, Boheim G, et al. 1993. Structural fluctuations between 2 conformational states of a transmembrane helical peptide are related to its channel-forming properties in planar lipid membranes. *Eur. J. Biochem.* 212:305

108. von Heijne G. 1984. Analysis of the distribution of charged residues in the N-terminal region of signal sequences: implications for protein export in prokaryotic and eukaryotic cells. *EMBO J.* 3:2315

109. von Heijne G. 1989. Control of topology and mode of assembly of a polytopic membrane protein by positively charged residues. *Nature* 341:456

110. von Heijne G. 1990. The signal peptide. *J. Membr. Biol.* 115:195

111. von Heijne G. 1991. Proline kinks in transmembrane α-helices. *J. Mol. Biol.* 218:499

112. von Heijne G. 1992. Membrane protein structure prediction—hydrophobicity analysis and the positive-inside rule. *J. Mol. Biol.* 225:487

113. von Heijne G, Gavel Y. 1988. Topogenic signals in integral membrane proteins. *Eur. J. Biochem.* 174:671

114. von Heijne G, Manoil C. 1990. Membrane proteins—from sequence to structure. *Protein Eng.* 4:109

115. von Heijne G, Wickner W, Dalbey RE. 1988. The cytoplasmic domain of *Escherichia coli* leader peptidase is a "translocation poison" sequence. *Proc. Natl. Acad. Sci. USA* 85:3363

116. Wang J, Pullman A. 1991. Do helices in membranes prefer to form bundles or stay dispersed in the lipid phase. *Biochim. Biophys. Acta* 1070:493

117. Weiss MS, Abele U, Weckesser J, Welte W, Schiltz E, Schulz GE. 1991. Molecular architecture and electrostatic properties of a bacterial porin. *Science* 254:1627

118. Weiss MS, Kreusch A, Schiltz E, Nestel U, Welte W, et al. 1991. The structure of porin from *Rhodobacter capsulata* at 1.8Å resolution. *FEBS Lett.* 280:379

119. Welply JK, Shenbagamurthi P, Lennarz WJ, Naider F. 1983. Substrate recognition by oligosaccharyltransferases. Studies on glycosylation of modified Asn-X-Ser/Thr tripeptides. *J. Biol. Chem.* 258:

120. Wessels HP, Spiess M. 1988. Insertion of a multispanning membrane protein occurs sequentially and requires only one signal sequence. *Cell* 55:61

121. Whitley P, Nilsson L, von Heijne G. 1993. A 3D model for the membrane domain of *Escherichia coli* leader peptidase based on disulfide mapping. *Biochemistry.* 32:8534

122. Whitley P, von Heijne G. 1993. The DsbA-DsbB system affects the formation of disulfide bonds in periplasmic but not in intramebraneous protein domains. *FEBS Lett.* 332:49

123. Wickner W. 1988. Mechanisms of membrane assembly: general lessons from the study of M13 coat protein and *Escherichia coli* leader peptidase. *Biochemistry* 27:1081

124. Wickner W, Driessen AJM, Hartl FU. 1991. The enzymology of protein translocation across the *Escherichia coli* plasma membrane. *Annu. Rev. Biochem.* 60:101

125. Wolfe PB, Wickner W. 1984. Bacterial leader peptidase, a membrane protein without a leader peptide, uses the same export pathway as pre-secretory proteins. *Cell* 36:1067

126. Woolfson DN, Mortishire-Smith RJ, Williams DH. 1991. Conserved positioning of proline residues in membrane-spanning helices of ion-channel proteins. *Biochem. Biophys. Res. Commun.* 175:733

127. Yeates TO, Komiya H, Rees DC, Allen JP, Feher G. 1987. Structure of the reaction center from *Rhodobacter sphaeroides:* Membrane-protein interactions. *Proc. Natl. Acad. Sci. USA* 84:6438

Annu. Rev. Biophys. Biomol. Struct. 1994. 23:193–213

ANNEXIN STRUCTURE AND MEMBRANE INTERACTIONS: A Molecular Perspective

Manal A. Swairjo and Barbara A. Seaton

Department of Physiology, Boston University School of Medicine, Boston, Massachusetts 02118

KEY WORDS: lipocortins, crystal structure, structural biology, calcium binding, phospholipids, vesicles, membrane fusion, calcium channels

CONTENTS

PERSPECTIVES AND OVERVIEW

The search for protein mediators of the intracellular calcium signal has led to the identification, in several laboratories, of a number of soluble proteins that bind to phospholipid membranes in a calcium-dependent manner (63). The initial names of these proteins (e.g. synexin, calectrins, chromobindins, calpactins, calcimedins, endonexins, and lipocortins) were based on their sources or in vitro properties. However, annexins constitute a family (for review, see 11, 19, 42), as evidenced by their cross-reactivity with specific antisera and their homologous amino acid and cDNA sequences (55). The term *annexin* (29), which derives from these proteins' property of annexing phospholipid membranes, has been suggested as a basis for a common nomenclature (20). The sequences and properties distinguish the annexin family from the calmodulin (EF hand), protein kinase C, and phospholipase A_2 families of calcium-binding proteins that play a role in signal transduction.

At least twelve annexins, numbered I–XII have been identified (see Table 1 for examples) (for more complete nomenclature tables, see 20, 51). They are widely distributed in nature, from simple eukaryotes through higher plants and animals, and occur in numerous cell types in the same species, where individual annexins have different organ, tissue, and subcellular distributions (11, 40, 42, 55). Immunocytochemical studies of annexins have shown that they reside subadjacent to plasma membranes (e.g. 24), near calcium-sequestering intracellular organelles (32), or even in the nucleus (50). However, some annexins have been found extracellularly, in lung lavage fluid (21), prostate fluid (31), and in the extracellular matrix (30). The differential distribution of certain annexins during development also has been studied (33, 39, 40).

Although the cellular functions of annexins remain uncertain, several potential functions have been assigned to them, based on in vitro properties. These properties include inhibition of phospholipase A_2 (reviewed in 59), anticoagulant activity (26), binding to cytoskeletal proteins (38), aggregation of membranes and vesicles (reviewed in 17), and calcium-selective channel activity (reviewed in 56).

Table 1 Common names of some annexin family members

Annexin	Synonym[a]
I	p35, calpactin II, lipocortin, chromobindin 9
II	p36, calpactin I heavy chain, protein I, chromobindin 8, PAP IV
IV	endonexin I, protein II, chromobindin 4, 32.5K calelectrin, PAP II, 35-β calcimedin
V	endonexin II, PAPI, VAC-α, 35K calelectrin, 35-γ calcimedin, calphobindin I, anchorin CII
VI	p68, p70, 73K, protein III, chromobindin 20, 67K calelectrin, 67K calcimedin, calphobindin II
VII	synexin

[a] PAP, placental anticoagulant protein; VAC, vascular anticoagulant protein. Annexins I–VI also have been identified as lipocortins I–VI, respectively (68).

The apparent dissociation constants of calcium binding to annexins fall between millimolar and micromolar values (42, 60, 61). The presence of phospholipids increases the binding affinity, but not to the level exhibited by cytosolic intracellular calcium-receptor proteins such as calmodulin (42). However, the higher calcium concentrations found at the membrane surface (relative to concentrations in the cytosol) probably enable annexins to bind calcium fully despite the comparatively low apparent calcium-binding affinity of annexins (17, 48).

Calcium specificity is an important characteristic of annexin in vitro properties. Intracellular cations such as magnesium cannot replace calcium without losing such properties as membrane binding (e.g. 1, 9, 14). Reportedly, zinc synergistically enhances calcium binding (1), which may occur through allostery between distinct zinc and calcium sites (43). Measurements of the stoichiometry of calcium binding indicate that as few as two and as many as ten calcium ions may be bound to one annexin molecule (4, 60, 61). Cooperativity between calcium sites has not been established definitively, though cooperativity of calcium-dependent phospholipid binding has been observed (18, 61).

Calcium likely exerts an effect on annexin membrane binding through the formation of the phospholipid-calcium-protein ternary complex (17). In the presence of calcium, apparent dissociation constants for phospholipid-vesicle binding to annexins have been estimated to be close to 10^{-10} M (65, 70), indicating very high affinity for phospholipids in bilayer or monolayer configurations. Annexins bind phospholipid monomers with low affinity (65), and annexin membrane-binding affinities depend strongly upon lipid composition. Anionic phospholipid membranes are strongly preferred or even required for annexin binding. Furthermore, binding hierarchies based on phospholipid head groups have been established for many individual annexins (1, 9).

ANNEXIN MOLECULAR STRUCTURE

Annexin sequences are characterized by a canonical motif in which a stretch of approximately 70 amino acids is repeated usually four times or, in the case of annexin VI, 8 times (27, 28). Most of the amino acid variations in this common core region are conservative replacements (35, 55). Annexins also have a highly variable N-terminal region, frequently referred to as the tail, that distinguishes different family members. This region varies in both sequence and length (35, 55) and is believed to determine individual annexin functions. Molecular weights range from 35 to 38 kDa for most four-domain annexins (55) and are 67 kDa for annexin VI (55) and 51 kDa for the four-domain annexin

VII, which has the longest variable region (12). These molecular weights are calculated from amino acid sequences and assume one polypeptide chain per molecule.

In 1990, Huber and coworkers (36) published the first annexin crystal structure, that of human annexin V. Crystal structures have since been determined for human (35, 37, 43), chicken (7), and rat (15) annexin V and human [des 1-33] annexin I (69). These molecular structures have confirmed the hypothesis, inferred from sequence data, that the repeating primary structure found in annexins corresponds to four homologous domains. These domains, which form the conserved core, appear to be responsible for calcium and membrane binding. We have less structural information about the variable N-terminal regions, which are either truncated (annexin I) or naturally short (annexin V) in the reported crystal structures.

Figure 1 shows the crystal structure of rat annexin V (15). The annexin core region contains mostly α-helical secondary structure as predicted by Taylor & Geisow (66), but the observed tertiary fold is novel. The four core domains each exhibit a helical arrangement characterized as a four-helix bundle (helices designated A, B, D, and E) with a fifth capping helix (C) crossing over the top (36). Within the helix bundle are two parallel helix-loop-helix substructures, held together by the capping helix and interhelical contacts. Each domain possesses its own conserved hydrophobic core. The structure appears to be unusually stable; annexin V, for example, is heat stable and protease resistant despite the absence of disulfide bonds (J Dedman, personal communication).

The four annexin domains form a planar cyclic arrangement, in which the N- and C-terminal regions of the polypeptide chain interact to hold domains 1 and 4 together noncovalently. Extensive hydrophobic contacts couple domains 2 and 3 and 1 and 4. In the center of this cyclic grouping lies an open area—a putative calcium channel—that is mostly hydrophilic and forms a funnel-shaped pore (36). A detailed model of the annexin V calcium channel has been presented (35, 41). However, the molecular surfaces of annexins are chiefly hydrophilic and lack the obvious exposed hydrophobic regions typical of membrane-spanning proteins. This and other structural observations have raised questions about possible mechanisms of channel formation, which are discussed in a later section.

The annexin molecule is slightly flattened and curved, with opposing convex and concave faces. The convex surface includes the interhelical loops that link the A and B helices and the D and E helices, respectively [designated the AB and DE loops (69)]. Considerable evidence supports the view that in the membrane-bound state, the convex surface of the

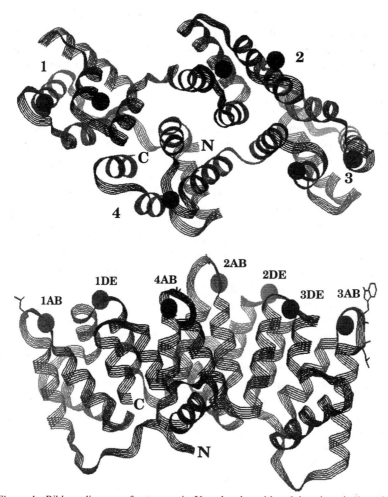

Figure 1   Ribbon diagram of rat annexin V molecule, with calcium ions indicated as shaded spheres, and domains designated by numerals. N and C termini are identified. (*Top*) View normal to bilayer plane, convex surface in foreground. (*Bottom*) Molecule rotated around *x* axis, 90° from above. View is from side, with convex surface on top and concave surface on bottom. The AB and DE calcium-binding loops from each domain are identified. Surface-exposed hydrophobic side chains in AB loops are shown.

annexin molecule lies along the plane of the phospholipid membrane (10, 22), with the loops in direct contact with membrane components. The concave surface includes the capping helices, an extended, non-helical connection between domains 2 and 3, and the N terminus, which also has an extended conformation. The N terminus thus faces the cytosol, where its variable sequence can be accommodated without perturbing calcium-dependent membrane binding. In several annexins, this region is also the site of in vitro phosphorylation by tyrosine kinases or protein kinase C (31). This orientation of the N terminus also allows it to participate in interactions with other intracellular proteins or membranes.

Calcium-Binding Sites

Calcium or lanthanide atoms have been identified in all but one [the hexagonal crystal form of human annexin V (35, 36)] of the published annexin crystal structures. These cations are localized at the loops of the convex surface. The liganding pattern in annexin calcium-binding sites differs from those seen in calmodulin-like (EF hand) proteins, which have more carboxylate ligands, fewer water ligands, and a longer calcium-binding loop (44; for a review of EF-hand proteins in this volume, see 52a). These structural differences (illustrated in Figure 2) are reflected in apparent calcium binding affinities: the K_d values for calmodulin and its homologues (63) are orders of magnitude lower than those of annexins. In annexins, the protein ligands consist of main-chain carbonyl oxygens and the carboxylate oxygens of an acidic side chain. Water molecules or other exogenous ligands may occupy the remaining coordination positions. The preponderance of carbonyl and water ligands suggests an open, flexible site, consistent with the surface location of these sites in the annexin molecule.

In terms of three-dimensional structure, annexin V calcium-binding sites fall into two classes, typified by the AB or DE loops. The characteristic AB sites are structurally related to the calcium- and phospholipid-binding sites of phospholipase A_2 (37). They were originally recognized in the annexin consensus sequence identified in 1986 (28). Structurally, these sites are formed by residues in the AB loops and an acidic residue in the DE loop, located approximately 40 residues distant, that provides bidentate carboxylate oxygens. The fully coordinated site with seven ligands forms a pentagonal bipyramid. Peptide carbonyl oxygen ligands are contributed by alternate loop residues in the canonical sequence. The first liganding residue in the loop donates a main-chain oxygen at one vertex of the bipyramid, and the opposite vertex is occupied by a water molecule. The other ligands are arranged equatorially around the calcium. In domain 3 of annexins I and V, the loop is slightly bent to accommodate a single-residue insertion, but the overall liganding geometry is the same as in other domains (15, 69).

In contrast, the DE calcium sites in annexins include only three ligand-donating residues: two peptide carbonyl oxygens from the DE loop and a bidentate carboxylate group from the E helix. This type of

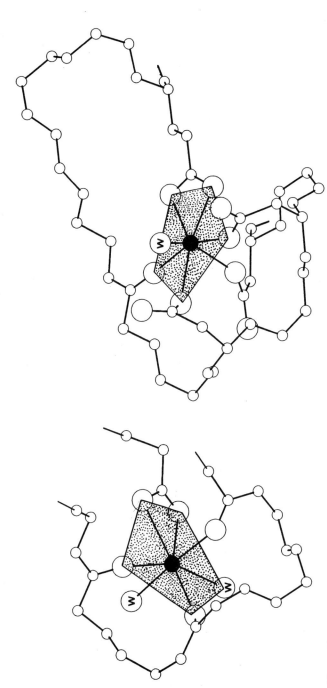

Figure 2 Comparison between calcium ligation in annexin AB loop (*left*) or calmodulin EF hand (*right*). Polypeptide backbones shown with coordinating oxygens (carbonyl, carboxylate, or water) are included. Calcium ions appear as black circles; oxygens, large circles; carbons and nitrogens, small circles. Water oxygens are marked W. Planes formed by equatorial ligands in the pentagonal bipyramidal configuration are shaded, with axial ligands above and below. Calcium-oxygen bonds are indicated. Annexin site includes three main-chain carbonyl oxygens, a bidentate carboxylate side chain (discontinuous with the rest of the loop), and two water molecules. Calmodulin site includes four carboxylate side chains, one of which is bidentate, a main-chain carbonyl oxygen, and a water molecule.

site could not be predicted from the sequence because the residues providing the main-chain carbonyl groups are not conserved. Up to three water-molecule ligands have been observed contributing to the coordination of calcium at this site (35, 69). In their survey of calcium binding proteins, McPhalen et al (44) noted that calcium binding affinities tend to decrease as the number of water oxygen ligands increases. Consistent with this trend, the annexin DE sites appear to bind calcium with lower affinity than the AB sites. However, the DE sites bind lanthanides with higher affinity than do the AB sites (35). The crystallographic data suggest that calcium binding at the AB site precedes that of its DE loop partner. Whether this observation indicates cooperativity between these sites is not clear.

Crystallographic evidence also indicates that calcium binding in different domains may be an ordered process (43). Comparison of annexin V crystal structures, some of which contain cations that compete with calcium for binding sites, indicates that the calcium affinity of the AB loops may be placed in the following descending domain order: 1, 4, 2, 3 (15, 43). This order implies that the AB calcium sites fill first in one half of the molecule, a phenomenon exhibited by calmodulin and troponin C. The crystal structures of annexin V show bound calcium in 0–4 of the AB sites, although none has calcium in only one site. Calcium binding in domains 1 and 4 might be cooperative, but these speculations need to be substantiated using other techniques.

In annexins, the two calcium sites reside close together in each domain but are well separated from those in other domains. In annexin V, for example, the calcium atoms in the AB and DE loops of the same domain are only 12 Å apart, while distances between calcium atoms in AB loops of different domains range from 28 Å (domains 3 and 4) to 61 Å (domains 1 and 3) (13). In addition to close proximity, highly conserved interactions between the AB and DE loops occur in each domain (15, 35).

The crystallographic evidence suggests that annexin calcium sites typically do not undergo major conformational changes upon binding calcium. However, in domain 3 of annexin V, calcium appears to trigger the formation of the AB site, which then allows the DE site to form (6a, 15, 64a). It is possible that similar transitions occurring in other domains have not been detected crystallographically, because of factors such as crystal packing or crystallization conditions. Currently, available data are not sufficient to indicate whether creation of additional sites by ligand binding could occur elsewhere in the molecule in this or other annexins, though the existence of such sites has been hypothesized (see below).

Huber et al (37) have proposed that calcium-binding leads to a hinge-bending motion involving the two halves of the annexin molecule. Superimposition of different annexin V structures shows small but significant changes in the relative orientation of the two halves of the molecule (37, 43). Initially, this relative motion appeared to be a calcium-induced conformational change. Upon comparison of more crystal structures, the trend seems less a function of calcium content than crystal packing; however, it is still premature to discount the possibility of a calcium-dependent domain motion.

Phospholipid Membrane Binding

Efforts to cocrystallize annexins with phospholipids or their analogues so far have been unsuccessful. Therefore direct observation of the protein-phospholipid complex has not been possible, though details of these interactions have been inferred from other data. For annexins, the dependence of the calcium affinity on membrane binding has led to the assumption that the calcium-filled sites are directly involved in protein-membrane binding. Comparisons are also made to phospholipase A_2, another calcium-dependent, membrane-binding protein that has been studied in the presence of phospholipid analogues (62). In these phospholipase A_2 structures, phosphoryl and acyl backbone carbonyl oxygens displace two coordinating water molecules to directly coordinate calcium from the phospholipid. Annexin binding sites may interact similarly with phospholipids. In some annexin structures, sulfate ions are bound in close proximity to calcium atoms (15, 35), supporting the possibility of phosphoryl binding sites.

Crystallographic studies have not clarified the structural basis for apparent lipid head-group specificity. Conserved basic residues located near the calcium sites may account for the preference for acidic phospholipids (35). However, no specific binding site has been identified for either head groups or lipid acyl chain. If head groups indeed bind specifically to annexins, their diversity suggests that their binding sites on the protein are very flexible or contain few actual determinants. Conceivably, binding sites may be created by specific conformational changes not yet revealed by crystallographic analysis. An alternative view holds that only the phosphate glycerol backbone region is required for phospholipid binding and that the apparent head-group specificity does not arise from actual binding of these moieties to the protein (48).

Annexin interactions with phospholipid bilayers may be facilitated by hydrophobic residues on the convex surface that are positioned to insert locally into the bilayer. In annexin V, these hydrophobic residues are found in the AB loops (Figure 1), where they extend away from the molecule. One such residue, a tryptophan in domain 3, exhibits a dramatic positional shift when the AB loop binds calcium: the side chain moves from a buried position in the protein hydrophobic core to a fully extended, solvent-exposed position (15). Fluorescence spectroscopic studies have detected this calcium-induced transition in solution and have noted that, in the presence of membranes, the tryptophan appears to insert into the membrane near the phospholipid phosphate-glycerol backbone region (47). This behavior and location is probably functionally important for annexin V. Tryptophan residues are frequently found at the lipid bilayer interface in membrane proteins, where they may be involved in stabilizing correct protein-membrane orientation and other electrostatic interactions (34).

Annexin interactions with phospholipid membranes differ greatly from phospholipase A_2 interactions with such membranes, despite some structural similarity in the calcium-binding sites of these proteins. Annexins bind to bilayer or micellar structures, and available evidence suggests that binding sites for membrane components reside on the protein surface rather than the interior. In contrast, phospholipase A_2 extracts phospholipid monomers from the bilayer into a relatively rigid, interior binding site, where hydrolysis is catalyzed (62). Therefore, the similarity in binding sites between these two otherwise unrelated classes of proteins appears to simply reflect low-affinity calcium binding at the membrane surface, rather than a more specific relationship based on common function or divergent evolution.

Annexin Self-Association and Quaternary Structure

Annexin II forms a heterotetramer, calpactin, in which two annexin II molecules combine with two smaller subunits that resemble the S-100 protein of the calmodulin family (17). Most other annexins form stable monomers, though calcium-dependent self-association has been observed (14, 57, 71). In addition, crystallization of annexins bound to phospholipid monolayers has been described in studies using image analysis of electron microscopic data (52, 53). Annexin self-association data provided through other techniques also may reflect crystallization rather than assembly of smaller oligomers. Since many annexins are present at high concentrations in cells, the property of forming crystalline arrays may be important for annexin function.

Crystalline arrays of trimeric annexin V in the membrane-bound state have been visualized through image analysis of electron micrographs of two-dimensional (2D) crystals (52) and inferred with chemical cross-linking (14). In the 2D crystals, the side-by-side trimeric protein-protein contacts leave the convex surface free to associate with the membrane surface. Repeating trimers appear in rhombohedral crystal forms of annexin V (15, 37), implying that the favorable lateral protein-protein contacts involved in 2D crystals may be utilized to build three-dimensional (3D) crystals as well. In solution, trimerization of annexin V requires both calcium and phospholipid membranes (14, 58). A growing consensus among investigators is that trimeric annexin V, perhaps as part of a crystalline array, is the active form of the protein, and this form has been implicated in processes such as enzyme inhibition (2). Annexin VI also forms trimeric 2D crystals on lipid monolayers (53). Similar crystallization was reported for 2D crystals of membrane-bound annexin IV, but these crystals were later discovered to be annexin V rather than IV (22).

Dimerization of annexins also may occur in a physiologically relevant context. At least one 3D crystal form of annexin V contains dimers that pack with their concave surfaces in close contact (43). This self-association is consistent with a mechanism proposed for membrane aggregation, though annexin V itself does not promote this event (see next section).

ANNEXIN INTERACTIONS WITH PHOSPHOLIPID MEMBRANES

Annexins: Transmembrane or Peripheral Membrane Proteins?

The calcium-dependent interaction of annexins with membrane bilayers is widely considered to be peripheral, although annexins exhibit some features of integral rather than soluble proteins. The easy purification of annexins from natural sources and the observed reversibility of their membrane binding caused by calcium chelators indicate that the proteins bind to the bilayer surface and do not solubilize in the bilayer core. However, bovine tissues contain annexin V and VI isoforms that are resistant to calcium chelators but can be solubilized with detergent (8).

The observed in vitro voltage-dependent calcium channel activity in certain annexins (56) has given rise to proposed mechanisms of interaction between annexin and membrane referred to in the following discussion as transmembrane or peripheral. In support of the transmembrane mechanism, the central hydrophilic pore and surrounding four-helix bundles in the annexin molecule are oriented perpendicular to the membrane bilayer. These features are consistent with those observed in current models of other ion-channel proteins. However, other aspects of annexin structure are inconsistent with this view. The annexin V helices with the correct orientation to span the membrane bilayer are, on average, 6–8 residues shorter than required for known membrane-spanning helices (36). In addition, the hydrophilic annexin surfaces are unlikely to insert into the hydrophobic bilayer without a massive rearrangement in protein tertiary structure. Such a rearrangement, though postulated for colicin (36), has never been documented for protein structures.

The peripheral mechanism of annexin-membrane interactions favors local perturbation of the membrane by the protein rather than complete insertion of the protein into the bilayer. In this mechanism, annexin binding to the membrane surface induces disorder on both sides of the membrane (illustrated in Figure 3), leading to increased ion permeability (35). The disorder may result from a direct interaction of annexin-bound calcium ions with the phosphoryl group of the underlying phospholipid, thus changing its geometry. Annexins also may contribute to local destabilization of the membrane by exerting a strong electrostatic field at the protein-membrane interface, leading to pore formation (electroporation effect) (35, 41).

The earliest evidence supporting the peripheral mechanism for annexin-bilayer interactions preceded the first annexin crystal structure determination. Newman and coworkers (53) found that the calcium-dependent binding of annexin VI to a phospholipid monolayer increases the surface pressure formed at the air-water interface. However, the surface pressure increase is smaller than that caused by peptides known to insert into monolayers. These results are consistent with partial penetration of annexins into the monolayer, causing steric or electrostatic perturbation of the monolayer. A small-angle neutron scattering

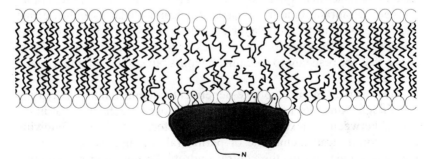

Figure 3 Cartoon suggesting a way that the annexin V molecule (*gray*) might bind to membrane in the peripheral model, creating local disorder in lipid bilayer. Convex protein surface includes the four AB loops with calcium ions shown as dots; N-terminal region shown facing cytosol.

(SANS) study of annexin V has found that the protein layer on the surface of small unilamellar vesicles (SUVs) is approximately 35 Å deep (58). In crystal structures, the annexin V molecule has a thickness of roughly 30 Å in the direction perpendicular to the membrane. Thus the SANS results support the view of a protein shell consisting of a single layer of annexin molecules situated on the vesicular surface, with little or no insertion of the molecule into the bilayer.

Effects of Annexin Binding on Membrane Parameters

The consequences of annexin V binding to SUV membrane components have been studied using NMR spectroscopy. Proton T_1 relaxation measurements of the phospholipid acyl-chain protons in the bilayer have detected no effect of annexin binding on the hydrocarbon-chain segmental motions. Yet changes in ^{31}P-NMR resonances from the phospholipid phosphate moiety under the same experimental conditions have shown a significant protein-induced effect on the phospholipid head groups of the inner and outer vesicular surfaces (MA Swairjo, MF Roberts, M-B Campos, JR Dedman & BA Seaton, unpublished results). Since the integrity of the vesicles did not change during the experiments, these results support the concept of local perturbation of membranes, induced by protein binding.

The formation of two-dimensional arrays of annexin molecules may be instrumental in creating local perturbations in membranes, through shape-determining effects. Cryoelectron micrographs of large unilamellar vesicles (LUVs), incubated with annexin V in the presence of calcium, show vesicles with multiple facets and sharp edges (2). The facets have been interpreted as rigid sheets, as large as 100×100 nm, of membrane-bound protein clusters that induce regional surface deformations in the membrane while the overall bilayer structure remains intact. Calcium promotes formation of these two-dimensional clusters, and ^{31}P-NMR spectral changes induced by calcium-dependent annexin V binding to phospholipid SUVs are consistent with reduced membrane curvature (MA Swairjo, MF Roberts, M-B Campos, JR Dedman & BA Seaton, unpublished results).

The effect of annexins on phospholipid lateral mobility and segregation has been investigated in several spectroscopic studies. Bazzi and coworkers have observed that annexin VI induces extensive calcium-dependent fluorescence quenching in small vesicles impregnated with phospholipids in which the head groups are fluorescently labeled (5, 6). These results are consistent with clustering of acidic phospholipids in association with annexin molecules rather than in extended regions of pure acidic lipids. Meers and coworkers (46) have conducted a similar fluorescence investigation of annexin V, using phospholipids with pyrene-labeled acyl chains. Their results suggest decreased lateral mobility of the phospholipids but no evidence of lipid segregation (46). In an electron paramagnetic resonance study, annexins IV and VI appear to reverse the lipid-segregating effects of calcium in large phosphatidylserine (PS)–phosphatidylcholine vesicles. Formation of the annexin-Ca^{2+}-phospholipid ternary complex may disrupt the $Ca^{2+}(PS)_2$ complex that would otherwise form extended patches (64). These various studies are in general agreement that annexin binding is incompatible with, and may disrupt, formation of extended patches of pure acidic phospholipid and therefore does not promote widespread lipid segregation.

EXAMPLES OF ANNEXIN IN VITRO FUNCTIONS: PROPOSED MOLECULAR MECHANISMS

Membrane Bridging by Annexins

One of the first in vitro properties of annexins to be identified was the calcium-dependent ability to aggregate negatively charged phospholipid vesicles (9, 67), adrenal chromaffin granules (18, 23, 71), and purified intracellular organelles (67). Aggregation frequently is accompanied by vesicle or membrane fusion (9). Kinetic analysis of liposomal fusion has revealed that annexins I and VII accelerate the aggregation of vesicles but do not mediate the fusion event itself (45, 49). The currently accepted view is that annexins are not fusogenic proteins but act as a glue or bridge bringing two membranes in tight contact, thus accelerating membrane fusion.

In studies using resonance energy transfer, Meers and coworkers found that the contact point between fusing vesicles aggregated with annexin I is minimal rather than extensive (49). A similar observation has been made in electron micrographs of fusing chromaffin granules (16). A minimal contact point is consistent with a controlled fusion process in which the point of contact is established by the annexin and the vesicular contents are retained in the fused vesicle. This process is unlike that induced by the effect of calcium on acidic phospholipid vesicles, in which large areas of contact and general vesicle lysis may result.

Various cofactors may act with annexins to promote fusion. In the presence of calcium, annexin I substantially increases the rate of fusion of PS-phosphatidylethanolamine vesicles with neutrophil plasma membrane preparations (25, 54). However, trypsin-treated plasma membranes cannot fuse with liposomes, and addition of purified annexins to the trypsin-treated membranes did not restore fusion properties (54). Similarly, annexin-catalyzed fusion of sonicated native biological membranes is decreased when the membranes are lipid extracted and resonicated (67). These results suggest that plasma membrane proteins other than annexins are required for fusion to occur (54, 67). The observation that whole cells do not fuse with liposomes, even in the presence of annexins, implicates components on the cytosolic side of the membrane in the fusion process (54). Annexin VII–mediated fusion of chromaffin granules and of liposomes is greatly assisted by the addition of unsaturated free fatty acids (16), which appear to act in vitro as cofactors that mediate the actual fusion process.

The mechanism by which some annexins bridge two membrane bilayers is not yet understood at the molecular level, though some aspects have been established. Researchers generally agree that the N-terminal region of annexins is critical for determining functions such as membrane bridging. Furthermore, N-terminus phosphorylation (68) or antibody treatment (49) strongly inhibits the membrane-aggregating effect of annexin I. Additional data have been provided through studies of annexin I_N-V_C, a chimeric protein engineered to have the N-terminal domain of annexin I and the core of annexin V (3). This protein exhibits phospholipid binding properties identical to those exhibited by annexin V. However, unlike annexin V, the chimera has the annexin I–associated ability to aggregate vesicles.

Many other aspects of membrane bridging remain controversial. Currently, three distinct hypotheses explain membrane bridging by annexins. For simplicity, these are distinguished in the following discussion as the one-annexin, two-annexin, and hydrophobic-bridge models.

In the one-annexin model, two membranes are bridged by a single annexin molecule that has undergone a conformational transition. Ellipsometry experiments investigating the adhesion of phospholipid vesicles to annexin I_N-V_C bound to a planar bilayer support this model. Andree and coworkers have shown that vesicle adherence is proportional to the surface coverage of bound annexin (3) , which is consistent with a single layer of protein (1, 52). When the annexin-coated bilayer is washed and incubated with protein-free vesicles, the vesicles adhere to the bilayer (3). These results indicate that a single layer of bound annexin is sufficient for membrane bridging. Meers and coworkers (49) obtained similar results in resonance energy transfer studies.

On a molecular level, two alternate mechanisms for the one-annexin model of membrane bridging have been suggested. In the first, the annexin molecule partially anchors itself to one membrane, using only some of the available binding sites on the convex surface of the protein. Then a conformational change, such as a hinge-bending motion between the two halves of the annexin molecule, allows the remaining binding sites on the convex surface to attach to a second membrane (49, 71). In the second mechanism, the annexin molecule binds to the first membrane fully, using all or most of the binding sites at the convex surface. This binding event induces a protein conformational change that exposes latent phospholipid binding sites elsewhere in the molecule (3), such as at the concave surface. Preliminary evidence is available to support each mechanism. However, neither proposed conformational change is supported by available crystallographic data, though much remains to be learned about the range of conformations that can be adopted by annexin molecules.

The two-annexin model arose from work performed in the late 1970s, primarily through the research of Creutz and coworkers on adrenal medullary chromaffin granule aggregation by annexin VII (for an overview, see 17). In this model, membranes are bridged through interactions between two annexins, each attached to a different membrane.

Resonance energy transfer experiments have provided evidence that the two-annexin model may operate at low calcium concentrations, whereas the one-annexin model may work at higher calcium levels (71). In these experiments, protein-protein interactions occurring on the same or different membranes could be distinguished. With annexins IV and VII, low calcium concentrations (<1 mM) enhance intermembrane energy transfer during aggregation of chromaffin granules, which suggests annexin molecules bound to different membranes interact (i.e. a two-annexin model). At high calcium concentrations (>1 mM), the same two annexins inhibit intermembrane energy transfer during aggregation. This inhibition may result from competition between the two modeled interactions in which conformational change in the annexin molecule disfavors the intermembrane annexin-annexin contacts. As a result, the one-annexin model interactions predominate under these conditions.

The third (hydrophobic bridge) model (57) is based on the assumption that the annexin molecule inserts across the lipid bilayer. In this model, calcium induces formation of highly hydrophobic polymers of annexin VII. The hydrophobic polymer inserts into two membranes simultaneously, thereby bridging and eventually fusing the membranes. This model would require a massive structural arrangement in the annexin core region that has not been observed. However, no detailed structural information is known for the large (167–189 residues), N-terminal region of annexin VII, which may impart unique properties to the entire molecule.

Molecular Models of Annexins as Ion Channel Proteins

The in vitro voltage-gated ion channel activity of annexins has been modeled for annexins V and VII. The model presented by Huber and coworkers (35, 41) is based on the crystal structure of human annexin V and electrostatic calculations. In this model, the hydrophilic central cavity acts as the calcium channel. The channel is funnel shaped, with the mouth facing the membrane surface. The inner sides of the funnel are lined with two ionic clusters that form numerous salt bridges. Each ionic cluster corresponds to a gate in the mechanical gating model. Purportedly, salt-bridge rearrangements that change the ion pairs in these clusters would change the protein conformation, leading to a change in ion conductance properties. In this model, the annexin molecule remains peripherally associated with the membrane and exerts its effects chiefly through electrostatic perturbation of the membrane. Experimental support for this model comes from studies of an annexin V variant in which a glutamic acid located in the center of the channel was mutated to serine. This mutation changes ion conductance properties without altering the protein's structure or organization on phospholipid monolayers (6a).

An alternative model, proposed by Pollard and coworkers, focuses on annexin VII (57). In this view, the molecule inserts across the membrane bilayer through a large-scale alteration in protein structure. The α-helices, most of which are amphipathic, reorient so that their polar surfaces face inward and apolar surfaces face outward. The resulting apolar sheath is in contact with the hydrophobic environment of the lipid bilayer. The original annexin domain structure rearranges to form a so-called TIM (named for triose phosphate isomerase) barrel, a donut-shaped structural motif that features a central hole lined with antiparallel β-sheets and surrounded by α-helices. The model predicts that the annexin AB and DE interhelical loops form an eight-member β-sheet structure around the hole, which acts as an ion-conducting pathway. This model structure, resembling a hollow screw penetrating the membrane, also forms the structural basis for the hydrophobic-bridge hypothesis of membrane fusion, described above.

Experimental support for this second ion channel model has yet to be presented, and the prediction of a massive conformational change in the annexin conserved core seems unlikely in view of available structural data on annexin V (6a, 10, 52). Circular dichroism studies of annexin V show no change between soluble and membrane-bound forms of the protein in the presence of calcium (MA Swairjo, unpublished results). Conceivably, through its unique N-terminal region, annexin VII could adopt a very different membrane-bound structure than annexin V.

Whether gated ion channel activity in annexins is important in vivo and whether the annexin monomer is the sole channel-forming unit are issues that need to be investigated further. Neither the relatively high cellular content found for many annexins nor their tendency to form extended protein sheets on membrane surfaces correlate well with the proposed ion channel function unless a regulatory mechanism, as yet unknown, exists in these cells. Distinctions also have to be made regarding the role of annexins in calcium-specific, voltage-gated ion conductance, as opposed to changes in ion permeability caused by perturbation of membrane properties.

CONCLUDING REMARKS

Considerably more structural information is needed to confirm the models and mechanisms described in this review, though each provides a useful starting point for further studies. Site-directed mutagenesis studies should be useful in identifying residues important for particular properties that may be related to function. Expansion of the data base of crystal structures will facilitate comparison between different annexins and between alternate conformational states. The structure of bovine liver annexin IV was recently solved (B Sutton & S Sprang, personal communication), and there are new structures of annexin I (S Raghunathan, RH Kretsinger, M Junker & CE Creutz, personal communication) and annexin V (64a; P Freemont, personal communication), with others in progress. More characterization is needed of the thermal properties of lipid bilayers with bound annexins, as well as details related to parameters such as ion permeability. The role of annexin self-assembly and interactions with other proteins also need to be explored further.

Molecular mechanisms of interactions between proteins and membranes remain a frontier of cell biology. The relationship between the structural biology of annexins and the dynamic behavior of membranes promises development of new lines of investigation. Their modular structures, oriented self-assembly, and membrane-binding properties suggest that annexins are unique cellular proteins that may point to a novel mode of mediating the intracellular calcium signal.

ACKNOWLEDGMENTS

We thank Drs. N Concha, J Dedman, J Head, M Kaetzel, and P Meers for comments on the manuscript and discussions. This work was supported by NIH grant #GM-44554 (BAS).

Literature Cited

1. Andree HAM, Reutelingsperger CPM, Hauptmann R, Hemker HC, Hermens WTh, Willems GM. 1990. Binding of vascular anticoagulant α (VACα) to planar phospholipid bilayers. *J. Biol. Chem.* 265:4923
2. Andree HAM, Stuart MCA, Hermens WTh, Reutelingsperger CPM, Hemker HC, et al. 1992. Clustering of lipid-bound annexin-V may explain its anticoagulant effect. *J. Biol. Chem.* 267:17907
3. Andree HAM, Willems GM, Hauptmann R, Maurer-Fogy I, Stuart MCA, Hermens WTh, et al. 1993. Aggregation of phospholipid vesicles by a chimeric protein with the N-terminus of annexin I and the core of annexin V. *Biochemistry* 32:4634
4. Bazzi MD, Nelsestuen GL. 1991. Highly sequential binding of protein kinase C and related proteins to membranes. *Biochemistry* 30:7970
5. Bazzi MD, Nelsestuen GL. 1991. Extensive segregation of acidic phospholipids in membranes induced by protein kinase C and related proteins. *Biochemistry* 30:7961
6. Bazzi MD, Nelsestuen GL. 1992. Interaction of annexin VI with membranes: highly restricted dissipation of clustered phospholipids in membranes containing phosphatidylethanolamine. *Biochemistry* 31:10406
6a. Berendes R, Voges D, Demange P, Huber R, Burger A. 1993. Structure-function analysis of the ion channel selectivity filter in human annexin V. *Science* 262:427
7. Bewley MC, Boustead CM, Walker JH, Waller DA, Huber R. 1993. Structure of chicken annexin V at 2.25-Å resolution. *Biochemistry* 32:3923
8. Bianchi R, Giambanco I, Ceccarelli P, Pula G, Donato R. 1992. Membrane-bound annexin V isoforms (CaBP33 and

CaBP37) and annexin VI in bovine tissues behave like integral membrane proteins. *FEBS Lett.* 296:158
9. Blackwood RA, Ernst JD. 1990. Characterization of Ca^{2+}-dependent phospholipid binding, vesicle aggregation and membrane fusion by annexins. *Biochem. J.* 266:195
10. Brisson A, Mosser G, Huber R. 1991. Structure of soluble and membrane-bound human annexin V. *J. Mol. Biol.* 220:199
11. Burgoyne RD, Geisow MJ. 1989. The annexin family of calcium-binding proteins. *Cell Calcium* 10:1
12. Burns AL, Magendzo K, Shirvan A, Srivastava M, Alijani M, et al. 1989. Calcium channel activity of purified human synexin and structure of the human gene. *Proc. Natl. Acad. Sci. USA* 86:3798
13. Concha NO. 1993. *The crystal structure of the rat annexin V protein, and its self-association on the surface of membranes.* PhD thesis. Boston Univ., Boston, MA. 153 pp.
14. Concha NO, Head JF, Kaetzel MA, Dedman JR, Seaton BA. 1992. Annexin-V forms calcium dependent trimeric units on phospholipid vesicles. *FEBS Lett.* 314:159
15. Concha NO, Head JF, Kaetzel MA, Dedman JR, Seaton BA. 1993. Rat annexin V crystal structure: Ca^{2+}-induced conformational changes. *Science* 261:1321
16. Creutz CE. 1981. *Cis*-unsaturated fatty acids induce diffusion of chromaffin granules aggregated by synexin. *J. Cell. Biol.* 91:247
17. Creutz CE. 1992. The annexins and exocytosis. *Science* 258:924
18. Creutz CE, Pazoles CJ, Pollard HB. 1978. Identification and purification of an adrenal medullary protein (synexin) that causes calcium-dependent aggre-

212   SWAIRJO & SEATON

gation of isolated chromaffin granules. *J. Biol. Chem.* 253:2858

19. Crompton MR, Moss SE, Crumpton MJ. 1988. Diversity in the lipocortin/calpactin family. *Cell* 55:1
20. Crumpton MJ, Dedman JR. 1990. Protein terminology tangle. *Nature* 345:212
21. Das SK, Chakrabarti P, Tsao FHC, Nayyar T, Mukherjee S. 1992. Identification of calcium-dependent phospholipid-binding proteins (annexins) from guinea pig alveolar type II cells. *Mol. Cell. Biochem.* 115:79
22. Driessen HPC, Newman RH, Freemont PS, Crumpton MJ. 1992. A model of the structure of human annexin VI bound to lipid monolayers. *FEBS Lett.* 306:75
23. Drust D, Creutz CE. 1988. Aggregation of chromaffin granules by calpactin at micromolar levels of calcium. *Nature* 331:88
24. Drust D, Creutz CE. 1991. Differential subcellular distribution of p36 (the heavy chain of calpactin I) and other annexins in the adrenal medulla. *J. Neurochem.* 56:469
25. Francis JW, Balazovich KJ, Smolen JE, Margolis DI, Boxer LA. 1992. Human neutrophil annexin I promotes granule aggregation and modulates Ca^{2+}-dependent membrane fusion. *J. Clin. Invest.* 90:537
26. Funakoshi T, Heimark RL, Hendrickson LE, McMullen BA, Fujikawa K. 1987. Human placental anticoagulant protein: isolation and characterization. *Biochemistry* 26:5572
27. Geisow MJ. 1986. Common domain structure of Ca^{2+} and lipid-binding proteins. *FEBS Lett.* 203:99
28. Geisow MJ, Fritsche U, Hexham JM, Dash B, Johnson T. 1986. A consensus amino-acid sequence repeat in *Torpedo* and mammalian Ca^{2+}-dependent membrane-binding proteins. *Nature* 320:636
29. Geisow MJ, Walker JH. 1986. New proteins involved in cell regulation by Ca^{2+} and phospholipids. *Trends Biol. Sci.* 11: 420
30. Genge BR, Wu LNY, Adkisson IV HD, Wuthier RE. 1991. Matrix vesicle annexins exhibit proteolipid-like properties. *J. Biol. Chem.* 266:10678
31. Haigler HT, Schlaepfer DD. 1992. Annexin I phosphorylation and secretion. See Ref. 51a, pp. 11–22
32. Hazarika P, Kaetzel MA, Sheldon A, Karin NJ, Fleischer S, et al. 1991. Annexin VI is associated with calcium-sequestering organelles. *J. Cell. Biochem.* 46:78
33. Hofmann C, Gropp R, von der Mark K. 1992. Expression of anchorin CII, a collagen-binding protein of the annexin family, in the developing chick embryo. *Dev. Biol.* 151:391
34. Hu W, Lee K-C, Cross TA. 1993. Tryptophans in membrane proteins: indole ring orientations and functional implications in the gramicidin channel. *Biochemistry* 32:7035
35. Huber R, Berendes R, Burger A, Schneider M, Karshikov A, et al. 1992. Crystal and molecular structure of human annexin V after refinement. *J. Mol. Biol.* 223:683
36. Huber R, Römisch J, Paques E-P. 1990. The crystal and molecular structure of human annexin V, an anticoagulant protein that binds to calcium and membranes. *EMBO J.* 9:3867
37. Huber R, Schneider M, Mayr I, Römisch J, Paques E-P. 1990. The calcium binding sites in human annexin V by crystal structure analysis at 2.0 Å resolution. *FEBS Lett.* 275:15
38. Ikebuchi NW, Waisman DM. 1990. Calcium-dependent regulation of actin filament bundling by lipocortin-85. *J. Biol. Chem.* 265:3392
39. Johnston PA, Perin MS, Reynolds GA, Wasserman SA, Südhof TC. 1990. Two novel annexins from *Drosophila melanogaster*. *J. Biol. Chem.* 265:11382
40. Kaetzel MA, Hazarika P, Dedman JR. 1989. Differential tissue expression of three 35-kDa annexin calcium-dependent phospholipid-binding proteins. *J. Biol. Chem.* 264:14463
41. Karshikov A, Berendes R, Burger A, Cavalié A, Lux H-D. 1992. Annexin V membrane interaction: an electrostatic potential study. *Eur. Biophys. J.* 20:337
42. Klee CB. 1988. Ca^{2+}-dependent phospholipid- (and membrane-) binding proteins. *Biochemistry* 27:6645
43. Lewit-Bentley A, Morera S, Huber R, Bodo G. 1992. The effect of metal binding on the structure of annexin V and implications for membrane binding. *Eur. J. Biochem.* 210:73
44. McPhalen CA, Strynadka NCJ, James MNG. 1991. Calcium-binding sites in proteins: a structural perspective. *Adv. Protein Chem.* 42:77
45. Meers P, Bentz J, Alford D, Nir S, Papahadjopoulos D, Hong K. 1988. Synexin enhances the aggregation rate but not the fusion rate of liposomes. *Biochemistry* 27:4430
46. Meers P, Daleke D, Hong K, Papahadjopoulos D. 1991. Interactions of annexins with membrane phospholipids. *Biochemistry* 30:2903
47. Meers P, Mealy T. 1993. Relationship between annexin V tryptophan expo-

sure, calcium, and phospholipid binding. *Biochemistry* 32:5411

48. Meers P, Mealy T. 1993. Annexin V binding to phospholipids: stoichiometry, specificity and the role of negative charge. *Biochemistry*. 32:11711

49. Meers P, Mealy T, Pavlotsky N, Tauber AI. 1992. Annexin I-mediated vesicular aggregation; mechanism and role in human neutrophils. *Biochemistry* 31: 6372

50. Mizutani A, Usuda N, Tokumitsu H, Minami H, Yasui K, et al. 1992. CAP-50, a newly identified annexin, localizes in nuclei of cultured fibroblast 3Y1 cells. *J. Biol. Chem.* 267:13498

51. Moss SE. 1992. The annexins. See Ref. 51a, pp. 1–9

51a. Moss SE, ed. 1992. *The Annexins*. London: Portland

52. Mosser G, Ravanat C, Freyssinet J-M, Brisson A. 1991. Sub-domain structure of lipid-bound annexin-V resolved by electron image analysis. *J. Mol. Biol.* 217:241

52a. Nakayama S, Kretsinger RH. 1994. Evolution of the EF-Hand family of proteins. *Annu. Rev. Biophys. Biomol. Struct.* 23:000–00

53. Newman R, Tucker A, Ferguson C, Tsernoglou D, Leonard K, Crumpton MJ. 1989. Crystallization of p68 on lipid monolayers and as three-dimensional single crystals. *J. Mol. Biol.* 206:213

54. Oshry L, Meers P, Mealy T, Tauber AI. 1991. Annexin-mediated membrane fusion of human neutrophil plasma membranes and phospholipid vesicles. *Biochim. Biophys. Acta* 1066:239

55. Pepinsky RB, Tizard R, Mattaliano RJ, Sinclair LK, Miller GT, et al. 1988. Five distinct calcium and phospholipid binding proteins share homology with lipocortin I. *J. Biol. Chem.* 263:10799

56. Pollard HB, Guy HR, Arispe N, de la Fuente M, Lee G, et al. 1992 Calcium channel and membrane fusion activity of synexin and other members of the annexin gene family. *Biophys. J.* 62:15

57. Pollard HB, Rojas E, Merezhinskaya N, Kuijpers GAJ, Srivastava M, et al. 1992. Synexin (annexin VII). See Ref. 51a, pp. 89–103

58. Ravanat C, Torbet J, Freyssinet J-M. 1992. A neutron solution scattering study of the structure of annexin-V and its binding to lipid vesicles. *J. Mol. Biol.* 226:1271

59. Russo-Marie F. 1992. Annexins, phospholipase A₂ and the glucocorticoids. See Ref. 51a, pp. 35–46

60. Schlaepfer DD, Haigler HT. 1987. Characterization of Ca^{2+}-dependent phospholipid binding and phosphorylation of lipocortin I. *J. Biol. Chem.* 262:6931

61. Schlaepfer DD, Mehlman T, Burgess WH, Haigler HT. 1987. Structural and functional characterization of endonexin II, a calcium- and phospholipid-binding protein. *Proc. Natl. Acad. Sci. USA* 84:6078

62. Scott DL, White SP, Otwinowski Z, Yuan W, Gelb MH, Sigler PB. 1990. Interfacial catalysis: the mechanism of phospholipase A₂. *Science* 250:1541

63. Smith VL, Kaetzel MA, Dedman JR. 1990. Stimulus-response coupling: the search for intracellular calcium mediator proteins. *Cell Reg.* 1:165

64. Sobota A, Bandorowicz J, Jezierski A, Sikorski AF. 1993. The effect of annexin IV and VI on the fluidity of phosphatidylserine/phosphatidylcholine bilayers studied with the use of 5-deoxylstearate spin label. *FEBS Lett.* 315:178

64a. Sopkova J, Renouard M, Lewit-Bentley A. 1993. The crystal structure of a new high-calcium form of annexin V. *J. Mol. Biol.* In press

65. Tait JF, Gibson D, Fujikawa K. 1989. Phospholipid binding properties of human placental anticoagulant protein-I, a member of the lipocortin family. *J. Biol. Chem.* 264:7944

66. Taylor WR, Geisow MJ. 1987. Predicted structure for the calcium-dependent membrane-binding proteins p35, p36, and p32. *Protein Eng.* 1:183

67. Tsao FHC. 1990. Purification and characterization of two rabbit lung Ca^{2+}-dependent phospholipid-binding proteins. *Biochim. Biophys. Acta* 1045:29

68. Wang W, Creutz CE. 1992. Regulation of chromaffin granule aggregating activity of annexin I by phosphorylation. *Biochemistry* 31:9934

69. Weng X, Luecke H, Song IS, Kang DS, Kim S-H, Huber R. 1993. Crystal structure of human annexin I at 2.5Å resolution. *Protein Sci.* 2:448

70. Yoshizaki H, Hashimoto Y, Arai K, Ohkuchi M, Shiratsuchi M, et al. 1991. Phospholipid-binding properties of calphobindin-II (annexin VI), an anticoagulant protein from human placenta. *Chem. Pharm. Bull.* 39:2617

71. Zaks WJ, Creutz CE. 1991. Ca^{2+}-dependent annexin self-association on membrane surfaces. *Biochemistry* 30: 9607

Annu. Rev. Biophys. Biomol. Struct. 1994. 23:215–45

NONRESONANCE RAMAN DIFFERENCE SPECTROSCOPY: A General Probe of Protein Structure, Ligand Binding, Enzymatic Catalysis, and the Structures of Other Biomacromolecules

Robert Callender and Hua Deng

Department of Physics, City College of the City University of New York, New York, NY 10031

KEY WORDS: vibrational spectroscopy, emerging technique, enzymes, active sites, energy-vibrational frequency correlations

CONTENTS

215

PERSPECTIVES AND OVERVIEW

Both infrared and Raman spectroscopies measure the vibrational frequency of a group of bonded atoms. The masses of the atoms and the force constants of the various bonds between the atoms determine this frequency, from which bond orders and bond lengths can be surmised (cf 29). The interactions that take place between molecular groups, such as hydrogen bonding, affect the force constants of certain bonds and, hence, vibrational frequencies. Thus, one can probe the energies of hydrogen bonds directly by examing shifts in the frequencies of certain bands from so-called Badger-Bauer relationships (2). This method for determining these parameters is very accurate; it is generally more accurate than probes of protein structure such as X-ray crystallographic and multidimensional NMR studies. On the other hand, while vibrational spectroscopy measures on a very fine scale, one cannot determine the full conformation or configuration of a protein from its vibrational spectrum—at least not at present. Hence, the information that these probes provide is quite synergetic.

Despite the obvious value vibrational spectroscopy could have in the determination of biomacromolecular structure, spectral crowding has greatly hampered its use. Many vibrational modes contribute to the spectrum of a protein at each frequency because the bandwidth of a given mode is relatively broad, making the spectrum very difficult to interpret. Selective measurements are usually necessary to obtain understandable results. Hence, resonance Raman spectroscopy is often performed using chromophores inside proteins. Because of resonance enhancement, the spectrum of the chromophore dominates the observed spectrum (cf 13, 49, 50). Also, Fourier transform infrared (FTIR) difference spectroscopy is widely used in systems that contain a photolabile chromophore, such as e.g. bacteriorhodopsin or the photosynthetic reaction center. In this technique, light is used to switch protein films from one state to another. This preserves the optical geometry to achieve a high degree of subtraction fidelity, and only those protein vibrational modes affected by the light are observed in the difference spectrum (cf 6–8, 41, 45). FTIR difference spectroscopy is also useful in studying proteins containing electrochemically switchable redox systems, such as cytochromes, hemoglobin, and the photosynthetic reaction center, so that one can control the state of the protein (reduced or oxidized) with the applied potential (cf 41). Although these methods are powerful and extremely useful in understanding the (very important) protein systems that fulfill the necessary experimental constraints for resonance Raman or light (redox)-induced

FTIR difference spectroscopy, they are not general methods for studying the structures of proteins or protein-ligand interactions as only certain systems and bonds can be studied.

In the past several years, very accurate nonresonance Raman difference spectroscopy, called simply Raman difference spectroscopy in this review, has emerged as a technically feasible, general method of probing protein structure (cf 10, 14, 19, 34, 42, 61). In such experiments, proteins are tagged in some way and the difference spectrum between the protein and its modified version measured. For example, one could measure a protein spectrum and the spectrum of a protein complexed with ligand. Subtraction of the two yields the spectrum of the bound ligand. Alternatively, an atom within a bond of interest could be labeled with a stable isotope (^2H, ^{13}C, ^{15}N, ^{18}O, etc), which shifts the frequency of the modes that involve the motion of the labeled atom. Subtraction of labeled and unlabeled protein spectra yields an isotopically edited difference spectrum that shows only those modes involving the labeled atom. These and other protocols, described below, provide sufficient selectivity and so yield an interpretable spectrum.

The analysis below suggests that discerning a particular band from the protein background requires a protein Raman signal with a signal-to-noise ratio in excess of 300/1; the Raman spectra of proteins can now be obtained in an hour with a signal-to-noise ratio of 1000/1. Moreover, water (H_2O or D_2O) generally has a very small Raman cross section, allowing the study of samples in their biological environment, and virtually the entire spectrum of a protein or protein-ligand complex can be measured. One can also obtain the spectrum of membrane-bound proteins (60). Thus, Raman difference spectroscopy can be used on most protein systems, and results are available in a relatively short period of time. Following similar protocols, investigators have recently successfully applied FTIR difference techniques to small proteins. This work was performed on samples in D_2O in order to move the intense and otherwise masking water absorption band from about 1640 cm^{-1}, the spectral region of interest for these experiments, down to 1200 cm^{-1} in order to study certain protein-ligand interactions (3, 47, 54, 55, 58, 59). This procedure may also develop into a general tool, particularly if some technique can be devised to overcome the problem of the strong water (H_2O or D_2O) absorption.

For the past few years, our laboratory has been developing techniques and protocols to perform Raman difference spectroscopy in order to better understand key aspects of protein structure in certain enzyme systems that interest us. The information we wanted was unavailable through other techniques, such as NMR and diffraction methods. These enzymes, it turned out, could also not be studied with res-onance Raman or FTIR difference spectroscopy, for the reasons outlined above. These studies showed the analysis potential for many other issues of protein structure of Raman difference spectroscopy; we have partially investigated some of these. This review is written for those who are interested in how proteins function and therefore are interested in their structures. For many problems, vibrational spec-troscopy is of real value, and Raman difference spectroscopy offers a method of measurement that can be used on most systems.

Virtually all work to date developing and using Raman difference spectroscopy of large molecules has been performed in our laboratory, and our work has essentially focused on proteins, so this review con-cerns only proteins. However, the methodology surely could be ex-tended to virtually any biomacromolecule and its assemblies. Indeed, the spectra of individual components of DNA assemblies were recently obtained using Raman difference spectroscopy (52).

GENERAL CONSIDERATIONS OF RAMAN DIFFERENCE SPECTROSCOPY

Raman Spectroscopy

In Raman spectroscopy, when light of a certain frequency (say ν_L since the light is usually produced by a laser) irradiates a sample, a (small) portion is scattered from the sample, and the frequency shifts by an amount corresponding to the frequency of a particular vibrational mode, ν_O. Thus, photons are emitted from the sample with a frequency of $\nu_L - \nu_O$. Because the frequency of the laser is known, the frequency of the vibrational mode can be determined. Figure 1 shows a Raman spectrometer set up. The universally used unit of the frequency is wav-enumbers (cm^{-1}), which is the reciprocal of the wavelength of ν_O ex-pressed in centimeters. The plotted spectrum is the intensity on the y-axis (usually in arbitrary units but proportional to the number of detected photons) versus frequency. Each peak in this plot cor-responds to the frequency of a vibrational mode.

Fluorescence is a general problem facing the execution of Raman spectroscopy. However, in the approach taken here, laser light in the visible (from the blue to the far red) is used to excite Raman scattering. This is known as nonresonance or classical Raman spectroscopy be-cause the protein samples under study, and their ligands, generally do not have visible-spectrum absorption bands. Thus, in principle, there is no fluorescence background because no absorption takes place; this chief advantage of the present approach is required for nonresonance Raman spectrscopy to function as a general probe. In practice, most biological samples contain trace amounts of impurities, and these may yield fluorescence. Of the 20 or so proteins we have studied over the past several years, about half of them were so contaminated. On the other hand, we have nearly always found purification routes (generally involving standard biochemical approaches) that have yielded samples sufficiently free of these impurities.

The characteristic time scale associated with vibrational spectroscopy is on the order of the vibrational motion ($\sim 10^{-13}$ s) or faster so that signal size and its characteristics are not affected by slow motions of the protein, such as tumbling or rotational motions, that affect NMR spectra. Thus large proteins are easy to study. In Figures 2 and 3 (see below), the Raman spectrum of a single phosphate group inside an $\sim$60-kDa protein is shown as is the spectrum of NADH bound to an $\sim$160-kDa protein. Certainly larger proteins may be studied as well.

In our work, we adapted a conventional Raman spectrometer to perform difference spectroscopy. The essential feature of the measurement is that the two parent spectra must be very accurate so that small differences between them show up without error in the difference spectrum. We first estimate the necessary accuracy of the spectrum, which is governed by essentially two parameters. One is the intensity of the parent spectra—both spectra must be large enough so that shot noise is small. The second is the spectral mismatch between the two spectra, because subtraction of two spectra that are not in register produces subtraction artifacts.

Anticipated Signal Size and Sources of Error in Raman Difference Spectroscopy

A typical protein contains a few hundred amino acid residues and has a weight of about 20–80 kDa. In Raman difference spectroscopy, most of the signal arising from the protein is subtracted out, and the question is how much signal-to-noise is necessary to detect the scattered light arising from a single vibrational mode from the protein background. The signal-to-noise ratios must be very high, but within the capabilities of present equipment. For example, a 40-kDa protein has approximately 4000 atoms, or 12,000 normal modes. Should about half these yield a signal, then 6000 bands comprise the spectrum. If we assume for this discussion that this signal is spread evenly over about 2000 cm^{-1} (not strictly valid, see below) and each band is 10 cm^{-1} in width, then some 30 normal modes contribute to the signal at each position of the observed spectrum. This estimate suggests that one must have a protein signal-to-noise ratio in excess of 300/1 to discern a particular band from the protein background (30 times stronger) with a signal-to-noise ratio of 10/1.

There are two sources of error in a protein spectrum that can adversely affect the signal-to-noise of the difference spectrum: so-called shot noise and systematic factors. Because shot noise arises from the statistical nature of the scattering process, it may be decreased with increased detected signal (signal-to-noise scales as the square root of the number of detected photons). Hence, much effort in recent technological developments of Raman spectroscopy has been devoted to more efficient collection optics and detectors. With biological samples in solution, to obtain shot noise of less than a percent of the protein Raman signal requires the use of optically fast detectors such as intensified diode arrays or charge-coupled devices, optical multichannel detector (OMA) systems. These instruments detect an entire portion of the spectrum simultaneously, and the spectrum of a protein in solution, at a concentration of a fraction of a millimolar, can be determined in about an hour with a signal-to-noise of better than 1000/1. Earlier work (32, 46) exploring Raman difference spectroscopy described Raman systems employing photomultiplier detectors. These spectrometer systems can yield an accurate difference spectrum, but take more than 100 times longer to do the measurement.

Systematic error factors comprise the most important experimental problem, and we have found the most critical determinant leading to an inaccurate subtraction of two spectra, say A and B, is that the signal from run A hits the OMA detector with a small spectral displacement with respect to the signal from run B. Consequently, the two spectra appear to be shifted in frequency, and identical signals present in the two runs do not subtract to zero but yield a difference spectrum resembling a derivative. The apparent frequency difference can be very small and yet yield a substantial difference intensity (e.g. 46, 61). The magnitude of the systematic error can be reduced to an effective shift in frequency between the two samples. For example, the maximum in the derivative signal, which we will call ΔI_{max}, can be calculated if the shape of the band is known. Assuming a Gaussian band shape with peak intensity of $I(0)$ and a full width at half maximum Γ, for small misalignments (61):

$$\Delta I_{max}/I(0) = 1.4(\delta/\Gamma).$$ 1.

where δ is the apparent frequency shift due to effective spectrometer misalignment. A Lorentzian line shape will change the numerical factor to 1.9. This equation shows that the apparent difference signal becomes significant whenever δ becomes large or Γ becomes small. Thus, how well the protein background subtracts out depends on the bandwidth of the protein band. A protein amide-I band is typically 50 cm^{-1} broad so that the apparent frequency shift, δ, must be kept to less than 0.1 cm^{-1} if we wish to maintain a $\Delta I_{max}/I(0)$ of 0.3% or better. Most proteins also contain sharp bands, such as the phenylalanine mode at 1004 cm^{-1}, which has a bandwidth of only 10 cm^{-1}. In this case, δ must be kept to less than 0.02 cm^{-1} to accurately subtract out this band. These are quite tight requirements for currently available spectrometer systems, but they are feasible, as shown below. That sharp bands are more difficult to subtract out than broad bands has been illustrated (61).

The Difference Raman Spectrometer Used in Our Studies

Our Raman spectra are measured using a conventional Raman spectrometer employing an optical multichannel analyzer (OMA) system as depicted in Figure 1 (10, 61). Typically, 100 mW of visible light from either an argon ion or krypton ion laser is used to excite Raman scattering, and a typical experiment takes one to two hours. We can detect about 1200 cm^{-1} of the Raman spectrum simultaneously. The parent spectra that make up the difference spectrum are obtained using a specially made split-cell cuvette, which is mounted on a translator stage–stepping motor combination. Each side of the split cell has an inside dimension of 3 × 2.5 mm and is loaded with 30 μl of sample in a typical experiment. Sample concentrations are about 1 mM; thus, approximately 2.4 mg of a 40-kDa protein are presently required.

We believe that advances in spectrometer technology, in terms of light collection and detector efficiency as well as sample cell configuration and involving no new principles, can be developed to reduce the amount of protein needed by as much as 100-fold. In fact, Peticolas and his coworkers have employed a Raman microscope system that requires only 2.5 μl of sample volume (42), and Carey and coworkers have demonstrated the measurement feasibility at a sample concentration of 100 μM (34).

Several precautions must be taken to minimize systematic errors. The entire spectrometer system, including the exciting laser, is mounted on a vibration-free table. Ambient room temperature is controlled to within ± 1.5°C and relative humidity to within ± 3%. Sample positioning is especially critical.

The protein solution is loaded into one side of the split cell cuvette,

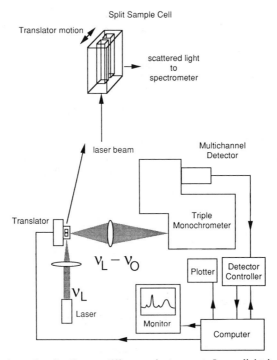

Figure 1 A schematic of a Raman difference instrument. Laser light is incident on a specially fabricated split cell from the bottom. The split cell has been designed to make the light paths in both halves as equal as possible in order to reduce subtraction artifacts. The Raman scattered light is collected by a monochrometer and multichannel detector combination. Scattered light is collected from one side of the split cell for 10–60 min, and this spectrum is stored in the computer, Then the cell is translated and scattered light is collected from the second side. The two spectra are then subtracted in the computer (see text) to form the difference spectrum.

e.g. the A side, while the altered protein in solution is loaded into the other. After measuring the Raman spectra of the two samples sequentially, one then calculates the Raman difference spectrum of the bound substrate from the two spectra stored in the laboratory computer. Matching the signal levels arising from A and B is very difficult. For example, small mismatches in alignment and/or sample concentration on the order of 1% are nearly always present. Therefore, the difference spectrum that nulls out the protein background signal is $A - xB$, where x is a numerical factor close but not identical to one. The parameter x is determined by trial subtractions that vary this parameter until the background peaks of the protein, which are generally relatively broad compared to those of the ligand, subtract out. Chen et al (14) discuss this procedure in more detail.

If we define subtraction fidelity as the ratio of the maximum false signal in the difference spectrum divided by the maximum signal in the parent spectra $[\Delta I_{max}/I(0)]$, the instrument depicted in Figure 1 has a fidelity of about 0.1%. Essentially, systematic factors determine this value, and it is measured by loading up both sides of the split cuvette in a test run with identical samples. Another procedure for assessing subtraction fidelity during a run involves taking interleaved spectra in an ABAB . . . AB sequence, adding every other A spectrum and subtracting this from the sum of the remaining A spectra. In such a subtraction, the resulting A − A or B − B difference should result only in simple shot noise.

AN EXAMPLE   One can perform many studies on bound ligands by measuring the Raman spectrum of the protein and the protein-ligand complex and subtracting these two. This type of difference spectrum provides the spectrum of the bound ligand as well as any signals that result from protein changes that are induced by the binding of ligand. While making solutions of the protein-ligand complex, one should determine whether or not the solution contains any free ligand. If so, the difference spectrum will also contain peaks caused by the free ligand. In all the work described here, the experimental conditions are such that the concentrations of free ligand were low enough to yield negligible signals.

Figure 2 shows early results (23). Spectrum a shows the Raman spectrum of lactate dehydrogenase (LDH) with bound NADH (i.e. reduced nicotinamide adenine dinucleotide). The nicotinamide group appears in Figure 2a for reference. Figure 2b shows the Raman spectrum of LDH itself. LDH is a tetramer with a molecular weight of about 160 kDa, containing four independently acting units. The strong broad protein band near 1660 cm^{-1} is the amide I band and arises from polypeptide backbone amide C=O stretching motions. The amide III region lies between 1230 and 1300 cm^{-1} and results from polypeptide backbone N-H in-plane bending and C-N stretching motions. The bands at 1340 and 1450 cm^{-1} are the γ-CH$_2$ and δ-CH$_2$ bands, respectively. The apparent difference between the LDH protein spectrum and the LDH/NADH binary complex spectrum is very small. Visually observing any difference in plots of the parent spectra is often impossible, but this example was chosen partly because a weak shoulder is barely observed near 1685 cm^{-1} in Figure 2a that is absent in Figure 2b. Figure 2d shows the difference spectrum between the LDH/NADH binary com-

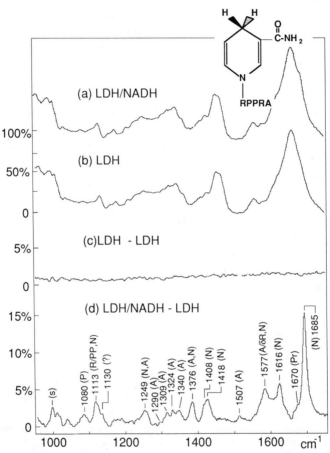

Figure 2 Raman spectra of (*a*) LDH/NADH binary complex and (*b*) LDH, at 4°C in 0.1 M phosphate buffer, pH 7.2. (*c*) Results of subtracting the spectrum from *b* of an otherwise identical run as in *b*, except that the second position of the split cell shown in Figure 1 containing LDH was moved into the laser interaction area. (*d*) Results obtained by calculating the difference between *a* and *b*. The scale in *c* or *d* is five times that in *a* or *b*, as shown on the *y* axis. Data are taken with the spectrometer system shown in Figure 1 using 100 mW of 488-nm irradiation from an argon ion laser and a resolution of 8 cm^{-1}. The molecular structure of the nicotinamide group of NADH is given in spectrum *a* for reference. Assignments of the peaks in *d* (23): A, adenine; N, nicotinamide; P, phosphate; Pr, protein; PP, pyrophosphate; R(δR), ribose; S, solvent; ?, unknown.

plex spectrum and that of LDH. The number of bands now observed in the difference spectrum, with very good signal-to-noise, is startling. The Raman bands in the difference spectrum are mostly from bound NADH, although some protein bands show up owing to the effect of NADH on the protein upon binding (see Figure 2 caption for assignment). Spectrum c shows the result of the control measurement of subtracting the spectra obtained from the A and B side of the cuvette, where both sides contain LDH. This difference spectrum is dominated by shot noise, which is about 0.5% of the protein's strongest (amide-I) peak in this example.

ISOTOPE EDITING   In general, the protein structure and conformation should change upon ligand binding. These alterations will be evident in the Raman difference spectrum, and signals from the protein should be present in a protein ligand–minus–protein difference spectrum. Figure 2d shows protein signals, but their size is generally smaller than those of the bound ligand. As a (very rough) rule of thumb, we have found that the Raman spectrum of a protein minus that of a perturbed protein (perturbed by bound ligand or mutated residue) is about 1% of that of the protein itself. This observation is consistent with the difference FTIR spectroscopic studies of proteins (e.g. 6, 55). Thus, in many cases, the signal from bound ligand will be similar in size, or smaller, than that arising from changes in protein structure. Moreover, some proteins are not stable without bound ligand. The strategy of isotope editing (40, 58) of the difference spectrum obviates these problems; here, isotopically labeled ligands are prepared, so that the frequency of those modes that involve motions of the isotope are shifted. Thus, a subtraction of the labeled ligand from the unlabeled one yields a difference spectrum of positive and negative peaks of just those modes, and all others cancel. In an experiment using labeled protein-ligand minus unlabeled protein-ligand, the protein bands subtract out.

In a recent study (20), the protein bands observed in a protein-ligand–minus–protein difference spectrum were completely dominant, and isotope editing was employed to remove these features. Figure 3 shows the Raman spectrum of phospho (a) and dephospho-phosphoglucomutase (b) in the P$\dot{-}$O stretch region. Phosphoglucomutase (PGM) catalyzes the interconversion of glucose 1-phosphate and glucose 6-phosphate. The active form of the enzyme contains a phosphorylated serine residue, and this phosphate group can be removed. The phosphate stretch bands for phosphate bound to PGM, and for bound glucose 1-phosphate and glucose 6-phosphate, were measured to study the catalytic mechanism of PGM, as discussed below. The difference spec-

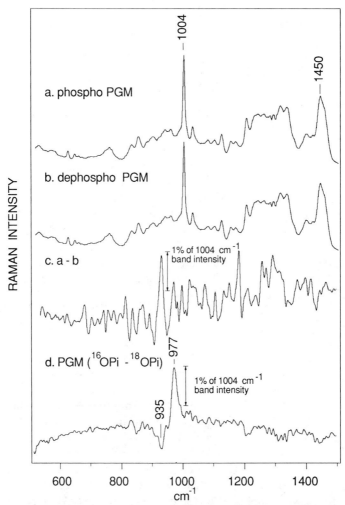

Figure 3 Raman spectra of phosphoglucomutase at pH = 7.4 at a temperature of 4°C. The approximate time for data accumulation for the protein spectra was 2 h; a 514.5-nm laser was used. (*a*) The spectrum of the phospho enzyme; (*b*) the spectrum of the dephospho form to the enzyme; (*c*) the difference spectrum between *a* and *b*; (*d*) the difference between two phospho forms of the enzyme, one containing ^{16}O-labeled phosphate and the other containing ^{18}O-labeled phosphate.

trum between phospho and dephospho enzyme spectra is surprisingly complicated (Figure 3c; discussed further below), and the phosphate stretch band cannot be assigned. The P≛^{16}O stretch shifts downward 35 cm^{-1} for P≛^{18}O, so ^{18}O-labeled phosphates were used to produce an edited spectrum. Figure 3d shows the difference Raman spectrum of PGM with ^{16}O-labeled minus ^{18}O-labeled phosphate, and all the protein peaks that are masking the phosphate stretch band in spectrum c now subtract out. The positive peak in spectrum d represents the P≛^{16}O stretch, and the negative peak the P≛^{18}O stretch. The background noise is simple shot noise (at a level of about 0.1% of the main bands of PGM). This experiment demonstrates the feasibility of measuring small molecules or small molecular fragments bound to an ~60-kDa protein with a signal-to-noise ratio of about 10/1.

A COMPUTATIONAL METHOD OF REDUCING SYSTEMATIC ERRORS   As discussed above, a slight misalignment of the two parent spectra on the detector gives rise to artifacts in the difference spectrum that have a derivative-like shape. In particular, this difference shows up when the two spectra are taken at different times, which makes the pooling of spectra, in order to reduce shot noise, difficult. One can eliminate or reduce these artifacts by shifting the frequency origin of one data set by a small amount before subtracting the two data sets (this may be done after the experiment because all data are stored in the computer). The amount of the shift can be calculated from the intensity and width of a band in the primary spectra and the unshifted difference spectrum that can be reasonably assumed to be, or is known to be, one that should subtract out in the difference spectrum, but does not.

An example of such a band is the prominent, but quite uninteresting, sharp protein band at 1004 cm^{-1} in the spectrum of PGM (Figure 3a), which arises from a phenylalanine ring mode. Its bandwidth in the primary spectra is measured, as is the magnitude of the peak-valley distance in the unshifted difference spectrum. These parameters are used in Equation 1 to calculate the shift required to null out this signal. This procedure was used recently to null out remnants of the phenylalanine 1004 cm^{-1} protein peak in some of the [^{16}O-^{18}O] PGM-phosphate difference studies (Figure 3d) (20). The shifts were typically less than 0.1 cm^{-1} (the data in Figure 3d is from unshifted parent spectra). Neither the positions nor the widths of the ^{16}O and ^{18}O phosphate stretches in the difference spectra were affected by the procedure, and additional artifacts in the difference spectrum from other protein bands in the parent spectra were also cleanly nulled. A complete description of this is to be published (J Burgner & R Callender, unpublished study).

COMPARISON OF DIFFERENCE RAMAN TO RESONANCE RAMAN SPECTROSCO-
PY   Because of its sensitivity and selectivity, resonance Raman spectroscopy is often the first choice in the study of ligand-protein or sub-
strate-enzyme interactions by vibrational spectroscopy when the
absorption maximum of the ligand or substrate is at a visible or UV
wavelength that is separate from that of the protein (54). However,
this method has two problems that can limit its usefulness. One is when
the bound ligand is photolabile. Raman difference spectroscopy can
be advantageous in this case because it can avoid unwanted photoreactions associated with the resonance Raman technique. For example, studies by Carey and coworkers (54, 54a, 55) on the acyl carbonyl group in [3-(5-methyl-2-thienyl)acryloyl]chymotrypsin compare
the results of the two techniques and also the results of FTIR. A similar
avoidance of light-induced photoreactions in resonance Raman studies
was accomplished in Raman difference studies of aspartate aminotransferase (19).

A second problem with resonance Raman spectroscopy is the oc-
casional presence of large masking fluorescence backgrounds. Fluorescence backgrounds are not present, in principle, when the frequency
of the laser excitation is not in resonance, as occurs in Raman difference spectroscopy. A recent study illustrates this by comparing resonance Raman versus nonresonance Raman spectroscopies (33).

STRUCTURES AND INTERACTIONS OF LIGANDS WITH PROTEINS PROBED BY RAMAN DIFFERENCE SPECTROSCOPY

How ligands bind to proteins is of central importance to biology. Upon
ligand binding, any number of structural changes may take place. Both
the ligand and/or the protein may change their structure; hydrogen
bonds and other electrostatic interactions may form between the ligand
and the protein at the binding site; and possible covalent bonds may
form. The now standard crystallographic and NMR (reviewed in 11)
approaches to studying this problem provide atomic-resolution pictures
placing the positions of atoms within the complex. However, the resolution of these pictures, at about 1–3 Å, while possibly sufficient to
place a particular atom to within 0.1–0.3 Å, is not sufficient to quantitate small but important changes in key bonds or the size of weak
forces such as hydrogen bonding, nor is it sufficient to probe whether
or not many small changes take place that, in the sum, are important.
In this context, vibrational spectroscopy is useful in that it provides
very-high-resolution pictures of the structure of groups of atoms and

bonds and of how these structures respond to noncovalent interactions. The following discussion does not review particular protein systems but rather groups the discussion into categories of structural information relevant to the binding of ligands to proteins, including the formation of covalent bonds, hydrogen bonding, and the effects of the ligand binding on the protein. In principle, one could also determine the molecular geometry of the bound ligand from vibrational spectroscopy. This is well documented (12, 48, 49), and we do not discuss it further here.

Covalent Bond Formation

A new covalent bond may form when a ligand binds to a protein. This new bond, characterized by a specific normal mode involving motions of the newly bonded atoms, will likely produce a new peak in the vibrational spectrum of the complex. The appearence of such a peak, when properly assigned, demonstrates the formation of the new bond.

For example, a Schiff base ($-C=N-$) linkage forms between the ϵ-amino group of active-site Lys258 of *E. coli* aspartate aminotransferase (AATase) and the carbonyl moiety of enzyme bound cofactor, pyridoxal 5′-phosphate (PLP). Recent Raman difference studies (28) examined the spectrum of the high and low pH forms of this complex, and Raman bands characteristic of Schiff base and protonated Schiff base were determined, respectively. A Y225F mutant form of the enzyme, in which the near-UV absorption of the bound PLP at high pH resembles that of an aldehyde rather than a Schiff base, was also studied. Evidence from isotope-edited Raman difference spectra proved conclusively that the near-UV spectrum is anomalous and that PLP is bound to Y225F at high pH as a Schiff base. A strong peak at 1630 cm^{-1} was observed for PLP bound to Y225F, which is characteristic of a Schiff base bond and not an aldehyde. Moreover, this band redshifted by 18 cm^{-1} in enzyme labeled with ^{15}N at Lys258 (28).

An inhibitor, α-methyl-L-aspartate (αMeAsp), complexed with enzyme-PLP was also studied because it is believed to be a Michaels complex of the enzyme. Four forms of the complex are possible because the inhibitor may, in principle, form a Schiff base with Lys258 (so-called internal Schiff base) or with PLP (the external Schiff base) and may be protonated or unprotonated. The Raman spectrum of αMeAsp bound to AATase complex contains a 1630 cm^{-1} band, which was assigned to the unprotonated internal Schiff base $C=N$ stretch mode based on a downshift of 18 cm^{-1} with ^{15}N labeling of the Lys258 ϵ nitrogen. This study also showed that the protonated external Schiff base form coexisted in this complex, a conclusion supported by the insensitivity of the observed $\nu_{C=NH^+}$ of the αMeAsp$-$ enzyme complex at 1655 cm^{-1} to lysine ^{15}N substitution. No significant amount of other two possible Schiff base forms, namely the protonated internal or unprotonated external forms, were found. Interestingly, the Raman study, which of course was performed on protein solutions, showed that the solution structure of the *E. coli* AATase-αMeAsp complex differs significantly from the reported crystal structures in terms of the equilibrium concentrations found amongst the four forms (18).

Hydrogen Bonding (and Weak Electrostatic Interactions)

The energies of hydrogen bonds and weak electrostatic interactions are on the order of 2–10 kcal/mol or more and play a major role in the structure of proteins and nucleic acids and their interactions with ligands (cf 30). H-bonding is generally considered a major determinant in the specificity of interactions between a protein and ligand, and these interactions are important to enzymatic catalysis (see below), although they have not been well characterized in proteins.

H-BOND ENERGIES FROM VIBRATIONAL FREQUENCIES   Clearly, hydrogen bonding affects the electronic distributions within bonds of localized modes (and hence force constants). Thus, the frequencies of particular modes may be sensitive to the strengths of H-bonding. Badger & Bauer (2) suggested quite some time ago that the enthalpy of formation of a hydrogen bond, ΔH, is linearly related to the vibrational frequency shift, $\Delta \nu$, of the O-H stretch frequency of an alcohol. A stronger hydrogen bond weakens the O-H bond and the stretch force constant; this weakening significantly decreases the observed stretching frequency. Numerous investigations of such thermodynamic correlations have shown that the relationship is often very direct and simple (cf 31). The general methodology of this body of work is to determine the association constants, enthalpies, and binding entropies of donor-acceptor pairs in organic solvents. Badger-Bauer relationships have been found for O-H, C=O, N-H, and other groups (reviewed in 17, 31, 56). The stated relationships are generally between ΔH and $\Delta \nu$, but ΔG versus $\Delta \nu$ relationships have also been derived (cf 31). The exact relationship depends on the nature of the group and nearby chemical constituents. Quantitative use of such relationships for a specific ligand then generally involves some sort of calibrating set of measurements. In general, the empirically derived relationships only extend over a fairly small range in ΔH (<10 kcal/mol). Theoretical development of this problem will greatly help define the accuracy and applicability of such relationships over wider ranges and in conditions other than those found in solution.

For example, the relationship between carbonyl stretch and hydrogen bond energy was recently investigated with ab initio calculations of H_2CO interacting with various cations and water (38). The shift in $C=O$ stretching frequency in H_2CO fits a linear correlation with the computed interaction energy, ΔE, having a slope of 0.5 kcal/mol for each wavenumber (cm^{-1}) of frequency shift—which agrees remarkably well with experiment (51). This study also addressed several important issues that the empirically observed correlations cannot. First, the linear relationship was found to hold up to an interaction energy of 27 kcal/mol, at which point the character of the donor-acceptor pair becomes covalent in nature. The empirical solution studies are limited to 5–10 kcal/mol in ΔE because model systems generally do not involve large hydrogen bond energies. Another important finding is that the linear correlation was found to be essentially independent of the nature of the cation and the distance between cation and the carbonyl oxygen (until the two were so close that the bond became more nearly covalent in character). The ΔE versus $\Delta \nu$ relationship differed among calculations in which the cation angle of approach to the carbonyl oxygen was varied; consequently, complete analyses of the experimental data will have to take this variation into account.

EXAMPLES OF H-BOND PROTEIN-LIGAND INTERACTIONS   Raman difference studies on two systems provide a basis of examining how well Raman difference spectroscopy tells us about hydrogen bonding of small molecules to proteins. The first system is the binding of substrates and coenzymes to the NAD dehydrogenases; the second is the binding of guanine nucleotides to a selected set of so-called G-proteins.

The NAD-linked dehydrogenases form a large class of oxidation-reduction enzymes needed for a variety of metabolic functions. Some of these have been studied with Raman difference spectroscopy: liver alcohol dehydrogenase (LADH), lactate dehydrogenase (LDH), malate dehydrogenase (cytoplasmic sMDH and mitochondrial mMDH), and dihydrofolate reductase (DHFR) (9, 10, 14, 15, 21–23, 62–64). These enzymes catalyze the reversible direct stereochemical transfer of a hydride ion, H^-, from either the pro-R or pro-S face of NADH (but not both) to the carbonyl of aldehyde or ketone carbon of substrate to form alcohol and NAD^+ (see, e.g. 26). The hydride transfer proceeds with a high degree of stereochemical fidelity. For example, the hydride transfer occurs from NADH's pro-R face with an error rate of $<1/10^8$ in LDH (1).

At the NADH protein-binding site (see Figure 2), hydrogen bonds are formed with the carboxamide $[-(C=O)NH_2]$ moiety of the nicotinamide headgroup. In Raman studies, this group is characterized by observation of the $C=O$ stretch and the $-NH_2$ rock mode. The $-NH_2$ rock mode is assigned to the 1113 cm^{-1} peak in Figure 2d for NADH bound to LDH. This band has shifted upward 30 cm^{-1} from its in-solution position at 1083 cm^{-1} (14, 23, 62). In the same way, the $C=O$ stretch of keto substrates bound to LDH and LADH shift upon binding (9, 22). Table 1 summarizes the observed frequency shifts, from which the interaction enthalpies are calculated from the Badger-Bauer relationships described above for the $C=O$ moieties. No accurate relationship has been derived for the $-NH_2$ groups. The reported hydrogen bond enthalpies are with respect to water.

It is sometimes useful to know the value of the hydrogen bond with respect to a nonhydrogen environment. A keto group forms a hydrogen bond with an interaction enthalpy estimated at about 4.5 kcal/mol from spectroscopic studies employing Badger-Bauer relationships (23). Thus, one must add approximately this amount to the values in Table

Table 1 Frequency shifts of certain vibrational bands and deduced binding energies of various coordinates[a]

Group	Wavenumbers (cm^{-1})		Reference
	$\Delta\nu$ (in situ, solution)	$-\Delta H$ (kcal/mol)	
$C{=}O$ stretch of bound substrates			
DABA in LADH	-94	-14	9
Pyruvate adduct in LDH	-35	-14	22
$C{=}O$ stretch of NAD's carboxamide group			
LDH	-10	-2.8	15, 21, 23
sMDH	-9	-2.5	15
mMDH	-9	-2.5	15
DHFR	$+5$	$+1.4$	64
$-NH_2$ rock of NAD's carboxamide group			
LDH	$+30$	~-3	15, 21, 23
LADH	$+30$	~-3	14
sMDH	$+35$	~-3	15
mMDH	-4	0	15
DHFR	$+35$	~-3	64
$-COO^-$ stretch of pyruvate's carboxylate			
LDH	-5		22

[a] Data are for the coenzymes NADH and NAD$^+$ and substrates of the NAD dehydrogenases, binding to the specified proteins as derived from Badger-Bauer relationships. The derived binding ΔH is expressed with respect to water. See text and the listed references for details.

1 to determine the absolute value of the hydrogen bond to the $C=O$ groups. The energies obtained from this analysis of the vibrational data are very useful in understanding some important properties of these complexes.

For example, the stereospecific nature of the hydride transfer step may be a result of relative positioning of the substrate and the coenzyme. For enzymes that are pro-S, only the pro-S hydrogen of NADH is positioned close to the carbonyl carbon of substrate, and the opposite is true for pro-R enzymes (about half of the 300 or so known dehydrogenases are pro-R and half are pro-S). The positioning apparently results from enzymic control of the conformation of the glycosidic bond between the nicotinamide ring and ribose group of NADH. Structural studies show that generally pro-R enzymes bind the nicotinamide ring in the *anti* conformation about the glycosidic bond, while pro-S binds the ring in the *syn* conformation. Assuming this is the case, the energy barrier to rotation about this bond, which is normally very small in solution, must adopt large values at the binding site. For LDH, a stereochemical transfer error rate of $<1/10^8$ suggests the barrier is greater or equal to 10.4 kcal/mol (1). The essential source of the energy barrier presumably arises from hydrogen-bond breaking between the carboxamide moiety and protein at the binding site, caused by rotation of the glycosidic bond from the normal *anti* conformation that NAD adopts when bound to LDH (15, 23). Assuming that enthalpic terms are entirely responsible for the energy difference between the *anti* and *syn* conformations, the value of 10.4 kcal/mol results from the addition of 3 kcal/mol for the hydrogen bond to $-NH_2$ and 7.3 kcal/mol for the hydrogen bond to $C=O$ of the carboxamide moiety (equal to the 2.8 kcal reported in Table 1, which is with respect to water, plus the 4.5 kcal/mol for breaking the water hydrogen bond to the keto group) (Table 1). Alternatively, LeReau & Anderson estimated a minimum energy difference of 8.2 kcal/mol in experiments on $PAAD^+$ in which the $-NH_2$ was replaced with a hydrogen to test the importance of the $-NH_2$ group of NAD (37). This value is satisfyingly close to the 7.3 kcal/mol difference in hydrogen bond energy estimated for the hydrogen bond to the carbonyl group alone.

One can use frequency shifts of appropriate spectroscopic marker bands and empirical relationships to relate the markers to interaction energies in order to probe the magnitude of various components of the binding enthalpy between protein and ligand. Such studies are quite important and can be applied to, for example, the rational design of drugs. One experimental study examined the binding of pyruvate to the LDH-NADH binary complex using the numbers given in Table 1

(24). The net total binding enthalpy is the result of numerous factors: the shift of pyruvate from water to enzyme and of structural water at the active site to solution, differences in coenzyme interactions with protein induced by substrate binding, and changes in the internal interactions within the enzyme produced by subtle or not-so-subtle protein conformational changes upon complex formation. The contribution to the net enthalpy of interaction by pyruvate should arise primarily from differences in interactions involving its carboxylate and carbonyl moieties. The value of about -17 kcal/mol for the overall binding enthalpy for pyruvate to LDH/NADH and the value of -14 kcal/mol derived for its carbonyl moiety (Table 1) is remarkably close. Thus, even though ligand binding may cause protein and other conformational changes, the net binding enthalpy of these changes seems to reflect the sum of several large, mostly compensating effects, which is consistent with recent theoretical studies (27). The hydrogen bond strengths reported in the Raman data for the $C=O$ groups of the substrates bound to LADH and LDH are unusually large for such bonds in proteins (cf 30) and are quite provocative. Given the assumptions inherent with the use of the empirical relationships, the value of 14 kcal/mol for the $C=O$ of pyruvate interacting with LDH has an error of perhaps ± 3 kcal/mol (24). Still the lower end of this range represents a hydrogen bond rarely reported inside proteins.

Another study along these lines looks at how the 6-keto and the 2-amino groups, the polar binding handles, of the purine ring of GDP interact with the EF-Tu and p21 proteins, which belong to the G-protein family (57). This protein family is involved in a variety of key cellular processes such as signal transduction, protein transport, and protein biosynthesis, and their activity is regulated by whether they bind GDP (inactive) or GTP (active). Because no Badger-Bauer-like calibrating empirical studies for the $C=O$ stretch and the $-NH_2$ deformation mode of GDP have been done, a quantitative relationship between frequency shift and ΔH is not known for these groups. However, one could glean some insight into the strengths of the interactions from the shifts themselves, assuming that at least a rough correlation does exist—a reasonable approximation in view of all the earlier studies.

The amine deformation mode of GDP, observed at 1646 cm^{-1} in solution, is shifted up by 8 and 16 cm^{-1} upon nucleotide binding to EF-Tu and p21, respectively, and the ketone stretch shifts down 15 and 10 cm^{-1} for GDP in EF-Tu and p21, respectively. The directions of the shifts indicate that the interaction between the keto and the amine groups are stronger for the two groups with either EF-Tu or p21 than with water; this is certainly reasonable because both proteins bind GDP very strongly (K_ds tighter than 10^{-9} M) and because the structure of the binding pockets is such that appropriate proton donors and acceptors are present to bind to the polar groups.

The hydrogen-bond strengths do not exhibit a consistent pattern in the binding of the carboxamide moiety of NAD to the NAD-dehydrogenases that have been studied (summarized in Table 1), and in the binding of GDP to the two G-proteins, despite the fact that the binding pockets for NADH among the dehydrogenases and for GDP by the G-proteins are much the same. For the NAD proteins, the H-bonds generally arise from a protein backbone C=O group that pairs with the −NH$_2$ moiety of NAD and a structural water that pairs with the C=O group. These observations indicate that the C=O group should bind more strongly to the proteins than to water, which is generally the case (15, 21). However, the C=O group of NAD actually binds more weakly to DHFR and inhibitor than to water (Table 1) (64). Similarly, interactions with the 6-keto and 2-amino positions are conserved in EF-Tu and p21 as well as among other members of the GTPase super family, as part of a NKXD motif. The 2-amino group of GDP is known to be only 3 Å or less away from an invariant Asp residue (Asp138 in EF-Tu and Asp119 in p21), while the 6-keto group is hydrogen bonded to the main-chain NH of a conserved alanine residue (Ala174 in EF-Tu and Ala146 in p21). However, the relative strengths of the hydrogen bonds formed with these groups and the two proteins are very different. If we assume that at least an approximate Badger-Bauer relationship holds between interaction energy and frequency shift of the marker bands, the hydrogen bonds can differ by up to a factor of two.

Ligand-Induced Changes in Protein Structure

How is the structure of a protein affected by the binding of a ligand? The standard method of studying this problem involves crystallographic or multidimensional NMR studies comparing the protein and the protein-ligand complex. The data shown in Figure 3c suggests that vibrational spectroscopy can also be helpful for this problem because of its high resolution. Figure 3c shows the difference spectrum of phospho-PGM minus dephospho-PGM, i.e. of two protein spectra from an ~60-kDa protein that differ only by the presence or absence of a single phosphate group (see above). The difference spectrum is surprisingly robust, but it has not yet been interpreted.

In general, an analysis would proceed as follows. The amide-I (~1660–1690 cm^{-1}) and amide-III (1230–1280 cm^{-1}) regions of the protein spectrum, which involve molecular motions of the polypeptide linkage, are sensitive to secondary structure. In addition, the characteristic signatures of the various residues in the spectrum provide useful structural information: the ionization states of histidines, carboxyls, etc; whether or not sulfide groups have formed disulfide linkages and, if not, the degree to which an S-H group is hydrogen bonded; the nature of how tyrosines have interacted with their environment; and so forth (see e.g. 12, 48). That the difference spectrum contains substantial structure essentially everywhere suggests, qualitatively and quite speculatively, that the presence of the single phosphate group has caused subtle changes throughout the protein. The size of the difference signal suggests that perhaps scores of residues find themselves in an altered environment. Crystallographic studies of PGM show minor changes between the two forms (44). However, the phosphate group forms an important bridging group between domains one and two of this four-domain protein. Evidence indicates that dephospho-PGM in the crystal state is stabilized by crystal-packing forces that are absent for PGM in solution (W Ray, private communication).

ENZYMATIC CATALYSIS

Enzymes perform two functions. One is to selectively bind the substrates that they catalyze. This feature is partly responsible for their ability to catalyze a particular chemical reaction (or a small set of reactions). Such chemical specificity is determined in part by the particular binding interactions between enzyme and substrate, and we presented examples above of how vibrational spectroscopy can be of help in studying these forces. Enzymes also lower the reaction barrier. This often involves bond distortion affecting the vibrational frequencies of the key internal modes that make up the reaction coordinates. For two enzymic problems, Raman difference spectroscopy has furthered our knowledge of enzymes' catalytic mechanisms. Before we discuss these examples, it is to be noted that resonance Raman spectroscopy has provided a wealth of information that has been invaluable in understanding some enzymes and for some internal coordinates; this body of work is very well reviewed (12, 49, 54). We emphasize that nonresonance Raman difference spectroscopy can extend this body of work because it is not tied to particular internal coordinates associated with chromophoric substrates. Rather, the entire set of coordinates that make up the reaction coordinate can be studied, one by one, as can any substrate. This feature of the technique should allow the study of most enzymic systems.

For example, the catalytic binding site of lactate dehydrogenase involves two domains. One binds the coenzyme, either NADH or NAD^+

(oxidized nicotinamide adenine dinucleotide), and the other binds a substrate, either pyruvate or lactate. NADH provides hydride ion, H^-, which attacks the aldehyde moiety of pyruvate to form the secondary alcohol, lactate, and NAD^+. The imidazole ring of His195 interacts with substrate and performs several important functions. The N3 nitrogen donates a proton to the carbonyl of pyruvate and accepts a proton from the alcohol of lactate, thus acting as a general acid-base catalyst. Its interaction with substrate (discussed above)—certainly with the carbonyl group of pyruvate—helps position the substrate properly for its interaction with the C4 hydrogen of NADH. This interaction also polarizes pyruvate's $C = O$ bond, promoting nucleophilic attack of H^-.

Figure 4 shows the reaction coordinate from pyruvate and NADH to the transition state and then to lactate and NAD^+. During reduction of pyruvate, the reaction scheme involves three important internal coordinates: the C4-H bond of the NADH coenzyme, the $C = O$ bond of pyruvate, and the hydrogen bond between the $C = O$ group and the imidazole ring. The properties of the C4-H bond have been studied by preparing NADH deuterated stereospecifically at the pro-R or the pro-S positions. This results in a localized C4-D stretch band that is unique in the difference spectrum. The frequency of the pro-R C4-H bond stretch of NADH does not change during formation of a binary LDH/NADH complex (25). This frequency is also not affected, apart from band narrowing, when oxamate, a substrate analogue, binds to form a ternary (LDH/NADH/oxamate) complex (16). This band narrowing was attributed to a stiffening of the binding site, which decreased the number of accessible states available to NADH and is essentially an entropic effect. Thus, the dominating ground-state enthalpic interaction in the reaction coordinate appears to be the hydrogen bond between

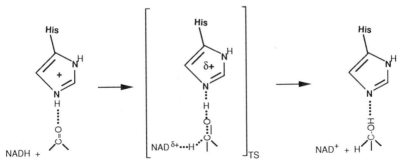

Figure 4   A simplified schematic of the reaction coordinate for the LDH-catalyzed reaction.

C = O and the imidazole ring, as suggested by the polarization of the
C = O bond of pyruvate when it binds to LDH (22).

As discussed above, one can characterize the strength of the H-bond
as well as the C = O bond order and bond length with the Badger-Bauer
relationships, and other empirical relationships [as developed, for example, in some recent studies of acyl-proteases (53–55, 59)], by using
the C = O stretch frequency as an internal probe. Keto (aldehyde)
groups inside enzymes have received much attention in vibrational
studies partly for technical reasons. For instance, the C = O stretch
sometimes lies in an otherwise spectroscopically silent region (higher
in frequency than the amide-I protein band near 1660 cm^{-1}). Thus,
FTIR measurements are feasible and have shown substantial bond polarization of a substrate keto group in triosephosphate isomerase (4,
35), in yeast aldolase (5), in phopholipase A_2 (47), and in citrate synthase (36). Recently, Wharton and his coworkers measured the C = O
stretch of a C = O containing substrate bound to chymotrypsin and
phospholipase A_2 by using FTIR difference spectroscopy and employing the isotope-editing techniques discussed above to remove the protein IR absorbance (47, 55, 58, 59). The stretch frequency of this particular keto group lies within the amide-I protein peak. Also, Carey
and his coworkers (cf 13, 54) and Peticolas and coworkers (cf 42) have
performed extensive resonance Raman studies on acyl-chymotrypsins
(and other proteases) made with chromophoric substrates.

In the case of lactate dehydrogenase, the C = O stretch of bound
pyruvate lies within the strong amide-I protein band but could be measured employing isotope-edited Raman difference spectroscopy (22,
24). The observation of substantial bond polarization of the bound keto
group implied that the total enthalpy of the essential reactant groups
is stabilized by 14 (± 3) kcal/mol from the C = O interaction with His195
(and other groups at the active site) relative to its interaction with water
(Table 1). Measurements of mutant lactate dehydrogenases that affect
the k_{cat} of this enzyme showed a definite correlation of rate of the
hydride transfer step with the C = O stretch frequency (24). This correlation was rationalized by supposing that the enthalpy of the transition state is stabilized to a greater extent than the ground state so
that the electrostatic interaction lowers the net reaction barrier. This
explanation seems plausible because the carbonyl moiety is substantially more polarized in the transition state, with more negative character on the oxygen. Also, the proton located on the imidazole in the
ground state is probably closer to the oxygen in the transition state,
as in Figure 5.

A numerical analysis of the correlation suggested that about $10^{5.5}$-fold of lactate dehydrogenase's 10^9-fold rate enhancement arises from the $C=O\cdots His195^+$ interaction. Thus, taken all together, vibrational studies on this protein have suggested that the catalytic mechanism arises from entropic factors (bringing the reactants together and holding them in a configuration appropriate for reacting) and bond polarization of the reacting $C=O$ coordinate. Note the high degree of precision in these results; the shift in frequency of 35 cm^{-1} for the $C=O$ stretch observed when pyruvate binds to lactate dehydrogenase represents a change in bond length of the $C=O$ group of only ~ 0.02 Å (53).

The enzymic mechanism of phosphoglucomutase (PGM) was recently studied using Raman difference spectroscopy (20, 43). This enzyme catalyzes the interconversion of glucose 1-phosphate and glucose 6-phosphate so that the bond-breaking step is the hydrolysis of the phosphate ester bond. Bound vanadate, when substituted for phosphate, likely behaves as a transition-state analogue. Thus, studies comparing the properties of phosphate to vanadate when bound to PGM compare the effect of the enzyme on the ground and transition states, respectively, upon binding.

The phosphate $P\rightleftharpoons O$ stretch frequency of bound phosphate groups was measured using isotope editing techniques and ^{18}O labeled samples (Figure 3). The frequencies of the dianionic phosphate $P\rightleftharpoons O$ stretch from either bound glucose 1-phosphate or glucose 6-phosphate did not differ from their values in solution, suggesting that a binding-induced distortion/polarization of the enzymic phosphate group in the ground state enzyme-substrate complex is not responsible for PGM's catalytic mechanism.

On the other hand, the frequency of the $V\rightleftharpoons O$ bonds within a vanadate group bound at the same site in the transition analogue complex involving glucose 1-phosphate 6-vanadate is much lower than for a normal vanadate in solution (20). A series of model studies of vanadate in solution (43) suggested the formation of a weak fifth bond between the central vanadium and some internal fifth-ligand atom of PGM, very likely the ΓO of Ser116. The addition of the fifth ligand draws electrons out of the three $V\rightleftharpoons O$ bonds, and this lowers the frequency of the $V\rightleftharpoons O$ stretch. Broadly speaking, the hydrolysis of a phosphate ester may proceed by either a dissociative (S_N1) or an associative (S_N2) mechanism. In the dissociative case, the ester bond breaks, which promotes nucleophilic attack. In the associative case, the phosphorus atom undergoes attack, which expels the ester group. The inference of a fifth bond to the phosphorus atom in the transition state supports an associative mechanism rather than a dissociative one (20). This finding contrasts with those of solution studies in which virtually all reactions involving hydrolysis of dianionic phosphate proceed via a dissociative mechanism.

PROPERTIES OF INDIVIDUAL RESIDUES AND THE EFFECTS OF MUTATION ON PROTEIN STRUCTURE

The previous two sections have emphasized what we can learn about the structures of ligands bound to their protein-binding sites from vibrational spectroscopy. Conceptually, Raman difference spectroscopy could report on the vibrational spectrum of an individual amino acid residue within a protein. This may be accomplished by forming the difference spectrum between a protein and its analogue: where a specific residue (or particular group of residues) is isotopically labeled; where a residue is mutated; or where its pH is altered so that a residue or group of residues are in a different ionization state. One can determine the pKs of ionizable residues or determine the effects of environmental factors imposed by the protein on a particular residue (as in conformations of particular bonds, H-bonding properties, and so-forth) as well as investigate how the mutation affects other residues.

In one study (62a), investigators titrated the various histidine residues of human transferrin to obtain the Raman difference spectra at different pHs (3.0–9.0) with respect to pH 8.9. About 12 ± 2 of the 18 residues titrated over this range. A titration curve with a pK_a of 6.08 ± 0.01 fit the data of histidine in solution, and 6.56 ± 0.02 was the average value of the 12 histidine residues inside transferrin. The study indicated that the technique had enough sensitivity to monitor a single histidine residue in an 80-kDa molecule and to determine the titration curve of one residue in a 40-kDa protein. Another study determined the pK_a values for thiol-thiolate equilibria of thioredoxin (39).

In an unpublished study, we obtained the Raman difference spectrum between a wild-type protein and a mutant, in which a serine replaced a carboxyl group. We are performing these measurements to determine the pK_a of the carboxyl because these groups are often at the active sites of enzymes and their ionization state is difficult to determine otherwise. Also, we wish to investigate how mutation affects the structure of the protein. Figure 5a shows the difference spectrum between wild-type dihydrofolate reductase (DHFR) and its D27S mutant, in which serine replaces Asp27, in 6 M urea (Y Chen, J Kraut & R Callender, unpublished data). This experiment should yield only the dif-

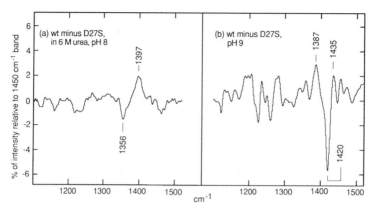

Figure 5 Difference spectra between wild-type (wt) dihydrofolate reductase (DHFR) and its D27S mutant in (*a*) 6 M urea and 10 mM Tris buffer, pH 8.1 and (*b*) 25 mM acetic acid, 15 mM phosphate, 15 mM Tris, and 200 mM KCl, pH 9.0.

ference spectrum of the Raman spectra of an aspartate with a serine without any other residue signatures because the concentration of urea is sufficient to unfold most of the protein (the spectrum of urea has been subtracted). The positive peak at 1397 cm^{-1} and the negative peak at 1356 cm^{-1} are then tentatively assigned to the carboxylate COO$^-$ symmetric stretch mode of Asp27 and a vibrational mode of Ser27, respectively, based on the observation that bands at similar (but not identical) positions are found in the solution aspartate and serine spectra. The scale of the *y*-axis refers to a percentage of the intensity of the protein 1450 cm^{-1} band; and the intensity of the observed bands in the difference spectrum are about right for the putative carboxylate and serine bands.

Figure 5*b* shows the difference Raman spectrum of wild-type DHFR and its D27S mutant in a buffer without urea. Which bands can be assigned to Asp27 or Ser27 in this spectrum is not obvious. Apparently, the network of interactions among protein residues is disturbed upon mutation of Asp27 to serine, and many Raman bands from various amino acids, which are sensitive to the environment, then become prominent in the difference spectrum. The character in this difference spectrum is similar to that found for PGM between the phospho and dephospho forms (see above; Figure 3*c*). Although an extensive analysis (which would follow the general outline sketched above for PGM) has not been done, the sharp and intense band at 1420 cm^{-1}, which is about three times more intense than the carboxylate COO$^-$ symmetric stretch band, probably arises from the ring N-H bending motion of one of DHFR's five protein tryptophan residues. The shift in frequency of this band from its normal position at 1435 cm^{-1} in water suggests that the ring nitrogen of this tryptophan in the wild-type DHFR is strongly hydrogen bonded, and its environment becomes much more hydrophobic in the D27S mutant. Further studies with specific mutated DHFR tryptophan residues should reveal which one is disturbed in the D27S mutant.

CONCLUSION

The above discussion clearly demonstrates the value of vibrational studies in answering important questions of the structures and functions of proteins and other biological macromolecules, as do many other investigations using resonance Raman and FTIR difference spectroscopies and other forms of vibrational spectroscopy. Their use has been limited because of the difficulty of assigning bands in a complicated protein spectrum. Because Raman difference spectroscopy deals directly with this problem and may be used on essentially any protein system, many problems of protein structure are now open to study. Moreover, the instrumentation is relatively inexpensive. Currently, an instrument can be purchased for about the price of a couple of high performance liquid chromatographs. Measurements may be performed rather quickly, on relatively small quantities of sample, and on protein solutions.

Some problems are particularly suited for Raman difference spectroscopy. One concerns characterization of the interactions between a protein and a ligand, indeed a very large area of protein research and one that is not well understood. Another has to do with investigations of the distortions of particular bonds, such as those that take place in enzymatic catalysis.

As suggested above, Raman difference spectroscopy may be useful for the study of how ligand binding or mutation changes the structure of a protein. The resolution of vibrational spectroscopy is very high compared with other techniques, and high-resolution pictures are needed in the study of these relatively poorly characterized, but very important, problems.

ACKNOWLEDGMENTS

The development of the techniques discussed here, and their applications, have been the enterprise of several colleagues. We acknowledge the efforts of Drs. TK Yue, D Chen, J van Beck, J Ball, J Burgner, D Mannor, G Weng, J Zheng, D Sloan, C Martin and students, Y-Q Chen, and D Xiao. Support from the National Institutes of Health (grants GM35183 and EYO3142) and the National Science Foundation (grant MCB-8912322) is gratefully acknowledged.

Literature Cited

1. Anderson VE, LaReau RD. 1988. Hydride transfer catalyzed by lactate dehydrogenase displays absolute stereospecificity at the C4 of the nicotinamide ring. *J. Am. Chem. Soc.* 110:3695–97
2. Badger RM, Bauer SH. 1937. Spectroscopic studies of the hydrogen bond. II. The shift of the O-H vibrational frequency in the formation of the hydrogen bond. *J. Chem. Phys.* 5:839–55
3. Baenziger JE, Miller KW, Rothschild KJ. 1992. Incorporation of the nicotinic receptor into planar mutilamellar films: characterization by fluorescence and Fourier transform infrared difference spectroscopy. *Biophys. J.* 61:983–92
4. Belasco JG, Knowles JR. 1980. Direct observation of substrate distortion by triosephosphate isomerase using fourier transform infrared spectroscopy. *Biochemistry* 19:472–77
5. Belasco JG, Knowles JR. 1983. Polarization of substrate carbonyl group by yeast aldolase: investigation by fourier transform infrared spectroscopy. *Biochemistry* 22:122–29
6. Braiman MS, Rothschild KJ. 1988. Fourier transform infrared techniques for probing membrane protein structure. *Annu. Rev. Biophys. Biophys. Chem.* 17:541–70
7. Breton J, Nabedryk E, Parson WW. 1992. A new infrared electronic transition of the oxidized primary electron donor in bacterial reaction centers: a way to assess resonance interactions between the bacteriochlorophylls. *Biochemistry* 31:7503–10
8. Breton J, Vermeglio A, ed. 1992. *The Photosynthetic Bacterial Reaction Center*, Vol. 2, *Structure, Spectroscopy, and Dynamics*. New York: Plenum
9. Callender R, Chen D, Lugtenburg J, Martin C, Ree KW, et al. 1988. The molecular properties of p-dimethylamino benzaldehyde bound to liver alchohol dehydrogenase: a Raman spectroscopic study. *Biochemistry* 27:3672–81
10. Callender R, Deng H, Sloan D, Burgner J, Yue TK. 1989. Raman difference

spectroscopy and the energetics of enzymatic catalysis. *Proc. Int. Soc. Opt. Eng.* 1057:154–60
11. Campbell AP, Sykes BD. 1993. The two-dimensional transferred nuclear overhauser effect: theory and practice. *Annu. Rev. Biophys. Biomol. Struct.* 22:99–122
12. Carey PR. 1982. *Biochemical Applications of Raman and Resonance Raman Spectroscopy*. New York: Academic
13. Carey PR, Tonge PJ. 1990. Chemistry of enzyme-substrate complexes revealed by resonance Raman spectroscopy. *Chem. Soc. Rev.* 19:293–316
14. Chen D, Yue KT, Martin C, Rhee KW, Sloan D, Callender R. 1987. Classical Raman spectroscopic studies of NADH and NAD$^+$ bound to liver alcohol dehydrogenase by difference techniques. *Biochemistry* 26:4776–84
15. Deng H, Burgner J, Callender R. 1991. Raman spectroscopic studies of NAD coenzymes bound to malate dehydrogenases by difference techniques. *Biochemistry* 30:8804–11
16. Deng H, Burgner J, Callender R. 1992. Raman spectroscopic studies of the effects of substrate binding on coenzymes bound to lactate dehydrogenase. *J. Am. Chem. Soc.* 114:7997–8003
17. Deng H, Callender R. 1993. Enzymatic catalysis and molecular recognition: the energetics of ligand binding to proteins as studies by vibrational spectroscopy. *Comments Mol. Cell. Biophys.* 8:137–54
18. Deng H, Goldberg JM, Kirsch JF, Callender R. 1993. Elucidation of the solution structure of the *Escherichia coli* aspartate aminotransferase-α-methyl-L-aspartate complex by isotope edited Raman difference spectroscopy. *J. Am. Chem. Soc.* 115:8869–70
19. Deng H, Manor D, Weng G, Chen C-X, Balogh-Nair V, Callender R. 1993. Difference Raman spectroscopic studies of ligand-protein interactions. *Proc. Int. Soc. Opt. Eng.* 1890:114–22
20. Deng H, Ray WJ, Burgner JW, Callen-

der R. 1993. A comparison of vibrational frequencies of critical bonds in ground state complexes and in a vanadate-based transition state complex of muscle phosphoglucomutase. Mechanistic implications. *Biochemistry.* 32: 12984–92

21. Deng H, Zheng J, Burgner J, Callender R. 1989. Hydrogen bonding and reaction specificity in lactate dehydrogenase studied by Raman spectroscopy. *J. Phys. Chem.* 93:4710–13

22. Deng H, Zheng J, Burgner J, Callender R. 1989. Molecular properties of pyruvate bound to lactate dehydrogenase: a Raman spectroscopic study. *Proc. Natl. Acad. Sci. USA* 86:4484–88

23. Deng H, Zheng J, Burgner J, Sloan D, Callender R. 1989. Classical Raman spectroscopic studies of NADH and NAD$^+$ bound to lactate dehydrogenase by difference techniques. *Biochemistry* 28:1525–33

24. Deng H, Zheng J, Clarke A, Holbrook JJ, Callender R, Burgner JW. 1994. The source of catalysis in the lactate dehydrogenase system, part II: ground state interactions in the enzyme·substrate complex. *Biochemistry.* In press

25. Deng H, Zheng J, Sloan D, Burgner J, Callender R. 1992. A vibrational analysis of the catalytically important C4-H bonds of NADH bound to lactate or malate dehydrogenase: ground state effects. *Biochemistry* 31:5085–92

26. Fersht A. 1985. *Enzyme Structure and Mechanism.* New York: Freeman

27. Gao J, Kuczera K, Tidor B, Karplus M. 1989. Hidden thermodynamics of mutant proteins: a molecular dynamics analysis. *Science* 244:1069–72

28. Goldberg JM, Zheng J, Deng H, Chen YQ, Callender R, Kirsch JF. 1993. The structure of the complex between pyridoxal 5'-phosphate and the tyrosine-225 to phenylalanine mutant of *Escherichia coli* aspartate aminotransferase determined by isotope edited classical raman difference spectroscopy. *Biochemistry* 32:8092–97

29. Gordy W. 1946. A relation between bond force constants, bond orders, bond lengths and the electronegativities of the bonded atoms. *J. Chem. Phys.* 14:305–20

30. Jeffrey GA, Saenger W. 1991. *Hydrogen Bonding in Biological Structures.* Berlin: Springer-Verlag

31. Joesten M, Schaad LJ. 1974. *Hydrogen Bonding.* New York: Marcel Dekker

32. Kiefer W. 1973. Raman difference spectroscopy with a rotating cell. *Appl. Spectrosc.* 27:253–57

33. Kim M, Carey PR. 1993. Observation of a carbonyl feature for riboflavin bound to riboflavin-binding protein in the red-excited raman spectrum. *J. Am. Chem. Soc.* 115:7015–16

34. Kim M, Owen H, Carey PR. 1993. A high-performance Raman spectroscopic system based on a single spectrograph, CCD, notch filters and a Kr laser ranging from the Near-IR to Near-UV regions. *Appl. Spectrosc.* In press

35. Komives EA, Change LC, Lolis E, Tilton RF, Petsko GA, Knowles JR. 1991. Electrophilic catalysis in triosephosphate isomerase: the role of histidine-95. *Biochemistry* 30:3011–19

36. Kurz LC, Drysdale GR. 1987. Evidence from fourier transform infrared spectroscopy for polarization of the carbonyl of oxaloacetate in the active site of citrate synthase. *Biochemistry* 26:2623–27

37. LaReau RD, Anderson VE. 1992. An inquiry into the source of stereospecificity of lactate dehydrogenase using substrate analogues and molecular modeling. *Biochemistry* 31:4174–80

38. Latajka Z, Scheiner S. 1990. Correlation between interaction energy and shift of the carbonyl stretching frequency. *Chem. Phys. Lett.* 174:179–84

39. Li H, Hanson C, Fuchs JA, Woodward C, Thomas JGJ. 1993. Determination of the pKa values of active-center cysteines, cysteines-32 and -35, in *Escherichia coli* thioredoxin by Raman spectroscopy. *Biochemistry* 32:5800–8

40. Manor D, Weng G, Deng H, Cosloy S, Chen CX, et al. 1991. An isotope edited classical Raman difference spectroscopic study of the interactions of guanine nucleotides with elongation factor Tu and H-*ras* p21. *Biochemistry* 30: 10914–20

41. Mäntele W. 1993. Reaction-induced infrared difference spectroscopy for the study of protein function and reaction mechanisms. *Trends Biochem. Sci.* 18: 197–202

42. Peticolas WL, Bajdor K, Patapoff TW, Wilson KJ. 1987. New methods of studying enzyme-substrate interactions using ultra violet resonance Raman and microscopic Raman difference technique. In *Studies in Physics and Theoretical Chemistry,* ed. J Stepanek, P Anzenbacher, B Sedlacek, pp. 249–70. Amsterdam: Elsevier

43. Ray JWJ, Burgner IJW, Deng H, Callender R. 1993. A comparison of internal chemical bonding in solutions of simple phosphates and vanadates. *Biochemistry.* 32:12977–83

44. Ray WJ, Post CB, Liu Y, Rhyu GI.

1993. Structural changes at the metal binding site during the phosphoglucomutase reaction. *Biochemistry* 32:48–57

45. Rothschild KJ. 1992. FTIR difference spectroscopy of bacteriorhodopsin: toward a molecular model. *J. Bioenerg. Biomembr.* 24:147–67

46. Rousseau DL. 1981. Raman difference spectroscopy as a probe of biological molecules. *J. Raman Spectrosc.* 10:94–99

47. Slaich PK, Primrose WU, Robinson D, Drabble K, Wharton CW, et al. 1992. The binding of amide substrate analogues to phospholipase A2. *Biochem. J.* 288:167–73

48. Spiro TG, ed. 1987. *Biological Applications of Raman Spectroscopy,* Vol. 1, *Raman Spectra and the Conformations of Biological Molecules.* New York: Wiley & Sons

49. Spiro TG, ed. 1987. *Biological Applications of Raman Spectroscopy,* Vol. 2, *Resonance Raman Spectra of Polyenes and Aromatics.* New York: Wiley & Sons

50. Spiro TG, ed. 1988. *Biological Applications of Raman Spectroscopy,* Vol. 3, *Resonance Raman Spectra of Heme and Metalloproteins.* New York: Wiley & Sons

51. Thijs R, Zeegers-Huyskens T. 1984. Infrared and Raman studies of hydrogen bonded complexes involving acetone, acetophenone, and benzopenone-I. Thermodynamic constants and frequency shifts of the ν_{OH} and $\nu_{C=O}$ stretching vibrations. *Spectrochem. Acta* 40A:307–13

52. Thomas GJ, Tsuboi M. 1993. Raman spectroscopy of nucleic acids and their complexes. *Adv. Biophys. Chem.* 3:1–69

53. Tonge PJ, Carey PR. 1990. Length of the acyl carbonyl bond in acyl-serine proteases correlates with reactivity. *Biochemistry* 29:10723–27

54. Tonge PJ, Carey PR. 1993. Raman, resonance Raman and FTIR spectroscopic studies of enzyme-substrate complexes. In *Biomolecular Spectroscopy,* ed. RJH Clarke, RE Hester, pp. 129–61. New York: Wiley & Sons

54a. Tonge PJ, Carey PR, Callender RH, Deng H, Ekrel I, Muhandiram R. 1993. Characterization of *trans* and *cis* 5-methylthienylacryloyl-chymotrypsin using Raman difference spectrscopy,

NMR, and kinetics: carbonyl environment and reactivity. *J. Am. Chem. Soc.* 115:8757–62

55. Tonge PJ, Pusztai M, White AJ, Wharton CW, Carey PR. 1991. Resonance raman and fourier transform infrared spectroscopic studies of the acyl carbonyl group in [3-(5-methyl-2-thienyl)acryloyl]chymotrypsin: evidence for artifacts in the spectra obtained by both techniques. *Biochemistry* 30:4790–95

56. Vinogradov SN, Linnel RH. 1971. *Hydrogen Bonding.* New York: Van Nostrand Reinhold

57. Weng G, Chen CX, Chen Z, Balogh-Nair V, Callender R, Manor D. 1994. The hydrogen bonding of G proteins with the guanine ring moiety of guanine nucleotides. *Protein Sci.* In press

58. White AJ, Drabble K, Ward S, Wharton CW. 1992. Analysis and elimination of protein perturbation in infrared difference spectra of acyl-chymotrypsin ester carbonyl groups by using isotopic substitution. *Biochem. J.* 287:317–23

59. White AJ, Wharton CW. 1990. Hydrogen-bonding in enzymatic catalysis. *Biochem. J.* 270:627–37

60. Yager P, Gaber BP. 1987. Membranes. See Ref. 48, pp. 81–133

61. Yue KT, Deng H, Callender R. 1989. Raman difference spectroscopy in measurements of molecules and molecular groups inside proteins. *J. Raman Spectrosc.* 20:541–46

62. Yue KT, Martin CL, Chen D, Nelson P, Sloan DL, Callender R. 1986. Raman spectroscopy of oxidized and reduced nicotinamide adenine dinucleotides. *Biochemistry* 25:4941–47

62a. Yue KT, Minghe L, Zheng J, Callender R. 1991. The determination of the pK_a of histidine in proteins by Raman difference spectroscopy. *Biochim. Biophys. Acta* 1078:296–302

63. Yue KT, Yang JP, Charlotte M, Lee SK, Sloan D, Callender R. 1984. A Raman study of reduced nicotinamide adenine dinucleotide bound to liver alchohol dehydrogenase. *Biochemistry* 23:6480–83

64. Zheng J, Chen YQ, Callender R. 1993. A study of the binding of NADP coenzymes to dihydrofolate reductase by Raman difference spectroscopy. *Eur. J. Biochem.* 215:9–16

Annu. Rev. Biophys. Biomol. Struct. 1994. 23:247–85

BIOLOGICAL APPLICATIONS OF OPTICAL FORCES

Karel Svoboda

Committee on Biophysics, Harvard University, Cambridge, Massachusetts 02138 and Rowland Institute for Science, 100 Edwin Land Boulevard, Cambridge, Massachusetts 02142

Steven M. Block

Rowland Institute for Science, 100 Edwin Land Boulevard, Cambridge, Massachusetts 02142 and Department of Molecular Biology, Princeton University, Princeton, New Jersey 08544

KEY WORDS: optical tweezers, optical trapping, radiation pressure, lasers, tensiometry

CONTENTS

247

1056–8700/94/0610–0247$05.00

PERSPECTIVES AND OVERVIEW

In the first part of the seventeenth century, the German astronomer Johannes Kepler proposed that the reason comet tails point away from the sun is because they are pushed in that direction by the sun's radiation. In his theory of electromagnetism of 1873, James Clerk Maxwell showed theoretically that light itself can exert optical force, or *radiation pressure,* but this was not demonstrated experimentally until the turn of the century. One reason for the lapse of nearly three centuries between hypothesis and verification is that radiation pressure is extraordinarily feeble. Milliwatts of power (corresponding to very bright light) impinging on an object produce piconewtons of force ($1 \text{ pN} = 10^{-12} \text{ N}$). The advent of lasers in the 1960s finally enabled researchers to study radiation pressure through the use of intense, collimated sources of light. An early pioneer of such studies was Arthur Ashkin of AT&T (Bell) Laboratories. By focusing laser light down into narrow beams, Ashkin and others demonstrated that tiny particles, such as polystyrene spheres a few micrometers in diameter, could be displaced and even levitated against gravity using the force of radiation pressure (1–3, 5, 6, 66). Ashkin's work on the effects of radiation pressure laid much of the groundwork for the development of laser-based atom trapping and cooling methods employed by today's physicists (2a, 33, 34).

One particular optical trapping scheme, proposed in 1978 and demonstrated in 1986 (2a, 10), simply consisted of bringing a beam of laser light to a diffraction-limited focus using a good lens, such as a microscope objective. Under the right conditions, the intense light gradient near the focal region can achieve stable three-dimensional trapping of dielectric objects. Optical traps employing this design do not trap atoms at room temperature, but they can be used to capture and remotely manipulate a wide range of larger particles, varying in size from several nanometers up to tens of micrometers. The term *optical tweezers* was coined to describe this single-beam scheme. In many respects, it resembles a scaled-down version of the tractor beam of popular science fiction. Ashkin and coworkers showed in 1987 that optical tweezers could manipulate living, as well as inanimate, material and that through proper choice of wavelength, optical damage to biological specimens could be minimized. Employing a continuous-wave (cw) near-infrared laser (Nd:YAG , $\lambda = 1064$ nm), Ashkin captured viruses, yeasts, bacteria, and protozoa (7, 11). Experiments in other laboratories during the past few years have begun to explore the rich possibilities afforded by optical trapping in biology. Although still in their infancy, laser-based optical traps have already had significant impact, mainly because they afford an unprecedented means to manipulate on the microscopic scale.

Optical forces are miniscule on the scale of larger organisms, but they can be significant on the scale of macromolecules, organelles, and even whole cells. A force of ten piconewtons, equal to one microdyne, can tow a bacterium through water faster than it can swim, halt a swimming sperm cell in its track, or arrest the transport of an intracellular vesicle. A force of this magnitude can also stretch, bend, or otherwise distort single macromolecules, such as DNA and RNA, or macromolecular assemblies, including cytoskeletal components such as microtubules and actin filaments. Mechanoenzymes such as myosin, kinesin, and dynein produce forces in the piconewton range. Optical traps are therefore especially well suited to studying mechanics or dynamics at the cellular and subcellular levels.

Recent reviews have covered the scope of the first generation of biological experiments (8, 20, 22, 23, 46, 54, 74, 88). The present discussion concentrates instead on current developments. It also deals with related technical issues, including a critique of optical trapping theory, considerations for instrument design and calibration, and novel approaches to using optical forces. Finally, we hope to communicate our sense of future directions for this growing field.

TRAPPING BASICS

Optical traps use radiation pressure, a term that refers generally to forces imparted to matter by the absorption, scattering, emission, or reradiation of light (i.e. by photons). Radiation pressure may manifest itself in several ways. Perhaps the most familiar form is the *scattering force,* which, following current usage, is defined as that force due to light scattering that is proportional to the light intensity and acts in the direction of propagation of light. This force may also be regarded as a consequence of the momentum delivered by the scattered photons. Optical tweezers, however, owe their trapping to the *gradient force,* which is instead proportional to the spatial gradient in light intensity and acts in the direction of that gradient. Other optical forces include, for example, the *optical binding force,* which is an interaction between particles in intense light (30, 31). All optical forces arise from the same physics.

The gradient force used by optical tweezers arises from fluctuating electric dipoles that are induced when light passes through transparent objects, which consequently experience a time-averaged force in the direction of the field gradient. When an object's dimensions are sub-stantially greater than the wavelength of light, i.e. when $d \gg \lambda$, a con-dition referred to as the Mie regime, a simple ray-optic picture suffices to explain the phenomenon (Figure 1). Rays of light carry momentum and are bent by refraction when passing through a dielectric sphere with a refractive index, n, greater than the surrounding medium. By conservation of momentum, the rate of change of momentum in the deflected rays conveys an equal and opposite rate of change in mo-

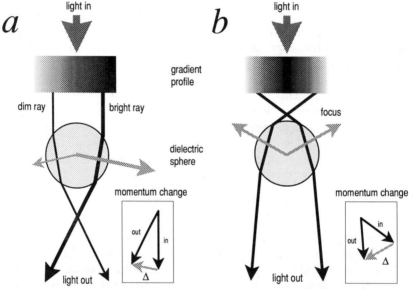

Figure 1   (*a*) A ray-optic picture of the gradient force. A parallel beam of light (*large gray arrow*) with a gradient in intensity (*shaded region;* the darker color indicates more light) shines through a transparent sphere with a higher refractive index than its back-ground. The relative thickness of the two representative rays (*black arrows*) symbolizes intensity. The rays are refracted, giving rise to the reaction forces shown acting through the sphere's center (*gray arrows*). The brighter right ray conveys more force than the dimmer left ray: the sum of all rays in the beam tends to pull the sphere rightwards towards the light. (*Inset*) A vector diagram indicating the change of momentum for the right ray. The difference in momentum (*gray arrow*) produces an equal and opposite reaction in the sphere. (*b*) A single beam trap. Light (*large gray arrow*) is brought to a focus: its beam profile has an intensity gradient (*shaded region*). Two representative rays (*black arrows*) pass through a transparent sphere located beyond the focus. The rays are bent, and reaction forces (*gray arrows*) pull the sphere upwards, towards the focus. (*Inset*) A vector diagram indicating the change of momentum in the left ray. The difference in momentum (*gray arrow*) produces an equal and opposite reaction in the sphere.

mentum to the sphere. The rate of change of momentum produces a force by Newton's Second Law.

When a dielectric sphere is placed in a light gradient, the sum of all rays passing through it generates an imbalance in force, tending to push the sphere towards the brighter region of the light. A focus functions as a trap because the strong light gradients in its neighborhood all point towards the center. Trapping is stable when the gradient force in the region beyond the focus is adequate to overcome the scattering force, which would otherwise propel the object out of the trap's center along the optical axis. This condition occurs, in practice, only with the steepest possible light gradients, e.g. those produced by a microscope objective of high numerical aperture (NA).

In the Rayleigh regime, where $d \ll \lambda$, light cannot be represented by rays, but trapping still occurs, and the magnitude of the trapping force is proportional to the field gradient. In this regime, objects can be represented as point dipole scatterers, simplifying theory. However, a focus cannot be represented as a point, but as a diffraction-limited region whose overall dimensions are close to λ. Unfortunately, most biological work falls into the intermediate regime ($d \approx \lambda$), where no dimensions can be neglected and calculations become difficult. Biological specimens further confound matters by tending to be nonspherical and inhomogeneous with respect to refractive index. Because of these complications, optical trapping theory is relatively immature. These and other considerations are discussed in greater detail in the trapping theory section of this review.

RECENT EXPERIMENTS

Optical traps have many intriguing applications (for reviews, see 8, 20, 22, 23, 46, 54, 74, 88). Ashkin & Dzeidzic used optical forces to stretch plant cell membranes into slender filaments to study their viscoeleastic properties (9). In collaboration with M Schliwa's group, they also used optical tweezers to estimate the force produced by moving vesicles in the giant amoeba *Reticulomyxa* spp. (12). The laboratories of K Greulich and M Berns have combined cw infrared optical tweezers with either pulsed ultraviolet or pulsed Nd:YAG laser microbeams, which function as optical scalpels, to cut and paste. With this arrangement, they performed various kinds of microsurgery, such as laser-assisted cell fusion (76). Greulich's group has employed optical scalpels to sever isolated chromosomes and optical tweezers to collect the pieces for eventual use in gene sequencing procedures (45, 71). They have also initiated studies bringing together killer T-cells and target cells with optical tweezers for studies of the immune response (71). Berns and colleagues have manipulated chromosomes or chromosome fragments in order to study cell division (19, 21, 56, 57, 85), and Aufderheide has repositioned micronuclei and small organelles in *Paramecium* spp. (13, 14). Much interest has focused on measuring the swimming force of sperm, and optical methods may potentially facilitate in vitro fertilization (36, 79). Optical tweezers can be used to separate individual cells out of a mixed culture, for example bacteria (11) or yeasts (47). In fact, a prototype sorter for eukaryotic cells has been built based on optical forces (28, 29), and a commercial version of optical tweezers has been developed that is well suited to sorting and picking operations (LaserTweezers® 1000, Cell Robotics, Inc., Albuquerque, NM). By calibrating the optical force against viscous drag, Block, Blair & Berg (24) measured the torsional compliance of bacterial flagella. This compliance mainly resulted from the hook, a flexible helical polymer consisting of ~150 polypeptides that connects the shaft of the bacterial rotary motor to the filament (25). Charon et al used optical tweezers, in combination with video-enhanced differential interference contrast (DIC) microscopy, to immobilize spirochete bacteria and establish that their periplasmic flagella rotate (32).

One especially powerful approach has been the use of materials strongly trapped by optical tweezers, such as polystyrene or silica microspheres, as tiny handles. Handles can be more refractile than biological material, supplying extra trapping force, and their shape and uniform size facilitate calibration. Chu and coworkers attached polystyrene spheres to one or more ends of single molecules of DNA, which can be visualized in fluorescence using intercalating dyes. Using this approach, they initiated studies of mechanical properties by stretching a molecule taught, then releasing one of its ends and following the relaxation to a random coil (33). Shepherd et al attached myosin molecules covalently to polystyrene spheres, then captured such spheres out of suspension using optical tweezers and deposited them directly onto actin cables derived from demembranated hair cell stereocilia (72). In the presence of ATP, the myosin molecules pulled the spheres unidirectionally along the length of the actin, providing a novel in vitro motility assay for myosin. Silica spheres coated with the motor protein kinesin were similarly captured and placed on axonemes or microtubules in the presence of ATP, whereupon they moved unidirectionally (26).

The use of optical tweezers improves the efficiency of in vitro moving-bead assays by several orders of magnitude, permitting one to work at such dilute concentrations of kinesin protein that beads carry just one motor molecule (26). Using an in vitro assay, Kuo & Sheetz (55) estimated the force produced by molecules of kinesin. Edidin et al (40) and Kucik et al (53) used particles attached to transmembrane proteins to monitor the motility in the plane of the membrane of these complexes in order to study diffusion and cytoskeletal transport. Svoboda et al (77) attached spherical handles to ghosts of human red blood cells and levitated such ghosts away from microscope chamber surfaces. The microscope chamber was then perfused with neutral detergents that dissolved the lipid membrane of the ghost, revealing the labile spectrin cytoskeleton and permitting study of its properties in the absence of complicating surface interactions. Kuo and colleagues (54) attached spherical handles to the outsides of cells and used optical tweezers to draw such particles away from the surface, pulling the membrane out into slender filaments resembling filapodia, which they dubbed "neopodia." Neopodia may provide a useful system for studying the dynamic reorganization of cytoskeletal elements in cells.

Recently, Svoboda et al (78) used beads carrying single molecules of kinesin to detect the tiny steps made by this mechanoenzyme as it moves along the microtubule substrate: this was accomplished by combining optical trapping with interferometric position detection. In related work, Simmons et al (75) are using a sophisticated double-trap arrangement, equipped with position detection and force feedback, for experiments to measure displacements and forces produced by single myosin molecules interacting with actin filaments stretched between handles. A later section of this review explores other uses of handles.

DESIGN CONSIDERATIONS

Building a Trap

Optical tweezers can be built into a conventional light microscope in several ways (22). Fundamentally, two rules must be observed. First, a single-mode laser beam should be introduced into the microscope in such a way as not to interfere with normal microscope function and brought to a tight focus at (or near) the specimen plane using an objective of high NA, typically ≥ 1.00. Arranging the optics so that the trap is parfocal with the specimen allows trapped objects to be visualized and improves the quality of the trap, because microscope optics are designed to minimize aberrations near the specimen plane. A high NA is essential to maximize the light gradient near the focal region and thereby to ensure stable trapping in the axial direction. Second, the effective diameter of the laser beam (usually taken to be the $1/e^2$ diameter of the Gaussian beam) should be adjusted to exactly fill, or somewhat overfill, the back pupil of the objective. Most often, this is accomplished by placing a laser beam expander (or some other lens pair) in the optical system before the light enters the microscope, but one can also use the natural laser beam divergence in combination with a longer beam path. Filling the back aperture of the objective assures that light converges to a tight, diffraction-limited spot.

Practical optical traps implement additional features, such as some means of shuttering or switching the laser to turn the trap on and off. A variable light level is also desirable. Laser attenuators may be built around neutral density filters or wedges, or, for polarized lasers, around variable-extinction devices (e.g. a rotating half waveplate in combination with a fixed polarizer), or acousto-optic modulators. The power in certain lasers, especially diode and diode-pumped lasers, may be readily altered by adjusting the operating current.

Often, the trap must be moved with respect to the specimen, which can be done either by moving the specimen or by moving the beam. In practice, both capabilities are helpful. Specimens can be positioned in the x-y plane by moving the microscope stage in the conventional way while leaving the trap fixed on the optic axis. This is especially useful when large-scale movements are required, i.e. over distances greater than the microscope field of view. A computerized, motorized stage can be used to automate movement, as in one commercial instrument (LaserTweezers® 1000, Cell Robotics). For small but accurate displacements, the sample may be mounted on an x-y piezoelectric stage. Movement of the trap in depth (the z-direction) is accomplished by focusing the microscope up or down (a process that also may be motorized), taking advantage of the parfocality of trap and specimen. Alternatively, the sample—or the objective, for that matter—can be placed on a vertical piezoelectric element. The trap can be displaced vertically with respect to the specimen plane by changing the parfocalizing optics, most often by moving an external lens controlling beam divergence.

Beam Steering

For rapid and convenient movement within the field, the trap may be steered in the specimen plane. To accomplish this, the laser beam must be scanned over the specimen while maintaining illumination across the full back aperture of the objective. This is essentially the same problem solved by laser scanning confocal microscopes, and solutions developed for those devices are readily adapted to optical tweezers.

Figure 2 shows four different schemes used for beam steering with

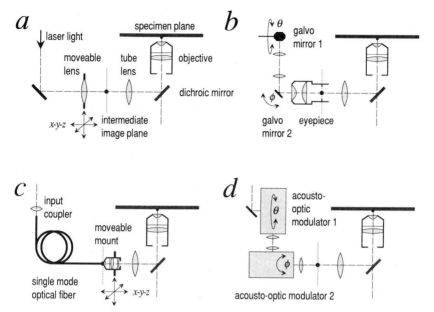

Figure 2   Four ways to scan the position of an optical trap in the specimen plane (see text). (*a*) Translating a moveable lens. (*b*) Rotating galvanometer mirrors. (*c*) Translating the end of an optical fiber. (*d*) Deflecting the beam with acousto-optic modulators (AOMs).

optical tweezers; objective lenses are drawn, for simplicity, with their rear focal plane at infinity. Figure 2*a* depicts an arrangement that is perhaps the most straightforward to build, in which the rear element of a two-lens telescope is moved by an *x-y-z* positioner (22). The front lens of the telescope may be the tube lens of the microscope that forms the intermediate image, or it may be some other lens external to the microscope light path. Translations of the rear lens in all three dimensions generate, to a good approximation, corresponding translations of the laser trap. This optical arrangement does not strictly produce the required rotation of the laser beam in the rear pupil of the objective, but it approximates that motion for small displacements, roughly within the center third of the field of view. Because it is mechanical and involves moving a relatively massive lens, it is slow, although scan rates to 100 Hz are still feasible (24). The scheme is simple, economical, lowest in terms of light loss, and quite stable (no drift), which may be vital to some specialized applications. It can be motorized and/or automated, if desired. It also provides for *z*-motion of the trap, in effect combining scanning and parfocality functions.

The scheme in Figure 2b is adapted directly from scanning confocal usage. Rotations of the galvanometer mirrors in θ and ϕ, which are placed in planes conjugate to the rear pupil of the objective, scan the beam in x and y. The first mirror is placed at the eyepoint of an eyepiece (or some other scan lens) that has been focused on the specimen. The 1:1 telescope lens pair between the galvanometer mirrors serves to image one mirror onto the other, so that they lie in conjugate planes, as well as to parfocalize the trap and image. An alternative is to place a single mirror at the eyepoint that can swivel in both θ and ϕ, driven through gimbal arrangement consisting of two nested galvanometers (not shown). The latter arrangement is somewhat slower, since one galvanometer must turn another one instead of just a lightweight mirror, but it may suffer less light loss. Although they are more costly and difficult to build, galvanometer-based scanners have a clear advantage of speed (rates up to several kilohertz), and they can scan the entire field of the microscope with minimal aberration. Moreover, they can be used to create multiple traps (84) and even different effective trap shapes (68). Most galvanometer mirrors are subject to small amounts of pointing jitter (5–100 μrad, p-p) that make their use problematic when absolute stability is required.

The scheme in Figure 2c is in many respects similar to that in 2a, except that the light is supplied by a single-mode optical fiber, the output of which is positioned at an intermediate image plane. An optical lever consisting of the lens arrangement shown moves the light-source position, which is steered mechanically with an x-y-z positioner (35). Optical fibers provide a convenient means of introducing laser light into an optical system.

The scheme in Figure 2d is similar to that in 2b, except that galvanometer mirrors are replaced by proportional acousto-optic modulators (AOMs). Such devices are quite expensive, relatively lossy (<85% transmittance per device), introduce aberrations, and are only capable of moderate deflections. However, they are unmatched for speed— frequencies approaching GHz are possible—and they have improved pointing stability over galvanometer mirrors. AOMs are best suited to specialized applications, such as force-feedback control.

The greatest light loss in optical trapping microscopes is sustained in the objective itself. Microscope manufacturers don't generally design lenses for transmittance in the near infrared, and as a result, antireflective coatings optimized for the visible spectrum can attenuate trapping lasers severely. The many optical surfaces present in compound lenses—up to 20 or more in the better objectives—do nothing to improve throughput. Numbers vary considerably, but in practice, one can only expect to get about half of the incident light through an objective of high numerical aperture, as shown in Table 1. Considerable care should be taken when measuring the transmittance of microscope objectives: the large divergence of light from the focus prevents one from simply placing a photodector behind the specimen position and getting a reliable measure of throughput. A better method is to use an optical bench to align two identical objectives facing one another on either side of a symmetric specimen (two coverglasses with immersion medium, with a water layer in the middle), and pass collimated laser light through the pair, in such as way as to fill the pupil of each objective. Measuring the light transmitted by such a pair circumvents the problems arising from divergence and provides a realistic simulation of the configuration actually used for trapping. Unfortunately, it requires two matched objectives. The transmittance data of Table 1 were acquired by this method; these do not take into account any additional losses sustained at the back aperture.

Trapping Lasers

To prevent damage by light absorption, most trapping lasers operate in the near infrared, where a window of transparency for biological material arises from two opposing trends (Figure 3). First, natural biological chromophores, such as hemoglobin (Figure 3) or the ubiquitous cytochromes, absorb increasingly less light towards the near infrared, dropping out beyond wavelengths of $\sim$800 nm. Second, water absorption rises dramatically as one goes farther into the infrared, peaking around 3 μm. An obvious compromise is the Nd:YAG laser at 1064 nm (or equivalently, the newer Nd:YLF laser at 1047 or 1053 nm), which is capable of the relatively high powers needed for trapping. Recently, single mode infrared diode lasers of sufficient power and beam quality

Table 1 Objective transmittances in the near infrared

Manufacturer	Type designation	Part number	Magnification	Numerical aperture	Transmittance at 1064 nm ($\pm 2\%$)
Carl Zeiss, Inc.	Plan Neofluar	44 04 80	$100 \times$	1.30 oil	59%
Carl Zeiss, Inc.	Plan Neofluar	44 04 66	$63 \times$	1.25 oil, iris	60%
Carl Zeiss, Inc.	Plan Apochromat	44 07 60	$63 \times$	1.40 oil	49%
Carl Zeiss, Inc.	Achrostigmat	44 02 55	$40 \times$	1.30 oil	49%
Nikon, Inc.	CF Fluor	85005	$100 \times$	1.30 oil	68%
Nikon, Inc.	CFN Plan Apochromat	85020	$60 \times$	1.40 oil	42%
Nikon, Inc.	CF Fluor	85004	$40 \times$	1.30 oil	74%

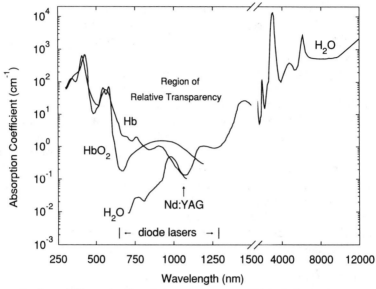

Figure 3 A graph illustrating the relative transparency of biological material in the near infrared region, showing the absorption of water and some common chromophores as a function of wavelength. Hb and HbO_2 stand for deoxyhemoglobin and oxyhemoglobin, respectively (at concentrations of 2×10^{-3} M). Water absorbs strongly beyond 2 μm. The wavelengths for Nd:YAG and diode lasers are indicated. Note the break in scale.

for trapping became available, and improved versions can be expected in the near future. Powers up to 1 W are now available commercially. Infrared diode lasers emit in narrow wavebands from ~780 to 1330 nm, with 820-860 nm being typical for trapping use. The tunable, externally pumped titanium sapphire laser can be varied continuously over the range of ~700–1100 nm. Table 2 serves as a comparative guide to lasers suitable for optical trapping.

Early work suggested that longer-term exposure to light at 1064 nm from a Nd:YAG laser produced photodynamic damage to cells, probably by optically pumping singlet molecular oxygen, a toxic free radical (22). Berns and colleagues have begun an important study of optical damage as a function of wavelength in the near infrared region using the tunable titanium sapphire laser, assaying chromosomal damage to mitotic cells (85). They covered the region from 700–840 nm, or roughly half the span of wavelengths available to this laser. Over this limited range, cells appeared minimally sensitive to irradiation around 700 nm and around 820 nm, but maximally sensitive at an intermediate value around 760 nm. The lower damage at 820 nm augurs well for the use

Table 2 Near infrared optical trapping lasers

Laser type	Gain medium	Wavelength (nm)	Power min–max (typical)	Some suppliers	Price range (1993, approximately)	Remarks
Conventional solid state (TEM$_{00}$ mode, cw)	Nd:YAG, Nd:YLF	1064, 1320 1047, 1053	0.5–20 W (1 W)	Coherent, CVI, Lee, Quantronix, Spectra-Physics, Spectron	$5,000–40,000	Most power; some alignment required; less stable; cooling water system required; least expensive for high power
Tunable solid-state (TEM$_{00}$ mode, cw)	Ti:Sapphire	~700–1100, variable	150 mW–3 W (1 W)	Coherent, E-O Schwartz, Spectra-Physics	$20,000–40,000	Tunable, power varies with wavelength; alignment required; less stable; requires multiwatt argon or Nd:YAG laser pump source and cooling system; most expensive
Diode-pumped solid state (TEM$_{00}$ mode, cw)	Nd:YAG, Nd:YLF	1064, 1320 1047, 1053	100 mW–4 W (300 mW)	Adlas, Amoco, Coherent, Laser Diode, Spectra-Physics	$10,000–40,000	Moderate power; turnkey operation, no alignment required; stable; usually thermoelectrically (TE) cooled; moderately expensive
Laser diode (single mode, cw)	GaAlAs, InGaAs, InGaAsP	780–1330 (850 typical)	40–250 mW (100 mW)	EG&G, Liconix, Melles Griot, Oki, Sharp, Sony, Spectra Diode Labs, Toshiba	$200–3000 (not including power supply, beam optics)	Lower power only; stable; beam circularization optics required; separate power supply required; TE cooling optional; nearly diffraction-limited; least expensive
Hybrid laser diode (single mode, cw) master oscillator power amplifier (MOPA)	InGaAs	985	1 W	Spectra Diode Labs	$10,000 (not including power supplies)	Highest power for single diode; stable; onboard TE cooler and beam circularization optics; three external power supplies required; nearly diffraction limited; relatively expensive

of diode lasers, which are convenient, economical, and available at this wavelength. Because minimal damage occurred at the extrema of the range, the wavelength spread needs to be extended in future study. Studying optical damage to biological systems on a case-by-case basis may also become necessary, since the mechanisms of photodamage are not well established. The situation is complex: damage most likely does not arise from heating, per se (22), but several types of deleterious photochemistry may be operating. Some toxicity may also arise from two-photon effects, which occur even with cw lasers at the high fluxes encountered near the trapping zone (80). The threshold for optical damage, or *opticution* (a colorful term due to Ashkin), sets the practical limit on the amount of light that can be delivered, and therefore on the optical force that can be usefully provided. Clearly, these limitations need to be better defined.

TRAPPING THEORY

Optical forces are sensitive to small perturbations in geometry, and therefore theoretical computation will probably never replace direct measurement. But theoretical models are nevertheless useful to suggest improvements in experimental geometry and choice of trapping materials. Comparisons between experiments and models may also reveal the presence of other forces. One possibility is the radiometric force, generated by thermal gradients resulting from residual absorption by the trapped particle (6). To date, force calculations have dealt only with spherical dielectrics, primarily because electromagnetic models for other geometries are harder to compute. Also, polystyrene and silica handles are spherical. Finally, any baseline lessons, parametric trends, and general wisdom can probably be transferred to the trapping of more complex specimens.

Optical forces are customarily defined by the relationship

$$F = \frac{Q n_m P}{c},$$

1.

where Q is a dimensionless efficiency, n_m is the index of refraction of the suspending medium, c is the speed of light, and P is the incident laser power, measured at the specimen (4). Q represents the fraction of power utilized to exert force. For plane waves incident on a perfectly absorbing particle, $Q = 1$. To achieve stable trapping, the radiation pressure must create a stable, three-dimensional equilibrium. Because biological specimens are usually contained in aqueous medium, the dependence of F on n_m can rarely be exploited to achieve higher trapping forces. Increasing the laser power is possible, but only over a limited range due to the possibility of optical damage. Q itself is therefore the main determinant of trapping force. It depends upon the NA, laser wavelength, light polarization state, laser mode structure, relative index of refraction, and geometry of the particle.

In the Rayleigh regime, trapping forces decompose naturally into two components. Since, in this limit, the electromagnetic field is uniform across the dielectric, particles can be treated as induced point dipoles. The scattering force is given by

$$\mathbf{F}_{\text{scatt}} = n_m \frac{\langle S \rangle \sigma}{c}, \tag{2.}$$

where

$$\sigma = \frac{8}{3} \pi (kr)^4 r^2 \left(\frac{m^2 - 1}{m^2 + 2} \right)^2 \tag{3.}$$

is the scattering cross section of a Rayleigh sphere with radius r (52). $\langle S \rangle$ is the time-averaged Poynting vector, n is the index of refraction of the particle, $m = n/n_m$ is the relative index, and $k = 2\pi n_m/\lambda$ is the wave number of the light. Scattering force is proportional to the energy flux and points along the direction of propagation of the incident light. The gradient force is the Lorentz force acting on the dipole induced by the light field. It is given by

$$\mathbf{F}_{\text{grad}} = \frac{\alpha}{2} \nabla \langle E^2 \rangle, \tag{4.}$$

where

$$\alpha = n_m^2 r^3 \left(\frac{m^2 - 1}{m^2 + 2} \right) \tag{5.}$$

is the polarizability of the particle (44). The gradient force is proportional and parallel to the gradient in energy density (for $m > 1$). Stable trapping requires that the gradient force in the $-\hat{z}$ direction, against the direction of incident light, be greater than the scattering force. Increasing the NA decreases the focal spot size and increases the gradient strength. Hence, in the Rayleigh regime, trapping forces in all directions increase with higher NA. For a trapped particle, the effect of $\mathbf{F}_{\text{scatt}}$ is to move the equilibrium trapping position down-beam from the laser focus. Although a decomposition into scattering and gradient forces is not strictly meaningful for larger particles, the nomenclature is nevertheless retained (see section on ray optics, below).

Most theoretical models have been limited to either Rayleigh or Mie scatterers. In the Rayleigh regime, Visscher & Brakenhoff (82) computed the dependence of axial forces on NA and wavelength. They used a form of the incident beam based on vector diffraction theory (64), valid for uniform illumination at the back aperture of a high NA objective. Models for Mie scatterers (15, 47a, 83, 92) have been based on the formalism of Roosen (65, 66) for the computation of optical forces caused by reflection and refraction at a spherical surface, and have neglected diffraction effects. But some of these computations assume a TEM_{00} mode structure at the focus (15, 47a, 92) that is only valid for low NA systems, since for higher NAs the paraxial approximation breaks down (38, 73). In a more generally applicable theory developed by Visscher & Brakenhoff, a high NA beam structure was used to compute axial trapping forces as a function of NA and index of refraction (83). They used the Poynting vector at a point on the sphere's surface to define the phase and angle of incidence. Although this strategy is physically incorrect (4), it probably gives qualitatively correct results. They predicted a maximum trapping force for $n = 1.65$ (for $r = 15 \ \mu m$, $NA = 1.3$, $\lambda = 1064$ nm), similar to the prediction of the ray-optics (RO) model described below. At this high index, however, the large scattering force will tend to accelerate particles in the neighborhood of the trap away from the focus and, in effect, make stable capture more difficult. Ashkin derived axial and trapping forces based on a simple RO model (4).

In the intermediate regime, where $r \leq \lambda \approx 1 \ \mu m$, recent electromagnetic (EM) calculations employing a more rigorous approach to the boundary value problem appear to describe trapping forces better than the RO model (16–18, 90, 91). Because the RO theory is the most complete, but the size regime of the EM theory arguably the most relevant, we discuss these two approaches in more detail.

Ray-Optics Theory

Building on the work of Roosen, Ashkin (4) computed optical forces for the Mie regime ($r \gg \lambda$). A known distribution of parallel rays enters the back focal plane of an objective, which is assumed to focus all rays to a point. Diffraction effects are neglected in this limit, by definition. The rays both reflect and refract at the surface of the sphere, giving rise to optical forces. The force, F, due to a single ray of power, P, is given by

$$\mathbf{F} = \frac{n_m P}{c}\left\{1 + R\cos 2\theta - \frac{T^2[\sin(2\theta - 2\epsilon) + R\cos 2\theta]}{1 + R^2 + 2R\cos 2\epsilon}\right\}\hat{\mathbf{k}} +$$

$$\frac{n_m P}{c}\left\{R\sin 2\theta - \frac{T^2[\sin(2\theta - 2\epsilon) + R\sin 2\theta]}{1 + R^2 + 2R\cos 2\epsilon}\right\}\hat{\mathbf{i}},$$

6.

where θ is the angle of incidence, ϵ is the angle of refraction, $\hat{\mathbf{k}}$ and $\hat{\mathbf{i}}$ are unit vectors parallel and perpendicular to the direction of the incident ray, and R and T are the Fresnel reflection and refraction coefficients (49). R and T are polarization dependent, and therefore so are the trapping forces. In Ashkin's notation, the coefficients of $\hat{\mathbf{k}}$ and $\hat{\mathbf{i}}$ represent the scattering and gradient forces, respectively. The force includes the effects of all internally reflected and refracted beams, hence, it is exact within the RO approximation. The overall force exerted by a beam with a given profile is simply the vector sum of the forces resulting from the ensemble of rays that comprise the beam. Figure 4 illustrates the basic geometry for ray-optic calculations.

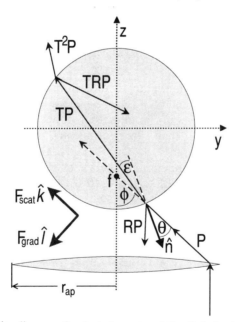

Figure 4 Ray-optics diagram of a single beam trap (after Ref. 4), shown with the objective below, as in an inverted microscope. The focus, f, is located on the z-axis. Variables: q, the angle of incidence for a ray; e, the angle of refraction; ϕ, the cone half-angle of the incident beam; $\hat{n}$, a surface normal; r_{ap}, the aperture radius. A single incident ray of power P gives rise to reflected and refracted rays of power RP, TP, T^2P, TRP, etc. Gray arrows indicate the directions of scattering and gradient forces. Note that the forces act through the center of the bead and do not exert torques.

In the RO regime, trapping forces are independent of sphere size, and the smallest forces occur in the $-\hat{z}$ direction. In this direction, the gradient force must overcome the axial scattering force. Therefore, the strongest trap is achieved by maximizing the restoring force in this direction, even at the expense of other force components. The RO theory predicts that *overfilling* the back pupil of the objective, i.e. $\omega_o > r_{ap}$, where ω_o is the beam radius of the TEM_{00} mode at the objective back aperture and r_{ap} is the lens aperture radius, leads to stronger trapping than simply filling the back pupil (4). This is because highly converging rays contribute disproportionately to the axial intensity gradient. The loss of laser power suffered by overfilling the back aperture is generally not a problem, because most trapping applications require only a few milliwatts at the specimen plane. For the same reason, objectives with the highest possible NA are most useful. In principle, laser mode profiles that concentrate a greater fraction of light at larger angles should do even better. Ashkin discusses use of the TEM_{01}^*, or donut mode, which has an intensity distribution of the form $I(r) = I_o(r/\omega_o)^2 \exp(-2r^2/\omega_o^2)$. Either overfilling the back aperture with the TEM_{00} mode or filling the back aperture with the TEM_{01}^* mode profile at NA = 1.3 should produce a ratio of forces in the strongest $(+z)$ and weakest $(-z)$ directions of 1.75–2.00. This ratio increases with decreasing axial gradients. In the $-z$ direction, the dependence of trapping forces on relative index of refraction should reach a maximum at $n = 1.69$. This observation implies that polystyrene particles ($n = 1.57$) should trap better than silica particles ($n = 1.47$). The decrease of trapping force at larger n (>1.69) results from a disproportionate increase in the scattering force. Theory predicts that the axial and transverse stiffnesses of the trap (i.e. dF/dz, dF/dy) increase towards the edge of the trapping zone.

One curious prediction of the RO model is that the transverse trapping efficiency should decrease with increasing NA (or decreasing focal spot size) over some range of NAs, i.e. that transverse forces vary nonmonotonically with transverse gradient fields. The fact that, under some circumstances, trapping due to the "gradient force" actually *decreases* with steeper gradients clearly shows that the simple decomposition into scattering and gradient forces breaks down outside the Rayleigh regime.

Electromagnetic Theory

Biological applications of optical tweezers often use spherical dielectric handles with diameters of 0.2–1.0 μm. For such particles, diffraction effects are significant. Moreover, for highly forcused beams, the vector character of the electromagnetic field cannot be neglected, as is generally the case in scalar theories that use the paraxial approximation. These factors enormously increase the difficulty of computing realistic forces in the intermediate size regime. The time-averaged force due to an arbitrary electromagnetic field, acting on an arbitrary particle, is given by the following integral over the surface enclosing the particle:

$$F_i = \left\langle \oint_s T_{ij} n_j da \right\rangle, \qquad\qquad 7.$$

where T_{ij} is the Maxwell stress tensor, n_j is the outward unit normal vector, and the brackets denote a temporal average. The appropriate form of the stress tensor has been the subject of some controversy. The consensus appears to be that for steady-state fields, the Minkowski form (49),

$$T_{ij} = \frac{1}{4\pi}\left[\epsilon E_i E_j + B_i B_j - \frac{1}{2}(\epsilon E_i E_i + B_i B_i)\delta_{ij} \right], \qquad 8.$$

where ϵ is the electric permittivity, is the correct one to use (18). The difficulty lies in deriving all six components of the electromagnetic field, E_i and B_i, at the surface of the particle, because the field includes contributions from the incident beam as well as the scattered and internal fields.

For incident light, the electromagnetic vector potential can be expanded in powers of the beam parameter, $s = \lambda/2\pi n_m \omega_o$, where λ is the wavelength and ω_o is the beam waist (38). The usual paraxial treatment for Gaussian laser beams is equivalent to a zeroth order approximation, i.e. it is valid for $\omega_o \gg \lambda$. Clearly, for highly focused beams, $\omega_o \leq \lambda$, this approximation is invalid. Even qualitative information gained by zeroth-order computations with Gaussian beams should be viewed with suspicion, because all axial fields are first order in s. Barton et al have derived all six electromagnetic field components in the focal region using a fifth-order correction to the paraxial Gaussian beam approximation (16). Their improved approximation is valid in the focal region of high NA objectives (within a 0.5-μm radius) illuminated by TEM$_{00}$ mode beams.

In related work, Barton and coworkers derived a theoretical framework to compute scattered and internal fields for a sphere illuminated by an arbitrary monochromatic wave (17). The force follows from knowledge of the field at the surface of the sphere and Equations 7 and 8. For example, they derived the radiation force and torque on a 5-μm-diameter water droplet (18). These calculations were in qualitative agreement with experiments in which polystyrene particles and glycerol droplets were levitated with focused laser beams (5).

Recently, Wright and coworkers (90) used EM theory and RO theory to compute the maximal axial trapping efficiency, Q_{max}, for polystyrene particles ($n = 1.57$), as a function of particle size (Figure 5). For small radii ($r < 0.1$ μm), trapping force scales with r^3, as expected for Rayleigh scatterers (Equation 5). The largest Q_{max} is predicted to be 0.14, corresponding to forces of 4.4 pN/mW. Their experimental measurements of Q_{max} for 1-μm-diameter silica spheres and 10-μm-diameter polystyrene spheres showed that EM theory gives better estimates for $r < 1$ μm than RO theory, and that RO theory gives acceptable results for $r > 10$ μm (at $\lambda = 1064$ nm). However, the discrepancy between EM theory and experiment for the 1-μm particle is still a factor of 3–5 depending upon the actual value used for objective transmittance (WH Wright, personal communication). The RO theory does somewhat better, but in general, measured Q values are low compared with theory. The discrepancy between theory and measurement may result from radiometric forces, but this remains to be determined. In the range 1–10 μm, neither EM nor RO theories seem to produce accurate results. Even a ninth-order correction does not help to prevent the breakdown of the EM theory for particles larger than 1 μm or the breakdown of the fifth-order Gaussian beam approximation far from

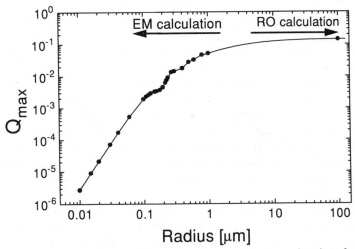

Figure 5 Computed maximum axial trapping efficiency (Q_{max}) as a function of sphere radius (redrawn from Ref. 90). Parameters were $n = 1.57$, $n_m = 1.33$, $\lambda = 1064$ nm. For the EM calculation, the spot size was 0.4 μm. For the RO calculation, the maximal cone half-angle was 60°.

the focus (WH Wright, personal communication). Wright et al also computed the axial trapping efficiency as a function of the distance between the sphere and the focus for a 1-μm-diameter silica sphere (90). In contrast to RO theory, the axial stiffness is predicted to decrease towards the edge of the trap. This behavior is in general agreement with our own measurements on 0.6-μm silica beads (see Figure 10a in the section on picotensiometers, below).

Although considerable work has gone into predicting optical forces, the agreement between theory and measurement is unsatisfactory; whether the quality of the measurements or of the models is responsible is unclear. Future force calibrations should be done with great care and combined with measurements of the beam profile at the focal plane, for comparison with theory (70, 91). The power actually delivered to the specimen ought to be reported, not merely the incident power to the system. Possibly, the microroughness of particle surfaces, a physical property not considered in any of these models, might contribute to scattering force (60). Finally, radiometric forces may play some role.

Parametric trends predicted by the EM and RO models have not been rigorously tested. One obvious candidate is the dependence of the axial trapping efficiency, Q_{max}, on particle radius. Another is the dependence of Q_{max} on the spot size and beam profile (91). It may be possible to apply self-consistent lattice models, in which the dielectric is represented as a collection of point dipoles on a lattice, to improve modeling. This approach has been successful in computing scattering by nonspherical objects (62).

FORCE MEASUREMENT

Calibration

Because current theory is unreliable in the computation of trapping force for particular objects and trapping geometries, these forces must be determined empirically. In most applications, forces are calibrated against viscous drag exerted by fluid flow. Calibration is facilitated by the fact that the Reynolds number is typically quite small for micron-sized objects: $Re = va\rho/\eta \approx 10^{-5}$, where v is the fluid velocity, a is the particle size, ρ is the particle density, and η is the fluid viscosity. Inertial forces are therefore entirely negligible, and the drag force on a stationary object if $F = \beta v$, where β is the drag coefficient and v is the fluid velocity (48). For a sphere of radius a, β is given by Stokes' Law: $\beta = 6\pi\eta a$. Drag forces on ellipsoids have also been derived in closed form (27, 48).

The maximal, or escape force, is typically measured in one of three ways (Figure 6):

1. Using a flow chamber, fluid is pumped past a stationary, trapped sphere at increasing velocity until the object just escapes (Figure 6a). The local fluid velocity is then measured by tracking the object immediately after leaving the trap, or by tracking some other object in the flow field in the same focal plane. This procedure requires only video microscopy and a flow chamber connected to a variable pump, but it has several drawbacks. First, since trapping is often done near a wall of the chamber, the shear field in the flow tends to push the trapped particle out of the focal plane towards the coverslip, and the force measured may differ from the actual force at the focal plane. Second, since only relatively slow particle velocities (~20 μm/s) can be measured with video methods, only small forces can be measured. Third, the method is confined to measuring transverse trapping forces.

2. The chamber containing fluid is moved past a stationary trapped sphere, and the velocity of the stage at which the bead escapes is measured (Figure 6b). In this case, a motorized or piezo-driven stage

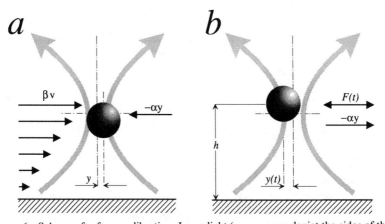

Figure 6 Schemes for force calibration. Laser light (*gray arrows* depict the sides of the beam profile) enters from below through a coverslip (*hatched*), as in an inverted microscope, and is focused to a narrow waist, whose center is marked by dashed lines. (*a*) The bead and chamber are held stationary while fluid is drawn past. The fluid drag force is balanced by the trapping force. Note that the shear field (*left arrows*) pushes the particle towards the coverglass. (*b*) The bead is held stationary while the chamber is moved, such that it experiences a force, $F(t)$. Note that the scattering force moves the axial equilibrium point down-beam from the center of the focus. Variables: h, the distance from coverglass surface; $y(t)$, the transverse position of the bead with respect to trap center; $F(t)$, the applied force on the bead (or, for thermal motion in a stationary chamber, the Langevin force); $-\alpha y(t)$, the transverse restoring force due to trap.

is needed. The main drawback to this method is that the drag must be corrected for the proximity to the coverglass surface, the effect of which can be large when the distance from the surface is comparable to the particle radius, as shown in Table 3. The viscous drag coefficient of a sphere with radius a whose center is a distance h from the surface is (48):

$$\beta = \frac{6\pi\eta a}{\left[1 - \frac{9}{16}(a/h) + \frac{1}{8}(a/h)^3 - \frac{45}{256}(a/h)^4 - \frac{1}{16}(a/h)^5\right]}. \qquad 9.$$

3. The optical trap is moved while the sample fluid remains stationary, and the velocity at which the bead escapes is recorded. This method is essentially equivalent to method 2 except that for some beam-steering configurations, notably those employing AOMs or galvanometer scan mirrors, larger velocities can be achieved and hence larger forces can be determined.

4. Axial trapping force can, in certain cases, be calibrated against gravity using an escape method. This approach is useful for particles that are sufficiently large and dense enough to have a negligible scale height, $h = kT/w$, where w is the net gravitational force acting on the object. The lower size limit is roughly 10 μm for polystyrene and 1 μm for silica particles. In principle, the gravity balance technique could

Table 3 Drag on a sphere near a planar surface (Faxen's Law)

$(h/a)^a$	Drag relative to $h = \infty$
1.01	2.97
1.10	2.36
1.25	1.92
1.50	1.62
1.75	1.47
2	1.39
3	1.23
4	1.16
5	1.10
10	1.06
50	1.01
∞	1.00

[a] Variables: h, distance above surface of center of sphere; a, sphere radius. The drag on the sphere at $h = \infty$ is given by Stokes' Law, $\beta = 6\pi\eta a$.

be extended to measuring lateral trapping by turning the microscope on its side.

Several groups have determined transverse trapping forces by using these methods (11, 12, 25, 55, 69), but the interpretation of calibration measurements is not necessarily straightforward. For instance, Sato et al (69) noted that the axial equilibrium trapping position is a function of transverse position. This effect would lead to an underestimate of force in experiments that strictly confine the particle to the equilibrium plane. Ashkin's computations suggest that this underestimate leads to only a small error ($\sim$5%), at least for larger particles (4).

Calibration against gravity has been used to measure the axial Q_{max} for various objectives (91). The size of the focal spot, ω_o, for these objectives was also measured with a knife-edge scanning technique. For both 1-μm silica particles and 20-μm polystyrene particles, Q_{max} is a strong function of objective NA (and ω_o). Q_{max} ranged from 0.132 to 0.023 for NAs of 1.3 to 0.8 with 20-μm polystyrene particles. In the same study, Wright et al (91) found that Q_{max} decreased dramatically with distance from the coverslip surface, an anticipated effect, given the increase in spherical aberration with depth. Misawa et al (60) measured Q_{max} using a technique similar to method 2 by moving the stage vertically and measuring the escape velocity. Axial forces were on the order of 1–5 pN for 2- to 11-μm polystyrene particles (NA = 1.3, P = 43 mW).

Several investigators have verified the strict proportionality between transverse force and laser power (cf 24, 69). But for small forces and large particles, the gravitational force should alter the axial trapping position in a power-dependent fashion. At the lowest powers, therefore, the transverse trapping force should scale with power with an exponent somewhat greater than unity.

Measurement of Trap Stiffness

Most force measurements have been made using variations of the escape-force method just described. Convenience, sensitivity, and versatility, however, can be greatly enhanced if the force is instead determined as a function of displacement from the trap center, i.e. if the trap stiffness is found. To accomplish this, the position within the trap must be measured to nanometer or better resolution. One approach is to use a video-based centroid tracking method (42), but the limited dynamic range ($\sim$30 Hz) and spatial resolution (a few nanometers) present severe limitations. Nanometer resolution at kilohertz bandwidths can be achieved by imaging the object onto a split photodiode detector: the difference voltage is proportional to displacement for motions up to the order of the particle radius (50, 51). The detector must be aligned with the optical trap at all times. An alternative arrangement is to use an optical trapping interferometer, in which the same laser light serves to produce both the trapping and interferometer functions (78). Displacement is proportional to the ellipticity developed by polarized light after recombination of the interferometer beams. In this setup, the detector zone and the trap remain intrinsically aligned (see below).

Physics of Trap Stiffness Measurements

For a harmonic potential, the equation of motion of a trapped particle subject to thermal motion can be solved exactly. If y is the displacement of the bead from the trap center, β is the viscous drag, and α is the stiffness of the trap, then for low Reynolds number, the equation of motion is

$$\beta \dot{y} + \alpha y = F(t), \qquad\qquad 10.$$

where $F(t)$ is an external driving force (Figure 6b). In the simplest case, $F(t)$ is the Langevin (thermal) force. The resulting dynamics is that of Brownian motion in a parabolic potential well, characterized by a Lorentzian power spectrum (86):

$$S_{yy}(f) = \frac{kT}{2\pi^3 \beta (f_0^2 + f^2)}. \qquad\qquad 11.$$

The corner frequency is $f_0 = \alpha(2\pi\beta)^{-1}$, and the mean square displacement of the particle is

$$\langle y^2 \rangle = 2\pi \int_0^{+\infty} S_{yy}(f) df. \qquad\qquad 12.$$

By the Equipartition Theorem, the mean square displacement is also equal to

$$\langle y^2 \rangle = kT\alpha^{-1}. \qquad\qquad 13.$$

These relationships suggest two ways to determine α by analysis of thermal fluctuations, both with inherent advantages. First, when the viscous drag is computable, e.g. for a spherical particle of known diameter located a known distance from the coverglass surface, the corner frequency, f_0, derived from a Lorentzian fit to the spectrum, gives a robust estimate of trap stiffness. A feature of this method is that the position detector itself need not be absolutely calibrated, because its calibration factor does not affect the corner frequency. Second, using a fully calibrated position detector, the mean square displacement, computed by integration of the power spectrum (Equation 13), provides a measure of the stiffness that is independent of drag force. Since the stiffness computed in this way scales with the second power of the calibration factor, a well-calibrated position detector is essential.

The foregoing discussion assumes that trapping stiffness is constant during thermal fluctuations, i.e. that the potential well is parabolic. This is clearly an approximation valid for small amplitudes. However, one may wish to map the optical force profile at larger displacements. One convenient method is to move the fluid chamber with a sinusoidal motion at frequency f and amplitude x_0 while holding the trap fixed. The force on the bead is then $F(t) = 2\pi i f \beta x_0 \exp(-2\pi i f t)$. Solving Equation 3 for this driving force gives the trajectory

$$y(t) = \frac{x_0 f}{\sqrt{f_0^2 + f^2}} \exp[-i(2\pi f t - \delta)], \qquad 14.$$

where the phase shift is $\delta = -\tan^{-1}(f_0/f)$. Both amplitude and phase shift can be used to determine f_0 and thereby the trapping stiffness. One particularly useful limit is $f/f_0 \ll 1$, where the amplitude becomes

$$|y(t)| = x_0 f/f_0. \qquad 15.$$

At a fixed driving level, the amplitude of motion can be measured as a function of frequency. This relationship provides a direct measure of the linearity in the trap force profile: deviations from linearity at a given amplitude imply that anharmonic contributions to the potential enter in at this level. Results of a typical force calibration using this method are shown in Figure 10 of the section on picotensiometers, below. Similarly, triangular waveforms can be used to map out the force profile (55).

Brownian Motion During Force Measurements

Microscopic objects in a viscous medium display significant Brownian motion, thereby introducing noise into all force measurements. One can measure an external force, $Q(t)$, which has a power spectral density $S_Q(f)$, by observing the motion of a single bead (Figure 3b) in the presence of a Langevin force $L(t)$, which has a white power spectral density $S_L(f) = 2kT\beta/\pi$. The equation of motion of the bead is given by Equation 10, setting $F(t) = Q(t) + L(t)$. The power spectrum of bead motion becomes

$$S_y(f) = \frac{S_Q(f) + S_L(f)}{\alpha^2(1 + \gamma^2)}, \qquad 16.$$

where $\gamma = f/f_0$, and the two terms in the numerator come from the signal and noise, respectively (61a). The signal-to-noise ratio (SNR) for this situation can then be expressed as

$$SNR = \left[\frac{\int_0^{f_b} S_Q(f)/(1 + \gamma^2)\, df}{(2kT\beta/\pi) \int_0^{f_b} 1/(1 + \gamma^2)\, df} \right]^{1/2}, \qquad 17.$$

where the upper limit of integration, f_b, is the measurement bandwidth. How does the SNR vary with the trap stiffness, α? In general, the SNR will depend on f_b and the exact shape of $S_Q(f)$, but two particular cases are of special interest. For a slowly varying external force—as is usually the case when calibrating traps or measuring forces exerted by mechanoenzymes—$S_Q(f)$ rolls off at a frequency $f_Q \ll f_0$. Here, it is experimentally advantageous to choose a lowpass filter frequency for force measurements such that $f_b \geq f_Q$. When this is done, $\gamma \ll 1$ and Equation 17 reduces to

$$SNR = \left[\pi/2kT\beta f_b \int_0^{f_b} S_Q(f)\, df \right]^{1/2},$$

a result that is independent of the trap stiffness. Another special case occurs for a white signal, where $S_Q(f) = S_Q(0) = constant$ out to some frequency $f \gg f_0$. Equation 17 reduces to $SNR = (\pi S_Q(0)/2kT\beta)^{1/2}$, once more independent of α. These two cases show that trapping force measurements, when appropriately filtered to maximize the SNR, can be made independent of the trap stiffness and need not be inversely proportional to the square root of that stiffness (75).

Picotensiometers

Several force transducers/tensiometers based on optical tweezers were recently constructed. For over 25 years, studies in physiology have focused on measuring the forces produced by muscle fibers. Analogous studies are now under way using modern in vitro motility assays, in which the action of just a few motor molecules at a time can be probed. In one such assay, myosin molecules are immobilized on a coverglass surface while actin filaments attached to silica beads are manipulated. For this work, S Chu, R Simmons, and J Spudich collaborated to develop a force transducer capable of exerting isometric tensions in the piconewton range over a bandwidth of several kilohertz (Figure 7). In

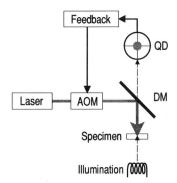

Figure 7 Simplified schematic of an isometric force transducer based on optical twee-zers (after Ref. 75). QD, quadrant detector with bead image cast upon it; AOM, acousto-optic modulator(s); DM, dichroic mirror. The output of the quadrant detector is used to generate a feedback error signal that deflects the trap in such a way as to prevent the specimen from moving, i.e. to achieve the isometric condition: this error signal is pro-portional to the force produced by the object.

their scheme, the trapped bead is imaged onto a quadrant detector, the output of which is fed back to an acousto-optic modulator operating in deflection mode. The feedback signal is used to servo the trap rapidly to counteract the force fluctuations, Brownian and otherwise, of the bead. This effectively stiffens the trap. The record of the feedback signal supplied provides a measure of the force required to keep the bead stationary. Using this arrangement, these workers plan to mea-sure the forces produced by small numbers of myosin molecules (75).

Svoboda et al (78) have developed an optical trapping interferometer (OTI) to measure the displacement of kinesin at subnanometer reso-lution while applying calibrated loads (Figure 8). In these assays, single kinesin molecules attached to silica beads are deposited by an optical trap onto microtubules immobilized on a coverglass surface. The sub-sequent motion of the beads is monitored by interferometry (39). The OTI takes advantage of standard differential interference-contrast op-tics in a modified inverted microscope. Polarized laser light is coupled to a single-mode, polarization-preserving fiber to eliminate pointing fluctuations of the laser. The beam is then introduced into the micro-scope at a point just below the objective Wollaston prism. This prism splits the light into two beams with orthogonal polarization; these are focused by the objective to two overlapping, diffraction-limited spots in the specimen plane. They function together as a single optical trap. A phase object located asymmetrically in the region illuminated by the two spots produces a relative retardation between the two beams.

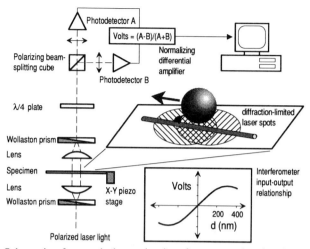

Figure 8 Schematic of an optical trapping interferometer, showing the optical components used for position detection (see text). (*Center*) A molecule of kinesin is shown pulling a bead along a microtubule in the direction shown by the arrow. (*Inset*) The output signal of this detector as a function of bead position.

When the beams interfere in the condenser Wollaston prism, elliptically polarized light results. The degree of this ellipticity provides a sensitive, nearly linear measure of displacement inside the trapping zone, in the direction of the Wollaston shear axis. A quarter waveplate, a polarizing beam–splitting cube, and a pair of photodiodes are used to measure the ellipticity. The normalized difference signal (V_{out}) carries the position information.

Detector noise is at or below 1 $\text{Å/Hz}^{1/2}$ (Figure 9). Since displacement information is encoded by the polarization of the laser light, this scheme is relatively insensitive to vibration, in contrast with imaging detectors, in which the position of the image with respect to the split photodiode carries the displacement information. Large laser light fluxes ensure that the detector does not become shot-noise limited at frequencies in excess of 100 kHz. The detector zone can be repositioned rapidly within the field of view of the microscope, because the same laser beam provides trapping and position sensing.

To calibrate the interferometer, a bead is immobilized on the coverslip surface and moved with a known waveform. The output voltage, V_{out}, is then measured as a function of displacement from the trap. This response function is approximately linear to ±150 nm. Fitting a cubic polynomial to the response function allows one to determine the correspondence between V_{out} and displacement up to ±200 nm from

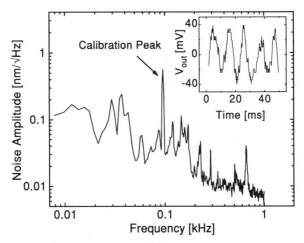

Figure 9 Sensitivity of the optical trapping interferometer. The graph shows the spectral noise density in response to a 100-Hz sinusoidal calibration signal of 1-nm amplitude. The large peak (*arrow*) corresponds to the signal; other peaks mainly result from acoustical interference and mechanical vibration. The raw detector output (*inset*) shows both the nanometer-sized signal and the noise, which is at the Ångstrom level.

the trap center to within a small error (~5%). Trap stiffness can be calibrated in any of the ways discussed above. Figure 10 shows the results of a typical force calibration.

Other Applications of Picotensiometry

Scanning force microscopy (SFM) has shown great potential for imaging nonconducting biological samples in solution at subnanometer resolution (63). In solid-supported Langmuir-Blodgett films, for example, single molecules can be imaged (41). However, on soft samples such as biological material, deformation caused by the heavy down-bearing force [typically nanonewtons (89)] of the mechanical cantilevers used in typical SFM systems limits resolution and frequently damages the specimen irreversibly. This suggests the use of optically trapped objects as sensing elements for SFM. Compared with mechanical cantilevers, probe stiffness could be reduced by three to five orders of magnitude. Ghislain & Webb have used a tensiometer similar to the design shown in Figure 8 to scan an optically trapped stylus (a pointed glass shard, ~1 μm in length), over a nanofabricated test specimen (43). They placed a photodiode detector down-beam from the specimen, between optical planes conjugate to the specimen and to the objective back aperture. This photodiode serves as a sensor for the axial (z-) position. Since the transparent stylus acts like a small lens,

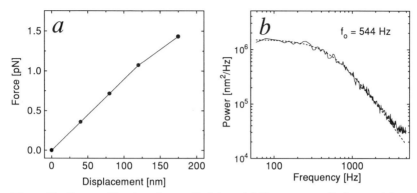

Figure 10 Force calibration of an optical trap. (*a*) Force versus displacement for a trapped silica bead (diameter ~0.6 μm; power ~14 mW), calibrated according to Equations 14 and 15 ($x_0 = 2$ μm; $\beta = 5.7 \times 10^{-6}$ pN s/nm). Stiffness is constant out to 150 nm ($\alpha = 9.0 \times 10^{-3}$ pN/nm), beyond which it decreases. (*b; Solid line*) The thermal noise spectrum of a trapped silica bead measured with the optical trapping interferometer (diameter ~0.6 μm; power ~28 mW). (*Dotted line*) The fit by a Lorentzian. The corner frequency of the Lorentzian (544 Hz) implies $\alpha = 1.9 \times 10^{-2}$ pN/nm.

axial probe displacements with respect to the focus modulate the light intensity at the detector. To take a picture, the stylus is placed in contact with the surface using optical tweezers and scanned while its z-position is recorded. In this way, Ghislain & Webb detected topographical features with a lateral resolution of ~20 nm. Microfabricated tips should improve the resolution of this promising technique of optical force microscopy.

Determinants of Trapping Forces

Even for perfect dielectric spheres, trapping forces depend on several factors, and most of the parameter space remains unexplored, either theoretically or experimentally. For example, in our system, 0.6-μm silica particles are stably trapped as far as 200 μm from the coverglass surface, whereas for 0.52-μm polystyrene particles, the trap develops an axial instability just 10 μm from the surface. This difference illustrates the need to calibrate forces under conditions similar to those used in an experiment. Increasing any of the following parameters should improve the trapping force: numerical aperture of the objective (but possibly not in the RO regime), index of refraction of the trapped object (but only up to $n = 1.69$), laser power, particle size, and laser frequency. The following effects degrade trapping forces: small optical misalignments, increasing distance from the coverglass surface, non-optimal coverglass thickness, incorrect choice of refractive index for the immersion oil, any additional sources of spherical aberration, back reflections and/or interference from scattered light, underfilling the objective back pupil, and laser beam wavefront distortion.

HANDLES

Biological macromolecules and macromolecular assemblies are often insufficiently refractile to be trapped alone with appreciable force. To facilitate trapping of such specimens, they are often attached to small refractile spheres, i.e. handles. One important consideration in handle attachment is surface chemistry. Unfortunately, no general principles seem to apply here. In certain cases, nonspecific attachment works quite well. For example, red blood cell cytoskeletons bind irreversibly to negatively charged silica bead surfaces, as do intact red blood cells and red cell ghosts (77). So, too, does native kinesin protein (26). Simple tricks sometimes produce favorable results: to attach handles to individual microtubules, we coated silica beads nonspecifically with avidin and bound these directly to biotinylated microtubules (R Stewart, K Svoboda & SM Block, unpublished data). Kuo & Sheetz (55) took a more elaborate approach, covalently linking bovine serum albumin (BSA) to carbodiimide-activated carboxylated polystyrene microspheres. The BSA was subsequently biotinylated and coated with avidin, and the avidin used to bind the beads to biotinylated microtubules. Actin filaments have been attached to silica beads by coating the beads with N-ethyl maleimide (NEM)-treated myosin or heavy meromyosin, which in turn binds tightly to actin (87).

Manufacturers (Polysciences, Bangs Laboratories, Seragen, Duke Scientific, etc) offer particles with a bewildering array of chemistries, including amine, carboxyl, and sulfate surface groups that facilitate coupling to proteins. Some form covalent linkages spontaneously using proprietary surface chemistry. Kits for attaching proteins to microspheres using antibody-based linkages or biotin-avidin are also available. Polystyrene beads come in a large assortment of sizes and colors, covering the useful size range for optical trapping (0.05–100 μm), and they are both round and homogeneous. Reasonably monodisperse silica beads in the 1-μm size range have only recently become commercially available (Bangs Laboratories). In the 0.5-μm size range, silica beads trap more readily than polystyrene. These advantages are partly offset by the relatively greater polydispersity in size and the smaller arsenal of surface chemistries of silica beads, which currently come with hydroxyl, amine, chloromethyl, or bromomethyl surface groups. However, several useful reagents are commerically available that chemically modify the surface of silica (Huls America).

The use of handles in biological applications of optical trapping will certainly continue to be important. In the future, aspherical designer handles, perhaps produced by microfabrication techniques, may provide substantially larger trapping efficiencies than spherical particles of the same volume, or may serve as better probes for the optical force microscope (above). The homogeneity, roundness, and size range of silica particles could be improved, as well as providing for larger variety of surface chemistries.

NOVEL TRAPPING GEOMETRIES

The use of optical tweezers for trapping is not without its disadvantages. Laser light must be focused to a tiny spot, generating enormous local fluxes ($\sim$5 MW/cm^2 for a 10-mW beam) and the possibility of optical damage. The size of the trapping zone is fixed and rather small, on the order of the light wavelength. The need for high NA objectives leads to short working distances and spherical aberrations that degrade trapping deeper into the sample chamber, away from the coverglass suface. In 1970, more than a decade before the single-beam gradient trap, Ashkin invented a stable optical trap based on two counter propagating beams that does not suffer from these problems. In this design, transverse trapping is supplied by the gradient force, but, in contrast to optical tweezers, the scattering force provides axial stability. Two counter propagating, coaxial beams with their waists separated by $\sim$100 μm in the longitudinal direction form a stable equilibrium point, z_{eq}, for dielectric particles. Particles that encounter the beam on either side of this point are drawn towards the optical axis by the gradient force and simultaneously accelerated towards z_{eq} by the scattering force. Once there, the scattering forces in the two beams balance. For equal beam powers, z_{eq} is located at the geometrical symmetry point. Because the two trapping beams need only be weakly focused, this type of trap provides a long working distance, and it was used in a prototype device for automated cell separation (29). Unfortunately, the trap is comparatively difficult to implement with a conventional microscope, and its stability is critically dependent on the axial alignment of the two beams: for small misalignments, trapped objects move in tiny circular orbits around z_{eq}.

A simpler manifestation of this two-beam trap, based on optical fibers, was recently demonstrated (37). The counter propagating beams are provided by two well-aligned, single-mode optical fibers, whose ends are placed opposite one another in the specimen plane and oriented perpendicular to the optical axis of the microscope. Because simple pigtail fibers coupled directly to diode lasers can be used and practically no additional optics are required, this design is perhaps the most economical optical trap of all (Figure 11). Strong forces transverse to the trapping beam axis (in the nanonewton range) can be achieved at relatively low power densities. The separation between the fiber ends (NA = 0.1) may be adjusted from 20 μm up to 280 μm and still capture particles from 0.1 to 10 μm in diameter, using laser power levels from 3 mW on up. One can alter the equilibrium position by reducing the power in one of the beams. A difficulty with this trapping arrangement is that the fibers must be aligned to within a micrometer or better, i.e. a fraction of the beam waist, to achieve stable trapping. Because stable fiber alignment in the current design depends on the mechanical support of the microscope slide, the trap is immobile in its present form. However, in principle this technical problem can be solved, and we can anticipate that a small trapping head will carry the fiber ends in alignment at some fixed separation and that this head can be moved throughout the microscope preparation on a conventional micromanipulator. Traps using counterpropagating beams should, in principle, be able to manipulate extremely high index particles (e.g. $n > 1.8$) that cannot be trapped by single beams owing to the loss of axial stability. With high index materials, still larger optical forces can be produced for a given laser power.

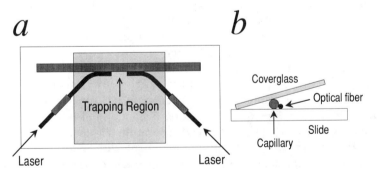

Figure 11 Schematic of the fiber-optic light force trap (after Ref. 37). (*a*) A 180-μm diameter glass capillary (*dark gray*) is sandwiched between a microscope slide (*white rectangle*) and a tilted coverglass (*light gray square*). Optical fibers (*black*) are channeled through two other short glass capillaries (*dark gray*) that are glued to the slide. The fibers are axially aligned by pressing them into the V-groove formed between the microscope slide and the capillary wall. (*b*) Side view, showing the V-groove.

Light-based radiation pressure has a direct acoustic analogue: both an acoustic scattering force and an acoustic gradient force are developed in interactions between matter and sound waves. Capitalizing on this analogy, Wu developed "acoustical tweezers" (93) based on a counterpropagating beam trap using 3.5 MHz ultrasonic transducers. A two-beam design was chosen to counteract the effect of acoustic streaming in the medium, which causes fluid to flow away from the transducers and would otherwise destabilize a single-beam trap. Thus far, the trap has been able to capture large (270-μm diameter) polystyrene spheres and clusters of frogs eggs. In principle, one could generate ultrasonic pressure waves with wavelengths smaller than those of visible light. However, acoustic lens technology lags far behind that of optical lenses, and it may prove difficult to focus acoustical waves to spot sizes smaller than those attainable with lasers. Nevertheless, acoustical tweezers may hold promise for several applications, particularly if they can be shown to produce significant forces without causing acoustic damage.

FUTURE DIRECTIONS

Prediction always carries an element of risk, but clearly optical forces stand poised to make important contributions to biological research. Light is a powerful tool. It can reach within sealed preparations—or even within living cells—to grasp and manipulate. Optical micromanipulators can work with double oil-immersion optics, affording the highest possible resolution in the light microscope. Displacements and forces produced by light can be controlled with extraordinary spatial and temporal precision. These properties bestow unique advantages upon optical force-based methods, as compared with conventional mechanical approaches.

Already, optical tweezers have been successfully used with a variety of different imaging techniques, including bright field (7, 11), phase contrast (21, 24), Nomarski DIC (22, 72), fluorescence (33, 75), and confocal microscopy (81). We anticipate that optical forces will eventually find applications in combination with microspectroscopy, light scattering, and perhaps even two-photon experiments.

Of particular interest is the latest generation of instruments, discussed above, which couple optical trapping with additional features. When combined with computer-driven, automated stages, optical traps can be used to sort and isolate a variety of items, including cells, sperm, and chromosomal fragments (20, 45). When combined with other laser techniques, such as optical scalpels, optical traps can assist in cellular microsurgery (20). When combined with sensitive position sensors, optical traps can be turned into tensiometers capable of measuring minute forces and displacements (75, 78), or into novel imaging devices capable of nanometer-scale resolution (43). When combined with beam scanners, optical traps can be used to grasp, orient, and maneuver many objects simultaneously, facilitating their use in microfabrication and/or microchemistry (58–61, 67, 68, 84). Finally, new designs for optical traps (37), as well as the advent of low-cost diode lasers, may help to make this technology both more powerful and more accessible to the rest of the biological community.

ACKNOWLEDGMENTS

We thank Sarah Ali, Arthur Ashkin, Michael Burns, Christoph Schmidt, and Linda Turner for comments on the manuscript; Winfried Denk and William Wright for discussions; Catherine Hirshfeld for help in preparing Table 1; Tom Deutsch and Kevin Schomacker for the data of Figure 3; Karl Aufderheide, Lucien Ghislain, Hiroaki Misawa, Mara Prentiss, William Wright, and Koen Visscher for sharing results in advance of publication; and the Rowland Institute for Science for supporting this work.

Literature Cited

1. Ashkin A. 1970. Acceleration and trapping of particles by radiation pressure. *Phys. Rev. Lett.* 24:156–59
2. Ashkin A. 1971. Optical levitation by radiation pressure. *Appl. Phys. Lett.* 19: 283–85
2a. Ashkin A. 1978. Trapping of atoms by resonance radiation pressure. *Phys. Rev. Lett.* 40:729–32
3. Ashkin A. 1980. Applications of laser radiation pressure. *Science* 210:1081–88
4. Ashkin A. 1992. Forces of a single-beam gradient laser trap on a dielectric sphere in the ray optics regime. *Biophys. J.* 61: 569–82
5. Ashkin A, Dziedzic JM. 1975. Optical levitation of liquid drops by radiation pressure. *Science* 187:1073–75
6. Ashkin A, Dziedzic JM. 1976. Optical levitation in high vacuum. *Appl. Phys. Lett.* 28:333–35

7. Ashkin A, Dziedzic JM. 1987. Optical trapping and manipulation of viruses and bacteria. *Science* 235:1517–20
8. Ashkin A, Dziedzic JM. 1989. Optical trapping and manipulation of single cells using infra-red laser beams. *Ber. Bus-enges. Phys. Chem.* 93:254–60
9. Ashkin A, Dziedzic JM. 1989. Internal cell manipulation using infrared laser traps. *Proc. Natl. Acad. Sci. USA* 86: 7914–18
10. Ashkin A, Dziedzic JM, Bjorkholm JE, Chu S. 1986. Observation of a single-beam gradient force optical trap for dielectric particles. *Opt. Lett.* 11:288–90
11. Ashkin A, Dziedzic JM, Yamane T. 1987. Optical trapping and manipulation of single cells using infrared laser beams. *Nature* 330:769–71
12. Ashkin A, Schuetze K, Dziedzic JM, Euteneuer U, Schliwa M. 1990. Force

generation of organelle transport measured in vivo by an infrared laser trap. *Nature* 348:346–48

13. Aufderheide KJ, Du Q, Fry ES. 1992. Directed positioning of nuclei in living *Paramecium tetraurelia:* use of the laser optical force trap for developmental biology. *Dev. Genet.* 13:235–40

14. Aufderheide KJ, Du Q, Fry ES. 1993. Directed positioning of micronuclei in *Paramecium tetraurelia* with laser tweezers: absence of detectable damage after manipulation. *J. Eukaryot. Microbiol.* 40:793–96

15. Bakker Schut TC, Hesselink G, de Grooth BG, Greve J. 1991. Experimental and theoretical investigations on the validity of the geometrical optics model for calculating the stability of optical traps. *Cytometry* 12:479–85

16. Barton JP, Alexander DR. 1989. Fifth-order corrected electromagnetic field components for a fundamental Gaussian beam. *J. Appl. Phys.* 66:2800–2

17. Barton JP, Alexander DR, Schaub SA. 1988. Internal and near-surface electromagnetic fields for a spherical particle irradiated by a focused laser beam. *J. Appl. Phys.* 64:1632–39

18. Barton JP, Alexander DR, Schaub SA. 1989. Theoretical determination of net radiation force and torque for a spherical particle illuminated by a focused laser beam. *J. Appl. Phys.* 66:4594–4602

19. Berns MW, Aist JR,Wright WH, Liang H. 1992. Optical trapping in animal and fungal cells using a tunable, near-infrared titanium-sapphire laser. *Exp. Cell Res.* 198:375–78

20. Berns MW, Wright WH, Steubing, RW. 1991. Laser microbeam as a tool in cell biology. *Int. Rev. Cytol.* 129:1–44

21. Berns MW, Wright WH, Tromberg BJ, Profeta GA, Andrews JJ, Walter RJ. 1989. Use of laser-induced optical force trap to study chromosome movement on the mitotic spindle. *Proc. Natl. Acad. Sci. USA* 86:4539–43

22. Block SM. 1990. Optical tweezers: a new tool for biophysics. In *Noninvasive Techniques in Cell Biology (Mod. Rev. Cell Biol. 9)*, ed. JK Foskett, S Grinstein, 15:375–402. New York: Wiley-Liss. 423 pp.

23. Block SM. 1992. Making light work with optical tweezers. *Nature* 360:493–95

24. Block SM, Blair DF, Berg HC. 1989. Compliance of bacterial flagella measured with optical tweezers. *Nature* 338:514–18

25. Block SM, Blair DF, Berg HC. 1991. Compliance of bacterial polyhooks mea-

sured with optical tweezers. *Cytometry* 12:492–96

26. Block SM, Goldstein LSB, Schnapp BJ. 1990. Bead movement by single kinesin molecules studied with optical tweezers. *Nature* 348:348–52

27. Brennen C, Winet H. 1977. Fluid mechanics of propulsion by cilia and flagella. *Annu. Rev. Fluid Mech.* 9:339–98

28. Buican TN, Neagley DL, Morrison WC, Upham BD. 1989. Optical trapping, cell manipulation, and robotics. *SPIE New Technol. Cytometry* 1063:190–97

29. Buican TN, Smyth MJ, Crissman HA, Salzman GC, Stewart CC, Martin JC. 1987. Automated single-cell manipulation and sorting by light trapping. *Appl. Opt.* 26:5311–16

30. Burns MM, Fournier J-M, Golovchenko JA. 1989. Optical binding. *Phys. Rev. Lett.* 63:1233–36

31. Burns MM, Fournier J-M, Golovchenko JA. 1990. Optical matter: crystallization and binding in intense optical fields. *Science* 249:749–54

32. Charon NW, Goldstein SF, Block SM, Curci K, Ruby JD, et al. 1992. Morphology and dynamics of protruding spirochete periplasmic flagella. *J. Bacteriol.* 174:832–40

33. Chu S. 1991. Laser manipulation of atoms and particles. *Science* 253:861–66

34. Chu S. 1992. Laser trapping of neutral particles. *Sci. Am.* 266;2:49–54

35. Chu S, Kron SJ. 1992. Method for optically manipulating polymer filaments. *US Patent #5079169*

36. Colon, JM, Sarosi PG, McGovern PG, Ashkin A, Dziedzic JM, et al. 1992. Controlled micromanipulation of human sperm in three dimensions with an infrared laser optical trap: effect on sperm velocity. *Fertil. Steril.* 57:695–98

37. Constable A, Kim J, Mervis J, Zarinetchi Z, Prentiss M. 1993. Demonstration of a fiber-optical light-force trap. *Opt. Lett.* 18:1867–69

38. Davis LW. 1979. Theory of electromagnetic beams. *Phys. Rev. A* 19:1177–79

39. Denk W, Webb WW. 1990. Optical measurements of picometer displacements of transparent microscopic objects. *Appl. Opt.* 29:2382–90

40. Edidin M, Kuo SC, Sheetz MP. 1991. Lateral movements of membrane glycoproteins restricted by dynamic cytoplasmic barriers. *Science* 254:1379–82

41. Garnaes G, Schwartz DK, Viswanathan R, Zasadzinski JAN. 1992. Domain boundaries and buckling superstruc-

tures in Langmuir-Blodgett films. *Nature* 357:54–57

42. Gelles J, Schnapp BJ, Sheetz MP. 1988. Tracking kinesin-driven movements with nanometer-scale precision. *Nature* 331:450–53

43. Ghishlain LP, Webb WW. 1993. Scanning force microscopy using an optical trap. *Opt. Lett.* 18:1678–80

44. Gordon JP. 1973. Radiation forces and momenta in dielectric media. *Phys. Rev. A* 8:14–21

45. Greulich KO. 1992. Chromosome microtechnology: microdissection and microcloning. *Trends Biotechnol.* 10:48–51

46. Greulich KO, Weber G. 1991. The laser microscope on its way from an analytical to a preparative tool. *J. Microsc.* 167:127–51

47. Grimbergen J, Visscher K, Gomes de Mesquita D. 1993. Isolation of single yeast cells by optical trapping. *Yeast* 9:723–32

47a. Gussgard R, Lindmo T, Brevik I. 1992. Calculation of trapping force in a strongly focused laser beam. *J. Opt. Soc. Am.* 9:1922–30

48. Happel J, Brenner H. 1991. *Low Reynolds Number Hydrodynamics.* Dordecht, the Netherlands: Kluwer Academic. 2nd ed. 553 pp.

49. Jackson JD. 1975. *Classical Electrodynamics,* p. 239. New York, NY: Wiley. 2nd ed.

50. Kamimura S. 1987. Direct measurements of nanometric displacements under an optical microscope. *Appl. Opt.* 26:3425–27

51. Kamimura S, Kamiya R. 1992. High-frequency vibration in flagellar axonemes with amplitudes reflecting the size of tubulin. *J. Cell Biol.* 116:1443–54

52. Kerker M. 1969. *The Scattering of Light and Other Electromagnetic Radiation,* pp. 32–37. New York, NY: Academic. 666 pp.

53. Kucik DF, Kuo SC, Elson EL, Sheetz MP. 1991. Preferential attachment of membrane glycoproteins to the cytoskeleton at the leading edge of lamella. *J. Cell Biol.* 114:1029–36

54. Kuo SC, Sheetz MP. 1992. Optical tweezers in cell biology. *Trends Cell Biol.* 2:116–18

55. Kuo SC, Sheetz MP. 1993. Force of single kinesin molecules measured with optical tweezers. *Science* 260:232–34

56. Liang H, Wright WH, He W, Berns MW. 1991. Micromanipulation of mitotic chromosomes in PTK-2 cells using laser-induced optical forces ("optical tweezers"). *Exp. Cell Res.* 197:21–35

57. Liang H, Wright WH, He W, Berns MW. 1993. Micromanipulation of chromosomes in PTK-2 cells using laser microsurgery (optical scalpel) in combination with laser-induced optical force (optical tweezers). *Exp. Cell Res.* 204:110–20

58. Misawa H, Koshioka M, Sasaki K, Kitamura N, Masuhara H. 1990. Laser trapping, spectroscopy, and ablation of a single latex particle in water. *Chem. Lett. Japan* pp. 1479–82

59. Misawa H, Koshioka M, Sasaki K, Kitamura N, Masuhara H. 1991. Spatial pattern formation, size selection, and directional flow of polymer latex particles by laser trapping technique. *Chem. Lett. Japan* pp. 469–72

60. Misawa H, Koshioka M, Sasaki K, Kitamura N, Masuhara H. 1991. Three-dimensional optical trapping and laser ablation of a single polymer latex particle in water. *J. Appl. Phys.* 70:3829–36

61. Misawa H, Sasaki K, Koshioka M, Kitamura N, Masuhara H. 1992. Multibeam laser manipulation and fixation of microparticles. *Appl. Phys. Lett.* 60:310–12

61a. Papoulis A. 1977. *Signal Analysis.* New York, NY: McGraw-Hill. 431 pp.

62. Purcell EM, Pennypacker CR. 1973. Scattering and absorption of light by nonspherical dielectric grains. *Astrophys. J.* 186:705–14

63. Radmacher M, Tillmann RW, Fritz M, Gaub HE. 1992. From molecules to cells: imaging soft samples with the atomic force microscope. *Science* 257:1900–5

64. Richards B, Wolf E. 1959. Electromagnetic diffraction in optical systems. II. Structure of the image field in an aplanatic system. *Proc. R. Soc. London Ser. A* 253:358–79

65. Roosen G. 1979. La lévitation optique de sphères. *Can. J. Phys.* 57:1260–79

66. Roosen G, Imbert C. 1976. Optical levitation by means of two horizontal laser beams: a theoretical and experimental study. *Physics Lett.* 59A:6–8

67. Sasaki K, Koshioka M, Misawa H, Kitamura N, Masuhara H. 1991. Laser-scanning micromanipulation and spatial patterning of fine particles. *Jpn. J. Appl. Phys.* 30:907–909

68. Sasaki K, Koshioka M, Misawa H, Kitamura N, Masuhara H. 1992. Optical trapping of a metal particle and a water droplet by a scanning laser beam. *Appl. Phys. Lett.* 60:807–9

69. Sato S, Ohyumi M, Shibata H, Inaba H. 1991. Optical trapping of small particles using a 1.3-micrometer compact In-

GaAsp diode laser. *Opt. Lett.* 16:282–84

70. Schneider M, Webb WW. 1981. Measurement of submicron laser beam radii. *Appl. Opt.* 20:1382–88

71. Seeger S, Manojembashi S, Hutter K-J, Futterman G, Wolfrum J, Greulich KO. 1991. Application of laser optical tweezers in immunology and molecular genetics. *Cytometry* 12:497–504

72. Shepherd GMG, Corey DP, Block SM. 1990. Actin cores of hair-cell stereocilia support myosin movement. *Proc. Natl. Acad. Sci. USA* 87:8627–31

73. Siegmann AE. 1986. *Lasers.* Mill Valley, CA: University Science. 1283 pp.

74. Simmons RM, Finer JT. 1993. Glasperlenspiel II: optical tweezers. *Curr. Biol.* 3:309–11

75. Simmons RM, Finer JT, Warrick HM, Kralik B, Chu S, Spudich JA. 1993. Force on single actin filaments in a motility assay measured with an optical trap. In *The Mechanism of Myofilament Sliding in Muscle Contraction,* ed. H Sugi, GH Pollack, pp. 331–36. New York, NY: Plenum

76. Steubing, RW, Cheng S, Wright WH, Numajiri Y, Berns MW. 1991. Laser induced cell fusion in combination with optical tweezers: the laser cell fusion trap. *Cytometry* 12:505–10

77. Svoboda K, Schmidt CF, Branton D, Block SM. 1992. Conformation and elasticity of the isolated red blood cell membrane skeleton. *Biophys. J.* 63:784–93

78. Svoboda K, Schmidt CF, Schnapp BJ, Block SM. 1993. Direct observation of kinesin stepping by optical trapping interferometry. *Nature* 365:721–27

79. Tadir Y, Wright WH, Vafa O, Ord T, Asch RH, Berns MW. 1990. Force generated by human sperm correlated to velocity and determined using a laser generated optical trap. *Fertil. Steril.* 53:944–47

80. Visscher K. 1993. *Optical manipulation and confocal microscopy,* pp. 73–77. PhD thesis, University of Amsterdam, Netherlands. 115 pp.

81. Visscher K, Brakenhoff GJ. 1991. Single beam optical trapping integrated in a confocal microscope for biological applications. *Cytometry* 12:486–91

82. Visscher K, Brakenhoff GJ. 1992. Theoretical study of optically induced forces on spherical particles in a single beam trap I: Rayleigh scatterers. *Optik* 89:174–80

83. Visscher K, Brakenhoff GJ. 1992. Theoretical study of optically induced forces on spherical particles in a single beam trap II: Mie scatterers. *Optik* 90:57–60

84. Visscher K, Brakenhoff GJ, Krol JJ. 1993. Micromanipulation by ''multiple'' optical traps created by a single fast scanning trap integrated with the bilateral confocal scanning microscope. *Cytometry* 14:105–14

85. Vorobjev IA, Liang H, Wright WH, Berns MW. 1993. Optical trapping for chromosome manipulation: a wavelength dependence of induced chromosome bridges. *Biophys. J.* 64:533–38

86. Wang MC, Uhlenbeck, GE. 1945. On the theory of the Brownian motion II. *Rev. Mod. Phys.* 17:323–41; Reprinted in *Selected Papers on Noise and Stochastic Processes,* ed. N Wax, pp. 113–32. New York, NY: Dover

87. Warrick HM, Simmons RM, Finer JT, Uyeda TQP, Chu S, Spudich JA. 1993. In vitro methods for measuring force and velocity of the actin-myosin interaction using purified proteins. *Methods Cell Biol.* 39:1–21

88. Weber G, Greulich KO. 1992. Manipulation of cells, organelles, and genomes by laser microbeam and optical trap. *Int. Rev. Cytol.* 133:1–41

89. Weisenhorn AL, Hansma PK, Albrecht TR, Quate CF. 1989. *Appl. Phys. Lett.* 54:2651–53

90. Wright WH, Sonek GJ, Berns, MW. 1993. Radiation trapping forces on microspheres with optical tweezers. *Appl. Phys. Lett.* 63:715–17

91. Wright WH, Sonek GJ, Berns, MW. 1993. A parametric study of the forces on microspheres held by optical tweezers. *Appl. Opt.* In press

92. Wright WH, Sonek GJ, Tadir Y, Berns MW. 1990. Laser trapping in cell biology. *IEEE J. Quantum Electron.* 26:2148–57

93. Wu J. 1991. Acoustical tweezers. *J. Acoust. Soc. Am.* 89:2140–43

Annu. Rev. Biophys. Biomol. Struct. 1994. 23:287–318

HIGH-PRESSURE NMR SPECTROSCOPY OF PROTEINS AND MEMBRANES

J. Jonas and A. Jonas*

Department of Chemistry, School of Chemical Sciences, and *Department of Biochemistry, College of Medicine, University of Illinois, Urbana, Illinois 61801

KEY WORDS: pressure denaturation, cold denaturation, phase diagrams, experimental techniques, water

CONTENTS

PERSPECTIVES AND OVERVIEW

Interest in pressure as an experimental variable has been growing in physicochemical studies of biochemical and biological systems. Two

287

recent (1992) international meetings on high pressure and biotechnology (6) and high pressure chemistry, biochemistry, and materials science (116) have dealt with this subject. As the rationale for using pressure as an experimental variable in studies of biochemical systems has already been thoroughly discussed (7, 36, 108, 119), this review highlights only the most important points: (*a*) First of all, changing the temperature of a biochemical system at atmospheric pressure produces a simultaneous change in thermal energy and volume; therefore, to separate the thermal and volume effects, one must perform high-pressure experiments. (*b*) Because noncovalent interactions play a primary role in the stabilization of biochemical systems, the use of pressure allows one to change, in a controlled way, the intermolecular interactions without the major perturbations produced by changes in temperature and/or chemical composition. (*c*) Pressure affects chemical equilibria and reaction rates. The following standard equations define the reaction volume, ΔV, and the activation volume, $\Delta V\ddagger$:

$$\Delta V = -\left[\frac{RT\partial \ln K}{\partial P}\right]_T, \qquad \Delta V\ddagger = -\left[\frac{RT\partial \ln k}{\partial P}\right]_T \qquad 1.$$

where K is the equilibrium constant, and k is the reaction rate. With the knowledge of ΔV and $\Delta V\ddagger$ values, one can draw conclusions about the nature of the reaction and its mechanism. (*d*) Studies (5) of simple liquids have indicated that volume (i.e. pressure) effects quite often determine the mechanism of a specific dynamic process, whereas temperature only changes the frequency of the motions without actually affecting the mechanism. (*e*) Although proteins are known to undergo pressure denaturation, few details are known about this important process or how it is related to thermal- or solvent-induced denaturation. (*f*) According to the high-pressure phase diagram of water, even at $-15°C$ water is still a liquid (20, 110). Therefore, protein solutions can be measured at subzero temperatures to investigate their cold-denaturation behavior. (*g*) Finally, the phase behavior and dynamics of phospholipid membranes can be explored more completely by carrying out experiments at high pressure. In fact, the lipid-phase transitions are influenced by pressure, and unique high-pressure gel phases are produced (119).

Pressures used to investigate biochemical systems range from 0.1 MPa to 1 GPa (0.1 MPa = 1 bar; 1 GPa = 10 kbar); such pressures only change intermolecular distances and affect conformations but do not change covalent bond distances or bond angles. In fact, pressures in excess of 30 GPa are required to change the electronic structure of a molecule (23).

Many excellent reviews discuss a wide spectrum of biochemical problems investigated with various high-pressure techniques. In particular, the monograph by Weber (105) addresses key issues in high-pressure studies of proteins. Of particular relevance to this review are the chapters dealing with effects of temperature and pressure on molecular associations and on single-chain proteins, and effects of pressure on oligomeric proteins and protein aggregates. In his review of the behavior of proteins under high pressure, Heremans (37) covers recent experimental high-pressure studies of protein compressibility, ligand-protein interactions, conformational transitions, and protein denaturation. In addition, he gives examples of high-pressure studies that may be of importance for industrial applications, such as high-pressure food processing. Weber (106) presents an in depth review of pressure dissociation of smaller oligomeric proteins, pointing out several important features encountered when dealing with equilibria of small-molecular complexes. According to Weber, a conformational drift of the monomers occurs after dissociation by pressure or dilution, which persists even after reassociation, leading to a deterministic, rather than a stochastic, nature of the thermodynamic equilibria. In another review, Weber (107) addresses the question of the relationship of interaction energy and entropy with volume, pressure, and temperature in protein aggregates.

Balny et al (7) cover both the experimental and theoretical aspects of recent high-pressure studies of proteins. They discuss the use of pressure as a tool for the investigation of enzyme mechanisms, and the association and dissociation of proteins and their interactions with other molecular systems. Frauenfelder et al (27) have carried out extensive high-pressure studies of myoglobin and the binding of CO and O_2 to myoglobin using a variety of experimental methods, including low temperature techniques. Silva (90) reviews the use of hydrostatic pressure to study protein-protein interactions of large aggregates and viruses. Of particular interest is the potential for the utilization of hydrostatic pressure to prepare noninfectious, whole-virus particles that are highly immunogenic (91). Interesting high-pressure experiments on protein-DNA interactions were recently reported by Villas-Boas et al (100). High-pressure vibrational spectroscopic studies of various aqueous biological systems are reviewed by Wong (120), who emphasizes work on model membrane systems and intact biological tissues and cells. Winter & Böttner (114) discuss the volumetric properties of model biological membranes.

Many additional reviews deal with the effects of pressure on a variety of biochemical and biological systems; however, the few we mention in the previous paragraphs illustrate the rapid development of the field of high-pressure biochemistry and biology (39) and the wide range of problems it encompasses. In the context of high-pressure studies of biochemical systems, we point out the growing importance of the industrial applications of high pressure in food processing and biotechnology (15, 35).

In view of the many high-pressure studies of biochemical systems using a variety of experimental techniques, even a brief overview of the entire field of high-pressure biophysics and biochemistry is too broad for this chapter. Therefore, we limit ourselves to a discussion of high-pressure NMR studies (8, 47). This recently developed high-pressure technique can provide unique information about the dynamics and structure of proteins and membranes. Despite the fact that NMR is one of the most important spectroscopic tools for the investigation of biochemical systems at ambient conditions, few high-pressure NMR studies on biological molecules have been reported to date. Wagner (102) investigated the pressure effects on the rotation of the Tyr35 and Phe45 aromatic rings in bovine pancreatic trypsin inhibitor (BPTI); Williams et al (112, 113) studied the effect of pressure on the dynamics and α-helical structure in several homopolypeptides; and Morishima and coworkers (66) investigated the effects of pressure on heme proteins. Also, Ludemann and his coworkers (33, 34) have studied the effects of pressure on the ionization of histidine and rotation of amide groups in peptides.

EXPERIMENTAL TECHNIQUES

Several monographs discuss in detail the standard techniques for generating and measuring pressures up to 1 GPa (10, 14, 28). Nearly all the components necessary for building a high-pressure setup, such as piston hand pumps, high-pressure tubing and valves, intensifiers, and high-pressure separators, are currently available from commercial sources. The high-pressure setup used for all biophysical experimental techniques consists of three main parts: (a) the pressure-generating system, (b) the pressure-measuring system, and (c) the biophysical-measuring device, which is located in a high-pressure vessel.

Figure 1 shows a schematic drawing of the high pressure–generating system used in our laboratory, illustrating the relative simplicity of the standard equipment used to generate high hydrostatic pressures (40, 50). This system can produce hydrostatic pressures up to 1 GPa. Prior to the application of the high-pressure NMR technique, many biophysical experimental techniques were used for the investigation of

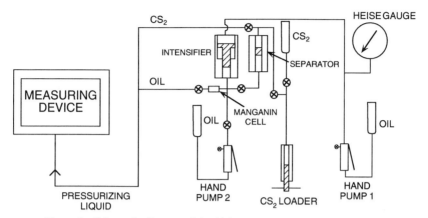

Figure 1   Schematic diagram of the high pressure–generating equipment.

various biochemical systems at high pressure. Table 1 lists the diverse experimental techniques, indicating the pressure range, temperature range, and the systems studied. This list is not exhaustive—rather it is illustrative of the wide range of experimental techniques that can be used in high-pressure studies of biochemical systems.

High-Pressure NMR Studies

Recent advances in superconducting magnet technology have resulted in the development of superconducting magnets capable of attaining a high homogeneity of the magnetic field over the sample volume, so that even without sample spinning, high resolution can be achieved. This ability to record high-resolution NMR spectra on dilute spin systems opened the new field of high-pressure NMR spectroscopy, which deals with pressure effects on biochemical systems.

In our laboratory, we have used high resolution, high-pressure NMR spectroscopy to investigate simple molecular liquids for two decades (40-42, 44–46, 48). Early on, we predicted that this high-pressure technique would be applied to studies of biological systems (111). However, initial progress in this area has been quite slow because of technical difficulties and the need for specialized equipment. The early studies (33, 34, 66, 102, 112, 113) used the capillary techniques introduced by Yamada (122), which, for the investigation of biochemical systems, are inherently limited by a restricted pressure range (maximum pressures of 150–200 MPa) and a very small sample volume, usually contained in a 1-mm-wide sample cell. The small sample volume markedly decreases the sensitivity and precludes the use of dilute biochemical sam-

Table 1 Main techniques used in high-pressure experiments on biochemical systems

Technique	Pressure range (MPa)	Temperature range (°C)	Systems studied[a]	References
Optical absorption	0.1–600	5–80	Proteins	29, 123
Fluorescence	0.1–950	20–80	Proteins	16, 17, 103, 104
Vibrational	0.1–3000[b]	30	Membranes	118, 121
spectroscopy	0.1–200	−260–30	Myoglobin	27
NMR	0.1–600	30–100	Proteins, membranes	47
X-ray scattering	0.1–100	25	Lysozyme	60
SANS[c]	0.1–300	25–70	Membranes	117
PVT measurements	0.1–250	0–90	Membranes	114
Light scattering	0.1–500	25–150	DNA	74
Dynamic light scattering	0.1–200	25	Hemocyanin	82
Circular dichroism	0.1–20	25–100	Gramicidin A	30
Stopped flow	0.1–150	5–50	Cytochrome oxidase	38, 59
Laser flash photolysis	0.1–200	20	Myoglobin	1
Differential scanning calorimetry	0.1–136	20–70	Anesthetics in liposomes	72
Gel electrophoresis	0.1–800	5–70	Oligomeric proteins; chymo-trypsinogen	65, 77
Temperature jump	0.1–200	25	β-cyclodextrin	73

[a] Illustrative examples.
[b] Diamond anvil cell.
[c] Small-angle neutron scattering.

ples, which are often necessary to prevent artifacts resulting from aggregation. Only recently (in 1988) did we succeed in developing high-pressure NMR probes (52) suitable for high-resolution and high-sensitivity experiments on biochemical systems.

High-Pressure, High-Resolution NMR Probes

Several features of NMR probe design (50) are essential for biochemical applications of the high-pressure NMR techniques: high resolution, high sensitivity, wide pressure and temperature ranges, large sample volume, reliable RF feedthroughs, contamination-free sample cells, ease of assembly and use, and suitability for superconducting magnets.

Figure 2 shows the design of the high-pressure vessel used for NMR studies with the 7.04 Tesla superconducting magnet (50). The vessel

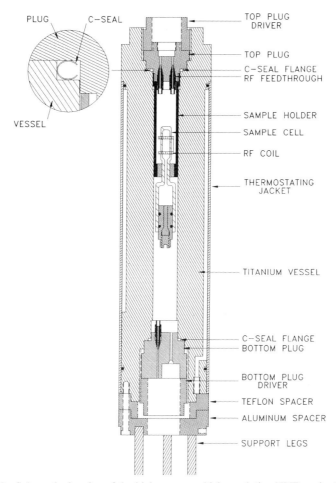

Figure 2   Schematic drawing of the high-pressure, high-resolution NMR probe (50) operating at a frequency of 300 MHz, pressure range from 0.1 to 600 MPa, and temperature range from −30 to 100°C. (*Inset*) The C-seal is shown in more detail.

is made of titanium alloy (RMI 6Al-2Sn-4Zr-6Mo) and is used for pressures up to 600 MPa. The 300 MHz NMR probe shown in Figure 2 has an excellent resolution and sensitivity, comparable to the performance characteristics of a commercial NMR probe made by General Electric for use at ambient pressure. In fact, one can achieve (50) an NMR line width of 1.2 Hz for a sample diameter of 10 mm at a proton frequency of 300 MHz (H_0 = 7.05 Tesla).

WATER—THE ANOMALOUS LIQUID AND SOLVENT

The hydrophobic effect is generally considered the dominant force of protein folding (21), and one can regard the role water plays in this effect as traditional or classic (21, 76, 96). However, recent studies (18, 53, 54, 58, 76, 83) suggest that water may be the key element in several other processes. For example, to explain the communication between distant sites within the protein, Kaminsky & Richards (53, 54) proposed a model that combines the structural changes in the protein matrix with changes in the surface hydration properties. The prevalent view that hydration water is bound to the protein surface is challenged in recent studies by Kennedy & Bryant (55) and Kimmich and collaborators (56, 57), who show that water in the hydration layer exhibits a high mobility. In addition, water seems to play an important role in allosteric regulation, as suggested by several studies (18, 83) dealing with osmolytic effects.

The reaction volume, ΔV (see Equation 1), for dissociation or unfolding of proteins can be considered (7) as the sum of several components, including the conformation ΔV term, the intramolecular interaction term, and the solvation term. Hence, one should note the anomalous behavior of water and heavy water at high pressure (43, 45, 49).

In contrast to simple molecular liquids, the effects of pressure on the dynamic structure of water are quite complex. The most interesting behavior of various transport and relaxation properties for water and heavy water occurs at temperatures between -15 and $40°C$ (20). In normal fluids, compression and increased packing significantly slow down all motions; in water, on the other hand, the T_1, the self-diffusion coefficients, the average residence time of a proton on a water molecule (62), and fluidity all reach a maximum with initial compression, and only further increases in pressures restrict motional freedom.

The anomalous motional behavior of water molecules with initial compression can be qualitatively interpreted in terms of a simple physical picture (45, 93) based on changes in the random hydrogen-bond network. The characteristic structural feature of liquid water is the local tetrahedral environment of each molecule, beyond which lies a randomized imperfect space-filling network of hydrogen-bonded molecules. By compressing liquid water in the low-temperature range, we cause the hydrogen-bond network to change from tetrahedral order toward a more compact packing arrangement. In water, the tendency of strongly directional forces to build an open, hydrogen-bond network competes with the tendency of external pressure to pack the molecules together more efficiently. Because the process for self-diffusion, shear viscosity, and reorientation of the water molecules requires the breaking and reforming of hydrogen bonds, breaking an already bent hydrogen bond should be easier than breaking an undistorted one. Initial compression, therefore, increases motional freedom, and only further compression slows down all the dynamic processes because of a more compact packing of the water molecules. Under high compression, the repulsive hard-core interactions begin to compete strongly with the directional forces that are responsible for the open structure of water at low pressures and low temperatures.

MODEL MEMBRANES AT HIGH PRESSURE

Interest in pressure as an experimental variable has been growing in studies of membranes by a variety of experimental techniques, including IR and Raman spectroscopy (119, 120), light transmission (80), fluorescence spectroscopy (16, 17), X-ray diffraction (94), neutron scattering (11, 115, 117), and NMR (48). By applying high pressure to membrane systems, one can observe changes in the dynamics of the component lipids and new pressure-induced phases (121). Temperature-pressure phase diagrams have been generated for several phospholipid systems (121).

In our laboratory, we have initiated systematic high-pressure NMR studies on model phospholipid membranes. Table 2 summarizes these studies, two of which are discussed in the next sections. First, we describe the use of high-pressure NMR to generate temperature-pressure phase diagrams for phospholipids in excess water (24) and illustrate the rich phase behavior produced by high pressure. Second, using our ^{31}P NMR study (78) of 1,2-dipalmitoyl-sn-glycero-3-phosphocholine (DPPC) and DPPC-tetracaine bilayers, we show how pressure affects the headgroup structure and motions.

Temperature-Pressure Phase Diagrams

High-pressure ^{2}H-NMR had not been used to probe the gel phases of a phospholipid until our studies (24, 25). Gel-state spectra were observed at several temperatures and pressures up to 500 MPa. In contrast to the liquid-crystalline (LC) state, the gel state (referring to several gel phases) is highly ordered.

The gel state is, in reality, made up of several phases, each with a particular structure. Most often studied are the $P_{\beta'}$ (pretransition) and $L_{\beta'}$ phases. Also present is a subtransition (L_c) phase that appears upon

Table 2   NMR studies of the pressure effects on model membranes[a]

System	Experiment	Result	References
DPPC[b]	Natural abundance[13]C, T_1, T_2	Phase transitions	52
DMPC[c]			
POPC[d]	[1]H 2D-NOESY	NOE build-up curves	51
DPPC-d$_{62}$	[2]H lineshapes	Phase diagram, order parameters, pressure reversal of the anesthetic effect of tetracaine	24, 25
DPPC (TTC)[e]	[31]P lineshapes, T_1	Structure and dynamics of the head group, phase diagram	78
DPPC-d$_2$ (2,2); (9,9); (13,13)	[2]H lineshapes, T_1, T_2	Order parameters, chain motions	unpublished data[f]
DPPC(TTC)	[1]H T_1, 2D-NOESY	Dynamics, location of TTC, spin diffusion	unpublished data[f]
DPPC-d$_{62}$-cholesterol	[2]H lineshapes	Phase diagram	unpublished data[f]

[a] Pressure range from 0.1 MPa to 500 MPa.
[b] DPPC, dipalmitoylphosphatidylcholine.
[c] DMPC, dimyristoylphosphatidylcholine.
[d] POPC, palmitoyloleylphosphatidylcholine.
[e] TTC, tetracaine.
[f] X Peng, S Samarasinghe & J Jonas.

prolonged refrigeration of the L$_{\beta'}$ phase. Less well known is the existence of other low-temperature/high-pressure phases. Wong et al (120, 121) have done extensive work in this area, using vibrational spectroscopic methods, and have shown the existence of at least five pressure-induced gel phases, which they have named GI through GV, corresponding to the increasing pressure of the transition. GI and GII correspond to P$_{\beta'}$ and L$_{\beta'}$, respectively, but the structure and dynamics of GIII, GIV, and GV have not been extensively studied by other methods.

In addition to Wong's studies, small-angle neutron diffraction (11) has shown the existence of a pressure-induced interdigitated phase in DPPC bilayers at pressures above 100 MPa and temperatures above 40°C.

Davis (19) originally demonstrated the changes of perdeuterated DPPC NMR spectral lineshapes associated with temperature changes at ambient pressure. However, at that time the complex phase behavior of this lipid was not known, variable pressure studies had not been performed, and a detailed analysis of lineshape changes with changes in conditions had not been attempted. We have shown that the gel state of DPPC bilayers exhibits various lineshapes that depend on the particular pressure and temperature and are characteristic of specific gel phases.

Two methods have been used to measure phase transitions in a quantitative way: direct measurement of the quadrupole splitting of the methyl group and first moment analysis. Figure 3 illustrates the phase transitions observed using these methods. The phases are labeled according to Wong (118) and Prasad (80). The LC-GI, GI/GII, GI/Gint, GI/GII, GII/GIII, and GIII/X transitions were all clearly identified using our ^{2}H-NMR spectral measurements.

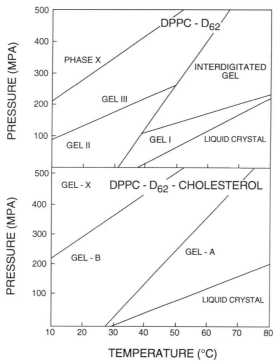

Figure 3 Pressure-temperature phase diagram of DPPC-d_{62} (*top*) and a DPPC-d_{62}-cholesterol mixture (*bottom*) as determined with the NMR methods described in the original references (24, 25). The diagram for pure DPPC agrees well with the partial phase diagrams reported in the literature (80, 112). The phase diagram for the DPPC-d_{62}-cholesterol mixture (80/20%) is reported for the first time (S Samarasinghe & J Jonas, unpublished data).

The use of pressure to study the gel phase has allowed us to observe phase changes that are not seen at ambient temperature. These data clearly show that the gel state cannot be thought of as a single phase beyond the $P_{\beta'}$ transition, undergoing gradual lineshape change in ^2H spectra with a gradual decrease in motion; rather, abrupt changes in motion and structure occur at phase transitions at specific temperatures and pressures.

Figure 3 (bottom) also shows the temperature-pressure phase diagram for a mixture (80/20%) of perdeuterated DPPC and cholesterol (S Samarasinghe & J Jonas, unpublished data). In agreement with the results of NMR studies (61, 101) of various phospholipid-cholesterol mixtures at ambient pressure, the barotropic phase diagram for the DPPC-cholesterol mixture is much simpler compared with that for pure DPPC (Figure 3, top). In fact, cholesterol eliminates the interdigitated gel phase seen in pure DPPC.

^{31}P NMR of the Phosphocholine Headgroup

Boulanger et al (9) reported that the addition of tetracaine (TTC) to phosphatidylcholine dispersions in water produced different effects depending on whether the anesthetic was positively charged (pH 5.5) or uncharged (pH 9.0). The changes in bilayer properties were monitored using ^2H and ^{31}P NMR spectroscopy (89). These results suggested that the headgroup undergoes a conformational change upon interaction with the anesthetic. Scherer & Seelig (88) have carried out thorough studies on the effects of electric charges on phospholipid headgroups by investigating mixtures of 1-palmitoyl-2-oleoyl-sn-glycero-3-phosphocholine (POPC) with charged amphiphiles. These authors recorded ^2H, ^{31}P, and ^{14}N NMR spectra for bilayers containing varying concentrations of amphiphiles and found that the charged amphiphiles have a major effect on the phosphocholine headgroup. The headgroups that are normally aligned parallel to the membrane surface in a pure phospholipid membrane change in orientation upon addition of a positively charged amphiphile, the N^+ end of the dipole moving toward the water phase. The same result was obtained with other positively charged anesthetics, as well as phospholipids and peptides.

MacDonald et al (64) extended the results obtained by Scherer & Seelig (88) in the LC phase to the gel state of 1,2-dimyristoyl-sn-glycero-3-phosphocholine (DMPC) using ^2H NMR spectroscopy of specifically choline-deuterated DMPC. These authors (64) provided evidence that the choline headgroup of phosphatidylcholine in the gel state also responds to charge changes at the membrane surface; thus, the response of the choline headgroup of phosphatidylcholine to surface charges is similar in the LC and the gel states of membrane lipids.

In a recent study (78), we measured the ^{31}P NMR lineshapes and ^{31}P spin-lattice relaxation times of pure DPPC bilayers and DPPC bilayers containing charged tetracaine as a function of pressure from 0.1 to 510 MPa at 50°C. The goals of the study were to determine the behavior of the headgroup in the LC phase and the various gel phases accessible at high pressure, to compare the pressure effects on pure DPPC bilayers with those observed for DPPC-tetracaine bilayers, and to determine whether the concept of a molecular electrometer as introduced by Scherer & Seelig (88) is also applicable for gel phases induced at high pressures. We determined ^{31}P NMR lineshapes with proton decoupling in the liquid crystalline state and various gel states of DPPC. The experimental ^{31}P NMR lineshapes for pure DPPC bilayers and bilayers containing TTC were evaluated, and the calculated chemical shift anisotropy, $\Delta\sigma$, values were plotted as a function of pressure in Figure 4 to permit a direct comparison between the $\Delta\sigma$ values obtained for pure DPPC and DPPC-TTC bilayers.

As indicated above, one of the objectives of this study was to examine our data in light of the results obtained by Scherer & Seelig (88) and MacDonald et al (64), who investigated the influence of membrane surface charges upon the conformation of the choline headgroup in various phosphatidylcholine bilayers. Our experimental results showed that the orientation of the headgroup changes upon the addition of the charged anesthetic, and that the difference in $\Delta\sigma$ for the pure DPPC

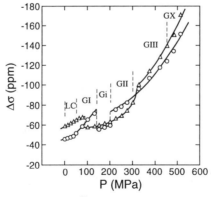

Figure 4   Pressure dependence of the ^{31}P chemical shift anisotropy ($\Delta\sigma$) values for DPPC bilayers (*circles*) and DPPC-TTC bilayers (*triangles*) at 50°C (78).

system and DPPC/TTC is not affected by the increasing pressure in the LC phase. In addition, we also provided supporting evidence for the proposal of MacDonald et al (64) that the choline headgroup of phosphatidylcholine responds to the surface-charge effects even in gel-state lipid membranes including high-pressure gel phases.

HEME PROTEINS

Heme proteins have key biological functions as O_2 binders in muscle (myoglobin), as O_2 transporters in blood (hemoglobin), and as electron carriers in energy metabolism (e.g. cytochrome c, cytochrome oxidase). The functional portion of these proteins is the heme, an Fe-protoporphyrin IX ring that is tightly bound in a hydrophobic cavity of these mostly α-helical proteins. At the center of the heme plane, the Fe^{2+} or Fe^{3+} ion is coordinated to four N atoms of the protoporphyrin ring, and axially to an amino acid residue of the protein, the so-called proximal His in myoglobin and hemoglobin. The sixth coordination position of the Fe^{2+} in deoxymyoglobin or deoxyhemoglobin is free, but it is occupied by the O_2 ligand in oxymyoglobin and oxyhemoglobin. Another ligand that commonly competes for this position is CO. The physiologically functional forms of myoglobin and hemoglobin contain Fe^{2+}, but the Fe^{3+} form predominates under oxidizing in vitro conditions. These oxidized forms are called metmyoglobin and methemoglobin. Normally the sixth coordination position of Fe^{3+} is occupied by water, but various anionic ligands, such as CN^-, N_3^-, and imidazole can readily bind in place of the water molecule. In the cytochromes, the reversible transformation from Fe^{2+} to Fe^{3+} is central to the electron-transport process.

Although the functional center of these proteins is the heme, numerous studies with model compounds have shown that the protein environment is critical in modulating their functions. Thus the same heme group has completely different functions in myoglobin and hemoglobin on the one hand, and the cytochromes on the other. For the same reason, myoglobin molecules from various animal species have different binding affinities for O_2.

In addition to the fundamental physiological roles of myoglobin and hemoglobin, studies of these proteins have examined them as models of protein structure since the initial elucidation of their three-dimensional structures in the late 1950s by J Kendrew & M Perutz. They are also models for ligand binding to proteins. Furthermore, hemoglobin serves as a classic example of allosteric proteins, which, through subunit interactions and regulatory ligands, can control binding of the main ligands at the multiple binding sites. Thus deoxyhemoglobin can exist in a strained or tense conformation (T) that is converted to a relaxed (R) conformation upon oxygenation. The oxyhemoglobin binds O_2 with progressively higher affinity, as the four hemes become occupied by the ligand.

Among the numerous experimental approaches that have been used to study heme proteins, high pressure combined with optical and NMR methods has provided special insights into their denaturation behavior, protein-protein interactions, the local structure in the heme pocket, and the kinetics and mechanisms of ligand binding. Recent synthesis of specific mutants of heme proteins opens a new and exciting avenue for the systematic modification of structure and function.

High-Pressure Studies

Table 3 summarizes selected high-pressure studies performed on heme proteins during the past two decades. The main experimental approaches have made use of visible, vibrational, and NMR spectroscopic methods in the pressure range from 0.1 to 800 MPa. High pressures (up to 800 MPa) depending on pH and temperature denature metmyoglobin, but lower pressures (100–200 MPa) cause more subtle structural changes in the heme cavity and in the interphases between hemoglobin subunits, promote the dissociation of protein complexes, and affect the binding kinetics of CO or O_2 to the heme.

The classic study of Zipp & Kauzmann (123) used the visible absorbance changes of the metmyoglobin heme to detect denaturation as a function of pressure (0.1–600 MPa), pH (4–13), and temperature (5–80°C). Assuming a two-state denaturation process, these authors determined ΔV values between -60 and -100 ml/mol, after careful corrections for the contributions of buffers that are sensitive to pressure at various temperatures and pHs. Their denaturation phase diagrams show clearly that extremes of pH and temperature, as well as high pressures, destabilize metmyoglobin, and stress the fact that each given pressure has a temperature range for optimal stability. In other words, low temperatures as well as high temperatures may denature metmyoglobin.

The physical changes in the heme cavity associated with the denaturation of methemoglobin by high pressure were later attributed by Ogunmola et al (75) to the change from the open crevice, high-spin structure to the closed crevice, low-spin structure, which is reflected in the changes of the visible spectrum of the heme. Although other regions of the protein were not probed, denaturation under such high-

Table 3 Studies of heme proteins at high pressures

Heme protein (ligand)	Pressure (MPa)	Temperature (°C)	pH	Spectroscopic method	Observations	References
MetMb[a]	0.1–600	5–80	4–13	Visible	Denaturation, thermodynamic parameters, ΔV	123
MetMb, MetHb[b], Mb, Hb (CN⁻, CO)	0.1–800	20	6	Visible	Denaturation, high spin-to-low spin conversion	75
Cyt c–cyt b_5[c] mutant complexes	0.1–100		7.4	Visible	Dissociation, ΔV	84, 85
Cyt c–cyt c oxidase complex	0.1–150	5	7	Visible	Dissociation equilibrium	59
Mb, Hb, heme models (CO, O_2)	0.1–300	20–25	7	Laser flash photolysis	Ligand binding kinetics, $\Delta V\ddagger$	2, 95
Mb (CO)	0.1–200	−43–57	5.5, 6.6	Visible, FTIR, pressure jump	Substate populations	3, 27
MetMb, MetHb, Mb, Hb (CN⁻, N_3^-, imidazole)	0.1–200	20	7	NMR	Small structural changes in the heme cavity, and in the quaternary structure of Hb	66–71

[a] Mb, myoglobin.
[b] Hb, hemoglobin.
[c] Cyt, cytochrome.

pressure conditions does not appear to lead to heme extrusion from the protein, but rather to a major structural rearrangement in its cavity.

At pressures up to 100–200 MPa, near neutral pH, and at physiological or ambient temperature, no major changes are detected in the optical spectra of heme proteins, but subtle structural effects can be observed with NMR (discussed in the next section). Here we summarize further pressure studies of heme proteins using optical methods.

Rogers and coworkers (84, 85) used optical absorbance changes to measure the dissociation constants for complexes of cytochrome c with cytochrome b_5 as a function of pressures up to 100 MPa. In a series of mutants of cytochrome b_5, several acidic residues, which are involved in salt-bridge formation, were replaced in the contact region with the cytochrome c with their corresponding amide analogues. The linear correlation of the ΔV values with the respective ΔG for the protein-protein dissociation, involving various single- and multiple-site mutants, led these authors to propose that the dissociation involves the breaking of protected salt bridges and the exposure and solvation of the charged groups. The solvation of a salt bridge is estimated to result in a decrease in volume of -25 to -30 ml/mol. Therefore, the -122 to -40 ml/mol ΔV values measured in this study correspond to the 5 to 1 salt bridges that are believed to stabilize the cytochrome c–cytochrome b_5 interaction. A similar study by Kornblatt et al (59) noted the dissociation of cytochrome c (minus the Fe^{3+}) from cytochrome c oxidase by pressures near 100 MPa.

Recent experiments have employed pressures up to 300 MPa to study the kinetics and mechanism of ligand rebinding to myoglobin, hemoglobin, and model compounds. In particular, CO and O_2 rebinding kinetics have been measured following dissociation of the ligands by laser flash photolysis. The pressure dependence of the rate constants has allowed the calculation of activation volumes ($\Delta V\ddagger$), and the proposal of various binding steps. Taube et al (95) used laser flash photolysis to study CO, O_2, isocyanide, and 1-methylimidazole recombination kinetics with myoglobin and model heme compounds. The bimolecular recombination rate constants as a function of pressure gave a negative $\Delta V\ddagger$ (-10.0 ml/mol) for CO rebinding to myoglobin, but positive $\Delta V\ddagger$ values (5.2–9.3 ml/mol) for all the other ligands. The negative $\Delta V\ddagger$ value indicates that bond formation is the rate-limiting step for CO, while the positive $\Delta V\ddagger$ values represent diffusion-limited processes, probably a gatelike conformational change in myoglobin. Rebinding of CO to protoheme, a model compound, over a pressure range from 0.1 to 300 MPa, in a viscous solvent gave negative $\Delta V\ddagger$ values up to 100 MPa and positive $\Delta V\ddagger$ values from 200 to 300 MPa. This result indicates that pressure changes the fast-reaction mechanism from an activation- to a diffusion-controlled one (97).

Adachi & Morishima (1) obtained similar results, showing that the positive $\Delta V\ddagger$ values for O_2 binding to myoglobin from diverse species (sperm whale, horse, and dog) were distinct in the iron-binding step as well as in the diffusion steps, suggesting that activation volumes are very sensitive to the amino acid residues in the path of the ligand. The millisecond and nanosecond kinetics of CO rebinding to the R-T-states of hemoglobin (98), and to the isolated α and β chains of hemoglobin (99), gave negative and distinct values for $\Delta V\ddagger$ at pressures up to 100 MPa and positive $\Delta V\ddagger$ at higher pressures.

As reported by others (97), the negative $\Delta V\ddagger$ values correspond to bond formation and may result from the $\sim$0.4-Å displacement of the Fe as CO is bound to the heme. Evidently, at high pressures, bond formation is accelerated and ligand migration is slowed down. Thus,

CO diffusion becomes the rate-limiting step, as found for other ligands (e.g. O_2) at all pressures. The $\Delta V\ddagger$ values for the isolated β subunits of hemoglobin are slightly smaller than for the α subunits, reflecting the well-known, higher structural flexibility of the β subunits (99).

In a recent report, Adachi et al (2) described the preparation and characterization of a site-specific mutant of human myoglobin in which Leu29 in the distal side of the heme was replaced by Ala or Ile. The pressure dependence of the second-order rate constants for the binding of CO and O_2 to these mutant myoglobins showed the expected signs but different magnitudes for $\Delta V\ddagger$ values for the Ile mutant, but an unexpected positive $\Delta V\ddagger$ for the overall binding of CO to the Ala mutant. Although the structural basis for these kinetic results is not completely understood, the amino acid environment of the heme evidently controls the kinetics and mechanism of ligand binding.

The infrared stretching bands of CO bound to myoglobin have indicated the existence of three or four states of very similar energy, corresponding to different angles of the CO dipole with respect to the heme plane (3, 27). Pressures up to 100 MPa change the relative distribution of these substates.

High-Pressure NMR Studies

Morishima and coworkers conducted all of the high-pressure NMR studies (for review, see 66) in the 1980s using a capillary glass NMR cell that was suitable for high-pressure measurements up to 200 MPa. Most of their experiments were performed in 0.1 M Tris-HCl buffer at 30°C on a Nicolet NT-300 spectrometer equipped with a 1280 computer system.

Morishima et al (71) attributed the chemical shift changes with increasing pressure of the heme methyl protons in metmyoglobin and methemoglobin, and their liganded forms, to the displacement of the high spin–to–low spin equilibrium towards the low-spin state. The low-spin state corresponds to the Fe atom in the plane of the heme, in contrast to the high-spin state in which the Fe atom is out of the plane. The ΔV values measured in this study were around -10 ml/mol and probably included protein structural changes in addition to the Fe displacement. Those liganded forms of the heme proteins that were purely low spin or high spin (i.e. were far away from equilibrium, e.g. CN^- complexes) were quite insensitive to pressure changes in this range but methemoglobin subjected to the highest obtainable pressures ($\sim$200 MPa) underwent structural changes similar to those described by Ogunmola et al (75) for metmyoglobin. In these cases, ligand exchange probably takes place in the sixth coordination position of the heme involving the replacement of water by the distal His, accompanied by high spin–to–low spin conversion, and major NMR and visible spectral changes.

Morishima & Hara (67, 69) analyzed the exchangeable NH signals in the paramagnetic-shifted region as a function of pressure for the CN^- complex of metmyoglobin. Pressure effects were much more significant on the distal His NH than on the proximal His signal, indicating that the distal side of the heme is more compressible. In addition, a comparison between horse and sperm whale myoglobin showed that the former is more sensitive to pressure effects and less stable than the sperm whale myoglobin.

Water in the sixth coordination position of metmyoglobin has a pK of 9.2. Ionization of this water molecule leaves an OH^- coordinated to the Fe and transfers a proton to the distal His. These chemical changes result in NMR spectral changes in the heme region, specifically in the heme methyl protons (66). At high pressures, the ionization equilibrium is shifted, giving pK values of 8.5 and 8.2 at 120 and 190 MPa, respectively. It is possible that compression of the heme cavity favors H-bond formation between water and the distal His, favoring proton transfer.

Morishima & Hara (68, 70) also studied the effects of pressure on the tertiary and quaternary structures of human hemoglobin. They used the ring current–shifted methyl resonances of E11 Val, as well as the heme methyl proton signals and the NH proton signals of the proximal His, to observe the effects of pressure. Their results showed significant shifts in the β chains, but no effects on the corresponding signals of the α subunits. Hemoglobin derivatives in the T $\leftrightarrow$ R allosteric equilibrium exhibited spectral changes for the T-state marker signals at 9.6 and 6.5 ppm, but no changes in the R-state marker signal at 6.0 ppm, when subjected to pressures up to 140 MPa (66). Morishima & Hara concluded that subtle changes are induced in the quaternary structure without producing the T $\leftrightarrow$ R transition.

Hemes with modified peripheral substituents, when reconstituted with the apoproteins, insert into the heme cavity in two orientations that differ by a 180° rotation from each other. Morishima (66) used NMR and high pressure to investigate the kinetics and $\Delta V\ddagger$ for the exchange and reorientation of the heme.

In addition to studying various forms of myoglobin and hemoglobin, Morishima (66) has investigated pressure effects on the structure of the Fe^{3+} and Fe^{2+} oxidation states of cytochrome c. From the hyperfine-shifted proton NMR spectra, aliphatic and aromatic proton signals, and amide proton exchange results at pressures up to 100 MPa, he concluded that the Fe^{3+} cytochrome c has much greater conformational flexibility than its Fe^{2+} counterpart.

PRESSURE DENATURATION OF PROTEINS

The use of NMR to follow pressure-induced unfolding of proteins is, so far, limited to our work. In the following sections four examples illustrate the new information obtained by combining high-resolution NMR techniques with high pressure. (*a*) In the study of pressure-induced reversible unfolding of lysozyme (87), we followed the effects of pressure on the behavior of several amino acid residues located in different regions of this small protein. (*b*) The results of the effects of amino acid substitution on pressure unfolding of staphylococcal nuclease (86) demonstrated the great potential of site-directed mutagenesis combined with high-pressure NMR in studies of protein stability. (*c*) In the experiment on the cold denaturation of ribonuclease A (X Peng, J Zhang & J Jonas, unpublished results), we took advantage of the depression of the freezing point of water by high pressure to carry out experiments on the unfolding of this protein well below 0°C. (*d*) In addition, we observed the pressure dissociation of Arc repressor (79) and the formation of a compact unfolded state of its monomer.

Pressure-Induced Reversible Unfolding of Lysozyme

Several studies reported in the literature provided the main motivation for our high-pressure NMR study (87) on hen egg white lysozyme. First of all, the high-pressure fluorescence experiments on lysozyme and lysozyme with bound tri-*N*-acetylglucosamine (tri-NAG) by Li et al (63) suggested that pressure denaturation of this protein is not a two-state process. Second, Kundrot & Richards (60) determined the crystal structure of lysozyme at a hydrostatic pressure of 100 MPa and found a differential compressibility in different regions of the protein. Third, Wedin et al (109) investigated the thermal denaturation of lysozyme, using high-resolution NMR and observing the NMR signals for various residues located in different regions of the protein.

We used high-resolution NMR to follow the effect of pressure on the equilibrium constant for the native and denatured forms of lysozyme by observing the proton resonances of the following amino acid residues: His15ϵ1, Leuδ2, Trp28ϵ3, Cys64α, and Trp108ϵ3. Because these residues lie in the regions for which Kundrot & Richards (60) determined different compressibilities, we were interested whether these differences would also be reflected in the determined reaction volumes (ΔV) for the individual residues. Dobson and coworkers (109) proposed that thermal denaturation of lysozyme is a cooperative two-state process because all the observed resonances corresponding to different residues gave equivalent ΔH and ΔS values for the unfolding process. Therefore, we felt that the determination of ΔV values for the same residues would contribute to resolving the fundamental questions of how pressure denaturation compares to thermal denaturation, and whether pressure denaturation of lysozyme is a cooperative, two-state process. As Weber and coworkers (63) observed that binding of tri-NAG, a substrate analogue, stabilizes the native form of lysozyme, we also studied the pressure denaturation of lysozyme with bound tri-NAG to determine the effect of this ligand on the unfolding process as reflected in the ΔV values obtained for residues located in or close to the active site.

The pressure effects on the high-resolution proton NMR spectra of D_2O solutions of hen egg white lysozyme at a pH of 3.9 and a temperature of 68.5°C were measured in the pressure range 0.1–500 MPa. Analogous experiments were performed for lysozyme with bound tri-NAG. The proton residues of interest in this study are localized in different structural regions of lysozyme and have sufficiently resolved proton spectra for accurate intensity measurements. His15ϵ1 has well-resolved native and denatured resonances, while the other residues only have resolved native resonances. His15ϵ1, Trp28ϵ3 and Trp108ϵ3, and Leu17δ2 are in α-helix structures, and Cys64α is in a β-sheet structure that is not compressible according to Kundrot & Richards (60).

From the experimental data, we calculated the ΔV values for these amino acid residues. Table 4 summarizes the means and standard deviations for the ΔV values calculated from the slopes of $\ln K_{eq}$ versus

Table 4 ΔV values calculated from the pressure dependence of the $\ln K_{eq}$ for five amino acid residues of lysozyme[a]

Residue	ΔV (ml/mol)[b]	
	Without tri-NAG	With tri-NAG
His15ϵ1	-11.8 ± 0.5	-12.0 ± 0.3
Leu17δ2	-10.2 ± 0.5	-10.6 ± 0.9
Trp28ϵ3	-10.8 ± 0.7	-10.4 ± 0.5
Cys64α	-9.3 ± 0.7	-10.9 ± 0.4
Trp108ϵ3	-10.3 ± 0.6	-18.1 ± 1.7

[a] In the presence and absence of tri-N-acetylglucosamine (tri-NAG) (87).
[b] The ΔV values are given as the mean ± standard deviation from seven independent experiments.

pressure plots, for all five amino acid residues. In the absence of tri-NAG, the ΔV values range from -9.3 ± 0.7 to -11.8 ± 0.5 ml/mol. Differences between the mean values that exceed the standard deviations can be considered statistically significant; therefore, the ΔV values for the three nonpolar residues, Leu17δ2, Trp28ϵ3, and Trp108ϵ3 are essentially equal, while those for His15ϵ1 and Cys64α are larger and smaller, respectively. This finding of statistically significant, although small, differences in ΔV values for several amino acid residues suggests that pressure denaturation resulting from changes in intermolecular distances is distinct from temperature denaturation and may provide novel information about the details of the protein-unfolding process. In addition, the relatively low ΔV value for Cys64α agrees with the low compressibility reported by Kundrot & Richards (60) for the β-sheet region.

In the presence of tri-NAG, Leu17δ2, His15ϵ1, and Trp28ϵ3 have the same ΔV values as in the absence of the substrate analogue, whereas Cys64α and Trp108ϵ3 have more negative ΔV values. In fact the ΔV for Trp108ϵ3 changes dramatically from -10.3 ± 0.6 to -18.1 ± 1.7 ml/mol. This large change in ΔV for Trp108ϵ3 is most likely related to the fact that tri-NAG occupies about half of the active site and produces a significant free volume in the immediate vicinity of the Trp108ϵ3 residue. Evidently Cys64α also senses the binding of the substrate analogue; its ΔV changes from -9.3 ± 0.7 to -10.9 ± 0.4 ml/mol in the presence of tri-NAG. The behavior of Cys64α in the absence (different ΔV compared to other residues) and presence of tri-NAG (similar ΔV to other residues) suggests the possible existence of multiple denaturation steps in lysozyme and a single-step process in lysozyme with bound tri-NAG, as observed by Weber and coworkers (63) by means of fluorescence measurements up to 1.1 GPa. To unequivocally prove or disprove the existence of multiple-pressure denaturated forms of lysozyme could only be accomplished by performing the high-pressure NMR experiments under experimental conditions comparable to those used in the fluorescence study of Weber's group (63). NMR experiments on lysozyme in the pressure range up to 900 MPa are in progress (X Peng & J Jonas, unpublished data).

Staphylococcal Nuclease

In contrast to lysozyme, staphylococcal nuclease does not contain sulfhydryl residues nor disulfide linkages; therefore, it is less stable in the face of pressure and other denaturing conditions. The native state of this protein exhibits structural heterogeneity linked to the *cis-trans* isomerization of prolyl peptide bonds. In a recent study, Royer et al

(86) used time-resolved and steady-state fluorescence, as well as high-resolution NMR, to investigate the effects of amino acid substitutions on the high-pressure denaturation of staphylococcal nuclease. These authors studied the pressure denaturation of two wild-type forms of this protein, WT (Foggi strain nuclease) and H124L (V8 strain nuclease), and several mutants of the V8 nuclease. The NMR experiments were performed on 3 to 5 mM solutions of both wild-type forms (WT and H124L) and the G79S and P47G + P117G mutants of the V8 nuclease, at 37°C and pH 5.1. The Hisε1 signals of His8, His46, and His121 were recorded as a function of pressures up to 500 MPa. Calculated ΔV values ranged from -47 to -65 ml/mol, and the midpoints of the pressure denaturation curves were between 92 and 310 MPa, depending on the stability of the protein. In fact, the P47G + P117G mutant did not denature even at pressures as high as 500 MPa. A comparison between the time-resolved fluorescence and NMR results indicated a correlation between the ΔV values reflecting the pressure stability of a particular mutant and its dynamic properties. A striking finding was that mutating either (or both) of the prolines that exhibit structural heterogeneity to glycine greatly affects the stability of staphylococcal nuclease under pressure.

In the discussion, the authors point out that the physical basis for the volume changes accompanying denaturation is very complex. They note that possible contributions to the decrease in volume upon denaturation (ΔV from -10 to -100 ml/mol for diverse proteins) may result, in part, from the existence of free volume in the folded proteins, from electrostriction of water caused by the exposure of buried ion-pairs, and from decreases in volume on exposure of hydrophobic residues to water. The authors conclude that a better characterization of the various contributions to ΔV will greatly improve our understanding of the relationship between structure, packing dynamics, and stability of proteins. Without doubt, this pioneering study shows the great promise of combining site-directed mutagenesis with high-pressure NMR studies of protein unfolding.

Cold Denaturation

All globular proteins appear to be subject to denaturation by low temperatures, referred to as *cold denaturation* (4, 81). Because this type of protein denaturation should occur at subzero temperatures in aqueous solutions at neutral pH, investigators have prevented freezing of water by different means, including protein solutions emulsified in oil (26), supercooled aqueous solutions (31), and cryosolvents such as methanol (32). Another way to depress the freezing point of aqueous protein solutions is to use high pressure, taking advantage of the high-pressure phase behavior of water (45). However, high pressure itself affects the stability of proteins and, at the present time, its relative role in denaturation is not clear.

In a recent study (X Peng, J Zhang & J Jonas, unpublished data), we carried out a cold denaturation experiment on ribonuclease A using high-resolution, high-pressure NMR techniques. The main goals were to provide additional proof that cold denaturation is a general process for globular proteins and to find out whether the structure of the cold-denatured protein is different from its heat-denatured and/or pressure-denatured forms. The main results of this study, shown in Figure 5, indicate that, at pressures of 300–500 MPa and a temperature of − 25°C, ribonuclease A undergoes reversible cold denaturation; furthermore, the ^{1}H NMR spectrum resembles the pressure-denatured form, but is distinct from the heat-denatured form obtained both at ambient pressure and at high pressure. A detailed conformational characterization of these various denatured states will be carried out using two-dimensional NMR techniques.

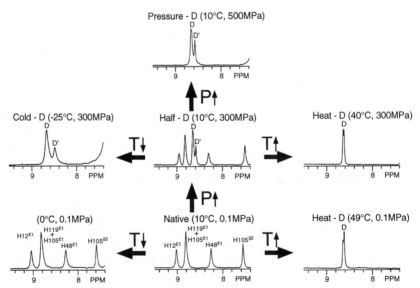

Figure 5 Comparisons of the histidine region of the ^{1}H NMR spectra among pressure-denaturated, cold-denaturated, and heat-denaturated states of ribonuclease A (X Peng, J Zhang & J Jonas, unpublished data).

Pressure Dissociation of Arc Repressor

The results of recent high-resolution NMR studies (79) of the pressure-induced dissociation and denaturation of Arc repressor clearly illustrate that pressure denaturation leads to a more controlled, less drastic perturbation to the protein structure than temperature or chemical denaturation. In fact, in these studies we show that pressure leads to molten globule or compact denatured states (22).

Arc repressor is a small DNA-binding protein of 53 amino acid residues that is dimeric (M_r = 13, 000) in solution. Breg et al (13) have proposed a tertiary-structure model for Arc repressor based on two-dimensional NMR data (12) and homology between Arc repressor and E. coli Met repressor. Silva et al (92) have used high-pressure fluorescence techniques and established that the Arc repressor dimer dissociates reversibly into monomers by increases of pressure at constant protein concentration or by dilution at constant pressure. The dissociated monomer is compact and has properties characteristic of a molten globule.

We used one-dimensional and two-dimensional NMR techniques to investigate the conformational changes during the pressure-induced dissociation and unfolding, temperature-induced denaturation, and urea-induced denaturation of Arc repressor (X Peng, J Silva & J Jonas, unpublished data).

According to Silva et al (92), 1.0 mM Arc repressor at 20°C and pH of 7.5 begins to dissociate into monomers at about 100 MPa and completely dissociates by 350 MPa. Our spectra in the pressure range 100–500 MPa show substantial overlap and line broadening of many resonances. Therefore our ^{1}H NMR spectra support the previously proposed molten-globule state of Arc repressor under high pressure (92). The ^{1}H NMR spectra of the dissociated state in the pressure range 350–500 MPa are substantially different from those of the native state (0.1 MPa, 20°C), the thermally denatured state (0.1 MPa, 70°C), and the urea-denatured state. The changes in the aliphatic region of the ^{1}H NMR spectra of Arc repressor, as a function of pressure, further suggest the appearance of a molten-globule state. The changes in both the linewidth and chemical shift in the pressure range 0.1 MPa–100 MPa indicate conformational changes prior to the dissociation of Arc repressor dimer.

To further characterize the structure of the molten-globule state of Arc repressor, two-dimensional NMR experiments were carried out at different pressures. Phase-sensitive two-dimensional correlated spectroscopy (COSY), two-dimensional nuclear Overhauser effect enhancement spectroscopy (NOESY), and exchange-correlated spectra were recorded.

The NOESY spectra for the αH-αH region of the β-sheet show NOE crosspeaks. Interestingly, NOEs between the α-Hs of Gln9 and Arg13 are observed throughout the pressure range studied, suggesting the proximity of these two residues. By contrast, no NOEs are observed between α-Hs of Gln9 and Arg13 in the NOESY spectrum of Arc repressor at 68°C nor in the NOESY spectrum of urea-denatured Arc repressor, suggesting that Gln9 and Arg13 are no longer close to each other in the thermally or urea-denatured states.

The chemical shift values of Asn11 at 68°C and in the urea-denatured state are smaller than their corresponding random coil values, suggesting the disruption of the β-sheet in the thermally and urea-denatured state. The observed NOEs between α-Hs of Gln9 and Arg13 and the α-Hs chemical shifts at pressures above 300 MPa suggest the presence of an antiparallel β-sheet in the Arc repressor monomer. The structure of an intramonomer β-sheet in the molten-globule state could be similar to the one proposed by Breg et al (13) as an alternative structure in the dimer. Our results indicate that, during pressure-induced dissociation, the intermonomer β-sheet in the native dimer is converted to an intramonomer β-sheet containing a γ-turn in the molten globule.

In the dissociated region (300–500 MPa), the substantial line broadening and overlap of many resonances result from the interconversion of different conformations of the molten globule, suggesting a high degree of conformational heterogeneity compared with the native state. The NMR results corroborate previous fluorescence lifetime data, which suggest considerable heterogeneity of states in this pressure range.

CONCLUDING REMARKS

This review has discussed the current status of the field of high-pressure, high-resolution NMR spectroscopy applied to proteins and model membranes. Clearly, the use of pressure as an experimental variable combined with the high information content of advanced NMR techniques provides a unique approach, particularly in studies of the protein-unfolding problem. The finding that pressure denaturation is less drastic than temperature and/or chemical denaturation may facilitate the detection, stabilization, and characterization of various partially folded intermediates.

The most promising future technical developments in this relatively young field will include the use of advanced two-dimensional and three-dimensional NMR techniques in high-pressure NMR studies of proteins and model membranes, as well as the development of high pressure, high-resolution NMR probes for high-field experiments. The major obstacle is related to the cost of wide bore, high-field superconducting magnets, rather than to the feasibility of the developments themselves. Several promising research directions can be readily identified: cold denaturation studies at high pressure and characterization of the cold-denatured and pressure-denatured states of proteins, and use of site-directed mutants in high-pressure NMR studies of proteins. In addition, systematic high-pressure experiments on model systems including peptides and polypeptides, and systematic studies of pressure effects on water in aqueous protein solutions, should be carried out to elucidate the physical nature and the relative role of the various contributions to the experimentally determined reaction volumes. In the area of model membranes, one can foresee studies of the pressure/temperature phase diagrams for various lipid systems and experiments on binary or ternary mixtures. Specifically, the structural and dynamic characterization of the various high-pressure gel phases is needed. And finally, high-pressure NMR spectroscopy can be used to investigate problems relevant to high-pressure food science and technology.

Given these likely developments and judging from the history of high-resolution NMR, which has become an indispensable tool in modern biophysics, biochemistry, and biology, we can foresee a major increase in research activities in the field of high-resolution NMR spectroscopy at high pressures.

ACKNOWLEDGMENTS

The work discussed in this review was supported in part by the National Institutes of Health grants PHS 1 RO1 GM42452 and PHS 5 RO1 HL16059, and by the National Science Foundation grant NSF CHE 90-17649.

Literature Cited

1. Adachi S, Morishima I. 1989. The effects of pressure on oxygen and carbon monoxide binding kinetics for myoglobin. A high pressure laser flash photolysis study. *J. Biol. Chem.* 264: 18896–18901

2. Adachi S, Sunohara N, Ishimori K, Morishima I. 1992. Structure and ligand binding properties of leucine 29 (B10) mutants of human myoglobin. *J. Biol. Chem.* 267:12614–21
3. Ansari A, Berendsen J, Braunstein D, Cowen BR, Frauenfelder H, et al. 1987. Rebinding and relaxation in the myoglobin pocket. *Biophys. Chem.* 26: 337–55
4. Antonino L, Kantz RA, Nakano T, Fox RO, Fink AL. 1991. Cold denaturation and ^2H_2O stabilization of a staphylococcal nuclease mutant. *Proc. Natl. Acad. Sci. USA* 88:7715–18
5. Artaki I, Jonas J. 1985. Pressure effect on the coupling between rotational and translational motions of supercooled viscous fluids. *J. Chem. Phys.* 82: 3360–70
6. Balny C, Hayashi R, Heremans K, Masson P, eds. 1992. *High Pressure and Biotechnology, Colloque INSERM.* Montrouge, France: John Libbey Eurotext
7. Balny C, Masson P, Travers F. 1989. Some aspects of the use of high pressure for protein investigations in solution. *High Pressure Res.* 2:1–28
8. Benedek GB. 1963. *Magnetic Resonance at High Pressures.* New York: Wiley-Interscience
9. Boulanger Y, Schreier S, Leitch LC, Smith ICP. 1980. Multiple binding sites for local anesthetics in membranes: characterization of the sites and their equilibria by deuterium NMR of specifically deuterated procaine and tetracaine. *Can. J. Biochem.* 58:986–95
10. Bradley ES, ed. 1965. *High Pressure Physics and Chemistry.* New York: Academic
11. Braganza LF, Worcester DL. 1986. Structural changes in lipid bilayers and biological membranes caused by hydrostatic pressure. *Biochemistry* 25: 7484–88
12. Breg JN, Boelens R, George AVE, Kaptein R. 1989. Sequence specific ^1H NMR assignment and secondary structure of the arc repressor of bacteriophage P22, as determined by two-dimensional ^1H NMR spectroscopy. *Biochemistry* 28:9826–33
13. Breg JN, Van Opheusden HS, Burgering MJM, Boelens R, Kaptein R. 1990. Structure of arc repressor in solution: evidence for a family of β-sheet binding proteins. *Nature* 346:586–89
14. Bridgman PW. 1949. *The Physics of High Pressures.* London: Bell
15. Cheftel JC. 1992. Effects of high hydrostatic pressure on food constitu-

ents: an overview. See Ref. 6, pp. 195–208
16. Chong PLG. 1988. Effect of hydrostatic pressure on the location of PRODAN in lipid bilayers and cellular membranes. *Biochemistry* 27:399–404
17. Chong PLG, Weber G. 1983. Pressure dependence of 1,6-diphenyl-1,3,5-hexatriene fluorescence in single-component phosphatidylcholine lyposomes. *Biochemistry* 22:5544–50
18. Colombo MF, Rau DC, Parsegian VA. 1992. Protein solvation in allosteric regulation: a water effect on hemoglobin. *Science* 256:655–59
19. Davis JH. 1979. Deuterium magnetic resonance study of the gel and liquid crystalline phases of dipalmitoyl phosphatidylcholine. *Biophys. J.* 27:339–58
20. DeFries T, Jonas J. 1977. Pressure dependence of NMR proton spin-lattice relaxation times and shear viscosity in liquid water in the temperature range −15°C to 10°C. *J. Chem. Phys.* 66: 896–901
21. Dill KA. 1990. Dominant forces in protein folding. *Biochemistry* 29:7133–55
22. Dill KA, Shortle D. 1991. Denatured states of proteins. *Annu. Rev. Biochem.* 60:5082–86
23. Drickamer HG, Frank CW. 1973. *Electronic Transition and the High Pressure Chemistry and Physics of Solids.* London: Chapman and Hall
24. Driscoll DA, Jonas J, Jonas A. 1991. High pressure ^2H nuclear magnetic resonance study of the gel phases of dipalmitoyl phosphatidylcholine. *Chem. Phys. Lipids* 58:97–104
25. Driscoll DA, Samarasinghe S, Adamy S, Jonas J, Jonas A. 1991. Pressure effects on dipalmitoyl phosphatidyl choline bilayers measured by ^2H nuclear magnetic resonance. *Biochemistry* 30: 3322–27
26. Franks F, Hatley R. 1985. Low temperature unfolding of chymotrypsinogen. *Cryo-Letters* 6:171–80
27. Frauenfelder H, Alberding NA, Ansari A, Braunstein D, Cowen BR, et al. 1990. Proteins and pressure. *J. Phys. Chem.* 94:1024–37
28. Hamann SD. 1957. *Physico-Chemical Effects of Pressure.* London: Butterworth
29. Hara K, Morishima I. 1988. High-pressure cell and its inner capsule for optical studies in liquids. *Rev. Sci. Instrum.* 59:2397–98
30. Harris RD, Jacobs M, Long MM, Ury DW. 1976. A high-pressure sample cell for circular dichroism studies. *Anal. Biochem.* 73:363–68

31. Hatley RHM, Franks F. 1986. Denaturation of lactate dehydrogenase at subzero temperatures. *Cryo-Letters* 7: 226–33
32. Hatley RHM, Franks F. 1989. The effect of aqueous methanol cryosolvents on the heat- and cold-induced denaturation of lactate dehydrogenase. *Eur. J. Biochem.* 184:237–40
33. Hauer H, Ludemann HD, Jaenicke R. 1982. Free activation energies and activation volumes for the amide rotation in some peptides studied by high pressure ^{1}H-high resolution NMR. *Z. Naturforsch.* 37c:51–56
34. Hauer J, Muller K, Ludemann, MD, Jaenicke R. 1981. The pressure dependence of the histidine ring protonation constant studied by ^{1}H HR-NMR. *FEBS Lett.* 135:135–38
35. Hayashi R. 1992. Utilization of pressure in addition to temperature in food science and technology. See Ref. 6, pp. 185–92
36. Heremans K. 1982. High-pressure effects on proteins and other biomolecules. *Annu. Rev. Biophys. Bioeng.* 11: 1–21
37. Heremans K. 1993. The behavior of proteins under pressure. See Ref. 116, pp. 443–69
38. Heremans K, Snauwaert J, Rijkenberg I. 1980. Stopped-flow apparatus for the study of fast reactions in solution under high pressure. *Rev. Sci. Instrum.* 51: 806–8
39. Jannasch HW, Marquis RE, Zimmerman AM, eds. 1987. *Current Perspectives in High Pressure Biology.* New York: Academic
40. Jonas J. 1972. Nuclear magnetic resonance measurements at high pressure. *Rev. Sci. Instrum.* 43:643–49
41. Jonas J. 1973. NMR studies in liquids at high pressure. *Adv. Magn. Reson.* 6:73–139
42. Jonas J. 1975. Nuclear magnetic resonance at high pressure. *Annu. Rev. Phys. Chem.* 26:167–90
43. Jonas J. 1977. Structure and motion in liquid water at high pressures. *Commun. Solid State Phys.* 8:29–35
44. Jonas J. 1978. Magnetic resonance spectroscopy at high pressure. *NATO ASI Sect. C* 41:65–110
45. Jonas J. 1982. Nuclear magnetic resonance at high pressure. *Science* 216: 1179–84
46. Jonas J. 1984. Pressure effects on the dynamic structure of liquids. *Acc. Chem. Res.* 17:74–80
47. Jonas J, guest ed. 1991. *High Pressure NMR in NMR Basic Principles and Progress,* ed. P Diehl, E Fluck, H Gunther, R Kosfeld, J Seelig. New York: Springer-Verlag
48. Jonas J. 1993. High pressure NMR studies of chemical and biochemical systems. See Ref. 116, pp. 393–441
49. Jonas J, DeFries T, Wilbur DJ. 1976. Molecular motions in compressed liquid water. *J. Chem. Phys.* 65:582–88
50. Jonas J, Koziol P, Peng X, Reiner C, Campbell DM. 1993. High resolution NMR spectroscopy at high pressures. *J. Magn. Reson.* 102B:299–309
51. Jonas J, Winter R, Grandinetti PJ, Driscoll D. 1990. High pressure 2D-NOESY experiments on phospholipid vesicles. *J. Magn. Reson.* 87:536–47
52. Jonas J, Xie CL, Jonas A, Grandinetti PJ, Campbell D, Driscoll D. 1988. High resolution ^{13}C-NMR study of pressure effects on the main phase transition in L-α-dipalmitoyl phosphatidylcholine vesicles. *Proc. Natl. Acad. Sci. USA* 85:4115–17
53. Kaminsky SM, Richards FM. 1992. Differences in hydrogen exchange behavior between the oxidized and reduced forms of *Escherichia coli* thioredoxin. *Protein Sci.* 1:10–21
54. Kaminsky SM, Richards FM. 1992. Reduction of thioredoxin significantly decreases its partial specific volume and adiabatic compressibility. *Protein Sci.* 1:22–30
55. Kennedy SD, Bryant RG. 1990. Structural effects on hydration: studies of lysozyme by ^{13}C solid NMR. *Biopolymers* 29:1801–6
56. Kimmich R. 1991. Reorientation mediated by translational diffusion as a mechanism for nuclear magnetic relaxation of molecules confined in surface layers, magnetic resonance imaging. 9: 749–51
57. Kimmich R, Nusser W, Greiting T. 1990. Molecular theory for nuclear magnetic relaxation in protein solutions and tissue: surface diffusion and free-volume analogy. *Colloids Surf.* 45:283–302
58. Kornblatt JA, Bon Hoa GH. 1990. A nontraditional role for water in the cytochrome *c* oxidase reaction. *Biochemistry* 29:9370–76
59. Kornblatt JA, Hoa GHB, Heremans K. 1988. Pressure-induced effects on cytochrome oxidase: the aerobic steady state. *Biochemistry* 27:5122–28
60. Kundrot CE, Richards FM. 1987. Crystal structure of hen egg-white lysozyme at a hydrostatic pressure of 1000 atmospheres. *J. Mol. Biol.* 193: 157–70

61. Laggner P, Lohmer K, Koyouvra R, Tenchov B. 1991. The influence of low amounts of cholesterol on the interdigitated gel phase of hydrated dihexadecylphosphatidylcholine. *Chem. Phys. Lipids* 58:153–61

62. Lamb WJ, Brown DR, Jonas J. 1981. The temperature and density dependence of the proton lifetimes in liquid water. *J. Chem. Phys.* 85:3883–87

63. Li TM, Hook JW III, Drickamer HB, Weber G. 1976. Plurality of pressure denatured forms in chymotripsinogen and lysozyme. *Biochemistry* 15:5571–80

64. MacDonald PM, Leisen J, Marassi FM. 1991. Response of phosphatidylcholine in the gel and liquid-crystalline states to membrane surface charges. *Biochemistry* 30:3558–66

65. Mitchell RM, Hawley SA. 1975. An electrophoretic study of reversible protein denaturation: chymotrypsinogen at high pressures. *Biochemistry* 14:3257–64

66. Morishima I. 1987. High pressure NMR studies of hemoproteins. See Ref. 39, pp. 315–32

67. Morishima I, Hara M. 1982. High-pressure NMR studies of hemoproteins. Pressure-induced structural changes in the heme environments of cyanometmyoglobin. *J. Am. Chem. Soc.* 104:6833–34

68. Morishima I, Hara M. 1983. High-pressure NMR studies of hemoproteins. The effect of pressure on the ternary and quaternary structures of human adult ferrous hemoglobin. *J. Biol. Chem.* 258:14428–32

69. Morishima I, Hara M. 1983. High-pressure nuclear magnetic resonance studies of hemoproteins. Pressure-induced structural changes in the heme environments of ferric low-spin metmyoglobin complexes. *Biochemistry* 22:4102–7

70. Morishima I, Hara M. 1984. High-pressure NMR studies of hemoproteins. The effect of pressure on the quaternary structure of hemoglobin. *Biochem. Biophys. Res. Commun.* 121:229–36

71. Morishima I, Ogawa S, Yamada H. 1980. High-pressure proton nuclear magnetic resonance studies of hemoproteins. Pressure-induced structural change in heme environments of myoglobin, hemoglobin, and horseradish peroxidase. *Biochemistry* 19:1569–75

72. Mountcastle DB, Biltonen RL, Halsey MJ. 1978. Effect of anesthetics and pressure on the thermotropic behavior of multilamellar dipalmitoylphosphatidylcholine liposomes. *Proc. Natl. Acad. Sci. USA* 75:4906–10

73. Nakatani H, Hiromi K. 1984. Kinetic study of β-cyclodextrin dye system by high-pressure temperature jump method. *J. Biochem.* 96:69–72

74. Nordmeier E. 1992. Effect of pressure on the helix-coil transition of calf-thymus DNA. *J. Phys. Chem.* 96:1494–1501

75. Ogunmola GB, Zipp A, Chen F, Kauzmann W. 1979. Effect of pressure on visible spectra of complexes of myoglobin, hemoglobin, cytochrome c, and horse radish peroxidase. *Proc. Natl. Acad. Sci. USA* 74:1–4

76. Otting G, Liepinsch E, Wüthrich K. 1991. Protein hydration in aqueous solution. *Science* 254:974–80

77. Paladini AA, Silva JL, Weber G. 1987. Slab gel electrophoresis of oligomeric proteins under high hydrostatic pressure. *Anal. Biochem.* 161:358–64

78. Peng X, Jonas J. 1992. High-pressure ^{31}P NMR study of dipalmitoyl phosphatidylcholine bilayers. *Biochemistry* 31:6383–90

79. Peng X, Jonas J, Silva J. 1993. Molten globule conformation of ARC repressor monomers studies by high pressure (^{1}H) NMR spectroscopy. *Proc. Natl. Acad. Sci. USA* 90:1776–80

80. Prasad SK, Shashidhar R, Gaber BP, Chandrasekhar SC. 1987. Pressure studies on two hydrated phospholipids—1,2-dimyristoylphosphatidylcholine and 1,2-dipalmitoyl-phosphatidylcholine. *Chem. Phys. Lipids* 43:227–35

81. Privalov PL. 1990. Cold denaturation of proteins. *CRC Crit. Rev. Biochem. Mol. Biol.* 25:281–305

82. Reinhart G, Gratton E, Mantulin WW. 1993. Dissociation of large oligomeric proteins by high hydrostatic pressure: dynamic light scattering studies. See Ref. 116, pp. 619–26

83. Robinson C, Sligar S. 1993. Mediation of molecular recognition by bound water: a mechanism for star activity of restriction endonucleases. *J. Mol. Biol.* 234:302–6

84. Rogers KK, Pochapsky TC, Sligar SG. 1988. Probing the mechanisms of macromolecular recognition: the cytochrome b_5-cytochrome c complex. *Science* 240:1657–59

85. Rogers KK, Sligar SG. 1991. Mapping electrostatic interactions in macromolecular associations. *J. Mol. Biol.* 221:1453–60

86. Royer CA, Hinck AP, Loh SN, Prehoda KE, Peng X, et al. 1993. Effects

of amino acid substitutions on the pressure denaturation of staphylococcal nuclease by fluorescence and nuclear magnetic resonance spectroscopy. *Biochemistry* 32:5222–32

87. Samarasinghe S, Campbell DM, Jonas A, Jonas J. 1992. High resolution study of the pressure-induced unfolding of lysozyme. *Biochemistry* 31:7773–78

88. Scherer PG, Seelig J. 1989. Electric charge effects on phospholipid headgroups: phosphatidylcholine in mixtures with cationic and anionic amphiphiles. *Biochemistry* 27:7720–28

89. Seelig J, Seelig A. 1980. Lipid conformation in model membranes and biological membranes. *Q. Rev. Biophys.* 13:19–61

90. Silva JL. 1993. Effects of pressure on large multimeric proteins and viruses. See Ref. 116, pp. 561–78

91. Silva JL, Luan P, Glaser M, Voss EW, Weber G. 1992. Effects of hydrostatic pressure on a membrane-enveloped virus: high immunogenicity of the pressure-inactivated virus. *J. Virol.* 66: 2111–17

92. Silva JL, Silveira CF, Correia Jr, Pones L. 1992. Dissociation of a native dimer to a molten globule monomer. Effects of pressure and dilution on the association equilibrium of arc repressor. *J. Mol. Biol.* 223:545–55

93. Stillinger FH, Rahman H. 1974. Molecular dynamics study of liquid water under high compression. *J. Chem. Phys.* 61:4973–80

94. Stomatoff J, Guillon GL, Cladis P. 1978. X-ray diffraction measurements of dipalmitoylphosphatidylcholine and a function of pressure. *Biochem. Biophys. Res. Commun.* 85:724–28

95. Taube DJ, Projahn HD, van Eldik R, Magde D, Traylor TG. 1990. Mechanism of ligand binding of hemes and hemoproteins. A high-pressure study. *J. Am. Chem. Soc.* 112:6880–86

96. Teeter MM. 1991. Water-protein interactions: theory and experiment. *Annu. Rev. Biophys. Biophys. Chem.* 20:577–600

97. Traylor TG, Luo J, Simon JA, Ford PC. 1992. Pressure-induced change from activation to diffusion control in fast reactions of carbon monoxide with hemes. *J. Am. Chem. Soc.* 114:4340–45

98. Unno M, Ishimori K, Morishima I. 1990. High-pressure laser photolysis study of hemoproteins. Effects of pressure on carbon monoxide binding dynamics for R- and T-state hemoglobins. *Biochemistry* 29:10199–10205

99. Unno M, Ishimori K, Morishima I. 1991. Pressure effects on carbon monoxide rebinding to the isolated α and β chains of human hemoglobin. *Biochemistry* 30:10679–85

100. Villas-Boas M, Silva JL, Clegg RM. 1993. Pressure studies on protein-DNA interactions. See Ref. 116, pp. 579–602

101. Vist MR, Davis JH. 1990. Phase equilibria of cholesterol/dipalmitoylphosphatidyl choline mixtures: ^{2}H nuclear magnetic resonance and differential scanning calorimetry. *Biochemistry* 29: 451–64

102. Wagner G. 1980. Activation volumes for the rotational motion of interior aromatic rings in globular proteins determined by high resolution ^{1}H NMR at high pressure. *FEBS Lett.* 112:280–84

103. Weber G. 1987. Dissociation of oligomeric proteins by hydrostatic pressure. *NATO ASI Ser. C* 197:401–20

104. Weber G. 1987. Fluorescence spectroscopy at high pressure: techniques and results. See Ref. 39, pp. 235–44

105. Weber G. 1992. *Protein Interactions.* New York: Chapman-Hall

106. Weber G. 1993. Pressure dissociation of the smaller oligomers: dimers and tetramers. See Ref. 116, pp. 471–87

107. Weber G. 1993. Relations of bond energies and entropy with volume, pressure and temperature in protein aggregates. See Ref. 116, pp. 489–509

108. Weber G, Drickamer HG. 1983. The effect of high pressure upon proteins and other biomolecules. *Q. Rev. Biophys.* 16:89–112

109. Wedin RE, Delepierre M, Dobson CM, Paulsen FM. 1982. Mechanism of hydrogen exchange in proteins from nuclear magnetic resonance studies of individual tryptophan indole NH hydrogens in lysozyme. *Biochemistry* 21:1098–1103

110. Wilbur DJ, DeFries T, Jonas J. 1976. Self-diffusion in compressed liquid heavy water. *J. Chem. Phys.* 65:1783–86

111. Wilbur DJ, Jonas J. 1975. Fourier transform NMR in liquids at high pressure. III. Spin-lattice relaxation in toluene-D_8. *J. Chem. Phys.* 62:2800–7

112. Williams RK, Fyfe CA, Bruck D, VanVeen L. 1979. Effect of hydrophobic side chains on the pressure-induced changes in the NMR spectra of water-soluble biopolymers. *Biopolymers* 18: 757–63

113. Williams RK, Fyfe CA, Epand RM, Bruck D. 1978. Pressure induced changes in the nuclear magnetic spec-

tra of a biopolymer in aqueous solution. *Biochemistry* 17:1506–9

114. Winter R, Böttner M. 1993. Volumetric properties of model biomembranes. See Ref. 116, pp. 545–60

115. Winter R, Christman MH, Bottner M, Thiyagarajan P, Heena RK. 1991. *Ber. Bunsenges Phys. Chem.* 95:811–20

116. Winter R, Jonas J, eds. 1993. *High Pressure Chemistry, Biochemistry and Materials Science, NATO ASI, Series C*, Vol. 401. Dordrecht, Netherlands: Kluwer Academic

117. Winter R, Pilgrim WC. 1989. A SANS study of high pressure phase transitions in model biomembranes. *Ber. Bunsenges. Phys. Chem.* 93:708–17

118. Wong PTT. 1987. High-pressure vibrational spectroscopy of aqueous systems: phospholipid dispersions and proteins. See Ref. 39, pp.287–314

119. Wong PTT. 1987. High-pressure studies of biomembranes by vibrational spectroscopy. *NATO ASI Ser. C* 197:381–400

120. Wong PTT. 1993. High pressure vibrational spectroscopic studies of aqueous biological systems: from model systems to intact tissues. See Ref. 116, pp. 511–43

121. Wong PTT, Siminovitch DJ, Mantsch HH. 1988. Structure and properties of model membranes: new knowledge from high pressure vibrational spectroscopy. *Biochim. Biophys. Acta* 947:139–71

122. Yamada Y. 1974. Pressure-resisting glass cell for high pressure, high resolution NMR measurements. *Rev. Sci. Instrum.* 45:640–42

123. Zipp A, Kauzmann W. 1973. Pressure denaturation of metmyoglobin. *Biochemistry* 12:4217–28

Annu. Rev. Biophys. Biomol. Struct. 1994. 23:319–48

MOLECULAR DIVERSITY AND FUNCTIONS OF GLUTAMATE RECEPTORS

Shigetada Nakanishi and Masayuki Masu

Institute for Immunology, Kyoto University Faculty of Medicine, Yoshida, Sakyo-ku, Kyoto 606, Japan

KEY WORDS: NMDA receptor, ligand-gated ion channel, G protein–coupled receptor, receptor structure, signal transduction

CONTENTS

INTRODUCTION

Glutamate is a major neurotransmitter that mediates synaptic excitation at a vast majority of synapses in the central nervous system. Glutamate is involved in many important brain functions, such as differentiation, neuronal cell survival and death, proliferation and the

319

1056–8700/94/0610–0319$05.00

development of neuronal and glial cells, and plastic changes in efficacy of synaptic transmission in adult and developing brains. Long-term potentiation (LTP) and long-term depression (LTD) typify the long-lasting changes in synaptic efficacy mediated by glutamate transmission and are believed to be underlying processes for information storage involved in memory acquisition and learning. Yet, massive stimulation of glutamate receptors under some pathological conditions such as brain ischemia, hypoxia, hypoglycemia, and epilepsy, can result in neurodegeneration and neuronal cell death. Glutamate neurotoxicity may also be related to certain neurodegenerative disorders, such as Huntington's disease, Alzheimer's disease, and amyotrophic lateral sclerosis.

Over the past few years, the diverse members of the glutamate receptors have been identified with molecular cloning techniques and characterized at the molecular level. This review focuses on the mechanisms underlying the diversification of the glutamate receptors and the characteristic structural features of the multiple glutamate receptors, in addition to discussing some of the physiological meanings of glutamate-receptor diversity. Space limitations prevent the inclusion of many important physiological, pharmacological, and pathological studies reviewed in other excellent articles (10, 17, 67, 70, 105, 133, 139).

PHARMACOLOGICAL CLASSIFICATION OF GLUTAMATE RECEPTORS

Previous electrophysiological and pharmacological studies have classified glutamate receptors into two distinct groups termed ionotropic receptors and metabotropic receptors (mGluRs) (70, 133, 139). Ionotropic receptors comprise ion channels that selectively permeate cations and are subdivided into three distinct subgroups according to their selective agonists: N-methyl-D-aspartate (NMDA), kainate, and α-amino-3-hydroxy-5-methyl-4-isoxazolepropionate (AMPA) (70). The latter two are sometimes referred to as non-NMDA receptors. mGluRs are coupled to intracellular second messengers via G proteins and belong to a category completely different from the ionotropic receptors (70, 105). mGluRs were found when excitatory amino acids stimulated inositol phosphate formation in brain slices, cultured neuronal cells, and *Xenopus laevis* oocytes injected with brain mRNA (83, 105, 112, 118). Another glutamate receptor, termed the L-2-amino-4-phosphonobutyrate (L-AP4) receptor, was reported in studies of a depressant action of L-AP4 on glutamate transmission. This receptor, however, needed to be characterized precisely (70).

MULTIPLICITY OF GLUTAMATE RECEPTORS

A functional cloning strategy that combines a *X. laevis* oocyte expression system and electrophysiology was used for molecular cloning and identification of each representative receptor group (39, 40, 47, 63, 64, 76). Numerous related genes were then isolated with cross-hybridization techniques and the polymerase chain reaction (PCR) method. The glutamate receptors are diversified by various cellular mechanisms characteristic of eukaryotic cells discussed below.

Gene Family

Tables 1–4 summarize diverse members of the glutamate receptor family. Both ionotropic and metabotropic receptors can be divided into several groups on the basis of their sequence similarities, their agonist and antagonist selectivities, and other properties. In both the ionotropic and metabotropic receptor families, receptors of the same subgroup share a 60–70% sequence similarity. This sequence similarity is much higher than for receptors from different subgroups (44, 89). To avoid confusion in the receptor nomenclature, the names of the rat receptors are used because almost all glutamate receptors were cloned and characterized from this species.

AMPA/KAINATE RECEPTORS   The AMPA/kainate receptor subunits can be divided into three subgroups according to their sequence similarities and responsiveness to AMPA and kainate. The first subgroup, consisting of GluR1–GluR4 (also referred to as GluRA–GluRD), form functional homomeric receptors or heteromeric receptors within the members of this receptor subgroup (12, 25, 39, 50, 80, 102, 119). These receptors expressed in *X. laevis* oocytes or cultured cells respond to kainate, AMPA, and quisqualate with a rank order of potencies of quisqualate > AMPA > kainate (12, 25, 39, 50, 80, 102, 119). Kainate evokes a nondesensitizing current, whereas AMPA elicits a rapidly desensitizing current (114). Kainate concentrations required to activate these receptors were several hundred-fold higher than the K_d value of high-affinity kainate-binding sites in brain preparations (39, 80, 102). Membranes prepared from cDNA-transfected cells showed a specific and saturable binding to ^{3}H-AMPA in all homomeric and heteromeric receptors. However, because of the low affinity of these homo- and

Table 1 Structural properties of cloned ionotropic glutamate receptors

Receptor	Subunit	Names (amino acids) Rat	Mouse	Human	Alternative splicing	RNA editing[a]	Chromosomal localization Rat[b]	Mouse[c]	Human[d]	References
AMPA/Kainate										
AMPA selective										
GluR1	GluR1/GluR-A/GluR-K1(907)	α1(907)		GluR1/HBGR1(906) GluH1 (907)	Flip/Flop	−		11	5q33	39, 50, 80, 94, 95, 102, 114, 119
GluR2	GluR2/GluR-B/GluR-K2(883)	α2(883)			Flip/Flop	+		3	4q32–33	12, 50, 80, 102, 114
GluR3	GluR3/GluR-C/GluR-K3(888)				Flip/Flop	−		X	Xq25–26	12, 50, 80,114
GluR4	GluR4/GluR-D(902)				Flip/Flop GluR-4c(884)	−		9	11q22–23	25, 50, 114
Kainate selective										
GluR5	GluR5-1(920)				GluR5-2a(856), 5-2b(905), 5-2c(934)	+		16	21q21.1–22.1	7, 113
GluR6	GluR6(908)	β2(864)				+		10		22, 75
GluR7	GluR7(919)					−		4		8, 59
KA-1	KA-1(956)					−				136
KA-2	KA-2(979)	γ2(979)	hum EAA2(980)			−				34, 48, 103
NMDA										
NR1	NMDAR1(938)	ζ1(938)	hNR1(938)		NMDAR1A(938), 1B(959), 1C(901), 1D(922), 1E(885), 1F(922), 1G(906), 1-3b(943)		3	2	9q34.3	37, 49, 76, 117, 138
NR2A	NMDAR2A/NR2A(1464)	ε1(1464)					10			45, 66, 72
NR2B	NR2B(1482)	ε2(1482)					4			56, 72
NR2C	NMDAR2C(1250) NR2C(962/1237)	ε3(1239)					10			45, 56, 72
NR2D	NMDAR2D-1(1356)	ε4(1323)			NMDAR2D-2 (1323)		1			44, 45

[a] Data from Ref. 115.
[b] Data from Ref. 55.
[c] Data from Ref. 30.
[d] Data from Refs. 23, 30, 49, 65, 95, 119.

Table 2 Properties of ionotropic glutamate receptors

Receptor	Subunit	Response of homomeric/ heteromeric receptors[a]	EC50 (μM)[b] DA[d]	KA	AMPA	Glu	QA	NMDA	Kd (nM)[c] AMPA	KA	DA	Ki (nM) KA	AMPA	Glu	QA	Rank order of agonist potencies	References
AMPA/ kainate	GluR1	+/+	1.8	36	1.3	9.2	0.15	-	+							QA > AMPA > Glu > KA	39, 80, 102
	GluR2	+/+	+	+	+	+	+	-	12	-		9,000		490	9	QA > AMPA > Glu > KA	50
	GluR3	+/+	+	130	36	+	+	-	+								80
	GluR4	+/+	+	+	+	+	+		+								50
	GluR5	+/+	1.2	34	3,000	631				73	2.1		~3,000	290	280	DA > KA > QA = Glu ≫ AMPA	113
	GluR6	+/+	-	1.0	-	31	11	-		95	59		>10,000	3,100	1,100	DA > KA > QA > Glu ≫ AMPA	8, 22, 59
	GluR7	-/-	-	-						77	12	63	>10,000	1,100	6,900	DA > KA > Glu > QA ≫ AMPA	8, 59
	KA-1	-/-	-	-				-		4.7	40						136
	KA-2	-/+	-	1.5	-	14	14	-	-	15	275		>5,000	200	18	KA > QA > DA > Glu ≫ AMPA	34, 103
NMDA	NR1	+/+			+	0.72	+	27					>10,000	480	58	KA > QA > DA > Glu ≫ AMPA	76
	NR2A	-/+				1.7		57									45, 66
	NR2B	-/+				0.8											56
	NR2C	-/+				0.7		32									45, 56
	NR2D	-/+				0.4											44

[a] +/+, Positively responded in both homomeric and heteromeric assemblies; -/+, positively responded in heteromeric assemblies with other subunits but not in a homomeric configuration; -/-, no response in either homomeric or heteromeric configuration.
[b] +, Positively responded but no EC50 value available; -, no response.
[c] +, Binding detectable but no Kd value available; -, no detectable binding.
[d] Abbreviations used: DA, domoate; KA, kainate; Glu, L-Glutamate; QA, quisqualate.

Table 3 Structures and properties of rat metabotropic glutamate receptors

Subgroup	Subtype (amino acids)	Second messenger	EC$_{50}$ (µM)[a]							Rank order of agonist potencies	Chromosomal localization (Rat)[b]	References
			Glu	ACPD	QA	Ibo	AP4	SOP	L-CCG-I			
I	mGluR1α(1199)	IP$_3$/Ca^{2+}	9	50	0.2	6	–		50	QA > Glu ≈ Ibo > ACPD ≈ L-CCG-I	1	2, 33, 40, 63, 124
	1β(906)	IP$_3$/Ca^{2+}	56	106	2.5	44						92
	1c(897)	IP$_3$/Ca^{2+}	13	130	0.8	60						93
	mGluR5(1171)	IP$_3$/Ca^{2+}	10	50	0.3	10				QA > Glu ≈ Ibo > ACPD	1	1
II	mGluR2(872)	cAMP ↓	4	5	~1000	35	–		0.3	L-CCG-I > Glu ≈ ACPD > Ibo > QA	8	33, 121
	mGluR3(879)	cAMP ↓	3	8	40	10	–			Glu > ACPD ≈ Ibo > QA	4	122
III	mGluR4(912)	cAMP ↓	5	±	±	–	0.5	4	50	AP4 > SOP ≈ Glu > L-CCG-I	20	33, 122
	mGluR6(871)	cAMP ↓	16	+	±	±	0.9	2.7		AP4 > SOP > Glu	10	78
	mGluR7(915)	cAMP ↓	1000			160	160	160		AP4 ≈ SOP > Glu		89

[a] +, Fairly effective but no EC$_{50}$ value available; ±, weakly effective; –, not effective. Abbreviations used: Glu, L-glutamate; QA, quisqualate; Ibo, ibotenate; SOP, L-serine-O-phosphate; L-CCG-I, (2S,1'S,2'S)-2-(carboxycyclopropyl)glycine.
[b] Data from Ref. 55.

Table 4 Structures and properties of other glutamate receptors and glutamate receptor–related proteins

Group	Names (amino acids)	Electrophysiological response and ligand binding	References
Function unknown	Rat, delta-1 (1013), mouse, δ-1 (1009)	No response	58, 137
	Rat, delta-2 (1009)	No response	58
Kainate-binding protein (KBP)	Frog, KBP (487)	^{3}H-kainate binding ($K_d = 5.6$ nM)	130
	Chick, KBP (487)	No response	29
Glutamate-binding protein (GluBP)	Rat, pGB-A2 (516)	^{3}H-glutamate binding ($K_d = 263$ nM) No response	54
Invertebrate glutamate receptors	*Drosophila melanogaster,* DGluR-I (991)	Response to KA ($EC_{50} = 75$ μM)	127
	D. melanogaster, DGluR-II (906)	Response to Glu ($EC_{50} = 35$ mM), Asp ($EC_{50} = 50$ mM)	107
	D. melanogaster, DNMDAR-I (997)	Weak response to glycine ($EC_{50} = 60$ μM) but not to Glu	126
	Lymnaea stagnalis, lGluR (917)	No response	42

heteromeric receptors for kainate, none of them showed any appreciable binding to ^{3}H-kainate (50). Antibodies raised against the cloned GluR1–GluR4 subunits immunoprecipitated a substantial amount of ^{3}H-AMPA binding but not any ^{3}H-kainate binding in membranes isolated from the rat brain (134). Thus, the receptors composed of the GluR1–GluR4 subunits are clearly AMPA selective.

GluR5–GluR7 and KA-1/KA-2 are classified as the second and the third subgroups of the AMPA/kainate receptors, respectively (7, 8, 22, 34, 48, 59, 75, 103, 113, 136). The homomeric expression of each subunit of both the GluR5–GluR7 subgroup and the KA-1/KA-2 subgroup in cultured cells showed ^{3}H-kainate binding with K_d values of 40–90 nM and 5–15 nM, respectively (8, 34, 48, 59, 113, 136). The GluR5–GluR7 and KA-1/KA-2 subgroups are thought to correspond to the low-affinity and high-affinity kainate-binding sites in the brain membranes, respectively (70, 139). Homomeric receptors composed of GluR5 and GluR6 evoked kainate responses in *X. laevis* oocytes or cultured cells, but those of GluR7, KA-1, and KA-2 did not (8, 22, 34, 59, 75, 103,

113, 136). The latter subunits may undergo rapid desensitization, may need other subunits to make functional heteromers, or may not be expressed functionally in heterologous expression systems.

NMDA RECEPTORS   The NMDA receptors consist of five different subunits. NR1 forms a functional homomeric receptor channel in *X. laevis* oocytes and shows all the properties characteristic of the NMDA receptors (49, 76, 138). This single NR1 polypeptide exhibits a voltage-dependent Mg^{2+} block, high Ca^{2+} permeability, potentiation by a low concentration of glycine, specific responses to various NMDA receptor agonists and antagonists, inhibition by Zn^{2+}, and activation by polyamines (49, 76, 138). In contrast to NR1, none of the four other subunits, termed NR2A–NR2D, showed any receptor-channel activity in a homomeric configuration or any heteromeric expression within the members of the NR2 subunits (44, 45, 56, 66, 72). However, the combined expression of individual NR2 subunits with NR1 markedly potentiated current responses to NMDA or glutamate (44, 45, 56, 66, 72) and produced the variability in NMDA receptor properties, as discussed in more detail below (44, 45, 56, 66, 72).

METABOTROPIC GLUTAMATE RECEPTORS   The mGluR family consists of at least seven distinct subtypes, termed mGluR1–mGluR7, which are subdivided into three subgroups on the basis of their sequence similarities, signal transduction mechanisms, and agonist selectivities (81, 89). They show 60-70% similarity within the same subgroup and about 40% similarity between different subgroups (81, 89). The signal transduction and agonist selectivities of individual subtypes as revealed in cultured cells by using DNA transfection and subsequent expression of each receptor subtype are as follows: mGluR1 and mGluR5 are coupled to the inositol trisphosphate $(IP_3)/Ca^{2+}$ signaling pathway and are potently activated by quisqualate (1, 2, 40, 63). The other five mGluR subtypes are coupled to the inhibition of the cAMP cascade (78, 89, 121, 122). mGluR2 and mGluR3 potently respond to *trans*-1-aminocyclopentane-1,3-dicarboxylate (ACPD), whereas mGluR4, mGluR6, and mGluR7 effectively interact with L-AP4 (78, 89, 121, 122). Recently, both ACPD and L-AP4 were found to inhibit cAMP formation in many neuronal cells and slice preparations (105). Furthermore, these compounds inhibit excitatory synaptic transmission by reducing glutamate release at the presynaptic site (105). The latter two subgroups correspond to the ACPD-sensitive and L-AP4-sensitive receptors, respectively.

OTHER RELATED PROTEINS   With molecular cloning, several other proteins were isolated as glutamate receptors, but have not yet been explicitly elucidated. Two mutually related proteins, termed delta-1 and delta-2, were isolated by cross-hybridization with the GluR1–GluR4 cDNAs or PCR amplification techniques (58, 137). Delta-1 and delta-2 show a significant homology with the other ionotropic receptors, including their large N-terminal regions, but show no specific current nor any appreciable binding to either ^{3}H-kainate or ^{3}H-AMPA, when expressed individually or together, or in combination with other ionotropic receptor subunits (58, 137). Therefore, the functions of delta-1 and delta-2 await clarification.

A different strategy for molecular cloning of ionotropic glutamate receptors is based on protein purification and subsequent cloning either by hybridization with oligonucleotides predicted from partial protein sequencing or by immunoscreening. Curiously, however, several proteins identified through this strategy were much smaller than, and different in many properties from, the ionotropic receptors described above. The small kainate-binding proteins (KBPs) were cloned from chick cerebellum and frog brain (29, 130). The KBPs showed a high sequence similarity with the AMPA/kainate receptors (29, 130). When the frog KBP was expressed in cultured cells, it exhibited a specific binding to ^{3}H-kainate. Various glutamate analogues with a rank order of potencies similar to those of GluR5–GluR7 displaced this binding (130). However, the KBP expressed in *X. laevis* oocytes showed no detectable electrophysiological response to any agonists (130). It is thus not certain whether the KBP requires other subunits to make an active form of the glutamate receptors or if it represents a different entity that possesses a distinct role other than the glutamate-gated channel function. Another small glutamate-binding protein was also purified and cloned from the rat brain (54). This purified protein, when incorporated into liposomes together with other putative subunit components, exhibits many properties characteristic of the NMDA receptor and was thought to represent a subunit component of the NMDA receptor-channel complex (60). However, the predicted protein sequence showed no similarity with any ionotropic receptors, nor did this protein evoke any response in *X. laevis* oocytes (54). Thus, the function of all of the small glutamate-binding proteins remains unknown.

Alternative Splicing

The diversity of the glutamate receptors results from the effective use of alternative splicing mechanisms. Before discussing these mechanisms in detail, we briefly describe the fundamental structures of the ionotropic receptors and metabotropic receptors. The hydrophobicity analysis indicated that all of the subunits of the AMPA/kainate and NMDA receptors have five hydrophobic segments, one at the N terminus that serves as a signal peptide, and four at the C-terminal side, which represents four transmembrane segments (TM1–TM4) (26, 81, 128). This hydrophobicity profile agrees with those of other ligand-gated ion channels such as the well-defined nicotinic acetylcholine receptors (9, 26, 128). Thus, both the AMPA/kainate and NMDA receptors were postulated to comprise four transmembrane segments with extracellular domains at both the N and C termini (Figure 1) (9, 26, 81, 128). Analogous to the nicotinic-receptor findings, evidence also indicates that TM2 is involved in channel-pore formation (14, 19, 41,

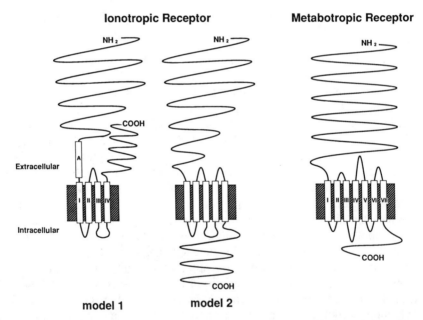

Figure 1 Transmembrane models of the ionotropic receptor subunits and the mGluR subtypes. Two models of the ionotropic receptors have been predicted, depending on whether the C terminus is placed on the extracellular side (model 1) or on the intracellular side (model 2). In model 1, two different assignments of four putative transmembrane segments have been proposed. One model predicts membrane-spanning domains consisting of four hydrophobic segments I, II, III, and IV (model 1A), while the other holds a different arrangement composed of segments A, I, III, and IV (model 1B). Transmembrane segment II of model 1A was evidenced to form a channel pore. In model 2, the number of transmembrane segments remains undefined. A model structure of the mGluR consisting of seven transmembrane segments with a large N-terminal extracellular domain and an intracellular C tail is generally accepted.

indicates that TM2 is involved in channel-pore formation (14, 19, 41, 129). However, several recent studies presented evidence contrary to (though without proof) the above structural architecture of the iono-tropic receptors and suggested that the C terminus following the TM4 segment is located on the cytoplasmic side. For the readers' conve-nience, however, the following discussion is based on a model structure (model 1A, Figure 1), in which the ionotropic receptors comprise four transmembrane segments with their N- and C-terminal regions on the extracellular side. All mGluR subtypes contain seven transmembrane segments (TM1–TM7) with an N-terminal domain on the extracellular side and a C-terminal tail on the cytoplasmic side (Figure 1). Therefore the mGluR family probably shares a common structural architecture with other members of G protein–coupled receptors (81, 105).

The splice variants of the AMPA-selective GluR1–GluR4 subunits, designated flip and flop, are generated by alternative splicing in the sequence between the TM3 and TM4 segments of these subunits (114). The flip and flop region spans 38 amino acid residues encoded on ad-jacent exons (114). The two splice isoforms of all GluR1–GluR4 sub-units showed no apparent difference in their agonist selectivity, but the glutamate-evoking steady-state current following a rapidly desen-sitizing current was much higher in the flip form than in the flop form (114). The expression sites and ontogeny were also found to be different between the flip and flop forms (71, 114).

The NR1 gene consists of 22 exons, spanning about 24 kilobase pairs (37). Alternative RNA splicing of this gene generates eight receptor isoforms that arise from splicing in or out of three alternative exons corresponding to exons 5, 21, and 22 (20, 37, 117). Exon 5 encodes 21 amino acids that can be inserted into the N-terminal domain, while exons 21 and 22 encode 37 and 38 amino acid residues that correspond to the last portion of the C terminus (20, 37, 117). The splicing out of exon 22 removes the stop codon present in the major isoform of NR1 and thus generates an unrelated C-terminal sequence of 22 amino acid residues (20, 37, 117). The homomeric receptors lacking an N-terminal insert expressed in $X.$ $laevis$ oocytes showed a high affinity for both glutamate and glycine and are markedly potentiated by a polyamine (20, 21, 79). These variants were activated by a submicromolar con-centration of Zn^{2+} and thus differed from the NR1 isoforms containing an insert, with which a low concentration of Zn^{2+} had no effect on NMDA response (37). The NR1 isoform lacking C-terminal insertions showed marked activity potentiation by protein kinase C (PKC) phos-phorylation (20, 21).

Alternative splicing also occurs in the C-terminal, cytoplasmic region of mGluR1 and generates three different isoforms, mGluR1α, mGluR1β, and mGluR1c (93, 121). All three splice isoforms are coupled to the same IP$_3$/Ca^{2+} second messenger with the same agonist selectivity (2, 40, 63, 92, 93, 121). However, mGluR1α comprises a large C-terminal sequence possessing several possible regulatory sites including phosphorylation sites and the SH3-binding consensus sequence (40, 63, 100), whereas mGluR1β and mGluR1c lack these characteristic sequences (93, 121). Furthermore, mGluR1α and mGluR1β /1c show different expression patterns; for example, mGluR1α predominates in the cerebellar Purkinje cells, whereas mGluR1β /1c is prominent in hippocampal pyramidal cells (24, 61). Alternative splicing of many other glutamate receptors, however, remains to be investigated.

RNA Editing

The third mechanism generating diversity of the glutamate receptors was uncovered by an unexpected observation that an amino acid critical for the channel conductance and ion permeability can be modified by an RNA-editing mechanism, the enzyme-directed, posttranscriptional change of a certain nucleotide of RNA transcripts. Among the AMPA-selective subunits, GluR2 is a key subunit that determines the current-voltage (I-V) relation and the Ca^{2+} permeability (14, 38). The homomeric GluR2 channel and the heteromeric assemblies containing GluR2 show a near-linear I-V relation and only weak Ca^{2+} permeability (12, 14, 38, 80). In contrast, the heteromeric assemblies lacking this subunit display a nonlinear I-V relation and a substantial Ca^{2+} permeability (12, 14, 38, 80). The presence of arginine at the TM2 segment of GluR2 characterizes this subunit; thus it differs from other subunits that contain glutamine at the corresponding position (14, 19, 41, 129). A glutamine codon (CAG) is encoded at the glutamine/arginine position in the genomic sequences for the GluR1–GluR6 subunits, even though an arginine codon (CGG) is found in cDNA sequences of the GluR2, GluR5, and GluR6 subunits (115). Thus, an RNA editing mechanism that alters adenosine to guanosine occurs posttranscriptionally in these RNA transcripts and determines the channel properties of the receptors containing these subunits.

Recently, RNA editing was also observed at two additional positions in the TM1 segment of GluR6—at one position with either isoleucine or valine and another with either tyrosine or cysteine (52). In contrast to GluR2, the presence of glutamine in the TM2 segment reportedly governs a low Ca^{2+} permeability, whereas arginine at this position determines a higher Ca^{2+} permeability if TM1 is fully edited (52). The combination of edited and unedited forms of GluR6 produces more diverse properties of the resultant receptor protein (52). Thus, RNA editing mechanisms play an important role in the generation of the functional diversity at least in the AMPA/kainate receptors.

A mammalian RNA-editing mechanism was first reported for apolipoprotein B (apo B) (36). Liver cells synthesize a large form of this protein, apo B100, whereas RNA editing of a CAA (Gln) to produce a UAA (stop) codon in apo B transcripts results in a small form, apo B48, in the small intestine (36, 123). Recently, a cDNA clone encoding a cellular component essential for intestinal apo B mRNA editing was isolated and characterized (123). The involvement of the same editing machinery in AMPA/kainate receptor editing remains undetermined.

Heteromeric Formation

The nicotinic acetylcholine receptors are pentameric proteins composed of four different kinds of subunits (9, 84). Like the nicotinic acetylcholine receptors, the ionotropic glutamate receptors were predicted to form a heteromeric assembly of different subunits. Antibodies raised against each of the GluR1–GluR4 subunits could co-immunoprecipitate the other three forms of the GluR subunits from solubilized membrane fractions of the rat brain (135). In addition, the immunoaffinity purification of rat brain membranes by the GluR2/GluR3 antibody showed that the GluR1–GluR4 subunits but no additional receptor subunits were copurified, suggesting that the native AMPA-selective receptors are exclusively composed of the GluR1–GluR4 subunits (135). Cross-linkage of the GluR subunits in synaptic membrane, followed by immunoblot analysis with the GluR2/GluR3 antibody, identified an oligomeric protein that is about five times larger than the single subunit, supporting the view that the AMPA-selective receptor is assembled in a pentameric structure (135).

The heteromeric assemblies of the GluR1-GluR4 subunits were also evidenced by electrophysiological characterization of these subunits. Expression of a single subunit of the GluR1–GluR4 subgroup induced a glutamate response, but combined expressions of these subunits further potentiated this response (12, 50, 80, 102). Furthermore, two distinct types of the AMPA receptors were characterized electrophysiologically in different neuronal cells. The receptors that resemble those containing GluR2 were identified in many neuronal cells (43), and the receptors that correspond to those lacking GluR2 were observed in a small population of hippocampal neuronal cells (43), retinal bipolar cells (27), and cerebellar Bergmann glial cells (13, 77).

The heteromeric assemblies of the kainate-selective receptors have not yet been extensively investigated. The homomeric expression of GluR5(R) and KA-2 showed no responses to any agonists (34, 103, 113) [in this and subsequent statements, (Q) and (R) stand for an unedited (glutamine) and edited (arginine) form of the receptor subunits]. However, the heteromeric expression of GluR5(R) and KA-2 induced clear kainate responses (34). In addition, the heteromeric expression of KA-2 with GluR5(Q) showed a kainate response whose desensitization kinetics were much faster than that of the homomeric GluR5(Q) channel (34). Furthermore, coexpression of KA-2 with either GluR6(Q) or GluR6(R) evoked AMPA responses, in contrast to the insensitivity of the homomeric GluR6(Q) or GluR6(R) channel to AMPA (34, 103). Thus, although KA-2 and the GluR5/GluR6 subunits share a low degree of sequence similarity, heteromeric assemblies can form among at least some of the subunits belonging to the kainate-selective subunits.

The NR2 subunits not only markedly potentiate the activity of NR1 but also confer some differences in responsiveness to agonists, antagonists, and open channel blockers (44, 45, 56, 72). The rank order of affinities for glutamate and glycine is NR2D/NR1 > NR2C/NR1 > NR2B/NR1 > NR2A/NR1, whereas the sensitivities to the NMDA receptor antagonist D-($-$)-2-amino-5-phosphonovalerate (AP5) and to Mg^{2+} block are ranked in the opposite oder (44). Furthermore, the single current conductances and their frequencies of the NR1/NR2A or NR1/NR2B channel and the NR1/NR2C channel agreed well with those characterized in hippocampal neuronal cells and large cultured cerebellar neuronal cells, respectively (116). NR1 may also form heteromeric assemblies containing more than two different NR2 subunits. Thus, the diversity of the ionotropic glutamate receptors is clearly generated at the level of heteromeric assemblies of different subunits.

Expression Pattern

Numerous in situ hybridization and immunohistochemical studies have been conducted and are still going on. This section discusses only interesting and important aspects of glutamate-receptor expression. The reader can find references to many important papers elsewhere (24, 61, 62, 68, 71, 87, 88, 90, 101, 109).

The different subunits or subtypes of glutamate receptors show different expression patterns in neuronal cells and glial cells. For example, NR1 mRNA is expressed in almost all neuronal cells (72, 76). In contrast, the NR2 mRNAs show overlapping but different expression patterns in various brain regions (45, 56, 72). The properties of the NMDA receptors characterized in different brain regions agree with those of the heteromeric assemblies predicted from the expression patterns of individual subunits (69). The anatomical and functional differences of the NR2 subunits thus provide at least some molecular basis for the diversity of the NMDA receptors.

The relation between the mRNA expression site and the receptor localization in individual neuronal cells is not as simple as expected. For example, there are some disparities between the radioligand binding sites of the NMDA receptors and the expression sites of NR1 mRNA. Autoradiographic and electrophysiological studies also suggested that the AMPA receptors and the NMDA receptors are colocalized in many neuronal cells and are clearly segregated in the distribution pattern from the kainate receptors (70, 139). In fact, the mRNAs for the AMPA-selective subunits and the NMDA receptor subunits are commonly expressed in many neuronal cells. However, the mRNAs encoding the kainate-selective subunits also overlap with the mRNAs for the AMPA-selective subunits in many brain regions (7, 34, 59, 136). Whether or not the observed discrepancy can be explained by the heterogenous nature of heteromeric assemblies of the different subunits largely remains to be determined.

Antibodies specific for different receptor subunits or subtypes were recently produced, and immunohistochemical and immunoelectron-microscopic studies have just begun to address whether individual receptors are localized at a postsynaptic site, a presynaptic site, or elsewhere. For example, immunoelectron analysis indicated that the GluR1–GluR4 subunits are localized in cell bodies, dendrites, and dendritic spines of certain subsets of neurons (62, 68, 90, 101). The colocalization of GluR1 and GluR2/GluR3 is also reported at postsynaptic sites of cultured hippocampal neurons, indicating that the AMPA-selective receptors indeed mediate an excitatory postsynaptic transmission (18). In the mGluR family, the IP_3/Ca^{2+}-coupled mGluRs are thought to excite many neurons postsynaptically (105). In contrast, the L-AP4-sensitive or ACPD-sensitive mGluR subtypes reportedly presynaptically inhibit synaptic transmission (105). The immunoreactivity of both mGluR1α and mGluR5 was located at the postsynaptic site (61, 109a), whereas mGluR2 is immunopositive at the presynaptic site and regulates transmitter release (31). Interestingly, mGluR2 is found at both dendrites and axons of cerebellar Golgi cells (H Ohishi, in preparation), suggesting a different function of this receptor subtype. The colocalization of different receptors or the subcellular localization of many other receptors, however, requires further study.

STRUCTURES OF GLUTAMATE RECEPTORS

Transmembrane Topology

Because the hydrophobicity analysis of the amino acid sequences of both AMPA/kainate receptors and NMDA receptors shows a profile common to the other members of ligand-gated ion channels, these receptors are predicted to comprise four transmembrane segments preceded and followed by extracellular domains at both the N-terminal and C-terminal sides (9, 26, 81). However, the amino acid sequences of the glutamate receptors diverge far from those of the other ligand-gated ion channels, prompting two proposals for models for the transmembrane arrangements in the ionotropic receptors, both of which assume four transmembrane-spanning domains (26, 81). Three of the putative transmembrane segments predicted by these two models are the same, but one model (model 1B) predicts that the three common transmembrane segments are C-terminal to a first transmembrane segment. The other (model 1A) holds that the different transmembrane segment precedes the second common transmembrane segment (Figure 1) (reviewed in 26).

The antibody raised against the N-terminal portion of GluR1 supported the above models, which localized the large N-terminal region on the extracellular side (68). However, recent evidence controverts the above two models and suggests that the large C-terminal tail is located on the intracellular side: (a) Immunoelectron microscopic analysis using the antibody to the C-terminal end of GluR1 placed this region on the cytoplasmic side of the membrane (62, 68, 90). (b) Most of the PKC phosphorylation sites are present in the C-terminal domain following the putative fourth transmembrane segment of the NR1 and probably NR2 subunits (74, 124). (c) Electrophysiological studies also suggested that the channel-forming transmembrane segment of the glutamate receptors, unlike the other ligand-gated ion channels, could traverse the membrane from the extracellular side to the intracellular side (19). These findings have led to the proposal of several new models in which the C terminus is intracellular rather than extracellular, as exemplified in model 2 in Figure 1 (74, 107a, 124). More direct evidence is required for the elucidation of the number of transmembrane segments, the sidedness, and the topology of the ionotropic receptors. In this review, however, we base our discussion on model 1A, assuming the presence of four transmembrane segments.

The mGluR family also exhibits a unique structure among the members of G protein–coupled receptors. This family shares no sequence similarity with any other members of the G protein–coupled receptors and contains a large hydrophilic sequence following a hydrophobic sequence at the N-terminal end and preceding seven hydrophobic segments at the C-terminal side. The mGluR family thus contains seven membrane-spanning domains preceded by a large extracellular N-terminal domain and followed by an intracellular C-terminal tail (81, 105).

Glutamate-Binding Domain

mGluR1 and mGluR2 have similar affinities for glutamate but respond in distinct patterns to quisqualate, ACPD, and (2S,1'R,2'R,3'R)-2-(2,3-dicarboxycyclopropyl)glycine (DCG-IV) (2, 31, 121). A series of chimeric receptors at the extracellular N-terminal domains of mGluR1 and mGluR2 was constructed, and changes in the agonist selectivities of the resultant chimeric receptors were then determined in *X. laevis* oocytes (120). This study demonstrated that about half of the N-terminal extracellular domain of mGluR is a determinant for the agonist selectivity of this receptor family, suggesting that this region is responsible for glutamate binding (120). An elegant computer-aided sequence analysis of mGluR independently reached the same conclusion (86). This analysis indicated that the N-terminal domain of mGluR and a number of bacterial periplasmic amino acid–binding proteins significantly share various structural parameters, including the presence of common hydrophobic cores, a similar distribution of hydrophobic residues, a sequence similarity in regions of helices and sheets, the absence of charged residues in buried regions, and a confined location of polar residues in surface regions. A structural model of the glutamate-binding site of mGluR was constructed on the basis of the above structural similarity by referring to the known tertiary structure of the bacterial amino acid–binding proteins (86). The validity of this model was confirmed by mutational analysis, in which ^{3}H-glutamate binding was abolished by substitutions of some amino acids (Ala165 and Ala188 in mGluR1) (86) in the putative glutamate-binding domain. The G protein–coupled receptors for small-molecule ligands such as adrenaline all possess small extracellular N-terminal domains and react with the corresponding ligands in their transmembrane pockets (85). Thus, the mode of ligand binding of mGluR differs from that of other G protein–coupled receptors interacting with small molecule transmitters.

The above computer-aided sequence analysis also revealed that two separate regions of the ionotropic receptors are related to the sequences of two kinds of bacterial amino acid–binding proteins (86). One homologous sequence corresponds to the sequence previously reported to share sequence similarity with the *Escherichia coli* glutamine-binding protein (80, 86). Mutational analysis in which certain amino acid substitutions of GluR1 reduced a glutamate-induced channel activity (125) also predicted that this region was a glutamate-bindng site. This homologous sequence is split into two portions by the putative TM1–TM3 segments. The other homologous sequence is located at the N-terminal half of the extracellular domain of the ionotropic receptors

(86). Because glutamate and glycine are required for the activation of the NMDA receptors, two binding sites may recognize these two amino acids (86). The putative extracellular glutamate-binding domains of both mGluRs and ionotropic receptors may be produced in soluble forms by recombinant DNA techniques. Thus, X-ray crystallography may be applied for resolution of tertiary structures in the glutamate-binding domains.

Channel Pore

Because GluR2 differentiates the current conductance and Ca^{2+} permeability of the AMPA-selective receptors, several laboratories studied a channel-forming transmembrane region by constructing a chimeric channel between GluR1 and GluR2 and by creating point mutations of particular amino acids on the basis of the sequence comparison of these receptors' subunits (11, 14, 19, 41, 129). These studies led to the conclusion that glutamine/arginine at the TM2 segment is a critical determinant of both Ca^{2+} permeability and the rectification property of the AMPA receptor-channels (11, 14, 19, 41, 129). Furthermore, replacement of arginine in the TM2 segment of GluR1 with asparagine resulted in a high Ca^{2+} permeability and blockade by Mg^{2+} (14), both of which are reminiscent of the NMDA receptors as described below. The arginine/glutamine at this position is a site responsible for blockade by the channel blocker Argiotoxin$_{636}$ (35).

All the NMDA receptor subunits contain asparagine at the position corresponding to glutamine or arginine of the TM2 segment of the AMPA/kainate receptors (44, 45, 49, 56, 66, 72, 76, 138). Systematic substitutions of single amino acids at the TM2 segment of NR1 or mutations of asparagines in different NR subunits were carried out to investigate the structural features that control Ca^{2+} permeation and channel blockade of the NMDA receptors (15, 73, 104). Substitutions of the asparagine of NR1 with glutamine and arginine reduced and abolished, respectively, both the Ca^{2+} permeability and the sensitivity to blockades by Mg^{2+} and the channel blocker MK801 (15, 73, 104). These observations demonstrate that the TM2 segment of NR1 forms part of the channel lining of the NMDA receptors. The above mutations of NR1 also altered the inhibitory effects of Zn^{2+}, the antidepressant desipiramine, and Argiotoxin$_{636}$, indicating that these inhibitors act at least partly as open channel blockers of the NMDA receptors (97, 104). The same substitutions of NR2A and NR2C with glutamine similarly reduced the Mg^{2+} blockade (15), indicating that the homologous asparagines in the NR2 subunits also form a channel pore. However, these mutations barely affected Ca^{2+} permeability. Asparagines of different NR subunits may be asymmetrically arranged in the channel pore and may thus contribute to distinct properties of the different NR2 subunits (15). All the above studies demonstrate that the TM2 segments of both AMPA/kainate receptors and NMDA receptors contain common structural motifs that form channel pores and control ion selectivity and channel conductance properties.

Phosphorylation Site

In glutamate transmission, the Ca^{2+} entry and subsequent activation of Ca^{2+}-dependent protein kinases are thought to be important for the induction of both LTP and LTD (10, 46). In one study, the targeted disruption of the α-Ca^{2+}/calmodulin-dependent kinase II gene abolished the induction of LTP and impaired spatial memory in mutant mice (110, 111), although the linkage of this enzyme in glutamate transmission is not yet well understood. Also, treatment of neuronal cells with phorbol ester reduced the sensitivity of the NMDA receptor to voltage-dependent Mg^{2+} blockade (16), and the PKC phosphorylation may be important in controlling synaptic plasticity (16).

Many of the glutamate receptors have consensus sequences for regulatory phosphorylations by protein kinase A (PKA), PKC, and Ca^{2+}/calmodulin-dependent kinase, and reports on the phosphorylation and regulation of glutamate receptors have recently accumulated (16, 98). The activation of PKA in $X.$ $laevis$ oocytes or transfected cells expressing the GluR1/GluR3 heteromeric receptor or the GluR6 homomeric receptor increased kainate-evoked currents (51). Mutations of the PKA consensus sequence (Ser666 and Ser684) at the second intracellular loop of GluR6 abolished the enhancement of the channel activity, suggesting that the PKA phosphorylation controls the channel activity of GluR6 (99, 132).

In the mouse NMDA receptors, phorbol ester markedly potentiated the NR1/NR2A and NR1/NR2B heteromeric receptors, but not the NR1/NR2C receptor, in $X.$ $laevis$ oocytes (56). The region responsible for different modulation by phorbol ester was assigned to the C-terminal portion of the NR2 subunits on the basis of the analysis of chimeric channels made between the NR2B and NR2C subunits (74). Phorbol ester also activated the homomeric NR1 receptor expressed in $X.$ $laevis$ oocytes, and the degree of this activation depended on the alternatively spliced isoforms of the NR1 subunit (20, 21). Most of the PKC phosphorylation sites are reportedly contained within a single alternatively spliced exon in the C-terminal region of NR1 (124). Thus, alternative splicing of the NR1 subunit not only confers the variability in NR1's channel properties but also distinguishes the PKC activation of the resultant receptors (124). Work on the phosphorylation of glutamate receptors has begun only recently, and our understanding of

the physiological role of the phosphorylation of glutamate receptors
will no doubt soon expand.

Other Possible Regulatory Sites

Both ionotropic and metabotropic receptors possess extremely large
extracellular domains that precede the putative membrane-spanning
domains. Thus, these regions may have some functions other than glutamate binding. In fact, the sequence in the middle portion of the extracellular domain of NR1 shows a significant sequence similarity with
the fatty acid-binding proteins (91). Analogous to the nicotinic acetylcholine receptors (129a, 140), the N-terminal portions may also participate in subunit assembly. The mGluR family is also unique in that
all mGluR subtypes possess a cluster of cysteine residues between the
putative glutamate-binding domain and the TM1 segment (86, 89). In
addition, mGluR1α and mGluR5 have large C-terminal cytoplasmic
regions composed of ~350 amino acids following the TM7 segment.
This region of mGluR1α possesses clusters of peculiar amino acid sequences including stretches of glutamine/proline and glutamic acid/as-
partic acid (40, 63). One of the proline-rich sequences agrees well with
the consensus sequence of the SH3-binding domain (100). Because
mGluR5 lacks the above peculiar sequences in the large C-terminal
region (1), mGluR1α and mGluR5, though coupled to the same IP_3/
Ca^{2+} signal transduction, may undergo different intracellular signaling
regulation.

IMPLICATIONS OF GLUTAMATE RECEPTOR DIVERSITY AND FUTURE PROSPECTS

Recent molecular characterization has revealed that the glutamate receptors are more diversified than previously evisioned. However, this
diversity is not unique among the receptor families of both ligand-gated
ion channels and G protein–coupled receptors (9, 85, 106). However,
the amino acid sequences of both ionotropic and metabotropic receptors markedly differ from the sequences of the other members of the
corresponding receptors. The following evolutionary events can account for this difference: both types of the glutamate receptors diverged
from the primordial receptors at a very early stage during evolution;
the rate of evolution of glutamate receptors was very rapid for some
unknown reasons; and convergence rather than divergence occurred
in the evolution of glutamate receptors. Because there is no particular
reason for either rapid evolution or convergence in forms of glutamate
receptors, the early evolutionary divergence of glutamate receptors is
the more easily accepted hypothesis. Whatever the explanation, the

observed differences in the glutamate receptors could reflect the specialization of some mechanisms underlying the functions of this receptor family. In fact, in contrast to the other small transmitter receptors, the N-terminal extracellular domain of mGluR is involved in binding to glutamate. In addition, the transmembrane topology of the ionotropic glutamate receptors may not be the same as that of the other members of ligand-gated ion channels. Although this receptor family also uses mechanisms commonly found in other receptors, the specialization of the glutamate receptors deserves more careful consideration for understanding the function of glutamate transmission.

Both ionotropic and metabotropic receptors have been observed for the same transmitter. The ionotropic glutamate receptors correspond to the nicotinic acetylcholine receptors and the $GABA_A$ receptors, whereas the mGluRs match the muscarinic acetylcholine receptors and the $GABA_B$ receptors. The ionotropic glutamate receptors differ markedly from the acetylcholine and GABA receptors in that the ionotropic gluatamate receptors are further divided, functionally and structurally, into two distinct groups of the receptors. Because we now know that some of the AMPA/kainate receptors are also permeable to Ca^{2+}, the distinction between the AMPA/kainate receptors and NMDA receptors with respect to the Ca^{2+} permeability has become less clear. All NMDA receptor subunits, however, contain asparagine at a key position of the channel pore and allow large amounts of Ca^{2+} to permeate through the pore, regardless of the subunit compositions.

As evidenced by this high Ca^{2+} permeability, the NMDA receptors play an important role in many integrative functions of glutamate transmission. The NMDA receptors are essential in inducing LTP in the hippocampus (10). The NMDA receptors are also important in refinement of synaptic connections in the developing visual system (28). Recently, these receptors were shown to be involved in synaptic elimination to establish specific connections between climbing fibers and Purkinje cells during cerebellar development (96). These receptors also regulate the migration of granule cells in the developing cerebellum (53). Although the role of mGluRs has not yet been well characterized, the functional cooperation of the AMPA/kainate receptors and mGluRs seems to be required for evoking LTD in Purkinje cells of the cerebellum (46). Furthermore, a recent study showed that mGluR participates in the induction of both NMDA receptor-dependent and NMDA receptor-independent forms of LTP in the hippocampus (4). Therefore, NMDA receptors and mGluRs might regulate excitatory transmission that is basically mediated through the AMPA/kainate receptors. Although this explanation may be oversimplified, important future investigations will examine what sorts of cooperative functions of different glutamate receptors are involved in the physiological functions of excitatory transmission.

Further investigation of the precise expression sites, intracellular localization, timing of expression, and regulation of individual receptor subtypes or subunits is essential for addressing the above questions. In fact, evidence indicating a specific role of a certain receptor subunit or subtype in glutamate transmission has been reported. The involvement of the NMDA receptors in neuronal cell death and survival has been characterized in detail in primary cultures of neonatal cerebellar granule cells by treatment with either high KCl depolarization or NMDA treatment (3). These treatments purportedly mimic the physiological stimulation of immature cerebellar granule cells during cerebellar development (3). Both treatments were known to induce the functional NMDA receptor (3), and a recent study has shown that this induction results from a specific up-regulation of NR2A mRNA among the different NMDA receptor subunits (6). Because the expression of NR2C mRNA predominates in adult granule cells (45, 56, 72), subunit switching of the NMDA recceptors may change the properties of granule cells and may thus be important in the development of granule cells (3). Another example of a specific expression of a receptor subtype is observed for mGluR6 (78) that probably participates in synaptic transmission between photoreceptor cells and ON-bipolar cells in the visual system (82, 108). Thus, more complete knowledge of the expression and regulation of a particular receptor subunit or subtype is prerequisite for understanding glutamate-mediated neuronal functions.

Glutamate was believed to act exclusively as an excitatory transmitter. ACPD and L-AP4, however, have been found to suppress synaptic transmission by inhibiting glutamate release in many neuronal pathways (105). It now turns out that the ACPD-sensitive and L-AP4-sensitive receptors correspond to mGluR2/mGluR3 and mGluR4/mGluR7, respectively. Thus, these mGluR subtypes appear to represent the autoreceptors that regulate glutamate release at the presynaptic sites. In fact, mGluR2 immunoreactivity has been found at the presynaptic sites in some neuronal cells (31). Also, the suppressive effect of ACPD and L-AP4 on glutamate release is reportedly mediated by inhibition of Ca^{2+} channels (105), though this mechanism still remains largely elusive. In the accessory olfactory bulb, mGluR2 is present at the granule cell dendrites and presynaptically suppresses inhibitory GABA transmission from granule cells to mitral cells (31). A granule cell forms typical divergent dendrodendritic synapses with numerous surrounding mitral cells. The above characterization of mGluR2 led to the proposal that the mGluR2 activation relieves an excited mitral cell from GABA inhibition but maintains the lateral inhibition of unexcited mitral cells, thus enhancing the signal-to-noise ratio between the excited mitral cells and their neighboring mitral cells. The results discussed here suggest that different glutamate receptors effectively cooperate in modulating the microcircuity between neuronal cells. Further investigation of the role of glutamate receptors in the modulation of not only glutamate transmission but also of other transmissions is important.

Finally, the complex functions of glutamate receptors need to be studied by a combination of different techniques and methods. Antisense techniques were used to investigate the involvement of NR1 in neuronal cell death in both cultured cells and ischemic animals (131). The microapplication method of a virus vector containing the GluR6 cDNA was used to define the role of this receptor in neurotoxicity in hippocampal pyramidal cells (5). The development of specific agonists and antagonists is also important, and new agonists and antagonists for mGluRs were effectively used for the examination of specific functions of these receptors (4, 31–33). A combination of PCR techniques with electrophysiology is useful for identification of a specific receptor in a single neuronal cell (57). Gene targeting of glutamate receptors will also provide new insight into the role of particular glutamate receptors in brain functions and dysfunction. On the basis of our knowledge of the molecular nature of different glutamate receptors, further studies of these receptors will undoubtedly be interesting and important for a better understanding of brain functions.

ACKNOWLEDGMENTS

We thank many people for sending copies of published and unpublished papers. We are specially grateful to GL Collingridge, T Honoré, RL Huganir, PH Seeburg, and S Zukin for access to unpublished work. This work was supported by research grants from the Ministry of Education, Science, and Culture of Japan and the Ministry of Health and Welfare.

Literature Cited

1. Abe T, Sugihara H, Nawa H, Shigemoto R, Mizuno N, Nakanishi S. 1992. Molecular characterization of a novel metabotropic glutamate receptor

mGluR5 coupled to inositol phosphate/ Ca^{2+} signal transduction. *J. Biol. Chem.* 267:13361–68
2. Aramori I, Nakanishi S. 1992. Signal

transduction and pharmacological characteristics of a metabotropic glutamate receptor, mGluR1, in transfected CHO cells. *Neuron* 8:757–65

3. Balázs R, Hack N, Jørgensen OS. 1992. Cerebellar granule cells and the neurobiology of excitatory amino acids. In *The Cerebellum Revisited*, ed. R Llinás, C Sotelo, pp. 56-71. New York: Springer-Verlag

4. Bashir ZI, Bortolotto ZA, Davies CH, Berretta N, Irving AJ, et al. 1993. Induction of LTP in the hippocampus needs synaptic activation of glutamate metabotropic receptors. *Nature* 363: 347–50

5. Bergold PJ, Casaccia-Bonnefil P, Xiu-Liu Z, Federoff HJ. 1993. Transsynaptic neuronal loss induced in hippocampal slice cultures by a herpes simplex virus vector expressing the GluR6 subunit of the kainate receptor. *Proc. Natl. Acad. Sci. USA* 90:6165–69

6. Bessho Y, Nawa H, Nakanishi S. 1994. Selective up-regulation of an NMDA receptor subunit mRNA in cultured cerebellur granule cells by K^+-induced depolarization and NMDA treatment. *Neuron*. In press

7. Bettler B, Boulter J, Hermans-Borgmeyer I, O'Shea-Greenfield A, Deneris ES, et al. 1990. Cloning of a novel glutamate receptor subunit, GluR5: expression in the nervous system during development. *Neuron* 5:583–95

8. Bettler B, Egebjerg J, Sharma G, Pecht G, Hermans-Borgmeyer I, et al. 1992. Cloning of a putative glutamate receptor: a low affinity kainate-binding subunit. *Neuron* 8:257–65

9. Betz H. 1990. Ligand-gated ion channels in the brain: the amino acid receptor superfamily. *Neuron* 5:383–92

10. Bliss TVP, Collingridge GL. 1993. A synaptic model of memory: long-term potentiation in the hippocampus. *Nature* 361:31–39

11. Bochet P, Dutriaux A, Lambolez B, Nalivaiko E, Rossier J, Prado de Carvalho L. 1991. A chimeric glutamate receptor subunit: discrete changes modify the properties of the channel. *Biochem. Biophys. Res. Commun.* 177:1183–87

12. Boulter J, Hollmann M, O'Shea-Greenfield A, Hartley M, Deneris E, et al. 1990. Molecular cloning and functional expression of glutamate receptor subunit genes. *Science* 249:1033–37

13. Burnashev N, Khodorova A, Jonas P, Helm PJ, Wisden W, et al. 1992. Calcium-permeable AMPA-kainate recep-

tors in fusiform cerebellar glial cells. *Science* 256:1566–70

14. Burnashev N, Monyer H, Seeburg PH, Sakmann B. 1992. Divalent ion permeability of AMPA receptor channels is dominated by the edited form of a single subunit. *Neuron* 8:189–98

15. Burnashev N, Schoepfer R, Monyer H, Ruppersberg JP, Günther W, et al. 1992. Control by asparagine residues of calcium permeability and magnesium blockade in the NMDA receptor. *Science* 257:1415–19

16. Chen L, Huang L-Y M. 1992. Protein kinase C reduces Mg^{2+} block of NMDA-receptor channels as a mechanism of modulation. *Nature* 356:521–23

17. Choi DW. 1992. Excitotoxic cell death. *J. Neurobiol.* 23:1261–76

18. Craig AM, Blackstone CD, Huganir RL, Banker G. 1993. The distribution of glutamate receptors in cultured rat hippocampal neurons: postsynaptic clustering of AMPA-selective subunits. *Neuron* 10:1055–68

19. Dingledine R, Hume RI, Heinemann SF. 1992. Structural determinants of barium permeation and rectification in non-NMDA glutamate receptor channels. *J. Neurosci.* 12:4080–87

20. Durand GM, Bennett MVL, Zukin RS. 1993. Splice variants of the *N*-methyl-D-aspartate receptor NR1 identify domains involved in regulation by polyamines and protein kinase C. *Proc. Natl. Acad. Sci. USA* 90:6731–35

21. Durand GM, Gregor P, Zheng X, Bennett MVL, Uhl GR, Zukin RS. 1992. Cloning of an apparent splice variant of the rat *N*-methyl-D-aspartate receptor NMDAR1 with altered sensitivity to polyamines and activators of protein kinase C. *Proc. Natl. Acad. Sci. USA* 89:9359–63

22. Egebjerg J, Bettler B, Hermans-Borgmeyer I, Heinemann S. 1991. Cloning of a cDNA for a glutamate receptor subunit activated by kainate but not AMPA. *Nature* 351:745–48

23. Eubanks JH, Puranam RS, Kleckner NW, Bettler B, Heinemann SF, McNamara JO. 1993. The gene encoding the glutamate receptor subunit GluR5 is located on human chromosome 21q21.1-22.1 in the vicinity of the gene for familial amyotrophic lateral sclerosis. *Proc. Natl. Acad. Sci. USA* 90:178–82

24. Fotuhi M, Sharp AH, Glatt CE, Hwang PM, von Krosigk M, et al. 1993. Differential localization of phos-

phoinositide-linked metabotropic glutamate receptor (mGluR1) and the inositol 1,4,5-trisphosphate receptor in rat brain. *J. Neurosci.* 13:2001–12
25. Gallo V, Upson LM, Hayes WP, Vyklicky L Jr, Winters CA, Buonanno A. 1992. Molecular cloning and developmental analysis of a new glutamate receptor subunit isoform in cerebellum. *J. Neurosci.* 12: 1010–23
26. Gasic GP, Hollmann M. 1992. Molecular neurobiology of glutamate receptors. *Annu. Rev. Physiol.* 54:507–36
27. Gilbertson TA, Scobey R, Wilson M. 1991. Permeation of calcium ions through non-NMDA glutamate channels in retinal bipolar cells. *Science* 251:1613–15
28. Goodman CS, Shatz CJ. 1993. Developmental mechanisms that generate precise patterns of neuronal connectivity. *Cell* 72/*Neuron* 10(suppl.):77–98
29. Gregor P, Mano I, Maoz I, McKeown M, Teichberg VI. 1989. Molecular structure of the chick cerebellar kainate-binding subunit of a putative glutamate receptor. *Nature* 342:689–92
30. Gregor P, Reeves RH, Jabs EW, Yang X, Dackowski W, et al. 1993. Chromosomal localization of glutamate receptor genes: relationship to familial amyotrophic lateral sclerosis and other neurological disorders of mice and humans. *Proc. Natl. Acad. Sci. USA* 90: 3053–57
31. Hayashi Y, Momiyama A, Takahashi T, Ohishi H, Ogawa-Meguro R, et al. 1993. Role of a metabotropic glutamate receptor in synaptic modulation in the accessory olfactory bulb. *Nature.* 366: 687–90
32. Hayashi Y, Sekiyama N, Nakanishi S, Jane DE, Sunter DC, et al. 1994. Analysis of agonist antagonist activities of phenylglycine derivatives for different cloned metabotropic glutamate receptor subtypes. *J. Neurosci.* In press
33. Hayashi Y, Tanabe Y, Aramori I, Masu M, Shimamoto K, et al. 1992. Agonist analysis of 2-(carboxycyclopropyl)glycine isomers for cloned metabotropic glutamate receptor subtypes expressed in Chinese hamster ovary cells. *Br. J. Pharmacol.* 107: 539–43
34. Herb A, Burnashev N, Werner P, Sakmann B, Wisden W, Seeburg PH. 1992. The KA-2 subunit of excitatory amino acid receptors shows widespread expression in brain and forms ion channels with distantly related subunits. *Neuron* 8:775–85

35. Herlitze S, Raditsch M, Ruppersberg JP, Jahn W, Monyer H, et al. 1993. Argiotoxin detects molecular differences in AMPA receptor channels. *Neuron* 10:1131–40
36. Hodges P, Scott J. 1992. Apolipoprotein B mRNA editing: a new tier for the control of gene expression. *Trends Biochem. Sci.* 17:77–81
37. Hollmann M, Boulter J, Maron C, Beasley L, Sullivan J, et al. 1993. Zinc potentiates agonist-induced currents at certain splice variants of the NMDA receptor. *Neuron* 10:943–54
38. Hollmann M, Hartley M, Heinemann S. 1991. Ca^{2+} permeability of KA-AMPA-gated glutamate receptor channels depends on subunit composition. *Science* 252:851–53
39. Hollmann M, O'Shea-Greenfield A, Rogers SW, Heinemann S. 1989. Cloning by functional expression of a member of the glutamate receptor family. *Nature* 342:643–48
40. Houamed KM, Kuijper JL, Gilbert TL, Haldeman BA, O'Hara PJ, et al. 1991. Cloning, expression, and gene structure of a G protein-coupled glutamate receptor from rat brain. *Science* 252:1318–21
41. Hume RI, Dingledine R, Heinemann SF. 1991. Identification of a site in glutamate receptor subunits that controls calcium permeability. *Science* 253: 1028–31
42. Hutton ML, Harvey RJ, Barnard EA, Darlison MG. 1991. Cloning of a cDNA that encodes an invertebrate glutamate receptor subunit. *FEBS Lett.* 292:111–14
43. Iino M, Ozawa S, Tsuzuki K. 1990. Permeation of calcium through excitatory amino acid receptor channels in cultured rat hippocampal neurones. *J. Physiol. (London)* 424:151–65
44. Ikeda K, Nagasawa M, Mori H, Araki K, Sakimura K, et al. 1992. Cloning and expression of the ε4 subunit of the NMDA receptor channel. *FEBS Lett.* 313:34–38
45. Ishii T, Moriyoshi K, Sugihara H, Sakurada K, Kadotani H, et al. 1993. Molecular characterization of the family of the N-methyl-D-aspartate receptor subunits. *J. Biol. Chem.* 268:2836–43
46. Ito M. 1989. Long-term depression. *Annu. Rev. Neurosci.* 12:85–102
47. Julius D, MacDermott AB, Axel R, Jessell TM. 1988. Molecular characterization of a functional cDNA encoding the serotonin 1c receptor. *Science* 241:558–64

48. Kamboj RK, Schoepp DD, Nutt S, Shekter L, Korczak B, et al. 1992. Molecular structure and pharmacological characterization of humEAA2, a novel human kainate receptor subunit. *Mol. Pharmacol.* 42:10–15

49. Karp SJ, Masu M, Eki T, Ozawa K, Nakanishi S. 1993. Molecular cloning and chromosomal localization of the key subunit of the human *N*-methyl-D-aspartate receptor. *J. Biol. Chem.* 268: 3728–33

50. Keinänen K, Wisden W, Sommer B, Werner P, Herb A, et al. 1990. A family of AMPA-selective glutamate receptors. *Science* 249:556–60

51. Keller BU, Hollmann M, Heinemann S, Konnerth A. 1992. Calcium influx through subunits GluR1/GluR3 of kainate/AMPA receptor channels is regulated by cAMP dependent protein kinase. *EMBO J.* 11:891–96

52. Köhler M, Burnashev N, Sakmann B, Seeburg PH. 1993. Determinants of Ca^{2+} permeability in both TM1 and TM2 of high affinity kainate receptor channels: diversity by RNA editing. *Neuron* 10:491–500

53. Komuro H, Rakic P. 1993. Modulation of neuronal migration by NMDA receptors. *Science* 260:95–97

54. Kumar KN, Tilakaratne N, Johnson PS, Allen AE, Michaelis EK. 1991. Cloning of cDNA for the glutamate-binding subunit of an NMDA receptor complex. *Nature* 354:70–73

55. Kuramoto T, Maihara T, Masu M, Nakanishi S, Serikawa T. 1994. Gene mapping of NMDA receptors and metabotropic glutamate receptors in the rat (*Rattus norvegicus*). *Genomics*. In press

56. Kutsuwada T, Kashiwabuchi N, Mori H, Sakimura K, Kushiya E, et al. 1992. Molecular diversity of the NMDA receptor channel. *Nature* 358:36–41

57. Lambolez B, Audinat E, Bochet P, Crépel F, Rossier J. 1992. AMPA receptor subunits expressed by single Purkinje cells. *Neuron* 9:247–58

58. Lomeli H, Sprengel R, Laurie DJ, Köhr G, Herb A, et al. 1993. The rat delta-1 and delta-2 subunits extend the excitatory amino acid receptor family. *FEBS Lett.* 315:318–22

59. Lomeli H, Wisden W, Köhler M, Keinänen K, Sommer B, Seeburg PH. 1992. High-affinity kainate and domoate receptors in rat brain. *FEBS Lett.* 307: 139–43

60. Ly AM, Michaelis EK. 1991. Solubilization, partial purification, and reconstitution of glutamate- and *N*-methyl-D-aspartate-activated cation channels from brain synaptic membranes. *Biochemistry* 30:4307–16

61. Martin LJ, Blackstone CD, Huganir RL, Price DL. 1992. Cellular localization of a metabotropic glutamate receptor in rat brain. *Neuron* 9:259–70

62. Martin LJ, Blackstone CD, Levey AI, Huganir RL, Price DL. 1993. AMPA glutamate receptor subunits are differentially distributed in rat brain. *Neuroscience* 53:327–58

63. Masu M, Tanabe Y, Tsuchida K, Shigemoto R, Nakanishi S. 1991. Sequence and expression of a metabotropic glutamate receptor. *Nature* 349: 760–65

64. Masu Y, Nakayama K, Tamaki H, Harada Y, Kuno M, Nakanishi S. 1987. cDNA cloning of bovine substance-K receptor through oocyte expression system. *Nature* 329:836–38

65. McNamara JO, Eubanks JH, McPherson JD, Wasmuth JJ, Evans GA, Heinemann SF. 1992. Chromosomal localization of human glutamate receptor genes. *J. Neurosci.* 12:2555–62

66. Meguro H, Mori H, Araki K, Kushiya E, Kutsuwada T, et al. 1992. Functional characterization of a heteromeric NMDA receptor channel expressed from cloned cDNAs. *Nature* 357:70–74

67. Meldrum B, Garthwaite J. 1990. Excitatory amino acid neurotoxicity and neurodegenerative disease. *Trends Phamacol. Sci.* 11:379–87

68. Molnár E, Baude A, Richmond SA, Patel PB, Somogyi P, McIlhinney RAJ. 1993. Biochemical and immunocytochemical characterization of antipeptide antibodies to a cloned GluR1 glutamate receptor subunit: cellular and subcellular distribution in the rat forebrain. *Neuroscience* 53:307–26

69. Monaghan DT, Anderson KJ. 1991. Heterogeneity and organization of excitatory amino acid receptors and transporters. In *Excitatory Amino Acids and Synaptic Transmission*, ed. HW Wheal, AM Thomson, pp. 33–54. San Diego: Academic

70. Monaghan DT, Bridges RJ, Cotman CW. 1989. The excitatory amino acid receptors: their classes, pharmacology, and distinct properties in the function of the central nervous system. *Annu. Rev. Pharmacol. Toxicol.* 29: 365–402

71. Monyer H, Seeburg PH, Wisden W. 1991. Glutamate-operated channels:

developmentally early and mature forms arise by alternative splicing. *Neuron* 6:799–810

72. Monyer H, Sprengel R, Schoepfer R, Herb A, Higuchi M, Lomeli H, et al. 1992. Heteromeric NMDA receptors: molecular and functional distinction of subtypes. *Science* 256:1217–21

73. Mori H, Masaki H, Yamakura T, Mishina M. 1992. Identification by mutagenesis of a Mg^{2+}-block site of the NMDA receptor channel. *Nature* 358: 673–75

74. Mori H, Yamakura T, Masaki H, Mishina M. 1993. Involvement of the carboxyl-terminal region in modulation by TPA of the NMDA receptor channel. *Neuroreport* 4:519–22

75. Morita T, Sakimura K, Kushiya E, Yamazaki M, Meguro H, et al. 1992. Cloning and functional expression of a cDNA encoding the mouse β2 subunit of the kainate-selective glutamate receptor channel. *Mol. Brain Res.* 14: 143–46

76. Moriyoshi K, Masu M, Ishii T, Shigemoto R, Mizuno N, Nakanishi S. 1991. Molecular cloning and characterization of the rat NMDA receptor. *Nature* 354:31–37

77. Müller T, Möller T, Berger T, Schnitzer J, Kettenmann H. 1992. Calcium entry through kainate receptors and resulting potassium-channel blockade in Bergmann glial cells. *Science* 256:1563–66

78. Nakajima Y, Iwakabe H, Akazawa C, Nawa H, Shigemoto R, et al. 1993. Molecular characterization of a novel retinal metabotropic glutamate receptor mGluR6 with a high agonist selectivity for L-2-amino-4-phosphonobutyrate. *J. Biol. Chem.* 268:11868–73

79. Nakanishi N, Axel R, Shneider NA. 1992. Alternative splicing generates functionally distinct N-methyl-D-aspartate receptors. *Proc. Natl. Acad. Sci. USA* 89:8552–56

80. Nakanishi N, Shneider NA, Axel R. 1990. A family of glutamate receptor genes: evidence for the formation of heteromultimeric receptors with distinct channel properties. *Neuron* 5: 569–81

81. Nakanishi S. 1992. Molecular diversity of glutamate receptors and implications for brain function. *Science* 258: 597–603

82. Nawy S, Jahr CE. 1990. Suppression by glutamate of cGMP-activated conductance in retinal bipolar cells. *Nature* 346:269–71

83. Nicoletti F, Iadarola MJ, Wroblewski JT, Costa E. 1986. Excitatory amino acid recognition sites coupled with inositol phospholipid metabolism: developmental changes and interaction with $α_1$-adrenoceptors. *Proc. Natl. Acad. Sci. USA* 83:1931–35

84. Numa S. 1989. A molecular view of neurotransmitter receptors and ionic channels. *Harvey Lect.* 83:121–65

85. O'Dowd BF, Lefkowitz RJ, Caron MG. 1989. Structure of the adrenergic and related receptors. *Annu. Rev. Neurosci.* 12:67–83

86. O'Hara PJ, Sheppard PO, Thøgersen H, Venezia D, Haldeman BA, et al. 1993. The ligand-binding domain in metabotropic glutamate receptors is related to bacterial periplasmic binding proteins. *Neuron* 11:41–52

87. Ohishi H, Shigemoto R, Nakanishi S, Mizuno N. 1993. Distribution of the messenger RNA for a metabotropic glutamate receptor, mGluR2, in the central nervous system of the rat. *Neuroscience* 53:1009–18

88. Ohishi H, Shigemoto R, Nakanishi S, Mizuno N. 1993. Distribution of the mRNA for a metabotropic glutamate receptor (mGluR3) in the rat brain: an in situ hybridization study. *J. Comp. Neurol.* 335:252–66

89. Okamoto N, Hori S, Akazawa C, Hayashi Y, Shigemoto R, et al. 1994. Molecular characterization of a new metabotropic glutamate receptor mGluR7 coupled to inhibitory cyclic AMP signal transduction. *J. Biol. Chem.* In press

90. Petralia RS, Wenthold RJ. 1992. Light and electron immunocytochemical localization of AMPA-selective glutamate receptors in the rat brain. *J. Comp. Neurol.* 318:329–54

91. Petrou S, Ordway RW, Singer JJ, Walsh JV Jr. 1993. A putative fatty acid-binding domain of the NMDA receptor. *Trends Biochem. Sci.* 18:41–42

92. Pickering DS, Thomsen C, Suzdak PD, Fletcher EJ, Robitaille R, et al. 1993. A comparison of two alternatively spliced forms of a metabotropic glutamate receptor coupled to phosphoinositide turnover. *J. Neurochem.* 61: 85–92

93. Pin J-P, Waeber C, Prezeau L, Bockaert J, Heinemann SF. 1992. Alternative splicing generates metabotropic glutamate receptors inducing different patterns of calcium release in *Xenopus* oocytes. *Proc. Natl. Acad. Sci. USA* 89:10331–35

94. Potier M-C, Spillantini MG, Carter NP. 1992. The human glutamate receptor cDNA GluR1: cloning, sequencing, expression and localization to chromosome 5. *DNA Seq.* 2:211–18

95. Puckett C, Gomez CM, Korenberg JR, Tung H, Meier TJ, et al. 1991. Molecular cloning and chromosomal localization of one of the human glutamate receptor genes. *Proc. Natl. Acad. Sci. USA* 88:7557–61

96. Rabacchi S, Bailly Y, Delhaye-Bouchaud N, Mariani J. 1992. Involvement of the *N*-methyl-D-aspartate (NMDA) receptor in synapse elimination during cerebellar development. *Science* 256: 1823–25

97. Raditsch M, Ruppersberg JP, Kuner T, Günther W, Schoepfer R, et al. 1993. Subunit-specific block of cloned NMDA receptors by argiotoxin$_{636}$. *FEBS Lett.* 324:63–66

98. Raymond LA, Blackstone CD, Huganir RL. 1993. Phosphorylation of amino acid neurotransmitter receptors in synaptic plasticity. *Trends Neurosci.* 16:147–53

99. Raymond LA, Blackstone CD, Huganir RL. 1993. Phosphorylation and modulation of recombinant GluR6 glutamate receptors by cAMP-dependent protein kinase. *Nature* 361:637–41

100. Ren R, Mayer BJ, Cicchetti P, Baltimore D. 1993. Identification of a ten-amino acid proline-rich SH3 binding site. *Science* 259:1157–61

101. Rogers SW, Hughes TE, Hollmann M, Gasic GP, Deneris ES, Heinemann S. 1991. The characterization and localization of the glutamate receptor subunit GluR1 in the rat brain. *J. Neurosci.* 11:2713–24

102. Sakimura K, Bujo H, Kushiya E, Araki K, Yamazaki M, et al. 1990. Functional expression from cloned cDNAs of glutamate receptor species responsive to kainate and quisqualate. *FEBS Lett.* 272:73–80

103. Sakimura K, Morita T, Kushiya E, Mishina M. 1992. Primary structure and expression of the γ2 subunit of the glutamate receptor channel selective for kainate. *Neuron* 8:267–74

104. Sakurada K, Masu M, Nakanishi S. 1993. Alteration of Ca^{2+} permeability and sensitivity to Mg^{2+} and channel blockers by a single amino acid substitution in the *N*-methyl-D-aspartate receptor. *J. Biol. Chem.* 268:410–15

105. Schoepp DD, Conn PJ. 1993. Metabotropic glutamate receptors in brain function and pathology. *Trends Pharmacol. Sci.* 14:13–20

106. Schofield PR, Shivers BD, Seeburg PH. 1990. The role of receptor subtype diversity in the CNS. *Trends Neurosci.* 13:8–11

107. Schuster CM, Ultsch A, Schloss P, Cox JA, Schmitt B, Betz H. 1991. Molecular cloning of an invertebrate glutamate receptor subunit expressed in *Drosophila* muscle. *Science* 254:112–14

107a. Seeburg PH. 1993. The molecular biology of mammalian glutamate receptor channels. *Trends Neurosci.* 16: 359–65

108. Shiells RA, Falk G. 1990. Glutamate receptors of rod bipolar cells are linked to a cyclic GMP cascade via a G-protein. *Proc. R. Soc. London Ser. B* 242: 91–94

109. Shigemoto R, Nakanishi S, Mizuno N. 1992. Distribution of the mRNA for a metabotropic glutamate receptor (mGluR1) in the central nervous system: an in situ hybridization study in adult and developing rat. *J. Comp. Neurol.* 322:121–35

109a. Shigemoto R, Nomura S, Ohishi H, Sugihara H, Nakanishi S, Mizuno N. 1993. Immunohistochemical localization of a metabotropic glutamate receptor, mGluR5, in the rat brain. *Neurosci. Lett.* 163:53–57

110. Silva AJ, Paylor R, Wehner JM, Tonegawa S. 1992. Impaired spatial learning in α-calcium-calmodulin kinase II mutant mice. *Science* 257:206–11

111. Silva AJ, Stevens CF, Tonegawa S, Wang Y. 1992. Deficient hippocampal long-term potentiation in α-calcium-calmodulin kinase II mutant mice. *Science* 257:201–6

112. Sladeczek F, Pin J-P, Récasens M, Bockaert J, Weiss S. 1985. Glutamate stimulates inositol phosphate formation in striatal neurones. *Nature* 317: 717–19

113. Sommer B, Burnashev N, Verdoorn TA, Keinänen K, Sakmann B, Seeburg PH. 1992. A glutamate receptor channel with high affinity for domoate and kainate. *EMBO J.* 11:1651–56

114. Sommer B, Keinänen K, Verdoorn TA, Wisden W, Burnashev N, et al. 1990. Flip and flop: a cell-specific functional switch in glutamate-operated channels of the CNS. *Science* 249: 1580–85

115. Sommer B, Köhler M, Sprengel R, Seeburg PH. 1991. RNA editing in brain controls a determinant of ion flow in glutamate-gated channels. *Cell* 67:11–19

116. Stern P, Béhé P, Schoepfer R,

Colquhoun D. 1992. Single-channel conductances of NMDA receptors expressed from cloned cDNAs: comparison with native receptors. *Proc. R. Soc. London Ser. B* 250:271–77

117. Sugihara H, Moriyoshi K, Ishii T, Masu M, Nakanishi S. 1992. Structures and properties of seven isoforms of the NMDA receptor generated by alternative splicing. *Biochem. Biophys. Res. Commun.* 185:826–32

118. Sugiyama H, Ito I, Hirono C. 1987. A new type of glutamate receptor linked to inositol phospholipid metabolism. *Nature* 325:531–33

119. Sun W, Ferrer-Montiel AV, Schinder AF, McPherson JP, Evans GA, Montal M. 1992. Molecular cloning, chromosomal mapping, and functional expression of human brain glutamate receptors. *Proc. Natl. Acad. Sci. USA* 89:1443–47

120. Takahashi K, Tsuchida K, Tanabe Y, Masu M, Nakanishi S. 1993. Role of the large extracellular domain of metabotropic glutamate receptors in agonist selectivity determination. *J. Biol. Chem.* 268:19341–45

121. Tanabe Y, Masu M, Ishii T, Shigemoto R, Nakanishi S. 1992. A family of metabotropic glutamate receptors. *Neuron* 8:169–79

122. Tanabe Y, Nomura A, Masu M, Shigemoto R, Mizuno N, Nakanishi S. 1993. Signal transduction, pharmacological properties, and expression patterns of two rat metabotropic glutamate receptors, mGluR3 and mGluR4. *J. Neurosci.* 13:1372–78

123. Teng B, Burant CF, Davidson NO. 1993. Molecular cloning of an apolipoprotein B messenger RNA editing protein. *Science* 260:1816–19

124. Tingley WG, Roche KW, Thompson AK, Huganir RL. 1993. Regulation of NMDA receptor phosphorylation by alternative splicing of the C-terminal domain. *Nature* 364:70–73

125. Uchino S, Sakimura K, Nagahari K, Mishina M. 1992. Mutations in a putative agonist binding region of the AMPA-selective glutamate receptor channel. *FEBS Lett.* 308:253–57

126. Ultsch A, Schuster CM, Laube B, Betz H, Schmitt B. 1993. Glutamate receptors of *Drosophila melanogaster:* primary structure of a putative NMDA receptor protein expressed in the head of the adult fly. *FEBS Lett.* 324:171–77

127. Ultsch A, Schuster CM, Laube B, Schloss P, Schmitt B, Betz H. 1992. Glutamate receptors of *Drosophila melanogaster:* cloning of a kainate-selective subunit expressed in the central nervous system. *Proc. Natl. Acad. Sci. USA* 89:10484–88

128. Unwin N. 1993. Neurotransmitter action: opening of ligand-gated ion channels. *Cell* 72/*Neuron* 10(Suppl.):31–41

129. Verdoorn TA, Burnashev N, Monyer H, Seeburg PH, Sakmann B. 1991. Structural determinants of ion flow through recombinant glutamate receptor channels. *Science* 252:1715–18

129a. Verrall S, Hall ZW. 1992. The N-terminal domians of acetylcholine receptor subunits contain recognition signals for the initial steps of receptor assembly. *Cell* 68:23–31

130. Wada K, Dechesne CJ, Shimasaki S, King RG, Kusano K, et al. 1989. Sequence and expression of a frog brain complementary DNA encoding a kainate-binding protein. *Nature* 342:684–89

131. Wahlestedt C, Golanov E, Yamamoto S, Yee F, Ericson H, et al. 1993. Antisense oligodeoxynucleotides to NMDA-R1 receptor channel protect cortical neurons from excitotoxicity and reduce focal ischaemic infarctions. *Nature* 363:260–63

132. Wang L-Y, Taverna FA, Huang X-P, MacDonald JF, Hampson DR. 1993. Phosphorylation and modulation of a kainate receptor (GluR6) by cAMP-dependent protein kinase. *Science* 259:1173–75

133. Watkins JC, Krogsgaard-Larsen P, Honoré T. 1990. Structure-activity relationships in the development of excitatory amino acid receptor agonists and competitive antagonists. *Trends Pharmacol. Sci.* 11:25–33

134. Wenthold RJ, Hunter C, Wada K, Dechesne CJ. 1990. Antibodies to a C-terminal peptide of the rat brain glutamate receptor subunit, GluR-A, recognize a subpopulation of AMPA binding sites but not kainate sites. *FEBS Lett.* 276:147–50

135. Wenthold RJ, Yokotani N, Doi K, Wada K. 1992. Immunochemical characterization of the non-NMDA glutamate receptor using subunit-specific antibodies. *J. Biol. Chem.* 267:501-7

136. Werner P, Voigt M, Keinänen K, Wisden W, Seeburg PH. 1991. Cloning of a putative high-affinity kainate receptor expressed predominantly in hippocampal CA3 cells. *Nature* 351:742–44

137. Yamazaki M, Araki K, Shibata A, Mishina M. 1992. Molecular cloning of a cDNA encoding a novel member of the mouse glutamate receptor channel

family. *Biochem. Biophys. Res. Commun.* 183:886–92

138. Yamazaki M, Mori H, Araki K, Mori KJ, Mishina M. 1992. Cloning, expression and modulation of a mouse NMDA receptor subunit. *FEBS Lett.* 300:39–45

139. Young AB, Fagg GE. 1990. Excitatory amino acid receptors in the brain: membrane binding and receptor autoradiographic approaches. *Trends Pharmacol. Sci.* 11:126–33

140. Yu X-M, Hall ZW. 1991. Extracellular domains mediating ϵ subunit interactions of muscle acetylcholine receptor. *Nature.* 352:64–67

Annu. Rev. Biophys. Biomol. Struct. 1994. 23:349–75
Copyright © 1994 by Annual Reviews Inc. All rights reserved

PROTEIN STRUCTURE–BASED DRUG DESIGN

Peter J. Whittle

Pfizer Central Research, Sandwich, Kent CT13 9NJ, United Kingdom

Tom L. Blundell

Imperial Cancer Research Fund Unit of Structural Molecular Biology, Department of Crystallography, Birkbeck College, Malet Street, London WC1E 7HX, United Kingdom

KEY WORDS: design cycles, protein modeling, structure determination, protein-ligand complexes, drug discovery

CONTENTS

PERSPECTIVES AND OVERVIEW

In the past, drug discovery usually consisted of the systematic modification of a chemical lead, using standard medicinal chemistry meth-

349

1056–8700/94/0610–0349$05.00

ods based upon cycles of synthesis and testing. The recent introduction of mechanized testing and rapid assay systems has enabled researchers to carry out very high throughput screening in the search for lead compounds, and the rapid growth of techniques for systematic generation of large numbers of novel compounds (e.g. random peptide and phage epitope libraries) suggests that these lead-generation methods are likely to play a significant role in drug discovery for some time to come. However, recent developments in biochemistry and recombinant DNA techniques now offer the possibility of radical new approaches to the generation of structural information relevant to the discovery process. For example, new techniques for the purification of small quantities of proteins allow their partial sequencing. DNA probes can be constructed on the basis of this amino acid–sequence information and used to clone and sequence the DNA coding for the protein. At the same time, site-directed mutagenesis has allowed us to make specific changes in enzymes, hormones, and other key factors in order to make them more useful for clinical applications.

Proteins, whether they are enzymes or membrane receptors, bind their ligands in specific conformations. The topographies of the complementary surfaces of the ligand and protein determine both affinity and specificity. Therefore, any methods that provide structural information on the nature of the interaction between ligand and protein could be used in the drug-design process. In this review we describe the progress that has been made in using three-dimensional structure as a basis for drug design. We briefly assess experimental methods that have successfully defined the structures and describe approaches to the use of this information to predict three-dimensional structures for real targets. We also review computational and graphic approaches to the design of novel molecules based upon the known structures of protein receptors, protein ligands, and protein-ligand complexes. Finally, we describe some examples of the use of structural information in drug design.

Design Cycles

Structure-based design is one component of multidisciplinary design cycles, as illustrated in Figure 1. If the molecule of interest is a protein, such as a monoclonal antibody or a growth factor, then the protein-engineering cycle is of value. In this cycle, the protein is cloned, expressed, and characterized kinetically, and the three-dimensional structure is defined, preferably as a complex with a ligand or a pseudosubstrate. When small, nonprotein ligands are of interest, the receptor-based drug design cycle is appropriate. In this cycle the three-

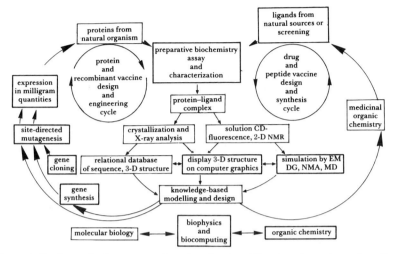

Figure 1 Design cycles for structure-based, rational modification of proteins and smaller ligands. MD, molecular dynamics; NMA, normal mode analysis; DG, distance geometry; EM, electron microscopy. Reprinted from Ref. 9, with permission.

dimensional structure of a protein-ligand complex is used as the basis for the design of a new ligand that is complementary to the protein (receptor) binding site. Often, only the structure of the receptor is known, and techniques are required to generate a novel molecule that is complementary in shape and electrostatics to the receptor topography. Chemical synthesis is then needed to realize the new design. In most cases we must go round the cycle several times, hoping to improve the design each time. Even if our aim is to design a nonprotein ligand, site-directed mutagenesis experiments on the protein receptor to test a hypothesis are often appropriate. Thus, protein engineering will probably find an important role in drug discovery as an alternative and complementary approach to chemical synthesis of new ligands in testing ideas about receptor-ligand affinity and specificity.

PROTEIN STRUCTURE

Growth of Structural Information About Proteins

Most target proteins for drug development participate in key regulatory steps in the human body or in an infectious organism. As such, they tend to be present in a few copies only, and often within specific cells. Their isolation and purification using traditional preparative biochemistry and in quantities required for routine assays has been a formidable challenge. This situation has been radically changed by the ability to clone and express proteins in a range of prokaryotic and eukaryotic cells, and even in whole animals and plants using transgenic organisms. Thus, many key target proteins are now becoming available in sufficient quantities to make them amenable not only to biological assays but also to NMR studies in solution and to crystallization for X-ray analysis.

Between 1970 and 1989 the number of protein three-dimensional structures defined by X-ray analysis increased linearly. There was an increase in the number of protein crystallographic groups worldwide, and also an improvement in technical capability, but this was not reflected in an increase in the rate of new structures being solved. Over the past few years, this position has changed radically as increasing numbers of eukaryotic proteins have been expressed, purified, and crystallized. The number of protein structures solved using X-ray analysis has begun to rise sharply with (as of January 1993) more than 1000 protein three-dimensional structures in the Brookhaven Data Bank (7), although not all of these are different proteins. Recombinant techniques have contributed to this advance in ways other than cloning and expression. They have allowed the isolation of stable domains of complex multidomain structures and have changed or removed the glycosylation patterns that make many extracellular eukaryotic proteins heterogeneous and unsuitable for crystallization. Recombinant methods have also been used to engineer more stable protein mutants for crystallization, to provide seleno-enzymes for use in multiple anomalous dispersion, and to introduce cysteines for binding heavy atoms for multiple isomorphous replacement.

The development of NMR methods has also produced many new structures (17, 72). These include small and relatively rigid disulfiderich proteins and an increasing number of larger proteins (M_r up to 20 kDa). Recombinant methods have been of value to NMR methodologies because they allow structure determination of small domains that are useful in drug discovery. NMR has a very strong advantage in this respect as the proteins need not be crystallized and flexible linker regions associated with globular domains create fewer problems for the analysis than they do for X-ray studies, where they often interfere with crystallization.

Structure Determination and Accuracy

The accuracy required of a protein structure depends upon the question addressed by the design process. Some processes are predicated on the assumption that a lead molecule will need to complement precisely a known binding site for a ligand, or match closely the presumed transition state structure of a reaction. These cases call for an accurate model at the highest resolution possible. Alternatively, the design process may exploit the structure to indicate the general availability of space to fill, hydrogen bonds to make, or electrostatic interactions to optimize. In these cases, simply a knowledge of the general topography of the binding site is often useful.

The accuracy of three-dimensional structures of proteins available for structure-based design reflects the method of structure determination: the refinement, the resolution, the number of restraints introduced in the structure analysis, the statistical indicators of agreement between the model and the experimental data, and the conformity of the model to stereochemistry found in proteins in general. The experimentalist can optimize most statistical parameters within the constraints of the data, but if the data are poor or the conformations, particularly of sidechains and loops, are incorrect, it is difficult to optimize them all at the same time. However, one can usually introduce a check on parameters that have not been restrained in the analysis. PROCHECK (37), for example, provides such a protein health check by analyzing the distribution of a range of conformational parameters and comparing them with expected distributions.

The correctness of the interpretation of protein structures often comes under serious scrutiny. These questions can relate to the overall topology, but errors are more likely to occur through local misalignment of the sequence with respect to the template, deriving either from experimental evidence (e.g. electron density) or from the use of an analogue in modeling or prediction. Several approaches now relate the propensity of an amino acid (41, 48), the knowledge-based potential (31), or the probability of amino acid substitution (49, 66) to the local environment in the proposed structure. Such approaches give a sequence-dependent indication of the probability that the structure is correct.

Comparative Modeling and Prediction

If the protein of interest is available in small quantities only, its sequence will likely be defined from the DNA sequence and the structure analysis will probably be carried out on recombinant protein. This means that the protein sequence will be available before the three-dimensional structure. For small proteins or domains, the lag between the availability of sequence information and the determination of the three-dimensional structure can be as short as a few months. For more complex proteins, years may pass before they are crystallized and structures solved. The question then arises as to whether our knowledge of protein sequence can be useful in modeling and prediction of three-dimensional structures. Investigators now widely agree that protein structures cannot be predicted by simulation of the folding pathway. The forces between the atoms of the protein, and particularly with the surrounding solvent and counterions, are not very well described, but more importantly, the computational problems are still beyond the scope of even the largest computers. However, proteins belong to families with a common fold. These include more than 1500 groups of homologous proteins that can be recognized by sequence searches alone, and probably between 500 and 700 that have common topologies or folds. These associations can provide a basis for comparative modeling if the common fold can be recognized from the sequence.

For proteins with sequence identities of <30%, profiles or templates are useful in the search for the common fold and alignment of the sequences. Toward this end, one can use structural information to identify key features in protein architecture and associate these with invariant or conserved sequences. The demonstration that relaxin could adopt the insulin fold (6), which was recently confirmed by X-ray analysis (24), serves as an example. A more systematic method is to project the restraints of the three-dimensional fold onto the one dimension of the sequence (57) and to compare sequence templates or profiles. The template search can also be approached by determining the propensity of an amino acid to occur in each class of local structural environment defined by solvent accessibility and secondary structure, as shown by Eisenberg and his colleagues (13). Alternatively, one can calculate amino acid substitution tables as a function of local environment (32, 41, 49). Each of these methods can be used to detect distantly related sequences that adopt a particular protein fold but none is successful at identifying all known topological relationships.

When a new sequence has been identified with a known fold, this information can be used to predict the three-dimensional structure of the protein. Systematic approaches are now being developed, for example, for rules that relate the side-chain dihedral angle with the residue type at equivalent positions in homologous proteins (61, 62). Most methods depend upon the assembly of rigid fragments (8, 11, 16, 33), often to select three sets of fragments that define the framework (8, 65); the structurally variable, mainly loop, regions; and the sidechains. These modeling procedures are very successful when the known structures cluster around that to be predicted and when the percentage sequence identity to the unknown is high (greater than 40%) (60).

In the absence of a common fold to guide the construction of a model, combinatorial approaches can be valuable (52). These depend upon the identification of secondary-structure elements using conformational propensities and residue patterns. The elements of secondary structure are then assembled by docking and/or by using rules concerning supersecondary structures.

COMPUTATIONAL APPROACHES TO STRUCTURE-BASED DESIGN

Once the three-dimensional structure of a target protein has been defined, preferably by experimental approaches but possibly through comparative modeling, then computational procedures are required to suggest ligands that will bind at the active site. One can accomplish this either by elaborating a known ligand or by searching for novel ligands that bind in the active-site cleft. In practice, the two approaches may not be so clearly distinguishable; even when the structure of an enzyme-ligand complex is known, computational and graphics searches for fragments that better complement the receptor topography are usually required.

Interactive Graphics Approaches

Structure-based design begins with the definition and graphical display of hydrogen bonds, molecular surfaces (28, 35), and electrostatic fields (26). In most laboratories, key interactions are identified visually, preferably from a series of three-dimensional structures of protein ligand complexes. In an interactive graphics approach, new designs are then explored manually in ways that might involve, for example, modification of groups on the ligand to optimize complementarity with receptor/enzyme subsites, optimization of a transition state isostere to reflect data from mechanistic studies, replacement of peptide bonds with groups that improve hydrolytic stability while maintaining key hydrogen bond interactions, or linking of adjacent side groups to increase the rigidity of the ligand. Although such an interactive approach has proved very useful in many laboratories, most of these steps can now be done using systematic computational approaches that fall into three classes: automated docking of whole molecules into receptor sites; precalculating potentials at grid points and fitting molecules to these potentials; and docking fragments and either joining them or growing them into real molecules.

Docking Molecules into Receptor Sites

With the advent of more powerful computers, several attempts were made to automate docking by the evaluation of electrostatic, steric, or more complex energy terms during a systematic search of rotational and translational space for the two molecules (34, 71). Although these methods had some successes, the simplification of the energy functions to achieve reasonable computational times proved a severe limitation. An attractive alternative appeared to be interactive or manual docking involving positioning of the molecules with constant feedback of the energy (15, 50, 64). The many degrees of freedom and modes of interaction, however, made this operation much too complex, even if clear objectives, such as optimizing specific interactions, were available.

Calculating Potentials at Points in the Binding Cleft

Precalculating terms for each point on a grid significantly reduces computational time. This approach, which was pioneered by Goodford (27) using electrostatic terms for probes (GRID), can be used to identify hydrogen-bonding sites within enzyme active sites. A similar approach is to use pseudoenergies calculated from pairwise distributions of atoms in protein complexes or crystals of small molecules. Probe molecules can then be fitted to these potentials and ranked according to energy.

Perhaps the most developed software of this kind is DOCK. This program creates a negative image of the target site by placing a set of overlapping spheres so that they fill the complex invaginations of the proposed binding site. The putative ligands are then placed into the site by matching X-ray or computer derived structures on the basis of a comparison of internal distances. Next, the candidates are ranked on the basis of their best orientations. Modification of this method has resulted in a directed DOCK, in which hydrogen-bond information is used and conformational flexibility is allowed (39). A related method (4) uses least squares fitting to maximize overlap of enzymes and putative ligands. Ligands can be examined at a rate of 10 to 100 per minute, enabling the examination of a database of 100,000 compounds in less than a week.

Genetic algorithms (51) and graph theory (40) can be used to generate molecular structures within constraints of an enzyme active site or a receptor binding site. In the graph theory method, surfaces are simplified to nodes and edges, which may represent steric or electrostatic features, and graphs are matched to receptor and ligand.

To be of use in drug discovery, such methods clearly depend upon the existence of large data bases of small molecule structures. Of these, the Cambridge Structure Data Base contains 100,000 crystal structures (2) and is an invaluable resource. However, chemical data bases such as the Fine Chemicals Directory are also of very great value as they can be generated in three-dimensional (3D) form by CONCORD (56).

Fragment Docking and Growing New Molecules

Considerable interest has focused on positioning fragments in the binding cleft of proteins of known structure and then developing algorithms to grow them into larger structures to fill the space available. These methods depend upon the exploration of electrostatic, van der Waals, or hydrogen bonding interactions involved in molecular recognition. Many build upon the work of Goodford (27) and can incorporate the GRID algorithm as a starting point.

GenStar (54) and GroupBuild (55) generate chemically reasonable structures to fill the active sites of enzymes. The proposed molecules give good steric contacts with the protein and have low energy conformers. They consist entirely of sp^3 carbons that are grown sequentially and can form rings. Alternatively, the program can start with a docked core or the structure of a fragment from an inhibitor complex. For each atom generated, several hundred candidate positions, representing different bond lengths and torsion angles, are scored on the basis of contacts with the enzyme.

The multiple copy simultaneous search (MCSS) method (29, 44) constructs a functionality map of the binding site by determining the energetically favorable positions and orientations of functional groups on the surface of proteins of known 3D structure. The method extends the approach of CHARMM and uses molecular dynamics calculations without nonbonding interactions between solvent molecules.   LUDI (12) positions molecules or new substituents of a lead compound into clefts of protein structures in such a way that hydrogen bonds are formed with the protein and hydrophobic pockets are filled with hydrocarbon groups. Interaction sites, which are discrete positions in space suitable to form hydrogen bonds or to fill a hydrophobic pocket, are first identified; these are derived from a statistical analysis of nonbonded contacts from the Cambridge Structural Database. The fragments are then fitted into the interaction sites using a standard library of 1000 fragments. Using a further library of 1200 link fragments, one can connect these into a single molecule. LUDI can also append new fragments to an existing molecule.

Many similar approaches that involve placing groups and then linking them into molecules are now being developed. For example CLIX (38) is a suite of computer programs that searches the Cambridge Data base for small molecules that have both geometrical and chemical complementarity to a defined binding site on a protein of known 3D structure. The future undoubtedly lies in bringing the best of these approaches together. A good example is LEAPFROG (R Kramer, TRIPOS Associates), which can suggest improvements to existing leads (OPTIMISE), propose new molecules expected to have good binding (DREAM), and support interactive design (GUIDE).

EXAMPLES OF STRUCTURE-BASED DESIGN

HIV Proteinase Inhibitors as AIDS Antivirals

In common with other retroviruses, human immunodeficiency virus (HIV), the causative agent of AIDS, codes for a proteinase that plays an essential role in the virus replication cycle. Inhibition of HIV proteinase is, therefore, a potential therapeutic approach for the treatment of AIDS (10). An early report by Toh et al (63), in which the authors suggested that retroviruses might code for a proteinase that is similar in mechanistic type to the aspartic proteinase family of mammalian and fungal enzymes, led to the rapid testing of known inhibitors of this class against the HIV proteinase. The majority of early inhibitor leads derived from this source. Four years later, confirmation that HIV-1 proteinase belongs to the aspartic proteinase family came with the publication, from three groups, of the crystal structure of the enzyme, which showed it to be a dimer composed of two 99–amino acid monomeric polypeptide chains (36, 47, 69). Each monomer supplies one active site aspartic acid residue and is related to the other monomer by a perfect C_2 axis of symmetry (Figure 2).

To use the crystal structure effectively in drug design, one should obviously know the mode of binding of inhibitors, and this information was initially provided by the publication of the crystal structure of a complex of synthetic HIV-1 proteinase bound to the reduced amide inhibitor, MVT-101 (Figure 3, top) (43).

Although the perfect two-fold symmetry of the native enzyme is disrupted, most notably by the asymmetric arrangement of the two flaps as they move down to bind the (asymmetric) inhibitor, this symmetry is broadly conserved in the hydrogen bonding pattern between enzyme and inhibitor (Figure 3, bottom). Crystal structures of HIV proteinase complexed with a wide range of inhibitors have now been published, and apart from some small variations, all bind in an extended conformation according to the generalized pattern shown in Figure 4 for a hydroxyethylene based inhibitor (70).

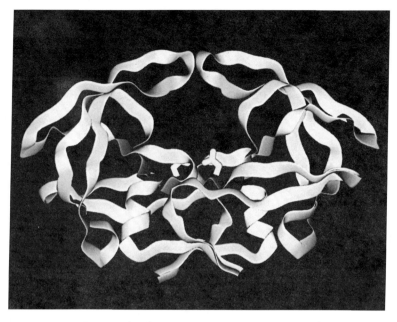

Figure 2   Ribbon diagram of native HIV-1 proteinase, showing the two identical monomers that each contribute one aspartic acid residue to the active site. Taken from coordinates 3HPV (36), obtained from the Protein Data Bank (PDB) (1, 7) at Brookhaven National Laboratory.

The detailed structural information that these studies have provided has been invaluable in enabling drug-design teams to tailor their inhibitor leads to optimize specific interactions at the active site, but the HIV proteinase field also exemplifies the way in which structural data can suggest novel inhibitor prototypes for synthesis. The hydrogen-bonding diagram in Figure 4 clearly shows an approximate two-fold symmetry in the interactions despite the asymmetrical nature of the inhibitor. Therefore, if a two-fold symmetrical inhibitor could be designed, with the symmetry axis coinciding with that of the enzyme dimer, then good inhibitory potency should result. In addition, because a symmetrical inhibitor would show less resemblance to the natural peptide substrate, one might expect inhibition of other, host, aspartic proteinases to be weaker. Both of these predictions have turned out to be correct. The first symmetrical inhibitor to be described was A-74704, a structure derived by taking a statine-, or hydroxyethylene-, based inhibitor in which the C_2 symmetry axis of the complexed enzyme coincides with the carbon atom to which the OH group is attached

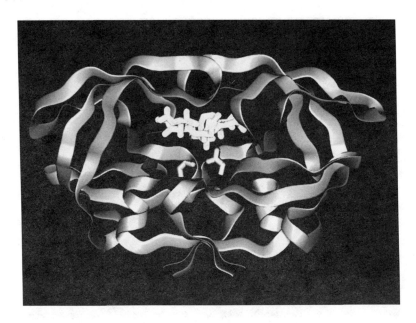

Figure 3 (*Top*) Ribbon diagram of HIV-1 proteinase complexed with MVT-101, showing the movement of the two flaps upon ligand binding. Taken from coordinates 4HVP (43), obtained from the PDB (1, 7) at Brookhaven National Laboratory. (*Bottom*) H-bonding pattern of MVT-101 bound to HIV-1 proteinase. Nle, norleucine. Other side chains are those of the natural amino acids indicated.

and eliminating all prime-side binding groups. Rotation of the remaining, nonprime, groups by 180°, in line with the C_2 symmetry of the enzyme, then generates the inhibitor structure that, except for the central carbon atom, has C_2 symmetry (Figure 5). The compound inhibits

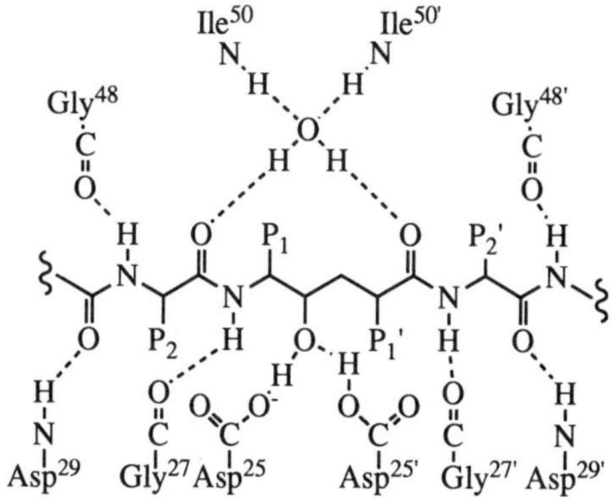

Figure 4   H-bonding pattern of a monostatine based inhibitor bound to HIV-1 proteinase.

HIV-1 proteinase with a K_i of 4.5 nM and shows no inhibition of the mammalian aspartic proteinases, renin and pepsin, at 10 μM (25).

The crystal structure of the complex of A-74704 bound to HIV-1 proteinase shows approximate C_2 symmetry, but the conformation of the flap residues could not be defined precisely at the available resolution. Figure 6 shows the hydrogen bond pattern between enzyme and inhibitor, which is exactly as predicted from the modeling studies.

Another important use of structural data for HIV proteinase in drug discovery programs is in the search for nonpeptide inhibitor leads, using only the enzyme active site as a starting point. Thus, DesJarlais et al (18) took the crystal structures of free and inhibitor-complexed HIV-1 proteinase and used their DOCK program to generate a 3D template of key potential binding sites that could be exploited by inhibitors. Mapping of this template to a structural data base for low-molecular-weight, nonpeptidic compounds led to the identification of haloperidol (structure below) as a potential inhibitor lead. This compound binds to HIV-1 and HIV-2 proteinases only weakly ($K_i \approx 100$ μM) and is therefore of no use as an anti-HIV drug per se, but other

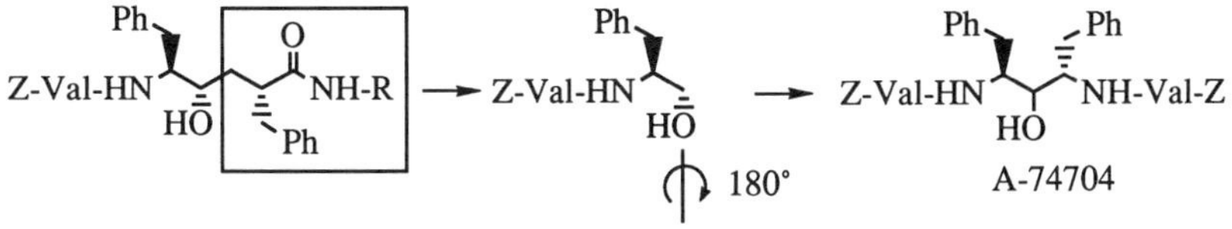

Figure 5   Generation of the symmetrical structure of the inhibitor A-74704. Z, benzyl-oxycarbonyl.

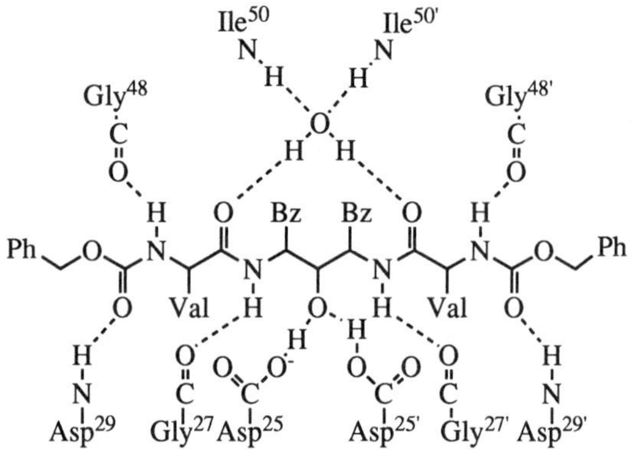

Figure 6 H-bonding pattern for the symmetrical inhibitor A-74704 bound to HIV-1 proteinase. Bz, benzyl; Ph, phenyl. Other side chains are those of the natural amino acids indicated.

analogues have been identified with greater potency. In a similar way, Bures et al (14) identified the nonpeptide inhibitor (compound 1, below) by generating a three-dimensional pattern of atoms, based upon the key interactions of the symmetrical inhibitor, A-74704, with the proteinase active site and then searching databases of small molecules, using their ALADDIN program, to identify structures that match the pattern.

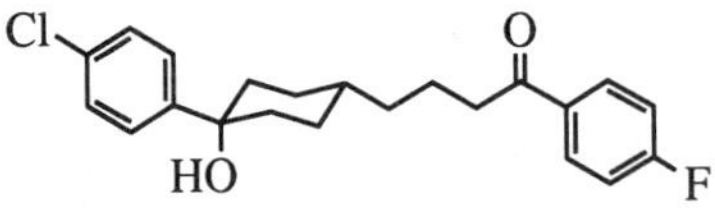

Haloperidol

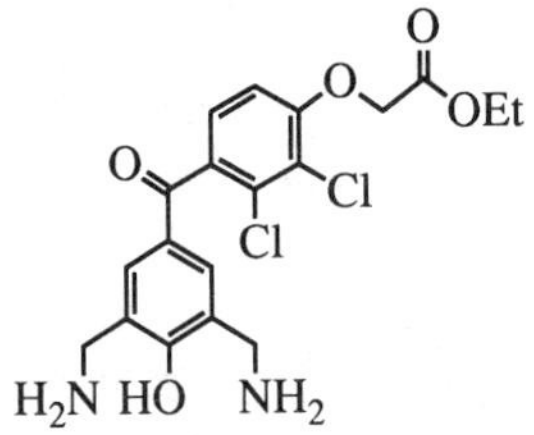

(1)

Purine Nucleoside Phosphorylase Inhibitors as Selective Immunosuppressants

Purine nucleoside phosphorylase (PNP) catalyzes the reversible phosphorolysis of the purine ribonucleosides (deoxy)guanosine and (deoxy)inosine to their respective bases and is an essential enzyme in the purine salvage pathway. Genetic deficiency of PNP leads to a selective impairment of the T-cell component (cell-mediated immunity) of the immune system, while B-cell function (humoral immunity) remains normal. Therefore, inhibitors of PNP that can suppress T-cell function in vivo may find clinical use, as T-cell selective immunosuppressants, in the prevention of organ transplant rejection or in the treatment of T-cell leukemias and psoriasis. No PNP inhibitors have yet been licensed for clinical use, which may be because potent enzyme inhibition (K_i < 10 nM) must be attained in vitro for effects on T-cell function to be observed in vivo, where PNP activity is high. Early, substrate-based inhibitors generally fell well short of this level of potency, except when phosphate groups were included in the structure, but this modification was not compatible with penetration of the inhibitor into the cell. With the determination of the crystal structure of human erythrocyte PNP by Ealick et al (23), the identification of potent, cell permeable PNP inhibitors by rational, structure-based design became a realistic possibility.

PNP exists in the crystal as a three-fold symmetric trimer, with each active site located close to the interface between subunits (Figure 7, top). The purine-binding site is generally hydrophobic in nature, but two polar residues (Glu201 and Lys244) form hydrogen bonds with N(1)-H and O(6), respectively, of guanine (Figure 7, bottom). Another important point, which became apparent when crystal structures of enzyme-inhibitor complexes were solved, is that a region of the polypeptide, residues 241–260, moves significantly upon binding of substrate or competitive inhibitor. Consequently, attempts to model inhibitors in the active site were only successful when the coordinates of the enzyme, as a bound complex, were used in the study.

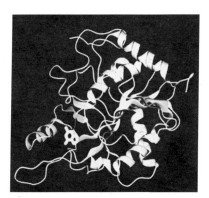 

Figure 7 (*Left*) Ribbon diagram of the human erythrocyte PNP monomer showing the position of guanine in the active site. (*Right*) Guanine binding site of human erythrocyte PNP showing the position of the Phe200, Glu201, and Lys244 side chains. Taken from coordinates IULB (22), obtained from the PDB (1, 7) at Brookhaven National Laboratory.

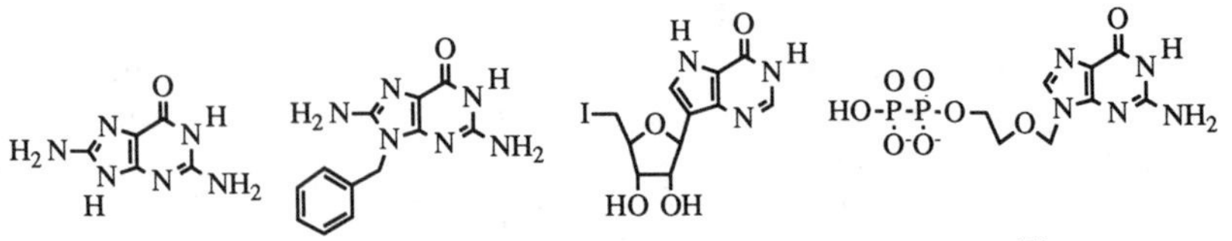

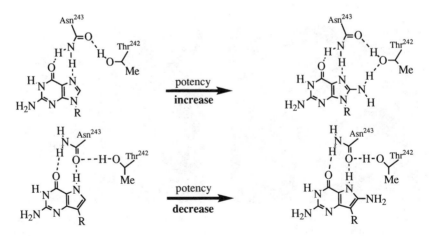

Figure 8 Structures of four PNP inhibitors for which crystallographic data, as bound ligands, have geen generated.

Analysis of the bound structures of some standard PNP inhibitors, such as 8-aminoguanine (compound 2, Figure 8), 9-benzyl-8-amino-guanine (compound 3, Figure 8), 5'-iodo-9-deazainosine (compound 4, Figure 8), and acyclovir diphosphate (compound 5, Figure 8) showed that the increase in inhibitory potency seen upon introduction of a lipophilic group at the purine 9-position results from an interaction with a hydrophobic region of the ribose binding site (22). The crystal structures also provided an explanation for the potency-enhancing effect of introducing an 8-amino substituent in the guanine, but not in the 9-deazaguanine, series (Figure 9). In the former series, the potency increase is a consequence of an additional hydrogen bond made with Thr242, but for the 9-deaza compounds, Asn243 has shifted position by ~2.5 Å to accommodate a hydrogen bond on N-7 of the deaza-guanine. A corresponding shift in Thr242 then prevents interaction of

Figure 9 H-bonding pattern of guanine- and 9-deazaguanine-based inhibitors bound to PNP.

the OH group of this residue with the N-8 amino group and, instead, places the methyl group in close proximity.

Further work to optimize the hydrophobic binding of the 9-substituent in the deazaguanine series was guided by crystallographic analysis of derivatives of this type and led to the identification of several compounds, e.g. (compound 6, below), which showed effects in vivo consistent with inhibition of PNP (46).

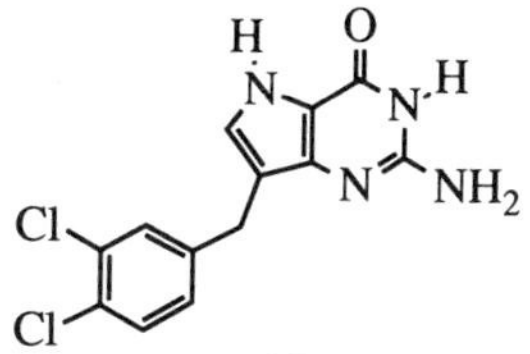

(6)

Thymidylate Synthase Inhibitors as Antiproliferative Agents

Thymidylate synthase (TS) catalyzes the reductive methylation of deoxyuridine monophosphate (dUMP) to thymidylate (dTMP) using the cofactor 5,10-methylenetetrahydrofolate as the one carbon source. Because this is the only de novo pathway for production of thymidylate, an essential DNA precursor, inhibition of TS has been recognized for many years as a potential chemotherapeutic approach to the treatment of diseases, such as cancer or psoriasis, which are caused by excessive cell proliferation. Before structural information became available for the enzyme, several different inhibitors had been described, which were based simply upon a knowledge of substrate, cofactor, and putative reaction intermediate. These include substrate analogues such as 5-fluorodeoxyuridine monophosphate (FdUMP; see structure below), the active metabolite of the anticancer agent 5-fluorouracil, and a range of folate antagonists, such as N^{10}-propargyl-5,8-dideazafolic acid (CB3717; see structure below). While this appoach has been effective in producing potent enzyme inhibitors, some of which have been used clinically, the close similarity of the compounds to the natural substrate or cofactor often led to toxicity as a consequence of interactions with other cellular enzymes. With the publication of the crystal structures of uncomplexed TS from *Lactobacillus casei* (30), and of the enzyme from *Escherichia coli* bound as a ternary complex with either substrate (dUMP) or analogue (FdUMP) and the folate antagonist CB3717 (42, 45), the possibility of using structure based design

FdUMP   CB3717

to identify specific and potent enzyme inhibitors became a realistic proposition.

In its native state, TS exists as a dimer of identical subunits related by a two-fold axis of rotation. The two separate active sites are formed at the interface between monomers, each of which contributes residues to each of the active sites (Figure 10, top). Upon binding of substrate and cofactor, a general closing down of the enzyme occurs around the reactants, but the six C-terminal residues move by 3.5–6.0 Å away from their exposed position in the uncomplexed enzyme to cover one face of the bound folate cofactor analogue. The binding site for the phosphate group of FdUMP is formed mainly from four arginine side chains, which also move position significantly upon substrate binding in order to facilitate the interaction with the phosphate group (Figure 10, bottom).

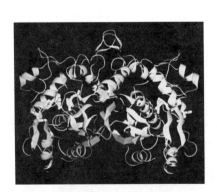
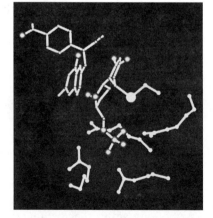

Figure 10 (*Left*) Ribbon diagram of *E. coli* TS bound to dUMP and CB3717 at each active site. (*Right*) Binding site of dUMP and CB3717 in *E. coli* TS, showing the position of the four arginine side chains around the phosphate group and the cysteine residue covalently linked to the substrate. Taken from coordinates 2TSC (45), obtained from the PDB (1, 7) at Brookhaven National Laboratory.

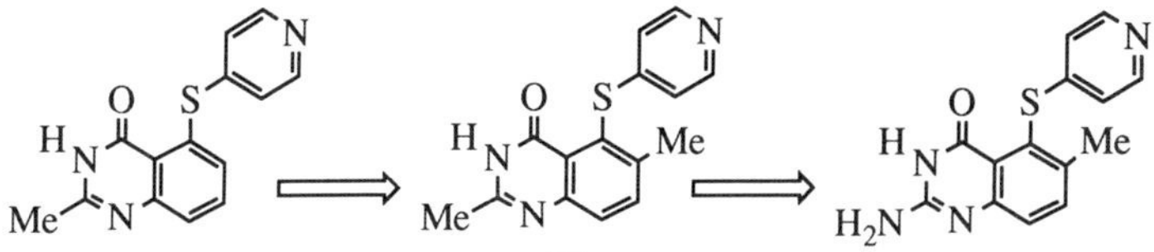

| Relative potency vs. E. coli TS | (7) 1 | (8) 20 | (9) 200 |

Figure 11   Structures and relative potencies of three TS inhibitors from the structure-based design program.

The overall aim of the drug design programs has been to use the available structural information to design novel, potent TS inhibitors that do not closely resemble either the substrate or cofactor and that are sufficiently lipophilic to enter cells by passive diffusion to reach their site of action. One approach has been to take the crystal structure of CB3717, bound to E. coli TS in a ternary complex with FdUMP, as a starting point and use the structural information generated on subsequent analogues to guide the synthesis program. In this way, the pyridine derivative (compound 7 in Figure 11) was identified initially as a lead compound (68). The crystal structure of compound 7, determined in a ternary complex with E. coli TS and FdUMP, then suggested a way of increasing binding affinity by incorporating an additional (hydrophobic) methyl group at C-6 of the quinazolinone unit, as in compound 8 (Figure 11). This compound was prepared and showed increased inhibitory potency, as predicted. Structural analysis of structure 8, when bound in the ternary complex, indicated other potential ways of increasing binding—for example, by replacing the C-2 methyl group with amino and thereby forming an additional hydrogen bond. This compound (#9, Figure 11) was prepared and, again, showed the expected increase in inhibitory potency. Thus, two small changes to the initial lead structure, based upon information derived from crystal structures of bound inhibitors, have increased potency 200-fold without the introduction of polar functionality that could affect cell penetration (Figure 11). Compound 9 is currently in clinical development as an anticancer agent.

A second way in which structural information has been used in the design of novel inhibitors is to start with the ternary enzyme structure and then remove the cofactor analogue, CB3717, to produce the active site conformation in the complexed state. This active site geometry has been used as the basis for de novo design using, for example, the GRID program of Goodford (27), to search for potential sites of interaction between the enzyme active site and hydrophobic or polar groups. Using this method, the two inhibitors, compounds 10 and 11, have been designed, starting from weakly active leads (3, 67). In a similar way, Shoichet et al (58) have utilized their molecular docking program, DOCK, to search the Fine Chemicals Directory for structures that are complementary to the active site of *L. casei* TS and have identified phenolphthalein (compound 12) by an iterative process of structure determination and similarity searching, again starting from only a poorly active lead.

(10)   (11)   (12)

Rhinovirus Canyon Binders as Agents for Treatment of the Common Cold

The picornaviridae are a family of positive-strand RNA viruses responsible for a range of human and animal diseases. The rhinoviruses constitute a particular subgroup of the picornavirus family and are the major causative agents of the common cold. Over 100 different rhinovirus serotypes have been identified, and for an antiviral agent to have clinical potential, activity against most, if not all, of these strains is essential. WIN 51711 (disoxaril; see below) is one of several structurally diverse antirhinovirus agents that inhibit a particular step in the virus-replication cycle—uncoating—which occurs after the virus has entered the host cell and involves the disruption of the protein shell to expose the viral RNA (20). Without this uncoating step, virus replication is blocked because translation of viral RNA cannot take place. The crystal structure of the human rhinovirus HRV-14 was published in 1985 (53), but there was no information at the time on the precise mechanism by which these compounds inhibited the uncoating process. This came the following year when the crystal structures of complexes of HRV-14 bound to WIN 51711, or to the close analogue, WIN 52084, were published (59). These inhibitors were shown to bind in a hydrophobic cavity located in the capsid protein VP1 under a canyon on the surface of the virus particle, which was subsequently shown to bind the host-cell receptor (Figure 12). Inhibitor binding results in a large

R = H; WIN 51711 (Disoxaril)
R = Me; WIN 52084

conformational change in one of the polypeptide strands in the floor of the cavity, and this may stabilize the virion particle to pH-mediated disassembly. Adsorption of the virion to the cell receptor is also decreased in the presence of inhibitor, and this may contribute to the antiviral activity of the uncoating inhibitors.

This report was the first to describe the detailed structural interaction of an antiviral agent with its site of action and was the impetus for

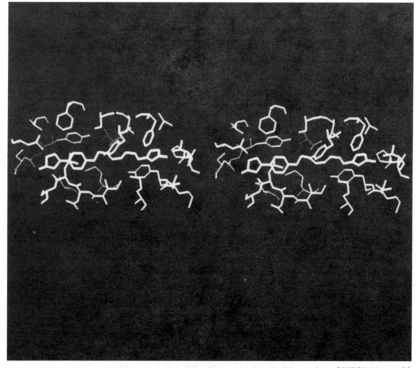

Figure 12   Stereo view of WIN 52084 bound in the hydrophobic cavity of HRV-14 capsid protein VP1. Taken from coordinates 2RSI (59), obtained from the PDB (1, 7) at Brookhaven National Laboratory.

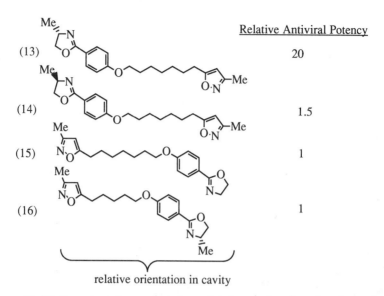

relative orientation in cavity

Figure 13   Binding orientations and relative antiviral potencies of a series of oxazoline-based inhibitors.

crystallographic studies on many similar agents aimed at defining precisely the structural requirements for potent, broad-spectrum, antirhinoviral activity. One of the main conclusions to come from this work is that, although the overall binding is almost entirely hydrophobic, and therefore essentially nondirectional, relatively small changes in inhibitor structure can significantly affect binding. For example, the (S) enantiomer (compound 13) of the methyl oxazoline inhibitor shows a higher binding affinity than the (R) enantiomer (compound 14), as a consequence of an interaction between the oxazoline methyl group and two residues, Leu106 and Ser107, on the surface of the canyon (59). This increased binding is reflected in a 13-fold difference in antiviral potency between the two isomers. Similarly, removing the oxazoline methyl substituent, or reducing the number of linking methylene groups from seven to five, as in compounds 15 and 16, respectively, results in a 180° change in orientation of binding in the cavity (Figure 13) (5).

Early results with the WIN series of compounds also showed that, although increasing the lipophilicity of the inhibitor generally led to improved antiviral potency, incorporation of bulky substituents on the phenyl ring, as in compound 17 (below) for example, was usually deleterious (21). When the crystal structures of further inhibitors bound to HRV-14 were solved, the reason for this lipophilicity ceiling became

(17) _inactive_

apparent. When the substituent on the phenyl group is over a certain size, the compounds are sterically blocked from entering the cavity by the side chains of the residues lining the pocket. By using all the structural data for uncoating inhibitors bound to HRV-14, it has been possible to generate a common volume that must be filled for a compound to be able to block the uncoating process. Similarly, by modeling into the binding pocket analogues that showed only weak binding, an exclusion volume could be generated that indicates those parts in the cavity where additional bulk in an inhibitor is not tolerated (19). This information is now being used to design inhibitors for which binding to the cavity has been optimized, and this should result in increased levels of antiviral activity against a wide range of isolates.

SUMMARY

Design cycles will undoubtedly play an increasingly important role in drug discovery in the coming years, as the amount of structural information on protein targets continues to rise. However, the traditional method of drug discovery, based upon random screening and systematic modification of leads by medicinal chemistry techniques, will probably not be abandoned completely because it has a potentially important advantage over more structure-based methods—namely, leads identified in this way are unlikely to show a close resemblance to the natural ligand or substrate. They may, therefore, have advantages in terms of patent novelty, selectivity, or pharmacokinetic profile. However, such leads could then serve as the basis for structure-based, rational modification programs, in which their interactions with target receptors are defined (as we have described) and improved molecules are designed.

A final important point to be made about structure-based design in drug discovery is that, while it can be of great use in the initial process of identifying ligands with improved affinity and selectivity in vitro, it can usually say very little about other essential aspects of the drug discovery process, e.g. the need to achieve an adequate pharmacokinetic profile and low toxicity in vivo. This observation reminds us that drug design is a multidisciplinary process, involving molecular biologists, biochemists, pharmacologists, organic chemists, crystallographers, and others. In order to be effective, therefore, structure-based design must be properly integrated into the overall discovery effort.

Literature Cited

1. Abola EE, Bernstein FC, Bryant SH, Koetzle TF, Weng J. 1987. Protein data bank. In *Crystallographic Databases— Information Content, Software Systems, Scientific Applications,* ed. FH Allen, G Bergerhoff, R Sievers, pp. 107–32. Bonn/Cambridge/Chester: Data Comm. Int. Union Crystallogr.
2. Allen FH, Bellard S, Brice MD, Cartwright BA, Doubleday A, et al. 1979. Cambridge crystallographic data centre—computer-based search, retrieval, analysis and display of information. *Acta Cryst. B* 35:2331
3. Appelt K, Bacquet RJ, Bartlett CA, Booth CLJ, Freer ST, et al. 1991. Design of enzyme inhibitors using iterative protein crystallographic analysis. *J. Med. Chem.* 34:1925
4. Bacon DJ, Moult J. 1992. Docking by least-squares fitting of molecular surface patterns. *J. Mol. Biol.* 225:849
5. Badger J, Minor I, Kremer MJ, Oliveira MA, Smith TJ, et al. 1988. Structural analysis of a series of antiviral agents complexed with human rhinovirus 14. *Proc. Natl. Acad. Sci. USA* 85:3304
6. Bedarkar S, Turnell WG, Blundell TL, Schwabe C. 1977. Relaxin has conformational homology with insulin. *Nature* 270:449
7. Bernstein FC, Koetzle TF, Williams GJB, Meyer EF Jr, Brice MD, et al. 1977. The protein data bank: a computer based archival file for macromolecular structures. *J. Mol. Biol.* 112:535
8. Blundell TL, Carney D, Gardner S, Hayes F, Howlin B, et al. 1988. Knowledge-based protein modelling and design. *Eur. J. Biochem.* 172:513
9. Blundell TL, Elliott G, Gardner SP, Hubbard T, Islam S, et al. 1989. Protein engineering and design. *Philos. Trans. R. Soc. London Ser. B* 324:447
10. Blundell TL, Lapatto R, Wilderspin AF, Hemmings AM, Hobart PM, et al. 1990. The 3-D structure of HIV-1 proteinase and the design of antiviral agents for the treatment of AIDS. *Trends Biochem. Sci.* 15:425
11. Blundell TL, Sibanda BL, Sternberg MJE, Thornton JM. 1987. Knowledge-based prediction of protein structure and the design of novel molecules. *Nature* 326:347
12. Bohm H-J. 1992. LUDI: rule-based automatic design of new substituents for enzyme inhibitor leads. *J. Comput. Aided Mol. Des.* 6:593
13. Bowie JU, Luthy R, Eisenberg D. 1991. A method to identify protein sequences that fold into a known three-dimensional structure. *Science* 253:164
14. Bures MG, Hutchins CW, Maus M, Kohlbrenner W, Kadam S, Erickson JW. 1990. Using three-dimensional substructure searching to identify novel, non-peptidic inhibitors of HIV-1 proteinase. *Tetrahedron Comput. Methodol.* 3:673
15. Busetta B, Tickle IJ, Blundell TL. 1983. Docker, an interactive program for simulating protein-receptor and substrate interactions. *J. Appl. Crystallogr.* 16:432
16. Claessens M, van Cutsem E, Lasters I, Wodak S. 1989. Modelling the polypeptide backbone with 'spare parts' from known protein structures. *Protein Eng.* 2:335
17. Clore GM, Gronenborn AM. 1991. Structures of larger proteins in solution: three- and four-dimensional heteronuclear NMR spectroscopy. *Science* 252: 1390
18. DesJarlais RL, Seibel GL, Kuntz ID, Furth PS, Alvarez JC, et al. 1990. Structure-based design of nonpeptide inhibi-

tors specific for the human immunodeficiency virus 1 protease. *Proc. Natl. Acad. Sci. USA* 87:6644

19. Diana GD, Kowalczyk P, Treasurywala AM, Oglesby RC, Pevear DC, Dutko FJ. 1992. CoMFA analysis of the interactions of antipicornavirus compounds in the binding pocket of human rhinovirus-14. *J. Med. Chem.* 35:1002

20. Diana GD, McKinlay MA, Otto MJ, Akullian V, Oglesby C. 1985. [[(4,5-Dihydro - 2 - oxazolyl)phenoxy]alkyl]isoxazoles. Inhibitors of picornavirus uncoating. *J. Med. Chem.* 28:1906

21. Diana GD, Treasurywala AM, Bailey TR, Oglesby RC, Pevear DC, Dutko FJ. 1990. A model for compounds active against human rhinovirus-14 based upon x-ray crystallographic data. *J. Med. Chem.* 33:1306

22. Ealick SE, Babu YS, Bugg CE, Erion MD, Guida WC, et al. 1991. Application of crystallographic and modelling methods in the design of purine nucleoside phosphorylase inhibitors. *Proc. Natl. Acad. Sci. USA* 88:11540

23. Ealick SE, Rule SA, Carter DC, Greenhough TJ, Babu YS, et al. 1990. Three-dimensional structure of human erythrocytic purine nucleoside phosphorylase at 3.2Å resolution. *J. Biol. Chem.* 265:1812

24. Eigenbrot C, Randal M, Quan C, Burnier J, O'Connell L, et al. 1991. X-ray structure of human relaxin at 1.5 Å. Comparison to insulin and implications for receptor binding determinants. *J. Mol. Biol.* 221:15

25. Erickson J, Neidhart DJ, VanDrie J, Kempf DJ, Wang XC, et al. 1990. Design, activity, and 2.8Å crystal structure of a C_2 symmetric inhibitor complexed to HIV-1 protease. *Science* 249:527

26. Gilson MK, Sharp KA, Honig BH. 1988. Calculating the electrostatic potential of molecules in solution: method and error assessment. *J. Comput. Chem.* 9:327

27. Goodford PJ. 1985. A computational procedure for determining energetically favourable binding sites on biologically important molecules. *J. Med. Chem.* 28:849

28. Goodsell DS, Mian IS, Olson AJ. 1989. Rendering volumetric data in molecular systems. *J. Mol. Graph.* 7:41

29. Grootenhuis PDJ, van Geerestein VJ, Haasnoot CAG, Karplus M. 1992. Molecular modelling of protein-ligand interactions. *Bull. Soc. Chim. Belg.* 101:661

30. Hardy LW, Finer-Moore JS, Montfort WR, Jones MO, Santi DV, Stroud RM. 1987. Atomic structure of thymidylate synthase: target for rational drug design. *Science* 235:448

31. Hendlich M, Lackner P, Weitckus S, Floeckner H, Froschauer R, et al. 1990. Identification of native protein folds amongst a large number of incorrect models—the calculation of low-energy conformations from potentials of mean force. *J. Mol. Biol.* 216:167

32. Johnson MS, Overington JP, Blundell TL. 1993. Alignment and searching for common protein folds using a data bank of structural templates. *J. Mol. Biol.* 231:735

33. Jones TH, Thirup S. 1986. Using known substructures in protein model building and crystallography. *EMBO J.* 5:819

34. Kuntz ID, Blaney JM, Oatley SJ, Langridge R, Ferrin TE. 1982. A geometric approach to macromolecule-ligand interactions. *J. Mol. Biol.* 161:269

35. Langridge R, Ferrin TE, Kuntz ID, Connolly ML. 1981. Real-time colour graphics in studies of molecular interactions. *Science* 211:661

36. Lapatto R, Blundell T, Hemmings A, Overington J, Wilderspin A, et al. 1989. X-ray analysis of HIV-1 proteinase at 2.7Å resolution confirms structural homology among retroviral enzymes. *Nature* 342:299

37. Laskowski RA, MacArthur MW, Moss DS, Thornton JM. 1993. PROCHECK—a program to check the stereochemical quality of protein structures. *J. Appl. Crystallogr.* 26:283

38. Lawrence MC, Davis PC. 1992. CLIX: a search algorithm for finding novel ligands capable of binding proteins of known three-dimensional structure. *Proteins Struct. Funct. Genet.* 12:31

39. Leach AR, Kuntz ID. 1992. Conformational analysis of flexible ligands in macromolecular receptor sites. *J. Comput. Chem.* 13:730

40. Lewis RA. 1993. Automated site-directed drug design: a method for generation of general three dimensional molecular graphics. *J. Mol. Graph.* 10:131

41. Luthy R, McLachlan AD, Eisenberg D. 1991. Secondary structure-based profiles: use of structure-conserving scoring tables in searching protein sequence databases for structural similarities. *Proteins Struct. Funct. Genet.* 10:229

42. Matthews DA, Appelt K, Oatley SJ, Xuong NgH. 1990. Crystal structure of *Escherichia coli* thymidylate synthase containing bound 5-fluoro-2'-deoxyuri-

374   WHITTLE & BLUNDELL

dylate and 10-propargyl-5,8,-dideazafolate. *J. Mol. Biol.* 214:923

43. Miller M, Schneider J, Sathyanarayana BK, Toth MV, Marshall GR, et al. 1989. Structure of complex of synthetic HIV-1 protease with a substrate-based inhibitor at 2.3Å resolution. *Science* 246:1149

44. Miranker A, Karplus M. 1991. Functionality maps of binding sites: a multiple copy simultaneous search method. *Proteins Struct. Funct. Genet.* 11:29

45. Montfort WR, Perry KM, Fauman EB, Finer-Moore JS, Maley GF, et al. 1990. Structure, multiple site binding, and segmental accomodation in thymidylate synthase on binding dUMP and an antifolate. *Biochemistry* 29:6964

46. Montgomery JA, Niwas S, Rose JD, Secrist III JA, Babu YS, et al. 1993. Structure-based design of inhibitors of purine nucleoside phosphorylase. 1. 9-(Arylmethyl) derivatives of 9-deazaguanine. *J. Med. Chem.* 36:55

47. Navia MA, Fitzgerald PMD, McKeever BM, Leu C-T, Heimbach JC, et al. 1989. Three-dimensional structure of aspartyl protease from human immunodeficiency virus HIV-1. *Nature* 337:615

48. Novotny J, Rashin JJ, Bruccoleri RE. 1988. Criteria that discriminate between native proteins and incorrectly folded model. *Proteins Struct. Funct. Genet.* 4:19

49. Overington JP, Johnson MS, Sali A, Blundell TL. 1990. Tertiary structural constraints on protein evolutionary diversity: templates, key residues and structure prediction. *Proc. R. Soc. London Ser. B* 241:132

50. Pattabiraman N, Levitt M, Ferrin TE, Langridge R. 1985. Computer graphics in real-time docking with energy calculation and minimization. *J. Comput. Chem.* 6:432

51. Payne AWR, Glen RC. 1993. Molecular Recognition using a binary genetic search algorithm. *J. Mol. Graph.* 11:76

52. Presnell SR, Cohen BI, Cohen FE. 1992. A segment-based approach to protein secondary structure prediction. *Biochemistry* 31:983

53. Rossmann MG, Arnold E, Erickson JW, Frankenberger EA, Griffith JP, et al. 1985. Structure of a human common cold virus and functional relationship to other picornaviruses. *Nature* 317:145

54. Rotstein SH, Murcko MA. 1993. GenStar—a method for de novo drug design. *J. Comput. Aided Mol. Des.* 7:23

55. Rotstein SH, Murcko MA. 1993. GroupBuild: a fragment-based method for de novo drug design. *J. Med. Chem.* 36:1700

56. Rusinko A III, Sheridan RP, Nilakantan R, Haraki KS, Bauman N, Venkataraghavan R. 1989. Using CONCORD to construct a large database of three-dimensional coordinates from connection tables. *J. Chem. Inf. Comput. Sci.* 29:251

57. Sali A, Blundell TL. 1990. Definition of general topological equivalence in protein structures. A procedure involving comparison of properties and relationships through simulated annealing and dynamic programming. *J. Mol. Biol.* 212:403

58. Shoichet BK, Stroud RM, Santi DV, Kuntz ID, Perry KM. 1993. Structure-based discovery of inhibitors of thymidylate synthase. *Science* 259:1445

59. Smith TJ, Kremer MJ, Luo M, Vriend G, Arnold E, et al. 1986. The site of attachment in human rhinovirus 14 for antiviral agents that inhibit uncoating. *Science* 233:1286

60. Srinivasen N, Blundell TL. 1993. An evaluation of the performance of an automated procedure for comparative modelling of protein tertiary structure. *Protein Eng.* 6:501

61. Summers NL, Carlson WD, Karplus M. 1987. Analysis of side-chain orientations in homologous proteins. *J. Mol. Biol.* 196:175

62. Sutcliffe MJ, Hayes FRF, Blundell TL. 1987. Knowledge-based modelling of homologous proteins. II. Rules for the conformations of substituted side chains. *Protein Eng.* 1:385

63. Toh H, Ono M, Saigo K, Miyata T. 1985. Retroviral protease-like sequence in the yeast transposon Ty-1. *Nature* 315:691

64. Tomioka N, Itai A, Iitaka Y. 1987. A method for fast energy estimation and visualization of protein-ligand interaction. *J. Comput. Aided Mol. Des.* 1:197

65. Topham C, McLeod A, Eisenmenger F, Overington JP, Johnson MS, Blundell TL. 1993. Fragment ranking in modelling of protein structure. Conformationally constrained environmental amino acid substitution tables. *J. Mol. Biol.* 229:194

66. Topham CM, Thomas P, Overington JP, Johnson MS, Eisenmenger F, Blundell TL. 1991. An assessment of COMPOSER: a rule-based approach to modelling protein structure. *Biochem. Soc. Symp.* 57:1

67. Varney MD, Marzoni GP, Palmer CL, Deal JG, Webber S, et al. 1992. Crystal-structure-based design and synthesis of benz[cd]indole-containing inhibitors of thymidylate synthase. *J. Med. Chem.* 35:663

68. Webber SE, Bleckman TM, Attard J, Deal JG, Kathardekar V, et al. 1993. Design of thymidylate synthase inhibitors using protein crystal structures: the synthesis and biological evaluation of a novel class of 5-substituted quinazolinones. *J. Med. Chem.* 36:733

69. Wlodawer A, Miller M, Jaskolski M, Sathyanarayana BK, Baldwin E, et al. 1989. Conserved folding in retroviral proteases: crystal structure of a synthetic HIV-1 protease. *Science* 245:616

70. Wlodawer A, Swain AL, Gustchina A. 1992. Comparison of crystal structures of inhibitor complexes of the human immunodeficiency virus protease. In *Molecular Aspects of Chemotherapy*, ed D Shugar, W Rode, E Borowski, pp. 173–86. Warsaw/Berlin: Springer-Verlag

71. Wodak SJ, Janin J. 1978. Computer analysis of protein-protein interactions. *J. Mol. Biol.* 124:323

72. Wuthrich K. 1989. Protein structure determination in solution by nuclear magnetic resonance spectroscopy. *Science* 243:45

Annu. Rev. Biophys. Biomol. Struct. 1994. 23:377–405
Copyright © 1994 by Annual Reviews Inc. All rights reserved

MOLECULAR NANOMACHINES: Physical Principles and Implementation Strategies

K. Eric Drexler

Institute for Molecular Manufacturing, Palo Alto, California 94301

KEY WORDS: nanotechnology, protein engineering, atomic force microscopy, supramolecular chemistry

CONTENTS

PERSPECTIVES AND OVERVIEW

In this review, I assess progress in the design and implementation of molecular machine systems by focusing on the fundamental principles of mechanosynthesis and emerging strategies for the synthesis and assembly of large ($>10^6$ atom) devices. This chapter describes existing knowledge and capabilities from the perspective of molecular systems engineering and examines key objectives in implementing molecular machine systems.

377

1056–8700/94/0610–0377$05.00

The range of structures termed molecular machines is extraordinarily diverse. Examples include pairs of trypticine moieties with aryl groups that mesh to enforce gearlike corotation (65), polymeric materials that can be driven through cycles of contraction and relaxation by changes in pH (99), zeolite catalysts, enzymes, and the bacterial flagellar motor. A recent review stated that "a molecular machine, commonly an assembly of polymeric molecules, is a structural fabrication that can convert energy from one form or location to another" (99, p. 819). This review instead focuses on a more restricted class of objects—those in which specific molecules combine to form "a structure consisting of a framework and various fixed and moving parts, for doing some kind of work" (35a); the quoted language is a dictionary definition of machine.

Theoretical studies of mechanically guided chemical synthesis (mechanosynthesis) have described some of the useful work that molecular machine systems can perform (18, 24, 61, 67); other studies describe how they can perform computation (20, 22, 24, 63). Thus, besides processing energy, molecular machine systems can also process matter and information. Among these processing functions, mechanosynthesis is of basic importance because it can be used to build molecular machine systems able to perform the other functions. Developing molecular machine systems capable of mechanosynthesis is thus a strategic objective.

In the next section, I compare solution synthesis and enzymatic synthesis with mechanosynthesis and describe the physical principles of mechanosynthetic systems and processes. This description helps define objectives for molecular machine research, indicating the size and nature of the required structures. In the following two sections, I review state-of-the-art in techniques for implementing molecular machine systems and use the requirements of mechanosynthesis to focus attention on key concerns. The first of these sections discusses techniques for molecular positioning using atomic force microscope technologies; a development approach based on these techniques would use mechanosynthesis to build molecular machines. The second reviews progress in protein engineering as a basis for the design and construction of complex functional devices; a development approach based on these techniques would build molecular machine systems via Brownian self-assembly of protein-like molecules to form supramolecular structures. Thus, mechanosynthesis provides a goal for molecular machine development, and AFM positioning and engineering of protein-like molecules provide alternative means toward that end.

MOLECULAR MACHINES FOR MECHANOSYNTHESIS

Suitable molecular machine systems can perform mechanosynthesis, and mechanosynthesis can build molecular machine systems (18, 24). This section first compares mechanosynthesis, enzymatic synthesis, and conventional solution-phase synthesis and then reviews the principles of mechanosynthesis and the implications of these principles for the design of mechanosynthetic devices and for the required capabilities of an underlying molecular machine technology.

Solution Synthesis, Enzymatic Synthesis, and Mechanosynthesis

Currently, chemical synthesis is conducted almost exclusively in solution, where reagent molecules move by diffusion and encounter one another in random positions and orientations. Solution-phase synthesis poses familiar problems of reaction specificity. Although many small-molecule reactions proceed cleanly and have high yields, large molecules with many functional groups present multiple potential reaction sites and, hence, can be converted into multiple products. Single-product yields of 99% are usually considered excellent, yet a sequence of 10,000 steps of this sort would have a net yield of $\sim 10^{-44}$, thus reliably yielding zero product molecules from any practicable amount of starting material.

Although a spectrum of intermediate cases can be identified, enzymatic synthesis differs significantly from the standard solution-phase model. Enzymatic reactions (11) begin with reagent binding, which places molecules in well-controlled positions and orientations. The resulting high effective concentrations (often augmented by strain energy, polarization, and catalytic groups) result in high reaction rates. The specificity of the binding interactions determines reaction geometries and results in highly specific reactions. Most alternative reagents will not bind in the active site, and among bound reagents, most alternative reaction geometries are excluded.

Mechanosynthesis as defined here differs from enzymatic catalysis (again, a spectrum of intermediate cases can be identified), yet many of the same principles apply. Anticipated molecular machine systems can position bound reagent molecules with respect to one another and guide the chemical reactions with a degree of specificity not found in solution-phase chemistry (24). The strain energy applied by enzymes is no greater than a fraction of the potential binding energy of the substrate (11), but power-driven mechanosynthetic devices can apply strains of bond-breaking magnitude (24). The provision of enzyme-like reaction environments is also feasible.

One can perform mechanosynthesis by using macroscopic devices, such as scanning tunneling and atomic force microscope (STM and AFM) mechanisms. The first clear example of a mechanically controlled synthesis (albeit of a noncovalent structure) was the arrangement of 35 xenon atoms on a nickel crystal to spell "IBM" (27). STM manipulation of atoms and molecules has been extended, for example, to CO bound to platinum and to silicon atoms on silicon (56). Although these processes still lack the control necessary to build molecular machine systems, they demonstrate the direct, mechanically guided rearrangement of the fundamental building blocks of matter.

Principles of Mechanosynthesis

Mechanosynthetic systems can use several effects to speed desired reactions and to suppress side reactions. Of these, the most basic is control of localized reaction probabilities by mechanical positioning of reactive groups. Solution phase processes provide a convenient point of reference and enable a description in terms of effective concentrations (a more direct description relies on transition-state theory).

EFFECTIVE CONCENTRATION   Consider a reaction between two groups, A and B, that can be attached either to separate molecules free to diffuse in solution or to a single, flexible molecule. The ratio of the intermolecular and intramolecular rate constants defines the effective concentration

$$\frac{k_{intra}(s^{-1})}{k_{inter}(M^{-1}s^{-1})} = C_{eff} \ (M).$$

Intramolecular reactions can be accelerated by electronic effects (in which case one might say that the reacting groups have been altered), by release of steric strain (a piezochemical effect), by differential solvation effects, or more commonly, by proximity and orientation. When groups A and B are linked by a flexible polymer, the effective concentrations take on conventional values (less than 55 M, the concentration of water molecules in water). When A and B are held in close proximity and in the correct alignment for a reaction, the effective concentration can be much higher. Thiols in proteins exhibit effective concentrations for disulfide formation of $>10^5$ M; in rigid organic molecules, effective concentrations can be $>10^9$ M, which is close to a theoretically calculated limit of about 10^{10} M (11). Where a structure holds two groups apart, the effective concentration can be essentially zero.

COMPLIANCE AND THERMAL MOTION   The effective concentration of a favorably positioned and oriented group is greater than or equal to the spatial probability density of a reference point in that group (e.g. a nuclear position) relative to a coordinate system based in the other group. This probability density can be calculated from the temperature and the potential energy surface of the system.

In terms of the compliances c (reciprocal stiffnesses, measured in m/N), the potential energy of a group positioned by a linear mechanical system is

$$V = \frac{1}{2} (\Delta x^2/c_x + \Delta y^2/c_y + \Delta z^2/c_z)$$

for a suitable choice of coordinates that measure displacement of one group with respect to another, provided that deformation of the groups themselves can be approximated as linear. (Conformational flexibility would violate this condition.)

PROBABILITY DENSITY AND EFFECTIVE CONCENTRATION   In both classical and quantum statistical mechanics, the probability density for a harmonic system is the product of the Gaussian probability densities along each of the coordinates. A comparison of classical and quantum mechanical results shows that the classical approximation is adequate for describing most mechanical systems of nanometer or larger scale at room temperature (24); quantum mechanical corrections become substantial (>0.1) only at extremes of low temperature, high stiffness, or low mass (e.g. for displacements of individual hydrogen atoms).

In the classical approximation, the Gaussian distribution for a single coordinate is characterized by a standard deviation

$$\sigma = \sqrt{c_x kT}.$$

At the peak of the Gaussian distribution, the local concentration of a group is

$$C_{\text{local}} = [1000 N_a \sqrt{c_x c_y c_z} (2\pi kT)^{3/2}]^{-1} \text{ (M)},$$

where N_a is Avogadro's number and energies are in joules. For a system with a compliance of 1 m/N along each of three axes, C_{local} approximately equals 400 M at 300 K. If the transverse compliance of the transition state is small compared with the compliance of the positioning mechanism (as is typical), the local concentration calculated above is approximately equal to the effective concentration (in the absence of orientational effects, which can increase the effective concentration by several orders of magnitude). This formulation neglects the steric interaction of the two reagent groups, which typically increases the effective concentration via excluded volume effects.

A useful model for many mechanosynthetic systems treats the positioning system as applying force along the z axis that presses a group against an unyielding wall. Neglecting stiffness along the z axis, the probability density function is exponential in z, while remaining Gaussian in x and y. The effective concentration is then

$$C_{local} = F[1000N_a\sqrt{c_x c_y}\, 2\pi(kT)^2]^{-1} \text{ (M)},$$

where F is the applied force in Newtons. For $F = 0.01$ nN, with a compliance of 1 m/N along each of remaining axes, $C_{local} \approx 150$ M at 300 K.

Rate increases from positioning are purely entropic: confining the reacting groups to a smaller volume of configuration space increases the frequency of reactive encounters. Positional control of reagents suppresses reactions at remote sites; along an axis with a compliance of 0.66 m/N, the effective concentration of a group at a distance of ~ 0.3 nm is 10^{-8} of the peak (in the absence of reactive groups from other sources). This effect is enthalpic: displacement of the group to a remote reaction site imposes a large strain energy on the supporting structure. Mechanical forces can reduce reaction energy barriers by applying a strain energy that is relieved by passage through the transition state. These favorable enthalpic effects are discussed elsewhere (24).

More accurate models of mechanosynthetic control can be developed from transition-state theory and knowledge of the reaction potential energy surface, but such models are beyond the scope of this review. Models based on effective concentration suffice to show how reaction rates at selected sites can be accelerated, while reactions at alternative, chemically equivalent sites can be suppressed. Provided that the desired reactions occur with high reliability (for a review of requisite conditions, see 24), mechanical control will permit syntheses with $\geqslant$ 10^6 sequential reactions to proceed with high yield.

Requirements for Mechanosynthetic Molecular Machinery

A mechanosynthetic device must bind reactive molecules (or groups) and position them relative to an object under construction. The device must be a structure of substantial size and stiffness capable of motion in several controllable degrees of freedom (ideally, six or more). These functional requirements resemble those of an industrial robot arm. Such a device differs substantially from known biological structures and solution-phase systems of small molecules or enzymes.

NEARLY DETERMINISTIC MACHINES   Conventional machines are nearly deterministic, which means they perform a specific series of operations at a predictable rate. Molecular machine systems can likewise be nearly deterministic, provided that the following conditions are met:

1. Mechanical stiffness is large enough to restrict thermal motion to acceptable bounds.
2. All energy barriers between acceptable states and error states are large relative to kT.
3. Input power drives the system through a specific sequence of acceptable states at an acceptable rate.

For a mechanosynthetic system, condition 1 requires that thermal fluctuations seldom bring a positioned group in contact with an inappropriate reaction site, condition 2 requires that the group (and other parts of the structure) not degrade or perform motions analogous to a gear slipping a tooth, and condition 3 requires that the positioning mechanism be driven along a suitable trajectory while binding the right sequence of reactive groups.

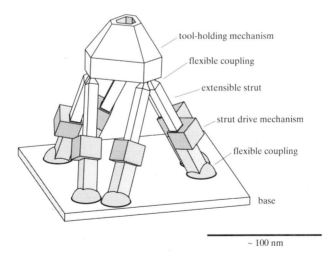

tool-holding mechanism

flexible coupling

extensible strut

strut drive mechanism

flexible coupling

base

~ 100 nm

Figure 1   Overall geometry of a mechanosynthetic device based on a Stewart platform. The lengths of the six struts are controlled externally, thus enabling the platform to be moved in six degrees of freedom.

A MECHANOSYNTHETIC POSITIONING MECHANISM   Figure 1 illustrates a class of positioning mechanisms based on a Stewart platform. The six struts have controllable lengths and form part of a rigid octahedral framework. Figure 2 illustrates a portion of the range of motion of such a device. The six-strut system gives control of all six degrees of translational and rotational freedom.

DIAMONDOID STRUCTURES   Structures made of diamondoid materials are well suited to molecular machine systems (19, 24, 60). Diamondoid materials are extremely stiff (Young's modulus typically 250–1000 GPa) and the units of design are individual atoms, which permits great freedom in specifying structures. Investigators have explored useful reactions for synthesizing diamondoid structures by using ab initio molecular orbital methods (67). Figure 3 illustrates a diamondoid bearing (60). Symmetry properties enable properly designed bearings of this class to rotate with energy barriers <0.001 kT (21, 24, 62). Diamondoid structures can serve as a basis for stiff, nearly deterministic systems able to perform mechanosynthetic operations in vacuum at high frequencies ($\sim 10^6$ s^{-1}) and with high reliability (error rates $<10^{-15}$) (24). Diamondoid systems are a natural long-term goal for molecular mechanical engineering, but their fabrication will require advanced mechanosynthetic capabilities.

POLYMERIC STRUCTURES   Molecular machine systems for mechanosynthesis can be developed in either of two ways: (a) mechanosynthetic capabilities first, which are then used to construct molecular machinery

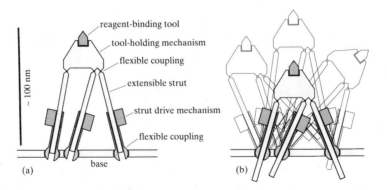

Figure 2   A two-dimensional diagram of a portion of the range of motion available to a Stewart platform like that in Figure 1.

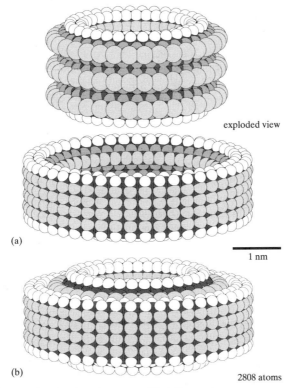

exploded view

(a)

1 nm

(b)

2808 atoms

Figure 3 A rotary bearing based on a modified diamond structure, designed and analyzed in collaboration with R Merkle at Xerox Palo Alto Research Center. Interlocking
ridges provide a large axial stiffness, while calculated rotational energy barriers are
<0.001 at 300 K. Fabrication of such structures will require mechanosynthesis.

or (*b*) molecular machinery first, which is then used to perform mechanosynthesis.

Either way, the initial products will be polymeric structures. Mechanosynthetic systems immersed in solution should enable the assembly of complex structures from monomers joined to form an extensively cross-linked polymer. Complex structures made by synthesis
and self-assembly will likely be built from polymeric building blocks
with fewer cross-links. The feasible Young's modulus for protein-like
structures is presumably no less than that of structural proteins: 4 GPa
for wool (containing alpha-helical keratin) (102), 10 GPa for silk (along
the beta-strand direction) (102), 10 GPa estimated for bacterial flagella

and *F*-actin (polymers of globular proteins) (73). The feasible modulus of elasticity for cross-linked polymeric structures is presumably in the range of biological and engineering polymers, for example, 1–14 GPa for various resins (97) and 100 GPa for cellulose (102). It may be feasible to stiffen self-assembled structures by incorporating grooves that bind stiffer polymeric chains or chemical precursors to chains or nets.

MECHANOSYNTHETIC POSITIONING WITH POLYMERIC STRUCTURES   The stiffness of a Stewart platform with respect to a surrounding framework structure will be of the same order as the stretching stiffness of one of the struts. A cylinder of modulus 10 GPa with a diameter of 15 nm and a length of 100 nm has a stretching compliance <0.06 m/N. This is a fraction of the tolerable compliance of a reliable mechanosynthetic device, and it provides a margin for additional compliances (e.g. flexibility in reactive groups). Among components of invariant shape, stiffness is proportional to scale, hence structures much smaller than this cylinder may not be adequate.

A more detailed examination of mechanosynthetic devices (24) describes means for binding appropriate reactive molecules and for using externally imposed pressure fluctuations to drive and control operations. The present survey of mechanosynthesis and the requirements it imposes on molecular machine design suffices to identify the fabrication of complex and stiff aperiodic structures as a key development problem.

SELF-REPLICATION   Self-replicating molecular systems have been developed from biological or chemical components. In the polymerase chain reaction, DNA strands replicate in the presence of reagents, enzymes, and cycling environmental conditions (66). RNA molecules can replicate in the presence of activated monomers and a polymerizing enzyme (26). Rebek has designed and synthesized simpler self-replicating molecules that employ DNA-like hydrogen bonding (83). In these systems, molecules serve as templates for the assembly of similar molecules. Both the biological and the chemical systems omit the metabolic complexity of a cell because the experimenter provides the molecular building blocks and other requirements. By employing similar simplifications, mechanosynthetic molecular machine systems driven by externally provided information can be made to build structures like themselves (24, 61).

FABRICATION VIA AFM-BASED MECHANOSYNTHESIS

Atomic force microscope technology (7) enables the placement of tips against surfaces with a positional precision of ~0.01 nm and forces as low as 0.01 nN (104). (Thermal drift, however, necessitates frequent corrections in order to maintain a position.) Hansma et al (40) have reviewed the use of AFMs for imaging. These devices have also been used for dissection and imaging of biomolecular structures, such as plasmids (39) and membrane gap junctions (44).

The degree of positional control, together with the relatively low compliance of the tip with respect to transverse displacements ($\ll 1$ m/N), suits AFMs for use as positioning mechanisms in a mechano-synthetic system. The chief remaining requirement is the stiff attachment of molecules (e.g. monoclonal antibody fragments) able to bind and orient reagent molecules from a dilute solution (23–25). A system of this sort has not yet been demonstrated, but the physical principles of each component are sufficiently well understood to enable an estimate of the likely properties. Anticipated effective concentrations are on the order of 100 M, which would provide localized reaction-rate accelerations (relative to background reactions) on the order of 10^8 (24). These accelerations should suffice to build structures containing $> 10^5$ monomers.

A possible sequence of objectives in pursuing this line of development includes: (a) binding desired molecules to tips in controlled orientations, (b) placing and bonding several reactive groups, and (c) building increasingly complex systems by extending these operations. This approach to molecular machine development has substantial advantages and has been reviewed quite recently (24). The balance of the present review focuses on self-assembling systems, which are more closely related to biological systems and hence to biophysical concerns.

FABRICATION VIA SYNTHESIS AND SELF-ASSEMBLY

Considerable research in organic synthesis focuses on building complex supramolecular structures (3, 46, 53, 55, 83, 105); some of these structures are intended as steps toward molecular machine systems. Biological molecular machine systems form through the self-assembly of folded polymeric structures, chiefly proteins. This section reviews progress in engineering protein-like molecules and its applicability to molecular machine development.

Constraints and Strategies for Self-Assembly

Each step in the self-assembly of a large structure, such as a molecular machine system, involves an encounter between two or more smaller units. All, or all but one, of the units must be soluble; any insoluble unit must be exposed to solvent (units may include solubility aids that are later removed). Each block must bind specifically and with reasonable kinetics; improper binding must be either rare or reversible. Finally, the resulting assembly must be either kinetically stable or stabilized by a further operation.

For stability, covalent bonds usually must join the smallest units: few other links between small molecules withstand thermal agitation at ordinary temperatures. Polymeric structures have natural advantages for making diverse structures from small units; they are used in biology, and some (peptides and DNA) have well-developed synthetic methodologies. Self-assembled structures must be stiff to serve as good machine components; this requirement favors structures with dense internal packings, ideally of rigid, bulky substructures.

When joining larger units, a combination of many weak interactions typically serves better than the formation of a few strong bonds: weak interactions can combine to give strong binding in a particular geometry but little binding in other geometries. This phenomenon enables reliable assembly steps. Large, asymmetrical structures suitable for use as machine systems could then be assembled using any of several different strategies. One is to give each subunit interface a unique structure with unique binding propensities (as in the ribosome) and mix blocks of all types simultaneously. Another strategy is to emulate solid-phase synthesis by using cyclic exposure to different subunits to control the sequence in which components are added. Structural control then results partly from intrinsic binding specificities and partly from an externally imposed sequence of operations. This approach falls outside recently described, biologically inspired models for controlling self-assembly (55).

The surfaces of assembled components must meet various functional constraints. These will presumably include provision of binding sites for other molecules, such as tools, auxiliary structural elements, and perhaps electronically active components. Binding of other molecules (perhaps followed by their polymerization) can provide a mechanism for altering surface structure after the primary self-assembly process. Binding these molecules may help in meeting the conditions (24) for interfacial sliding with small energy barriers and thereby facilitate the design and fabrication of bearing surfaces.

Candidate Polymer Systems

Self-assembly of polymeric structural units does not demand individual units with stably folded conformations. Nonetheless, building with stable folded units appears advantageous with respect to ease of design, assembly kinetics, and avoidance of unwanted aggregation. Accordingly, the ability to design and synthesize polymers that form stably folded structures is an important objective.

NUCLEIC ACIDS   Ease of synthesis and ease of designing matching structures are two reasons for using nucleic acids as building materials. Nonlinear structures can be engineered from DNA; for example, Chen & Seeman have made a framework containing eight DNA junctions, which form a structure with the connectivity of a cube (8). However, the size and geometry of base-paired nucleotides, as well as the presence of a charged backbone, render the design of dense structures awkward. Furthermore, biological systems have (with a few striking exceptions) exploited proteins rather than nucleic acids as a basis for molecular machinery and structural components. Although nucleic acids deserve further consideration, protein-like materials seem more attractive.

STANDARD PROTEINS   Naturally occurring molecular machines are built chiefly of standard proteins, which are unbranched polymers of the 20 genetically encoded amino acids. Engineered standard proteins, which can often be made by biological means, can closely resemble natural models, thereby facilitating their design. The chief disadvantages of standard proteins are the limited choices of monomers and chain topology. The de novo design of standard proteins was recently reviewed (89), and successful efforts indicate that engineering of standard proteins could provide a path to complex molecular machine systems. This review, however, focuses on the advantages gained from working with a broader class of structures.

PROTEIN-LIKE MOLECULES   A primary motivation for engineering standard proteins is to understand the relationship between structure and stability in natural proteins (95). When engineering nonstandard, protein-like molecules, however, the primary motivation is to take the knowledge gained from engineering standard proteins and use it to make structures that fold more stably and predictably than natural or engineered standard proteins. Potentially useful differences from standard proteins include use of nonstandard amino acids and nonlinear chain topologies, as discussed below.

Researchers can incorporate nonstandard amino acids into proteins by using chemically aminoacylated tRNA in RNA-directed protein synthesis in vitro (4, 9, 72). These techniques have been used to probe protein stability (28, 59), thereby extending and confirming the results of more conventional mutational studies (95).

Scientists continue to review and improve methods for solid-phase peptide synthesis (30, 49); these methods enable wholesale use of nonstandard amino acids. Synthesis of chains that contain over 30 amino acid residues is now routine, although certain sequences are more difficult than others. To the extent that difficult sequences can be predicted (101), experimenters can avoid them by imposing suitable constraints during design (an option not available when making a predetermined natural product). Protein-like molecules ($\geq$50 residues) can be constructed either directly or by linking several shorter peptides. The latter approach presents serious difficulties if the links must be peptide bonds (e.g. to make a standard protein) but lesser difficulties if links are nonpeptide bonds (e.g. disulfide or metal-ligand bonds) formed between deprotected chains.

OTHER POLYMERS   Starburst dendrimers (98) form a diverse class of highly ordered three-dimensional molecular structures. Examples thus far, however, have had high symmetry or flexibility, which precludes their use as building blocks for self-assembled molecular machine systems. Future developments could remove these limitations.

Design of Proteins and Protein-Like Molecules

Natural proteins provide a reference model for the design of a broader class of protein-like molecules. Although the overall thermodynamics of protein stability remain controversial (81, 107), the influence of incremental changes in structure is comparatively well understood (1, 95). Accordingly, differences between standard proteins and proposed protein-like molecules can be used to estimate differences in folding stability. Rose & Wolfenden recently reviewed general issues in protein stability (91).

Yun-yu et al (108) have argued that present methods for computing free energy differences cannot accurately predict the effect of mutations on protein stability because of the difficulty of sampling enough conformations to compute entropic contributions. This prediction limitation, however, need not present difficulties for design. Consider a set of structural changes, each of which is of a type that is statistically favorable but individually uncertain. Because effects on stability are approximately additive, researchers can reliably predict that the joint effect of many such changes will be large and positive.

DESIGN AND STABILITY OF STANDARD PROTEINS   DeGrado (13), Mutter & Vuilleumier (70), and Richardson et al (88, 89) have reviewed various aspects of the design of peptides and proteins. Several of the latter have been designed de novo. The first was α_4 (14, 15, 86), which has been used as a basis for several subsequent modifications and refinements (37, 38, 82, 85). Others include a 79-residue de novo design (Felix) deliberately modeled on natural protein sequences; this structure folded successfully but with low stability (an estimated 0.8 kcal/ mol) (41). Felix, a four-α-helix design, was as successful on the first try as a β-sheet design (by the same group) was on the ninth attempt; this difference was attributed to the greater modularity of helices and the lesser solubility of β-sheet structures. Another four-helix bundle structure has been designed to present a desired immunogenic determinant (47). A 242-residue α/β-barrel protein has been designed and appears to fold correctly (35). A major conclusion drawn from de novo protein design is the importance of negative design, which seeks not only to stabilize a desired fold but to destabilize alternative folds and patterns of aggregation (14, 88).

Until recently, proteins designed de novo have shown NMR spectra characteristic of disordered cores (89); by modifying an earlier design, Raleigh & DeGrado (82) produced a protein with more native-like characteristics, including a distinct melting transition. These modifications replaced multiple Leu residues (which made up the entire core of α_4) with β-branched and aromatic residues and introduced shape complementarity into the packing interactions between helices. A separate effort, which yielded an even more well-ordered core, modified the α_4 design by adding two zinc binding sites (38).

NATURAL PROTEINS ARE NEEDLESSLY DESTABILIZED   Free energies of protein unfolding are favorable by about 5–20 kcal/mol (17), which corresponds to probabilities of occupying the unfolded state of about 10^{-4} to 10^{-15}. Because protein folding times are about 10^{-1} to 10^3 s (11), the mean waiting time to observe an unfolding event in an intact protein with a stability of 15 kcal/mol is over 100 years, which is longer than the lifespan of most organisms.

This waiting time is significant for protein design: because natural selection can only operate on events that occur, evolution has no direct mechanism for favoring proteins much more stable than those observed. The upper end of the stability range observed in vitro could be explained by the presence in vivo of denaturing influences, such as solutes, mechanical stresses, or elevated temperatures, which lead to selection for high stability. Alternatively, stability may sometimes correlate with other evolutionarily favored properties. Finally, free energies of unfolding for highly stable proteins in water are typically extrapolated from data on unfolding in · concentrated guanidinium chloride, which may introduce errors.

Because random mutations tend to destabilize any particular folded structure, evolutionary processes (either neutral or adaptive) tend to carry proteins to the threshold of significant instability. Accordingly, the consistently low stability of natural proteins is quite compatible with the goal of constructing artificial proteins of high stability (18). The infeasibility of predicting the folding of natural proteins is also compatible with the goal of designing proteins that fold predictably (18), as has been demonstrated (14).

Improving Stability, Predictability, and Solubility

The design of soluble, stably folded structures can play a central role in the technology of self-assembling molecular machine systems. This section reviews techniques and strategies that appear useful for designing such structures based on existing knowledge of protein stability and the opportunities offered by nonstandard amino acids and chain topologies.

BRANCHED CHAINS   Mutter has observed that branched chains have a lower conformational entropy in the unfolded state (because of excluded volume effects) and that branched protein-like structures consistent with a desired fold can be expected to fold more stably and predictably. His laboratory has synthesized several structures (termed template-assembled synthetic proteins) that confirm these predictions (68–70).

Applying the same principle with a different synthetic methodology, Hahn et al synthesized a stable 73-residue peptide that had four helical branches (36). They included a substrate-binding site with catalytic residues patterned on chymotrypsin; this peptide cleaved ester substrates at ~0.01 the rate of chymotrypsin, with a similar substrate affinity.

LOOPED CHAINS   Linking a polymer to form a loop decreases its entropy, and fold-compatible cross-links accordingly favor the folded state by reducing the entropy of unfolding (79). Researchers have developed computer-aided design software for identifying potential loops and disulfide bridges between already-defined structures (74) and used engineered disulfide bonds to stabilize natural proteins (75).

Rizo & Gierasch (90) recently reviewed conformationally constrained peptides containing nonstandard structures. Cross-links between residues i and $i + 4$ can be used to stabilize an α-helix. Formation of amide bonds between side chains during solid-phase synthesis has introduced multiple cross-links in good yields (29).

METAL-ION BINDING   Coordination of side-chain ligand groups to a metal ion can result in branched or looped structures of increased stability. Because metal ions can bind selectively to deprotected peptides under mild conditions, they can be incorporated late in an assembly sequence. Metal-ion binding can be quite specific because different groups have affinities for different metals and complexation can be reversible. Furthermore, Cr(II) and Co(II) are labile with respect to ligand exchange, but Cr(III) and Co(III) are relatively inert. Experimenters have introduced the labile forms into metal binding sites in proteins and then oxidized them to the exchange-inert species (100). This process could be useful in self-assembly because it combines the advantages of reversible, cooperative binding with those of a stable product.

Regan (84) recently reviewed the design of metal-binding sites in proteins; among the design efforts reported, the success rate was high. Regan & Clarke modified α_4 to incorporate a binding site for Zn(II) with two His and two Cys ligands; the resulting protein bound Zn(II) with an estimated dissociation constant of 2.5×10^{-8} M and was significantly stablized (85). Handel & DeGrado modified a de novo protein design (α_4) to incorporate a three-His Zn(II) binding site and observed both binding and substantial stabilization (37). They subsequently incorporated two such sites, which yielded a structure in which the core's stability was comparable to that of a natural protein (38). In a separate line of development, Pessi et al have engineered a three-His binding site in a protein modeled on a portion of an antibody variable domain (77). Hellinga & Richards designed a metal binding site that appears to bind Hg(II) as they predicted but binds Cu(II) in an unexpected mode (42, 43).

Metal complexes can stabilize isolated helices. One way to achieve such stability is to bind metal ions to pairs of nonstandard, metalligating residues (92); another approach results in an exchange-inert Ru(III) complex that binds pairs of histidine residues (32).

Metal complexes can also link separate peptide chains. For example, researchers have bound various divalent metal ions to assemble triple-helix bundle proteins in which amphipathic peptides are linked to a 2,2'-bipyridene functionality at their N termini (34, 54). A stable Ru(II) complex has been used to make a four-helix bundle protein by linking four pyridyl functionalities, each at the N-terminus of an amphiphilic peptide (33). These structures have branched topologies, the advantages of which were discussed earlier in this review.

MATCHED HYDROGEN-BONDED PAIRS   Unlike nucleic acids, standard proteins lack specific pair-wise interactions between monomers (with the exception of cysteine pairing to form disulfides). A study surveying multiple protein structures found no tendency for specific pairs of hydrophobic side chains to associate in protein cores and no tendency for specific pairs to be surrounded by better packed neighbors (6). [In any specific protein, however, the backbone geometry might impose stringent constraints on the allowable set of side chains and conformations (80).]

Nielson et al used standard solid-phase synthesis techniques to prepare polyamides that consisted of thymine-linked aminoethylglycyl units; these polymers bind tightly to DNA with sequence recognition (71). The use of a wider range of hydrogen-bonding groups in this manner would presumably enable the design of protein-like structures containing interfaces that had DNA-like complementarity.

REDUCED BACKBONE FLEXIBILITY   Substituting non-Gly for Gly residues or Pro for non-Pro residues decreases the conformational entropy of the unfolded state, thereby stabilizing the folded state (provided that these substitutions are compatible with the folded geometry) (58). Expected improvements are about 1 kcal/mol per residue replaced; observed improvements in natural proteins are smaller but comparable. Helices are stabilized by α-methyl-α-amino acids (dialkylglycines); difficulties in chain synthesis can be overcome by incorporating them as the C-terminal components of protected dipeptides (2).

REDUCED SIDE-CHAIN FLEXIBILITY   In several proteins, a buried side chain has multiple conformations discernible in X-ray structures (96), but most buried structures have no conformational freedom. Consequently, burial of flexible structures during folding imposes an entropic cost. The estimated $T\Delta S$ costs for burial of residues in a well-packed core (78) are substantial: Ile, -0.89; Leu, -0.78; Met, -1.61; Phe, -0.58; Val, -0.51 (all in kilocalories per mole at 300 K).

Protein-like molecules can incorporate nonstandard amino acids that have lower conformational entropy per unit volume in the unfolded state. Examples might include amino acids with side chains containing cyclohexyl, norbornyl, or adamantyl moieties. Assuming these amino acids are incorporated into folded structures that have similar core packing densities, strain energies, and so forth, this reduction in conformational entropy will contribute directly to increasing fold stability. Furthermore, by limiting side-chain flexibility, this strategy should decrease the likelihood of alternative core packings in the folded state and yield a structure of improved predictability and mechanical stability.

INCREASED PACKING DENSITY   Richards found that the packing density of protein interiors (the fraction of the volume inside the van der Waals surface) is like that of crystals of small organic molecules, 0.70–0.78 (87). The local packing densities within a single protein vary from <0.60 to >0.85; poor side-chain packing correlates with good backbone hydrogen bonding (e.g. in regular secondary structure), while dense side-chain packing correlates with regions of less regular hydrogen bonding (87).

High packing density tends to correlate with stronger van der Waals interactions and burial of more hydrophobic area; hence, provided bad steric contacts are avoided, greater packing density should correlate with greater fold stability and greater mechanical stiffness, which would improve components for molecular machine systems. The variable packing densities in natural proteins suggest that improvements are usually possible. By providing additional side-chain options that add to the set of available shapes, the use of nonstandard amino acids multiplies the number of possible core packings and hence the number of packings with unusually high densities.

Several algorithms identify densely packed sets of side chains and conformations compatible with a specified backbone structure. Some investigators assume that side chains always occupy approximately rotameric states (local minima of strain energy) (16, 80). In other algorithms, simulated annealing is used to search for low-energy packings of a specified set of side chains, including nonrotameric conformations (45, 52).

A rotameric algorithm successfully identified a repacking of a substantial region of the core of a natural protein (42, 43). Another rotameric algorithm that included a molecular mechanics energy, a solvation energy, and an entropic term (also based only on rotameric states) gave good predictions of the relative catalytic efficiency of over 40 related enzyme-substrate combinations and was used to design an altered enzyme that is both highly active and selective for a nonnatural substrate (106). These successes with standard amino acids suggest that the potential of nonstandard amino acids for increasing packing densities can in fact be successfully exploited.

REDUCED TORSIONAL STRAIN   A study of high-quality X-ray structures shows that roughly 20% of side chains are nonrotameric (i.e. have at least one torsion deviating by more than 20° from the optimal, rotameric angle); each has a strain energy of more than 1 kcal/mol (94). Even in a protein of only 70 residues, a mean strain energy of 1.5 kcal/mol for 20% of the side chains implies a destabilizing energy of 21 kcal/mol, which is greater than the net stability of the folded state. For a 300-residue protein, the estimated destabilization is 90 kcal/mol.

From a fold-prediction perspective, the prevalence of nonrotameric side chains presents difficulties for rotamer-based algorithms (16, 80). From a fold-design perspective, however, this situation presents some opportunities: if rotamer-based algorithms succeed in designing a dense, hydrophobic core, the resulting structure will be less strained and hence more stable (perhaps by >20 kcal/mol) than an analogous natural protein. Core designs with a relaxed rotameric constraint will have a trade-off between increasing density and decreasing strain. Adding nonstandard side chains to the set of options shifts this trade-off curve in a favorable direction.

REDUCED BAD CONTACTS   The mechanical compliances associated with torsional deformations and nonbonded contacts are comparable (though nonlinearities make this a rough comparison). Consequently, one would expect that packing forces, in storing a given amount of energy in torsional strain, would store a comparable amount of energy in bad van der Waals contacts. This effect would more or less double the total strain energy associated with nonrotameric torsions in side chains.

INCREASED CORE HYDROPHOBICITY   Dill concludes that hydrophobicity is the chief force driving protein folding and that the pattern of hydrophobicity along a chain chiefly determines the general pattern of its fold (17). Hydrophobicity patterns have been a primary concern in de novo designs. The α_4 design has an extraordinarily hydrophobic core and hydrophilic surface and an extremely high stability—~15.4 kcal/mol in one version (38). The Felix design does not exaggerate hydrophobicity contrasts and has an unusually low stability—~0.8 kcal/mol (41).

Based on a reinterpretation of the calorimetric studies of protein unfolding performed by Privalov & Gill (81) and on electrostatic calculations, Yang et al (107) have concluded that desolvation of peptide units and other polar structures has a large enthalpic cost (~1 kcal/mol per residue) even if these structures are hydrogen bonded in the folded state. This largely cancels the favorable effects of burying and desolvating hydrophobic side chains.

The cost of burying polar structure suggests strategies for increasing fold stability:

1. Increase the bulk of hydrophobic side chains, thereby decreasing the relative amount of polar structure in the interior.
2. Avoid burying polar side chains in the interior. About 7% of the residues in a typical natural protein have polar side chains that are ≥95% buried (11). A calculation of the fraction of buried side-chain structure that is polar gives a value of 9.8% (5).

Handel et al argue that buried polar structures provide interactions more specific than hydrophobic contacts and thus play an important role in organizing protein core structures (38). Their use of polar residues to construct metal-binding sites clearly demonstrates this effect, and metal binding can increase folding stability, much as cross-links do. Use of a metal ion–binding strategy is consistent with avoiding most buried polar structures, such as ion pairs and hydrogen-bonded side chains.

Perfluoroalkylated amphiphilic molecules are bulkier and more hydrophobic than their hydrogenated analogues and readily form supramolecular assemblies (51). Fluorinated side chains could also prove useful in engineering protein-like molecules.

NONAQUEOUS SOLVENT SYSTEMS   Many water-soluble enzymes remain catalytically active after being lyophilized and dispersed in anhydrous organic solvents such as octane and toluene (50). Furthermore, many are stable to temperatures >100°C and appear to have less conformational flexibility than in water (103). Antibody-hapten binding remains strong and specific in anhydrous organic solvents (93). Because natural proteins (which have evolved under selective pressures favoring marginal stability in aqueous media) can often tolerate anhydrous organic solvents, the design of stable protein-like molecules for anhydrous media is unlikely to prove difficult. The decreased flexibility of proteins in anhydrous media suggests that protein-like molecules may perform better as machine components in the absence of water.

IMPROVED AQUEOUS SOLUBILITY   Good water solubility is routinely achieved in engineered helical proteins with a high density of hydrophilic side chains on the surface. Ionic side chains are strongly hydrophilic, and engineered salt bridges can stabilize folded structures. Helix formation, for example, is promoted by the presence of i, $i+4$ salt bridges between Glu$^-$ and Lys$^+$ (57). Extensive use of such side chains also makes folding more predictable by providing a strong contrast in hydrophobicity between surface and interior residues.

SUMMARY   Evolution does not maximize the stability of natural proteins. Designs chosen from a larger set of possible structures, with attention focused on maximizing stability, should have substantially greater stability. Table 1 summarizes estimated contributions from the stabilizing mechanisms discussed in this section. The estimated total suggests that application of the strategies reviewed here can increase folding stability by >100 kcal/mol. Even a less thorough and only par-

Table 1   Feasible stabilization of a nonstandard 70-residue structure[a]

Structural feature	Stability increment (kcal/mol)
Looped chains[b]	16
Metal ion binding[c]	16
Reduced backbone flexibility[d]	14
Reduced side-chain flexibility[e]	7
Increased packing density[f]	14
Reduced torsional strain[g]	21
Reduced bad contacts[h]	10
Increased core hydrophobicity[i]	5
Sum of estimated increments	103

[a] All changes are relative to a typical 70-residue natural protein with no disulfide cross-links and assume a design in which all structural features are compatible.

[b] Based on the change in conformational entropy from forming four 10-residue loops (79).

[c] Taken as equal to b.

[d] Assumes a 1 kcal/mol increment per five residues through use of dialkylglycines.

[e] Assumes an average improvement of 0.1 kcal/mol per residue through substitution of bulky, inflexible side chains for more flexible side chains in the core.

[f] Exploitation of nonstandard side chains is assumed to increase packing density by 4% from the mean for proteins (0.74) to a high value for organic crystals (0.78), which is less than dense packings observed in proteins (>0.85) (87). The stability increment is estimated from the 1.1 kcal/mol stabilization, which results from filling a cavity the size of a methylene group (48).

[g] See text; assumes successful core packing with nearly rotameric side chains.

[h] Estimated at about 0.5 (g).

[i] Reduction of buried polar groups by 7% through avoidance of buried polar side chains—assuming 1 kcal/mol per polar residue removed.

tially successful application of these strategies can likely produce structures of excellent stability.

Several of the stabilizing mechanisms discussed here decrease the entropy of the unfolded state: branched chains, looped chains, reduced backbone flexibility, and reduced side-chain flexibility; metal-ion binding is sometimes stable enough to act in this manner. Because these mechanisms operate by reducing the number of possible conformations, they reduce not only the entropy of the unfolded state but the number of potential misfolded states as well. Accordingly, they can be expected to reduce the likelihood that a designed molecule will fold to an approximately correct state but with a disordered core. Stabilization by reduced conformational entropy thus acts to increase folding predictability, thereby acting as an implicit form of negative design (89).

Most of the stabilizing mechanisms discussed here have been demonstrated experimentally, although not all in one molecule. Applied in combination, they seem more than adequate to allow the design of stable protein-like structures of ~70 residues, while leaving extensive freedom in design of the molecular surface, and hence of intermolecular interactions.

Supramolecular Assembly of Folded Polymers

Cram emphasizes the importance of preorganization in self-assembly (10). Folding preorganizes a polymer and places its surface groups in a distinct spatial pattern. Binding interactions between two folded structures can be strong and selective, as illustrated by quaternary structures and protein-antibody binding. Large structures offer more opportunities for complementarity and cooperative binding than do smaller structures; hence the many successes in designing supramolecular assemblies of smaller molecules (10, 53, 55, 105) encourage confidence regarding the design of binding interactions among protein-like molecules.

If one models monomers as cubes, then a family of protein-like molecules consisting of $4 \times 4 \times 4 = 64$ monomers would have 16 monomers exposed on each face. If each monomer site permits only five variations in polarity (e.g. nonpolar, hydrogen-bond donor, hydrogen-bond acceptor, positive ion, or negative ion) and only two variations in geometry (bump or hollow), then each monomer site can have one of $5 \times 2 = 10$ functionally distinct structures, and each face can have one of 10^{16} different structures. If we use one face structure as a reference, only $\sim 10^{-4}$ of a set of randomly generated structures will be complementary in polarity and geometry at more than half of the monomer sites. This calculation suggests that accidental complementarity will be rare, except in regular structures (e.g. the arrays of hydrogen-bonding groups found at the edge of β-sheet).

Most of the previously described strategies for improving fold stability are applicable to designing surfaces for tight, specific binding. The exceptions are altered chain topologies and backbone flexibility, which are irrelevant in already folded structures, and strong hydrophobicity, which would be incompatible with aqueous solubility. Of the others, metal-ion binding can drive quaternary assembly of natural proteins (31), and complementarity of hydrogen bonds and ionic species is common in antibody binding interfaces (12). Dense, low-strain packing of relatively inflexible structures is as favorable in the interface between molecules as in the interior of a single molecule.

Interfaces in quaternary structures are commonly hydrophobic (11), but studies of antibody-protein complexes demonstrate that hydrophilic protein surfaces can bind tightly in water (12). Pellegrini & Doniach successfully used computer simulation of intermolecular interactions to identify the binding sites of three antibodies to hen egg white lysozyme (76), thus suggesting that binding can be modeled well enough to support design.

A sequence of objectives in pursuing the development of molecular machine systems via self-assembly might be as follows:

1. Develop a more routine ability to design stable, globular, protein-like structures.
2. Design protein-like structures that assemble to form densely packed regular arrays.
3. Extend this design capability to assemble complex aperiodic structures of good mechanical stiffness.
4. Design and build complex structures with sliding interfaces, forming components for molecular machine systems.

SUMMARY AND CONCLUSIONS

The goal of constructing artificial molecular machine systems able to perform mechanosynthesis is beyond the immediate reach of current laboratory techniques. Nonetheless, these systems can already be modeled in substantial detail, and existing techniques enable steps toward their implementation.

Mechanosynthetic systems will rely on mechanical positioning to guide and control the molecular interactions of chemical synthesis. The effective concentration of a mechanically positioned species depends on the temperature and on the stiffness of the positioning system. These concentrations can be large (>100 M) and localized on a molecular scale. Background concentrations can approach zero, thus enabling precise molecular control of the locations and sequences of synthetic operations. Researchers have developed concepts for mechanosynthetic systems and defined general technology requirements.

One approach to the fabrication of molecular machine systems is the development of AFM-based mechanosynthetic devices. These would position molecules by binding them to (for example) antibody fragments attached to an AFM tip. Development of suitable monomers, binding sites, and reaction sequences would then be a basis for the fabrication of complex mechanical structures.

Biological molecular machine systems rely on the self-assembly of folded polymers. A review of progress in protein engineering suggests that we have the means to design and synthesize protein-like molecules with well-defined structures and excellent stability. Success in this effort provides a basis for the design of self-assembling systems, and experience with the design and supramolecular assembly of smaller molecules is encouraging regarding the success of this next step.

Development of a molecular machine technology promises a wide range of applications. Biological molecular machines synthesize proteins, read DNA, and sense a wide range of molecular phenomena. Artificial molecular machine systems could presumably be developed to perform analogous tasks, but with more stable structures and different results (e.g. reading DNA sequences into a conventional computer memory, rather than transcribing them into RNA). Self-assembling structures are widely regarded as a key to molecular electronic systems (55, 64), which therefore share an enabling technology with molecular machine systems. Finally, studies suggest that the use of molecular machine systems to perform mechanosynthesis of diverse structures (including additional molecular machine systems) will enable the development and inexpensive production of a broad range of new instruments and products (18, 24, 61). Laboratory research directed toward this goal seems warranted.

ACKNOWLEDGMENTS

I thank W DeGrado, B Imperiali, D Nitecki, C Peterson, F Richards, J Richardson, and K Ulmer for helpful comments on a precursor to this paper, and J Bonaventura, J Bottaro, M Edelstein, B Erickson, T Kaehler, M Krummenacker, R Merkle, and J Ponder for helpful discussions. This work has been supported in part by grants from the Institute for Molecular Manufacturing.

Literature Cited

1. Alber T. 1989. Mutational effects on protein stability. *Annu. Rev. Biochem.* 58:765–98
2. Altmann E, Altmann K-H, Nebel K, Mutter M. 1988. Conformational studies on host-guest peptides containing chiral α-methyl-α-amino acids. *Int. J. Pept. Protein Res.* 32:344–51
3. Anelli PL, Ashton PR, Ballardini R, Balzani V, Delgado M, et al. 1992. Molecular Meccano. 1. [2]Rotaxanes and a [2]catenane made to order. *J. Am. Chem. Soc.* 114:193–218
4. Bain JD, Switzer C, Chamberlin AR, Benner SA. 1992. Ribosome-mediated incorporation of a non-standard amino acid into a peptide through expansion of the genetic code. *Nature* 356:537–39
5. Baumann G, Frömmel C, Sander C. 1989. Polarity as a criterion in protein design. *Protein Eng.* 2:329–34
6. Behe MJ, Lattman EE, Rose GD. 1991. The protein-folding problem: the native fold determines packing, but does packing determine the native fold? *Proc. Natl. Acad. Sci. USA* 88: 4195–99
7. Binnig G, Quate CF. 1986. Atomic force microscope. *Phys. Rev. Lett.* 56: 930–33
8. Chen J, Seeman N. 1991. Synthesis from DNA of a molecule with the connectivity of a cube. *Nature* 350:631–33
9. Chung H-H, Benson DR, Schultz PG. 1993. Probing the structure and mechanism of Ras protein with an expanded genetic code. *Science* 259:806–9
10. Cram DJ. 1986. Preorganization— from solvents to spherands. *Angew. Chem. Int. Ed. Engl.* 25:1039–1134
11. Creighton TE. 1993. *Proteins: Structures and Molecular Properties.* New York: Freeman. 507 pp. 2nd ed.
12. Davies DR, Padlan EA, Sheriff S. 1990. Antibody-antigen complexes. *Annu. Rev. Biochem.* 59:439–73
13. DeGrado WF. 1988. Design of peptides and proteins. *Adv. Protein Chem.* 39: 51–124
14. DeGrado WF, Regan L, Ho SP. 1987. The design of a four-helix bundle protein. *Cold Spring Harbor Symp. Quant. Biol.* 52:521–26
15. DeGrado WF, Wasserman ZR, Lear JD. 1989. Protein design, a minimalist approach. *Science* 243:622–28
16. Desmet J, De Maeyer M, Hazes B, Lasters I. 1992. The dead-end elimination theorem and its use in protein side-chain positioning. *Nature* 356: 539–42
17. Dill KA. 1990. Dominant forces in protein folding. *Biochemistry* 29:7133–55
18. Drexler KE. 1981. Molecular engineering: an approach to the development of general capabilities for molecular manipulation. *Proc. Natl. Acad. Sci. USA* 78:5275–78
19. Drexler KE. 1986. *Engines of Creation: The Coming Era of Nanotechnology.* New York: Anchor/Doubleday. 298 pp.
20. Drexler KE. 1987. Molecular machinery and molecular electronic devices. In *Molecular Electronic Devices II,* ed. FL Carter, pp. 549–71. New York: Dekker
21. Drexler KE. 1987. Nanomachinery: atomically precise gears and bearings. *Proc. IEEE Micro Robot. Teleoperators Workshop.* Hyannis, Massachusetts
22. Drexler KE. 1988. Rod logic and thermal noise in the mechanical nanocomputer. In *Molecular Electronic Devices,* ed. FL Carter, R Siatkowski, H Wohltjen, pp. 39–56. Amsterdam: North-Holland
23. Drexler KE. 1991. Molecular tip arrays for molecular imaging and nanofabrication. *J. Vac. Sci. Technol. B* 9:1394–97
24. Drexler KE. 1992. *Nanosystems: Molecular Machinery, Manufacturing, and Computation.* New York: Wiley. pp. 556
25. Drexler KE, Foster JS. 1990. Synthetic tips. *Nature* 343:600
26. Eigen M, McCaskill J, Schuster P. 1988. Molecular quasi-species. *J. Phys. Chem.* 92:6881–91
27. Eigler DM, Schweizer EK. 1990. Positioning single atoms with a scanning tunnelling microscope. *Nature* 344: 524–26
28. Ellman J, Mendel D, Schultz PG. 1992. Site-specific incorporation of novel

backbone structures into proteins. *Science* 255:197–200
29. Felix AM, Wang C-T, Heimer EP, Campbell RM, Madison VS, et al. 1989. Solid-phase synthesis and biological activity of highly potent cyclic and dicyclic (lactam) analogs of growth hormone releasing factor. In *Proceedings of Peptides: Chemistry, Structure and Biology (Proc. 11th Am. Pept. Symp.)*, ed. JE River, GR Marshall, pp. 226–28. Leiden, The Netherlands: ESCOM
30. Fields GB, Noble RL. 1990. Solid phase peptide synthesis utilizing 9-fluorenylmethoxycarbonyl amino acids. *Int. J. Pept. Protein Res.* 35:161–214
31. Frankel AD, Bredt DS, Pabo CO. 1988. Tat protein from human immunodeficiency virus forms a metal-linked dimer. *Science* 240:70–73
32. Ghadiri MR, Fernholz AR. 1990. Peptide architecture. Design of stable α-helical metallopeptides via a novel exchange-inert RuIII complex. *J. Am. Chem. Soc.* 112:9633–35
33. Ghadiri MR, Soares C, Choi C. 1992. Design of an artificial four-helix bundle metalloprotein via a novel ruthenium(II)-assisted self-assembly process. *J. Am. Chem. Soc.* 114:4000–2
34. Ghadiri MR, Soares C, Choi C. 1992. A convergent approach to protein design. Metal ion-assisted spontaneous self-assembly of a polypeptide into a triple-helix bundle protein. *J. Am. Chem. Soc.* 114:825–31
35. Goraj K, Renard A, Martial JA. 1990. Synthesis, purification and initial structural characterization of octarellin, a de novo polypeptide modelled on the α/βbarrel proteins. *Protein Eng.* 3:259–66
35a. Guralnik DB, ed. 1970. *Webster's New World Dictionary*. New York: World
36. Hahn KW, Klis WA, Steward JM. 1990. Design and synthesis of a peptide having chymotrypsin-like esterase activity. *Science* 248:1544–47
37. Handel T, DeGrado WF. 1990. De novo design of a Zn^{2+}-binding protein. *J. Am. Chem. Soc.* 112:6710–11
38. Handel TM, Williams SA, DeGrado WF. 1993. Metal ion–dependent modulation of the dynamics of a designed protein. *Science* 261:879–85
39. Hansma HG, Vesenka J, Siergerist C, Kelderman G, Morrett H, et al. 1992. Reproducible imaging and dissection of plasmid DNA under liquid with the atomic force microscope. *Science* 256:1180–84
40. Hansma PK, Elings VB, Marti O, Bracker CE. 1988. Scanning tunneling microscopy and atomic force microscopy: application to biology and technology. *Science* 242:209–16
41. Hecht MH, Richardson JS, Richardson DC, Ogden RC. 1990. De novo design, expression, and characterization of Felix: a four-helix bundle protein of native-like sequence. *Science* 249:884–91
42. Hellinga HW, Richards FM. 1991. Construction of new ligand binding sites in proteins of known structure. I. Computer-aided modeling of sites with pre-defined geometry. *J. Mol. Biol.* 222:763–85
43. Hellinga HW, Richards FM. 1991. Construction of new ligand binding sites in proteins of known structure. II. Grafting of a buried transition metal binding site into *Escherichia coli* thioredoxin. *J. Mol. Biol.* 222:787–803
44. Hoh JH, Lal R, John SA, Revel J-P, Arnsdorf MF. 1991. Atomic force microscopy and dissection of gap junctions. *Science* 253:1405–8
45. Holm L, Sander C. 1992. Fast and simple Monte Carlo algorithm for side chain optimization in proteins: application to model building by homology. *Proteins Struct. Funct. Genet.* 14:213–23
46. Kaszynski P, Friedli AC, Michl J. 1992. Toward a molecular-size "Tinkertoy" construction set. Preparation of terminally functionalized [n]-staffanes from [1.1.1]propellane. *J. Am. Chem. Soc.* 114:601–20
47. Kaumaya PTP, Berndt KD, Heidorn DB, Trewhella J, Kezdy FJ, Goldberg E. 1990. Synthesis and biophysical characterization of engineered topographic immunogenic determinants with αα topology. *Biochemistry* 29:13–23
48. Kellis JT Jr, Nyberg K, Sali D, Fersht AR. 1988. Contribution of hydrophobic interactions to protein stability. *Nature* 333:784–86
49. Kent SBH. 1988. Chemical synthesis of peptides and proteins. *Annu. Rev. Biochem.* 57:957–89
50. Klibanov AM. 1989. Enzymatic catalysis in anhydrous organic solvents. *Trends Biochem. Sci.* 14:141–44
51. Krafft M-P, Giulieri F, Riess JG. 1993. Can single-chain perfluoroalkylated amphiphiles alone form vesicles and other organized supramolecular systems? *Angew. Chem. Int. Ed. Engl.* 32:741–43
52. Lee C, Subbiah S. 1991. Prediction of

protein side-chain conformation by packing optimization. *J. Mol. Biol.* 217:373–88

53. Lehn J-M. 1988. Supramolecular chemistry—scope and perspectives: molecules, supermolecules, and molecular devices. *Angew. Chem. Int. Ed. Engl.* 27:89–112

54. Lieberman M, Sasaki T. 1991. Iron(II) organizes a synthetic peptide into three-helix bundles. *J. Am. Chem. Soc.* 113:1470–71

55. Lindsey JS. 1991. Self-assembly in synthetic routes to molecular devices. Biological principles and chemical perspectives: a review. *New J. Chem.* 15: 153–80

56. Lyo I-W, Avouris P. 1991. Field-induced nanometer-to atomic-scale manipulation of silicon surfaces with the STM. *Science* 253:173–76

57. Marqusee S, Baldwin RL. 1987. Helix stabilization by Glu⁻ . . . Lys⁺ salt bridges in short peptides of de novo design. *Proc. Natl. Acad. Sci. USA* 84: 8898–8902

58. Matthews BW, Nicholson H, Becktel WJ. 1987. Enhanced protein thermostability from site-directed mutations that decrease the entropy of unfolding. *Proc. Natl. Acad. Sci. USA* 84:6663–67

59. Mendel D, Ellman JA, Chang Z, Veenstra DL, Kollman PA, Schultz PG. 1992. Probing protein stability with unnatural amino acids. *Science* 256: 1798–1802

60. Merkle RC. 1991. Computational nanotechnology. *Nanotechnology* 2:134–41

61. Merkle RC. 1992. Self replicating systems and molecular manufacturing. *J. Br. Interplanet. Soc.* 45:407–13

62. Merkle RC. 1993. A proof about molecular bearings. *Nanotechnology* 4: 86–90

63. Merkle RC. 1993. Two types of mechanical reversible logic. *Nanotechnology* 4:114–31

64. Mirkin CA, Ratner MA. 1992. Molecular electronics. *Annu. Rev. Phys. Chem.* 43:719–54

65. Mislow K. 1989. Molecular machinery in organic chemistry. *Chemtracts Org. Chem.* 2:151–74

66. Mullis K, Faloona F, Scharf S, Saiki R, Horn G, Erlich H. 1986. Specific amplification of DNA in vitro: the polymerase chain reaction. *Cold Spring Harbor Symp. Quant. Biol.* 51(P1):263–73

67. Musgrave CB, Perry JK, Merkle RC, Goddard WA III. 1991. Theoretical studies of a hydrogen abstraction tool for nanotechnology. *Nanotechnology* 2:187–95

68. Mutter M, Altmann E, Altmann K-H, Hersperger R, Koziej P, et al. 1988. The construction of new proteins. Artificial folding units by assembly of amphiphilic secondary structures on a template. *Helv. Chim. Acta* 71:835–47

69. Mutter M, Tuchscherer GG, Miller C, Altmann K-H, Carey RI, et al. 1992. Template-assembled synthetic proteins with four-helix-bundle topology. Total chemical synthesis and conformational studies. *J. Am. Chem. Soc.* 114:1463–70

70. Mutter M, Vuilleumier S. 1989. A chemical approach to protein design—template-assembled synthetic proteins (TASP). *Angew. Chem. Int. Ed. Engl.* 28:535–676

71. Nielsen PE, Egholm M, Berg RH, Buchardt O. 1991. Sequence-selective recognition of DNA by strand displacement with a thymine-substituted polyamide. *Science* 254:1497–1500

72. Noren CJ, Anthony-Cahill SJ, Griffith MC, Schultz PG. 1989. A general method for site-specific incorporation of unnatural amino acids into proteins. *Science* 244:182–88

73. Oosawa F, Asakura S. 1975. *Thermodynamics of the Polymerization of Protein.* London: Academic

74. Pabo CP, Suchanek EG. 1986. Computer-aided model-building strategies for protein design. *Biochemistry* 25: 5987–91

75. Pantoliano MW, Ladner RC, Bryan PN, Rollence ML, Wood JF, Poulos TL. 1987. Protein engineering of subtilisin BPN': enhanced stabilization through the introduction of two cysteines to form a disulfide bond. *Biochemistry* 26:2077–82

76. Pellegrini M, Doniach S. 1993. Computer simulation of antibody binding specificity. *Proteins Struct. Funct. Genet.* 15:436–44

77. Pessi A, Bianchi E, Crameri A, Venturini S, Tramontano A, Sollazzo M. 1993. A designed metal-binding protein with a novel fold. *Nature* 362:367–69

78. Pickett SD, Sternberg MJE. 1993. Empirical scale of side-chain conformational entropy in protein folding. *J. Mol. Biol.* 231:825–39

79. Poland DC, Scheraga HA. 1965. Statistical mechanics of noncovalent bonds in polyamino acids. VIII. Covalent loops in proteins. *Biopolymers* 3:379–99

80. Ponder JW, Richards FM. 1987. Ter-

tiary templates for proteins. *J. Mol. Biol.* 193:775–91

81. Privalov PL, Gill SJ. 1988. Stability of protein structure and hydrophobic interaction. *Adv. Protein Chem.* 39:191–234

82. Raleigh DP, DeGrado WF. 1992. A de novo designed protein shows a thermally induced transition from a native to a molten globule-like state. *J. Am. Chem. Soc.* 114:10079–81

83. Rebek J Jr. 1992. Molecular recognition and self-replication. *J. Mol. Recogn.* 5:83–88

84. Regan L. 1993. The design of metal-binding sites in proteins. *Annu. Rev. Biophys. Biomol. Struct.* 22:257–81

85. Regan L, Clarke ND. 1990. A tetrahedral Zinc(II)-binding site introduced into a designed protein. *Biochemistry* 29:10878–83

86. Regan L, DeGrado WF. 1988. Characterization of a helical protein designed from first principles. *Science* 241:976–78

87. Richards FM. 1977. Areas, volumes, packing, and protein structure. *Annu. Rev. Biophys. Bioeng.* 6:151–76

88. Richardson JS, Richardson DC. 1989. The de novo design of protein structures. *Trends Biochem. Sci.* 14:304–9

89. Richardson JS, Richardson DC, Tweedy NB, Gernert KM, Quinn TP, et al. 1992. Looking at proteins: representations, folding, packing, and design. *Biophys. J.* 63:1186–1209

90. Rizo J, Gierasch LM. 1992. Constrained peptides: models of bioactive peptides and protein structures. *Annu. Rev. Biochem.* 61:387–418

91. Rose GD, Wolfenden R. 1993. Hydrogen bonding, hydrophobicity, packing, and protein folding. *Annu. Rev. Biophys. Biomol. Struct.* 22:381–415

92. Ruan F, Chen Y, Hopkins PB. 1990. Metal ion enhanced helicity in synthetic peptides containing unnatural, metal-ligating residues. *J. Am. Chem. Soc.* 112:9403–4

93. Russell AJ, Trudel LJ, Skipper PL, Groopman JD, Tannenbaum SR, Klibanov AM. 1989. Antibody-antigen binding in organic solvents. *Biochem. Biophys. Res. Commun.* 158:80–85

94. Schrauber H, Eisenhaber F, Argos P. 1993. Rotamers: to be or not to be? An analysis of amino acid side-chain conformations in globular proteins. *J. Mol. Biol.* 230:592–612

95. Shortle D. 1992. Mutational studies of protein structures and their stabilities. *Quart. Rev. Biophys.* 25:205–50

96. Smith JL, Hendrickson WA, Honzatko RB, Sheriff S. 1986. Structural heterogeneity in protein crystals. *Biochemistry* 25:5018–27

97. Tapley BD, Poston TR. 1990. *Eschbach's Handbook of Engineering Fundamentals.* New York: Wiley. 4th ed.

98. Tomalia DA, Naylor AM, Goddard WA III. 1990. Starburst dendrimers: molecular-level control of size, shape, surface chemistry, topology, and flexibility from atoms to macroscopic matter. *Angew. Chem. Int. Ed. Engl.* 29:138–75

99. Urry DW. 1993. Molecular machines: how motion and other functions of living organisms can result from reversible chemical changes. *Angew. Chem. Int. Ed. Engl.* 32:819–41

100. Van Wart HE. 1988. Introduction of exchange-inert metal ions into enzymes. *Methods Enzymol.* 158:95–110

101. Van Woerkom WJ, Van Nispen JW. 1991. Difficult couplings in stepwise solid phase synthesis: predictable or just a guess? *Int. J. Peptide Protein Res.* 38:103–13

102. Vincent JFV. 1982. *Structural Biomaterials.* New York: Wiley

103. Volkin DB, Staubli A, Langer R, Klibanov AM. 1991. Enzyme thermoinactivation in anhydrous organic solvents. *Biotechnol. Bioeng.* 37:843–53

104. Weisenhorn AL, Hansma PK, Albrecht TR, Quate CF. 1989. Forces in atomic force microscopy in air and water. *Appl. Phys. Lett.* 54:2651–53

105. Whitesides GM, Mathias JP, Seto CT. 1991. Molecular self-assembly and nanochemistry: a chemical strategy for the synthesis of nanostructures. *Science* 254:1312–19

106. Wilson C, Mace JE, Agard DA. 1991. Computational method for the design of enzymes with altered substrate specificity. *J. Mol. Biol.* 220:495–506

107. Yang A-S, Sharp KA, Honig B. 1992. Analysis of the heat capacity dependence of protein folding. *J. Mol. Biol.* 227:889–900

108. Yun-yu S, Mark AE, Cun-xi W, Fuhua H, Berendsen HJC, van Gunsteren WF. 1993. Can the stability of protein mutants be predicted by free energy calculations? *Protein Eng.* 6:289–95

Annu. Rev. Biophys. Biomol. Struct. 1994. 23:407–39

GLOBAL STATISTICS OF PROTEIN SEQUENCES: Implications for the Origin, Evolution, and Prediction of Structure

Stephen H. White

Department of Physiology and Biophysics, University of California, Irvine, California 92717

KEY WORDS: protein secondary structure, protein databases, amino acid frequencies, protein sequence lengths, protein sequence randomness, stochastic modeling of protein sequences

CONTENTS

1056–8700/94/0610–0407$05.00

PERSPECTIVES AND OVERVIEW

Statistical analyses have played a central role in studies of protein sequences and their evolution since the early studies of Ycas (92). One of the major thrusts of statistical studies has been to identify relatively short oligopeptide sequences associated with specific structural and functional features that occur with high significance within complete sequences (15, 22, 33, 83). A recent review by Karlin et al (44) describes reliable general methods for finding sequence patterns of possible functional and structural importance that are unlikely to occur by chance. These methods are examples of local statistical studies (see 91) because they focus on subsequences. The present review is concerned with global studies that consider the general statistical characteristics of entire sequences. Given the large sizes of current protein databases and their rapid rates of growth, an understanding of the global statistics of proteins is of fundamental importance and may be useful for improving the accuracy of structure-prediction algorithms, the creation of appropriate mathematical models, and the development of guidelines for the ab initio design of proteins.

One approach to global statistics is to catalog how often properties or features of proteins occur and to provide mathematical means and variances. A slightly more sophisticated approach is to characterize the frequency distributions by means of probability density functions. The approach I prefer, and which forms the basis for the work described in this review, is to begin with a stochastic model for protein sequences, calculate the density functions expected, and then examine the extent to which collections of sequences satisfy the expectations of the model. The use of an explicit stochastic model is helpful for clarifying one's thinking and may, in the ideal case, reveal new biological principles.

This review is not meant to be a comprehensive account of statistical studies of protein sequences. Rather, it presents a point of view about the origin, evolution, and prediction of protein structure that I have found useful for thinking about proteins. The viewpoint, which may at first be discomfiting to some readers, emerged from work begun several years ago in collaboration with Russell Jacobs. It is formalized by the random origin hypothesis (ROH), which asserts that proteins originated by stochastic processes according to simple rules (87, 90, 91). The hypothesis leads to the conclusion that the earliest proteins were examples of mathematically random sequences. The perplexing part of the work is that modern protein sequences, in the main, have the characteristics expected for the primordial ones. The useful part, independent of one's acceptance or rejection of the underlying hypothesis and its consequences, is that it provides a consistent and useful mathematical basis for characterizing the statistical properties of large collections of protein sequences.

This review begins with a general discussion of the stochastic nature of protein sequences. I then discuss the ROH and how the resulting stochastic model can be used for the practical purposes of characterizing and exploring protein sequence databases. Finally, I consider the results of an analysis of a representative protein database in the context of the origin, evolution, and prediction of three-dimensional structure.

THE STOCHASTIC NATURE OF PROTEIN SEQUENCES

The first hint of the stochastic nature of protein sequences arose from cryptographic and information theory analyses undertaken by Gamow & Ycas (26) as part of an effort to break the genetic code. Ycas (92) concluded from the limited number of sequences then available that no evidence supported the nonrandom occurrence of dipeptide pairs. Subsequent investigators using larger databases have sought the nonrandom occurrence of oligopeptides of various sizes (1, 15, 48, 49, 55, 94). Although many oligopeptides occur more frequently than would be expected by chance, randomness is still a dominant tendency.

The early observation of Ycas (92) led Gates & Fisher (28) to assume that proteins were random heteropolymers for the purpose of estimating the dimensions of soluble proteins based upon simple geometric considerations (24) and observations regarding the frequency of hydrophobic residues. One of their important conclusions, subsequently confirmed by several laboratories (39, 52), was that some of the hydrophobic residues had to be exposed on the surface of the protein. Janin (39) showed that the mathematical relation between protein molecular weight and the numbers of residues buried and exposed accurately obeyed the model of Gates & Fisher (28) and thereby supported implicitly the assumption that protein sequences can be treated as random heteropolymers. Dill and his colleagues (11, 13) have also used the Gates & Fisher approach successfully in their analyses of protein folding and stability.

These approaches show that the random heteropolymer model is useful in terms of gross protein geometry but they do not consider the folding patterns of real proteins. Ptitsyn & Finkelstein (23, 66, 67), however, have shown that many of the basic folding patterns of proteins can be arrived at by assuming protein sequences to be random. That is, many of the patterns observed in proteins appear to be a natural consequence of random protein sequences. We (90) came to a similar conclusion regarding membrane proteins. Ptitsyn (66) concluded that "primary structures of proteins are basically just the examples of random amino acid sequences which have only been 'edited' during biological evolution in order to impart to them the additional (functional) meaning and the additional stability" (66, p. 45). Ptitsyn inferred the randomness of protein sequences from the fact that one could arrive at basic folding motifs from the assumption of sequence randomness. We (91) adopted Ptitsyn's inference as the null (random origin) hypothesis and examined explicitly several aspects of the randomness of protein sequences.

The null-hypothesis assertion that protein sequences are indistinguishable from random sequences should not, under any circumstances, be interpreted as meaning that specific protein sequences are arbitrary or irrelevant to the determination of three-dimensional structure. Clearly, a particular sequence will have a specific and invariant three-dimensional structure under normal physiological conditions. The assertion instead simply means that a protein sequence can be considered mathematically as a sequence of independent events. That is, real protein sequences are indistinguishable from the ones expected by the random selection of amino acids (with replacement) from a pool containing the different kinds of amino acids in proportion to their frequencies of occurrence in the sequence. Karlin et al (44) refer to this as the independence random model. If some rule was followed in the selection of the amino acids, then collections of sequences would generally fail tests for sequence randomness. However, regardless of the rejection or acceptance of the null hypothesis, important insights into the protein-folding and structure-prediction problems will be obtained. If the null hypothesis must be rejected in certain cases, then special distributions may be revealed that improve structure prediction. If the null hypothesis cannot be rejected, then distribution patterns characteristic of random sequences are preferred. That would imply that the lengthwise distribution of amino acids for proteins designed de novo should tend to satisfy mathematical criteria for randomness.

The independent random model is a biologically reasonable hypothesis because protein evolution proceeds by means of random mutations (14, 25, 40, 46, 47). The use of the model is further justified when one considers that about 10^{112} unique sequences can be formed from 100 amino acids chosen to reflect the amino acid composition typical of soluble proteins. This number is so large [the age of the universe is only about 10^{17} seconds (65)] that it is unlikely that the entire sequence space could have been explored systematically during the history of the biosphere and especially during the primordial era. In my opinion, random sampling would have been the most efficient way of exploring sequence space so that the earliest proteins likely originated by chance from within the space. Hence, mathematically random sequences would be the most likely ones (51, 80, 90, 91). If the ability to fold into a compact structure is a general characteristic of heteropolymers, as the work of Dill and his colleagues suggests (7, 51), then a broad range of sequence characteristics would have been sampled, by chance, at the earliest stages of evolution. If the successful primordial sequences were mathematically random, then we should not be surprised to find evidence of the randomness preserved in modern sequences.

STOCHASTIC MODEL FOR COLLECTIONS OF PROTEIN SEQUENCES

Of the many features of protein sequences amenable to statistical analysis, the most fundamental ones are: (*a*) the lengthwise distribution of amino acids, because it determines three-dimensional structure; (*b*) sequence length, because protein stability depends on it; and (*c*) amino acid frequencies, because they must reflect broad stability requirements and genetic-code utilization. A consideration of the first two features led to the random origin hypothesis (ROH) (91) and the so-called no-exon model (NE model) (87). Here, I extend the model to include a consideration of the frequencies in the context of the code-table amino acid probabilities of the universal genetic code [but see Jukes (42) regarding the universality and evolution of the code].

A growing body of evidence (61, 74, 93) indicates that RNA preceded proteins and DNA in the evolution of the biosphere (32, 60, 63, 85). The ROH takes this as a given and assumes the existence of a primitive system for the coding, translation, and synthesis of protein sequences that, at some point, resulted in a protein synthetic "big bang" that produced a very large number of random heteropeptide sequences (90). This idea gains stature from the recent finding (61) that ribosomal RNA can apparently catalyze peptide bond formation. Because the ability to fold into compact structures places few restrictions on the space of possible amino acid sequences (51), the ROH assumes that a significant fraction of the random sequences could have folded into protoproteins and that sequence length was an important determinant of stability. Of these protoproteins, only those that could catalyze some advantageous chemical reaction or serve some useful structural function were selected for preservation in the primitive genome as primitive proteins.

The ROH has three corollaries that are formalized in the NE model: 1. The amino acid sequences of the primitive proteins would be examples of random sequences. 2. The length distribution of the primitive sequences would be determined solely by two independent processes: (*a*) the lengthwise statistics of nucleic acid begin and end signals uniformly randomly distributed along the genome that delimited primitive genes or their transcribed messages and (*b*) a probability of folding into a compact structure that increases with sequence length (11, 86). 3. The density of amino acid frequencies in the collection of protoprotein sequences, and possibly in the primitive sequences, would reflect the frequencies of their codons in the genome. This model completely ignores the widely held view that the primordial proteins were pieced together by exon-splicing in order to increase sequence length and is therefore referred to as the no-exon model (87).

The first corollary means that the primitive sequences would be representative examples of sequences formed according to standard combinatorial formulas using the codon frequencies as probabilities. Given the extraordinarily large number of combinations possible, one cannot catalog all of the possible sequences. However, one can ask whether or not the sequences selected have lengthwise distributions consistent with a random sample of sequence space. The second corollary implies that the distribution of lengths will be the product of two probability densities: one describing the distribution of intervals between begin and end signals and the other the probability of folding into a compact structure. The amino acid probability densities will have distributions about the mean frequencies (probabilities) determined by the density of lengths and the stochastic fluctuations in the numbers of amino acids of a given type. The following sections summarize the methods for testing these expectations.

Lengthwise Distributions of Amino Acids

One can test the hypothesis that the lengthwise distribution of objects is random in many different ways. In my experience, the run test (59, 84) is, overall, the simplest and most sensitive general test. Furthermore, the run test statistic has a particularly convenient interpretation that is useful for characterizing sequences. Mood (58) developed a complete general theory of the statistical distribution of runs that can be applied to a sequence of 20 kinds of objects (amino acids) but it is more informative and useful to reduce the sequence to a binary one by assigning a value of 1 to the amino acids of interest and 0 to all others.

The use and interpretation of the binary run test applied to protein sequences has been discussed in detail (90, 91).

A run is a subsequence of one or more identical objects bounded at either end by an unlike object. A random sequence will have neither too few (e.g. 0000011111) nor too many (e.g. 0101010101) runs. For a sequence of length $L = a + b$ consisting of a ones and b zeros, with a and $b \geq 0$, the expected number of runs μ_{ex} of ones and zeros will be:

$$\mu_{ex} = \frac{2ab}{a + b} + 1. \tag{1.}$$

If one generates by a single random process a large number of sequences of length L with fixed a and b, the observed number of runs μ_{ob} should fluctuate about the expected value with a variance

$$\sigma^2 = \frac{2ab(2ab - a - b)}{(a + b)^2(a + b - 1)}. \tag{2.}$$

The run test statistic

$$r_o = \frac{\mu_{ob} - \mu_{ex}}{\sigma} \tag{3.}$$

compares the observed and expected number of runs. This statistic will be normally distributed with mean $r_m = 0$ and variance $\sigma^2 = 1$ [the so-called $N(0,1)$ distribution] provided $a \approx b \geq 10$. If $a \ll b$ or if $a + b < 20$, r_o will not be normally distributed so that the probability density must be calculated from the combinatorial formulas (see appendix of 91).

Values of r_o for a collection of sequences can be used in two ways (see 91 for a complete discussion): (a) to decide if a single sequence can be considered random or (b) to decide if the collection is equivalent to one produced by a single random process. In the first case, one adopts the null hypothesis H_0 that the sequence is random. Because r_o is distributed normally when H_0 is true, the two-tailed probability $P(r > r_o)$ of a random sequence having a value of r greater than r_o can be calculated. H_0 is rejected if $P(r > r_o) \leq \alpha$, where α is the level of significance (usually 0.05). This means that H_0 is rejected if $|r_o| \geq 2$. In the second case, if the number density $n(r_o)$ of the collection of sequences is $N(0,1)$, one can conclude that the collection is equivalent to one produced by a single random process. If $n(r_o)$ is not $N(0,1)$, one cannot say much about the processes that produced it without resorting to extensive analysis and modeling. The practical approach we have adopted is to declare all sequences with $|r_o| < 2$ as random and to characterize the extent of randomness by the fraction of sequences

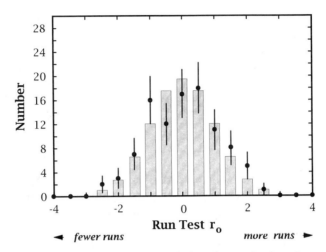

Figure 1   The distribution of the run test statistic r_o for a collection of 100 randomly produced binary sequences of length 24 containing 12 ones. The bars show the normal distribution and the points the observed distribution (the lines through the points show the expected standard deviation). Sequences with $r_o < 0$ have fewer runs than expected so that the ones tend to cluster together. If $r_o > 0$, the ones do not cluster enough, which results in too many runs. Modified from Ref. 91.

lying within these bounds. In most cases we have found that the distributions tend to be $N(r_m, \sigma^2)$ so that the mean r_m and standard deviation σ provide information about the general tendencies of the collection.

Figure 1 summarizes the general features of the run test, comparing the $n(r_o)$ of a collection of 100 sequences produced randomly with the $N(0,1)$ distribution. Note that r_o is a useful parameter for characterizing the extent to which the ones and zeros in a sequence tend to clump together: If r_o is negative, the runs are fewer than expected (the ones or zeros clump together), whereas a positive r_o indicates too many runs and the ones or zeros tend to avoid one another. The same idea can be applied to r_m to understand the global tendencies of a collection of sequences.

Distributions of Lengths of Protein Sequences

If the begin and end signals that define a reading frame in a nucleotide sequence are uniformly randomly distributed, then the intervals Z_i between begin and end signals will be exponentially distributed random variables. If the probability of the resulting protein folding into a compact structure increases linearly with Z_i or exponentially in the form

$1 - \exp(Z)$, the probability density function $f_Z(z)$ for the lengths Z will be

$$f_z(z) = \frac{\alpha\beta}{(\beta - \alpha)} [\exp(-\alpha z) - \exp(-\beta z)], \qquad\qquad 4.$$

where α and β are parameters related to the probabilities of end and begin signals and the probability of folding (87). Figure 2 illustrates this

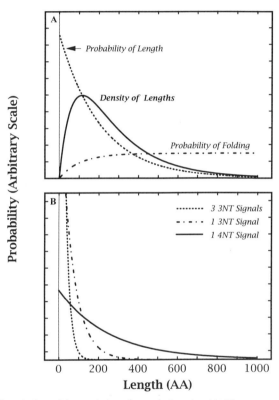

Figure 2   A description of the statistics of protein lengths. (*A*) The no-exon model based upon the random origin hypothesis (see text) assumes the interaction of two independent events: the probability of a length (*dotted curve*) determined by the statistics of start and end signals distributed uniformly randomly along a nucleotide sequence and the probability that a sequence of a given length will fold into a compact structure (*dot-dashed curve*). The density of lengths that results (*solid curve*) is, basically, a gamma distribution with parameter 2. See Equations 4 and 5. (*B*) The probability-of-length curves (Equation 11) that result from assuming that the stop codons are coded by three trinucleotides (3NT), one trinucleotide, or one tetranucleotide (4NT). Notice that the tail of the 4NT curve is very similar to the tail on the density of lengths in panel *A*. Modified from Ref. 87.

distribution for a case in which the probability of folding increases exponentially. Here, α does not equal β. If the probability of folding increases linearly with sequence length, then α equals β and Equation 4 reduces to the gamma distribution with parameter 2:

$$f_Z(z) = \alpha^2 \cdot z \cdot \exp(-\alpha z). \hspace{2cm} 5.$$

Distribution of Frequencies of Amino Acids

If a sequence is random, then the number of amino acids n_i of a specified type should fluctuate from sequence to sequence according to binomial statistics so that, for a large population of sequences, the expected mean and variance would be

$$\bar{n}_i = p_i \cdot L_k \hspace{3cm} 6a.$$

$$\sigma_i^2 = p_i(1 - p_i)L_k, \hspace{2.5cm} 6b.$$

where p_i is the probability of an amino acid of type i and L_k is the total number of amino acids in the sequence. Figure 3 shows the fluctuation in the combined frequencies of hydrophobic residues for a set of 500 protein sequences and demonstrates that the binomial behavior is a reasonable first approximation. The solid curves in the figure are the mean $\pm 3\sigma$ calculated from Equation 6. The majority of sequences in

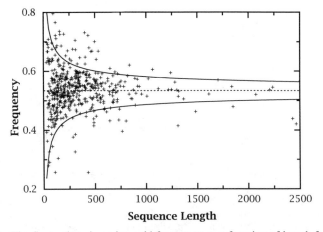

Figure 3 The fluctuations in amino acid frequency as a function of length for 500 sequences chosen at random from the 1992 Superfamily Set of protein sequences. The frequency is that of a set of hydrophobic amino acids that include A, V, I, L, F, C, M, W, Y, P, and G. The mean frequency μ (0.54) is indicated by the dashed line and the expected range of fluctuations by the solid curves ($= \mu \pm 3\sigma$) calculated from Equation 6.

a population are sufficiently long that the binomial distribution can be approximated by the normal distribution

$$N(n_i, k) = \frac{\exp(-[n_i - \bar{n}_i]^2/2\sigma_i^2)}{\sigma_i\sqrt{2\pi}} N_k.$$ 7.

where N_k is the number of sequences of length L_k. The NE model assumes that the probabilities p_i are determined by the relative numbers of codons in the genetic-code table so that probabilities for amino acids coded by 1, 2, 3, 4, or 6 codons are, respectively, 0.0164, 0.0328, 0.0492, 0.656, and 0.0984.

The number densities defined by Equations 6 and 7 depend upon length, which in turn is distributed according to Equation 4 or 5. In other words, the distribution of amino acid frequencies is determined by a collection of binomial distributions weighted by the distribution (density) of lengths. One can derive the expected distribution of frequencies for the entire population of N_T sequences by considering the distribution of frequencies for the N_k sequences in the length domain L_k, where $k = 1 \ldots m$ and $L_k = L_k - 1 + \Delta L$. However, a better method is to simulate the expected density of frequencies by means of random-variable generating algorithms (72). A collection of random-length variables obeying Equation 4 can be generated from

$$X_L = -\frac{1}{\alpha} \ln(rnd[1]) - \frac{1}{\beta} \ln(rnd[1]),$$ 8.

where $rnd[1]$ is a random number between 0 and 1. For each of the length variables produced by Equation 8, one can generate a n_i using the Box-Muller generating function

$$X_n = \bar{n}_i + \sigma_i\sqrt{-2 \ln(rnd[1])}\cdot\cos(2\pi\cdot rnd[1])$$ 9.

and the $\bar{n}_i$ and σ_i given by Equation 6.

STATISTICAL CHARACTERISTICS OF A REPRESENTATIVE PROTEIN DATABASE

The International Protein Identification Resource (PIR) sequence database (29, 62) contains more than 20,000 sequences divided among more than 3000 superfamilies. Because the sequences within superfamilies, by definition, have a high degree of similarity, the full set of PIR sequences is degenerate. Furthermore, the number of members of each superfamily is highly variable so that the full database is biased toward the large superfamilies. Therefore, we (91) devised the so-called

Superfamily Set of sequences, which contains the first member of each superfamily encountered in the VAX-tape PIR1.SEQ files of the various releases of the database. Statistical analyses were limited to the PIR1 sequences because they have been fully verified and their superfamily data systematized in the accompanying PIR1.CDX files. A superfamily database was created by merging the *.SEQ and *.CDX files so that each entry contained a line of superfamily numerical data. The Superfamily Set of sequences was selected from this database with the additional constraints that sequences have a minimum length of 21 amino acids, be complete sequences (no fragments), and be unambiguous [i.e. any sequence with an amino acid designated B (Asx), Z (Glx), or X (unknown) was rejected]. The last PIR issue of each of the past several years has been used to create the 1988 through 1992 Superfamily Sets so that the statistical stability of the Sets could be verified. Although the Superfamily Set of protein sequences grew from 1789 sequences in 1989 to 2912 in 1992, no statistically significant variations in global properties have been detected.

Lengthwise Distribution of Amino Acids

Using the run test and the 1989 Superfamily Set, we (91) examined the lengthwise distributions of the individual amino acids and various combinations of them. The surprising result of the study was that, regardless of the type of amino acid(s) examined, the chance that a randomly chosen sequence would be indistinguishable from the random expectation was always 90% or better. Figure 4 shows two examples of the run test results for the 1992 Superfamily Set for a set of hydrophobic residues and a set of residues with a strong α-helix propensity (54). Although the densities of r_o values are not $N(0,1)$, they are remarkably close. The density's mean value r_m is a particularly valuable property because it indicates the global tendencies of amino acids to cluster together or to avoid each other more than would be expected by chance. The class of amino acids with the strongest tendency to cluster together are those with an α-helix propensity, as shown in Figure 4B. Positively charged amino acids also tend to cluster together, but negatively charged ones (as a group) and those with a β-sheet propensity do not (91). These observations suggest that the run test can be used to identify preferential associations (or avoidances) among amino acids that may not be apparent from considerations of secondary or other obvious structural classifications alone. Indeed, using a smaller randomly selected subset of sequences, one can examine the clustering tendency of every possible combination of amino acid (SH White & RE Jacobs, unpublished data).

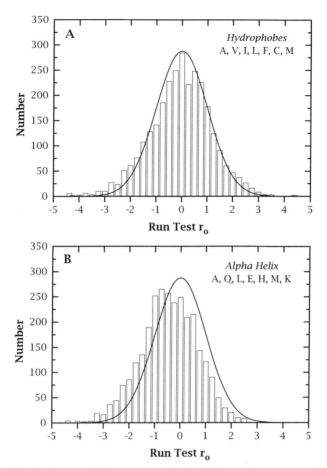

Figure 4 The distribution of the run test r_o for the 2912 protein sequences in the 1992 Superfamily Set. The solid curves are the expected normal $[N(0,1)]$ distributions and the bars the observed distributions. (*A*) Hydrophobic amino acids. (*B*) Amino acids with a strong α-helix propensity (54). Notice in panel *B* that the observed distribution is shifted dramatically to the left, indicating that amino acids with a strong α-helix propensity generally cluster together much more often than would be expected from chance.

Density of Protein Lengths

The run-test data provided convincing evidence that randomness was a central feature of protein sequences (90, 91). Thus, the finding that the lengths of protein sequences also obeyed simple stochastic principles was not surprising (86, 87). The density of sequence lengths for the 1992 Superfamily Set shown in Figure 5*A* compares very favorably

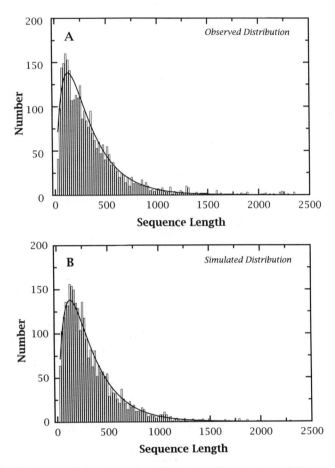

Figure 5   The observed (*A*) and simulated (*B*) density of lengths in the 1992 Superfamily Set of protein sequences. The solid curves in panels *A* and *B* are identical and were obtained by fitting Equation 4 to the observed density (*bars, panel A*). The simulation method is described in the text.

with the stochastic simulation shown in Figure 5*B*. Careful examination of the densities of the 1989 Superfamily Set and sets of *Escherichia coli* and human sequences reveal that Equation 4 or 5 describes the densities with very high significance (87), but N. Schumacher has developed a test of significance for determining which of the two distributions best describes a given set of sequences (see 87). This test indicates that the *E. coli* sequences are described by Equation 5 while human sequences are described by Equation 4. Therefore, the probability of folding increases more rapidly with length for human sequences than for *E. coli* sequences. Disulfide bond formation is probably responsible for the difference (86). These results indicate that Equations 4 and 5 are useful for characterizing populations of protein sequences. But, as discussed more fully below, the fact that the observed length distributions adhere closely to a simple stochastic model has important implications for the early evolution of proteins.

Amino Acid Frequencies

The random variable–generating functions of Equations 8 and 9 were used to generate 2912 sequences using the code-table probabilities for p_i and values of α and β determined from a nonlinear-least-squares fit of Equation 4 to the observed density of lengths (Figure 5A). Figure 6 shows the simulated density of frequencies obtained using the six-codon probability along with the observed densities for arginine and leucine, which have six codons. The widths of the observed densities are broader than predicted by the simulation and the means are shifted to lower values.

Table 1 summarizes the results of the statistical analyses of the densities of frequencies for the complete set of natural amino acids. Two conclusions can be reached. First, except for tyrosine, all of the ob-

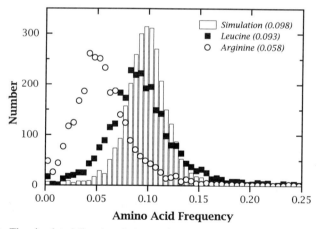

Figure 6 The simulated (*bars*) and observed (*squares, circles*) densities of amino acid frequencies in the 1992 Superfamily Set of protein sequences. The simulation (see text) used the six-codon code-table probability of 0.098. Leucine (*squares*) and arginine (*circles*) are each represented by six codons in the genetic code, but their observed probabilities are significantly lower than expected. The widths of both the leucine and arginine densities are much larger than expected because there is not a fixed probability p_i of leucine or arginine (Equation 6) for the sequences in the database.

Table 1 Means (μ) and standard deviations (σ) of the distributions of amino acid frequencies for the 1992 Superfamily Set of 2912 protein sequences

Amino acid[a]	Distribution (μ)	Z score[b] (codon μ)	Distribution (σ)	Z score[b] (codon σ)
Ala (4)	0.0783	+37	0.0376	+78
Arg (6)	0.0576	−96	0.0342	+38
Asn (2)	0.0441	+46	0.0239	+61
Asp (2)	0.0514	+75	0.0222	+51
Cys (2)	0.0183	−59	0.0234	+58
Gln (2)	0.0390	+25	0.0228	+55
Glu (2)	0.0600	+110	0.0298	+95
Gly (4)	0.0670	+4	0.0332	+60
His (2)	0.0220	−44	0.0153	+11
Ile (3)	0.0572	+43	0.0274	+50
Leu (6)	0.0933	−12	0.0344	+39
Lys (2)	0.0595	+108	0.0341	+120
Met (1)	0.0256	+53	0.0138	+36
Phe (2)	0.0392	+26	0.0202	+40
Pro (4)	0.0492	−47	0.0298	+46
Ser (6)	0.0683	−71	0.0276	+15
Thr (4)	0.0573	−24	0.0250	+26
Trp (1)	0.0135	−17	0.0114	+16
Tyr (2)	0.0324	−1.6	0.0182	+28
Val (4)	0.0667	+3	0.0252	+27

[a] The number of code-table codons for each amino acid is in parentheses.

[b] The Z scores measure the extent to which the observed means and standard deviations differ from the expected means and standard deviations of the simulated distributions using the codon probabilities of the universal genetic-code table. The scores are calculated as described by White & Jacobs (91). The scores represent the number of standard deviations by which the observed values of μ and σ differ from those expected from the simulations (see text). The means and standard deviations for the simulated distributions for 2912 sequences are: 1 codon, 0.0164 ± 0.0094; 2 codons, 0.0328 ± 0.0133; 3 codons, 0.0492 ± 0.0166; 4 codons, 0.0656 ± 0.0187; 6 codons, 0.0984 ± 0.0229.

served means are different from the means expected from the code-table probabilities with extremely high significance. This finding is not surprising because the accumulated mutations in proteins are not random (see 76). Beyond that, however, the results in Table 1 show that modern proteins are broadly and strongly biased away from the codon probabilities. These biases are undoubtedly related to general requirements for protein stability, and one can suppose that they arose very early in evolution. Under the ROH, the amino acid composition of the collection of primitive proteins would certainly have reflected fundamental stability requirements. Second, the widths of all of the observed densities are much broader than expected with extremely high significance. This is easily interpreted to mean that a fixed amino acid probability p_i is not a characteristic of the biosphere. However, the range of p_i does appear to be limited, because any of the observed frequency densities can be accurately simulated by allowing the p_i in Equation 6 to fluctuate according to a normal distribution. This is accomplished during the simulation by using the Box-Muller algorithm of Equation 9 to generate a p_i prior to generating a n_i. The density of valine frequencies, for example, can be simulated quite well using $p_i = 0.067$ with a standard deviation of 0.03.

A final point must be made about the densities of amino acid frequencies. One's first impulse when faced with distributions such as those of Figure 6, which are characterized by a mean and a standard deviation, is to assume that amino acid frequencies are somehow imprecise. That view is correct if one draws a single sequence by chance from a large population; the density of frequencies indicates the likelihood of drawing a sequence with a particular frequency from the collection. However, the density itself is based upon almost 3000 sequences and is therefore defined with great accuracy. Because of this fact, one can claim with extreme confidence that, say, the mean frequency of glutamine (0.0390 in Table 1) is different from the expected value of 0.0328, which comes from the code-table probability. If one assumes that the mean and standard deviation of the simulated two-codon density is the true one, then one can ask about the fluctuations in the mean and standard deviation of multiple collections of 2912 sequences drawn from an infinite collection. Standard statistical methods (see 87) show that the standard deviation of the mean frequency of glutamine from collection to collection will be about 0.0002. Hence, the observed 0.0390 differs by 25σ from the expected value of 0.0328!

ORIGIN, EVOLUTION, AND PREDICTION OF PROTEIN STRUCTURE

It is remarkable that the minimal assumptions of the random origin hypothesis and the no-exon model capture so well the essential statistical features of a representative set of protein sequences. Although the results of the analysis of the 1992 Superfamily Set clearly reveal significant deviations from the random expectation, one must be impressed by how well the NE model reproduces the fundamental properties of the collection. Yet, our experience as biologists causes us to rebel against the notion that biological structure has an underlying randomness. How can a molecular structure as beautiful as triose phosphate isomerase result from a random sequence? The same experience also compels us to inquire about the consequences of the ROH in practical terms. Does it help resolve or clarify any important problems of modern biology? The remainder of this review is devoted to these questions.

Stochastic Sequences and the Origin of Structure

THE HYDROPHOBIC CORE   The regions of protein sequences that are rich in hydrophobic residues (i.e. hydrophobes) define the interiors of globular proteins, the interfaces between protein subunits, and the lipid-spanning segments of membrane proteins (8, 11, 12, 20, 45). Thus, the lengthwise distribution of these residues along sequences gives rise to the basic structure. The hydrophobe-rich regions are easily detected by hydropathy plots that result from moving an averaging or summing window along a sequence of numbers representing the hydrophobicity values of the amino acids comprising the sequence (20, 50, 71, 88). A simplified hydropathy plot of the seven-helix membrane protein bacteriorhodopsin (bR) (Figure 7A) was produced using a binary hydrophobicity scale (90) that assigns a value of 1 to hydrophobes and 0 to all others so that the sliding window simply counts the number of hydrophobes in the window at each amino acid position. The plot reveals peaks that apparently occur at regular intervals; one might therefore suppose that this sequence is nonrandom. However, this supposition is not correct. The run test r_o value for this sequence is -0.009, and it is therefore perfectly random from the mathematical point of view (90, 91).

Sequences that appear similar overall to bR are easily produced using a random number generator, as shown in Figure 7B. Although I purposely chose for this figure a randomly produced sequence that yields a hydropathy plot vaguely like that of bR, only three trials were required to obtain it.

How does the regularity of the hydropathy plot, and therefore the clustering of the hydrophobes, arise? A simple experiment reveals the answer. Select by chance 300 balls from a large container of black (hydrophobes) and white balls and lay them one after another in a line. Then subdivide them into contiguous segments (windows) of 20 balls and count the number of black balls in each window. If the container contained 70% black balls (the typical frequency of hydrophobes in membrane proteins), the average window will contain 14 black balls. However, the number will fluctuate according to simple binomial statistics and the probability of finding a few windows containing 16 to 18 balls (Figure 7) is reasonably high. Figure 7B has five such windows. How often will one of these windows be encountered as we move along the sequence? The answer is, on average, every $60 = 300 / 5$ balls.

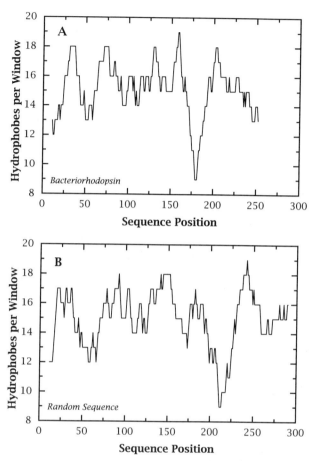

Figure 7 Hydropathy plots of bacteriorhodopsin (*A*) and a random sequence (*B*) with the same frequency of hydrophobes. The plots are implemented using a binary hydrophobicity scale that assigns a value of 1 to the amino acids A, V, I, L, F, C, M, W, Y, P, and G and 0 to all others. The sliding window had a width of 21 amino acids and summed the values so that the ordinates of the curves represented the number of hydrophobic residues per window at each sequence position. See text.

This number is also subject to statistical fluctuations that should have a standard deviation of approximately $\sqrt{60} \approx 8$ so that a peak can be expected to occur every 60 ± 16 residues. Therefore, hydrophobicity peaks with a quasiperiodic behavior are an expected feature of random sequences, and the hydrophobicity plot of Figure 7*B* should not come as a surprise.

STATISTICAL CHARACTERIZATION OF HYDROPATHY PLOTS   Formalizing the above ideas using binomial statistics provides useful insights to the relationship between frequency of hydrophobes and basic structural features of proteins. Figure 8A summarizes the statistics of window occupancy for the hydropathy plots of Figure 7 and compares them with the binomial distribution expected for $n = 0 \ldots 21$ events with a probability of 0.7. Although the hydropathy plot statistics differ somewhat from the perfect binomial distribution, they are well within the fluctuations expected by chance. This simple analysis demonstrates in fact another way of testing the hypothesis that a sequence is a random one. More important, it allows one to see how, in a gross way, a simple change in the frequency of hydrophobes can affect the basic structure. Two binomial distributions for hydrophobe frequencies of 50 and 70% are compared in Figure 8B. Apparently an amino acid sequence containing 50% hydrophobes (typical of soluble proteins) will have a much lower window occupancy than the 70% case (typical of membrane proteins). Thus, soluble proteins with their smaller clusters of hydrophobes are destined to have structural characteristics that differ from membrane proteins.

CHARACTERISTIC LENGTHS OF SECONDARY STRUCTURE   The binomial statistics of hydropathy plots provide a means of establishing a relationship between amino acid frequency and characteristic structural lengths. For example, because in folded soluble proteins the hydrophobic cores are generally defined by α-helices and β-strands terminated by reverse turns (71), one expects the frequency of hydrophobes to affect the lengths of buried secondary structure. As a result, the so-called natural window size for hydropathy plots can be used to estimate the average length of protein secondary structure (90).

What is meant by the natural window size? In general, the choice of window size is arbitrary except for the perception that a length appropriate for the structure sought should be used (89). In Figure 7, for example, a window of 21 amino acids was chosen because one expects transmembrane helices to have lengths of that size. If the longest clusters of hydrophobes in a sequence define the lengths of secondary structure, then the problem reduces to one of establishing the size of the window required to contain the highest number of hydrophobes that are likely to be encountered. In Figure 8B, the window occupancies of interest are those on the far right of the distribution. The highest window occupancy will likely be the mean occupancy plus three standard deviations.

The standard deviation of the binomial distribution with parameters

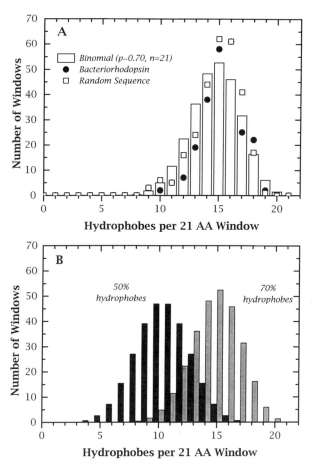

Figure 8 Binomial statistics of window occupancy for binary-scale hydropathy plots. Bars represent calculated binomial distributions. (*A*) The points show the observed distributions of window occupancy for the hydropathy plots of Figure 7. (*B*) Binomial distributions computed for random sequences containing 50 and 70% hydrophobes that are characteristic of soluble and membrane proteins, respectively. See text.

W and f is $\sigma_b = [W \cdot f(1 - f)]^{1/2}$, where $W \cdot f$ is the mean window occupancy. The natural window length is thus given by $W = W \cdot f + 3[W \cdot f(1 - f)]^{1/2}$, which is easily solved to yield

$$W = 9f/(1 - f).$$ 10.

The fraction of hydrophobes for globular proteins is typically 0.55, which results in a W of 11 amino acids that compares favorably with the average lengths of secondary structure in globular proteins (43).

This value is also the natural window size for hydrophobicity plots of globular proteins and happens to coincide with the size that Kyte & Doolittle (50) arrived at empirically. For membrane proteins with a hydrophobe frequency of 0.7, $W = 21$, which is the expected minimum length of transmembrane helices (20, 88).

AMPHIPHILIC SECONDARY STRUCTURE   Amphiphilic α-helices are a common feature of proteins and can serve to define secondary-structure boundaries between the exterior and interior of globular proteins. They tend to have a 3.6-residue periodicity in the polar-nonpolar distribution of their amino acids. This periodicity causes a peak at about 100° in the Fourier power spectrum of the sequence of hydrophobicity values, indicating a high hydrophobic moment (9, 19). A helical wheel diagram (75) of a 12-residue amphiphilic helix formed using the binary hydrophobicity scale yields the sequence 110011011001, which produces a very strong Fourier peak at 100° as expected. This sequence is an example of a random sequence, as its run test r_o is small.

How often will random sequences have high hydrophobic moments characteristic of amphiphilic helices? This question can be answered by generating a large number of random binary sequences and examining their hydrophobic moments and run test values. When this is done, one finds that 8–12% of the sequences ($f = 0.5$; $L = 12$ to 24) have statistically significant Fourier peaks at 100° and that the probability of such peaks increases drastically in the vicinity of $r_o = 0$ (91). This is a very large percentage from the perspective of evolution. A similar percentage is observed for amphiphilic β-strands (Fourier peak at 180°) with the general pattern 10101010 (unpublished observation). As expected, the percentage of sequences with high β-strand hydrophobic moments increased as r_o became more positive because the pattern involves an increased number of runs (see Figure 1).

These considerations show that the most fundamental patterns of hydrophobicity that we use to characterize the basic structural features of proteins are common features of random sequences. Workers in the laboratories of Fisher (24, 28), Ptitsyn (23, 66, 67), and Dill (7, 51), as noted earlier, have come to the same conclusion. Therefore, one must conclude that not only is three-dimensional structure consistent with sequence randomness, it seems to be a fundamental feature.

Evolution of Structural Diversity: the Roles of Introns and Stop Codons

The conventional and widely accepted view of the origin of the rich diversity in sequence, size, and structure of modern proteins is that they have evolved from a small set of starter sequences with lengths of 30 to 50 amino acids by means of gene duplication, exon shuffling, and random mutations (2, 14, 16–18, 31, 37, 56). The most modern version of this starter set hypothesis is that of Dorit et al (17), who have proposed a limited universe of exons, several thousand in number, from which all proteins have been constituted. They suggest that modern exons are descendants of the original genes that encoded the starter sequences. The main impetus for these ideas was the discovery of intervening sequences (introns) and the frequent observation that protein subdomains are often encoded by exons. Studies of introns and exon splicing have provided, perhaps, the main support for the starter set hypothesis [see the thorough reviews in the recent volume edited by Stone & Schwartz (82)]. Beyond that, the early notion that the first proteins must have been comprised of regular repeating oligopeptide sequences (18, 56) steered thinking away from the possibility that these proteins were random sequences despite the observations of Ycas (92) and the insight and influence of Monod (57). The random origin hypothesis as embodied in the no-exon model is an appealing alternative to the starter-set hypothesis because of its simplicity, which surely must have been of singular importance in a feeble biosphere.

The most crucial issue in both the starter-set and no-exon models is the length of protein sequences. Clearly, length plays a major role in protein stability (11). The strong length dependence of the frequencies of some amino acids, particularly cysteine, reinforces this view (86). Senapathy (77) has examined the lengthwise distribution of stop codons in DNA sequences and found that the intervals between stop codons can be accurately described by a negative exponential. More precisely stated, he observed that the intervals Z_i between stop codons are exponentially distributed random variables. As noted earlier, this is the expected distribution if the stop codons are uniformly randomly distributed along the sequence. Senapathy's observation thus verifies one of the principal assumptions of the NE model and permits the probability of finding a reading frame of length Z, which would be calculated from the equation

$$P_Z(z) = \epsilon \exp(-\epsilon z), \qquad\qquad 11.$$

where ϵ is the frequency of stop codons.

Senapathy (77) measured and compared the distributions of intervals between stop codons in DNA sequences and in computer-generated random nucleotide sequences. Although the distributions of the intervals in both cases could be described by Equation 11, the maximum interval for simulated sequences (with $A = T = G = C$) was 200 codons, whereas for DNA the maximum for the sequences used was 2000 codons. That 200 codons is the upper limit expected in a random sequence can be verified by setting ϵ in Equation 11 equal to the probability that any three consecutive nucleotides encode a stop codon. A plot of Equation 11 with $\epsilon = 3[(1/4)^3] = 0.047$ appears in Figure 2B and is designated 3 3NT Signals because of the three stop codons. From his analysis, Senapathy argued that selective evolutionary pressure must have eliminated stop codons, and suggested that introns evolved to accomplish this through the transformation of stop codons into splice-junction signals (35, 78).

Senapathy's argument assumes that three trinucleotide stop codons were present in the primitive genetic code. Given that the genetic code itself has a complex evolutionary history (64) that has probably proceeded by means of changes in stop codons (41), this is a weak assumption. If only a single trinucleotide stop codon was present, as in *Tetrahymena thermophilia* (34), then ϵ would decrease to $(1/4)^3 = 0.0156$, causing the interval between codons to increase significantly (Figure 2B). However, one could go even further and assert that the primordial stop codons could have been encoded by four or more nucleotides (87). If a single tetranucleotide signal is considered, ϵ becomes $(1/4)^4 = 0.0039$ and the length distribution increases drastically as shown in Figure 2B. This exponential tail should be compared to the tail of the length distribution in Figure 2A, which was calculated from $\epsilon = 0.0048$ derived by fitting Equation 5 to the Superfamily Set length distribution. Degenerate (m-fold) higher order (n) nucleotide sequences with $\epsilon = m[(1/4)^n]$ could yield a similar value, but Occam's razor favors the simplest case: a tetranucleotide.

Bossi & Roth (4) discovered that the efficiency of suppressor tRNA is influenced by nucleotides outside the stop codons, and Bossi (3) subsequently showed that the nucleotide immediately following the codon was responsible. In an extensive recent analysis, Brown et al (5, 6) unequivocally showed that the adjacent nucleotide strongly affects the release of polypeptides from ribosomes in both prokaryotes and eukaryotes. In fact, the effect is so striking that Brown et al declared "that the stop codon and the nucleotide following it comprise a tetra-nucleotide stop signal" (6, p. 6339). This conclusion provides experimental confirmation of the prediction of the NE model.

The NE model, the experimental observation of tetranucleotide stop signals, and the evolution of the genetic code by stop-codon takeover (53) suggest that the evolution of translation-termination processes was of greater importance to the early evolution of proteins than gene duplication or exon shuffling. However, these latter processes have clearly been of great importance in protein evolution, and one can therefore envision, instead of a starter set of small proteins, an initial set of protein sequences, produced according to the NE model, that were diverse in sequence, length, and structure from the beginning (87). This scenario eliminates the need for gene duplication and exon shuffling as precursors to diversity and, consequently, a limited universe of exons. It shifts the length question from the complexities of intervening sequences to questions about the statistical distribution of stop codons in the genome, the evolution of the genetic code, and the regulation of translation termination (87).

The Problem of Predicting Structure

The prediction of three-dimensional protein structure from sequence has proven to be one of the most elusive goals of modern molecular biology and biophysics. Even the more limited goal of accurately predicting secondary structure has been difficult to attain despite 25 years of research [see reviews by Fasman (21) and Garnier (27)]. The accuracy of secondary structure prediction for nonhomologous proteins is currently stalled at about 65% (30, 68, 70) and the prospects for significant improvement in the near future seem grim. The sequence motif studies of Rooman & Wodak (70) suggest that a database of 1500 high-resolution protein structures will be required to achieve accuracies of 85–90%. Qian & Sejnowski (68) are more pessimistic; they conclude from neural network analyses that predictive schemes based solely on local sequence information cannot surpass the 65% barrier. The global statistics of sequences discussed here support this point of view in that virtually any aspect of sequences examined thus far yield broad distributions. Efforts to distinguish specific classes of proteins by their positions within the distributions have been disappointing. The breadths of the distributions seem to indicate that ambiguities will always be present in purely statistical approaches to structure prediction.

Garnier (27) has outlined two reasons for these ambiguities. First, no apparent torsion-angle restrictions prevent any of the 20 amino acids from occurring within virtually any type of secondary structure (30). Second, our present database of a few hundred high-resolution proteins has sampled a statistically insignificant number of the sequences that can form secondary structure. Assuming a typical secondary-structure length of 10 amino acids, 20^{10} ($\approx 10^{13}$) sequences are possible. If one considers a length of 17 amino acids, as is often used in secondary structure–prediction schemes (27), the number rises to about 10^{22} sequences. Numbers of these magnitudes make the Rooman & Wodak (70) estimate seem optimistic. Indeed, Gibrat et al (30) suggest that the

65% limit exists because that is the maximum amount of information contained within the local sequence necessary for specifying the conformation of a given residue. Rackovsky (69) has come to a similar conclusion based upon an analysis of the occurrence of tetrapeptides in secondary structure.

Arguments similar to Garnier's can be applied to the complete three-dimensional structure of proteins, as shown by extensive simulations and mathematical analyses. Chan & Dill (7) explored the types of structure that can be formed by compact heteropolymers folding on three-dimensional lattices and showed that the formation of secondary structure is very common and a natural consequence of steric constraints. Dill notes that "there are simply very few possible ways to configure a compact chain, and most of them involve helices and sheets" (12, p. 7148). This conclusion is equivalent to Garnier's (27) first reason for the failure of prediction algorithms. Lau & Dill (51) have explored the other reason for prediction inaccuracy, i.e. the large diversity of sequences that can have a given type of structure, by means of simulations. They conclude that the number of sequences coding for the same native structure is likely to be extraordinarily large, perhaps greater than 10^{21} for a protein 100 amino acids long. Similar conclusions, based on spin-glass model results, have been reached by Shakhnovich & Gutin (79, 80). These various simulations and analyses are entirely consistent with the fact that three-dimensional structure is more highly conserved than amino acid sequence, as first shown for the cytochromes c (10, 81). I believe that this is a necessary condition for evolution to proceed. If the stability of a structure were limited to a very narrow region of sequence space, random mutations would be intolerable.

The structure-prediction problem, in the end, involves finding global solutions based upon minuscule samples of an extremely large and degenerate space of sequences. Given the difficulty of this problem, how can statistical approaches help? There are two fundamental ways. First, statistical approaches will become extremely useful if we know precisely what clues we are seeking. As we learn more about the physical chemistry of the protein-folding problem, we can develop stronger statistical tests. The results of the run test (Figure 4) indicate that any sequence chosen from a population has a 90% or better chance of being mathematically random (91). Thus, nonrandomness itself is not a sufficient condition for structure prediction. To be sure, one can develop strong tests to detect interesting features of sequences that occur more often than expected by chance (44), but these are exceptions as must be the case when one seeks events that stand out at a significance of

1% or less. All protein structures are interesting, but unfortunately they mostly have sequences that are mathematically random. The most successful structure prediction schemes are likely to be ones such as hydropathy plots that detect features that are structurally important even in random sequences (Figure 7). Of course, in their present form, many of the peaks (or lack of them) in hydropathy and related plots can be ambiguous (91), even for highly nonrandom sequences (88).

The second way that statistics can help, and help immediately, is in the selection of an appropriate database of proteins of known three-dimensional structure (3D database). Such a database represents a sample of sequence space and must therefore be equivalent statistically to the parent set. Most efforts over the years have not addressed this issue. In the earliest days when the number of proteins of known structure was small, the general rule was the more the better, so that a 3D database such as that of Kabsch & Sander (43) was particularly important. Sander & Schneider (73) have more recently developed methods for expanding the effective size of the full 3D database using sequence homology.

Also, Hobohm et al (36) have developed methods for selecting a representative 3D database (~150 structures) that maximizes the number of structures while minimizing redundancies. The issue of redundancy, especially of 3D structure in the database of proteins of unknown structure, is a very important one that needs to be addressed more carefully. Holm & Sander (38), for example, have recently reported the surprising finding that the membrane-insertion domain of colicin A closely resembles the globin fold. From the point of view of secondary-structure prediction via the calculation of secondary-structure propensities, the 3D database should have the same kinds of redundancies as the set of proteins of unknown structure. A related but unsolved (and perhaps unsolvable) problem is that of assuring that the 3D set contains examples of all folding motifs.

The global statistical properties of the Superfamily Set of proteins should be useful for judging whether or not a 3D database is a representative sample. White & Jacobs (91) have discussed the standard statistical methods for doing this. Consider, for example, run test results such as those of Figure 4 that yield means μ and standard deviations σ for the population. Take these as the correct values for the extant sequences. If one draws a random sample of, say, 100 sequences from this parent population, the μ and σ will rarely be precisely the same as the parent set because of the usual statistical fluctuations. How close to the parent's values must the sample's values be to assure a good chance that the sample is fair? If one repeatedly draws random

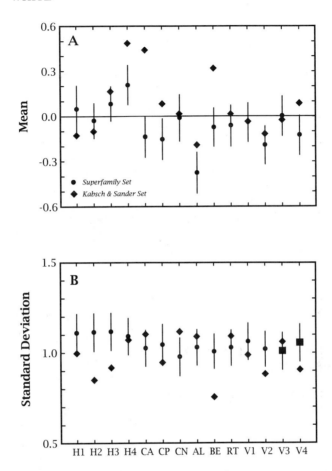

Amino Acid Class

Figure 9 Statistical comparison of the run test r_o statistics for the 82 sequences of the proteins in the Kabsch & Sander (43) three-dimensional database with the statistics of the 1989 Superfamily Set of protein sequences (91). The abscissa indicates the 14 amino acid classes examined (described in detail in 91). In brief, H1 through H4 represent four different classes of hydrophobic amino acids; CA, CP, and CN indicate all charged amino acids (CA), positive charge (CP), and negative charge (CN); AL, BE, and RT respectively represent amino acid residues with strong α-helix, β-sheet, and reverse-turn propensities (54); V1 through V4 represent four different side-chain volume classes with the numbers indicating the volume quartile rank beginning with the smallest amino acids. (*A*) Comparisons of the mean r_o values. Solid circles indicate the means of the 1989 Superfamily Set. The lines through the points represent the spread of mean r_o values expected for multiple 82-sequence samples drawn from the Superfamily Set. (*B*) Comparisons of the standard deviations of the densities of the r_o values. The lines through the solid circles have the same meaning as in panel *A*.

subpopulations (with replacement), one can establish a range of values that will include 95% of the observations so that if a sample's μ and σ fall outside the range, the sample is probably not representative. If μ_p and σ_p arc the values for the parent set and μ_s and σ_s the values for a sample of size n, then one can determine the allowable ranges from (91)

$$| \mu_s - \mu_p | \leq 2\sigma_p/\sqrt{n} \qquad\qquad 12.$$

$$\sigma_s = [\sqrt{(2n - 1)} \pm 2] \cdot \sigma_p/\sqrt{2n}. \qquad\qquad 13.$$

Figure 9 shows an example of the application of this idea to the Kabsch & Sander (43) 3D database. Here the statistical parameters for the run test distributions obtained from 14 different classes of amino acids (91) were used for the comparison. There are some glaring deviations relative to the 1989 Superfamily Set statistics. In principle, one should be able to select an appropriate 3D database that falls within the expected limits. The difficulty is finding a set that not only conforms to appropriate run test statistics but also to sequence length and amino acid frequency.

EPILOGUE

Jacques Monod (57) thought deeply about the fundamental issues of the origin and evolution of proteins and expressed them elegantly in his classic 1970 monograph, *Chance and Necessity*. Based upon a small number of protein sequences and a large amount of insight, he wrote: "From the work on these sequences, and after systematically comparing them with the help of modern means of analysis and computing, we are now in a position to deduce the general law: it is that of chance" (57, p. 96). And further: "In the ontogenesis of a functional protein are reflected the origin and descent of the whole biosphere. And the ultimate source of the project that living things represent, pursue, and accomplish is revealed in this message—in this neat, exact, but essentially indecipherable text that primary structure constitutes. [The sequence] in its make-up discloses nothing other than the pure randomness of its origin. But such, precisely, is the profounder meaning of this message which comes to us from the most distant reaches of time" (57, p. 98). The work reviewed in this article supports this viewpoint. Although randomness seems contrary to the beautiful structures that are revealed to us through X-ray crystallography, it resolves the dilemma of how the structures of life could evolve in a chaotic physical world that is driven forward by increasing entropy. This randomness, however, greatly complicates the prediction of structure from sequence.

ACKNOWLEDGMENTS

I am grateful to Dr. Russell Jacobs for his early contributions to the work reviewed here. I am pleased to acknowledge the advice and criticisms of the "Wednesday Afternoon Group" that consisted of Prof. Howard Tucker, Prof. Mark Finkelstein, Mr. Norbert Schumacher, and Mr. Les Vernon of the Mathematics Department. The research of my laboratory is supported by the National Science Foundation (DMB-8807431) and the National Institutes of Health (GM-46823).

Literature Cited

1. Black JA, Harkins RN, Stenzel P. 1976. Non-random relationships among amino acids in protein sequences. *Int. J. Peptide Protein Res.* 8:125–30
2. Blake CCF. 1983. Exons—present from the beginning? *Nature* 306:535–37
3. Bossi L. 1983. Context effects: translation of UAG codon by suppressor tRNA is affected by the sequence following UAG in the message. *J. Mol. Biol.* 164:73–87
4. Bossi L, Roth JR. 1980. The influence of codon context on genetic code translation. *Nature* 286:123–27
5. Brown CM, Stockwell PA, Trotman CNA, Tate WP. 1990. The signal for termination of protein synthesis in prokaryotes. *Nucleic Acids Res.* 18:2079–86
6. Brown CM, Stockwell PA, Trotman CNA, Tate WP. 1990. Sequence analysis suggests that tetra-nucleotides signal the termination of protein synthesis in eukaryotes. *Nucleic Acids Res.* 18: 6339–45
7. Chan HS, Dill KA. 1990. Origins of structure in globular proteins. *Proc. Natl. Acad. Sci. USA* 87:6388–92
8. Chothia C. 1984. Principles that determine the structure of proteins. *Annu. Rev. Biochem.* 53:537–72
9. Cornette JL, Cease KB, Margalit H, Spouge JL, Berzofsky JA, DeLisi C. 1987. Hydrophobicity scales and computational techniques for detecting amphipathic structures in protein. *J. Mol. Biol.* 195:659–79
10. Dickerson RE, Timkovich R, Almassy RJ. 1976. The cytochrome fold and the evolution of bacterial energy metabolism. *J. Mol. Biol.* 100:473–91
11. Dill KA. 1985. Theory of the folding and stability of globular proteins. *Biochemistry* 24:1501–9
12. Dill KA. 1990. Dominant forces in protein folding. *Biochemistry* 29:7133–55
13. Dill KA, Alonso OV, Hutchinson K. 1989. Thermal stability of globular proteins. *Biochemistry* 28:5439–49
14. Doolittle RF. 1979. Protein evolution. In *The Proteins,* ed. H Neurath, RL Hill. 4:1–118. New York: Academic
15. Doolittle RF, ed. 1990. *Methods in Enzymology,* Vol. 183, *Molecular Evolution: Computer Analysis of Protein and Nucleic Acid Sequences.* San Diego: Academic. 736 pp.
16. Dorit RL, Gilbert W. 1991. The limited universe of exons. *Curr. Opin. Struc. Biol.* 1:973–77
17. Dorit RL, Schoenbach L, Gilbert W. 1990. How big is the universe of exons? *Science* 250:1377–82
18. Eck RV, Dayhoff MO. 1966. Evolution of the structure of ferredoxin based on living relics of primitive amino acid sequences. *Science* 152:363–66
19. Eisenberg D, Weiss RM, Terwilliger TC. 1982. The helical hydrophobic moment: a measure of the amphiphilicity of α-helix. *Nature* 299:371–74
20. Engelman DM, Steitz TA, Goldman A. 1986. Identifying nonpolar transbilayer

helices in amino acid sequences of membrane proteins. *Annu. Rev. Biophys. Biophys. Chem.* 15:321–53

21. Fasman GD. 1989. The development of the prediction of protein structure. See Ref. 22, pp.193–316

22. Fasman GD, ed. 1989. *Prediction of Protein Structure and the Principles of Protein Conformation.* New York: Plenum. 798 pp.

23. Finkelstein AV, Ptitsyn OB. 1987. Why do globular proteins fit the limited set of folding patterns. *Prog. Biophys. Mol. Biol.* 50:171–90

24. Fisher HF. 1964. A limiting law relating the size and shape of protein molecules to their composition. *Proc. Natl. Acad. Sci. USA* 51:1285–91

25. Fitch WM, Margoliash E. 1967. A method for estimating the number of invariant amino acid coding positions in a gene using cytochrome *c* as a model case. *Biochem. Genet.* 1:65–71

26. Gamow G, Ycas M. 1958. The cryptographic approach to the problem of protein synthesis. See Ref. 92a, pp.63–69

27. Garnier J. 1990. Protein structure prediction. *Biochimie* 72:513–24

28. Gates RE, Fisher HF. 1971. Restrictions of sequence on the thickness of globular protein molecules. *Proc. Natl. Acad. Sci. USA* 68:2928–31

29. George DG, Barker WC, Hunt LT. 1986. The protein identification resource (PIR). *Nucleic Acids Res.* 14:11–15

30. Gibrat JF, Robson B, Garnier J. 1991. Influence of the local amino acid sequence upon the zones of the torsional angles-ϕ and angle-ψ adopted by residues in proteins. *Biochemistry* 30:1578–86

31. Gilbert W. 1978. Why genes in pieces?. *Nature* 271:501

32. Gilbert W. 1986. The RNA world. *Nature* 319:618

33. Gribskov M, Devereux J. 1991. *Sequence Analysis Primer.* New York: Stockton. 279 pp.

34. Hanyu N, Kuchino Y, Nishimura S. 1986. Dramatic events in ciliate evolution: alteration of UAA and UAG termination codons to glutamine codons due to anticodon mutations in two *Tetrahymena* tRNAs(Gln). *EMBO J.* 5:1307–11

35. Harris NL, Senapathy P. 1990. Distribution and consensus of branch point signals in eukaryotic genes: a computerized statistical analysis. *Nucleic Acids Res.* 18:3015–19

36. Hobohm U, Scharf M, Schneider R,

Sander C. 1992. Selection of representative protein data sets. *Protein Sci.* 1:409–17

37. Holland SK, Blake CCF. 1990. Proteins, exons, and molecular evolution. See Ref. 82, pp.10–42

38. Holm L, Sander C. 1993. Globin fold in a bacterial toxin. *Nature* 361:309

39. Janin J. 1979. Surface and inside volumes in globular proteins. *Nature* 277:491–92

40. Jukes TH. 1969. Evolutionary pattern of specificity regions in light chains of immunoglobulins. *Biochem. Genet.* 3:109–17

41. Jukes TH. 1982. Possible evolutionary steps in the genetic code. *Biochem. Biophys. Res. Commun.* 107:225–28

42. Jukes TH. 1990. Genetic code 1990. Outlook. *Experientia* 46:1149–57

43. Kabsch W, Sander C. 1983. Dictionary of protein secondary structure: pattern recognition of hydrogen-bonded geometrical feature. *Biopolymers* 22:2577–2637

44. Karlin S, Bucher P, Brendel V, Altschul SF. 1991. Statistical methods and insights for protein and DNA sequences. *Annu. Rev. Biophys. Biophys. Chem.* 20:175–203

45. Kauzmann W. 1959. Some factors in the interpretation of protein denaturation. *Adv. Protein Chem.* 14:1–63

46. Kimura M. 1968. Evolutionary rate at the molecular level. *Nature* 217:624–26

47. King JL, Jukes TH. 1969. Non-Darwinian evolution. *Science* 164:788–98

48. Klapper MH. 1977. The independent distribution of amino acid near neighbor pairs and in polypeptides. *Biochem. Biophys. Res. Commun.* 78:1018–24

49. Klapper MH. 1977. Amino acid frequency distributions in proteins. *Fed. Proc.* 36:837

50. Kyte J, Doolittle RF. 1982. A simple method for displaying the hydropathic character of a protein. *J. Mol. Biol.* 157:105–32

51. Lau KF, Dill KA. 1990. Theory for protein mutability and biogenesis. *Proc. Natl. Acad. Sci. USA* 87:638–42

52. Lee B, Richards FM. 1971. The interpretation of protein structures: estimation of static accessibility. *J. Mol. Biol.* 55:379–400

53. Lehman N, Jukes TH. 1988. Genetic code development by stop codon takeover. *J. Theor. Biol.* 135:203–14

54. Levitt M. 1978. Conformational preferences of amino acids in globular proteins. *Biochemistry* 17:4277–85

55. McCaldon P, Argos P. 1988. Oligopep-

tide biases in protein sequences and their use in predicting protein coding regions in nucleotide sequences. *Proteins Struct. Funct. Genet.* 4:99–122

56. McLachlan AD. 1972. Repeating sequences and gene duplication in proteins. *J. Mol. Biol.* 64:417–37

57. Monod J. 1971. *Chance and Necessity. An Essay on the Natural Philosophy of Modern Biology.* New York: Knopf. 199 pp.

58. Mood AM. 1940. The distribution theory of runs. *Ann. Math. Stat.* 11:367–92

59. Mood AM, Graybill FA, Boes DC. 1974. *Introduction to the Theory of Statistics.* New York: McGraw-Hill. 564 pp.

60. Nisbet EG. 1986. RNA and hot-water springs. *Nature* 322:206

61. Noller HF, Hoffarth V, Zimniak L. 1992. Unusual resistance of peptidyl transferase to protein extraction procedures. *Science* 256:1416–19

62. Orcutt BC, George DG, Dayhoff MO. 1983. Protein and nucleic acid data base systems. *Annu. Rev. Biophys. Bioeng.* 12:419–41

63. Orgel LE. 1986. RNA catalysis and the origins of life. *J. Theor. Biol.* 123:127–49

64. Osawa S, Jukes TH. 1988. Evolution of the genetic code as affected by anticodon content. *Trends Genet.* 4:191–98

65. Peebles PJE, Schramm DN, Turner EL, Kron RG. 1991. The case for the relativistic hot big bang cosmology. *Nature* 352:769–76

66. Ptitsyn OB. 1985. Random sequences and protein folding. *J. Mol. Struct.* 123: 45–65

67. Ptitsyn OB. 1987. Protein folding: hypotheses and experiments. *J. Protein Chem.* 6:273–94

68. Qian N, Sejnowski TJ. 1988. Predicting the secondary structure of globular proteins using neural network models. *J. Mol. Biol.* 202:865–84

69. Rackovsky S. 1993. On the nature of the protein folding code. *Proc. Natl. Acad. Sci. USA* 90:644–48

70. Rooman MJ, Wodak SJ. 1988. Identification of predictive sequence motifs limited by protein structure data base size. *Nature* 335:45–50

71. Rose GD, Roy S. 1980. Hydrophobic basis of packing in globular proteins. *Proc. Natl. Acad. Sci. USA* 77:4643–47

72. Ross SM. 1989. *Introduction to Probability Models.* San Diego: Academic. 544 pp.

73. Sander C, Schneider R. 1991. Database of homology-derived protein structures and the structural meaning of sequence alignment. *Proteins Struct. Funct. Genet.* 9:56–68

74. Sassanfar M, Szostak JW. 1993. An RNA motif that binds ATP. *Nature* 364: 550–53

75. Schiffer M, Edmundson AB. 1967. Use of helical wheels to represent the structures of proteins and to identify segments with helical potential. *Biophys. J.* 7:121–35

76. Schulz GE, Schirmer RH. 1979. *Principles of Protein Structure.* New York: Springer-Verlag. 314 pp.

77. Senapathy P. 1986. Origin of eukaryotic introns: a hypothesis, based on codon distribution statistics in genes, and its implications. *Proc. Natl. Acad. Sci. USA* 83:2133–37

78. Senapathy P. 1988. Possible evolution of splice-junction signals in eukaryotic genes from stop codons. *Proc. Natl. Acad. Sci. USA* 85:1129–33

79. Shakhnovich EI, Gutin AM. 1989. Formation of unique structure in polypeptide chains. Theoretical investigation with the aid of a replica approach. *Biophys. Chem.* 34:187–99

80. Shakhnovich EI, Gutin AM. 1990. Implications of thermodynamics of protein folding for evolution of primary sequences. *Nature* 346:773–75

81. Smith EL, Margoliash E. 1964. Evolution of cytochrome *c. Fed. Proc.* 23: 1243–47

82. Stone EM, Schwartz RJ, eds. 1990. *Intervening Sequences in Evolution and Development.* New York: Oxford Univ. Press. 203 pp.

83. von Heijne G. 1987. *Sequence Analysis in Molecular Biology.* San Diego: Academic. 188 pp.

84. Wani JK. 1971. *Probability and Statistical Inference.* New York: Appleton-Century-Crofts. 315 pp.

85. Westheimer FH. 1986. Polyribonucleic acids as enzymes. *Nature* 319:534–36

86. White SH. 1992. The amino acid preferences of small proteins: implications for protein stability and evolution. *J. Mol. Biol.* 227:991–95

87. White SH. 1993. The evolution of proteins from random amino acid sequences. II. Evidence from the statistical distributions of the lengths of modern protein sequences. *J. Mol. Evol.* 38: In press

88. White SH. 1994. Hydropathy plots and the prediction of membrane protein to-

pology. In *Membrane Protein Structure: Experimental Approaches,* ed. SH White. New York: Oxford Univ. Press. In press

89. White SH, Jacobs RE. 1990. Observations concerning topology and locations of helix ends of membrane proteins of known structure. *J. Membr. Biol.* 115: 145–58

90. White SH, Jacobs RE. 1990. Statistical distribution of hydrophobic residues along the length of protein chains—implications for protein folding and evolution. *Biophys. J.* 57:911–21

91. White SH, Jacobs RE. 1993. The evolution of proteins from random amino acid sequences. I. Evidence from the

lengthwise distribution of amino acids in modern protein sequences. *J. Mol. Evol.* 36:79–95

92. Ycas M. 1958. The protein text. See Ref. 92a, pp.70–102

92a. Yockey HP, ed. 1958. *Symposium on Information Theory in Biology.* New York: Pergamon. 418 pp.

93. Zaug AJ, Cech TR. 1986. The intervening sequence RNA of *Tetrahymena* is an enzyme. *Science* 231:470–75

94. Zielenkiewicz P, Plochocka D, Rabczenko A. 1988. The formation of protein secondary structure. Its connection with amino acid sequence. *Biophys. Chem.* 31:139–42

Annu. Rev. Biophys. Biomol. Struct. 1994. 23:441–71

PERSPECTIVES ON THE PHYSIOLOGY AND STRUCTURE OF INWARD-RECTIFYING K$^+$ CHANNELS IN HIGHER PLANTS: Biophysical Implications for K$^+$ Uptake

Julian I. Schroeder, John M. Ward, and Walter Gassmann

Department of Biology and Center for Molecular Genetics, University of California San Diego, La Jolla, California 92093-0116

KEY WORDS: K$^+$ transport, guard cell, anomalous rectifier, metal toxicity, salt tolerance

CONTENTS

441

1056–8700/94/0610–0441$05.00

INTRODUCTION

Voltage-dependent K^+ channels comprise a heterogeneous group of ion channels in the plasma membrane of eukaryotic cells. These K^+ channels play major roles in controlling central physiological processes such as excitability, K^+ transport, secretion, and cellular homeostasis in animal and plant cells (35, 54, 56, 59, 121). In spite of the great diversity in the functions and modes of regulation of K^+ channels, recent molecular biological studies have suggested that most eukaryotic voltage-dependent K^+ channels are members of a superfamily of genes that share common ancestral origins (1, 59). Several subfamilies of K^+ channel genes have been identified, most of which are depolarization-activated (so-called outward-rectifying) K^+ channels (59, 100).

K^+ channels belonging to another general class are activated by membrane hyperpolarization, thereby allowing K^+ influx, and are therefore referred to as inward-rectifying K^+ channels (61, 122). As shown by recent cloning and functional characterization of cDNAs that encode plant and animal inward-rectifying K^+ channels, the general structures of these plant (3, 125) and animal (55, 68, 150) inward K^+ channels differ. However, plant inward-rectifying K^+ channels do show some remarkable structural similarities to outward-rectifying K^+ channels in animal systems (1, 3, 111, 125). Therefore, inward-rectifying K^+ channel clones from higher plants may provide a unique model system for understanding voltage-dependent gating.

The emphasis of plant research on the physiological roles of ion channels has led to newly derived biophysical models that have profound implications for many plant signal-transduction and transport processes. While membrane potential control is one important function of K^+ channels in higher plants, inward-rectifying (K_{in}^+) channels have further been suggested to provide a major pathway for K^+ uptake into plant cells (93, 122). The electrogenic proton-extruding ATPase is ubiquitous in the plasma membrane of plant cells. It hyperpolarizes the membrane to sufficiently negative potentials (128, 135) to open K_{in}^+ channels and drive physiological K^+-uptake fluxes through these channels at physiological cytosolic K^+ concentrations of ~ 100 mM and extracellular K^+ concentrations in the low-affinity range of ≥ 0.3 mM K^+ (7, 117, 121, 122, 125). Plant cell resting potentials lie in the range from ~ 120 to -220 mV owing to the activity of proton ATPases (128, 135).

Cellular K^+ uptake plays a major role in plant growth and development (39, 88). K^+-uptake transporters in plant cells interact with several other metals (cations), such as Na^+ and Al^{3+}, that are detrimental to plant growth (34, 43, 89). Conversely, Ca^{2+} reduces the toxic effects of these metals on K^+ uptake (65, 69). The question can now be addressed whether and to what extent channel block or permeation contribute to important metal ion effects on cellular K^+ transport and plant growth, as discussed in this review. Several cytosolic modulation mechanisms of K_{in}^+ channels have been found and may reflect the importance of K^+ channel regulation for cellular processes. We review the reported modulation mechanisms.

Recent reviews have provided excellent overviews of ion channel classes and their general electrical properties in higher plants (49, 60, 90, 120, 137, 138, 142) and of the structure and function of animal outward-rectifying K^+ channels (16, 59). First, we discuss the physiology and electrical properties of K_{in}^+ channels in plant cells. We then examine the primary structure of K_{in}^+ channel cDNAs and discuss the implications of K^+ channel and cation transporter structure for fundamental physiological processes, including ion selectivity, metal block, hyperpolarization-induced activation, and cytosolic regulation.

PHYSIOLOGICAL FUNCTIONS OF PLANT K_{in}^+ CHANNELS

K_{in}^+ Channels and K^+ Uptake

Potassium is the most abundant cellular cation in plants. The transport of K^+ across the plasma membrane is important for diverse tissue-specific and cell-specific processes related to plant growth and development, such as germination, ion uptake in roots, leaf movement, regulation of stomatal aperture, nutrient storage, and nutrient transport in the vascular transport tissues (39, 89, 90, 105). Research on guard cells has revealed a role of K^+ channels in cellular K^+ uptake (121, 122).

Guard cells regulate the aperture of stomatal pores in the leaf epidermis, thus controlling gas exchange between the leaf and the atmosphere. The accumulation of K^+ and anions in guard cells mediates opening of stomatal pores. Patch-clamp studies on *Vicia faba* (bean) guard cells have led to the identification of time- and voltage-dependent K_{in}^+ channels, resulting in the hypothesis that these channels provide a major pathway for K^+ uptake during stomatal opening (121, 122). In brief, detailed studies on guard cells showed that K_{in}^+ channels can carry physiological K^+-uptake fluxes (117, 121, 122, 140) and that the extracellular K^+ dependence of the K_{in}^+ conductance correlates to the major low-affinity K^+-uptake transporters in plants (29, 117). K_{in}^+ channels display no significant inactivation over periods lasting many minutes (115), thereby allowing long-term K^+ uptake driven by proton pumps (7, 140). Aluminum, which inhibits stomatal opening (114), blocks K_{in}^+ channels in guard cells (115). The alkali metal ion selectivity of these channels (115) correlates with effects of various cations on stomatal opening (105), and an increase in K_{in}^+ currents at acidic extracellular pH is consistent with proton enhancement of K^+ uptake (12). In addition, proton-extruding pumps in the plasma membrane of guard cells sufficiently hyperpolarize cells to activate K_{in}^+ channels and drive physiological K^+ fluxes through these channels (140). Finally, recent studies have shown that K_{in}^+ channels are inactivated by Ca^{2+}-dependent signaling mechanisms, which correlates to physiological inhibition of K^+ uptake by Ca^{2+} during stomatal movements (13, 30, 79, 83, 118, 124).

As in guard cells, inward-rectifying K^+ channels may play a role in mediating fluxes of K^+ into the motor cells (which regulate osmotically driven movements of leaflets) of *Samanea saman* (64, 93). Findings on mesophyll cells of oat led to the conclusion that K_{in}^+ channels can mediate K^+ influx corresponding to an increase of the internal K^+ concentration by 0.12 M per hour under physiological conditions (67). Inward-rectifying K^+ channels have also been identified in various plant species and cells, including aleurone layer cells of barley (18); suspension culture cells of *Arabidopsis thaliana,* maize, and tobacco (22, 63, 143); guard cells of maize (32); mesophyll cells of *A. thaliana* (131); root membranes of rye (146); and root hair cells of wheat (36).

This broad distribution points to a fundamental role of these K^+ channels in plant cells. The two main functions suggested for K_{in}^+ channels are: (*a*) the regulation of membrane potential and (*b*) proton pump-driven K^+ uptake in connection with osmoregulation, transport, nutrition, and cellular responses. We refer to K^+ uptake as meaning the accumulation of K^+ by various plant cell types from the extracellular space and, when directly referred to, from soil solutions. Together with nitrogen and phosphate, K^+ is one of the three main macronutrients administered in fertilizers to enhance crop productivity. Classical flux studies of plant K^+ uptake in tissues and cells have revealed at least two major mechanisms of K^+ uptake, responsible for low-affinity and high-affinity K^+ uptake, respectively (28, 29).

HIGH-AFFINITY K^+ UPTAKE   In various higher plant cells and tissues, a high-affinity K^+-uptake mechanism that contributes greatly to K^+ uptake was found with an apparent affinity (K_m) for K^+ in the range of 10–30 μM. Tracer flux studies indicate that high-affinity K^+ uptake saturates at approximately 200 μM external K^+ (29, 96). This uptake mechanism is induced by low (micromolar) external K^+ concentrations

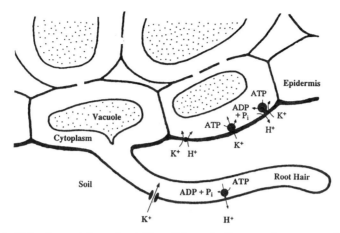

Figure 1 Potassium uptake and nutrition. Schematic diagram of a cross-section of a root epidermal cell layer. Shown in the plasma membrane of a root hair cell are two known transporters: the inward-rectifying K^+ channel and H^+-ATPase. Hypothetical high-affinity mechanisms for K^+-uptake transporters appear in the plasma membrane of a neighboring epidermal cell (from left to right): K^+-H^+ symporter, K^+-ATPase, and K^+-H^+-exchange ATPase (see text). The spatial separation of K^+ transporters serves illustrative purposes only. (Figure modified from Ref. 39. Reprinted with permission, © 1989, Jones and Bartlett Publishers.)

(26, 33). However, the precise mechanism for high-affinity K^+ uptake in higher plants remains unknown. Figure 1 shows three proposed mechanisms, which are based on physiological studies of K^+ uptake in plants and are analogous to known uptake mechanisms in prokaryotes and other eukaryotes. The three proposed high-affinity mechanisms are: K^+-H^+ exchange ATPases, K^+-uptake ATPases (73), and K^+-H^+ cotransporters (symporters) that would allow influx of both K^+ and H^+ driven by the transmembrane pH gradient and membrane potential (96), as found in *Neurospora crassa* (109), and analogous to Na^+-K^+ symporters found in algae (152). For example, a high-affinity K^+-H^+ symporter allowing simultaneous uptake of one K^+ per proton would be able to accumulate K^+ against a 3.8×10^6-fold concentration gradient at a membrane potential of -150 mV and a pH gradient of 1.5 units.

All of the above mechanisms could depolarize the plasma membrane that was suggested from membrane potential recordings (96). The mechanistic bases of higher plant transporters have remained poorly understood because of the inability to perform direct voltage clamp recordings on most plant tissues. Recent voltage clamp studies on heterologously expressed H^+-nitrate cotransporters (141), as well as patch clamp studies on isolated root epidermal cells (36), provide the means to unequivocally resolve electrogenic (nonelectroneutral) uptake mechanisms. Functional properties of a recently cloned high-affinity K^+ uptake transporter from wheat roots correlate to K^+-H^+ symporter characteristics (D Schachtman & J Schroeder, unpublished data).

LOW-AFFINITY K^+ UPTAKE   The major low-affinity K^+-uptake mechanism in various higher plant cells displays an apparent affinity for K^+ in the range of 4–16 mM and allows enhanced K^+ uptake at ≥ 0.3 mM extracellular K^+ as shown in numerous tracer flux studies (28, 29). Because expression of the high-affinity mechanism is reduced at elevated extracellular K^+ (26, 33), the low-affinity mechanism presumably contributes significantly to K^+ uptake at external K^+ concentrations above approximately 0.3 mM. In several studies, 50–90% of hundreds of different soil samples had soil solution K^+ concentrations ranging from 0.3 to 5 mM (39, 88, 106). K^+ concentrations at the surface of roots may be ~50% lower for soil solution K^+ concentrations of 0.3 mM owing to an equilibrium of exchangeable soil-bound K^+, K^+ diffusion, cell-wall buffering, and depletion resulting from K^+ uptake (39, 88). Depletion can be greater at lower K^+ concentrations. Free K^+ concentrations recorded using several techniques in cell walls of various plant tissues ranged from ~1 to 15 mM (15, 77, 149). These data suggest that the low-affinity K^+-uptake mechanism is important for higher plant cell K^+ uptake and nutrition. Recent cloning of a first high-affinity K^+ transporter (D Schachtman & J Schroeder, unpublished data), which plays a major role for K^+ uptake, will allow detailed molecular studies of the interaction of the two K^+ uptake mechanisms.

Plant inward-rectifying K^+ channels are well-suited to serve as a low-affinity K^+-uptake system; when cellular K^+ conductance was analyzed, the apparent affinity for K^+ of the channels ranged from ~3 to 5 mM K^+. K_{in}^+ channels in *Vicia faba* guard cells could carry physiological K^+-uptake fluxes at external K^+ concentrations of 0.3 mM (117). Data indicate a balance between an active outward H^+ pump current and an inward K^+ current in these cells (140).

A major site of K^+ uptake from soils is the root epidermis, with additional uptake provided by cortical cells (Figure 1) (39, 88). Root hairs are tubular outgrowths of epidermal cells of the root and allow access to soil in which nutrients are less depleted (39, 88). Recent studies on root hair cells of wheat demonstrated the presence of inward-rectifying K^+ channels in this cell type (Figure 1) (36). K_{in}^+ channels in root hairs allow K^+ uptake at external K^+ concentrations of 0.5 mM and possibly lower (36) and are blocked by Al^{3+} concentrations

(50% inhibition at $\sim$7 M free Al^{3+}) (36) that inhibit cation uptake (34, 89). These results are physiologically relevant for K^+ nutrition based on the K^+ dependence of the major low-affinity K^+-uptake mechanism, on the distribution of soil solution K^+ concentrations (39, 88, 106), and on the ability of root hairs to grow into soils of undepleted nutrients (39, 88). It is possible that different specialized cell types utilize different combinations or types of K^+ transporters, depending on physiological requirements. Furthermore, it cannot be excluded that additional low-affinity mechanisms are also likely to function in higher plant K^+ uptake (28).

In addition to providing a pathway for K^+ uptake, inward-rectifying K^+ channels can contribute to membrane potential control by regulating the membrane resistance and/or by acting as sensors of extracellular K^+ levels, similar to other K^+ channels (54). In guard cells, at low external K^+ concentrations ($\leq$1 mM), these channels have a low open probability at membrane potentials more positive than the K^+ equilibrium potential (117). This open probability may lead to a low level of K^+ efflux, sufficient to hyperpolarize plant cells towards the K^+ equilibrium potential. Because many nutrients, irrespective of their charge (e.g. glucose) are taken up by electrogenic cotransport with protons in higher plants (87, 107, 110, 141), this hyperpolarization may contribute indirectly to electrogenic uptake processes (117).

The cytosolic K^+ concentration in plant cells is maintained within the range of approximately 60–150 mM (39, 88). The uptake of K^+ against the K^+ concentration gradient via channels is made possible in plants by the negative membrane potential generated by the H^+-ATPase (physiological resting potentials $\sim$ −120 to −220 mV) (128, 135) (Figure 1). The membrane potential generated by the H^+-ATPase could theoretically approach potentials of −300 mV (101), which have been recorded in some cases in fungi and algae (109, 128, 137). These strong negative membrane potentials would theoretically allow channel-mediated K^+ accumulation against a 100,000-fold gradient. Consistent with this supposition, transformation of a yeast mutant deficient in high-affinity K^+ uptake with a putative K_{in}^+ channel gene enabled this mutant to take up K^+ at 0.6 μM external K^+ (125). This result indicates that K_{in}^+ channels can contribute to K^+ uptake at low micromolar K^+ concentrations when other K^+-uptake transporters are disabled. However, in plants K_{in}^+ channels are not the physiological pathway for high-affinity K^+ uptake that saturates at $\sim$200 μM external K^+ (29).

Furthermore, at low external K^+ concentrations, K^+ uptake may occur at membrane potentials that are not sufficiently negative to enable channel-mediated K^+ uptake (40). This evidence may be limited in the low-affinity K^+ concentration range (≥ 0.3 mM K^+) because of the accuracy of measurements by standard techniques of cytosolic and cell-wall K^+ concentrations and of the membrane potential. In particular, patch clamp measurements have shown that the background membrane resistances of plant and animal cells are approximately 10 times larger than predicted by classical microelectrode studies. For example, typical plant and animal cells have whole-cell membrane resistances of ≥ 20 GΩ (~ 0.07 S·m^{-2}) (8a, 36, 54, 117). Classical membrane potential recordings with high-quality impalement (seal) resistances of 500 MΩ, at low nutrient levels that produce large membrane resistances, would therefore result in apparent potentials 20–50 mV more positive than actual plant-cell resting potentials after consideration of H^+ pump current densities and plasmodesmatal coupling (36, 36a). [In addition, when using K^+ acetate-filled microelectrodes, correction of liquid junction potentials results in actual resting potentials ~ 10–15 mV more negative than those directly recorded (11, 95).] Furthermore, Ca^{2+} leakage through the site of impalement may inhibit K_{in}^+ channels (13, 79, 118). Because of the above considerations, membrane potential recordings would result in an underestimation of K^+-channel contribution to K^+ uptake at external K^+ concentrations in the physiologically important range from 0.3 to 2 mM K^+. At present, tracer flux studies on intact cells and tissues provide a relatively good assessment for physiological K^+-uptake contributions showing measurable low-affinity K^+ uptake at ~ 0.3 mM K^+ (28, 29), although molecular biophysical mechanisms cannot be distinguished in these flux studies.

Why Do Plant Cells Take Up K^+ via K_{in}^+ Channels?

In guard cells, other higher plant cells, and yeast, biophysical, pharmacological, cell biological, and genetic studies have all strongly supported the model that inward-rectifying K^+ channels can function as proton pump-driven K^+-uptake transporters. Although channel-mediated K^+ uptake may occur in some animal epithelial cells and in glial K^+ buffering (e.g. 144), this mechanism appears to be uncommon in most prokaryotes and eukaryotes. Apart from the energetic considerations discussed above, a valid question is why do higher plant cells use a channel mechanism for K^+ uptake. The answers we propose, in addition to the above-reviewed data, are necessarily speculative, but they will help to summarize and interpret findings on K_{in}^+ channels:

1. High-affinity K^+ transporters (Figure 1) fall into the pump or co-transporter classes of proteins, which have turnover rates in the range of 10^2 to 10^4 ions per second (54) and saturate and/or are

repressed at >200 μM K^+ (26, 29, 33). The rate of translocation of ions through channels lies in the range of 10^6 to 10^7 per second, comparable only to the fastest diffusion-limited enzyme reaction rates (54). Therefore, the number of K^+-transporter proteins needed in the plasma membrane would be minimal, although K^+ ions must be taken up in large numbers.

2. Plant cells are faced with unstable and fluctuating environmental conditions (39, 88). K_{in}^+ channels, in conjunction with proton pumps, can respond over a wide low-affinity range of K^+ concentrations by influencing the membrane potential and shifting their activation potential to ensure K^+ uptake (117, 125). K_{in}^+ channels may also provide a backup K^+-uptake mechanism for environmental or genetic conditions that reduce or abolish high-affinity K^+ uptake and the associated depolarization (Figure 1).

3. K^+ channels contribute to the plasma membrane potential (117). This activity could support cellular homeostasis and indirectly modulate the uptake of other nutrients translocated via electrogenic proton-coupled cotransporters (107, 110, 141).

4. Though highly specific, the data suggest that the selectivity filter of certain K_{in}^+ channels does not completely exclude other cations such as NH_4^+ and Ca^{2+} (31, 111, 115). Therefore, K_{in}^+ channels or other cation channel classes may also be involved in the uptake of other cationic nutrients (see below).

In conclusion, the function of K_{in}^+ channels as long-term K^+-uptake transporters differs when compared with the main functions of other K^+ channels. Within the framework of plant membrane biophysics, they appear well-adapted to enable K^+ uptake into specialized cells under variable conditions.

BASIC ELECTRICAL PROPERTIES OF PLANT K_{in}^+ CHANNELS

As current research emphasizes the physiological and cell biological functions of K_{in}^+ channels, most studies have incorporated the whole-cell patch clamp technique. Several single-channel studies have also been performed on guard cells (118, 121, 122) and other higher plant cells (18, 36, 67, 93, 111, 146). Plant K_{in}^+ channel currents activate slowly in response to hyperpolarization of the plasma membrane (Figure 2, top). The half-time of activation lies in the range of 25–400 ms (18, 32, 67, 93, 122). Activation kinetics can also differ; for example, K_{in}^+ channels of maize guard cells activate more rapidly than do those of bean guard cells (32). The membrane potential at which K_{in}^+ channels

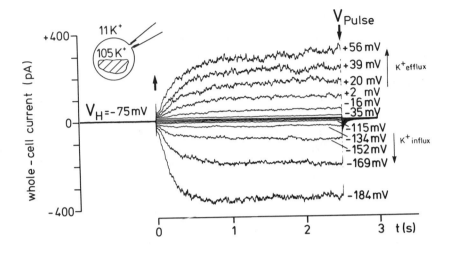

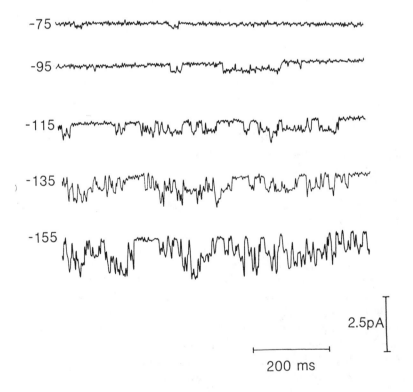

activate (activation potential) depends on many cellular parameters, including the equilibrium potential for K^+ (E_K^+) (18, 117) and the intracellular Ca^{2+} concentration (118). At external K^+ concentrations ≥ 1 mM, the activation potential of the guard cell K_{in}^+ channel is negative of the K^+ equilibrium potential; thus net K^+ efflux through the channel is prevented (117). However, the dependence of the activation potential of K_{in}^+ channels on the K^+ equilibrium potential in plant cells (18, 22, 67, 115, 122, 140) is generally weaker than for inward-rectifying K^+ channels from animal cells (44). Increases in the free cytoplasmic Ca^{2+} concentration within the physiological range (0.1 –1.5 μM) cause an apparent shift in the activation potential of K_{in}^+ channels to more negative potentials, effectively reducing K_{in}^+ channel activity (13, 30, 79, 118).

Plant K_{in}^+ channels remain active during continuous hyperpolarizations of many minutes (115). This characteristic—the lack of inactivation (Figure 2, top)—of plant K_{in}^+ channels indicates that these channels can function as a pathway for long-term K^+ influx. The absence of inactivation distinguishes plant K_{in}^+ channels from most animal K^+ channels, which display several rapid and slow rates of voltage-dependent inactivation (for reviews, see 16, 54, 59).

The selectivity of K_{in}^+ channels is typical of highly selective K^+ channels; K^+ is more permeant than any other physiological ion. In general, these channels are selective for K^+ over Rb^+ and NH_4^+, both of which also permeate the channels. Guard cells have the permeability sequence $K^+ > NH_4^+ \approx Rb^+ \gg Na^+ > Li^+ > Cs^+$ (115). This selectivity sequence varies in K_{in}^+ channels in different higher plant cells (18, 67, 115, 131), as is the case for selectivity sequences of animal K^+ channels (70).

In several studies, single K_{in}^+ channel currents were found to correlate to many of the macroscopic (whole-cell) current characteristics. The selectivity, voltage dependence (Figure 2, bottom), and time de-

---

Figure 2   Voltage-dependent K^+ channels in the plasma membrane of guard cells. (*Top*) Inward-rectifying (downward deflections) and outward-rectifying K^+ channel currents (upward deflections) resulting from voltage pulses to hyperpolarized and depolarized potentials, respectively. Pulse potentials (indicated to the right of recorded currents) were applied to a single guard cell between the arrows (for details see 122; reproduced with permission from 120). (*Bottom*) Activation of single K_{in}^+ channels bathed in 11 mM K^+ by negative membrane potentials ranging from -75 to -155 mV, indicated on the left of traces recorded in an outside-out patch. More hyperpolarized holding potentials increase the activation of K_{in}^+ channels (for details see 118; reproduced with permission from 118).

pendence of single channels account for the ion selectivity, slow activation, and deactivation observed at the whole cell level (93, 121, 122). The conductance of single K_{in}^+ channels depends on the genotype and the concentration of external K^+. In symmetrical 225 mM KCl, guard cell K_{in}^+ channels have a conductance of ~37 pS (121), while the conductance decreases to ~15–40 pS in different plant cells at K^+ concentrations of ~100 mM (18, 36, 67, 93, 111, 122). We have found that the conductance decreases further to 5–8 pS when single channels are measured with ~11 mM K^+ in the external solution (Figure 2, bottom) (18, 118). Cytosolic Ca^{2+} inhibits both single K_{in}^+ channels and whole-cell K_{in}^+ currents (118). Inward-rectifying K^+ channels in most higher plant cells studied to date exhibit rapid open-closed transitions (flickers) in the submillisecond and millisecond time range, which is reminiscent of rapid flicker in many other types of ion channels (54) and may reflect important ion permeation and block properties of K^+ channels (9, 25, 42).

In summary, plant K_{in}^+ channels activate slowly in response to hyperpolarization, remain active during prolonged hyperpolarization, are selective for K^+, and respond to the external K^+ concentration by changing the activation potential to minimize K^+ efflux. Some electrical properties of K_{in}^+ channels in plants differ significantly from K^+ channels in animal systems. The activity of plant K_{in}^+ channels may be optimized for proton pump-driven K^+ uptake and plant membrane potential regulation.

CLONING AND FUNCTIONAL CHARACTERIZATION OF K_{in}^+ CHANNEL cDNAs

Yeast Expression: A Powerful System to Study Transporters

Yeast cells, like plant cells, contains a proton-extruding ATPase in the plasma membrane that provides the driving force for K^+ uptake. *Saccharomyces cerevisiae* mutants in which two K^+-transport systems were deleted have been obtained (66, 104). Complementation of these yeast mutants resulted in two cDNAs, *AKT1* and *KAT1*, cloned from *Arabidopsis thaliana* (3, 125). The proteins encoded by *AKT1* and *KAT1* share some amino acid identity with outward-rectifying K^+ channels from animals in a putative voltage-sensing region (S4), in a domain that contributes to ion selectivity (named P, H5, or SS1-SS2), and in the predicted membrane-spanning topology of the core region of the protein (3, 125). In spite of these structural similarities of *A. thaliana* cDNAs to outward-rectifying K^+ channels, *AKT1* and *KAT1* restored potassium uptake to yeast mutants deficient in K^+ influx (3, 125). On the basis of guard cell studies, K^+ uptake has been ascribed to plant inward-rectifying K^+ channels rather than outward-rectifying K^+ channels (122). As expected, transformation of these K^+ uptake–deficient yeast strains with a plasmid encoding Shaker outward-rectifying potassium channels does not complement K^+ uptake into yeast (R Gaber, personal communication), because Shaker K^+ channels do not allow steady-state K^+ influx.

The function of several higher plant ion-transporter genes can be accurately determined by expression in *Xenopus laevis* oocytes (14, 19, 85, 111, 141). Detailed studies showed that mRNA from the single cDNA *KAT1* was sufficient to achieve heterologous expression of the major functional properties of plant K_{in}^+ channels in *X. laevis* oocytes, including the time and voltage dependence, ion selectivity, block by TEA and Ba^{2+}, single-channel conductance (111), lack of inactivation, and dependence on the external K^+ concentration (D Schachtman & J Schroeder, unpublished data). Whether additional β-subunits contribute to K_{in}^+ channel function, as in animal cation channels (10a, 54), remains unknown. K^+ uptake–deficient yeast mutants should provide a powerful system to isolate, mutate, and further characterize additional animal and plant cation transporters that convey passive or active K^+ influx.

Structural Features of K_{in}^+ Channel Genes

The primary structure of plant K_{in}^+ channels differs significantly from the first inward-rectifying (i.e. anomalous rectifier) K^+ channels recently cloned from animal systems (55, 68, 150). In contrast to plant K_{in}^+ channels (Figure 3*a*), animal inward-rectifying K^+ (IRK) channels possess only two main hydrophobic domains (S5 and S6) (68), which surround a consensus sequence for the domain implicated in K^+ selectivity (P-domain; see Figure 3*c*). The ability to form a functional K^+ channel with a P-domain surrounded by two hydrophobic domains supports models in which S5, P, and S6 contribute substantially to the central pore region of K^+ channels (27, 68). In addition, animal IRKs show only a truncated putative voltage sensor (55), which may reflect block-related gating-independent activation of IRKs (84).

Plant K_{in}^+ channels, however, show a remarkable homology to members of the outward-rectifying K^+ channel superfamily. This finding poses interesting questions with regard to voltage-dependent regulation (see below). Four full-length clones of the K_{in}^+ channel family have been isolated from *A. thaliana,* including *KAT1* (3), *AKT1* (125), PCAT14 (K Ketchum & CW Slayman, personal communication), and

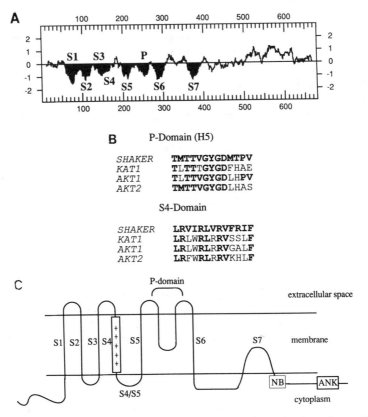

Figure 3 Structural analysis of higher plant K_{in}^+ channels. (*a*) Hydropathy profile of KAT1 shows that K_{in}^+ channels have one hydrophobic domain more (S7) than Shaker channels (Hopp & Wood analysis, window size 19). (*b*) Alignment of conserved regions of K^+ channel P and S4 domains. Three *A. thaliana* K_{in}^+ channel sequences, KAT1 (3), AKT1 (125), and AKT2 (Y Cao et al, unpublished data), are compared with those of the Shaker K^+ channel (100). Amino acids identical to those in the Shaker sequence are printed in boldface. (*c*) Model representation of the proposed membrane topology of K_{in}^+ channels. The putative selectivity filter and mouth-forming domain (P), a putative voltage-sensing domain (S4), and consensus sequences for nucleotide binding (NB) and ankyrin domains (ANK) are indicated.

AKT2 (Y Cao et al, unpublished data). In addition, DNA amplification (PCR) has been used to isolate partial sequences of K_{in}^+ channel genes from several plant tissues, including wheat and tomato (D Schachtman, A Ichida & J Schroeder, unpublished data).

   Analysis of the hydropathy profiles of the K_{in}^+-channel clones *KAT1*, *AKT1*, and *AKT2* show the presence of seven major hydrophobic domains (Figure 3*a*). The hydrophobic domains S1–S6 can be aligned with the core hydrophobic membrane-spanning domains S1–S6 from the superfamily of outward-rectifying K$^+$-channel genes (3, 125), while S7 is unique to plants (Figure 3). Within the entire core region (S1–S6), the level of amino acid similarity between KAT1 and Shaker (100) is low (26%). The levels of similarities between KAT1 and Eag (40%) (145), or KAT1 and cyclic GMP–regulated channels (35%) (62) are the highest in this region. Pairwise alignments of these animal ion channels from different subfamilies show low levels of similarity in the core region (e.g. Shaker to cGMP $\approx$ 26%; Eag to cGMP = 36%). Specialized domains (P and S4) are more conserved between K$_{in}^+$ channels and animal channels (Figure 3b). Their possible physiological functions are discussed in the following sections.

K$_{in}^+$ CHANNEL SELECTIVITY AND BLOCK

Putative Structural Domains for K$_{in}^+$ Channel Block and Ion Selectivity

The molecular structure by which K$^+$-uptake transporters in plant cells promote uptake of nutrients such as K$^+$ and NH$_4^+$, while reducing permeation and block by toxic cations such as Na$^+$, Cs$^+$, and Al^{3+}, has important environmental and agricultural implications (34, 39, 43, 123). The structural domains that form the extracellular channel mouth and the K$^+$ selectivity filter of plant cation-uptake channel clones may be of prime significance for these processes, yet they remain unknown. Determining ion channel topologies by using antibodies has proven difficult. On the other hand, mapping by site-directed mutagenesis of the structural domains responsible for ion selectivity and extracellular and intracellular channel block has provided compelling evidence regarding K$^+$-channel mouths and the selectivity filter (20, 80–82, 147; for reviews 16, 59).

The highest degree of homology between plant K$_{in}^+$ channels and animal K$^+$ channels is found in the pore region (P region; Figure 3b) (3, 125; A Ichida, Y Cao, D Schachtman & J Schroeder, unpublished data). Detailed mutagenesis studies in animal systems have shown that the relatively small P region (approximately 25 amino acids in length) plays major roles in depolarization-activated K$^+$ channels in determining extracellular charybdotoxin block (80, 81) and extracellular and intracellular TEA block (20, 82, 147). Flanking sequences of the P region of outward-rectifying K$^+$ channels have been implicated as major structural motifs contributing to the extracellular mouth of K$^+$ channels (Figure 3c) (16, 59). Conversely, the S4/S5 linker, the central part of the P domain, and the C-terminal region of the S6 domain (Figure 3c) have been implicated as structural components of the intracellular mouth of outward-rectifying K^+ channels (Figure 3c) (20, 78, 129, 147). Furthermore, the P region contributes significantly to the single-channel conductance and the selectivity of depolarization-activated K^+ channels with respect to NH_4^+, Ca^{2+}, and Na^+ (46, 50, 51, 148). Mutagenesis studies of regions in Na^+ channels analogous to the P region have shown that site-directed mutations in this domain can convert Na^+ channels to Ca^{2+}-permeable channels (52). Detailed reviews have appeared on the effects of individual amino acid substitutions on K^+-channel selectivity and block (16, 59).

The following sections discuss models for K_{in}^+ channel and cation transporter involvement in physiologically important stresses related to cation transport and nutrition. The models represent simplifications of cation stress mechanisms and focus on hypothetical contributions of K_{in}^+ channels to these stresses without discussion of other important mechanisms. The following discussion can serve as a basis for novel approaches for studying these topics at the molecular biophysical level.

In higher plants, various cations interact with K^+ uptake. Some cations are also nutrients, such as NH_4^+ and Ca^{2+} (39, 48, 69), and others, which are toxic, can decrease or compete with K^+ uptake, such as Cs^+, Na^+, and Al^{3+} (34, 43, 89, 126). Extracellular Na^+, Cs^+, Ca^{2+} and Al^{3+} ions block plant K_{in}^+ channels (18, 31, 67, 121, 122). K_{in}^+ channels show 50% block at 1 mM Na^+ and 0.25 mM Cs^+ at -175 mV and 100 mM external K^+ (67). The block of K_{in}^+ channels by Ca^{2+}, Na^+, and Cs^+ occurs in a voltage-dependent manner; block is enhanced at more negative potentials (17, 67). This phenomenon can be interpreted with a model in which the blockers need to enter the channel pore to produce channel block (54, 70). Cations that produce a voltage-dependent block of K_{in}^+ channels may therefore also have a low permeability through these channels if they can exit the channel via the cytosolic channel mouth after entering the pore (54, 70). Single amino acids in the P region may determine possible differences in block and permeability between K_{in}^+ and cation channels. For example, deletion or mutation of one or two amino acids in the selectivity filter-forming P region of outward-rectifying K^+ channels greatly enhances the Na^+ and Ca^{2+} permeability of these channels, while also increasing the block by extracellular Ca^{2+} (50, 51).

Possible Interactions of Na^+ with K^+-Uptake and Cation Transporters

Na^+ influx is toxic to plant growth (43). Na^+ tolerance in plants is determined by many different genetic, metabolic, and transport components (39, 43, 98). Osmolyte production (136) and several transport processes, including Na^+ exclusion at the root epidermis, Na^+ extrusion, vacuolar Na^+ loading, and Na^+ exclusion from shoots, contribute significantly to Na^+ tolerance (43). Vacuolar loading of Na^+ is mediated by the Na^+-H^+ exchanger in the tonoplast (43). Outward-rectifying K^+ channels in plant cells allow cation efflux (92, 120) and therefore may contribute to Na^+ extrusion or Na^+ transport to shoots, which requires ion efflux from xylem parenchyma cells during xylem loading. A positive Na^+ equilibrium potential may exclude this possibility. Outward-rectifying channels that are permeable to Na^+ have been described in higher plants (131, 133). These may serve as good examples for studying structural determinants of K^+ channel selectivity. Na^+-extruding pumps may also account for Na^+ efflux, as in yeast and algae (45, 137).

Conceptually, the ionic selectivity of K_{in}^+ channels may contribute to the ability of the root to exclude Na^+ uptake. Tracer flux studies show that Na^+ influx into plant cells occurs mainly via the low-affinity K^+-uptake mechanism rather than the high-affinity K^+-uptake transporter, when extracellular K^+ is present (102, 103). In the absence of extracellular K^+, the high-affinity transporter also allows significant Na^+ uptake (102, 103). These data suggest a role for K_{in}^+ channels and other cation transporters in Na^+ toxicity and Na^+ exclusion in the presence of K^+ (117). Interestingly, relatively high levels of Na^+ in the extracellular space of plant cells and high ratios of Na^+-to-Ca^{2+} concentrations in the soil solution are required to produce salt stress (43). High Na^+ concentrations occur under saline conditions and pose a serious problem to plant growth and agricultural production (e.g. toxic effects at ~20–200 mM Na^+ depending on the plant species) (43). The high Na^+ concentrations required to produce salt stress correlate with findings indicating that K^+ channels function in the millimolar concentration range (117) and that high extracellular sodium concentrations (e.g. >100 mM Na^+) may produce measurable Na^+ influx through or block of K_{in}^+ channels in some tissues (18, 31, 67, 121). On the other hand, expression of *KAT1* in oocytes shows minute Na^+ permeation (111) and no significant block of K_{in}^+ channels by Na^+ (W Gassmann & J Schroeder, unpublished data). In one study, Na^+ influx through outward-rectifying K^+ channels did not vary between wheat species differing in Na^+ tolerance (112). However, based on the multi-ion–pore nature of K^+ channels, significant net Na^+ influx through these depolarization-activated K^+ efflux channels is thermodynamically and electrostatically unlikely (54, 112). For future studies it will be important to know the general mechanism (e.g. Na^+ exclusion or extrusion) and location of transport processes leading to differential

Na^+ tolerance, and to study the appropriate transporter in an identified cell type.

Many flux and growth studies have shown that Ca^{2+} interacts with Na^+ and K^+ transport during nutrient uptake by the plant. In this regard, elevation of extracellular Ca^{2+} enhances the Na^+ exclusion process in higher plants (43, 69). Data indicate that extracellular Ca^{2+} interacts with K_{in}^+ channels (17, 31). Extracellular Ca^{2+} (17), as well as an increase in cytosolic Ca^{2+} (13, 79, 118), inhibit K_{in}^+ channels, which may reduce the major low-affinity Na^+ influx component into plant cells (102, 103). Ca^{2+} may also posttranscriptionally modify the selectivity of cation channels. Interestingly, in animal systems, removal of extracellular Ca^{2+} dramatically increases the Na^+ permeability of both outward-rectifying K^+ (4, 5) and Ca^{2+} channels (2, 53). Such an increase in Na^+ influx through plant cation channels induced by reduction in Ca^{2+} could be of major physiological importance for the effects of Ca^{2+} on Na^+ uptake. The hypothesis that effects of Ca^{2+} and Na^+ on plant cation channels may contribute to physiologically important cation interactions during plant transport requires detailed analysis.

Aluminum Toxicity and Block of K_{in}^+ Channels

Aluminum exerts toxic effects on cation uptake in higher plants at much lower concentrations than Na^+ (34, 41, 89). Aluminum is the third most abundant element by weight in the outer lithosphere of the earth (75), and complexed, nontoxic forms predominate in soils (34, 123). However, when soil pH is lower than 4.5–5.0, Al^{3+} can be solubilized and reaches soil solution concentrations toxic to plant growth (34, 65). The uptake of Al^{3+} into plant cells can disturb several metabolic processes (47). In spruce trees as well as in crop plants, one of the early effects of solubilized Al^{3+} on the epidermis of plant roots is a dramatic inhibition of the cations Ca^{2+}, K^+, NH_4^+, and Mg^{2+} (34, 41, 57, 89, 123). As shown for Na^+ stress, at elevated extracellular concentrations, Ca^{2+}, Mg^{2+}, and K^+ compete with Al^{3+} and ameliorate its toxicity (65).

In guard cells, we have found that Al^{3+} blocks K_{in}^+ channels (115), which correlates with Al^{3+} inhibition of stomatal opening (114). In root hair cells, phytotoxic concentrations of Al^{3+} block K_{in}^+ channels, with half-maximal inhibition at $\sim 7~\mu M$ free Al^{3+} at 11 mM external K^+, 0.2 mM $CaCl_2$, and pH 4.5 (36). The finding that Al^{3+} inhibition is reversible and not voltage dependent suggests a contribution by extracellular Al^{3+} block (36).

In the presence of Al^{3+}, both Ca^{2+} and K^+ uptake can progress in an Al^{3+}-tolerant wheat cultivar, while Al^{3+} inhibits Ca^{2+} and K^+ uptake in an Al^{3+}-sensitive cultivar (57, 89). Whether the Al^{3+}-tolerant K^+-uptake component is located in the root apex, as has been shown for the Al^{3+}-tolerant Ca^{2+}-uptake component (57), remains to be determined. In these two cultivars, possible Al^{3+} tolerance mechanisms include differential Al^{3+} inhibition of one uptake mechanism for both K^+ and Ca^{2+}, of multiple uptake transporters, or of a central regulatory component [e.g. secretion of Al^{3+} chelators (23a)].

Further research is required to determine whether and to what extent the effects of Na^+, Ca^{2+}, NH_4^+, and Al^{3+} on K_{in}^+ and other cation channels contribute to physiologically, environmentally, and agriculturally important cation interactions during plant nutrient uptake. The functional mechanisms of other cation-uptake transporters in the plasma membrane of higher plant cells will need to be identified, such as high-affinity K^+-uptake transporters and Ca^{2+}, Mg^{2+}, and NH_4^+ uptake transporters, and the effects of metals on these transporters will have to be analyzed, as such toxic effects would be significant.

VOLTAGE-DEPENDENT K_{in}^+ CHANNEL ACTIVATION

In plant cells, the hyperpolarization-induced activation of K_{in}^+ channels is of major importance for the role of these channels as K^+ uptake transporters in plant cells while limiting K^+ efflux (117, 122). Studies of animal K^+ channels indicate that two main mechanisms may be responsible for voltage-dependent channel activation: cytosolic channel block and intrinsic voltage-induced gating. The term *gating* refers to the movement of charged residues in the electrical transmembrane field, which in turn may open or close ion channels (54), and is discussed in depth in a chapter by Bezanilla & Stefani in this volume (10a; see also 16, 59).

Channels belonging to the superfamily of outward-rectifying K^+ channels show intrinsic voltage-induced gating. These channels contain five to seven positively charged residues located within the stretch of hydrophobic amino acids that constitutes the fourth transmembrane (S4) domain. The S4 domain probably represents a significant voltage-sensing domain in outward-rectifying K^+ channels that undergoes transmembrane movement in response to depolarization, which in turn produces channel activation (74, 76). On the other hand, many animal inward-rectifying K^+ (IRK) channels are regulated by cytosolic Mg^{2+} (84; but see 127). Depolarization of the membrane leads to rapid voltage-dependent Mg^{2+} block of these channels. In the absence of cytosolic Mg^{2+}, these channels can lose certain inward-rectifying properties (84).

Whether activation of K_{in}^+ channels in higher plants is mediated by hyperpolarization-induced gating or by cytosolic blocker removal has not been clearly determined. Differences in the structure of K_{in}^+ and IRK channels may suggest dissimilar activation mechanisms. In plants, macroscopic K_{in}^+ channel currents show a steep voltage-dependent activation and a strong voltage dependence of deactivation times (67, 122). In particular, the voltage dependence of deactivation time constants of inward-rectifying K^+ channels in guard cells (J Schroeder, unpublished) is very similar, but inverted, to the voltage dependence of deactivation time constants of outward-rectifying K^+ channels in guard cells that have been modeled as gating events (32, 115). Although several characteristics of guard cell K_{in}^+ channels suggest an intrinsic voltage-dependent gating mechanism that produces activation, direct evidence for this hypothesis is limited.

The conserved S4 domains in animal voltage-dependent K^+, Na^+, and Ca^{2+} channels have been modeled as voltage sensors (27). However, the cGMP-regulated channel from photoreceptors, which is largely voltage-insensitive, also contains an S4 domain with five positive charges (62). All currently cloned members of hyperpolarization-activated plant K_{in}^+ channels have five positively charged residues in the S4 domain (Figure 3b,c) (3, 125; Y Cao et al, unpublished data).

One might hypothesize that this S4 domain contributes to hyperpolarization-induced activation of K_{in}^+ channels. The S4 domain in K_{in}^+ channels may contribute to hyperpolarization-induced activation in several ways, because of higher-order protein-structure effects. K_{in}^+ channels may close when S4 moves toward the extracellular membrane side upon depolarization, and K_{in}^+ channels may open when S4 moves to the cytoplasmic side upon hyperpolarization. In such a model, the structure of the channel gate (27), in addition to the S4 voltage sensor, may be of central importance for channel opening by hyperpolarization.

Outward-Rectifying K^+ Channels

One can gain further insight into the mechanisms underlying hyperpolarization-induced K_{in}^+ activation by determining the structure of depolarization-activated K^+ channels in plants. These outward-rectifying K^+ channels (K_{out}^+) have been described in the plasma membrane of algae, higher plant cells, and yeast (Figure 2a) (10, 49, 91, 137, 138). Research on the action potentials in *Nitella* and *Chara* has shown that repolarization is associated with potassium efflux (9, 21, 35, 94, 134, 137). Detailed reviews on K_{out}^+ channels in plants have appeared (49, 90, 137, 138).

In guard cells, a striking feature of K_{out}^+ channels is that they display many features similar to K_{in}^+ channels (121, 122) (Figure 2). Although these two K^+ channel types have opposite voltage dependencies (Figure 2, top), they share other general properties such as time-dependent activation on similar time-scales (Figure 2a) (122), block by extracellular Ba^{2+} (122), and similar single-channel properties of a main conductance state (122; for review see 49, 138). Currents of both K_{in}^+ and K_{out}^+ channels are saturated at strong polarizations (9, 42, 121, 122). In guard cells, the saturation of outward-rectifying K^+ currents has been suggested to result from a bipolar gating mechanism (11). Single-channel studies have conversely suggested that macroscopic K^+ current saturation is a consequence of ion permeation, on the basis of data showing saturation of single-channel currents and/or rapid block of K^+ channels at strong polarizations (9, 25, 42).

The general similarities of K_{out}^+ and K_{in}^+ channel behavior in plants, as briefly outlined above, suggest that K_{out}^+ channel structures may provide some insight into the opposite activation mechanisms of these two channel types (Figure 2a). At present, clones of K_{out}^+ channels in plants have not yet been functionally identified.

CYTOSOLIC MODULATION OF K_{in}^+ CHANNELS

Evidence from several laboratories shows that inward-rectifying K^+ channels in higher plant cells are highly modulated by cytosolic second messengers and regulatory enzymes. These studies on K_{in}^+ channels have been performed mainly on guard cells, which have recently emerged as a powerful model system for elucidating cellular transport and signaling (6, 83, 105, 120, 151). In guard cells, elevation in the cytosolic Ca^{2+} concentration inhibits K_{in}^+ channels (118). Furthermore, inositol 1,4,5 trisphosphate (IP$_3$) and GTP-γ-S inhibited K_{in}^+ channels in guard cells, and both of these activities were reversed by coinjection of Ca^{2+} buffers (13, 30). Further work is needed to understand the mechanisms of putative GTP-binding protein–mediated increases in cytosolic Ca^{2+} of guard cells. The Ca^{2+}-induced inhibition of K_{in}^+ channels may contribute to Ca^{2+} inhibition of stomatal opening (24) and reduction of K^+ uptake (83). The modulation of K_{in}^+ channels causes an ~50% change in whole-cell currents in some cases (30, 79), which may not suffice to modulate proton pump–driven K^+ uptake. This modulation would, however, have a profound effect on membrane potential control, due to the significant changes in membrane resistance at physiological hyperpolarized potentials.

Microinjection of caged Ca^{2+} or IP_3 triggers stomatal closing (38). These data show that Ca^{2+} alone is sufficient to trigger stomatal closing. The phytohormone abscisic acid (ABA), which inhibits stomatal opening and induces stomatal closing, causes a rise in the cytosolic Ca^{2+} concentration of guard cells (37, 86, 119). Abscisic acid triggers Ca^{2+} release from intracellular organelles and activates Ca^{2+}-permeable nonselective channels in the plasma membrane of guard cells (38, 86, 119). Variability in ABA-triggered Ca^{2+} elevations (38, 119) and other findings have led to the suggestion that additional second messenger processes are involved in guard-cell signal transduction (for review see 6, 116, 151). One of these can be the ABA-induced alkalinization of the cytoplasm of guard cells (58), which activates K_{out}^+ channels (12).

Whether Ca^{2+} inhibits K_{in}^+ channels by direct interaction with the ion channel protein or with an associated regulatory protein was recently addressed. Ca^{2+}-induced dephosphorylation of K_{in}^+ channels in guard cells, via the Ca^{2+}-dependent protein phosphatase 2B (PP2B, or calcineurin) has been suggested as a mechanism for K^+ channel inhibition (79). In particular, the immunosuppressant complexes cyclosporin A–cyclophilin and FK506-FK506–binding protein are highly specific inhibitors of PP2B (79). These complexes counteracted the Ca^{2+}-induced inhibition of K_{in}^+ channels (79). Furthermore, a constitutively active PP2B fragment inhibited K_{in}^+ channels in the absence of elevated cytosolic Ca^{2+} concentrations. Taken together, these data suggest that Ca^{2+} activation of PP2B produces K_{in}^+-channel inhibition, via dephosphorylation of K_{in}^+ channels or an associated regulatory protein. Another type of K^+ channel in *A. thaliana* that shows instantaneous inward-rectification may be activated by phosphorylation, because it is stimulated by ATP and by light, which should increase ATP levels (130).

In contrast, recent results show a reduction in K_{in}^+-channel currents in guard cells by okadaic acid (139), a potent inhibitor of protein phosphatase 2A (PP2A). These data suggest inhibition of K_{in}^+ channels by phosphorylation of channel or regulatory proteins rather than dephosphorylation. These apparently opposing models—that both dephosphorylation (79, 130) and phosphorylation (139) inhibit K_{in}^+ channels—do not necessarily contradict one another. The two studies focus on modulators of two different phosphatases (PP2A and PP2B), and parallel regulatory pathways are possible. Ca^{2+} may also directly modulate K_{in}^+ channels. In this regard, it is interesting that the Ca^{2+}-activated K^+ channel, Slowpoke, recently cloned from *Drosophila* is directly activated by Ca^{2+} (97), although this K^+ channel clone shows no clear homology to known consensus sequences for Ca^{2+}-binding domains (8).

In plants, lipid metabolites are probably involved in various signal transduction processes (for review, see 23). Various lysolipids and free fatty acids activate the plasma membrane proton pump of higher plants (99, 113), which provides the driving force for K^+ uptake through K_{in}^+ channels. In guard cells, diacylglycerols activate ion pumping, which is required for stomatal opening (71). Whether other fatty acids also activate the plasma-membrane proton pump in guard cells remains to be determined. Phosphatidylcholine (PC) and phosphatidylethanolamine (PE) are hydrolyzed by phospholipase A2, which is abundant in plants (113). Two metabolites produced by phospholipase A2, linolenic acid and linoleic acid, are the major unsaturated fatty acids in plant cells (108). Recent data show that, in guard cells, linolenic acid and arachidonic acid, but not other fatty acids, enhance stomatal opening and greatly potentiate inward-rectifying K^+ channel currents (72).

Whether cytosolic modulation processes converge on a single regulatory domain, such as a phosphorylation site of plant K_{in}^+ channels, remains to be answered. Plant K_{in}^+ channel clones have several possible phosphorylation sites. In addition, all plant K_{in}^+ channel clones and the partial clones isolated have a highly conserved domain showing weak homology to a cyclic nucleotide binding sequence (Figure 3c) (125). Although the existence of cyclic AMP in plants is uncertain (132), the high degree of conservation of this domain among K_{in}^+ channels suggests an important role for K_{in}^+ channel function. Cytosolic modulation of K_{in}^+ channels suggests that K_{in}^+ channel regulation is important for plant-cell responses to physiological signals by regulating transport, the membrane resistance, and membrane potential. Heterologous expression of K_{in}^+ channel clones in *X. laevis* oocytes and recordings in excised membrane patches provide a potent system for determining direct modulators of K_{in}^+ channels and for studying direct effector-target interactions of putative second messengers and modulatory enzymes from higher plants.

PERSPECTIVES

K^+ transport and membrane potential regulation play central roles in many cellular processes during growth and development of higher plants. Biophysical, cell biological, pharmacological, and molecular genetic studies have supported the hypothesis (122) that K_{in}^+ channels represent a major low-affinity K^+-uptake transporter in specialized higher plant cells. A detailed study of the structure-function relationship of K_{in}^+ channels will not only lead to valuable insights regarding plant membrane potential control and K^+ transport, but should also broaden the knowledge of fundamental biophysical functions of ion channels in general, such as voltage-dependent activation and ion permeation.

Correlations of K^+ channel properties to Al^{3+} and Na^+ stress and Ca^{2+} interaction suggest possible involvement of K_{in}^+ channels and other cation transporters in the physiology and tolerance of metal stresses. Studies of transporter function in transformed yeast and oocytes provide potent genetic and biophysical model systems to investigate these possibilities. Furthermore, analysis of dominant K_{in}^+ channel and transporter variants in mutant or transgenic plants should enable the investigation of the contribution of these transporters to cation uptake in various cell types under physiological and metal stress conditions. Other metabolic and transport processes, yet to be identified at the molecular level, also play major roles during metal stress. The biophysical and mechanistic bases of electrogenic cation uptake transporters have remained poorly understood because of the difficulties associated with direct voltage clamp recordings on plant tissues, but these can now be circumvented (e.g. 141). A molecular biological analysis of cation transport and metal stress interactions is just beginning with the study of K_{in}^+ channels and will need to be extended to other transport and regulatory mechanisms. The combination of biophysical analyses, molecular biological studies, high resolution patch clamp recordings, and the use of genetic mutants in yeast and model plants such as *A. thaliana* will likely provide significant advances towards answers to the many remaining questions, simplified models, and interesting investigation-demanding and tentative correlations presented in this review.

ACKNOWLEDGMENTS

We thank Mary Beth Hiller, Judie Murray, and Melinda Marcus for assistance in the preparation of the manuscript. We thank our many colleagues for information concerning published and unpublished research. We are grateful to Drs. Emanuel Epstein, Bertil Hille, Heven Sze, Winslow Briggs, Chris Miller, Nick Spitzer, Mary Bisson, and Stu Brody for comments on the manuscript. We thank André Läuchli, Tony Glass, Mary-Helen Goldsmith, and members of our laboratory for discussions. Research in the laboratory of the authors was supported by NSF grant MCB9004977, USDA Grant No. 92-37304-7757, and NSF Presidential Young Investigator Award (JIS) and a NSF Plant Biology Fellowship (JMW).

Any *Annual Review* chapter, as well as any article cited in an *Annual Review* chapter, may be purchased from the Annual Reviews Preprints and Reprints service. 1-800-347-8007; 415-259-5017; email: arpr@class.org

Literature Cited

1. Aldrich R. 1993. Potassium channels— advent of a new family. *Nature* 362: 107–8
2. Almers W, McCleskey EW. 1984. Non-selective conductance in calcium channels of frog muscle: calcium selectivity in a single-file pore. *J. Physiol.* 353:585–608
3. Anderson JA, Huprikar SS, Kochian LV, Lucas WJ, Gaber RF. 1992. Functional expression of a probable *Arabidopsis thaliana* potassium channel in *Saccharomyces cerevisiae*. *Proc. Natl. Acad. Sci. USA* 89:3736–40
4. Armstrong CM, Lopez-Barneo J. 1987. External calcium ions are required for potassium channel gating in squid neurons. *Science* 236:712–14
5. Armstrong CM, Miller C. 1990. Do voltage-dependent K$^+$ channels require Ca^{2+}? A critical test employing a heterologous expression system. *Proc. Natl. Acad. Sci. USA* 87:7579–82
6. Assmann SM. 1993. Signal transduction in guard cells. *Annu. Rev. Cell Biol.* 9:345–75
7. Assmann SM, Simoncini L, Schroeder JI. 1985. Blue light activates electrogenic ion pumping in guard cell protoplasts of *Vicia faba*. *Nature* 318:285–87
8. Atkinson NS, Robertson GA, Ganetzky B. 1991. A component of calcium activated potassium channels encoded by the *Drosophila slo* locus. *Science* 253:551–55
8a. Barry PH, Lynch JW. 1991. Liquid junction potentials and small cell effects in patch-clamp analysis. *J. Membr. Biol.* 121:101–17
9. Bertl A, Gradmann D. 1987. Current-voltage relationship of potassium channels in the plasma membrane of *Acetabularia*. *J. Membrane Biol.* 99:41–49
10. Bertl A, Slayman CL, Gradmann D. 1992. Calcium-dependent and voltage-

dependent ion channels in *Saccharomyces cerevisiae*. *Philos. Trans. R. Soc. London Ser. B* 338:63–72
10a. Bezanilla F, Stefani E. 1994. Voltage-dependent gating of ionic channels. *Annu. Rev. Biophys. Biomol. Struct.* 23:819–46
11. Blatt MR. 1988. Potassium-dependent bipolar gating of K$^+$ channels in guard cells. *J. Membr. Biol.* 102:235–46
12. Blatt MR. 1992. K$^+$ channels of stomatal guard cells: characteristics of the inward rectifier and its control by pH. *J. Gen. Physiol.* 99:615–44
13. Blatt MR, Thiel G, Trentham DR. 1990. Reversible inactivation of K$^+$ channels of *Vicia* stomatal guard cells following the photolysis of caged inositol 1,4,5-trisphosphate. *Nature* 346: 766–69
14. Boorer KJ, Forde BG, Leigh RA, Miller AJ. 1992. Functional expression of a plant plasma membrane transporter in *Xenopus* oocytes. *FEBS Lett.* 302:166–68
15. Bowling DJF. 1987. Measurement of the apoplastic activity of K$^+$ and Cl$^-$ in the leaf epidermis of *Commelina communis* in relation to stomatal activity. *J. Exp. Bot.* 38:1351–55
16. Brown AM. 1993. Functional bases for interpreting amino acid sequences of voltage-dependent K$^+$ channels. *Annu. Rev. Biophys. Biomol. Struct.* 22:173–98
17. Busch H, Hedrich R, Raschke K. 1990. External calcium blocks inward rectifier potassium channels in guard cell protoplasts in a voltage and concentration dependent manner. *Plant Physiol.* 93:14 (Abstr.)
18. Bush DS, Hedrich R, Schroeder JI, Jones RL. 1988. Channel-mediated K$^+$ flux in barley aleurone protoplasts. *Planta* 176:368–77
19. Cao Y, Anderova M, Crawford NM, Schroeder JI. 1992. Expression of an

outward-rectifying potassium channel from maize mRNA and complementary RNA in *Xenopus* oocytes. *Plant Cell* 4:961–69

20. Choi KL, Mossman C, Aubé J, Yellen G. 1993. The internal and quaternary ammonium receptor site of *Shaker* potassium channels. *Neuron* 10:533–41

21. Cole KS, Curtis HJ. 1938. Electrical impedance of *Nitella* during activity. *J. Gen. Physiol.* 22:37–64

22. Colombo R, Cerana R. 1991. Inward rectifying K$^+$ channels in the plasma membrane of *Arabidopsis thaliana*. *Plant Physiol.* 97:1130–35

23. Coté GG, Crain RC. 1993. Biochemistry of phosphoinositides. *Annu. Rev. Plant Physiol. Plant Mol. Biol.* 44:333–56

23a. Delhaize E, Ryan PR, Randall PJ. 1993. Aluminum tolerance in wheat (*Triticum aestivum* L.). II. Aluminum-stimulated excretion of malic acid from root apices. *Plant Physiol.* 103:695–702

24. De Silva DLR, Cox RC, Hetherington AM, Mansfield TA. 1985. Synergism between calcium ions and abscisic acid in preventing stomatal opening. *New Phytol.* 101:555–63

25. Draber S, Shultze R, Hansen U-P. 1992. Fast switching and coupled excitation of the Cs$^+$-blocked K$^+$-channels in tonoplast vesicles of *Chara corallina* as directly resolved in the time series of pipette current. *Int. Workshop on Plant Membrane Biology, 9th, Monterey, CA.* p. 182

26. Drew MC, Saker LR, Barber SA, Jenkins W. 1984. Changes in the kinetics of phosphate and potassium absorption in nutrient-deficient barley roots measured by a solution-depletion technique. *Planta* 160:490–99

27. Durrell SR, Guy HR. 1992. Atomic scale structure and functional models of voltage-gated potassium channels. *Biophys. J.* 62:238–50

28. Epstein E. 1976. Kinetics of ion transport and the carrier concept. In *Transport in Plants*, Vol. 2, Part B, *Tissues and Organs*, pp. 70–94. New York: Springer-Verlag

29. Epstein E, Rains DW, Elzam OE. 1963. Resolution of dual mechanisms of potassium absorption by barley roots. *Proc. Natl. Acad. Sci. USA* 49: 684–92

30. Fairley-Grenot K, Assmann SM. 1991. Evidence for G-protein regulation of inward K$^+$ channel current in guard cells of fava bean. *Plant Cell* 3:1037–44

31. Fairley-Grenot KA, Assmann SM. 1992. Permeation of Ca^{2+} through K$^+$ channels in the plasma membrane of *Vicia faba* guard cells. *J. Membr. Biol.* 128:103–13

32. Fairley-Grenot KA, Assmann SM. 1993. Comparison of K$^+$-channel activation and deactivation in guard cells from a dicotyledon (*Vicia faba* L.) and a graminaceous monocotyledon (*Zea mays*). *Planta* 189:410–19

33. Fernando M, Mehroke J, Glass ADM. 1992. De novo synthesis of plasma membrane and tonoplast polypeptides of barley roots during short-term K$^+$ deprivation. In search of the high-affinity K$^+$ transport system. *Plant Physiol.* 100:1269–76

34. Foy CD, Chaney RL, White MC. 1978. The physiology of metal toxicity in plants. *Annu. Rev. Plant Physiol.* 29: 511–66

35. Gaffey CT, Mullins LJ. 1958. Ionic fluxes during the action potential in *Chara*. *J. Physiol. London* 144:505–24

36. Gassmann W, Schroeder JI. 1993. Inward-rectifying K$^+$ channel currents in root hairs of wheat. *Plant Physiol.* 102: 150

36a. Gassmann W, Ward JM, Schroeder JI. 1993. Physiological roles of inward-rectifying K$^+$ channels. *Plant Cell* 5: 1491–93

37. Gilroy S, Fricker MD, Read ND, Trewavas AJ. 1991. Role of calcium in signal transduction of *Commelina* guard cells. *Plant Cell* 3:333–44

38. Gilroy S, Read ND, Trewavas AJ. 1990. Elevation of cytoplasmic calcium by caged calcium or caged inositol trisphosphate initiates stomatal closure. *Nature* 346:769–71

39. Glass ADM. 1989. *Plant Nutrition. An Introduction to Current Concepts.* Boston: Jones and Bartlett. 234 pp.

40. Glass ADM, Dunlop J. 1979. The regulation of K$^+$ influx in excised barley roots. The relationships between K$^+$ influx and electrochemical potential differences. *Planta* 145:395–97

41. Godbold DL, Fritz E, Hüttermann A. 1988. Aluminum toxicity and forest decline. *Proc. Natl. Acad. Sci. USA* 85: 3888–92

42. Gradmann P, Klieber HG, Hansen UP. 1987. Reaction kinetic parameters for ion transport from steady-state current-voltage curves. *Biophys. J.* 51: 569–85

43. Greenway H, Munns R. 1980. Mechanisms of salt tolerance in nonhalophytes. *Annu. Rev. Plant Physiol.* 31: 149–90

K$_{in}^+$ CHANNELS IN HIGHER PLANTS 467

44. Hagiwara S, Miyazaki S, Rosenthal NP. 1976. Potassium current and the effect of cesium on this current during anomalous rectification of the egg cell membrane of a starfish. *J. Gen. Physiol.* 67:621–38
45. Haro R, Garciadeblas B, Rodríguez-Navarro A. 1991. A novel P-type ATPase from yeast involved in sodium transport. *FEBS Lett.* 291:189–91
46. Hartmann HA, Kirsch GE, Drewe JA, Taglialatela M, Joho RH, Brown AM. 1991. Exchange of conduction pathways between two related K$^+$ channels. *Science* 251:942–44
47. Haug A. 1984. Molecular aspects of aluminum toxicity. *CRC Crit. Rev. Plant Sci.* 1:345–73
48. Haynes RJ, Goh KM. 1978. Ammonium and nitrate nutrition of plants. *Biol. Rev.* 53:465–10
49. Hedrich R, Schroeder JI. 1989. The physiology of ion channels and electrogenic pumps in higher plant cells. *Annu. Rev. Plant Physiol.* 40:539–69
50. Heginbotham L, Abramson T, MacKinnon R. 1992. A functional connection between the pores of distantly related ion channels as revealed by mutant K$^+$ channels. *Science* 258:1152–55
51. Heginbotham L, MacKinnon R. 1993. Use of chimeras to localize regions determining ion selectivity in potassium channels. *Biophys. J.* 64:A16
52. Heinemann SH, Terlau H, Stühmer W, Imoto K, Numa S. 1992. Calcium channel characteristics conferred on the sodium channel by single mutations. *Nature* 356:441–43
53. Hess P, Tsien RW. 1984. Mechanism of ion permeation through calcium channels. *Nature* 309:453–56
54. Hille B. 1992. *Ionic Channels of Excitable Membranes.* Sunderland, MA: Sinauer. 607 pp. 2nd ed.
55. Ho K, Nichols CG, Lederer WJ, Lytton J, Vassilev PM, et al. 1993. Cloning and expression of an inwardly rectifying ATP-regulated potassium channel. *Nature* 362:31–38
56. Hodgkin AL, Huxley AF. 1952. A quantitative description of membrane current and its application to conduction and excitation in nerve. *J. Physiol. London* 117:500–44
57. Huang JW, Grunes DL, Kochian LV. 1993. Aluminum effects on calcium (^{45}Ca^{2+}) translocation in aluminum-tolerant and aluminum-sensitive wheat (*Triticum aestivum* L.) cultivars: differential responses of the root apex

versus mature root regions. *Plant Physiol.* 102:85–93
58. Irving HR, Gehring CA, Parish RW. 1992. Changes in cytosolic pH and calcium of guard cells precede stomatal movements. *Proc. Natl. Acad. Sci. USA* 89:1790–94
59. Jan LY, Jan YN. 1992. Structural elements involved in specific K$^+$ channel functions. *Annu. Rev. Physiol.* 54:537–55
60. Johannes E, Brosnan JM, Sanders D. 1991. Calcium channels and signal transduction in plant cells. *Bioessays* 13:331–36
61. Katz B. 1949. Les constantes electriques de la membrane du muscle. *Arch. Sci. Physiol.* 2:285–99
62. Kaupp UB, Niidome T, Tanabe T, Terada S, Bönigk W, et al. 1989. Primary structure and functional expression from complementary DNA of the rod photoreceptor cyclic GMP-gated channel. *Nature* 342:762–66
63. Ketchum KA, Shrier A, Poole RJ. 1989. Characterization of potassium-dependent currents in protoplasts of corn suspension cells. *Plant Physiol.* 89:1184–92
64. Kim H, Coté GG, Crain R. 1993. Potassium channels in *Samanea saman* protoplasts controlled by a biological clock. *Science* 260:960–62
65. Kinraide TB, Parker DR. 1987. Cation amelioration of aluminum toxicity in wheat. *Plant Physiol.* 83:546–51
66. Ko CH, Gaber RF. 1991. TRK1 and TRK2 encode structurally related K$^+$ transporters in *Saccharomyces cerevisiae*. *Mol. Cell Biol.* 8:4266–73
67. Kourie J, Goldsmith MHM. 1992. K$^+$ channels are responsible for an inwardly rectifying current in the plasma membrane of mesophyll protoplasts of *Avena sativa*. *Plant Physiol.* 98:1087–97
68. Kubo Y, Baldwin TJ, Jan YN, Jan LY. 1993. Primary structure and functional expression of a mouse inward rectifier potassium channel. *Nature* 362:127–33
69. LaHaye PA, Epstein E. 1969. Salt toleration by plants: enhancement with calcium. *Science* 166:395–96
70. Latorre R, Miller C. 1983. Conduction and selectivity in potassium channels. *J. Membr. Biol.* 71:11–30
71. Lee Y, Assmann SM. 1991. Diacylglycerols induce both ion pumping in patch-clamped guard-cell protoplasts and opening of intact stomata. *Proc. Natl. Acad. Sci. USA* 88:2127–31
72. Lee Y, Lee HJ, Crain RC, Lee A, Korn SJ. 1994. Polyunsaturated fatty

acids modulate stomatal aperture and two distinct K$^+$ channel currents in guard cells. *Cell. Signal.* In press.

73. Leonard RT, Hotchkiss CW. 1976. Cation-stimulated adenosine triphosphatase activity and cation transport in corn roots. *Plant Physiol.* 58:331–35

74. Liman ER, Hess P, Weaver F, Koren G. 1991. Voltage-sensing residues in the S4 region of a mammalian K$^+$ channel. *Nature* 353:752–56

75. Lindsay WL. 1979. *Chemical Equilibria in Soils.* New York: Wiley & Sons. 449 pp.

76. Logothetis DE, Movahedi S, Satler C, Lindpainter K, Nadal-Ginard B. 1992. Incremental reductions of positive charge within the S4 region of a voltage-gated K$^+$ channel results in corresponding decreases in gating charge. *Neuron* 8:531–40

77. Long JM, Widders IE. 1990. Quantification of apoplastic potassium content by elution analysis of leaf lamina tissue from pea (*Pisum sativum* L. cv Argenteum). *Plant Physiol.* 94:1040–47

78. Lopez GA, Jan YN, Jan YN. 1993. Mutations in the S6 domain affecting conductance, TEA and barium blockade in the permeation pathway of the *Shaker* potassium channel. *Biophys. J.* 64:113

79. Luan S, Li W, Rusnak F, Assmann SM, Schreiber SL. 1993. Immunosuppressants implicate protein phosphatase regulation of K$^+$ channels in guard cells. *Proc. Natl. Acad. Sci. USA* 90:2202–6

80. MacKinnon R, Heginbotham L, Abramson T. 1990. Mapping the receptor site for charybdotoxin, a poreblocking potassium channel inhibitor. *Neuron* 5:767–71

81. MacKinnon R, Miller C. 1989. Mutant potassium channels with altered binding of charybdotoxin, a pore-blocking peptide inhibitor. *Science* 245:1382–85

82. MacKinnon R, Yellen G. 1990. Mutations affecting TEA blockade and ion permeation in voltage-activated K$^+$ channels. *Science* 250:276–79

83. MacRobbie EAC. 1986. Calcium effects in stomatal guard cells. In *Molecular and Cellular Aspects of Ca^{2+} in Plant Development*, ed. AJ Trewavas, D Marmé, pp. 383–84. New York: Plenum

84. Matsuda H. 1991. Magnesium gating of the inwardly rectifying K$^+$ channel. *Annu. Rev. Physiol.* 53:289–98

85. Maurel C, Reizer J, Schroeder JI,

Chrispeels MJ. 1993. The vacuolar membrane protein γ-TIP creates water specific channels in *Xenopus* oocytes. *EMBO J.* 12:2241–47

86. McAinsh MR, Brownlee C, Hetherington AM. 1990. Abscisic acid–induced elevation of guard cell cytosolic Ca^{2+} precedes stomatal closure. *Nature* 343:186–88

87. McClure PR, Kochian LV, Spanswick RM, Shaff JE. 1990. Evidence for cotransport of nitrate and protons in maize roots. I. Effects of nitrate on the membrane potential. *Plant Physiol.* 93:281–89

88. Mengel K, Kirkby EA. 1982. *Principles of Plant Nutrition.* Worblaufen-Bern, Switzerland: International Potash Institute. 655 pp.

89. Miyasaka SC, Kochian LV, Shaff JE, Foy CD. 1989. Mechanisms of aluminum tolerance in wheat. An investigation of genotypic differences in rhizosphere pH, K$^+$, and H$^+$, transport, and root-cell membrane potentials. *Plant Physiol.* 91:1188–96

90. Moran N. 1990. The role of ion channels in osmotic volume changes in *Samanea* motor cells analyzed by patch-clamp methods. *The Pulvinus: Motor Organ for Leaf Movement*, ed. RL Satter, HL Gorton, TC Vogelmann, pp. 142–59. Rockville, MD: Am. Soc. Plant Physiologists

91. Moran N, Ehrenstein G, Iwasa K, Bare C, Mischke C. 1984. Ion channels in plasmalemma of wheat protoplast. *Science* 226:835–38

92. Moran N, Ehrenstein G, Iwasa K, Mischke C, Bare C, Satter RL. 1988. Potassium channels in motor cells of *Samanea saman*. A patch-clamp study. *Plant Physiol.* 88:643–48

93. Moran N, Satter RL. 1989. K$^+$ channels in plasmalemma of motor cells of *Samanea saman*. In *Plant Membrane Transport*, ed. J Dainty, MI DeMichelis, E Marré, F Rasi-Coldogno, pp. 529–30. Amsterdam: Elsevier Science. 712 pp.

94. Mummert H, Gradmann D. 1976. Voltage dependent potassium fluxes and the significance of action potentials in *Acetabularia. Biochim. Biophys. Acta* 443:443–50

95. Neher E. 1992. Correction for liquid junction potentials in patch clamp experiments. *Methods Enzymol.* 207:123–31

96. Newman IA, Kochian LV, Grusak MA, Lucas WJ. 1987. Fluxes of H$^+$ and K$^+$ in corn roots. Characterization

and stoichiometries using ion-selective microelectrodes. *Plant Physiol.* 84: 1177–84

97. Olcese R, Toro L, Pérez G, Kavanaugh MP, North RA, et al. 1993. Macroscopic (cut-open oocyte) and reconstituted (bilayer) single channel currents of *Slowpoke* Ca-activated K channels. *Biophys. J.* 64:A200 (Abstr.)

98. Omielan JA, Epstein E, Dvorák J. 1991. Salt tolerance and ionic relations of wheat as affected by individual chromosomes of salt-tolerant *Lophopyrum elongatum. Genome* 34:961–74

99. Palmgren MG, Sommarin M, Ulvskov P, Jørgensen PL. 1988. Modulation of plasma membrane H$^+$ ATPase from oat roots by lysophosphatidylcholine, free fatty acids and phospholipase A$_2$. *Physiol. Plant.* 74:11–19

100. Papazian DM, Schwarz TL, Tempel BL, Jan YN, Jan LY. 1987. Cloning of genomic and complementary DNA from *Shaker*, a putative potassium channel gene from *Drosophila. Science* 237:749–53

101. Poole RJ. 1978. Energy coupling for membrane transport. *Annu. Rev. Plant Physiol.* 29:437–60

102. Rains DW, Epstein E. 1967. Sodium absorption by barley roots: the role of the dual mechanisms of alkali cation transport. *Plant Physiol.* 42:314–18

103. Rains DW, Epstein E. 1967. Sodium absorption by barley roots: its mediation by mechanism 2 of alkali cation transport. *Plant Physiol.* 42:319–23

104. Ramos J, Contreras P, Rodríguez-Navarro A. 1985. A potassium transport mutant of *Saccharomyces cerevisiae. Arch. Microbiol.* 143:88–93

105. Raschke K. 1975. Stomatal action. *Annu. Rev. Plant Physiol.* 26:309–40

106. Reisenauer HM. 1964. Mineral nutrients in soil solution. In *Environmental Biology*, ed. PL Altman, DS Dittmer, pp. 507–8. Bethesda, MD: Fed. Am. Soc. Exp. Biol.

107. Riesmeier JW, Willmitzer L, Frommer WB. 1992. Isolation and characterization of a sucrose carrier cDNA from spinach by functional expression in yeast. *EMBO J.* 11:4705–13

108. Robinson T. 1980. *The Organic Constituents of Higher Plants.* North Amherst, MA: Cordus

109. Rodríguez-Navarro A, Blatt MR, Slayman CL. 1986. A potassium-proton symport in *Neurospora crassa. J. Gen. Physiol.* 87:649–74

110. Sauer N, Friedländer K, Gräml-Wicke U. 1990. Primary structure, genomic organization and heterologous expression of a glucose transporter from *Arabidopsis thaliana. EMBO J.* 9:3045–50

111. Schachtman DP, Schroeder JI, Lucas WJ, Anderson JA, Gaber RF. 1992. Expression of an inward-rectifying potassium channel by the *Arabidopsis* KAT1 cDNA. *Science* 258:1654–58

112. Schachtman DP, Tyerman SD, Terry BR. 1991. The K$^+$/Na$^+$ selectivity of a cation channel in the plasma membrane of root cells does not differ in salt-tolerant and salt-sensitive wheat species. *Plant Physiol.* 97:598–605

113. Scherer GFE, André B. 1989. A rapid response to a plant hormone: auxin stimulates phospholipase A$_2$ *in vivo* and *in vitro. Biochem. Biophys. Res. Commun.* 163:111–17

114. Schnabl H, Ziegler H. 1975. The influence of aluminum ions on the movement of the stomata in *Vicia faba* epidermis. *Zur Pflanzenphysiol.* 74:394–403

115. Schroeder JI. 1988. K$^+$ transport properties of K$^+$ channels in the plasma membrane of *Vicia faba* guard cells. *J. Gen. Physiol.* 92:667–83

116. Schroeder JI. 1992. Plasma membrane ion channel regulation during abscisic acid–induced closing of stomata. *Philos. Trans. R. Soc. London Ser. B* 338: 83–89

117. Schroeder JI, Fang HH. 1991. Inward-rectifying K$^+$ channels in guard cells provide a mechanism for low-affinity K$^+$ uptake. *Proc. Natl. Acad. Sci. USA* 88:11583–87

118. Schroeder JI, Hagiwara S. 1989. Cytosolic calcium regulates ion channels in the plasma membrane of *Vicia faba* guard cells. *Nature* 338:427–30

119. Schroeder JI, Hagiwara S. 1990. Repetitive increases in cytosolic Ca^{2+} of guard cells by abscisic acid activation of nonselective Ca^{2+}-permeable channels. *Proc. Natl. Acad. Sci. USA* 87: 9305–9

120. Schroeder JI, Hedrich R. 1989. Involvement of ion channels and active transport in osmoregulation and signaling of higher plant cells. *Trends Biochem. Sci.* 14:187–92

121. Schroeder JI, Hedrich R, Fernandez JM. 1984. Potassium-selective single channels in guard cell protoplasts of *Vicia faba. Nature* 312:361–62

122. Schroeder JI, Raschke K, Neher E. 1987. Voltage dependence of K$^+$ channels in guard cell protoplasts. *Proc. Natl. Acad. Sci. USA* 84:4108–12

123. Schulze ED. 1989. Air pollution and forest decline in a spruce (*Picea abies*) forest. *Science* 244:776–83
124. Schwartz A. 1985. Role of calcium and EGTA on stomatal movements in *Commelina communis*. *Plant Physiol.* 79:1003–5
125. Sentenac H, Bonneaud N, Minet M, Lacroute F, Salmon J, et al. 1992. Cloning and expression in yeast of a plant potassium ion transport system. *Science* 256:663–65
126. Sheahan JJ, Ribeiro-Neto L, Sussman MR. 1993. Cesium-insensitive mutants of *Arabidopsis thaliana*. *Plant J.* 3: 647–56
127. Silver MR, DeCoursey TE. 1990. Intrinsic gating of inward rectifier in bovine pulmonary artery endothelial cells in the presence or absence of internal Mg^{2+}. *J. Gen. Physiol.* 96:109–33
128. Slayman CL. 1987. The plasma membrane ATPase of *Neurospora*: a proton pumping electroenzyme. *J. Bioenerg. Biomembr.* 19:1–20
129. Slesinger PA, Jan YN, Jan YN. 1993. The S4-S5 cytoplasmic loop forms part of the inner mouth of the *Shaker* potassium channel pore. *Biophys. J.* 64: 114
130. Spalding EP, Goldsmith MHM. 1993. Activation of K^+ channels in the plasma membrane of *Arabidopsis* by ATP produced photosynthetically. *Plant Cell* 5:477–84
131. Spalding EP, Slayman CL, Goldsmith MHM, Gradmann D, Bertl A. 1992. Ion channels in *Arabidopsis* plasma membrane. Transport characteristics and involvement in light-induced voltage changes. *Plant Physiol.* 99:96–102
132. Spiteri A, Viratelle OM, Raymond P, Rancillac M, Labouesse J, Pradet A. 1989. Artefactual origins of cyclic AMP in higher plant tissues. *Plant Physiol.* 91:624–28
133. Stoeckel H, Takeda K. 1989. Calcium-activated, voltage-dependent, non-selective cation currents in endosperm plasma membrane from higher plants. *Proc. R. Soc. London Ser. B* 237:213–31
134. Stoeckel H, Takeda K. 1993. Plasmalemmal, voltage-dependent ionic currents from excitable pulvinar motor cells of *Mimosa pudica*. *J. Membr. Biol.* 131:179–92
135. Sussman MR, Harper JF. 1989. Molecular biology of the plasma membrane of higher plants. *Plant Cell* 1: 953–60
136. Tarczynski MC, Jensen RG, Bohnert HJ. 1993. Stress protection of transgenic tobacco by production of the osmolyte mannitol. *Science* 259:508–10
137. Tazawa M, Shimmen T, Mimura T. 1987. Membrane control in the Characeae. *Annu. Rev. Plant Physiol.* 38: 95–117
138. Tester M. 1990. Plant ion channels: whole-cell and single-channel studies. *New Phytol.* 114:305–40
139. Thiel G, Blatt MR. 1992. Phosphatase antagonist okadaic acid inhibits K^+ currents in intact *Vicia faba* guard cells. *Int. Workshop on Plant Membrane Biology, 9th, Monterey, CA*
140. Thiel G, MacRobbie EAC, Blatt MR. 1992. Membrane transport in stomatal guard cells: the importance of voltage control. *J. Membr. Biol.* 126:1–18
141. Tsay Y-F, Schroeder JI, Feldmann KA, Crawford NM. 1993. The herbicide sensitivity gene CHL1 of Arabidopsis encodes a nitrate-inducible nitrate transporter. *Cell* 72:705–13
142. Tyerman SD. 1992. Anion channels in plants. *Annu. Rev. Plant Physiol. Plant Mol. Biol.* 43:351–73
143. Van Duijn B, Ypey DL, Libbenga KR. 1993. Whole-cell K^+ currents across the plasma membrane of tobacco protoplasts from cell-suspension cultures. *Plant Physiol.* 101:81–88
144. Verkhratsky A, Hoppe D, Kettenmann H. 1991. K^+ channel properties in cultured mouse Schwann cells: dependence on extracellular K^+. *J. Neurosci. Res.* 28:210–16
145. Warmke J, Drysdale R, Ganetzky B. 1991. A distinct potassium channel polypeptide encoded by the *Drosophila eag* locus. *Science* 252:1560–62
146. White PJ, Tester MA. 1992. Potassium channels from the plasma membrane of rye roots characterized following incorporation into planar lipid bilayers. *Planta* 186:188–202
147. Yellen G, Jurman M, Abramson T, MacKinnon R. 1991. Mutations affecting internal TEA blockade identify the probable pore-forming region of a K^+ channel. *Science* 251:939–42
148. Yool AJ, Schwarz TL. 1991. Alteration of ionic selectivity of a K^+ channel by mutation of the H5 region. *Nature* 349: 700–4
149. Zucker-Lowen C, Satter RL. 1989. Light-promoted changes in apoplastic K^+ activity in the *Samanea saman* pulvinus, monitored with liquid membrane microelectrodes. *Planta* 179: 421–27

150. Kubo Y, Reuveny E, Slesinger PA, Jan YN, Jan LY. 1993. Primary structure and functional expression of a rat G-protein-coupled muscarinic potassium channel. *Nature* 364:802–6

151. MacRobbie EAC. 1992. Calcium and ABA-induced stomatal closure. *Phi-los. Trans. R. Soc. London Ser. B* 338: 5–18

152. Smith FA, Walker NA. 1989. Transport of potassium by *Chara australis*. I. A symport with sodium. *J. Membr. Biol.* 108:125–37

Annu. Rev. Biophys. Biomol. Struct. 1994. 23:473–507

EVOLUTION OF THE EF-HAND FAMILY OF PROTEINS

Susumu Nakayama[1] *and Robert H. Kretsinger*

Department of Biology, University of Virginia, Charlottesville, Virginia 22901

KEY WORDS: calcium, homologue, exon shuffling, congruence

CONTENTS

OVERVIEW

Classification is one of the fundamental tasks of science. Ordering organisms and proteins not only lets us glimpse potential evolutionary paths, but provides insight into the structures and functions of the proteins as well as into the peregrinations of the relevant DNAs.

---

[1] Present address: Department of Biochemistry, Nagasaki University School of Medicine, 12-4 Sakamoto 1-chome, Nagasaki 852, Japan.

1056–8700/94/0610–0473$05.00

In this chapter, we summarize characteristics of the EF-hand proteins, review our classifications, present interpretations, and pose several questions. We rely heavily on five papers (5, 31, 41–43) and could accept responsibility for this review having only recently completed those analyses.

CHARACTERISTICS OF EF-HAND PROTEINS

EF-Hand Domains

Table 1 lists the 31 known subfamilies of EF-hand proteins. Crystal structures are available for several parvalbumins (PARV) (1, 39, 50) troponins C (TNC) (27, 53) and calmodulins (CAM) (10, 47, 64) as well as for intestinal calcium-binding protein (ICBP, in S100) (61), sarcoplasm calcium-binding protein (SARC) (65), and recoverin (visinin, VIS) (17). The crystal structures (49, 71) of the S1 fragment of molluscan myosin show the conformations of both the regulatory light chain (RLC) and the essential light chain (ELC).

These structures confirm the ability of several algorithms to distinguish the amino acid sequences of EF-hand homologues from many similar analogues (32). Most investigators use the mnemonic of Figure 1 because it is easily applied and reflects several structural and functional characteristics. It misses very few true EF-hands, but it can give false positives. Usually, we compare a candidate sequence against our data base of 996 known EF-hand domains. Consistently, EF-hand homologues score over 10 identity of 29 length when compared with representatives of several EF-hand subfamilies. Although this test is very sensitive, it is more difficult to apply manually than is the traditional mnemonic of Figure 1.

Calcium Coordination

The crystal structures, hundreds of sequences, and many functional studies support the description of the canonical calcium-binding loop found in the legend to Figure 1. In the domains 1 that bind calcium in the S100/ICBP subfamily, the Glu at $-Z$ provides two ligands; four ligands come from carbonyl oxygens; and the seventh comes from water. ELC represents a second, and totally unanticipated, variation on the canonical domain. A third of the domains probably do not bind calcium. However, given that the calcium coordinations of neither the S100 nor the ELC variant domains were anticipated, some caution is required in generating models. In general, the (inferred) noncalcium-binding domains show greater variation in sequence than do those that bind calcium.

Table 1 Subfamilies of EF-hand homologues

Name	Abbreviation	Occurrence[b]	Function/structure known[c]	\ Domain[a] 1	2	3	4	5	6	7	8
Calmodulin	CAM	A/Pl/F/Pr	+/X	1	2	3	4				
				1	2	3	4				
Troponin C	TNC	A	+/X	*1*	*2*	3	4				
				1	*2*	3	4				
Essential light chain myosin[d]	ELC	A/F	+/X	*1*	*2*	3	4				
				1	*2*	3	4				
Regulatory light chain myosin	RLC	A	+/X	1	2	3	4				
				1	2	3	4				
Troponin, nonvertebrate	TPNV	A	?/?	3	2	3	4				
Cal1 (*Caenorhabditis*)[e]	CAL	A	+/?	1	2	3	4				
				1	2	**Ur**	4				
Squidulin (*Loligo*)[e]	SQUD	A	?/?	**Od**	2	3	4				
CDC31, or caltractin	CDC	F/Pr	?/?	**Od**	*Ev*	3	4				
				1	2	3	4				
Calcium-dependent protein kinase[f]	CDPK	Pl	+/?	**Od**	4	3	4				
				Ur	2	**Od**	2				
LAV1 (*Physarum*)[e,f]	LAV	F	?/?	3	**Ev**	**Ur**	**Ev**				
				Ur	**Ev**	**Ur**	**Ev**				
EHF5	EHF5	Pr	?/?	*Od*	4	*Od*	4				
				Ur	*Ev*	*Ur*	*Ev*				
Calcineurin B	CLNB	AF	+/?	**Ev**	**Ev**	**Od**	**Ev**				
				Od	**Od**	3	2				
p24 Thyroid protein (*Canis*)[e]	TPP	A	?/?	**Od**	**Od**	**Od**	**Od**[g]				
				1	2	3	4				

Table 1 *Continued*

Name	Abbreviation	Occurrence[b]	Function/structure known[c]	Domain[a]							
				1	2	3	4	5	6	7	8
Calbindin 28 kDa	CLBN	A	?/?	**3**	*Ev*	**3**	*Ev*	**3**	*Ev*		
				3	*Od*	**3**	**2**	**1**	**2**		
Parvalbumin	PARV	A	?/X		**3**	**3**	**4**				
					2	**3**	**2**				
S100, intestinal calcium binding protein[d]	S100	A	?/X	*Ur*	*Ev*	**3**	*Ev*				
				Od	**2**	**3**	**2**				
Diglycerol kinase[gh]	DGK	A	+/?	*Ev*	**2**						
				Od	*Ev*						
α-Actinin[e]	ACTN	A	+/?	*Od*	**4**						
				Ur	**2**						
Protein phosphatase (*Drosophila*)[e,f]	PPTS	A/Pr	+/?	**3**	*Unknown*[i]	**2**	*S*				
				3		**2**	**2**				
Strongylocentrotus calcium-binding protein[e]	SPEC	A	?/?	*Od*	**2**	*Od*	*Ev*				
				Ev	**2**	*Ev*	**2**				
Lytechinus purpuratus SPEC resembling protein	LPS	A	?/?	**2**	**4**	*Ev*	**4**	**2**	**4**	*Ev*	**4**
				2	**2**	*Ev*	**2**	**2**	**2**	*Ev*	**2**
Aequorin and luciferin binding protein	AEQ	A	+/?	*Ev*	(**4**)[j]	*Ev*	**4**				
				Ev	(*Ur*)	*Ur*	*Ev*				
Calcium vector protein (*Branchiostoma*)[b,e]	CVP	A	?/?	*Ur*	*Ev*	*Ev*	*Ev*				
1F8 and TB17	1F8	Pr	?/?	*Od*	*Ur*	*Od*	*Ur*				
				Od	*Ev*	*Od*	*Od*				

Protein	Abbrev.	Origin	Fn/Str	Domain 1	Domain 2	Domain 3	Domain 4	Domain 5
Calpain and sorcin[j]	CALP	A	+/?	C / C	C / C	C / C	C / C	C / Ur
Membrane-associated protein (*Plasmodium*)[f,k]	PFS	Pr	?/?	Ur / Ur	C / Ur	Ur / Ur	C / Ur	C / Ur
Sarcoplasm calcium-binding protein	SARC	A	?/X	S / S	S / S	S / S	S / S	
Visinin and recoverin	VIS	A	+/X	S / Ev	C / 2	Ur / 1	S / 4	
Calcium-binding protein (*Saccharopolyspora*)[e]	CMSE	Prokaryote	?/?	S / Od	S / 4	Od / 4	Od / Od	
Tetrahymena calcium-binding protein	TCBP	Pr	?/?	Ur / 4	S / 2	Ur / 4	S / 2	
CAM related gene product (*Homo*)[e]	CRGP	A	?/?	Ur / Od	S / Ur	S / 2	S / Ur	

[a] The first row indicates the domain origin as determined by protein sequence, and the second row the domain origin as determined by cDNA sequence. A single row means that only protein sequence was used for the determination. Boldface type indicates inferred calcium binding, italics not, and boldface italic type that both binding and not binding have been inferred in different representatives. 1, 3, Od(d) and 2, 4, Ev(en) refer to the branches to the four domains of the precursor protein of CAM, TNC, ELC, and RLC. C refers to the domain from which all four domains of CALP evolved, and S refers to the precursor branch of all four domains of SARC. Ur is the ur-domain that gave rise to OD and Ev as well as to C and S.

[b] A, animal; Pl, plant; F, fungus; Pr, protist.

[c] +, Function known; X, X-ray or NMR structure known; ?, function or structure not known.

[d] Noncanonical calcium-binding domains are sometimes present.

[e] Probable EF-hand subfamily, designated unique.

[f] The structural (LAV, ACTN) or catalytic (CDPK, PPST) domain of the protein precedes the EF hand.

[g] A 17-residue insertion occupies position −Z in TPP.

[h] Each of DGK's EF hands are preceded by approximately 100 residues and followed by a catalytic domain.

[i] Although these regions do not score as EF hands, they occur between two EF hands, 1 and 3, and might have diverged beyond recognition.

[j] Only the large subunit has a catalytic domain.

[k] Each of the five EF hands are preceded and followed by other domains.

```
CANONICAL
                    ------ loop ------
     ---- helix E -------             ------ helix F ------
                    1 1 1 1 1 1 1 1 1 1 2 2 2 2 2 2 2 2 2 2
     1 2 3 4 5 6 7 8 9 0 1 2 3 4 5 6 7 8 9 0 1 2 3 4 5 6 7 8 9
     E n * * n n * * n X * Y * Z G ‡ I-X * *-Z n * * n n * *(n)


S-100, domain 1
                    -8      -5 -3      0          +5
                                                  2 2 2 2 2 2 2 2
     1 2 3 4 5 6 7 8 9                            1 2 3 4 5 6 7 8 9
     * n * * n n * * n * * *EG D * **L * K * E n * * n n * * *
                       X      Y   Z   -Y          -Z
                       =O     =O =O   =O


ELC,   domain 1
                                    1 1 1 2 2 2 2 2 2 2 2 2
     1 2 3 4 5 6 7 8 9              7 8 9 0 1 2 3 4 5 6 7 8 9
     $ n * * V F $ L F D FWD GRD G * V D A n K n G D n n R C L
                       X   -X  -Y
                       Y   Z       -Z
                       =O  =O      =O
```

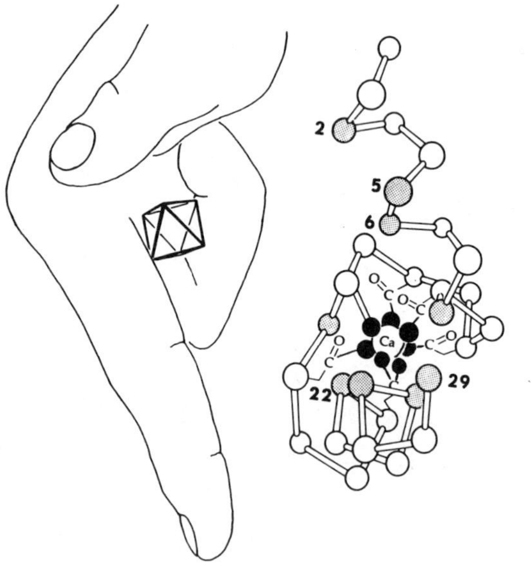

Figure 1   The canonical EF-hand consists of an α-helix (E, residues 1–11), a loop around the calcium ion, and a second α-helix (F, residues 19–29). The α-carbons (cartoon, stippled), indicated by n [residues 2, 5, 6, 9, 17, 22, 25, 26, and (29)], usually have hydrophobic side chains. They point inward and interact with the homologous residues of a second EF-hand domain, related to the first by a local two-fold axis, to form a hydrophobic core. Ile, Leu, or Val at residue 17 attaches the loop to the hydrophobic core. An asterisk indicates variable residues, often hydrophilic; Gly at position 15 permits a sharp bend in the calcium-binding loop. Residues specifically indicated reflect a strong consensus;

Pairs of Domains

Usually EF-hands occur in pairs of adjacent domains, though PARV, which has three domains, and *Plasmodium falciparum* membrane surface protein (PFS), which has five, are exceptions. The two domains of a pair are related by an approximate two-fold rotation axis. Each pair is hemispherical with the calcium-binding sites on the outer curved surface. The flat surface is more or less hydrophobic depending on whether or not calcium is bound. In PARV, the third domain, which does not bind calcium, provides a cap, which covers the hydrophobic surface of the pair of domains. Both aequorin (AEQ) and the Thr/Ser protein phosphatase (PPTS) have three well-defined domains, which are listed in Table 1 as 1, 3, and 4. The residues between domains 1 and domains 3 do not not appear to contain EF-hands (Table 1, footnote d). However, these residues might have diverged beyond recognition and might still pair with domain 1. As with calcium coordination, one can expect the unexpected from the 23 subfamilies of unknown structure. For instance, a domain might pair with an EF-hand that is not adjacent in sequence or with one from another molecule.

Tandem EF-hands are attached to the C termini of larger non-EF-hand domains in seven of the subfamilies. In diacylglycerol kinase (DGK), which has two EF-hands, and in the membrane-associated proteins of *Plasmodium* (PFS), which has five, there are also large non-EH-hand domains on the C-terminal sides of the EF-hand domains. The other five subfamilies have either four [calcium-dependent protein kinase (CDPK), LAV1 of *Physarum polycephalum* (LAV), PPTS, and

---

they are not invariant. The Ca^{2+} ion is coordinated by an oxygen atom, or bridging water molecule, of the side chains of residues 10 (X), 12 (Y), 14 (Z), and 18 ($-$X). The ligand at vertex $-$Y is the carbonyl oxygen of residue 16. Usually residue 21 ($-$Z) is Glu and is the sixth residue to coordinate calcium. It binds with both oxygen atoms contributing the sixth and seventh oxygens of a pentagonal bipyramid whose axis is 10 (X)–18 ($-$X).

In the S100 subfamily, two residues are inserted into the first loop of the domains 1 that are inferred to bind calcium. The Glu at $-$Z coordinates with both atoms of its carboxylate group. Four carbonyl oxygens—X, Y, Z, and $-$Y—coordinate calcium. The seventh ligand is the oxygen of water.

Loop 1 of ELC of *Aquipecten irradiens,* and probably of *Patinopecten yessoensis* and *Todarodes pacificus,* also has two residues inserted, but not at positions homologous to those inserted in loop 1 of S100. Asp10 coordinates calcium or magnesium with both carboxylate oxygen (X) and carbonyl oxygen (Y); Asp12 (Trp is inserted between 11 and 12) coordinates with both carbonyl oxygen (Z) and carboxylate ($-$X); Asp14 (Arg is inserted between 13 and 14) uses its carboxylate ($-$Y), and a carbonyl oxygen comes from position 16 ($-$Z). The $ . . . $ in the molluscan ELCs is either Glu . . . Asp or Asp . . . Glu.

the calpains of CALP] or two [α-actinin (ACTN)] EF-hands. The catalytic regions of the four enzymes—DGK, CDPK, PPTS, and calpain—are each homologues of different non-EF-hand proteins.

The relationship of one pair of domains, referred to as a lobe, to other parts of the molecule varies. In TNC and CAM the 11- or 8-residue linker between pair 1,2 and pair 3,4 is an α-helix, as seen in the crystal structure and deduced from solution studies with small angle X-ray scattering (26) or with nuclear magnetic resonance (29). The second, or F, α-helix of domain 2, the linker, and the first, or E, α-helix of domain 3 form one continuous central helix eight or seven turns long. A similar dumbbell shape is inferred for monomeric ELC and for RLC. However, when bound to a target, CAM (28, 40), ELC, and RLC (49,71) show varying degrees of bending in the 2,3 linker—hence the term, flexible tether (45). In contrast, in the crystal structure of SARC, the 15-residue linker is bent. Lobes 1,2 and 3,4 fit tightly together. The relationships between lobes can vary widely, especially in calbindin (CLBN), which has six EF-hand domains and in the *Lytechinus pictus* SPEC-like protein (LPS), which has eight.

Calcium as a Secondary Messenger

The oversimplified paradigm of decades past holds that the concentration of free Ca^{2+} ion in the cytosol of an unstimulated eukaryotic cell is $\sim 10^{-17.2}$ M. Following stimulation, $[Ca^{2+}]$ rises to $\sim 10^{-5.8}$ M. An *apo*-EF-hand protein binds calcium and changes conformation. In its *calci*-form, it activates a target enzyme or structural protein.

The actual situation is more complex. The rise in calcium concentration following stimulation may oscillate with different phases and amplitudes in different parts of the cell (6). The effective concentration of Ca^{2+} ion adjacent to the membrane surface may exceed $10^{-5.0}$ M.

In the so-called quiescent cell, some EF-hand domains coordinate magnesium. The concentration of the free Mg^{2+} ion in the cytosol is nearly constant about $10^{-2.5}$ M. For many calcium-binding proteins, and certainly most EF-hand proteins, the ratio of affinities for Ca^{2+} and for Mg^{2+} is about $10^{4.2}$. Sites with high affinity for calcium, e.g. $K_d \approx 10^{-7.2}$ M, would have an affinity for magnesium of (for example) $K_d \approx 10^{-3.0}$ M and would be filled with magnesium in the resting cell. Thus, calcium entering a cell first binds to the weaker sites, sometimes referred to as calcium specific, which are unoccupied.

Kretsinger (30) suggested that all of the proteins that bind messenger calcium are members of the EF-hand homologue family. Probably other membrane-associated proteins, such as annexins (reviewed in 59), that have lower calcium affinities can also bind messenger calcium because of its higher effective concentration near the membrane.

The functions of only 13 of the 31 subfamilies are known. CAM is inferred (usually) to be a monomer in the resting cell. Upon binding calcium it interacts with and activates a score of target enzymes or structural proteins. TNC (and perhaps TPNV from nonvertebrates) is the third component of troponin, which includes the tropomyosin-binding protein, TnT, and the inhibitory component, TnI. One molecule each of ELC and RLC bind to the myosin head. TNC, ELC, and RLC remain bound in their respective complexes whether or not calcium is bound. Similarly, four molecules of CAM are part of the hexadecamer phosphorylase kinase *b*. Several other homologues are components of heterocomplexes and do not dissociate upon release of calcium, for example: the small subunit, CLNB, of the protein phosphatase, calcineurin; the homodimer, ACTN, that links the ends of thin filaments to Z lines or to membranes; and p10 (p11) a member of S100 that, as a dimer, is part of the heterotetramer calpactin (annexin II). CDPK, DGK, PPTS, and CALP are calcium-modulated enzymes, supposedly via their EF-hands. Not all EF-hand proteins interact with other molecules. The function of PARV, which served as the rosetta stone for the entire family, has yet to be determined; however, it probably functions in temporal buffering and/or transport of calcium.

With the possible exception of S100 when it functions as a growth factor (67) and avian thymic hormone, a member of PARV (8), all EF-hand proteins are found in the cytosol or associated with cytosolic membranes. Of the innumerable extracellular calcium-binding proteins, some may have calcium-binding loops similar to those of EF-hands; however, none appear to be EF-hand homologues (32).

In summary, members of a subfamily can differ significantly in calcium coordination and function. Conversely, (members of) different subfamilies can have converged toward similar characters. Most of the subfamilies appear to have radiated rapidly from a few precursors, as suggested by the lack of systematic correlation of structure or function with branching patterns of subfamilies (domains) relative to one another.

CLASSIFICATION

Procedures

We have described the procedures for generating dendrograms in detail along with citations to sequences (41–43). Dendrograms depend on the correct alignment of amino acid sequences within the EF-hand domains. Within subfamilies the assignment of insertions and deletions is quite clear. Between subfamilies, we optimized these alignments by

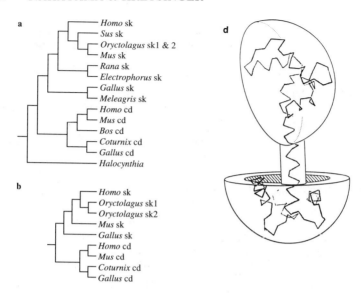

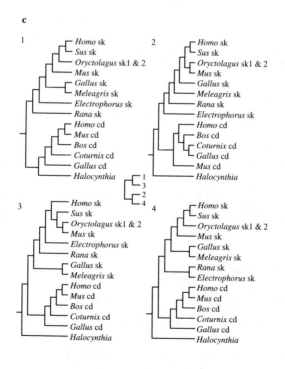

considering the relatedness of the domains. However, the relationships among domain subfamilies depends on the alignments—admittedly a cyclic process. Alignments of sequences before, between, and after domains (collectively, interdomains) is usually unambiguous within subfamilies, quite reliable between congruent subfamilies (as discussed in the next section), and near random between noncongruent subfamilies.

The dendrograms of Figures 2–11 are minimum mutation distance algorithms as frequently used in studies of molecular evolution. Most of the dendrograms are robust and statistically reliable by several criteria. For instance, the inclusion or omission of several sequences chosen at random does not significantly alter the relationships among the other domains. Inevitably, each branch length bears some uncertainty because of the stochastic nature of the evolutionary process. These errors are difficult to estimate. Often a small change in branch length can significantly change branch order and inferred evolutionary pathway. We have compared the minimum mutation distance scores of the lowest score (best) tree with similar ones that might better reflect evolution. Those subfamilies with 10 or more members are very robust; our reference group consists of CAM (36 different protein sequences), TNC (14 sequences), ELC (26 sequences), RLC (29 sequences), CALP (15 sequences), and SARC (11 sequences) as well as PARV (31 sequences) and S100 (27 sequences). Collectively, CAM, TNC, ELC, RLC, CALP, and SARC are designated CTER/CS. The relationships of domains within and especially among the other 23 subfamilies are more tentative.

Congruence

Congruence is fundamental to our classification. To describe this concept and to illustrate the relevant procedures and terminology, we discuss in some detail the TNC subfamily. Figure 2 shows the lowest-scoring dendrogram for 56 domains of the 14 TNCs. All domains 1 cluster together as do all domains 2, all domains 3, and all domains 4. The branching order within each of the domain groups is very similar

←——

Figure 2 (*a*) A dendrogram, based on protein sequence, relating the 56 domains of 14 TNCs. All domains 1 cluster together, as do all domains 2, etc. Domains 1 and 3 are more closely related as are domains 2 and 4. All four are similar to the dendrogram based on the full length of TNC (*b*). (*c*) The dendrogram based on the available encoding DNAs; two genes of *Oryctolagus cuniculus* encode identical protein sequences. (*d*) The α-carbon trace as seen in the crystal. Abbreviations are: cd, cardiac muscle; sk, skeletal muscle.

but not identical. The four domains of TNC are congruent. Congruence is a necessary but not sufficient character of the domains within any subfamily.

The most parsimonious interpretation, that is, the one demanding the fewest assumptions, is that all of the known TNC genes evolved from one precursor TNC gene in an organism that was an ancestor to all extant chordates.[2] The lack of perfect parallelism among all four domain trees reflects the stochastic nature of mutation and fixation, not an error in sequence determination nor in computation. Since we have inferred that all TNCs descended from a common TNC, we can compute a dendrogam of the TNCs using the complete sequence—four EF-hand domains plus interdomains—161 residues instead of only 29.

In the dendrogram for the complete sequence, and in the four-domain dendrograms, the cardiac TNCs form one cluster and the skeletal TNCs another, i.e. *Homo sapiens* cardiac TNC is more similar to *Mus musculus* cardiac TNC than it is to *H. sapiens* skeletal TNC. This implies that the organism ancestral to these vertebrates already had both cardiac and skeletal TNCs. The TNC of *Halocynthia roretzi*, a protochordate, branches prior to the cardiac, skeletal branch. The gene-duplication event that gave rise to cardiac and skeletal forms occurred in the organism that was an ancestor of vertebrates but not of protochordates.

One can make a similar dendrogram for all of the domains of the CAMs, TNCs, ELCs, and RLCs. All of the domains 1, from all four subfamilies, cluster together as do all domains 2, all domains 3, and all domains 4. That is, the domains 1 of CAM more closely resemble the domains 1 of RLC than they do other domains of CAM. Because these four subfamilies are definitely congruent with one another and because they contain 420 of 996 domains in the data base, we use their dendrogram as a reference and call them CTER. They evolved from a single four-domain molecule in the organism that was an ancestor of all eukaryotes. This is a powerful conclusion, since within TNC, ELC, and RLC the only sequences available outside of the animal kingdom is that of *P. polycephalum* and *Dictyostelium discoideum* ELC, and of *D. discoideum* RLC. If TNC, ELC, and RLC had evolved from a precursor molecule in an organism ancestral to animals only, the CAM from animals would more closely resemble TNC, ELC, and RLC than CAM from plants, fungi, and protists, but this is not the case. Unless the precursor genes of TNC, ELC, and RLC have been deleted in the

---

[2] Chordates are defined as animals with, at some stage of development, a notochord, a dorsally situated central nervous system, and gill clefts.

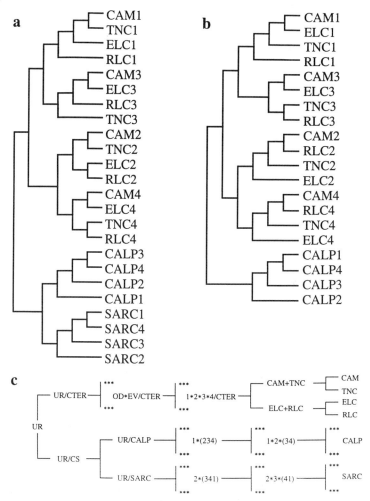

Figure 3 (*a*) A dendrogram relating the 24 domain clusters of CAM, TNC, ELC, RLC, CALP, and SARC (CTER/CS). The individual domains within each cluster were constrained to the relationship derived from protein sequence data for each of the six subfamilies when that subfamily was analyzed as illustrated in Figure 2. (*b*) The relationship of the 20 domain clusters of CTER and CALP; eDNA data is not available for SARC. (*c*) The inferred evolutionary pathway. The Ur-EF-hand domain gene duplicated to form UR/CTER and UR/CS. The CTER subfamilies are congruent; a UR/CTER domain gene duplicated and fused to form OD*EV/CTER. In turn, this duplicated and fused to form 1*2*3*4/CTER, the common precursor to all CAMs, TNCs, ELCs, RLCs, and other subfamilies that are congruent with CTER. Subsequent gene duplications, without fusions, produced the precursors of the four subfamilies of CTER. The UR/CS gene duplicated without fusion to form UR/CALP and UR/SARC UR/SARC. Within each lineage, CALP and SARC, gene duplications and fusions formed four domain precursors. The remaining 95 (119 − 24) domain clusters of 25 (31 − 6) subfamilies are classified relative to this summary dendrogram as having branched from 1, 3, Od; 2, 4, Ev; C; S; or Ur (Table 1).

plant, fungi, and protist ancestors, these three proteins should be present in these three kingdoms.

Because in CTER the domains 1 are most closely related to the domains 3, and the domains 2 are closely related to domains 4, we contend that the four-domain precursor of CTER evolved by gene duplication and splicing from a two-domain precursor, which we call Odd*Even or ODEV. This precusor in turn evolved from a single EF-hand precursor, or ur-domain, UR/CTER (Figure 3). Support for this interpretation is the reconizable homology of interdomains 1,2 and interdomains 3,4.

In contrast, a dendrogram of domains of CALP, SARC, and CTER shows that the four domains of CALP cluster together and the four domains of SARC cluster together (Figure 3). Neither CALP nor SARC are congruent with other subfamilies. This finding of total congruence within CTER and no congruence of either CALP or SARC outside of the subfamily is highly significant. Whereas CAM, TNC, ELC, and RLC all evolved from a single four-domain precursor by gene duplication, CALP evolved from a single EF-hand, UR/CALP, by gene duplication and splicing and SARC evolved from an UR/SARC by duplication and splicing (Figure 3).

Domain Grouping and Branching Order

The CTER/CS dendrogram is based on 524 domains out of a total of 996. It provides a reference point for the classification of the remaining 25 subfamilies. Each of their 95 subfamily domains is related to CTER/CS [Figures 3 and 6 (see below); Table 1]. Because several of these subfamilies have only a single or few members of known sequence, the placement relative to the CTER/SC tree is much less reliable than the reference dendrogram itself.

Encoding DNA

We have also generated dendrograms using DNA derived either from DNA sequences complementary to messenger RNA (cDNA) or from genomic sequences (gDNA); we refer to these as e(encoding)DNA. The bookkeeping is complicated because eDNA sequences are not available for all protein sequences. For several proteins of CTER, several different eDNAs encode identical protein sequences. In addition, several pseudogene sequences are related to CAM. For TNC, ELC, RLC, CALP, PARV, and S100, the dendrograms computed from protein sequences and the dendrograms computed from eDNA sequences are very similar. Furthermore, the dendrogram from the DNA sequences of intron 3 + 1/1 (defined in Table 2) of ELC is almost the same as those computed from protein and from eDNA sequences.

This near identity of dendrograms derived from independent data sets strongly supports both the underlying concept as well as the computational procedures. Table 1 also shows the branching patterns, relative to CTER/CS, for the 25 subfamilies for which eDNA data is available. The differences in branching pattern deduced from the protein and from the eDNA in some subfamilies may reflect small sample size and great evolutionary distance. For PARV (31 protein, 6 eDNA) and S100 (27 protein, 18 eDNA), the branch origins agree reasonably well.

CAM is the one subfamily within which the protein and eDNA dendrograms differ significantly (see section on calmodulin contradiction).

Table 2a   Positions and phases of known EF-hand introns[a]

		CAM 12	TNC 4	ELC 14	RLC 7	CAL 1	CDC 1	CLBN 1	PARV 3	S100 4	DGK : 1	SPEC : 4	LPS 1	CALP : 2	TCBP 1	CRGP 1
02	−17/1	−	−	−	−	−	−	−		−	+	−	−−	+	−	−
04	−10/0	B	+	+	B	−	−	−		−	−	+	+−	−	+	−
06	−03/1	−	−	−	−	−	−	−		−	−	−	−+	−	−	−
08	1.01/1	B	+	+	−	−	−	−		−	+	+	+−	−	−	−
10	1.05/0	−	−	−	B	−	−	−		−	−	−	−−	−	−	−
12	1.10/0	B	−	−	−	−	+	−		−	−	−	−−	+	−	−
14	1.15/1	B	−	−	−	−	−	+		−	−	−	−−	−	−	−
16	1.21/0	−	−	−	B	−	+	−		−	+	−	−−	−	−	−
18	1.+1/1	−	−	−	B	−	−	−		−	−	−	−−	−	−	−
20	1.+7/0	−	−	−	−	−	−	+	+	−	−	−	−−	−	−	+
22	2.03/0	−	−	−	−	−	+	−	−	−	+	−	−−	+	−	−
24	2.12/1	B	+	B	−	−	−	+	−	−	−	+	++	−	−	−
26	2.21/1	B	−	−	−	−	−	−	−	−	−	−	−−	−	−	−
28	2.22/0	−	−	−	−	−	−	+	−	−	−	−	−−	−	−	−
30	2.+3/0	B	−	−	−	−	−	−	−	−	−	−	−−	−	−	−
32	2.+3/1	−	−	−	B	−	−	−	−	−	−	−	−−	+	−	−
34	2+12/0	−	−	−	−	−	−	−	−	−	+	−	−−	−	−	−
36	3.05/0	−	−	−	−	−	−	+	−			−	−−	−	+	
38	3.11/2	−	+	−	−	−	−	−	−			−	−−	−	−	
40	3.12/0	B	−	−	−	−	−	−	−			−	−−	−	−	
42	3.15/1	−	−	−	B	−	−	−	−			−	−−	−	−	
44	3.20/2	−	−	−	B	−	−	−	+			+	++	−	−	
46	3.24/0	B	−	−	−	+	+	+	−			−	−?	−	−	
48	3.+1/1	−	−	+	−	−	−	−	−			−	−?	−	−	
50	3.+6/1	−	−	−	−	−	+	−	−			−	−?	−	−	
52	4.04/0	−	−	−	B	−	−	−	−			−	−?	−	−	
54	4.04/1	−	−	−	−	−	−	−	−			−	−?	+	−	
56	4.07/2	B	−	−	−	−	−	−	−			−	−?	−	−	
57	4.08/0	−	−	−	B	−	−	+	−			−	−?	−	−	
58	4.21/1	B	+	+	−	−	−	−	+			+	+?	−	−	
60	4.22/0	B	−	−	−	−	−	−	−			−	−?	+	−	
62	4.24/2	−	−	−	−	−	+	+	−			−	−?	−	−	
64	4.+9/0								+							
66	5.12/0								+							
68	5.+7/0								+							

Table 2b   Distribution of introns in the CTER, CAL, and CDC subfamilies[b]

	04	08	10	12	14	16	18	22	24	26	30	32	38	40	42	44	46	48	50	52	56	57	58	60	62
CAM vert.	+	+	.	.	.	.	.	.	+	.	.	.	.	+	.	.	.	.	.	.	.	.	+	.	.
CAM vert.(II)	+	+	.	.	.	.	.	.	+	.	.	.	.	+	.	.	.	.	.	.	.	.	+	.	.
CAM Dros.	+	+	.	.	.	.	.	.	+	.	.	.	.	.	.	.	.	.	.	.	.	.	+	.	.
CAM Aplysia	+	+	.	.	.	.	.	.	+	.	.	.	.	.	.	.	.	.	.	.	.	.	+	.	.
CAM Cand.+Schizo.	+	.	.	.	.	.	.	.	.	.	.	.	.	.	.	.	.	.	.	.	.	.	+	.	.
CAM Asper.	+	.	.	+	+	.	.	.	.	+	.	.	.	.	.	.	.	.	.	.	.	.	.	.	.
CAM Plasmod.	.	.	.	.	+	.	.	.	.	.	.	.	.	.	.	.	.	.	.	.	.	.	.	.	.
CAM Chlamy.	.	.	.	.	+	.	.	.	.	.	+	.	.	.	.	.	+	.	.	.	+	.	.	+	.
CAM Prot.+Fun.	.	.	.	.	.	.	.	.	.	.	.	.	.	.	.	.	.	.	.	.	.	.	.	.	.
CAL	.	.	.	.	.	.	.	.	.	.	.	.	.	.	.	.	+	.	.	.	.	.	.	.	.
CDC caltractin Chl.	.	.	.	+	.	+	.	+	.	.	.	.	.	.	.	.	+	.	+	.	.	.	.	.	+
CDC CDC31 Sacchar.	.	.	.	.	.	.	.	.	.	.	.	.	.	.	.	.	.	.	.	.	.	.	.	.	.
TNC	+	+	.	.	.	.	.	.	+	.	.	.	+	.	.	.	.	.	.	.	.	.	+	.	.
ELC vert.	+	+	.	.	.	.	.	.	+	.	.	.	.	.	.	.	.	+	.	.	.	.	+	.	.
ELC Dros.	+	+	.	.	.	.	.	.	.	.	.	.	.	.	.	.	.	+	.	.	.	.	+	.	.
RLC Rat. sk.	+	.	+	.	.	.	+	.	.	.	.	+	.	.	.	+	.	.	.	+	.	.	.	.	.
RLC Dros. sk.	+	.	+	.	.	.	.	.	.	.	.	.	.	.	.	.	.	.	.	.	.	.	.	.	.
RLC Caeno. 1	+	.	.	.	.	+	.	.	.	.	.	+	.	.	.	.	.	.	.	.	.	+	.	.	.
RLC Caeno. 2	.	.	.	.	.	+	.	.	.	.	.	+	.	.	.	.	.	.	.	.	.	+	.	.	.
RLC Rat. smth.	.	.	.	.	.	.	+	.	.	.	.	.	.	+	.	.	.	.	.	.	.	.	.	.	.
RLC Dros. non.	.	.	.	.	.	.	.	.	.	.	.	.	.	.	.	.	.	.	.	+	.	.	.	.	.

[a] The location of each intron has been tabulated in terms of its position and phase. For instance at (about) 10 residues before the first domain an intron is found at phase (class) 0, i.e. between coding triplets. Intron "-10/0" is found in some (indicated by B) CAMs and some RLCs as well as in all known TNC, ELC, SPEC, TCBP, and LPS genes (Figure 11d). A phase 1 intron (between first and second encoding base), 4.21/1, at residue 21 of domain 4 is found in some CAMs and in all known TNC, ELC, PARV, SPEC, and LPS genes (Figure 11e). Thirty-four intron sites, numbered 2, 4, . . . 68 to permit insertions such as #57, have been found in the EF-hand family. The number below the subfamily indicates the number of gDNA sequences available.

[b] The congruent subfamilies—CAM, TNC, ELC, RLC, CAL, and CDC—are listed in terms of the distributions of introns among the 35 distinct sites.

Subfamilies

Most of the assignments of proteins to subfamilies are unambiguous. Similarities in function reflect similarities in amino acid sequence. The few uncertainties are discussed in the context of the subfamily in question.

CAM (calmodulin) presumably exists in the cytosol of all cells of all eukaryotes. It plays a major role in transducing the information in a pulse of messenger Ca^{2+} ions into a change in conformation and reactivity of over a score of target enzymes and structural proteins (3, 56, 66).

The CAM data base is complex, perhaps reflecting its functions. It contains 29 different protein sequences. The CAMs of the genera *Homo, Oryctolagus, Rattus, Mus, Bos,* and *Xenopus* as well as one CAM of *Gallus* and *Arbacia* are identical. The CAMs of *Drosophila* and *Aplysia* are also identical. Animal CAM is highly conserved; those of plant, protist, and fungi are slightly less so. For several genera, e.g. *Homo* (3), multiple genes encode identical protein sequences; hence

43 eDNAs encode the 29 proteins. Seven pseudogenes increase the protein sequences to 36 and the eDNA to 50. Thirty gDNA sequences encode 20 different CAM sequences, including the 7 pseudogenes. Figure 11 (below) shows dendrograms based on eDNA, protein, 3' base sequences, and sequences of introns − 10/0 and 4.21/1. These trees are very different.

TNC (troponin C), together with TnI and TnT, forms troponin. In resting skeletal muscle TNC has two equivalents of calcium or magnesium bound in sites 3 and 4 and neither calcium nor magnesium in the lower affinity sites 1 and 2. When calcium enters the cell, it is bound first to the empty sites (1 and 2), thereby relieving the productive interaction of the head of myosoin with the actin filament. A similar mechanism occurs in cardiac muscle; however, only domain 2 binds calcium (11, 22).

ELC (essential, or enzymatic, light chain of myosin) is essential for the ATPase activity of myosin, although its ease of extraction from and reconstitution of myosoin varies with species. Whether ELC imparts calcium sensitivity to any muscle has not yet been determined (71; reviewed in 49). Within vertebrates, the ventricular and atrial cardiac forms cluster separately, as do the cardiac and smooth muscle forms,

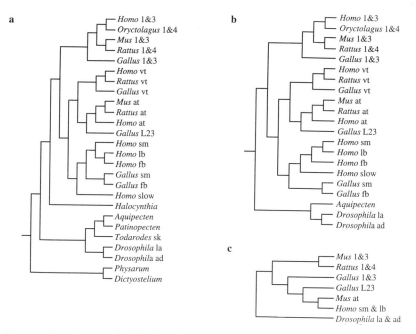

Figure 4   Dendrograms for ELC are based on the sequences of protein (*a*), eDNA (*b*), and intron 3 + 01/1 (*c*), as described in Table 2.

and all of these are distinct from the two isoforms of skeletal muscle (Figure 4). The molluscan and insect forms comprise a distinct subgroup, but only the molluscan form in the first loop has the Trp and Arg insertion apparently associated with its unique calcium coordination (Figure 1). The light chain from *P. polycephalum* clusters with ELC.

RLC (regulatory light chain of myosin) imparts calcium sensitivity to muscle either by directly binding calcium in skeletal muscle or via

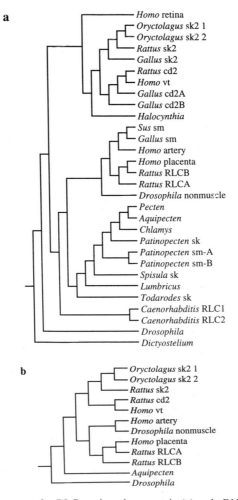

Figure 5   Dendrograms for RLC are based on protein (*a*) and eDNA (*b*) sequences.

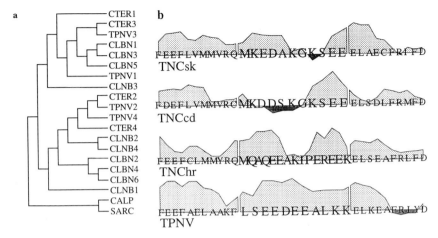

Figure 6   (*a*) The relationships of the four domains of TPNV, the six domains of CLBN, and the four domains of CLNB are shown relative to CTER/CS. (*b*) The predicted helix-forming tendencies of the central helices of TNC from *H. sapiens* skeletal (THCsk) and cardiac (TVCcd) muscle, and from *Halocynthia roretzi* (TNChr), as well as the helices of TPNV from *Astacus leptodactylus*. Each TNC is predicted to have a region in its 2,3 linker that is inclined to bend; in contrast, the linker of TPNV is strongly predicted to be an α-helix. Stippled shading above horizontal line indicates a tendency to form α-helices; solid shading below the line indicates a tendency not to form α-helices.

its phosphorylation by myosin light chain kinase, a CAM-regulated enzyme. As in ELC and TNC, the protein and eDNA dendrograms are very similar (Figure 5).

TPNV (troponin C from arthropods) clusters into a distinct subfamily; it is not congruent with TNC. Wnuk et al (68) found that TPNV interacts with TnI and TnT and restores calcium sensitivity to skinned rabbit fast-twitch fibers. The 2,3 linkers of various TNCs, as well as CAMs, are predicted to have regions inclined to bend or flex; in contrast, the linker of TPNV is strongly predicted to be helical (Figure 6*b*). The branching order, 3*2*3*2 (Figure 6*a* and Table 1), indicates the duplication and fusion of a 3*2 precursor gene. It will be interesting to see whether classification anticipates an alternate function.

The gene for CAL (*cal-1* of *Caenorhabditis elegans*) is present in one copy per haploid genome (52). It is congruent with CTER, but its domains branch outside of those four subfamilies.

SQUD (squid calcium-binding protein) is congruent with CTER but distinct from CAM. It is also found in optic lobe of *Loligo pealei* (25). The functions of both CAL and SQUD are unknown.

CDC (*CDC31* gene) of *Saccharomyces cerevisiae*, a fungus, and caltractrin of *Chlamydomonas reinhardtii*, a protist, consistently cluster together and are placed in the same subfamily. Both are (nearly) congruent with CTER. Baum et al (4) speculated that CDC is localized in the spindle pole body and plays a regulatory role in the organization of microtuble arrays. Taillon et al (62) summmarized the evidence that centrin (caltractin) " . . . is involved in the formation of fibers, the fibers can have diverse morphologies, and the fibers show calcium-dependent contraction" (p. 1622).

CDPK (calcium dependent protein kinase) is found in several isoforms in higher plants. In its full length of 610 residues, it is synergistically stimulated by calcium up to 0.1 mM free ion and by lysophosphatidylcholine and phosphatidylinositol (24, 55). The junction region between the catalytic domain and the four EF-hands is highly conserved. Harper ct al (24) argued by analogy to CAM's binding to calmodulin-dependent protein kinase that " . . . the junction domain in DPK functions as an autoinhibitor that is regulated by its neighboring calmodulin-like domain" (p. 3289).

LAV (LAV1 cDNA) was identified as a plasmoidal-specific mRNA of *P. polycephalum*. The linker between EF-hand domains 2 and 3 consists of a single Leu. The function of this 355-residue protein is unknown (36).

EFH5 is the product of the EF-hand 5 gene originally identified in *Trypanosoma brucei* (TbEFH5), recently in *T. cruzi* (TcCUB) (2), and in *Leishmania tarentolae* (LtEFH5) (DA Campbell, MG Elgort, J Fleischmann & U Kurath, in preparation). The TbEFH5 gene is transcribed as a polycistronic precursor RNA. It follows the CAM gene C by 111 bp and precedes ubiquitin-EP52/1 by 116 bp. It is presumbably under the control of a single distant upstream promoter (69). The three gene products are most similiar to one another in domains 1, 3, and 4; however, LtEFH5 domain 2 most closely resembles CAM domains 2. The inferred calcium-binding ability of domains 1–4 of the TbEFH5 gene product is $- + + -$, respectively; for domains 1–4 of both TcCUB and LtEFH5, it is $- - - -$. Whether EFH5 performs the same function in the three organisms remains to be seen. The three EFH5 proteins are tentatively placed in the same subfamily, in part, because all three genes are just upstream of the ubiquitin EP52 genes.

CLNB (calcineurin B, or the regulatory subunit of calmodulin-dependent protein phosphatase 2B) is N-myristylated and remains attached to the catalytic subunit A in the absence of calcium. CLNB is found in both animals and yeast (35).

TPP [thyroid protein (p24)] can be phosphorylated at Ser40, which occurs in the first calcium-binding loop at position $- Y$ (38). The fourth domain contains an inserted Glu after Ser at the Y vertex. The putative calcium coordination might be either SEDTE or DSDTE, similar to the calcium binding of domain 3, which is DSDTD. More unusual is the insertion of 17 residues—EFQDYYSGVSASMDTDE—at the Glu at $-Z$. Whether this insertion results in an F helix five turns longer and/or in altered calcium affinity is unknown.

The CLBN (28-kDa calbindin and calretinin) proteins are both selectively expressed in various vertebrate tissues in addition to the intestine, from which calbindin was first isolated, and the retina, which was the initial source of calretinin. The two proteins are congruent and have been tentatively placed in the same subfamily. The three pairs of domains—1,2; 3,4; and 5,6—certainly evolved by recent gene triplication and fusion (44).

PARV (parvalbumin) is found in numerous tissues of vertebrates (Figure 7). It occurs in highest concentration in the muscles of poikilotherms (i.e. cold-blooded animals). It binds two equivalents of calcium with high affinity, and most of it occurs in the magnesium form in the resting cell. Following stimulation of muscle and the relatively slow release of magnesium, it can bind calcium and might thereby help to relax the muscle and prevent tetany (21). Its possible functions in other tissues are unknown. The two major subgroups correspond to the α and β forms, but the PARVs in the genera *Latimeria, Triakis,* and *Amphiuma,* which are usually called α, split off before the α,β branch. Oncomodulin, whose concentration increases in several tumors, closely resembles *Raja clavata* and *Latimeria chalumnae* β. Its crystal structure (1) is similar to other PARVs. The avian thymic protein of *Gallus gallus* (8) clusters with *Graptemys geographica* and *Amphiuma means* βs. Most animals have several isoforms with no obvious correlation of tissue or function.

S100 is considered to comprise a single subfamily because all of its members are congruent and contain the unique first domain, described in Figure 1, or a deleted form thereof (Figure 8). One half consists of intestinal calcium-binding proteins (ICBP, sometimes called calbindin 9K though this is not closely related to calbindin 28K, which contains six EF-hands) plus MIF-related protein (MRP)-8. These proteins are all monomeric. In contrast, S100β and S100α, in the other half of the subfamily, are dimers. p10 is a dimer and also forms part of the tetramer calpactin (annexin II). ICBP may be involved in transporting calcium across cell; its concentration increases following administration of vitamin D. The functions of none of the members of S100 are known (15).

DGK (diacylglycerol kinase) from mammalian leucocytes contains

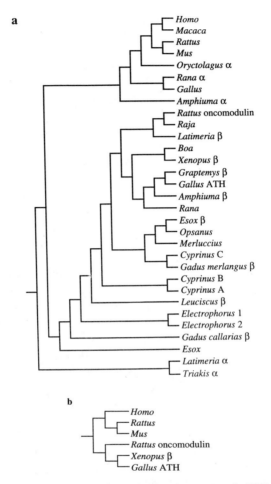

Figure 7 Dendrograms of PARV are based on protein (*a*) and eDNA (*b*) sequences.

two EF-hand domains at its N terminus. DGK " . . . attenuates the level of the second messenger DG in signal transduction, and therefore possibly modulates protein kinase C" (54, p. 151).

ACTN (α-actinin) forms an elongated dimer of monomer M_r 100,000. It cross-links actin filaments and is found in the Z-line of skeletal muscle. In nonmuscle cells, it links the ends of thin filaments to organelles or to membranes. The two EF-hand domains at the C terminus impart calcium sensitivity to the nonmuscle cells. The EF-hands of muscle ACTN do not bind calcium and the cross-linking function is not calcium sensitive (19).

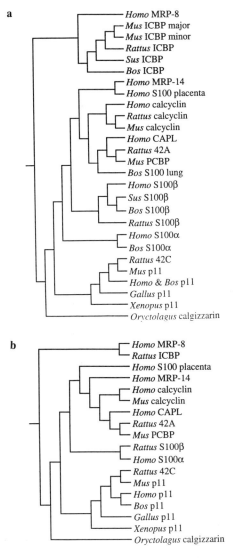

a

b

Figure 8 Dendrograms of the S100 subfamily are based on protein (*a*) and eDNA (*b*) sequences.

PPTS (Ser/Thr protein phosphatase) is encoded by the *Drosophila melanogaster* retinal degeneration C (*rdgC*) gene. Residues 153–393 are homologous with the catalytic domains of types 1, 2A, and 2B Ser/Thr protein phosphates. "The *rdgC* gene product appears to be required in a pathway initiated by rhodopsin stimulation, but distinct from the subsequent steps of the phototransduction cascade" (57, p. 669). "Young *rdgC* flies show normal visual function, but develop photoreceptor degeneration and a degraded reponse to light stimuli if maintained in the light" (57, p. 669). There are 56 residues between the first and second (of three) EF-hands. As in AEQ, this region may contain an EF-hand diverged beyond recognition (see Table 1).

SPEC (*Strongylocentrotus purpuratus* ectodermal protein) mRNAs are expressed in the aboral ectodermal cells during the gastrula and pluteus stages of sea urchin development (23). The 5′ and 3′ untranslated sequences are more highly conserved than are the coding regions.

LPS (*Lytechinus pictus* SPEC-resembling protein) genes (LpS1) in aboral ectoderm cells are activated early in devclopment (70). They contain eight EF-hands and evolved by duplication and fusion of a four-domain precursor. Xiang et al (70) proposed that LpS1 and the gene encoding SPEC share a more recent ancestor and note the high degree of sequence divergence. We confirm that for each of the eight domains of LPS, the more similar protein and eDNA sequences are from subfamilies other than SPEC. Xiang et al argue that, nevertheless, the spatial expression patterns of all the genes remain identical. The five intron sites in the SPEC genes are shared in LPS 1–4. Of these five, two are shared in LPS 5–8, and one is not yet sequenced. The LPS 5–8 intron − 03/1 (position 06, Table 2) may correspond to SPEC 1.01/1 (position 08).

AEQ (aequorin) is the luciferase of hydrozoa. Following binding of three Ca^{2+} ions, it catalyzes the oxidative decarboxylation of tightly bound luciferin with the emission of a photon, $\lambda = 469$ nm. Luciferin-binding protein of anthozoa is in the same subfamily with AEQ but is not an enzyme. Upon binding calcium its luciferin becomes available to a luciferase (discussion in 33). AEQ is about 189 residues long and can occur in numerous isoforms in one organism. Residues 44–107 might correspond to a fourth EF-hand. PPTS exhibits a similar ambiguity: domains 2 and 3 appear to be a pair of domains, a lobe, and domain 1 is followed by a region of undetermined homology.

CVP (calcium vector protein) is extracted from the muscle of *Branchiostoma lanceolatum* and is inferred to be involved in contraction; however, no target has been identified (12). CVP has a disulfide link between Cys16 (domain 1, position 2) and Cys78 (domain 2, position 26). PARV, TNC, or CAM could accommodate the homologous S-S bond with only slight distortion.

1F8 and TB17 were isolated from trypanosomes. Immunofluorescence indicated that 1F8 is located in the flagellum (16). Infected animals developed antibodies against 1F8.

CALP (calpain or calcium-activated neutral protease) is a heterodimer. The larger (M_r 80,000) catalytic subunit contains a domain homologous to the sulfhydryl proteases, and the C terminus has four EF-hands. The smaller (M_r 30,000) subunit consists of four EF-hands. It exists in two forms, μ that binds calcium at micromolar concentration, and m that binds at millimolar concentration. The μ and m forms cluster separately and both cluster away from the four EF-hands of the L (large) subunit (18, 51). Sorcin, a monomer, is congruent with μ and m calpain as well as with the four domains of the L subunit (7). The supposed target of sorcin has not been found. For a dendrogram of CALP, see Figure 9.

PFS [*Plasmodium falciparum* surface protein (Pfs40)], is the major calcium-binding protein of this malaria parasite. In gametes and zygotes it can be labeled with ^{125}I and has an N-terminal secretory signal sequence (48). Whether the five EF-hand domains are cytosolic or extracellular has not been determined. All five EF-hand domains branch deep in the CTER/CS tree, from either Ur or CALP; their pairings (1,2 and 3,4; or 2,3 and 4,5) cannot be inferred.

SARC (sarcoplasm calcium-binding protein) is found in the sarcoplasm of invertebrates. In the crystal structure (65), lobe 3,4 makes many contacts with lobe 1,2 (Figure 10). No target has been found and it may have a buffering or transport function.

VIS is found in the retinas of *G. gallus* (visinin) and of *Bos taurus* (recoverin). In the dark, bound cGMP keeps open Na$^+$ and Ca^{2+} chan-

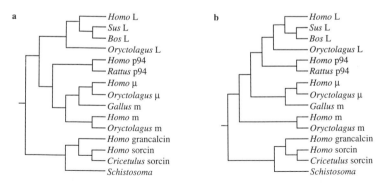

Figure 9   Dendrograms for CALP are based on protein (*a*) and eDNA (*b*) sequences.

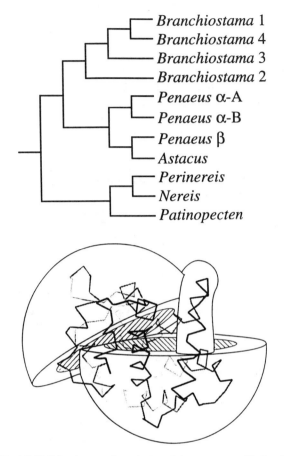

Figure 10 (*Top*) SARC dendrogram based on protein sequences. (*Bottom*) The α-carbon drawing from the crystal structure.

nels. Following absorption of a photon by rhodopsin, an enzyme cascade results in the hydrolysis of cGMP, thereby closing the channel and reducing the concentration of cytosolic calcium. Recoverin (14) is unique in that it activates rod guanylate cyclase when it is in the *apo* state, thereby leading to recovery of the dark state. Cancer-associated retinopathy is characterized by auto-antibodies that bind to recoverin at specific sites in the retina (46). Another member of the subfamily has been cloned from a rat brain library (34).

CMSE (calcium-modulated protein from *Saccharopolyspora erythraea*) is the only known EF-hand homologue from a prokaryote (60). Its function and origin remain unknown.

TCBP (*Tetrahymena pyriformis* calcium-binding protein) occurs in two isoforms of 23 (207 residues) and 25 (218 residues) kDa (63). Its suggested involvement in ciliary reversal has yet to be confirmed.

CRGP (CAM-related gene product) is encoded by the T+ gene, which contains a transposon-like human repeat element, THE 1 (13). The function of this 79-residue protein is unknown.

INTRONS

Gilbert proposed, with later elaboration (20), that exons encode structural domains and that exon shuffling played a major role in the evolution of contemporary proteins. Introns should define the boundaries of domains and facilitate the exon-duplication and -translocation process. Several genes, for example those encoding low-density lipoprotein (58), conform to this model.

Table 2 summarizes the positions and phases of known EF-hand introns. Some subfamilies exhibit several patterns, e.g. nine within CAM, for which 30 genomic sequences are available. Of 35 different intron sites, within 15 subfamilies, 13 occur between domains and 22 occur within domains. This pattern indicates that exons do not correspond to or define the structural and functional EF-hand domain. Furthermore, it implies that exon shuffling did not play a significant role in the complex process of gene duplication, translocation, and splicing inferred from the branching patterns of Table 1 and from the distribution of EF-hand genes throughout the chromosomes.

CAM of *S. cerevisiae* has only one intron, while CAM of vertebrates has five. The CAM gene(s) in the common ancestor of fungi and animals may have had five introns and lost four in the fungus lineage, or it may have had one and gained four in the animal lineage. Parsimony cannot distinguish which is more likely.

A dendrogram based on whether each site in CAM does or does not have an intron bears little resemblance to the dendrograms based on either protein or DNA sequences. We suggest that introns in the EF-hand family have been inserted and deleted frequently in the course of evolution and that their evolution cannot easily be reconstructed from extant sequences. Although Lee et al (37) worked with a less complete data set and did not distinguish congruent subfamilies, their conclusion still seems valid: " . . . it appears that the majority of the gene members of the EF-hand superfamily have acquired introns independently after the genesis of a four-domain primordial ancestor from the original one-domain progenitor and after the divergence of this multigene family" (p. 189).

CHROMOSOMAL DISTRIBUTIONS

Berchtold (5) summarized the chromosomal assignments of genes encoding EF-hand proteins. Except for S100α, genes within subfamilies are not linked, nor are subfamilies clustered. *H. sapiens* has 27 known loci for members of CAM, ELC, CALP, PARV, S100, and CLBN, and *M. musculus* has 8 loci for ELC, RLC, PARV, and S100. For instance, the three genes encoding the identical CAM sequence are located at 14q24-q31, 2p21.1-p21.3, and 19q13.2-113.3, and the pseudo- and cal-modulin-like genes are at 17, 7pter-p13, 10p13-ter. These data indicate, as pointed out by Berchtold (5), that selective pressure was not present to maintain chromosomal clustering, that chromosomal translocations occurred before these species diverged, and that " . . . evolution of various EF-hand proteins involved numerous gene duplications, trans-locations, assemblies, and other rearrangements" (p. 495).

CALMODULIN CONTRADICTION

Figure 11*a* shows a condensed dendrogram of 23 terminal nodes computed from the sequences of 50 different eDNA sequences. Figure 11*b* shows a condensed dendrogram of 7 nodes based on 29 different protein sequences. There is strong similarity between the dendrograms computed from eDNA and from amino acid sequences for each of TNC, ELC, RLC, CALP, PARV, and S100. Yet the eDNA and protein den-drograms for CAM are significantly different.

The dendrogram based on the first 200 bases 3′ to the termination codons (Figure 11*c*) shows little similarity to either the protein tree or to the eDNA tree. In dendrograms based on the sequences of introns − 10/0 and 4.21/1 (Figures 11*d,e*), as well as on intron position (not shown), TNCs and RLCs are interspersed with CAMs. By contrast, a dendrogram based on the sequences of introns 3 + 01/1 of ELC (Figure 4*c*) is parallel to its protein and eDNA trees.

The similarity of eDNA and protein dendrograms for TNC, ELC, RLC, SARC, PARV, and S100 might reflect the fact that all of the sequences are from animals. The branches in Figure 11*a* that lead to animal CAMs are drawn more heavily. The eDNA dendrogram for animals shows little relation to the species from which the CAMs come. The contradiction cannot be ascribed to paralogy, the inadvertant com-parison of alternate isoforms, because we use the protein sequence encoded by the DNA sequence under investigation. If mRNA or gDNA sequences encoding CAM are subject to special selective forces, we fail to recognize them.

The chordate and echinoderm lineages diverged 600 million years ago. Among animal CAMs, sequences differ by, at most, six residues. The β branch contains CAMs from *Arbacia punctulata, Aplysia californica,* and *D. melanogaster.* The two isoforms from *A. punctulata* are found in the α and the β branches; however, their eDNAs cluster together. The three classes of vertebrate genes (I, II, and III), which encode identical α amino acid sequences, have diverged significantly with as many as 85 differences over the length of 444 (3 × 148) bases.

The inclusion of pseudogenes as eDNA and their deduced protein sequences further complicates the dendrograms but does not alter the relationships described above for protein and eDNA trees. *H. sapiens* and *Gallus* pseudogenes (0) cluster outside all CAM eDNAs. *H. sapiens* pseudogenes 1, 2, and 3 (and *Rattus norvegicus* 1 and 3) cluster near *H. sapiens* and *R. norvegicus* II, implying that II was the source of these three pseudogenes. The deduced amino acid sequences are supposedly subject to no selective pressure and they differ by 7–35 residues from vertebrate CAM.

CONCLUSIONS

The following conclusions can be drawn from these studies:

1. In multidomain proteins, one should identify and classify proteins in terms of their constituent domains. Congruence must be established before entire protein sequences can be compared.
2. The relationships within EF-hand subfamilies are highly significant and help to focus experiments on several structural and functional questions.
3. CAM, TNC, ELC, and RLC are congruent with one another. The four domains of CALP evolved from a single CALP precursor domain; the four domains of SARC evolved from a UR/SARC domain. The CTER/SC dendrogram provides a reference tree for estimating the origins of the domains of the other 25 subfamilies.
4. Several of the subfamilies evolved by complex combinations of gene duplications, translocations, and splicings. This is reflected both in their diverse domain origins and in their chromosomal locations.
5. Even within CTER, and its congruent subfamilies and certainly for the other subfamilies, we cannot recognize a pattern or sequence of subfamily origins. The several subfamilies seem to have radiated from a point. This may reflect turbulent speciation events or more likely multiple mutations whose order we cannot reconstruct.

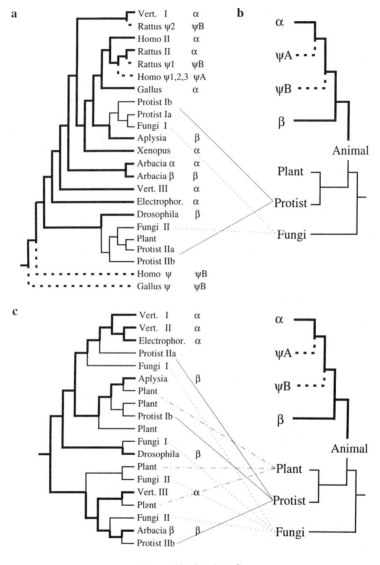

Figure 11 (Continued)

6. Functional and physical properties, such as calcium coordination, vary within subfamlies. We do not recognize a systemic variation of characteristics among subfamilies; homoplasy is rampant.

7. Because many of the subfamilies are represented by multiple isoforms, one must exercise extreme caution in using EF-hand proteins as markers to follow the evolution of species.

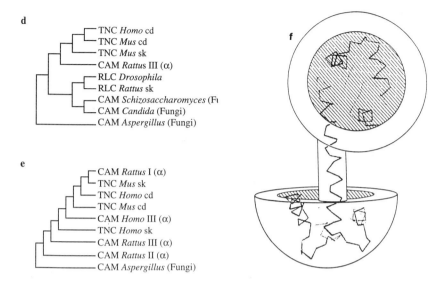

Figure 11   The dendrogram of CAM based on 50 eDNA sequences and simplified to 23 terminal nodes (*a*) is compared with that based on 36 different protein sequences condensed to 7 terminal nodes (*b*). The bold branches lead to animal CAMs. Dashed branches lead to pseudogenes. (*c*) A comparison of the dendrogram based on the 200 bases 3' to the termination codon with that for protein. (*d, e*) Dendrograms based on introns −10/0 and 4.21/1, which are common to the indicated subgroups of CAM, TNC, and RLC (Table 2). (*f*) The α-carbon trace as seen in the crystal.

8. The distributions of introns in the encoding genes refutes the hypothesis that exons correspond to EF-hand domains; exon shuffling did not play a significant role in the evolution of this family.

9. The dendrograms based on encoding DNA are parallel within stochastic fluctuation to those based on protein sequence for TNC, ELC, RLC, CALP, PARV, and S100.

10. The classifications of CAM by protein and by nucleic acid sequences present several intriguing and unresolved contradictions.

NOTE ADDED IN PROOF

Zhao et al (72) sequenced a gene from *P. falciparum* that encodes an inferred protein kinase. The C-terminus contains four EF-hands, all of which probably bind calcium. The origins of all four domains, as judged by both protein and eDNA sequences are deep within the dendrogram. They are not congruent with any other subfamily and comprise the thirty-second subfamily. The DNA that encodes PFPK contains four introns: one between domains 1 and 2 and one each within domains 2, 3, and 4.

ACKNOWLEDGMENTS

The help and advice of Hiroshi Kawasaki has been invaluable, as was the support from NASA NAGW-1233.

Literature Cited

1. Ahmed FR, Rose DR, Evans SV, Pippy ME, To R. 1993. Refinement of recombinant oncomodulin at 1.30 Å resolution. *J. Mol. Biol.* 230:1216–24
2. Ajioka J, Swindle J. 1993. The calmodulin-ubiquitin associated genes of *Trypanosoma cruzi:* their identification and transcription. *Mol. Biochem. Parasitol.* 57:127–36
3. Baba ML, Goodman M, Berger-Cohn J, Demaille JG, Matsuda G. 1984. The early adaptive evolution of calmodulin. *Mol. Biol. Evol.* 1:442–45
4. Baum P, Furlong C, Byers B. 1986. Yeast gene required for spindle pole body duplication: homology of its product with Ca^{2+}-binding proteins. *Proc. Natl. Acad. Sci.* 83:5512–16
5. Berchtold, MW. 1993. Evolution of EF-hand calcium-modulated proteins. V. The genes encoding EF-hand proteins are not clustered in mammalian genomes. *J. Mol. Evol.* 36:489–96
6. Berridge MJ. 1993. Inositol triphosphate and calcium signalling. *Nature* 361:315–25
7. Boyhan A, Casimir CM, French JK, Teahan CG, Segal AW. 1992. Molecular cloning and characterization of grancalcin, a novel EF-hand calcium-binding protein abundant in neutrophils and monocytes. *J. Biol. Chem.* 267:2928–33
8. Brewer JM, Wunderlich JK, Kin D-H, Carr MY, Beach GG. Ragland WL. 1989. Avian thymic hormone (ATH) is a parvalbumin. *Biochem. Biophys. Res. Commun.* 160:1155–61
9. Deleted in proof
10. Chattopadhyaya R, Meador WE, Means AR, Quiocho FA. 1992. Calmodulin structure refined at 1.7 Å resolution. *J. Mol. Biol.* 228:1177–92
11. Collins JH. 1991. Myosin light chains and troponin C: structural and evolutionary relationships revealed by amino acid sequence comparisons. *J. Muscle Res. Cell Motil.* 12:3–25
12. Cox JA. 1990. Calcium vector protein and sarcoplasmic calcium binding proteins from invertebrate muscle. In *Stimulus Response Coupling: The Role of Intracellular Calcium-Binding Proteins,* ed. JR Dedman, VL Smith, pp. 83–107. Boston: CRC Press
13. Deka N, Wong E, Matera AG, Kraft R, Leinwand LA, Schmid CW. 1988. Repetitive nucleotide sequence insertions into a novel calmodulin-related gene and its processed pseudogene. *Gene* 71:123–34
14. Dizhoor AM, Ray S, Kumar S, Niemi G, Spencer M, et al. 1991. Recoverin: a calcium sensitive activator of retinal rod guanylate cyclase. *Science* 251: 915–18
15. Donato R. 1991. Perspectives in S-100 protein biology. *Cell Calcium* 12:713–26
16. Engelman DM, Krause K-H, Blumin JH, Kim KS, Kirchhoff LV, Donelson JE. 1989. A novel flagellar Ca^{2+}-binding protein in trypanosomes. *J. Biol. Chem.* 264:18627–31
17. Flaherty KM, Zozulya S, McKay DB, Stryer L. 1993. Three-dimensional structure of recoverin. A calcium sensor in vision. *Cell* 75:709–16
18. Fox JEB, Taylor RG, Taffarel M, Boyles JK, Goll DE. 1993. Evidence that activation of platelet calpain is induced as a consequence of binding of adhesive ligand to the integrin, glycoprotein IIb-IIIa. *J. Cell Biol.* 120: 1501–7
19. Fyrberg E, Kelly M, Ball E, Fyrberg

C, Reedy MC 1990. Molecular genetics of *Drosophila* alpha-actinin: mutant alleles disrupt Z disc integrity and muscle insertions. *J. Cell Biol.* 110:1999–2011

20. Gilbert W. 1985. Genes-in-pieces revisited. *Science* 228:832–24
21. Gilles J-M, Thomason DB, LeFevre J, Kretsinger RH. 1982. Parvalbumin and muscle relaxation: a computer simulation study. *J. Muscle Res. Cell Motil.* 3:377–98
22. Grabarek Z, Tao T, Gergely J. 1992. Molecular mechanism of troponin-C function. *J. Muscle Res. Cell. Motil.* 13:383–93
23. Hardin PE, Angerer LM, Hardin SH, Angerer RC, Klein WH. 1988. Spec2 genes of *Strongylocentrotus purpuratus*. Structure and differential expression in embryonic aboral ectoderm cells. *J. Mol. Biol.* 202:417–31
24. Harper JF, Binder BM, Sussman MR 1993. Calcium and lipid regulation of an *Arabidopsis* protein kinase expressed in *Escherichia coli*. *Biochemistry* 32:3282–90
25. Head JF 1989. Amino acid sequence of a low molecular weight, high affinity calcium-binding protein from the optic lobe of the squid *Loligo pealei*. *J. Biol. Chem.* 264:7202–9
26. Heidorn DB, Trewhella J. 1988. Comparison of the crystal structure and solution structures of calmodulin and troponin C. *Biochemistry* 27:909–15
27. Herzberg O, James MNG. 1988. Refined crystal structure of troponin C from turkey skeletal muscle at 2.0 Å resolution. *J. Mol. Biol.* 203:761–79
28. Ikura M, Kay LE, Krinks M, Bax A. 1992. A triple resonance multi-dimensional NMR study of calmodulin complexed with the binding domain of skeletal muscle myosin light chain kinase: indication of a conformational change in the central helix. *Science* 256:632–38
29. Ikura M, Spera S, Barbato G, Kay LE, Krinks M, Bax A. 1991. Secondary structure and side-chain ¹H and ¹³C resonance assingment of calmodulin in solution by heteronuclear multi-dimensinal NMR spectroscopy. *Biochemistry* 30:9216–28
30. Kretsinger RH. 1975. Hypothesis: Calcium modulated proteins contain EF hands. In *Calcium Transport in Contraction and Secretion*, ed. E Carafoli, F Clementi, W Drabikowski, A Margreth, pp. 469–78. Amsterdam: North-Holland

31. Kretsinger RH, Nakayama S. 1993. Evolution of EF-hand calcium-modulated proteins. IV. Exon shuffling did not determine the domain compositions of EF-hand proteins. *J. Mol. Evol.* 36:477–88
32. Kretsinger RH, Tolbert D, Nakayama S, Pearson W. 1991. The EF-hand, homologs and analogs. In *Novel Calcium Binding Proteins*, ed. C Heizmann, pp. 17–38. Heidelberg: Springer Verlag
33. Kumar S, Harrylock M, Walsh KA, Cormier MJ, Charbonneau H. 1990. Amino acid sequence of the Ca²⁺-triggered luciferin binding protein of *Renilla reniformis*. *FEBS Lett.* 268:287–90
34. Kuno T, Kajimoto Y, Hashimoto T, Mukai H, Shirai Y, et al. 1992. cDNA cloning of neural visinin-like Ca²⁺-binding protein. *Biochem. Biophys. Res. Commun.* 180:1219–25
35. Kuno T, Tanaka H, Mukai H, Chang C-D, Hiraga K, et al. 1991. cDNA cloning of a calcineurin B homolog in *Saccharomyces cerevisiae*. *Biochem. Biophys. Res. Commun.* 180:1159–63
36. Laroche A, Lemieux G, Pallotta D. 1989. The nucleotide sequence of a developmentally regulated cDNA from *Physarum polycephalum*. *Nucleic Acids Res.* 17:10502
37. Lee VD, Stapleton M, Huang B. 1991. Genomic structure of *Chlamydomonas* caltractin. Evidence for intron insertion suggests a probable genealogy for the EF-hand superfamily of proteins. *J. Mol. Biol.* 221:175–91
38. Lefort A, Lecocq R, Libert F, Lamy F, Swillens S, et al. 1989. Cloning and sequencing of a calcium-binding protein regulated by cyclic AMP in the thyroid. *EMBO J.* 8:111–16
39. McPhalen CA, Sielecki AR, Santarsiero BD, James MNG. 1994. Refined X-ray structure of rat parvalbumin, a mammalian α-lineage parvalbumnin, at 2.0 Å resolution. *J. Mol. Biol.* 235: In
40. Meador WE, Means FA, Quiocho FA. 1992. Target enzyme recognition by calmodulin: 2.9 Å structure of calmodulin-peptide complex. *Science* 257:1251–55
41. Moncrief ND, Goodman M, Kretsinger RH. 1990. Evolution of EF-hand calcium modulated proteins. I. Relationships based on amino acid sequences. *J. Mol. Evol.* 30:522–62
42. Nakayama S, Kretsinger RH. 1993. Evolution of EF-hand calcium-modulated proteins. III. Exon sequences

confirm most dendrograms based on protein sequences: calmodulin dendrograms show significant lack of parallelism. *J. Mol. Evol.* 36:458–76

43. Nakayama S, Moncrief ND, Kretsinger RH. 1992. Evolution of EF-hand calcium modulated proteins. II. Domains of several subfamilies have diverse evolutionary histories. *J. Mol. Evol.* 34:416–48

44. Parmentier M, Lefort A. 1991. Structure of the human brain calcium-binding protein calretinin and its expression in bacteria. *Eur. J. Biochem.* 196:79–85

45. Persechini A, Kretsinger RH. 1988. The central helix of calmodulin functions as a flexible tether. *J. Biol. Chem.* 263:12175–78

46. Polans AS, Buczyłko J, Crabb J, Palczewski K. 1991. A photoreceptor calcium binding protein is recognized by autoantibodies obtained from patients with cancer-associated retinopathy. *J. Cell Biol.* 112:981–89

47. Rao ST, Wu S, Satyshur KA, Ling K-Y, Kung C, Sundaralingam M. 1993. Structure of *Paramecium tetraurelia* calmodulin at 1.8 Å resolution. *Protein Struct.* 2:436–47

48. Rawlings DJ, Kaslow DC. 1992. A novel 40-kDa membrane-associated EF-hand calcium-binding protein in *Plasmodium falciparum. J. Biol. Chem.* 267:3976–82

49. Rayment I, Rypniewski WR, Schmidt-Bäse K, Smith R, Tomchick DR, et al. 1993. Three-dimensional structure of myosin subfragment-1: a molecular motor. *Science* 261:50–57

50. Roquet F, Declerq J-P, Tinant B, Rambaud J, Parello J. 1992. Crystal structure of the unique parvalbumin component from muscle of the leopard shark (*Triakis semifasciata*). The first X-ray study of an α-parvalbumin. *J. Mol. Biol.* 223:705–20

51. Saito K-I, Elce JS, Hamos JE, Nixon RA. 1993. Widespread activation of calcium-activated neutral proteinase (calpain) in the brain in Alzheimer disease: a potential molecular basis for neuronal degeneration. *Proc. Natl. Acad. Sci. USA* 90:2628–32

52. Salvato M, Sulston J, Albertson D, Brenner S. 1986. A novel calmodulin-like gene from the nematode *Caenorhabditis elegans. J. Mol. Biol.* 190:281–90

53. Satyshur KA, Pyzalska D, Greaser M, Sundaralingam M. 1993. Structure of chicken skeletal muscle troponin-C at 1.78 Å resolution. *Acta Crystallogr. D.* In press

54. Schaap D, de Widt J, van der Wal J, Vandekerckhove J, van Damme J, et al. 1990. Purification, cDNA-cloning and expression of human diacylglycerol kinase. *FEBS Lett.* 275:151–58

55. Schaller GE, Harmon AC, Sussman MR. 1992. Characterization of calcium- and lipid-dependent protein kinase associated with the plasma membrane of oat. *Biochemistry* 31:1721–27

56. Scheibel LW. 1992. Role of calcium/calmodulin-mediated processes in protozoa. *Int. Rev. Cytosol.* 134:165–242

57. Steele FR, Washburn T, Rieger R, O'Tousa JE. 1992. Drosophila retinal degeneration C (rdgC) encodes a novel serine/threonine protein phosphatase. *Cell* 749:669–76

58. Südhof TC, Goldstein JL, Brown MS, Russell DW. 1985. The LDL receptor gene: a mosaic of exons shared with different proteins. *Science* 228:815–22

59. Swairjo MA, Seaton D. 1994. Annexin structure and membrane interactions: a molecular perspective. *Annu. Rev. Biophys. Biomol. Struct.* 23:193–213

60. Swan D, Cortes J, Hale RS, Leadley PF. 1989. Cloning, characterization and heterologous expression of the *Saccharopolyspora eythraea* (*Streptomyces erythraeus*) gene encoding an EF-hand calcium-binding protein. *J. Bacteriol.* 171:5614–19

61. Szebenyi DME, Moffat K. 1986. The refined structure of vitamin D-dependent calcium-binding protein from bovine intestine. Molecular details, ion binding, and implications for the structure of other calcium-binding proteins. *J. Biol. Chem.* 261:8761–77

62. Taillon BE, Adler SA, Suhan JP, Jarvik, JW. 1991. Mutational analysis of centrin: an EF-hand protein associated with three distinct contractile fibers in the basal body apparatus of *Chlamydomonas. J. Cell Biol.* 119:1613–24

63. Takemasa T, Takagi T, Kobayashi T, Konishi K, Watanabe, Y. 1990. The third calmodulin family protein in *Tetrahymena*. Cloning of the cDNA for *Tetrahymena* calcium-binding protein of 23 kDa (TCBP-23). *J. Biol. Chem.* 265:2514–17

64. Taylor DA, Sack JS, Maune JF, Beckingham K, Quiocho FA. 1991. Structure of a recombinant calmodulin from *Drosophila melanogaster* refined at 2.2-Å resolution. *J. Biol. Chem.* 266(191):21375–80

65. Vijay-Kumar S, Cook WJ. 1992.

Structure of a sarcoplasmic calcium-binding protein from *Nereis diversicolor* refined at 2.0 Å resolution. *J. Mol. Biol.* 224:413–26

66. Williams RJ. 1992. Calcium and calmodulin. *Cell Calcium* 13:355–62

67. Winningham Major F, Staecker JL, Barger SW, Coats S, Van Eldik LJ. 1989. Neurite extension and neuronal survival activities of recombinant S100 beta proteins that differ in the content and position of cysteine residues. *J. Cell. Biol.* 109:3063–71

68. Wnuk W, Schoechlin M, Kobayashi T, Takagi T, Konishi K, et al. 1986. Two isoforms of troponin C from crayfish. their characterization and a comparison of their primary structure with the tertiary structure of skeletal troponin C. *J. Muscle Res. Cell Motil.* 7:67–68

69. Wong S, Morales TH, Neigel JE, Campbell DA. 1993. Genomic and transcriptional linkage of the genes for calmodulin, EF-hand 5 protein, and ubiquitin extension protein 52 in *Trypanosoma brucei. Mol. Cell. Biol.* 13:207–16

70. Xiang M, Ge T, Tomlinson CR, Klein WH. 1991. Structure and promoter activity of the LpS1 genes of *Lytechinus pictus. J. Biol. Chem.* 266:10524–33

71. Xie X, Harrison D, Schlichting I, Sweet R, Kalabokis VN, et al. 1994. Structure of the regulatory domain of scallop myosin at 2.8 Å resolution. *Nature.* In press

72. Zhao Y, Kappes B, Franklin RM. 1993. Gene structure and expression of an unusual protein kinase from Plasmodium falciparum homologous at its carboxyl terminus with the EF hand calcium-binding proteins. *J. Biol. Chem.* 286:4347–54

Annu. Rev. Biophys. Biomol. Struct. 1994. 23:509–39

THE BACTERIAL FLAGELLAR MOTOR

Stephan C. Schuster

Division of Biology, California Institute of Technology, Pasadena, California 91125

Shahid Khan

Department of Physiology and Biophysics, Albert Einstein College of Medicine, Bronx, New York 10461

KEY WORDS: molecular motor, chemiosmotic device, bioenergetics, macromolecular assembly

CONTENTS

1056–8700/94/0610–0509$05.00

PROLOGUE

It has been known for some time that bacterial flagella are powered by remarkable rotary motors and that flagellar rotation is energized by transmembrane-proton, or sodium, electrochemical gradients rather than ATP (7). Recently, a combined assault of genetic, biochemical, and biophysical approaches has laid the groundwork for elaboration of the molecular mechanism: (a) A set of proteins, defects in which abolish motor function, has been identified and their interactions are being characterized. (b) New structural components of flagellar bases that are likely to harbor the motor machinery have been visualized. (c) The steady-state relations between the electrochemical potentials, motor torque, and velocity have been determined in detail sufficient to constrain construction of explicit molecular models. This chapter reviews the current understanding of the operation of the bacterial flagellar motor in the light of emerging principles underlying motile phenomena and their regulation. General reviews on bacterial motility have been published (37, 41, 62). Caplan & Kari-Ivanov (18) have written a review on the flagellar motor, focused on analysis of motor models.

OPERATIONAL CHARACTERISTICS

All bacterial flagella studied thus far rotate (81) (Figure 1). Viscous, rather than inertial forces, dominate flagellar rotation (4). Biophysicists take special interest in studies of flagellar rotation because, as often noted (e.g. 18), these experiments monitor the action of a small ensemble of force-generating units. The number of force-generating units is approximately 10 per motor, as indicated by stepwise resurrection of rotation of tethered, nonmotile mutant bacteria (9). Spontaneous fluctuations in the rotation speed of both individual filaments and tethered cells have been analyzed (24, 49, 53).

Bacterial flagellar motors are energized by transmembrane electrochemical ion gradients, not ATP (58). Energy balance requires downhill transport of at least 1000 protons per revolution for the ~10 Hz rotation of metabolizing, tethered *Escherichia coli*. This number is a small fraction of the total steady-state proton circulation in metabolizing bacteria (4). Quantitative studies in intact bacteria of the relationship between electrochemical potentials and rotation speed have relied on measurements, based on radiolabeled cations and weak-acid uptake, of potentials in metabolizing bacteria (see 41).

Alternatively, in certain bacteria motility can be artificially energized. Artificial energization involves deenergization by starvation or

Tethered cell (10–20Hz)   Bead on polyhooks (170Hz)

Flagellar bundle rotation (60–270Hz)   Filament rotation (200Hz)

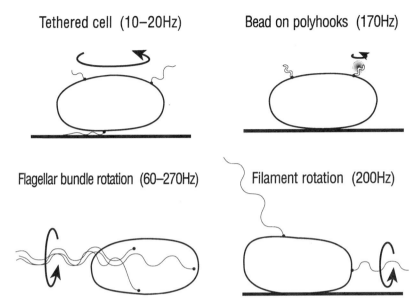

Figure 1   How flagellar rotation is measured. (*a*) Tethered cell. Tethered *Escherichia coli* typically spin at ~10–20 Hz. Using rotating electric fields, rotation can be increased up to 600 Hz or reversed up to -200 Hz. Tethered cell torque is between 10^{-17} and 10^{-18} Nm (36). (*b*) Bead on polyhook. Rotations of up to 170 Hz of antibody-coated beads on polyhooks or flagellar stubs, imaged via pinhole onto photomultiplier, have been measured (8). (*c*) Flagellar bundle rotation. Rotation of *E. coli* flagellar bundles, evident as a high-frequency jitter in photomultiplier readouts of swimming cell tracks, was measured at ~270 Hz at 32°C. *Streptococcus* spp. flagellar bundle rotation varied between 120 and 60 Hz because of changes in the viscosity of the medium (61). (*d*) Filament rotation. Single filaments imaged onto photomultipliers using laser dark-field microscopy, a technique that avoids illumination of the cell body, have been observed to rotate at ~170 Hz when anaerobically energized (53).

respiratory poisons, followed by imposition of known electrical or pH gradients that are maintained long enough to allow motility measurements. Such measurements have shown that the rotation sense changes direction upon reversal of the energizing ion gradient. The flagellar motor's rotation speed varies linearly with the driving potential and with hydrodynamic drag over a large range.

In addition, preparations of *E. coli* and *Salmonella typhimurium* cell envelopes that lack the cytoplasm but have functional flagella (23) have been valuable for defining requirements for flagellar rotation and switching and for dissecting the effects of pharmacological manipulations.

Flagellar motors of most bacteria are bidirectional and switch at random between periods of clockwise or counterclockwise rotation. *E. coli* flagellar motors do so about once per second (82). Pauses in motion have also been observed for *E. coli* and *S. typhimurium* flagella. Individual flagellar filaments can often switch rotation sense without producing detectible changes in rotation speed (4) and independently of other filaments on the same cell (63). Counterclockwise-rotating flagella can bundle together to propel the cell. The flagellar bundle flies apart and the cells tumble when a sufficient number of flagella pause or switch to clockwise rotation, which initiates polymorphic transitions of filament waveform (64).

Linear Phenomenological Relations

Early work on artificially energized, tethered streptococci uncovered a remarkably linear relationship between tethered-cell rotation speed and the energizing potential (43). Investigators have also discovered linear relationships between tethered *E. coli* cell-envelope rotation and proton potential (71) and between sodium-powered alkaliphilic *Bacillus firmus* swimming-cell speed and sodium potential (33). These relationships have been taken to imply that the motor operates close to thermodynamic equilibrium (18). If so, studies in this regime should have limited value for identifying the mechanistic processes limiting rotation.

More recent studies have examined threshold and saturation effects of the speed-potential relation. Artificially energized, tethered streptococci decreased speed as a linear function of potential upon shift-down to lower potentials, but increased speed nonlinearly upon shift-up (Figure 2). The linear plots extrapolated back to the origin, indicating absence of a threshold. The hysteresis implied that the nonlinearity evident during shift-up resulted from rotation barriers that dissipated upon rapid rotation. Swimming cells have a distinct threshold, but this is probably because rotation of more than one flagellum is required to enable peritrichously flagellated bacteria such as *E. coli* to swim.

Flagellar rotation does saturate as a function of proton potential. Saturation speed depends upon internal pH but is independent of whether the proton potential is applied as a chemical or electrical potential. In recent experiments, a minimal kinetic scheme accounted for the saturation behavior in terms of proton-binding site pK effects, implying that the pH dependence dominantly reflects the proton transfer chemistry (44). Given that the permeability of the energizing protons is determined by interaction with a localized region, analogous to other membrane channel–ion-pore interactions, simulated fits to the data

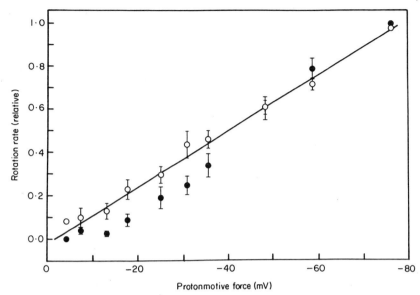

Figure 2   Tethered cell rotation dependence on rotation. Tethered streptococci, when artificially energized by a potassium-diffusion potential, will rotate for many minutes, allowing measurements of single-cell rotation at different potential values obtained by flow-cell exchange of buffers with varying potassium concentration. The aggregate behavior of 10 cells subjected to successive increments (*closed circles*), then decrements (*open circles*), of the proton potential, is shown. Bars denote standard errors. Taken from Ref. 49 with permission.

indicated that such a region was located on the cytoplasmic side of the transmembrane electrical field. The saturation speed of motor-ion dissociation reactions was decreased by substituting deuterons for protons to power streptococci (61) or *E. coli* (10) or by substituting lithium for sodium to power *Vibrio alginolyticus* (60). Hence, these reactions partially limited unloaded flagellar rotation. Such manipulations did not affect flagellar rotation at high loads.

Several laboratories are conducting on-going studies of the relation between torque and rotational velocity. The data on hand indicate that torque varies linearly with velocity over a large range (36, 61). Tethered cell rotation and rotation of flagellar bundles in swimming cells represent the high-load and unloaded extremes of this range, respectively; internal friction is considered negligible (7). A number of papers have been recently published that utilize rotating electric fields to spin tethered cells in both the negative and positive directions. At low frequency rotation, cells were entrained to the field. A linear relation between torque and rotation speed was evident between the −20 to 50 Hz regime, which could be investigated using this method (Figure 3). An elegant methodology (6a) was developed to spin cells up to 600 Hz upon high-frequency (0.50 to 2.25 MHz) rotation of the electric field. The cells spin owing to induction of charged dipoles in both the cell and surrounding medium that are slightly out of phase with the electric field. A region of constant torque at low speeds followed by a linear decrease was obtained in such measurements. Furthermore, sharp resistance was encountered when cells were spun backwards. High torques could overwhelm this resistance, but this resulted in irreversible damage, as evidenced by failure of the cells to spin under their own power. Reasons for the different results obtained using the two measurements are not presently clear.

Only one study of the proton flux through the flagellar motor has been published (67). Flagellar antibody was used to block flagellar rotation by agglutinating flagellar bundles of artificially energized swimming streptococci, and the resulting decrease in the inward proton flux correlated with swimming speed. The flux remained proportional to rotation speed upon changing either proton potential or viscosity of the media. This proportionality was consistent with near-to-equilibrium operation of the flagellar motor.

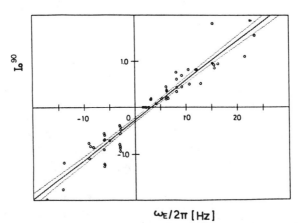

$\omega_E/2\pi$ [Hz]

Figure 3 Rotating electric field measurements of torque-frequency relationships in tethered *E. coli*. The magnitude of the electric field was proportional to the current applied to the experimental chamber. Below a certain threshold current, synchronization between electric field and tethered cell rotation was broken and the cell reverted to its natural frequency. Variation of threshold current (Io^{90}) with electric field rotation frequency ($E/2$). Torque is expected to be a linear function of both parameters. Sixty three data points from eleven cells (~2 Hz natural rotation frequency) are shown. Taken from Ref. 36 with permission.

Reversibility is another criterion of close-to-equilibrium operation. In artificially energized streptococci, pH shifts of either sign produced transient rotation of the bacteria (7). A subsequent study using a mutant strain incapable of pH taxis showed that reversal of the sign of the imposed gradient reversed rotation sense (43). Such measurements imply that mechanical rotation of flagellar filaments should lead to efflux or influx of protons even though this has not been demonstrated directly. In apparent contrast, outwardly directed pH shifts did not elicit rotation of tethered *E. coli* cell envelopes (71). As noted elsewhere (see Figure 10 of 44), asymmetry of proton flux and, hence, flagellar rotation can arise because of pK differences in residues comprising the proton transport pathway of the flagellar motor.

Bidirectionality

Tethered *E. coli* and *S. typhimurium* switch rotation sense rapidly (~1 ms) without detectible changes in rotation speed (7). Recently, persuasive evidence that pausing intervals also occur has been obtained from video analysis of the rotation of tethered cells, bead-decorated flagellar filaments, the counter-rotation of cells with flagella linked together by bivalent antibodies (24), and direct, laser dark-field based measurements of single-filament rotation (53). Examination of non-chemotactic mutants established a tight correlation between switching and pausing, implying that pausing was a result of futile switching events. Kuo & Koshland (54) also used computer-assisted video analysis of tethered *E. coli* to examine motor-switching kinetics. Their dwell-time histograms for wild-type bacteria deviated from the single-exponential distributions reported earlier (15), but they did not discuss reasons for the discrepancy.

Several factors involved in altering motor clockwise-counterclockwise rotation bias have been identified. Control of motor switching by the chemotaxis machinery has, understandably, been studied the most extensively. The chemotaxis protein, CheY, is the component thought to interact most directly with flagellar motors for the following reasons: (*a*) Mutant bacteria gutted for all Che proteins rotate only counterclockwise. They rotate clockwise only upon plasmid-based expression of CheY, but not other Che (i.e chemotaxis) protein components (96). (*b*) Incorporation of CheY in cell-envelope preparations restores clockwise rotation (72). Extensive in vitro biochemistry and analysis of chemotaxis mutants have established that phosphorylation of CheY protein is correlated with its ability to restore clockwise rotation of flagellar motors (16). The CheY concentration dependence of motor clockwise-counterclockwise rotation bias was determined using whole cell immunoblots. In contrast to wild-type bacteria, single exponential dwell-time histograms were obtained when CheY was overexpressed in a gutted strain. However, the duration of both clockwise and counter-clockwise rotation intervals depended upon CheY concentration, ruling out switch models in which only two kinetic states were postulated, one for each rotational direction (15, 48). An apparent Hill coefficient of 5.5 indicated cooperativity of CheY-motor interactions. Because CheY and not the phosphorylated species was used, the cooperativity could not be interpreted simply as binding of multiple CheY molecules to the flagellar switch (54). Cell-envelope data have suggested that factors in addition to CheY phosphorylation may be required for clockwise flagellar rotation (2). Factors that have been shown to affect motor clockwise/counterclockwise rotation bias directly or indirectly through interaction with chemotaxis signaling components are small metabolites (i.e acetate) (3), ions (i.e calcium) (88), and the proton potential itself (48).

Speed Fluctuations

Flagella rotate smoothly at constant speed for many minutes, allowing study of both spontaneous and forced speed changes. The rms (root mean square) variation in photomultiplier-based measurements of rotation speeds of both tethered cells (7) and flagellar filaments (53) of mutant strains that rotate only counterclockwise is small. The larger variation (~30%) in the frame-by-frame displacement of videoimages of tethered wild-type *E. coli* has been ascribed to pausing events (24).

While fully energized, tethered bacteria rotate smoothly, and de-energized bacteria frequently lock up (7). Therefore, period-by-period variation in cell rotation was studied as a function of energy level by artificially energizing a counterclockwise-only-rotating mutant of a motile *Streptococcus* strain. In the regime where proton-motive force and rotation speed shared a linear relation (i.e > −35 mV), the cells exhibited unhindered Brownian drift. In the hysteresis regime below −35 mV, the bacteria paused at periodic angular positions (49). Thus, barriers to flagellar rotation do not influence running torque above proton potential energies of $\sim 1.5kT$.

During tethered cell rotation, flagellar motors operate at high load (67) and tethered cell running torque should be proportional to the number of force generators. This number was estimated by analyzing the ressurrection of rotation of tethered, nonmotile *E. coli* cells, using plasmid based overexpression to complement defective or absent motor proteins (Figure 4). This study noted that the erroneous estimate reported earlier (13) resulted from frequent hesitations of the single

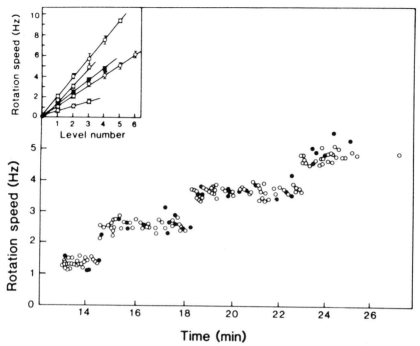

Figure 4   Stepwise resurrection of flagellar motors. Plasmids containing the wild-type *motA* gene linked to the *lac* promoter were transduced in an *E. coli* MotA mutant strain. Cells were tethered in a flow cell and expression of the MotA protein induced by a flow of isopropyl thiogalactoside (IPTG). The transitions in rotation speed observed in one tethered cell that started to rotate upon IPTG induction are shown. (*Inset*) Constant speed increments between levels were observed, as demonstrated by the linear plots of the mean values at discrete rotation speed levels for this cell (*filled circles*) and four other cells (*open circles*). Filled and open circles denote clockwise and counterclockwise intervals, respectively. Taken from Ref. 9 with permission.

ressurrected cell whose maximal and initial speeds were compared. However, a systematic study of fluctuations at the lowest versus higher speeds was not made.

Methods for jumping external pH and potential have been developed based on utilization of caged compounds and patch electrodes. pH jumps produced by photorelease of caged protons sped up rotating tethered cells within 15 ms (80). Starting up locked deenergized cells upon caged proton photorelease took substantially longer (~100 ms) (49). The locked motor may reflect a rigor state of the force-generating units. Electrical potential jumps were produced by patch pipette–induced hyperpolarization of whole bacteria. Upon hyperpolarization, flagellar filaments increased rotation speed within 5 ms (39). A large leakage current was unavoidable in these measurements because of the porous outer wall, and this leakage prevented quantitative analysis. Given an unloaded rotation speed of ~200 Hz (Figure 1), ~10 independently acting force generators (Figure 4), and at least 1000 protons per revolution (67), one can estimate a minimum transit time per proton per force generator of <0.1 ms. Therefore, speed-up times probably reflect the temporal resolution of the experimental protocols rather than the rate of the reactions limiting cycle time.

One should remember that the rotating cell or filament can interact with the antibody-coated glass surface, and the filament tether or stuck cells, which are assumed to be stationary in fluctuation measurements, can shift position. Single filaments and bead-coated polyhooks are the smallest structures that have been directly observed to rotate. Damping out of high-frequency fluctuations by the flexible hook [a 130-subunit polymer of hook protein (62)] coupling the rigid filament to the cell wall is significant even for unloaded filament rotation (14) and is much more severe for tethered cells, limiting prospects of utilizing speed fluctuations for dissection of the unusually fast mechanochemical cycle (< 0.1 ms) of flagellar motors.

MACROMOLECULAR ARCHITECTURE

Motor Proteins

The phrase *bacterial flagellar motor* refers to an as yet structurally ill-defined entity at the base of the bacterial flagellum responsible for flagellar rotation. As such, it includes machinery for transporting the energizing ions through the cytoplasmic membrane; for bidirectional force generation, including both rotor and stator parts; and for switching. By comparison, the term *molecular motor* has evolved on the basis of genetic and in vitro motility assays to denote the minimal fragment capable of producing movement along a static track (89, 93). Thus, gene-sequence analysis together with in vitro motility assays have defined, for example, a common motor domain of about 350 amino acids for the kinesin superfamily, capable of both ATP hydrolysis and microtubule binding.

The genetics of *E. coli* and *S. typhimurium* motility have been instrumental in the identification of flagellar motor parts. Of particular interest are *mot* mutant strains that can assemble, but not rotate, their flagella. The analysis of bacterial motility mirrors the development of bacterial genetics. The first *S. typhimurium mot* mutants were isolated in the 1950s (86); the 1960s and early 1970s saw systematic screening and complementation of motility mutants, followed by cloning, over-expression, and purification of the relevant proteins (62). Remarkably, despite the large number of genes (~40) required for assembly of the flagellum, defects in only five proteins are known (MotA, MotB, FliG, FliM, and FliN) to give rise to the Mot phenotype. Of these defects, only *motA* and/or *motB* deletions still allow assembly of the flagellum. The three Fli proteins were suggested to form a structural complex, the so-called switch complex, based on supressor mutation analysis (97). CheY and CheZ (for reviews, see 17, 32, 85), which are thought to control motor switching by transient interaction with the switch proteins, complete this short list of motor components.

Genes coding for all these proteins have been cloned and sequenced. Antibodies have been generated against the purified proteins and used to estimate copy numbers in wild-type bacteria and to localize the proteins to cellular fractions and flagellar basal structures (Table 1). Finally, one should remember that active involvement of other flagellar basal structural proteins in energization and switching of flagellar rotation cannot be ruled out, even though *mot* mutants have not been isolated in these proteins thus far.

Table 1 Motor proteins[a]

Protein	Mol wt (kDa)	Copies		Location	
		Cell	Motor	Cell	Motor
MotA	31	600	~11	Membrane	IMP ring
MotB	37	120	11 or 22	Membrane	IMP ring
FliG	37	3700	~27	Cytoplasm	Outer MS ring
FliM	38	?	<100	Cytoplasm	C ring
FliN	16	?	<100	Cytoplasm	C ring
CheY	14	12,000	?	Cytoplasm	?
CheZ	24	24,000	?	Cytoplasm	?

[a] Cloning, overexpression and cell fractionation experiments have provided estimates of cellular concentration and location (50, 65, 74, 84, 95). Fli proteins have been localized to the flagellar basal body using immunoelectron microscopy (28). The isolation of motile fusion mutants indicates that both FliF-FliG and FliM-FliN are paired in a 1:1 stoichiometry (27), implying 27 FliG copies per motor match the number of FliF copies (38). The C ring, if comprised entirely of FliM and FliN, would contain ~100 copies of each. The flagellar intramembrane ring particles visualized with freeze-fraction electron microscopy, if comprised of MotA-MotB as commonly supposed, contain one MotA per particle, as particle and MotA transmembrane domain widths are comparable. Interactions of CheY and CheZ with the intact motor, if any, have not been determined. Estimates of total cellular protein imply a substantial cellular pool of MotA and FliG, but not MotB.

MotA and MotB

MotA-MotB complexes presumably form the proton channels and torque generators of the motor (6). The *motA* and *motB* genes, which are adjacent in the *mocha* operon, both code for integral membrane proteins (62). DNA sequence analysis and proteolyic digestion studies indicate that MotA has four transmembrane-spanning helices (11). Alkaline phosphatase fusions have shown that MotB has a single membrane-spanning helical region with a large, periplasmically located, C-terminal domain that could serve as anchor to the cell wall (20). The idea that MotA conducts protons rests on the fact that coexpression of MotA with a MotB fragment impairs cell growth by increasing the leakiness of the cytoplasmic membrane to protons, as established by proton uptake measurements on *E. coli* membrane vesicles. Coexpression of mutant MotA alleles that abolish motility, together with the MotB fragment, does not impair cell growth (10). In addition, overexpression of MotA alone or MotB alone, or both together, does not impair cell motility or growth, even at 50-fold greater levels of overexpression (86). Hence, MotA alone, or complexed with full-length MotB, probably does not conduct protons in the absence of other motor components.

Mutant analysis provides a potent approach for linking protein structure and function. This approach has been applied extensively to the Mot proteins. A priori, impairment or loss of motility could result from defective binding of the mutant proteins to motor components or defective proton transfer or force generation. Dominant mutant proteins that impaired motility of wild-type bacteria, presumably by displacing wild-type proteins from the motor apparatus, were isolated in both MotA and MotB (10–12). Nonfunctional dominant mutations clustered in the transmembrane domain of MotA but were also found in both periplasmic and transmembrane segments of MotB. Dominant alleles could not be isolated in a truncated MotB lacking the 17 C-terminal amino acids, implying that this segment mediated MotB binding to the motor (86). Slow-swimming alleles were also isolated. Slow-swimming MotA mutants retained running torque in the tethered-cell assay. Thus, the MotA mutations affected processes limiting rotation speed, but not the number or efficiency of the force-generating units.

Analysis of speed fluctuations indicated that the number of force-generating units was reduced in MotB slow-swimming alleles. Deuterium isotope–effect data suggested that proton transfers might be the rate-limiting reactions affected by the MotA mutations (10). The mutations mapped to the cytoplasmic domain of MotA (11), in agreement with physiological data that the reactions limiting transport occur after the protons have crossed the profile of the transmembrane electric field (44). Alternatively, however, slow swimming might result from tighter binding of the dominant mutant alleles to rotor components; here, deuterium-hydrogen exchange in the cytoplasmic domain would simply affect MotA conformation. The contention that nonfunctional, dominant MotA alleles implicate residues involved in proton transport (11) also presents problems. Loss of pore-forming function is suggested by the fact that strains expressing the mutant MotA proteins do not show the impaired growth that characterizes strains expressing the wild-type MotA together with the MotB fragment. However, interactions of MotA with the MotB fragment coexpressed in these studies may not reflect its interactions with full-length MotB. High-resolution structure and transient-state kinetic measurements were neccessary for characterization of bacteriorhodopsin proton-transfer mutants (52), and unambigous evaluation of mutant phenotypes in the absence of such information is difficult.

FliG, FliM, and FliN

These proteins are required for energization, switching, and assembly of the flagellum. Cell fractionation and electron microscopy of switch-protein overproducers have shown that the proteins are in the cytosol and do not form structural aggregations (65, 74; SC Schuster, unpublished data). FliG is adjacent to FliF in one operon, while FliM and FliN are adjacent in another operon. Hydrophobic, transmembrane-spanning segments are absent in the deduced protein sequences, and three-residue mixed-charge clusters characterize the FliG sequence (50). FliG and FliM sequences isolated from various species are strongly homologous among themselves compared with Mot protein sequences. All are relatively weakly conserved (62).

Spontaneously generated or genetically engineered fusion proteins represent an elegant approach for investigating switch protein interactions. Sequencing of mutant alleles revealed two mutant strains carrying FliF-FliG fusions that were nevertheless motile. For one of these fusions, about a third of the *fliG* gene was truncated, indicating that this portion was not required for motility (27). More recently, motile clockwise-biased strains carrying FliM-FliN fusions have been constructed (R Macnab, personal communication). These findings imply that if these proteins form a structural complex as suggested by genetic-supressor mutation data, then FliF and FliG, and analogously FliM and FliN, complex to each other in a 1:1 stoichiometry.

The interactions of the chemotaxis protein, CheY, with the switch proteins have been studied through both genetic supression analysis and biochemical assays. The atomic structure of CheY, a single-domain protein that is structurally homologous to H-Ras, is known to 1.7-Å resolution (84). CheY is phosphorylated at Asp57 in vitro by CheA or by small-molecule phosphate donors (32). CheY is also acetylated, at Lys109, even though a physiological role for the latter covalent modification remains to be established. Mutations that abolish CheY phosphorylation produce smooth-swimming bacteria. Supressor CheY mutations against FliG and FliM map to helical loop regions on the CheY protein that are some distance away from the phosphorylation site (75). NMR studies are beginning to define the substantial conformational changes that accompany phosphorylation of CheY protein (17). Numerous FliG, FliM, and FliN *mot* and CheY/CheZ suppressor *che* mutants have been sequenced. FliN contains many *mot* mutations, which suggests that it may play an important role in force generation. Meanwhile, *che* mutations predominate in FliM. However, the *che* suppressor mutations are not allele specific (35, 83).

Recently, CheY–switch protein binding was studied in vitro. The switch proteins were overexpressed, specifically labeled with ^{14}C-leucine, purified, and isolated by sonication rather than detergent solubilization. FliM was found to bind specifically to Sepharose beads carrying CheY—such binding depends upon the phosphorylation level of CheY and is unaffected by the other two switch proteins (94). The biochemical data are not in agreement with genetic reversion analyses showing that mutations on the motor face of CheY suppress both FliG and FliM mutations and vice versa. Nevertheless, these studies provide the first evidence that CheY may switch the direction of flagellar rotation by directly binding to the motor.

CheZ catalyzes dephosporylation of CheY in vitro (16, 85). Switch-protein mutant alleles that suppress CheZ mutations have also been isolated, but whether this suppression reflects direct physical interaction is uncertain because of the lack of allele specificity. CheZ probably does not bind to the motor in the absence of CheY, because overexpression of CheZ in the absence of CheY does not affect rotation bias (54 and references therein).

Motor Structure

The base of the bacterial flagellum is embedded in the cytoplasmic membrane. Because transmembrane electrochemical gradients provide the fuel for flagellar rotation, the flagellar motor machinery must form part of the membrane-embedded flagellar base.

Current understanding of *E. coli/S. typhimurium* flagellar basal structure is schematized in Figure 5. It has been known for some time that the flagellar filament is contiguous basally with two distinct segments, a thicker hook segment followed by a thinner rod segment. The rod is encircled by L and P ring structures as it passes through the outer membrane and terminates in the MS-ring complex. The hook, the rod, and the L, P, and MS rings are collectively referred to as the hook basal-body (HBB) complex.

Recent work (90) has shown that the entire MS ring and proximal rod of the HBB complex is comprised of FliF, a 65-kDa protein. This rules out ideas that torque might be generated by rotation of the M ring relative to the S ring. Estimates of copy numbers for FliF and other HBB polypeptides have come from gel autoradiography (38) and scanning transmission electron microscopy analysis (84); FliF is present in approximately 27 copies per flagellum. Neither *mot* nor *che* alleles have been isolated thus far in genes coding for BBB polypeptides. Thus, the role, if any, of the HBB structure in the switching or energization of flagellar rotation cannot be evaluated.

It has been recently established that two additional structural modules comprise the flagellar base. These modules are the focus of current structural research on the flagellar motor, since analysis of motor mutants and labeling with antibodies prepared against cloned gene products has indicated that these structures are comprised, at least partially, of the known motor proteins: MotA, MotB, FliG, FliM, and FliN. As Figure 5 shows, these structures consist of, first, rings of intramembrane particles encircling the flagellar rod, absent in *motA-motB* deletion mutants (45) and, second, structures contiguous with the cytoplasmic face of the MS ring of the HBB complex, which are absent in *mot* alleles of FliG, FliM, and FliN (46) and shown by antibody-labeling experiments to contain all three proteins (28).

INTRAMEMBRANE PARTICLE RINGS   Found in all flagellated species studied thus far (42), these particles are unusually tall and may be highlighted by rotary-shadowing. After subtraction of the metal coat, each particle has a diameter of ~5 nm, as visualized in freeze-fracture replicas. The flagellar ring structures of *E. coli* and other bacteria contain about 10–12 particles (Figure 6, left). About 14–16 particles per ring are also found in other flagellated species such as *Streptococcus* spp. *E. coli* particle rings are missing in mutants lacking either *motA* or *motB*, but reappear with concomitant restoration of motility upon plasmid-based expression of the Mot proteins in the mutant bacteria (45). The peripheral, modular nature of the particle rings suggests that they

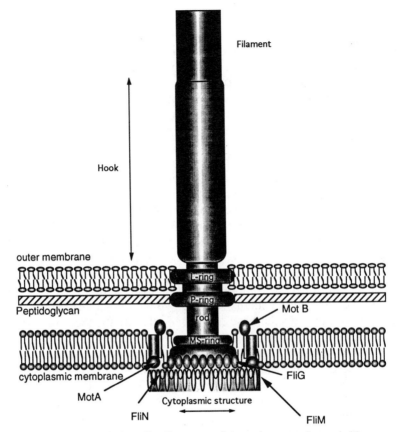

Figure 5 Components of the flagellar motor. Schematic portraying probable arrangement of motor proteins at the flagellar base. Two intramembrane particles (each comprised of a MotA and MotB protein), extended MS-containing FliG (only nine copies
shown), and cytoplasmic structure–containing FliM and FliN (12 copies shown) are schematized. The structure is thought to contain twice as many copies of FliG (i.e 27) as
copies of MotA (~11), while copy numbers of FliM and FliN are not known (Table 1).
The cytoplasmic module is at least fourfold thicker than portrayed.

may assemble one at a time onto preexisting flagella, consistent with
their being comprised of Mot proteins synthesized late in the hierarchy
of expression of the flagellar regulon. This finding would also be in
qualitative accord with physiological data indicating that expression of
the Mot proteins induces a stepwise increase in force production (9),
though there is a discrepancy in the observed number of steps and
particles.

Therefore, each ring particle is probably a MotA-MotB complex that

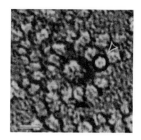
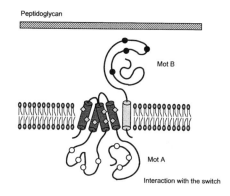

Figure 6 Force-generators of the flagellar motor. Positions of dominant nonfunctional and slow-swimming alleles of both MotA and MotB are indicated. (*Left*) Electron micrographs of a freeze-fracture replica of a flagellar particle ring. Arrow on the micrograph points out one intramembrane particle (*circled*). (*Right*) Model for the MotA and MotB complex based on the hydropathy of the protein sequences. One hypothesis is that the particles consist of a 1:1 MotA:MotB complex. Bar = 10 nm.

conducts protons responsible for the energization of the flagellar motor, though this supposition remains to be proven. If so, the diameter of the particles would accomodate one MotA protein four-helix bundle, while the large periplasmic domain of MotB would explain the unusual height of the particles. Figure 6 (right) diagrams this hypothesis, and positions functional mutations in the postulated MotA-MotB complex. Finally, the morphology of flagellar particle rings of the sodium-powered alkalophilic bacilli is identical to those of proton-powered neutrophilic bacilli (46). Again, the particles are ~5 nm in diameter. This observation rules out the possibility that the ion selectivity reflects different oligomerization states of the channel proteins (59).

CYTOPLASMIC BASAL STRUCTURE AND OTHER HBB-ASSOCIATED STRUCTURES   In both *E. coli* and *S. typhimurium,* additional structures associated with the HBB complex have been isolated upon glutaraldehyde fixation (22) and by use of protocols that avoid the extremes of pH and ionic strength traditionally used for purification of flagellar basal structures (28, 40, 77). These additional structures protude basally out from the MS-ring complex; they are, therefore, inferred to be located in the cytoplasm (Figure 5) and are referred to as *cytoplasmic basal structures.* Thin-section electron microscopy of polarly flagellated bacteria and rapidly frozen, freeze-substituted *S. typhimurium* cell envelopes has also provided evidence for cytoplasmically located basal structure (reviewed in 42). Morphological differences are apparent in *S. typhimurium* cytoplasmic basal structures isolated using different protocols and visualized in cell-envelope thin sections. Image averaging procedures have been applied to determine that a large (60-nm diameter), cytoplasmic ring structure, termed the C ring, is isolated associated with the HBB complex if acid pH (pH 2.5) treatment and cesium chloride density gradient centrifugation are avoided (28). Isolation of C ring–containing HBB complexes, however, involved exposure to pH 10.0 in order to reduce contamination by outer membrane vesicles. Isolation of basal flagellar fragments is carried out at near-neutral pH (40). Cytoplasmic basal structures isolated as part of basal flagellar fragments (40) or those obtained in glutaraldehyde-fixed flagella (22) seem to contain axially located rod and disc substructures within, and in addition to, an outer cask-like structure that could correspond to the C ring. The cytoplasmic structures visualized in cell-envelope thin sections also seem to contain axially located rod-like substructures and, furthermore, are larger in size (47). It remains possible, therefore, that cytoplasmic basal flagellar structures are degraded by exposure to pH 10 and the detergent solubilization steps common to all isolation protocols.

Nevertheless, antibody-labeling studies have shown that the more extended C ring–containing HBB complex contains all three proteins, FliG, FliM, and FliN. FliG seems to be closely associated with the MS-ring complex, since immunoblots showed that FliG, but not FliM or FliN, was still present, albeit to a reduced extent, upon treatments that degraded the C-ring component (28). FliF-FliG fusion mutants are motile and basal structures isolated from such mutants may be decorated with both FliF and FliG antibodies (27). Mutants obtained by construction of FliM-FliN fusions are also motile (R Macnab, personal communication). The facts imply that FliG is localized at the periphery of the MS ring, whereas the C ring contains FliM and FliN. Overexpression of FliN resulted in resurrection of motility in mutant *E. coli* containing little or no functional FliN (32), but in contrast to MotA and MotB resurrection experiments, rapidly fluctuating speed transitions rather than discrete, stepwise increments were observed. This may reflect unstable intermediates during C-ring assembly. Indeed, labile protein-protein associations seem to characterize the entire flagellar cytoplasmic structure; several *mot* point mutations in either one of the switch proteins drastically affect isolation of the cytoplasmic module in basal flagellar fragment preparations (40).

In summary, little is known regarding the polypeptide composition of the recently described *E. coli/S. typhimurium* cytoplasmic basal flagellar structures, and even their morphological description may be incomplete. Regular occurrence of, as well as functional roles for, the putative cytoplasmic substructures visualized in basal flagellar fragment and glutaraldehyde-fixed preparations and cell-envelope thin sections remain to be established. Importantly, however, the FliG, FliM, and FliN proteins have been shown to be present in C ring–containing HBB complexes, even though the extended MS and C rings may also be comprised of other proteins responsible for scaffolding or regulation of flagellar assembly.

In polarly flagellated bacteria such as *Wolinella succinogenes,* a large disk structure of up to 200-nm diameter comprises part of the flagellar basal body. The disk is located in the periplasm, being attached to the inner side of the outer membrane (77). The HBB L-P ring complex is found at the center of the disk. The *W. succinogenes* disk contains as many as 2200 monomers assembled into an Archimedian spiral and 12 spokes radiating from the L-P ring complex to the rim of the structure (26, 77a). The disk is the second largest structural component, following the filament, of polar flagella. It is not known whether intramembrane particle rings, consisting of 12 particles per ring as in *E. coli,* are part of the basal structure of the *W. succinogenes* flagellum. Nevertheless, it is attractive to suppose that the spokes serve to bolt intramembrane ring particles, one per spoke, onto the disk, thereby providing a rigid support for torque generation. Alternatively, the disk structures may play a role in positioning the polar flagellum. In line with the latter alternative, analogous structures have not been found thus far at flagellar bases of peritrichous bacteria such as *E. coli.*

The flagellar motor, if comprised solely of the Mot and switch proteins, will be made up of the intramembrane particle and C-ring structures. These structures are positioned ~40 nm from the center of the flagellum (Figure 5). The ressurrection experiments (Figure 4) indicate that there are approximately 10 independently acting force generators per flagellum. The stall torque of the flagellar motor is $\sim 5 \times 10^{-18}$ Nm (Figure 3). Given a 40-nm radial distance and 10 force generators, this value converts to an isometric force of ~10 pN per force generator. A 40-nm radial distance yields a circumferential distance of ~250 nm. Proton flux measurements (67) suggest that the proton flux through the flagellar motor is tightly coupled to rotation, with ~1240 protons being expended per revolution. Thus, one force generator traverses an effective distance of ~250 nm per revolution, expending ~124 protons in the process. For tightly coupled mechanisms in which a fixed incremental displacement (i.e. step) results per proton translocated, this yields a step size of ~2 nm. Flagella can rotate up to 300 Hz (6a, 61). This would convert to a maximum linear speed of (250 × 300) nm/s, or 75 μm/s.

COMPARISON WITH OTHER MOLECULAR MOTORS

Torque Production

The bacterial flagellum is not the only organelle capable of rotary motion. The rotary movement of the axostyle of dinoflagellates may be caused by actin filaments arranged in a cylindrical geometry (87). Squid neuronal kinesin rotates as well as translocates microtubules, as evidenced by observations that the motor tracks single protofilaments that follow a tilted path relative to the microtubule long axis (29). In vitro motility assays have also shown that motor proteins such as 14S axonemal dynein (92) can generate both torque and thrust. Whether flagellar motor force generators are capable of torque production or whether the rotation of the flagellum is solely a consequence of the rotary geometry of its motor apparatus is not known. As noted in the previous section, forces produced at high load by flagellar motor-force generators are impressive; thus, the force production probably requires anchorage to rigid cytoskeletal or exoskeletal (i.e cell wall) structures. However, this is not a universal requirement for all membrane-associated motors. *Acanthamoeba* spp. myosin I moves actin filaments by binding directly to planar, purified phospholipid films, but it does so at low velocities (0.2 μm/s) (98).

Mechanochemistry

The past decade has witnessed explosive· growth in the biochemical identification and characterization of motor proteins (93). Motor proteins differ greatly in their operational characteristics. The force-generating units of the flagellar motor compare favorably with the fastest, strongest ATP-driven motors (55, 92) in maximal force and speed. A shorter cycle time might reflect the fact that ion transport machinery, unlike that for ATP hydrolysis, does not need to utilize binding energy to accelerate chemical-reaction rates. Ion dissociations limit unloaded flagellar rotation frequencies. Thus, dissociation of the transported or utilized fuel molecule seems to be the rate-limiting process generally found in molecular motors. Under metabolizing conditions, the energy liberated from transmembrane transport of one proton ($\sim 3 \times 10^{-13}$ ergs) is comparable to that liberated from hydrolysis of one ATP molecule. Flagellar motors can operate at torque and, probably, efficiency values that are an order of magnitude greater than that obtained under physiological (i.e free-swimming) conditions. Analogous examples are found in other motile systems [e.g. the motors that move chromosomes during mitosis (68)].

Force (or torque)-velocity curves provide more detailed information regarding motor operation than estimates of maximal force and speed alone. Extrapolation about the properties of the elemental force–generating units from force-velocity data involving multiple motors is not straightforward. Force-velocity relationships in kinesin-driven motility depend upon the ratio of dead to active motors and are, possibly, a function of the fraction of the duty cycle the motor spends attached to its track (31). Different force-velocity curves result depending upon the use of isotonic or auxotonic conditions (19). During flagellar rotation, the hook is wound up so that the motor force–generating units work against an elastic resistance [i.e. conditions approximating auxotonic contraction (21)], but the elasticity of the filament tether has not been considered in published work. This reservation aside, torque-velocity measurements indicate a consensus torque-velocity regime at high speeds. In contrast, both myosin and kinesin decrease, rather than increase, speed in vitro upon application of negative load (31).

Detailed measurements of variation of motor proton flux with torque will be neccessary in order to interpret torque velocity data in terms of a mechanochemical scheme. Measurements of rotation-dependent flux are a start, but estimates of total flux are what are required. Torque velocity data have been interpreted in terms of proton-transfer chemistry (36, 61), but there is no compelling reason to assume that proton-transfer kinetics determine torque-velocity relationships.

The remarkable property of the *Streptococcus* spp. flagellar motor— that it can be driven clockwise by inwardly directed and counterclockwise by outwardly directed potentials, respectively—has no parallel among ATP-powered motors. Motility of ATP motors driven by a negative phosphate potential remains to be demonstrated. Perhaps, different binding energies of substrate and products effectively make reversal of the ATPase cycle kinetically unfeasible, which would be analogous with the modulation of the reversibility of flagellar motors by pK shifts (44).

Bidirectionality

What are the mechanisms whereby bidirectional force may be generated? A unidirectional motor may attach to its track in different orientations, thereby generating bidirectional force. Examples where this occurs are not presently known. It is known that scallop myosin crossbridges can rotate and bind to actin filaments of the opposite polarity. However, the direction is determined by the actin filaments and the sliding velocity is an order of magnitude lower in the wrong (180° rotated) orientation. A formal equivalent of this strategy, advanced in models for flagellar rotation (see below), is that the polymer that serves as a track switches between conformations of opposing polarity. Another strategy for bidirectional force generation could involve an interacting complex of two antagonistic, unidirectional motors. The kinesin-like *ncd* motor protein provides an example of a motor that generates force in the opposite direction along the microtubule track when compared with other members (i.e. conventional kinesin) of its (i.e. kinesin) superfamily (93). However, the facts that clockwise and counterclockwise rotation speeds are equal over a wide range of external load and that both rotation modes are observed at the lowest speed level during resurrection of nonmotile mutants (Figure 4) favor a single force-generating species. Another example of bidirectional movement that may involve a single motor is dynein from *Reticulomyxa filosa,* of which phosphorylated and nonphosphorylated forms power movement in opposite directions (76). Interestingly, phosphorylation underlies switching of the flagellar motor as well. The frequent (~1 s) bidirectional switching of flagellar motors constitutes perhaps the most fascinating aspect of this motor system.

Cellular and Environmental Controls

In eukaryotic cells, the multiplicity of microtubule- and actin-based motors presumably allows the cell, through differential expression and positioning of motor proteins, to adjust its motile functions to environmental changes and proceed through different stages of its cell-cycle or developmental program with high efficiency. In some cases, flagellated bacteria express a different type and/or number of motors in response to environmental perturbation. Thus, *Vibrio parahaemolyticus* has a single, sodium-powered polar flagellum in sea-water, but grows lateral arrays of proton-powered flagella for swarming in semisolid media. The polar flagllum presumably senses the high load resulting from increased medium viscosity and then initiates expression of lateral flagellar genes (1). In *E. coli,* expression of the flagellar regulon and, hence, the number of flagella per cell depends upon levels of metabolites such as glucose. Cell-cycle control of motility also occurs, as illustrated by the well-studied example of the polar flagellum of *Caulobacter crescentus,* in which both flagellar expression and positioning depend on cell cycle–linked cues (62). Because we do not yet understand the mechanochemical properties of bacterial flagellar motor proteins at the single-molecule level, we cannot correlate different motor-protein sequences with function.

MODELING THE BACTERIAL FLAGELLAR MOTOR

Ideas regarding force generation within the flagellar motor have sought to explain its remarkable bidirectionality and apparently reversible operation. Motor models have been recently reviewed in detail (18; see also 6a). The models shown in Figure 7, in addition to being the most well developed analytically, illustrate the major ideas that have influenced workers in the field.

Electrostatic Models

Conceptually, the most direct class of models are electrostatic ones, in which the ion flux generates electrostatic force via interaction with charges positioned on the rotor. The first electrostatic model was proposed nearly two decades ago (30). Only recently, however, has a comprehensive electrostatic model been proposed that accounts in a satisfactory way for most physiological data (8). Structurally, Berry's model borrows the geometry first used by Läuger to explain bidirectionality (56). Läuger postulated that both the rotor and stator components contained rows of proton-binding sites that were mutually tilted with respect to each other. Berry modified this geometry, envisioning the arrays as comprised of rows of alternating positive and negative charge (8). PK shifts allow switching without invoking gross conformational changes. A general difficulty with electrostatic models is assembly of the motor machinery, because highly charged surfaces are postulated to exist in a low dielectric for force generation to occur.

Elastic Linkages

Force generation via stretch of elastic linkages was first proposed by Huxley for muscle contraction (34). Berg & Anderson first suggested that elastic crossbridge elements could power flagellar rotation in their rotation hypothesis (5). Berg & Khan (6) coupled this suggestion to a specific structural geometry and developed it to explain physiological

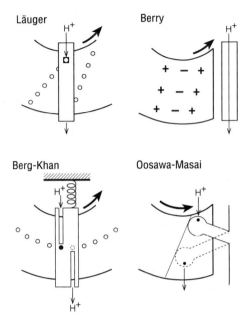

Figure 7 Selected models of flagellar rotation. In all cases, an intramembrane ring particle, assumed to comprise one channel force–generating unit, is shown contacting the
rotor (MS or C ring). (*Top left*) Läuger. Proton-binding sites are formed only upon overlap
of half-proton binding sites on the rotor and channel. Because of the tilted array of charges
on the rotor, the inward flux of protons exerts torque on the rotor. Conformational
changes of the rotor that reverse the angle of tilt of the rotor arrays reverse rotation
sense (56). Elastic linkages were incorporated in a later version of the model (57), and
the stochastic behavior of this model was analyzed (51). (*Top right*) Berry. Torque is
produced by electrostatic interaction between alternating lines of charge on the rotor
and the energizing protons in the channel. Shifts in pK cause switching of rotation sense
as the shifts change the occupancy of the channel proton–binding sites. At low proton
occupancies, channel protons interact with the negative lines of charge, and inward flux
produces counterclockwise rotation. At high proton occupancies, empty channel proton–
binding sites effectively constitute an outward flux of holes that interact with the positive
lines of charge to produce clockwise rotation (8). (*Bottom left*) Berg-Khan. The channel
complex is attached by elastic linkages to the cell wall. Proton flux through the outer
channel protonates sites on the rotor. The charged site restricts thermal motions of the
complex away from it. Motions that bring the inner channel into line with this site allow
deprotonation and proton transport into the cytoplasm and also allow, concurrently,
protonation at the adjacent proton-binding site. When the rotor is held stationary, the
protonations and deprotonations bias the thermal motions of the channel complex,
stretching the elastic linkages until the elastic energy gained equals that dissipated by
transmembrane transport of a proton (43). Reversal of the channel configuration reverses
rotation sense. Energetics of the model when rotor rotation is rapid relative to the drift
of the channel complexes have been analyzed (18, 66). (*Bottom right*) Oosawa-Masai.
The channel has crossbridge domains that interconvert between an outwardly and inwardly oriented configuration. The protonated forms of these configurations bind to the

tethered cell data. The elastic crossbridge elements responsible for force generation were envisaged conducting protons, but a ring of proton-binding sites on the rotor was required to complete the proton-conducting pathway such that transmembrane transit of protons was only possible upon movement of the crossbridges relative to the rotor. It was explicitly supposed that the intramembrane ring particles observed using freeze-fracture (Figures 5 and 6) could be such crossbridge elements, connected by elastic linkages to a rigid outer-membrane based support. The linkages were sufficiently weak such that each particle (crossbridge element) could thermally diffuse (jiggle), traversing proton-binding sites arrayed around the MS-ring periphery. The jiggle of the crossbridge elements made possible protonations-deprotonations of the MS-ring binding sites and was, in turn, biased by their proton occupancy, which reflected the sign and magnitude of the proton gradient. The motor geometry proposed by Läuger may also be modified to incorporate elastic linkages (57). Stochastic simulations of the Läuger model have revealed that the force constant of the elastic linkage is an important parameter in determining both steady-state and transient behavior of the flagellar motor (51).

Conformational Change

Conformational transitions of crossbridging elements that attach between stationary and mobile components at different orientations represent another strategy for force production. Conformational transitions, typically assumed to be instantaneous in theoretical treatments, produce strain in bound crossbridges, which leads to force development. Hill and coworkers (25) have detailed this force-generation strategy for muscle contraction. Oosawa and coworkers (69, 70) have advanced a model of the flagellar motor in which such crossbridge elements were envisaged lying along the interface between the M and S rings. This geometry is not consistent with recent structural data but can be made so without undue difficulty (Figure 7).

In Berry- and Oosawa-type models, coupling is loose because transmembrane transit of the energizing ions can occur in the absence of flagellar rotation. Even so-called tight coupling models will exhibit

---

rotor at different angular tilts; torque results from configurational transitions of the bound crossbridges (70). Unprotonated forms of these configurations may also bind to the rotor but with opposite angular tilt. Proton flux is loosely coupled to torque production via a reversible crossbridge cycle (69). Conformational changes, either of the rotor or of the crossbridges, that lead to formation of rotor-crossbridge attachments of opposite angular tilt, will switch rotation sense.

loose coupling upon relaxation of appropriate constraints. On the other hand, loose-coupled models can, upon appropriate choice of parameters, yield fairly tight coupling (8). Perhaps a more substantial difference between models concerns the pathway of the energizing protons. In loose-coupled models, proton binding sites on both rotor and stator components are not required for completion of the proton pathway. This is a simpler, and thus more attractive, alternative than the arrays of half-proton binding sites and staggered half-channel complexes postulated in the Läuger and Berg-Khan models, respectively. Indeed, it is not clear exactly what a half-proton binding site is.

Models provide a conceptual framework that can be compared with ideas generated from the study of analogous systems. One may ask, for example, whether motor proteins are derived from a prototypical motor molecule. Models are neccessary to tackle these and similar issues. As Figure 7 indicates, proposed mechanisms of flagellar rotation share ideas among themselves and with models proposed for other motile systems. Their value lies in being explicit, not in being correct. Caplan & Kari-Ivanov (18), in their discussion of the development of motor models, show that the properties of Läuger's model, modified to incorporate elastic linkages, are energetically equivalent to those of the Berg-Khan model. Indeed, the idea that force generation could occur by bias of the thermal motion of elastic linkages is the central contribution of the Berg-Khan model. The model was not a synthesis of available experimental data, which, at that time, indicated simply that tethered-cell rotation occurred close to thermodynamic equilibrium. Nor have all of its predictions been fulfilled. For example, the proposed structural geometry has proved only partially correct. Furthermore, while gating of ion transport by protein motions of the channel is possible, no channel complexes have been found with the particularly convenient feature of two sets of half-channels that allow for bidirectionality, each with a stagger identical to the spacing between adjacent proton-binding sites on the rotor. However, this model did show, by explicit construction, how rapid proton association-dissociations could generate adequate force and speed through mass-action biasing of the Brownian motion of elastic elements. This was an important departure from earlier ideas that linked elementary angular displacements of the flagellum directly to proton movements (see 7). The notion that the chemical fuel, whether ATP or protons, could be utilized to bias the ever-present thermal motions of motor molecules has gained ground in recent thought on ATP-powered motors (21, 91). Furthermore, binding of protons to flagellar motor proteins can, in principle, generate force by simply increasing the flexibility of elastic linkages, as has been suggested for ATP motors (21). In this case, directionality is determined by stereochemically precise rotor-stator interactions, as the myosin S1 structure suggests might occur for actomyosin (73).

EPILOGUE

Rotary motion and energization by electrochemical ion gradients instead of ATP set bacterial flagellar motors apart from the actin and microtubule-based flagellar motors found in eukaryotic cells. It remains to be seen whether the characteristics reflect either a profound difference in the mechanism or tactical variations on a common strategy. It is, perhaps, not a coincidence that determination of the molecular mechanism of flagellar rotation reduces to the task of discriminating between a limited set of strategies currently under debate for other motors.

ACKNOWLEDGMENTS

We are grateful to all colleagues who submitted material in advance of publication and those who critiqued the manuscript. SCS was supported by a fellowship from the Max-Planck-Gessellschaft. SK was supported by the Barnard Davis summer fellowship from the Marine Biological Laboratory (MBL) and grant R01GM36936 from the National Institutes of Health.

Literature Cited

1. Atsumi, McCarter L, Imae Y. 1992. Polar and lateral flagellar motors of marine *Vibrio* are driven by different ionmotive forces. *Nature* 355:182–84
2. Barak R, Eisenbach M. 1992. Correlation between phosphorylation of the chemotaxis protein CheY and its activity at the flagellar motor. *Biochemistry* 31:1821–26
3. Barak R, Welch M, Yanovsky A, Oosawa K, Eisenbach M. 1992. Acetyladenylate or its derivative acetylates the chemotaxis protein CheY in vitro and increases its activity at the flagellar switch. *Biochemistry* 31:10099–100107

4. Berg HC. 1974. Dynamic properties of bacterial flagellar motors. *Nature* 249: 77–79
5. Berg HC, Anderson RA. 1973. Bacteria swim by rotating their flagellar filaments. *Nature* 245:380–82
6. Berg HC, Khan S. 1982. A model for the flagellar rotary motor. In *Mobility and Recognition in Cell Biology*, ed. H Sund, C Veeger, pp. 485–97. Berlin: De Gruyter
6a. Berg HC, Turner L. 1993. Torque generated by the flagellar motor of *Escherichia coli. Biophys. J.* 65:2201–16
7. Berg HC, Manson M, Conley M.P

1982. Dynamics and energetics of flagellar rotation in bacteria. *Soc. Exp. Biol. Symp.* 35:1–31

8. Berry RM. 1993. Torque and switching in the bacterial flagellar motor and electrostatic model. *Biophys. J.* 64:961–73

9. Blair DF, Berg HC. 1988. Restoration of torque in defective flagellar motors. *Science* 242:1678–81

10. Blair DF, Berg HC. 1990. The MotA protein of Escherichia coli is a proton-conducting component of the flagellar motor. *Cell* 60:439–49

11. Blair DF, Berg HC. 1991. Mutations in the MotA protein of *Escherichia coli* reveal domains critical for proton conduction. *J. Mol. Biol.* 221:1433–42

12. Blair DF, Kim D, Berg HC. 1991. Mutant MotB proteins in *Escherichia coli*. *J. Bacteriol.* 173:4049–55

13. Block SM, Berg HC. 1984. Successive incorporation of force-generating units in the bacterial rotary motor. *Nature* 309:470–72

14. Block SM, Blair DF, Berg HC. 1989. Compliance of bacterial flagella measured with optical tweezers. *Nature* 338:514–18

15. Block SM, Segall JS, Berg HC. 1983. Adaptation kinetics in bacterial chemotaxis. *J. Bacteriol.* 154:312–23

16. Bourret RB, Borkovitch KA, Simon MI. 1991. Signal transduction pathways involving protein phosphorylation in prokaryotes. *Annu. Rev. Biochem.* 60:401–41

17. Bourret RB, Drake SK, Chervitz SA, Simon MI, Falke JJ. 1993. Activation of the phospho-signaling protein, CheY. Analysis of activated mutants by ^{19}F-NMR and protein engineering. *J. Biol. Chem.* 268:13089–96

18. Caplan SR, Kara-Ivanov M. 1993. The bacterial flagellar motor. *Int. Rev. Cytol.* 147:97–164

19. Chaen S, Oiwa K, Shimmen T, Iwamoto H, Sugi H. 1989. Simultaneous recordings of force and sliding movement between a myosin coated glass microneedle and actin cables in vitro. *Proc. Natl. Acad. Sci. USA* 86:1510–14

20. Chun S-Y, Parkinson JS. 1988. Bacterial motility: membrane topology of the *Escherichia coli* MotB protein. *Science* 239:276–78

21. Cordova NJ, Ermentout B, Oster GF. 1992. Dynamics of single-motor molecules: the thermal ratchet model. *Proc. Natl. Acad. Sci. USA* 89:339–45

22. Driks A, DeRosier D. 1990. Additional structures associated with the flagellar basal body. *J. Mol. Biol.* 211:669–72

23. Eisenbach M, Adler J. 1980. Bacterial cell envelopes with functional flagella. *J. Biol. Chem.* 256:8807–14

24. Eisenbach M, Wolf A, Welch M, Caplan SR, Lapidus IR, et al. 1990. Pausing, switching and speed fluctuations of the bacterial flagellar motor and their relation to motility and chemotaxis. *J. Mol. Biol.* 211:511–63

25. Eisenberg E, Hill T, Chen, Y-D. 1980. Cross-bridge model of muscle contraction: quantitative analysis. *Biophys. J.* 29:195–227

26. Engelhardt H, Schuster SC, Bauerlein E. 1993. An Archimedian spiral: the basal disk of the Wolinella flagellar motor. *Science* 262:1046–48

27. Francis NR, Irikura VM, Yamaguchi S, DeRosier DJ, Macnab RM. 1992. Localization of the *Salmonella typhimurium* flagellar switch protein to the cytoplasmic M-ring face of the basal body. *Proc. Natl. Acad. Sci. USA* 89:6304–8

28. Francis NR, Sosinsky GE, Thomas D, DeRosier DJ. 1993. Isolation, characterization and structure of bacterial flagellar motors containing the switch-complex. *J. Mol. Biol.* In press

29. Gelles J, Schnapp BJ, Sheetz M. 1988. Tracking kinesin-driven movements with nanometer-scale precision. *Nature* 331:450–53

30. Glagolev AN, Skulachev VP. 1978. The proton pump is the molecular engine of motile bacteria. *Nature* 268:360–62

31. Hall K, Cole DG, Yeh Y, Scholey JM, Baskin RJ. 1993. Force-velocity relationships in kinesin-driven motility. *Nature* 364:457–59

32. Hazelbauer GL, Berg HC, Matsumura P. 1993. Bacterial motility and signal transduction. Meeting review. *Cell* 73:15–22

33. Hirota N, Imae Y. 1983. Na[+]-driven flagellar motors of an alkalophilic *Bacillus* strain YN-1. *J. Biol. Chem.* 258:10577–81

34. Huxley AF. 1957. Muscle structure and theories of contraction. *Prog. Biophys. Biophys. Chem.* 7:255–318

35. Irikura VM, Kihara M, Yamaguchi S, Sockett H, Macnab RM. 1993. *Salmonella typhimurium fliG* and *fliM* mutations causing defects in assembly, rotation and switching of the flagellar motor. *J. Bacteriol.* 175:803–10

36. Iwazawa J, Imae Y, Kobayashi S. 1993. Study of the torque of the bacterial flagellar motor using a rotating electric field. *Biophys. J.* 64:925–33

37. Jones CJ, Aizawa, S-I. 1991. The bacterial flagellum and the bacterial flagel-

lar motor: structure, assembly and function. *Adv. Microb. Physiol.* 32:109–72
38. Jones CJ, Macnab RM, Okino H, Aizawa, S-I. 1990. Stoichiometric analysis of the flagellar hook-basal body complex of *Salmonella typhimurium*. *J. Mol. Biol.* 212:377–87
39. Kami-ike, N, Kudo S, Hotani H. 1991. Rapid changes in flagellar rotation induced by external electric pulses. *Biophys. J.* 60:1350–55
40. Khan IH, Reese TS, Khan S. 1992. The cytoplasmic component of the bacterial flagellar motor. *Proc. Natl. Acad. Sci. USA* 89:5956–60
41. Khan S. 1990. Motility. In *The Bacteria: A Treatise on Structure and Function*, 12:301–43. San Diego: Academic
42. Khan S. 1993. Gene to ultrastructure: the case of the flagellar basal body. *J. Bacteriol.* 175:2169–74
43. Khan S, Berg HC. 1983. Isotope and thermal effects in chemiosmotic coupling to the flagellar motor of Streptococcus. *Cell* 32:913–19
44. Khan S, Dapice M, Humayun I. 1990. Energy transduction in the bacterial flagellar motor: effects of load and pH. *Biophys. J.* 57:779–96.22
45. Khan S, Dapice M, Reese TS. 1988. Effects of *mot* gene expression on the structure of the flagellar motor. *J. Mol. Biol.* 202:575–84
46. Khan S, Ivey DM, Krulwich TA. 1992. Membrane ultrastructure of alkaliphilic *Bacillus* species studied by rapid-freeze electron microscopy. *J. Bacteriol.* 174:5123–26
47. Khan S, Khan IH, Reese TS. 1991. New structural features of the flagellar base in *Salmonella typhimurium* revealed by rapid-freeze electron microscopy. *J. Bacteriol.* 173:2888–96
48. Khan S, Macnab RM. 1980. The steady state counterclockwise/clockwise ratio of bacterial flagellar motors is regulated by protonmotive force. *J. Mol. Biol.* 138:563–99
49. Khan S, Meister M, Berg HC. 1985. Constraints on flagellar rotation. *J. Mol. Biol.* 184:645–56
50. Kihara M, Homma M, Kutsukake K, Macnab RM. 1989. Flagellar switch of *Salmonella typhimurium*: gene sequences and deduced protein sequences. *J. Bacteriol.* 171:3247–57
51. Kleutsch B, Läuger P. 1990. Coupling of proton flow and rotation in the bacterial flagellar motor: stochastic simulation of a microscopic model. *Eur. Biophys. J.* 18:175–91
52. Krebs MP, Khorana HG. 1993. Mech-

anism of light-dependent proton translocation. *J. Bacteriol.* 175:920–28
53. Kudo S, Magariyama Y, Aizawa S-I. 1990. Abrupt changes in flagellar rotation observed by laser dark-field microscopy. *Nature* 346:677–80
54. Kuo SC, Koshland, DE Jr. 1989. Multiple kinetic states for the flagellar motor switch. *J. Bacteriol.* 171:6279–87
55. Kuo SC, Sheetz MP. 1993. Force of single kinesin molecules measured with optical tweezers. *Science* 260:232–34
56. Läuger P. 1977. The proton pump is a molecular engine of motile bacteria. *Nature* 268:360–62
57. Läuger P. 1988. Torque and rotation rate of the flagellar motor. *Biophys. J.* 53:53–66
58. Larsen SH, Adler J, Gargus JJ, Hogg RW. 1974. Chemomechanical coupling without ATP: the source of energy for motility and chemotaxis in bacteria. *Proc. Natl. Acad. Sci. USA* 71:1239–43
59. Lear JD, Wasserman ZR, DeGrado WF. 1988. Synthetic ampipathic peptide models for protein ion channels. *Science* 240:1177–81
60. Liu JZ, Dapice M, Khan S. 1990. Ion selectivity of the *Vibrio alginolyticus* flagellar motor. *J. Bacteriol.* 172:5236–44
61. Lowe G, Meister M, Berg HC. 1987. Rapid rotation of flagellar bundles in swimming bacteria. *Nature* 325:637–40
62. Macnab RM. 1992. Genetics and biogenesis of bacterial flagella. *Annu. Rev. Genet.* 26:131–58
63. Macnab RM, Han DP. 1983. Asynchronous switching of flagellar motors on a single bacterial cell. *Cell* 32:109–17
64. Macnab RM, Ornston MK. 1977. Normal-to-curly flagellar transitions and their role in bacterial tumbling. Stabilization of an alternative quaternary structure by mechanical force. *J. Mol. Biol.* 112:1–30
65. Malakooti J, Komeda Y, Matsumura P. 1989. DNA sequence analysis, gene product identification and localization of flagellar motor components of *Escherichia coli*. *J. Bacteriol.* 171:2728–34
66. Meister M, Caplan R, Berg HC. 1989. Dynamics of a tightly coupled model for flagellar rotation. *Biophys. J.* 55:905–14
67. Meister M, Lowe G, Berg HC. 1987. The proton flux through the bacterial flagellar motor. *Cell* 49:643–50
68. Nicklas RB. 1988. The forces that move chromosomes in mitosis. *Annu. Rev. Biophys. Biophys. Chem.* 17:431–50
69. Oosawa F, Hayashi S. 1986. Coupling between flagellar motor rotation and

proton flux in bacteria. *J. Phys. Soc. Japan* 52:4019–28

70. Oosawa F, Masai J. 1982. Mechanism of flagellar motor rotation in bacteria. *J. Phys. Soc. Japan* 51:631–41

71. Ravid S, Eisenbach M. 1984. Minimal requirements for rotation of bacterial flagella. *J. Bacteriol.* 158:1208–10

72. Ravid S, Matsumura P, Eisenbach M. 1986. Restoration of flagellar clockwise rotation in bacterial envelopes by insertion of the chemotaxis protein CheY. *Proc. Natl. Acad. Sci. USA* 83:7157–61

73. Rayment I, Holden HH, Whittaker M, Yohn CB, Lorenz M, et al. 1993. Structure of the actin-myosin complex and its implications for muscle contraction. *Science* 261:58–65

74. Roman SJ, Frantz BB, Matsumura P. 1993. Gene sequence, overproduction, purification and determination of the wild-type level of the *Escherichia coli* flagellar switch protein FliG. *Gene.* 133: 103–8

75. Roman SJ, Meyer M, Volz K, Matsumura P. 1992. A chemotactic signaling surface on CheY defined by suppressors of flagellar switch mutations. *J. Bacteriol.* 174:6247–55

76. Schliwa M, Shimizu T, Vale RD, Euteneur U. 1991. Nucleotide specificities of anterograde and retrograde organelle transport in *Reticulomyxa* are indistinguishable. *J. Cell Biol.* 112:1199–1203

77. Schuster SC, Bauerlein E. 1992. Location of the basal disk and a ringlike cytoplasmic structure, two additional structures of the flagellar apparatus of *Wolinella succinogenes. J. Bacteriol.* 174:263–68

77a. Schuster SC, Bauerlein E. 1989. Basal body associated disks as new structural elements of the flagella apparatus of *Wolinella succinogenes. Biol. Chem. Hoppe Seyler* 370:9580–83

78. Sellers JR, Kachar B. 1990. Polarity and velocity of sliding filaments: control of direction by actin and of speed by myosin. *Science* 249:406–8

79. Sheetz MP, Spudich JA. 1983. Movement of myosin-coated fluorescent beads on actin cables in vitro. *Nature* 303:31–35

80. Shimada K, Berg HC. 1987. Response of the flagellar rotary motor to abrupt changes in extracellular pH. *J. Mol. Biol.* 193:585–89

81. Silverman M, Simon M. 1974. Flagellar rotation and the mechanism of bacterial motility. *Nature* 249:73–74

82. Sockett E, Yamaguchi S, Kihara M, Irikura VM, Macnab RM. 1992. Molecular analysis of the flagellar switch protein FliM of *Salmonella typhimurium. J. Bacteriol.* 174:793–806

83. Sosinsky GE, Francis NR, DeRosier DJ, Wall JS, Simon MN, Hainfeld J. 1992. Mass determination and estimation of subunit stoichiometry of the bacterial hook basal-body complex of *Salmonella* flagella by scanning transmission electron microscopy. *Proc. Natl. Acad. Sci. USA* 89:4801–5

84. Stock JB, Lukat GS, Stock A. 1991. Bacterial chemotaxis and the molecular logic of intracellular signaling networks. *Annu. Rev. Biophys. Biophys. Chem.* 20:109–36

85. Stocker BAD, Zinder ND, Lederberg J. 1953. Transduction of flagellar characters in *Salmonella. J. Gen. Microbiol.* 9:410–33

86. Stolz B, Berg HC. 1991. Evidence for interactions between MotA and MotB, torque-generating elements of the flagellar motor of *Escherichia coli. J. Bacteriol.* 173:7033–37

87. Tamm SL. 1978. Laser microbeam study of a rotary motor in termite flagellates: evidence that the axostyle generates torque. *J. Cell Biol.* 73:76–92

88. Tisa L, Adler J. 1993. Calcium ions are involved in *Escherichia coli* chemotaxis. *Proc. Natl. Acad. Sci. USA* 89: 11804–8

89. Toyoshima YY, Kron SJ, McNally EM, Neibling KR, Toyoshima C, Spudich JA. 1987. Myosin subfragment 1 is sufficient to move actin filaments in vitro. *Nature* 328:536–39

90. Ueno T, Oosawa K, Aizawa, S-I. 1992. M-Ring, S-ring and proximal rod of the flagellar basal body of *Salmonella typhimurium* are composed of subunits of a single protein, FliF. *J. Mol. Biol.* 227: 672–77

91. Vale RD, Oosawa F. 1990. Protein motors and Maxwell's demons: does mechanochemical transduction involve a thermal ratchet? *Adv. Biophys.* 26:97–134

92. Vale RD, Toyoshima YY. 1988. Rotation and translocation of microtubules in vitro induced by dyneins from Tetrahymena cilia. *Cell* 52:459–69

93. Walker RA, Sheetz MP. 1993. Cytoplasmic microtubule associated motors. *Annu. Rev. Biochem.* 62:429–52

94. Welch M, Oosawa K, Aizawa, S-I, Eisenbach M. 1993. Phosphorylation-dependent binding of a signal molecule to the flagellar switch of bacteria. *Proc. Natl. Acad. Sci. USA* 90:8787–91

95. Wilson LM, Macnab RM. 1990. Co-

overproduction and localization of the *Escherichia coli* motility proteins MotA and MotB. *J. Bacteriol.* 172:3932–39

96. Wolfe AJ, Conley MP, Kramer TJ, Berg HC. 1987. Reconstitution of signaling in bacterial chemotaxis. *J. Bacteriol.* 169:1878–85

97. Yamaguchi S, Aizawa, S-I, Kihara M, Isomura M, Jones CJ, Macnab RM.

1986. Genetic evidence for a switching and energy-transducing complex in the flagellar motor of *Salmonella typhimurium. J. Bacteriol.* 168:1172–79

98. Zot GZ, Doberstein SK, Pollard T. 1992. Myosin-I moves actin filaments on a phospholipid substrate: implications for membrane targeting. *J. Cell Biol.* 116:367–89

Annu. Rev. Biophys. Biomol. Struct. 1994. 23:541–76

H-DNA AND RELATED STRUCTURES

Sergei M. Mirkin

Department of Genetics, University of Illinois at Chicago, Chicago, Illinois 60612

Maxim D. Frank-Kamenetskii[1]

Institute of Molecular Genetics, Russian Academy of Sciences, Moscow 123182, Russia

KEY WORDS: DNA structure, triple-helical DNA, nuclease hypersensitivity, DNA polymerase, promoters, telomeres

CONTENTS

PERSPECTIVES AND OVERVIEW

The discovery of the crystal form of Z-DNA by Alex Rich and his coworkers in 1979 (123) and the subsequent demonstration of Z-DNA

[1]Present address: Center for Advanced Biotechnology and Department of Biomedical Engineering, Boston University, Boston, Massachusetts 02215.

541

and cruciform formation in supercoiled plasmids (71, 97, 116) stimulated interest in unusual DNA conformations and their possible biological role(s). Observations by Larsen & Weintraub (68) and Hentchel (41) that promoters of eukaryotic genes in both active chromatin and supercoiled plasmids show hypersensitivity toward S1 nuclease indicated to many researchers that unusual structures might be formed at those sites (127). Numerous studies revealed that S1 sensitivity was associated with homopurine-homopyrimidine stretches (reviewed in 128). This finding was surprising because homopurine-homopyrimidine sequences could adopt neither cruciform nor Z-DNA structures. Slippage loops (41, 80, 87, 112), left-handed helices (19, 84, 105), triple helices (20, 69), and quarter helices (47) had been discussed in the literature; but the controversial data on fine mapping of S1 cleavage sites did not permit definite conclusions about the nature of any unusual structures in the homopurine-homopyrimidine tracts.

Such conclusions were finally enabled by two-dimensional gel electrophoresis of supercoiled DNAs carrying a homopurine-homopyrimidine insert (75, 76, 91). These studies revealed beyond any doubt that an unusual structure was formed and, remarkably, that this structure was stabilized by hydrogen ions—hence the name ''H form'' for the unusual structure (Figure 1). The main element of the H form is an intramolecular triple helix formed by the entire pyrimidine strand and half of the purine strand; the other half of the purine strand remains single stranded. The triple helix is stabilized by CG^*C^+ and TA^*T base

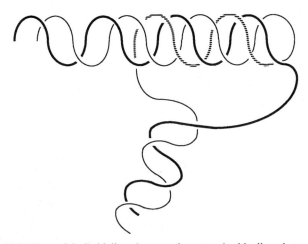

Figure 1 H-DNA model. Bold line, homopurine strand; thin line, homopyrimidine strand; dashed line, the half of the homopyrimidine strand donated to the triplex.

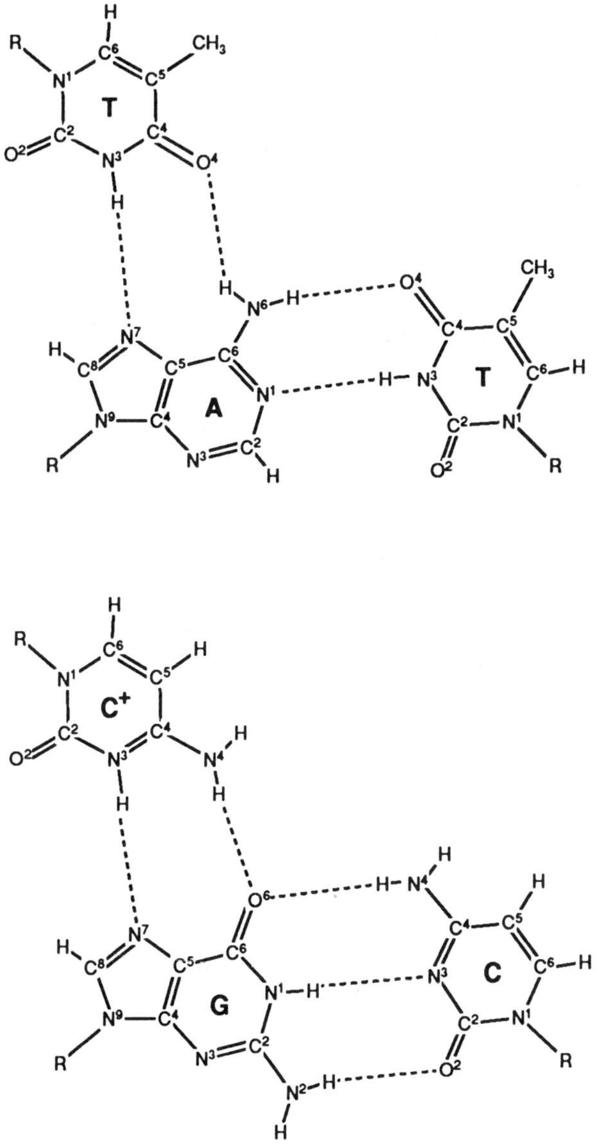

Figure 2   TA*T and CG*C$^+$ base triads.

triads (Figure 2). Numerous studies using mutational analysis and chemical probing have substantiated this model (see reviews 32, 33, 96, 128, 129, and references therein).

H-DNA was the first example of an intramolecular DNA triplex. It has become clear in recent years that an entire family of H-like DNA structures exists whose members differ in the chemical nature of their triplexes; such structures can exist in different isomeric forms depending on ambient conditions and sequences. Similarly, the variety of sequences known to be able to adopt the H-DNA structure has significantly increased during the last few years. We review these recent findings and discuss factors affecting the structure and stability of H-DNA.

The discovery of H-DNA stimulated speculations about its possible biological role. However, until very recently, efforts by many groups to find H-DNA in vivo remained unsuccessful. Now several reports have appeared that provide the first reliable indications that H-DNA may exist in vivo. Intriguing biochemical data are available that show the influence of H-DNA on replication and transcription. We discuss these data along with other biological applications.

CANONICAL H-DNA

In order to study a structure of homopurine-homopyrimidine stretches in supercoiled DNA Lyamichev et al (75) chose a method called two-dimensional (2-D) gel electrophoresis of DNA topoisomers. This method, first described by Wang et al (125), is based on the dependence of the mobility of circular DNA in the gel on its torsional tension. The mobility of DNA topoisomers, i. e. circular DNA molecules that are chemically identical but differ in their supercoiling, will increase until saturation with an increase of the number of supercoils in the first direction of gel electrophoresis. If a structural transition occurs, accompanied by the release of some superhelical stress, the mobility of the corresponding topoisomers decreases. Thus, the topoisomer under transition co-migrates with a less supercoiled one. Electrophoresis in a second direction, perpendicular to the first, is used to resolve co-migrating topoisomers. At this stage an intercalating dye (usually chloroquine) is added to the buffer. The dye intercalates into the DNA duplex and relaxes negative superhelical tension, thus converting non-B-DNA segments into B conformation. As a result, the mobility of previously co-migrated topoisomers becomes different according to their actual linking difference. In the final picture, one can see a gradual increase of topoisomer mobility until a sharp drop appears, reflecting the transition (Figure 3). From its 2-D pattern, one can determine two important characteristics of a structural transition. First, it is easy to calculate the number of supercoils released during transition. If the length of the sequence adopting a new conformation is known, one can deduce the topological status of the new conformation. Second, it is easy to calculate the number of supercoils necessary for the transition. This makes it possible to estimate the free energy of a transition under given ambient conditions.

Lyamichev et al (75) studied a cloned sequence from a spacer between the histone genes of the sea urchin *P. miliaris.* It contained a $d(G-A)_{16}$ stretch that had been found to be hypersensitive to S1 nuclease (41). First, the structural transition was demonstrated without any enzymatic or chemical modification. The pH dependency of the transition was remarkable (Figure 4). One can see that at acidic pH, the transition occurs under low torsional tension, while at neutral pH it is almost undetectable. Because pH-dependence had never been observed before for non-B-DNA conformations (cruciforms, Z DNA, bent DNA, etc), the investigators concluded that a novel DNA conformation had been formed, which they called H-DNA.

Treatment of the DNA topoisomer mixture with S1 nuclease before gel electrophoresis removed from the 2-D pattern topoisomers that

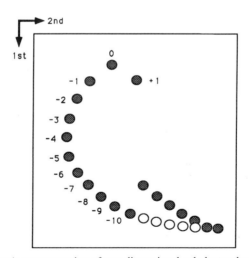

Figure 3 Schematic representation of two-dimensional gel electrophoresis. The structural transition occurs in topoisomers starting from number -11 and accompanies the release of four supercoils. Filled circles show the DNA topoisomers where the transition took place; empty circles show the mobility of corresponding topoisomers where no transition occurred.

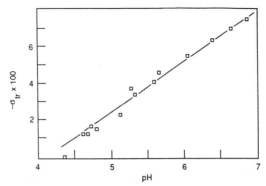

Figure 4   Dependence of the superhelical density of the B-to-H transition on pH for the d(TC)$_n$·d(GA)$_n$ sequence (75).

adopted the H conformation. S1 cleavage sites are located in a small d(G-A)$_{16}$ stretch inside the whole 509-bp insert, so it seemed reasonable to conclude that the observed structural transition was due to this DNA segment. Because the mobility drop accompanying the transition corresponded to three superhelical turns, and an unusual structure was formed in the 32-bp-long stretch, the investigators concluded that the H form must be topologically equivalent to unwound DNA.

The N3 position of cytosine seemed the most probable protonation site. Among free nucleotides it has the highest pK value for protonation, and this pK value had been known to increase substantially when protonated cytosines were involved in different structures.

A theoretical consideration of B-to-H transitions noted by Lyamichev et al (75) allowed predictions about the number of protonation sites in the structure. Let *m* be the number of base pairs within DNA undergoing transition from B- to H-DNA. The free energy of transition will be:

$$\Delta F = \Delta F_o - (RT/r)\ln(1 + 10^{pK_t - pH}) \qquad 1.$$

where *r* is the number of base pairs per protonated site in H-DNA, pK_t is the pK value of cytosine within the structure, and ΔF_o is the free energy of H-DNA formation with all protonation sites unoccupied. At pH values below pK_t, the stability of the protonated structure is strongly pH-dependent:

$$\Delta F = \Delta F_o^* + pH(RT/r)2.3 \qquad 2.$$

Equation 2 predicts a linear dependence of the free energy of H-DNA stabilization on pH. As one can see from Figure 4, a linear pH-dependence of supercoiling density required for H-DNA formation was indeed observed experimentally. Equation 2 leads to a simple equation for the superhelical density of transition:

$$\sigma_{tr} = (0.1/r)\,(\mathrm{pH_o} - \mathrm{pH}),\qquad\qquad 3.$$

where $\mathrm{pH_o}$ is the value of the pH at which the H form is extruded in linear, topologically unconstrained DNA. The slope of the linear part of the experimental dependence curve (Figure 4) directly showed that the variable, r, was equal to 4, i.e. there was one protonation site per 4 bp of the insert. Because this curve represents data for the $d(G-A)_n$ stretch, half of the cytosines must be protonated for H-DNA formation to occur.

A model of H form DNA was proposed by Lyamichev et al (76) (Figures 1 and 5). It consists of an intramolecular triple helix formed by the pyrimidine strand and half of the purine strand; the other half of the purine strand is single stranded. As Figure 1 shows, this structure is topologically equivalent to unwound DNA. Two isoforms of H form are possible: one single-stranded in the 5' part of the purine strand and the other single-stranded in the 3' part (Figure 5). The existence of single-stranded purine stretches in H-DNA may explain its hyperreactivity to S1 nuclease.

TA*T and CG*C$^+$ base triads stabilize the triple helix (Figure 2). Thymines or protonated cytosines from the third strand interact with adenines or guanines, respectively, from AT or GC base pairs via Hoogsteen rules (43). The protonation of cytosines is crucial for the formation of CGC$^+$ base triads. This observation explains the pH dependency of the structural transition. It is also clear that only one half of the cytosines must be protonated for Hoogsteen hydrogen bonding, while the remaining cytosines form Watson-Crick hydrogen bonds. It

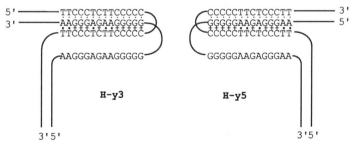

Figure 5 Two isoforms of H-DNA (91). Watson-Crick hydrogen bonds are labeled by points, nonprotonated Hoogsteen hydrogen bonds are shown by squares, and protonated Hoogsteen hydrogen bonds are shown by plus symbols.

is important that the triads be isomorphous such that good stacking in a triple helix is possible. The formation of triplexes, first suggested by Felsenfeld et al (28) for mixtures of homopurine and homopyrimidine polyribonucleotides, has been documented further in many studies (69, 92).

The H-DNA model suggested several obvious predictions. First, it should be true for several simple repeats including d(G)n·d(C)n and d(A)n·d(T)n. However, the features of the transition for these two sequences should be different. For d(G)n·d(C)n one must expect a substantial pH dependence, and since r should be 2 rather than 4, the slope of the experimental dependency of σ_{tr} on pH should be twice that observed for d(G-A)n·d(T-C)n. Using 2-D gel electrophoresis for cloned d(G)n·d(C)n sequences, the pH-dependent structural transition was indeed observed (77), and the maximal slope of the experimental pH-dependency curve actually corresponded to the predicted value $r = 2$ at 200 mM Na$^+$.

For d(A)n·d(T)n, one would expect a pH-independent structural transition, since TAT triads do not require base protonation. However, for a long time all attempts to detect this transition remained unsuccessful. Using single-strand-specific nucleases and chemicals as probes, Fox (30) found that d(A)n·d(T)n stretches adopt the H conformation under the influence of DNA supercoiling at pH 8. It turned out that even those very sensitive approaches detected H-DNA formation for only very long (69 bp) stretches. It is not yet clear why shorter sequences refuse to form H-DNA. This refusal may be due to an unusual helical conformation (B'-DNA) of d(A)n·d(T)n which is characterized by high propeller twist, contains additional bifurcated hydrogen bonds (22, 95), and does not wrap around nucleosomes (66). The rigidity and enhanced stability of this structure may prevent initiation of H-DNA formation for short tracts.

A less trivial prediction regarding sequence requirements of H-DNA formation is based on the importance of TA*T and CG*C$^+$ triad isomorphism. When the pyrimidine-rich strand folds back to form a triplex, cytosines from one half of the homopurine-homopyrimidine sequence should interact with GC but not AT base pairs in its other half. Conversely, thymines in one half should interact with AT but not GC base pairs from the other half. Thus, a homopurine-homopyrimidine sequence must be a mirror repeat to form H-DNA. Regular sequences d(G-A)n·d(T-C)n, d(G)n·d(C)n, and d(A)n·d(T)n are mirror repeats. One would expect that irregular homopurine-homopyrimidine sequences with mirror symmetry must adopt H conformation as well.

This hypothesis was proved by Mirkin et al (91) in studies of cloned mirror repeated homopurine-homopyrimidine sequences with different point substitutions:

AAGGGAGAA<u>A</u>GGGGTATAGGGG<u>A</u>AAGAGGGAA   a.

AAGGGAGAA<u>A</u>GGGGTATAGGGG<u>G</u>AAGAGGGAA   b.

AAGGGAGAA<u>G</u>GGGGTATAGGGG<u>A</u>AAGAGGGAA   c.

AAGGGAGAA<u>G</u>GGGGTATAGGGG<u>G</u>AAGAGGGAA   d.

The first sequence is a perfect mirror repeat with the exception of the central TATA box. Both (b) and (c) contain an A-to-G substitution in either the left or right half of the mirror repeat (underlined). Though the homopurine-homopyrimidine nature of the stretch is undisturbed, both (b) and (c) are no longer mirror repeats. The last sequence combines both point substitutions, such that the mirror symmetry is restored. The first and last sequences must adopt the H conformation, while the second and the third should not—or should form it only at higher negative superhelicity. The results of 2-D gel-electrophoretic study of the corresponding supercoiled plasmid DNAs (Figure 6) were in full agreement with the above predictions.

It was concluded, therefore, that any mirror repeated homopurine-homopyrimidine sequence could form H-DNA. Such a sequence was called an H palindrome. Most natural S1-hypersensitive sequences show no sequence homology but contain prominent H palindromes (91). Thus, it is likely that the H form is the structural basis for DNA S1 hypersensitivity.

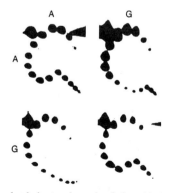

Figure 6   Two-dimensional gel electrophoresis of plasmids carrying H palindromes with point substitutions (91). In DNA samples with mirror repeated homopurine-homopyrimidine inserts (*top left, bottom right* corners), transition to the H form occurred at much lower superhelicity than in the other two DNAs, where mirror symmetry was destroyed by point mutations.

Final proof of the correctness of the H-form model was obtained by chemical probing of H-DNA (39, 40, 44, 48, 57, 120, 121). Several reagents were used that are reactive toward different bases and sensitive to particular DNA conformations (for review see 72, 128). Briefly, diethyl pyrocarbonate (DEPC) carboxyethylates purines at the N7-position in the single-stranded or Z conformation. Thus, it should react with single-stranded purines in the H form. Dimethyl sulfate (DMS) methylates the N7-position of guanines in the double- and single-stranded states. The N7-position of some guanines in H-DNA are involved in Hoogsteen hydrogen bonding. Methylation protection of guanines when in the H form is expected. Osmium tetroxide (OsO$_4$) forms osmate esters with the C5-C6 double bond of single-stranded thymines. It should interact with the thymines in the central part of the pyrimidine strand that are looped out in the H form. Chloroacetaldehyde (CAA) forms ethenoderivatives with the base-pairing positions of adenines, cytosines and, less prominently, guanines. It must interact with single-stranded purines and cytosines in H-DNA. All of these modified residues are detectable at a nucleotide resolution after piperidine cleavage, followed by sequencing gel electrophoresis.

Several groups found a unique pattern of chemical modification of different H palindromes in supercoiled DNA under acidic pH. The 5' portion of the purine-rich strand was hypersensitive towards DEPC and CAA, while its 3' half was relatively resistant (39, 40, 44, 48, 57, 120, 121). Conversely, for DMS, clear methylation protection of guanines in the 3' part of the purine strand, compared to its 5' half was observed (48, 121). Finally, OsO$_4$ and CAA were found to modify specifically the central part of the pyrimidine strand (39, 40, 44, 57, 120). These results support the H form model. They also reveal that different sequences preferentially adopt one of the two possible isomeric forms of the H-DNA in which the 5' part of the purine strand is unstructured.

The structural features responsible for the difference between the two isoforms have been identified by Htun & Dahlberg (45). They have shown that the isoform with the looped out 5' half of the purine strand (designated H-y3) is preferentially formed at high superhelical densities. (Note that DNA samples with a high level of DNA supercoiling were used in most chemical probing experiments.) The other isoform with the looped out 3' half of the purine strand (designated H-y5) is observed at lower superhelical density. A simple three-dimensional modeling of H-DNA formation showed that formation of the H-y3 releases one superhelical turn more than the H-y5 isoform, such that the former becomes more favorable at high superhelical density. Recent studies show that the mechanisms underlying preferential isomerization into the H-y3 conformation are more complex. Apparently, the presence of bivalent cations makes the H-y5 isoform preferable (50). What is more surprising, the loop sequence plays an important role for the direction of isomerization (49, 114). Systematic studies of factors contributing to isomerization are yet to be provided.

The energetics of the B-to-H transition is still poorly understood. A simple thermodynamic treatment shows that when the cooperative transition of the n bp insert into the H form occurs, the superhelical density of the transition is determined from the equation (78):

$$\Delta F(n - 3) + F_n + \Delta G = 0, \qquad\qquad 4.$$

where $n - 3$ base pairs actually form a triplex (due to the existence of a loop), ΔF is the free energy per base pair of the triplex part of H-DNA, F_n is the length-independent energy of nucleation of the H form, and ΔG is the change in superhelical energy accompanying the transition. ΔG may be also determined as (31):

$$\Delta G = 10RTN[(\sigma + n/N)^2 - \sigma^2], \qquad\qquad 5.$$

where N is the total number of base pairs in DNA and σ is a superhelical density. Equations 4 and 5 yield:

$$-\sigma_{tr} = n/2N + \Delta F/20RT + (F_n - 3\Delta F)/20RTn. \qquad\qquad 6.$$

This consideration allows one to estimate both ΔF and F_n by comparing experimentally determined superhelical densities of B-to-H transitions for regular homopurine-homopyrimidine repeats of varying length. Studies of this question for $d(G-A)_n \cdot d(T-C)_n$ and $d(G)_n \cdot d(C)_n$ inserts showed that the nucleation energy of the B-to-H transition is 18 kcal/mol (78), which is close to the corresponding value for cruciform extrusion.

To what extent may DNA tolerate deviations from the mirror symmetry and/or the homopurine-homopyrimidine character of a sequence? This issue was addressed by studying sequences like:

5'-AAGGGAGAA<u>X</u>GGGGTATAGGGG<u>Y</u>AAGAGGGAA-3',

where X and Y are any DNA bases. For X = Y = A or X = Y = G, the sequences corresponded to perfect mirror repeats and easily adopted H conformation (see above). Using two-dimensional gel electrophoresis and S1 mapping, Belotserkovskii et al tested H-DNA formation for all other mismatches (10). They showed that the H conformation is actually possible for all X and Y, though in cases other than X = Y = A/G the transition requires greater superhelical stress. Quantitative analysis of the data made it possible to estimate the energy cost of triplex formation due to all possible mismatched base triads (Table 1). These data were later confirmed in studies of intermolecular DNA triplexes with different noncanonical triads (79, 89). The only notable contradiction between the two series of data is the AT*G triad, which appeared advantageous in intermolecular triplexes (36, 124) but is not among the favorable triads in H-DNA (10). The reason for this difference is not clear. Energies are within the range of 3–6 kcal/mol—i.e. similar to the energy cost of mismatches in a B-DNA. Sequence requirements for triplex formation are thus similar to the sequence requirements for complementary recognition in a duplex. Though costly, the incorporation of noncanonical triads into H-DNA would significantly increase the number of sequences that could adopt this conformation.

As noted above, H-DNA formation requires DNA supercoiling and/ or acidic pH. The positive effect of these factors is evident: DNA supercoiling compensates for the high nucleation energy of H-DNA formation, while protonation of cytosines makes the CG*C$^+$ base triads favorable. Other stabilization factors have recently been revealed.

Belotserkovskii et al (9) studied the influence of oligonucleotides complementary to the single-stranded homopurine stretch in H-DNA on the stability of an intramolecular triplex. They found that such oligonucleotides stabilized H-DNA under high pH values (pH 7.0) where H-DNA alone rapidly flops into the B conformation. To explain this finding it is useful to consider the elementary steps in the H-to-B transition. The transition involves two energetically unfavorable processes: a disruption of a Hoogsteen pair, and an increase of negative superhelical stress. These processes are at least partly compensated by the energetically favorable formation of the Watson-Crick pair. In the case of oligonucleotide-associated H-DNA, formation of a Watson-Crick pair occurs at the cost of disruption of duplex base pairs formed by the oligonucleotide. In this case every step in H-to-B transition is less

Table 1 Energy cost for H-DNA formation for mismatched triads (10)

Triad	ΔE kcal/mol	Triad	ΔE kcal/mol
CG*T	2.9	AT*T	5.1
CG*A	2.9	TA*A	5.1
GC*T	3.6	AT*A	5.1
AT*C	3.6	GC*G	5.1
GC*C	4.4	TA*C	5.1
CG*G	4.4	TA*G	5.1
AT*G	5.1	GC*A	5.8

favorable by the energy of one Watson-Crick base pair, δF_o. For a transition consisting of many sequential steps, the lifetime of the oligonucleotide-associated H-DNA is (2):

$$\vartheta' = \vartheta \, s^m, \qquad\qquad\qquad 7.$$

where ϑ is the lifetime of H-DNA, $s = \exp (\delta F_o/kT)$, and m is the length of the oligonucleotide. Because the δF_o for a Watson-Crick pair is about 10, association of a 14-nucleotide-long oligonucleotide with H-DNA would increase its lifetime by a factor of 10^{14}. Thus, addition of oligonucleotides kinetically traps DNA in the H conformation (9).

An interesting hypothesis of Reaban & Griffin (108; see also discussion in 109, 117) was that the H (or *H) form may be transiently extruded as a result of transcriptionally driven supercoiling and stabilized by the uptake of newly synthesized RNA molecules (see the section below on Detection of H-DNA in vivo). The data in Ref. 9 show that such stabilization is actually possible.

Another stabilizing factor was described by Lee and coworkers (37, 38). They found that pyrimidine-rich oligonucleotides complementary to the single-stranded purine stretch in H-DNA causes dimerization of plasmids carrying the corresponding H-forming sequences under conditions favorable for triplex extrusion. As discussed above, these oligonucleotides may associate with H-DNA or they may form an intermolecular triplex with the homopurine-homopyrimidine stretch in a B conformation (9). The authors suggested that dimerization is caused by the interaction of a single oligonucleotide with two independent plasmid molecules. It appeared that the presence of the polyamines spermine and spermidine favors plasmid dimerization under neutral pH. Independent studies showed that polyamines stabilize putative intermolecular triplexes as well (93). Because the density of a negative charge is higher in triplexes than in duplexes, the stabilizing effect of polyamines on triplex formation is probably caused by the reduction of repulsion between phosphate backbones upon binding of polyamines to DNA. Polyamines are normal components of eukaryotic cells, present in the nucleus (reviewed in 118). Thus, their stabilizing effect may play an important role in H-DNA formation in vivo.

*H-DNA

A related conformation was first described by Kohwi & Kohwi-Shigematsu (57). They studied the structure of $d(G)_n \cdot d(C)_n$ stretches in supercoiled DNA in the presence of Mg^{2+} ions using the single-stranded DNA-specific reagent chloroacetaldehyde. They observed an unusual pattern of chemical hyperreactivity under neutral pH in the presence of magnesium ions. In this case, the central part of the purine strand and the 5' half of the pyrimidine strand were hyperreactive. The authors concluded that an H-DNA-like structure was formed in which the entire purine strand and half of the pyrimidine strand formed Py·Pu·Pu triplex. (They called it H'-DNA, but in current literature it is more often called *H-DNA, the designation we use here.) This conclusion was later supported by 2-D gel electrophoresis (98). The structural transition for the $d(G)_{46}·d(C)_{46}$ insert was observed at neutral pH in the presence of Mg^{2+} ions. The transition occurred at high superhelical stress ($\sigma_{tr} = -0.06$) and was accompanied by the release of 5 supercoils. Thus, like H-DNA, *H-DNA is topologically equivalent to unwound DNA.

For several years $d(G)_n·d(C)_n$ tracts remained the only sequences shown to adopt *H conformation (57, 62). It was not clear whether this type of triplex could be formed by other sequences. Surprisingly, however, recent studies have shown that *H-DNA is much more versatile than canonical H-DNA with respect to sequence requirements.

Using nuclease and chemical probing, Azorin and his coworkers (12, 13) found that $d(G-A)n·d(T-C)n$ stretches adopt *H configuration when in a supercoiled state. The structural units of such triplex are CG*G and TA*A base triads (Figure 7). In this case, Zn^{2+} rather than Mg^{2+} ions stabilize the structure (see below). In all of the above cases, the H-r3 isoform of *H-DNA dominated.

The analysis of *H-DNA benefited significantly from numerous studies of the formation of intermolecular Py·Pu·Pu triplexes during recent years. In particular, it was shown that nonorthodox TA*T and protonated CG*A$^+$ base triads may successfully incorporate into such triplexes (5, 82). Less stable, but still possible, are TA*C and GC*T triads (6). These observations permitted the design of experiments which showed that *H-like structures can be formed by sequences that are neither homopurine-homopyrimidine nor mirror repeats.

One example is *H-DNA consisting of intervening CG*G and TA*T triads. To form such a structure, guanines in the purine-rich strand should be arranged in a mirror repeated way, while thymines concentrated in one half of the purine strand should be reflected by adenines in the other half (Figure 8). As a result, such sequences would be neither homopurine-homopyrimidine (because they contain thymines in otherwise purine-rich strands) nor mirror repeated (because A and T bases are positioned in an inverted repeated way). The asymmetric character of such sequences leads to the existence of two subclasses with adenines in either the 5' part or the 3' part of the purine-rich strand. This

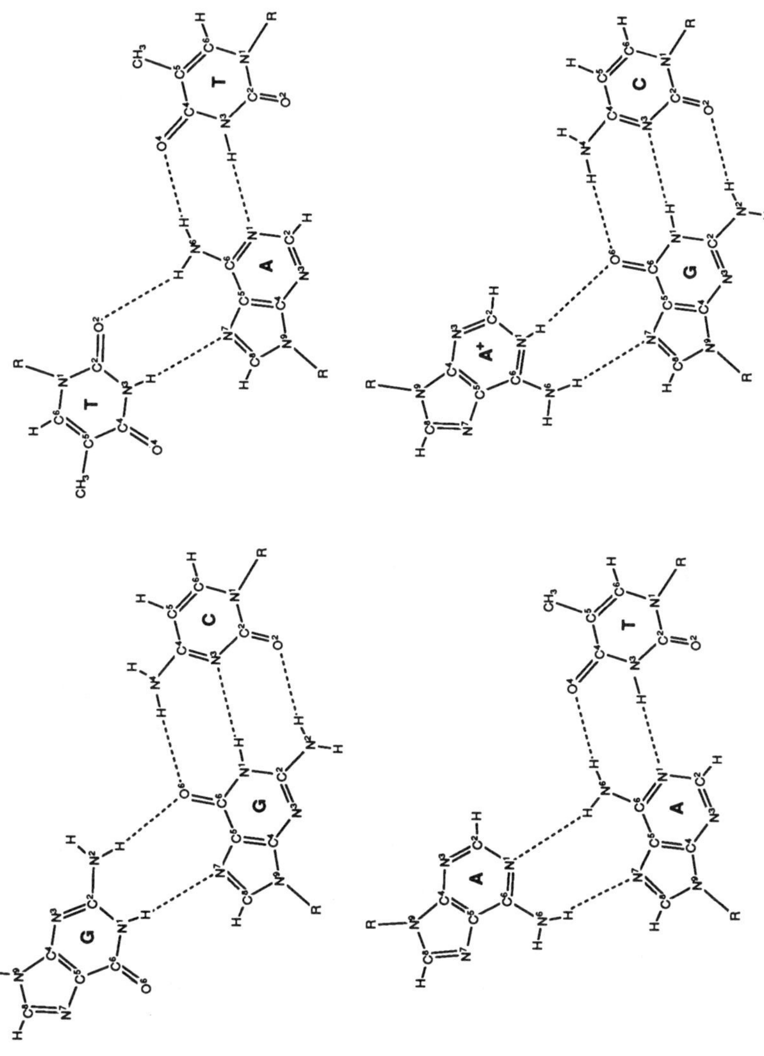

Figure 7 *H-DNA-forming triads: CG*G, TA*A, TA*T, and CG*A⁺.

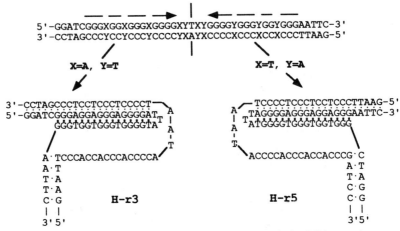

Figure 8 *H-DNA consisting of CG*G and TA*T base triads. GC base pairs are arranged as mirror repeats (shown by arrows flanking a vertical line representing the pseudosymmetry site), while AT base pairs are arranged as inverted repeats. Depending on the relative location of the adenines and thymines, either the H-r3 or the H-r5 isomer of *H-DNA is formed (27). Points, Watson-Crick hydrogen bonds; squares, Hoogsteen hydrogen bonds.

causes differences in triad composition between the two isoforms of *H-DNA for these subclasses (Figure 8). Using fine chemical probing of supercoiled plasmids with corresponding sequences in the presence of Mg^{2+} Dayn et al (27) showed that they indeed form the *H conformation. It is interesting that here the sequence content of the triplex appeared to be more important than topological differences between isoforms. Both sequences form triplexes composed of CG*G and TA*T triads; thus, H-r3 and H-r5 isoforms were stable for different sequences.

Malkov et al (82) observed *H-DNA formation for the sequence $G_{10}TTAA(AG)_5$ which is not mirror repeated. This asymmetry again leads to differences in triads between different isoforms: CG*G and CG*A triads in the H-r3 configuration and CG*G and TA*G triads in the H-r5 configuration. Chemical probing showed that only the H-r3 isoform was formed. Thus, *H-DNA is formed by CG*G and CG*A triads. It is surprising that this transition occurred under acidic pH and did not require bivalent cations—a combination of phenomena never observed before for *H-DNA. It was suggested, therefore, that protonation of adenines is crucial for stability of $CG*A^+$ triads. Figure 7 represents all triads shown to be involved in *H-DNA formation. Be-

Table 2 Formation of Py·Pu·Pu triplexes in the presence of different bivalent cations (81)

| Bivalent metal cation | $dC_n \cdot dG_n \cdot dG_n$ | | $d(TC)_n \cdot d(GA)_n \cdot d(GA)_n$ | |
	*H-DNA	Intermolecular triplex	*H-DNA	Intermolecular triplex
Ba^{2+}	No data	−	No data	−
Ca^{2+}	+	+	−	−
Mg^{2+}	+	+	−	−
Cd^{2+}	No data	+	+	+
Co^{2+}	−	+	+	+
Mn^{2+}	+	+	+	+
Zn^{2+}	−	+	+	+
Ni^{2+}	No data	+	−	+

cause those triads are not strictly isomorphous, triad isomorphism is not so crucial for the formation of *H-DNA as for that of H-DNA.

One of the most complicated questions about *H-DNA and Py·Pu·Pu triplexes in general is their dependence on bivalent cations. First of all, it is not clear why some bivalent cations are so efficient in stabilizing these triplexes, while others are not. This situation with H-DNA and Py·Pu·Py triplexes is quite different; in that case the requirement for hydrogen ions is evident. Second, cation requirements are different for different sequences (Table 2) (11–13, 23, 57, 59, 62, 85). While *H-DNA formed by $d(G)n \cdot d(C)n$ sequences is stabilized by Ca^{2+}, Mg^{2+}, and Mn^{2+}, the same structure formed by $d(G-A)n \cdot d(T-C)n$ is formed in the presence of Zn^{2+}, Mn^{2+}, Cd^{2+}, and Co^{2+}. Similar effects are observed for intermolecular triplexes (81). It is not yet clear whether differences in cation requirements are caused by variations in neighboring triads or by changes in the GC content between different triplexes. Recent data indicate that moderate changes in GC content (from 75% to 63%) switch cation requirement from Mg^{2+} to Zn^{2+} for a particular sequence to form *H-DNA (110). However, because changing GC-content necessarily changes the sequence itself, only studies of many different *H-forming sequences can answer this question.

H-DNA-LIKE STRUCTURES

Triplex-containing structures, originally represented only by canonical H-DNA, actually comprise an entire family of structures (113) formed by various sequences, not necessarily homopurine-homopyrimidine.

Under superhelical stress they are stabilized by a variety of means, including acidic pH, bivalent cations, etc. We have already discussed the best-studied representatives of this family, namely H- and *H-DNA. Even those structures exhibit significant versatility in sequence requirements, in isomeric forms, and in conditions favoring their formation. In this section, we discuss other members of this family which are more unusual yet.

Nodule DNA

Two independent groups (63, 99) described a composite DNA triplex formed by sequences $d(G)_n \cdot d(C)_n$ and $d(A-G)_n \cdot d(T-C)_n$ (Figure 9). To adopt such a structure two thirds of the pyrimidine strand form an H-like triplex with one third of the purine strand, while the rest of the pyrimidine strand is involved in an *H-like triplex with two thirds of the purine strand. The resulting structure, called nodule DNA, contains only few unpaired DNA bases at the tips of both triplexes. Formation of nodule DNA was detected by chemical and nuclease probing, which showed sites reactive towards single-strand-specific agents and nucleases situated at one third the distance from both ends of the inserts.

As discussed above, H-DNA is stable at acidic pH while *H-DNA is stabilized by bivalent cations. Therefore, one would expect nodule DNA to exist within a narrow range of ambient conditions; and indeed nodule DNA formed by $d(G)_n \cdot d(C)_n$ is detected under mild acidic pH in the presence of bivalent cations (63). For $d(A-G)_n \cdot d(T-C)_n$ this structure was only observed at neutral pH in the presence of cobalt hexamine (99).

Nodule DNA formation was detected for relatively long regular homopurine-homopyrimidine inserts, while shorter inserts adopted orthodox intramolecular triplexes. This could be easily explained. Compared with H- and *H-DNA, the nodule conformation has a higher nucleation energy owing to a larger number of junctions between different conformations, whereas it has a lower elongation energy because the single-stranded region (inherent in H and *H forms) is lacking.

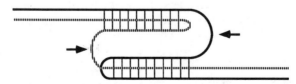

Figure 9   Nodule DNA (63, 99). Bold line, homopyrimidine strand; dashed line, homopurine strand. Arrows show single-stranded stretches that demonstrate nuclease and chemical hyperreactivity.

Eclectic DNA

Several studies described the formation of unusual DNA structures by telomeric repeats. Telomeric ends of eukaryotic chromosomes contain the redundant consensus $d[T_{1-3}(T/A)G_{1-4}]$, which is tandemly repeated up to 15 kb in length in the double-stranded state, followed by a $3'$ overhang containing two repeats of the G-rich strand alone (reviewed in 130). The structure of the ends of chromosomes is beyond the scope of this paper and is reviewed by Williamson in this volume (128a). We concentrate here on a special problem—an unusual structure adopted by telomeric sequences cloned within supercoiled plasmids.

Interest in this problem was initiated by Budarf & Blackburn (17), who found that the cloned *Tetrahymena* telomeric repeat, $d(G_4T_2)n$, exhibits hypersensitivity to S1 nuclease. Because these data looked similar to those that led to the discovery of H-DNA, this problem was attacked using 2-D gel electrophoresis, chemical and enzymatic probing, and oligonucleotide binding—i.e. all the methods previously successful for H-like DNA structures (9, 74, 122).

These studies of cloned repeats of *Tetrahymena* $(T_2G_4)n$, human $(T_2AG_3)n$, and yeast $(TG_3TGTG)n$ revealed that all these sequences behave similarly. 1. Two-dimensional gel electrophoresis proved that these sequences adopt an unusual structure(s) topologically equivalent to unwound DNA. 2. As in the case of H-DNA, the transition was strongly pH dependent. 3. In all cases, complementary Py-rich, but not Pu-rich, oligonucleotides bound with plasmids carrying unusual structures. Thus, an unusual protonated DNA structure was formed, and at least some portion of the Pu-rich strand was single stranded.

These results were puzzling. They reflected what one would expect if telomeric sequences adopted an H-like structure, but the sequences themselves were not homopurine-homopyrimidine mirror repeats. In the first attempt to explain these data, for the case of the *Tetrahymena* telomeric sequence, Lyamichev et al proposed a so-called C,A-hairpin model (74). The main component of this structure is a hairpin formed by the pyrimidine-rich strand and stabilized by antiparallel C^*C^+ and A^*A^+ pairs. The purine-rich strand is mainly unstructured (Figure 10A). The requirement for base protonation explains the pH-dependence of the transition. The possibility of the formation of an antiparallel C^*C^+ hairpin was later confirmed in a study of single-stranded telomeric sequences using absorbance thermal denaturation, chemical probing, and gel electrophoresis (1).

However, the results of more detailed investigation by chemical and enzymatic probing of the human telomeric repeat proved to be incon-

A

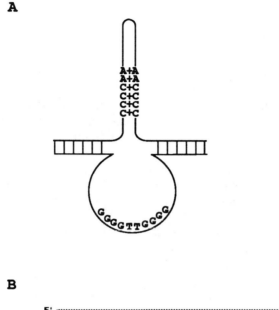

B

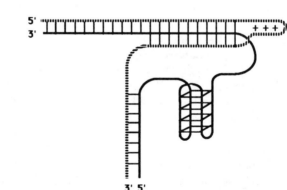

Figure 10   Models of unusual structures formed by telomeric repeats at acidic pH under superhelical stress. (*A*) C,A-hairpin (74). The C-rich strand forms a hairpin stabilized by C*C$^+$ and A*A$^+$ base pairs, while the G-rich strand is unstructured. (*B*) Eclectic DNA (122). The structure includes a nonorthodox triplex, quadruplex, C,A-hairpin, and unstructured regions. Bold line, G-rich strand; dashed line, C-rich strand.

sistent with the C,A-hairpin model. Clear-cut asymmetry in chemical reactivity within each strand was observed, whereas the C,A-structure implies a symmetrical pattern of modification. As a result, an alternative model, called "eclectic DNA," was proposed (Figure 10B; 122). It was called eclectic because it combines two unusual elements: 1. a nonorthodox triplex containing both regular CG*C$^+$ triads and mis-matched AT*A and AT*T triads, and 2. a quadruplex formed by part of the Pu-rich strand (a detailed discussion of quadruplex DNA is presented elsewhere in this volume). As discussed above, both AT*A and AT*T triads discourage triplex formation. Nevertheless, the proposed model fits Voloshin et al's chemical and nuclease modification data best (122).

Two-dimensional gel-electrophoretic studies of cloned *Tetrahymena* repeats showed that the nucleation energy for the formation of the unusual structure is unexpectedly low: 7 kcal/mol (8). This low energy requirement may result from the formation of the quadruplex, which makes initiation of the eclectic structure more favorable than that of the H-DNA containing unstructured single-stranded region. The lower nucleation energy can make the formation of H-like triplexes with mismatched triads possible, especially for long sequences that dramatically release superhelical stress upon transition.

Elucidation of the protonated DNA structures formed by telomeric sequences awaits further studies. The exact configuration for a given telomeric repeat may depend on its length, base composition, ambient conditions, etc. Mutational analyses similar to those provided for H-DNA would also be useful in addressing the problem.

H-Like Structure Formed by Parallel-Stranded DNA

A highly unusual *H-like structure was described by Klysik et al (56). They studied a d(A)$_{15}$·d(T)$_{15}$ segment in which the orientation of the two strands was parallel rather than antiparallel as in normal double-helical DNA (reviewed in 109). The authors synthesized a DNA duplex in which a central parallel-stranded segment was flanked by normal antiparallel-stranded regions, and inserted it into plasmid DNA. Circular DNAs with varying levels of DNA supercoiling were obtained in vitro, and the influence of torsional stress on the structure of the ps d(A)$_{15}$·d(T)$_{15}$ stretch was studied by 2-D electrophoresis and chemical probing. Both methods revealed a structural transition within the parallel-stranded segment under the influence of DNA supercoiling. Chemical modification data were consistent with the formation of an intramolecular triplex stabilized by TA*A base triads. (As in *H DNA, two homopurine strands in such a triplex are antiparallel; as in *H-DNA, only one of two possible isoforms dominated.) The nucleation energy of this unusual structure was estimated as 10 kcal/mol, which is lower than the H-DNA value of 18 kcal/mol. This reduction may result from the lower stability of the parallel-stranded insert relative to antiparallel sequences.

DETECTION OF H-DNA IN VIVO

Sequences that can form H-DNA are widespread throughout the genome of eukaryotes (7, 83) but are not common among eubacteria. However, the direct detection of H-DNA in eukaryotic cells is difficult owing to the great complexity of genomic DNA. Therefore, most of the studies of H-DNA in vivo exploit *Escherichia coli* as a convenient model system and artificially design constructs containing triplex-forming sequences.

The first direct detection of H-DNA in vivo was carried out by Karlovsky et al (51). Investigators there studied the structure of a $d(T-C)_{16} \cdot d(A-G)_{16}$ stretch cloned into a plasmid vector. They employed OsO_4 as a tool for H-DNA detection in vivo. It modifies the central part of the homopyrimidine strand when in H-DNA but not when in B-DNA. It can also penetrate bacterial cells, making possible chemical probing in vivo. *E. coli* cells containing the corresponding plasmid were incubated with OsO_4, then plasmid DNA was isolated, and the sites of in vivo modification were detected by sequencing. H-DNA could be formed in *E. coli* cells under a specific set of conditions. First, it was detected only in cells treated by the antibiotic chloramphenicol prior to modification. Chloramphenicol, an inhibitor of bacterial protein synthesis, causes (among other effects), an increase in superhelical density of plasmids within cells up to -0.055 (26). This density increase was shown to provoke the formation of unusual DNA structures, including Z-DNA and cruciforms (26, 115). Thus, it is reasonable to suggest that this same increase in superhelicity caused H-DNA formation. Second, H-DNA was observed only if cells were additionally pre-incubated in a buffer with a pH below 5.2. Such incubation should drop the intracellular pH somewhat, making H-DNA formation more likely.

A more detailed study of H-DNA formation in *E. coli* cells was provided by Usery & Sinden (119). These authors used chemical probing of a plasmid bearing an H-forming $d[(G-A)_7TA(G-A)_7]$ insert. The central TA dinucleotide in this sequence is a target for trimethylpsoralene photobinding in double-helical DNA but not in the H form. Since this chemical penetrates *E. coli* cells, it is a convenient tool for the detection of H-DNA in vivo. Using this approach Usery & Sinden found that an H-y3 isomer of H-DNA may form in normal cells without chloramphenicol treatment, but the higher level of DNA supercoiling in topoisomerase I mutants enhances its formation. Growth conditions were also significant: H-DNA formation was most prominent in bacterial cells grown in a synthetic medium at pH 5.0. These authors proposed that this pH supposedly decreases intracellular pH to 7.1 instead of the standard 7.8. Finally, H-DNA occurrence depended on the stage of *E. coli* culture growth, being more pronounced in stationary than in exponential phase.

Similar approaches were used for the detection of *H-DNA. Kohwi et al (60) used chloroacetaldehyde for the detection of this structure in *E. coli* cells. Chloroacetaldehyde specifically modifies one half of the homopyrimidine strand in *H conformation and may enter bacterial cells. Kohwi et al found that $d(G)_n \cdot d(C)_n$ stretches within bacterial plasmids may form *H-DNA. This structure was detected for inserts longer than 35 bp capable of adopting *H conformation under physiological ionic strength at reasonable supercoiling density (58). *H-DNA was observed only after chloramphenicol treatment of cells.

In summary, these studies show that H- and *H-DNA may in principle exist within bacterial cells. Clearly the level of DNA supercoiling in vivo is the major limiting factor in the formation of these structures. Environmental conditions during *E. coli* growth also significantly contribute to the appearance of H-DNA.

Recently it became clear that, while the steady-state level of DNA supercoiling is determined by the balance of DNA gyrase and Topo I (reviewed in 126), the local level of supercoiling strongly depends on transcription. Elongating RNA polymerase creates domains of high negative and positive supercoiling upstream and downstream of itself, respectively (73) which may influence the formation of unusual DNA structures. Indeed, transcription was found to drive cruciform and Z-DNA formation when corresponding DNA sequences were located upstream of promoters (25, 106). Quite recently similar observations were made for *H-DNA (61). $d(G)_n \cdot d(C)_n$ stretches were cloned upstream from a regulated promoter in an *E. coli* plasmid, and the structure of this stretch was studied by chloroacetaldehyde probing. Investigators found that induction of transcription provokes *H-DNA formation for stretches longer than 32 bp. *H-DNA formation in turn stimulated homologous recombination between direct repeats flanking the $d(G)_n \cdot d(C)_n$ insert. The authors suggested that the change in DNA geometry accompanying H-DNA formation brings flanking DNA sequences into close proximity, stimulating strand exchange.

There are also indirect indications of H-DNA formation in vivo. Klysik and coworkers (100) found that a GATC site situated in an H-forming sequence is undermethylated in vivo by *dam* methyltransferases. In vitro, formation of H-DNA prevented *dam* methylation. The authors suggested that the formation of H-DNA in vivo may be responsible for the observed undermethylation.

Two other studies concerned the influence of H motifs on transcription in vivo. A homopurine-homopyrimidine mirror repeat artificially designed in the transcribed portion of a bacterial gene significantly decreased gene expression due to premature transcriptional termination (111). Sarkar & Brahmachari speculated that H-DNA formation is responsible for transcriptional termination. Reaban and Griffin suggested that a possible mechanism of such termination is the interaction of an RNA chain with the H-DNA transiently extruded by local negative supercoiling upstream of RNA polymerase (108). Conversely, an H motif placed upstream of the β-lactamase promoter increased its activity (52). Because this promoter's activity strongly depends on DNA topology, the authors suggested that changes in topology associated with H-DNA formation are responsible for the elevation of transcription.

Other interpretations of these results are also possible. For example, chloramphenicol treatment completely abolished the undermethylation effect described above. Because in most cases chloramphenicol stimulated H-DNA formation (see above), this result does not support the proposed model. An alternative explanation is that some proteins in *E. coli* cells can bind H motifs that in turn effect different genetic processes in vivo. Additional studies are required to clarify this issue.

The only data on triplex DNA detection in eukaryotic cells were obtained using antibodies against triplex-helical DNA (70). It was found that these antibodies interact with eukaryotic chromosomes. Note, however, that interpretation of these interesting results is hindered by the fixation procedure used for antibody staining.

H-DNA AND DNA POLYMERIZATION

The biological role of H-DNA, if any, remains to be established. Recently, it has become clear that intramolecular triplexes significantly influence DNA polymerase activity in vitro. Dayn et al (27) studied DNA polymerization on DNA templates containing sequences that form *H-DNA consisting of CG*G and TA*T base triads (Figure 8). As discussed above, in supercoiled DNA, either the H-r3 or the H-r5 isomer of *H-DNA is formed, depending on the design of a particular sequence. It turned out that DNA polymerase terminates at specific sites on both DNA chains within supercoiled templates containing such sequences. The location of the termination sites was different for distinct *H-forming stretches but in all cases coincided precisely with triplex boundaries as defined by chemical probing. Dayn et al suggested, therefore, that formation of *H-DNA prior to DNA synthesis causes DNA polymerase to terminate. The difference in the location of termination sites is not surprising because the H-r5 and the H-r3 isomers contrast in chain polarity. Since DNA polymerase moves in a 3' to 5' direction along the template strand, it would face the triplex either at the end or at the middle of an *H motif, depending on the nature of the isomer (Figure 11).

An unexpected twist in DNA polymerase–triplex relations came from studies showing that H-DNA may be formed in the course of DNA polymerization. The first data obtained by Manor and his co-authors showed that d(G-A)$_n$ or d(C-T)$_n$ inserts within single-stranded

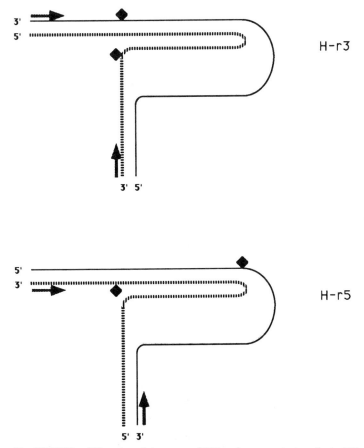

Figure 11   *H-DNA within a template causes DNA polymerase to terminate (27). Location of termination sites (shown by diamonds) differs between the H-r3 and the H-r5 isomers. Solid line, Py-rich strand; dashed line, Pu-rich strand. Growing DNA chains are shown by arrows.

DNA templates cause partial termination of DNA polymerases (4, 67). Termination sites were always located in the center of the insert. In explanation of these results, Baran et al (4) suggested that when the newly synthesized DNA chain reaches the center of the homopolymer sequence, the remaining homopolymer stretch folds back, forming a stable triplex (Figure 12A). As the result, DNA polymerase finds itself in a kind of trap and is unable to continue elongation.

For double-helical DNA templates another mechanism of polymerase-driven triplex formation is also possible. Many DNA polymerases can displace the nontemplate DNA strand in the course of DNA synthesis (reviewed in 65). The displaced strand may fold back, promoting the formation of an intramolecular triplex downstream of the replication fork. Conditions for DNA polymerization in vitro—i. e. neutral pH and high magnesium concentration—are optimal for the formation of *H-DNA. Thus, if a DNA polymerase meets a potential *II-forming sequence, displacement of the purine-rich strand could provoke triplex formation (Figure 12B) which, in turn, could lead to termination of DNA synthesis. This hypothesis was recently proven by Samadashwily et al (110) in their studies of DNA polymerization on open circular DNAs. T7 DNA polymerase terminated exactly at the pseudosym-

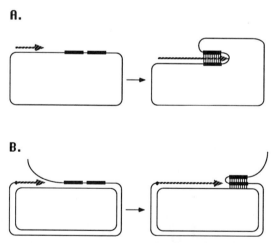

Figure 12 DNA polymerase–driven triplex formation blocks polymerization. Black boxes represent the two halves of a homopurine-homopyrimidine mirror repeat involved in the formation of an intramolecular triplex; the striated arrow depicts the newly synthesized DNA chain. (*A*) Single-stranded DNA template (4). (*B*) Double-stranded DNA template (110). The diamond shows the original nick in the double-helical template providing a 3'-OH end for DNA polymerase.

metry site of *H-motifs when the purine-rich strand was displaced. When the pyrimidine-rich strand was displaced, no termination occurred. The model gained support from the observation that mutations within such motifs which destroyed *H potential released polymerization termination, while compensatory mutations restoring the *H-forming ability restored termination as well.

Prevention of further elongation by DNA polymerase-driven triplex formation may serve as an efficient mechanism of DNA polymerase self-termination. Consequently, H motifs may be considered suicidal sequences for DNA polymerization. Clearly, the actual replication fork contains not only DNA polymerase but a complex of replication proteins, including helicases, SSB proteins, primases, topoisomerases, etc. Recently it was found that the DNA-helicase activity of the SV40 T-antigen is inhibited by triplex formation (101). However, detailed studies on the role of H-DNA in reconstituted replication systems have not yet been provided.

Only fragmentary data are available on the role of H motifs in the regulation of replication in vivo. One example concerns polyomavirus-transformed rat cells. Polyomavirus DNA integrates in a particular chromosomal site (88), and treatment of the cells with mitomycin C leads to the amplification of virus DNA and adjacent cellular sequences (3). The boundary of the amplified DNA segment lies within a homopurine-homopyrimidine stretch, $d(G-A)_{27} \cdot d(C-T)_{27}$, located 2 kb from the viral DNA. Because this sequence causes premature termination of replication in vitro, it was suggested that this DNA motif could be a natural replication terminator. This hypothesis gained support from the observation that when the corresponding DNA segment was cloned into SV40 DNA it caused a pausing in replication fork progression (107).

Another case is the *dhfr*-amplicon. It contains an unusual cluster of simple-repeats, including $d(A-C)_{18}$, $d(A-G)_{21}$, $d(G)_9$, and $d(A-G)_{27}$, which is located 2 kb 3' of the *dhfr* origin of replication (18, 90). This cluster, when cloned at either side of the SV40 origin in the pSV011 episome, reduced its replication up to twofold, and, when placed on both sides of the origin, blocked replication almost completely (15). Based on in vitro data, the authors speculated that the triplex-forming repeats within this cluster may play a key role in termination of DNA replication in vivo (15).

Although these data make the idea of H-DNA involvement in the regulation of replication promising, this hypothesis is far from proved. Alternative ideas (e.g. protein binding, or changes in chromatin structure) may explain the results as well. Future studies, including direct detection of H-DNA in vivo, are crucial for the evaluation of this hypothesis.

H-MOTIFS IN EUKARYOTIC PROMOTERS

As noted above, the studies that led to the discovery of H-DNA were initiated by the detection of S1 hypersensitivity within eukaryotic promoters—hypersensitivity associated with homopurine-homopyrimidine stretches (reviewed in 128). In many cases, it was then found that the formation of H-DNA did indeed account for nuclease hypersensitivity. In other cases, however, the formation of canonical H-DNA seems unlikely because of the insufficient length of homopurine-homopyrimidine motifs or the lack of proper symmetry within them. Thus other structures, which may be related to H-DNA, must be responsible for nuclease hypersensitivity. There is a growing body of data on the structure-functional dissection of H motifs in eukaryotic promoters. We describe below several of the best-studied cases showing the significance of H motifs in promoter function.

One well-characterized example is the promoter of the *Drosophila* heat-shock gene *hsp26*. At approximately the -100 position of the promoter it contains a $d(C-T)_{10} \cdot d(A-G)_{10}$ stretch (34) crucial for the heat shock response of the promoter in vivo (35). Careful nuclease and chemical probing led to the conclusion that this sequence adopts an H conformation in vitro (34). However all attempts to detect H-DNA in vivo using genomic footprinting have been unsuccessful (35). A *Drosophila* nuclear protein that binds preferentially to the pyrimidine-rich strand of this sequence was found (34). It is not yet clear whether or not the H-forming potential of the target sequence is important for protein binding.

Another case is the promoter of the chicken β^A-globin gene, which contains a $d(G)_{18} \cdot d(C)_{18}$ string approximately 200 bp upstream of the transcriptional start site. Detailed structural studies of this stretch (57, 62) revealed that it can exist in either H or *H conformation, depending on environmental conditions in vitro. No attempt has yet been made to determine the structure of this string in vivo. Chicken erythroid cells contain a zinc-dependent protein called BGP1 that specifically targets this sequence (21). This protein binds to the G-rich strand of the stretch.

The human c-*myc* gene contains a nuclease-hypersensitive element, called NHE or NSE, located 125 bp upstream of the P1 promoter start site (14, 54, 104). Several groups have suggested that formation of H-like DNA is responsible for nuclease sensitivity in this promotor (29, 104). Two different structures have been discussed, both containing numerous mismatches and looped out single- and double-stranded DNA stretches. The NSE is important for c-*myc* transcription (24, 104). This sequence serves as a binding site for a protein(s), presumably a transcriptional activator (24, 104). Cloning and sequencing of a gene coding for a protein that binds to the c-*myc* NSE, called NSEP-1, has been reported (64). This protein binds preferentially to the pyrimidine-rich strand—not only to the NSE in the *myc* promoter, but also to several other H-forming sequences from different promoters, including c-Ki-*ras*, EGF-R, etc. The authors suggested that NSEP-1 recognizes structural rather than sequence similarities of the homopurine-homopyrimidine stretches, presumably their ability to form H-DNA. Postel et al have described a different protein binding to the same element, called PuF (104). This protein has recently been cloned and sequenced. It appears to be identical to the previously described nm23-H2 nucleoside diphosphate kinase, which is a candidate supressor of tumor metastasis (103).

Homopurine-homopyrimidine stretches showing S1 hypersensitivity are common in so-called TATA-less promoters. These promoters are unusually GC-rich, have no TATA or CAAT boxes, and contain numerous transcriptional start sites. It is not immediately clear whether the elevated frequency of the homopurine-homopyrimidine stretches has a functional significance or is a simple result of high sequence redundancy. One well-studied case is the mouse c-Ki-*ras* oncogene promoter. The S1-hypersensitive element is located approximately 100 bp upstream of the multiple transcriptional start-sites area and is important for promoter function (42). A nuclear protein(s) that specifically binds to this element was identified by band-shift assay (42). Pestov et al (102) found that H-DNA formed by a 27-bp-long H palindrome is responsible for nuclease cleavage. It is thus reasonable to believe that the H-forming motif in the c-Ki-*ras* promoter is a positive *cis*-acting transcriptional element. Similar conclusions have been reached for several other TATA-less promoters, including human c-*ets*-2 (86) and EGF-R (46).

All the cases described here share significant similarities. H-forming sequences appear to be important for transcriptional regulation. These sequences serve as targets for nuclear proteins, presumably transcriptional activators. And these proteins, when characterized, often bind preferentially to either the purine-rich or the pyrimidine-rich strand of the H motifs. This unusual binding pattern may dramatically influence the equilibrium between different DNA conformations of the promoter.

Numerous hypotheses have been offered about the role of H-motifs in promoter functioning. In our view it is reasonable to suggest that local changes in DNA structure may regulate the interaction between promoter DNA and specific regulator proteins. In support of this hypothesis are numerous reports describing eukaryotic proteins preferentially binding to either the homopurine- or the homopyrimidine strand of H motifs (16, 53, 94). Recently, the partial characterization of a protein that preferentially binds to triple-helical DNA has also been reported (55). A study of Kohwi & Kohwi-Shigematsu (58) additionally support this idea. The authors studied the influence of $d(G)_n$ stretches of varying length on the activity of a downstream minimal promoter. It turned out that an initial increase in the length of the $d(G)_n$ stretch caused a progressive activation of transcription, but a further increase in the length restored the original level of promoter activity. There was a clear reverse correlation between the ability of a stretch to form *H configuration in vitro and its ability to activate transcription in vivo. The authors concluded that short $d(G)_n$ stretches served as binding sites for a transcriptional activator; while longer stretches adopted a triplex configuration that prevented activator binding.

Despite the wealth of data and hypotheses, no direct evidence indicates that the structural features of H motifs are involved in transcriptional regulation in vivo. Further studies addressing this issue are needed.

CONCLUSIONS

As in the cases of other unusual DNA structures (Z-DNA, parallel-stranded DNA, cruciforms, quadruplexes), the triplex H form and its related structures have been extensively studied in solution in recent years using a variety of physical and chemical methods. A large body of data has been accumulated about the versatility of H-like DNA structures and the factors affecting their stability. A variety of intramolecular triplexes can be formed by quite different sequences under a wide range of ambient conditions. In coming years we will likely encounter many more such structures.

As in the cases of other unusual structures, the biological roles of H-DNA remain obscure in spite of numerous speculations and repeated attempts to attack the problem. In recent years, accurate in vitro studies have demonstrated clear-cut effects of H-DNA-forming sequences on the function of different purified enzymes, the first of which was DNA polymerase. Both the crucial role of intramolecular triplexes in these effects and the possibility of H-DNA formation in vivo have been demonstrated; but we still lack a single example of the direct involvement of H-DNA in any biological process. Nevertheless, the versatility of the intramolecular triplexes makes it unlikely, in our opinion, that these structures play no role in normal or pathological biological processes.

ACKNOWLEDGMENTS

We thank our colleagues who have participated in the discovery and studies of H-DNA, including VI Lyamichev, ON Voloshin, BP Belotserkovskii, VA Malkov, AG Veselkov, ON Danilevskaya, AV Vologodskii, VN Dobrynin, VN Soyfer, A Dayn, DG Pestov, GM Samadashwily, M Vojtiskova, and E Palecek; Randal Cox for proofreading the manuscript; and the NIH, ACS, and Soros Foundation for financial support.

Any *Annual Review* chapter, as well as any article cited in an *Annual Review* chapter, may be purchased from the Annual Reviews Preprints and Reprints service.
1-800-347-8007; 415-259-5017; email: arpr@class.org

Literature Cited

1. Ahmed S, Henderson E. 1992. Formation of novel hairpin structures by telomeric C-strand oligonucleotides. *Nucleic Acids Res.* 20:507–11
2. Anshelevich VV, Vologodskii AV, Lukashin AV, Frank-Kamenetskii MD. 1984. Slow relaxational processes in the melting of linear biopolymers: a theory and its application to nucleic acids. *Biopolymers* 23:39–58
3. Baran N, Lapidot A, Manor H. 1987. Unusual sequence element found at the end of an amplicon. *Mol. Cell. Biol.* 7:2636–40
4. Baran N, Lapidot A, Manor H. 1991. Formation of DNA triplexes accounts for arrests of DNA synthesis at $d(TC)_n$ and $d(GA)_n$ tracts. *Proc. Natl. Acad. Sci. USA* 88:507–11
5. Beal PA, Dervan PB. 1991. Second structural motif for recognition of DNA by oligonucleotide-directed triple-helix formation. *Science* 251:1360–63
6. Beal PA, Dervan PB. 1992. The influence of single base triplet changes on the stability of a pur·pur·pyr triple helix determined by affinity cleaving. *Nucleic Acids Res.* 20:2773–76
7. Beasty AM, Behe MJ. 1988. An oligopurine sequence bias occurs in eukaryotic viruses. *Nucleic Acids Res.* 16:1517–28
8. Belotserkovskii BP, Frank-Kamenetskii MD. 1993. Study of pH-dependent

structural transition in telomeric sequences by two-dimensional gel electrophoresis. *Electrophoresis* 14:266–70
9. Belotserkovskii BP, Krasilnikova MM, Veselkov AG, Frank-Kamenetskii MD. 1992. Kinetic trapping of H-DNA by oligonucleotide binding. *Nucleic Acids Res.* 20:1903–8
10. Belotserkovskii BP, Veselkov AG, Filippov SA, Dobrynin VN, Mirkin SM, Frank-Kamenetskii MD. 1990. Formation of intramolecular triplex in homopurine-homopyrimidine mirror repeats with point substitutions. *Nucleic Acids Res.* 18:6621–24
11. Beltran R, Martinez-Balbas A, Bernues J, Bowater R, Azorin F. 1993. Characterization of the zinc-induced structural transition to *H-DNA at a $d(GA·CT)_{22}$ sequence. *J. Mol. Biol.* 230:966–78
12. Bernues J, Beltran R, Casasnovas JM, Azorin F. 1989. Structural polymorphism of homopurine-homopyrimidine sequences: the secondary DNA structure adopted by a $d(GA·CT)_{22}$ sequence in the presence of zinc ions. *EMBO J.* 8:2087–94
13. Bernues J, Beltran R, Casasnovas JM, Azorin F. 1990. DNA sequence and metal-ion specificity of the formation of *H-DNA. *Nucleic Acids Res.* 18: 4067–73
14. Boles TC, Hogan ME. 1987. DNA

structure equilibria in the human c-*myc* gene. *Biochemistry* 26:367–76

15. Brinton BT, Caddle MS, Heintz NH. 1991. Position and orientation-dependent effects of a eukaryotic Z-triplex motif on episomal DNA replication in COS-7 cells. *J. Biol. Chem.* 266:5153–61

16. Brunel F, Alzari PM, Ferrara P, Zakin MM. 1991. Cloning and sequencing of PYBP, a pyrimidine-rich specific single strand DNA-binding protein. *Nucleic Acids Res.* 19:5237–45

17. Budarf M, Blackburn EH. 1987. S1 nuclease sensitivity of a double-stranded telomeric DNA sequence. *Nucleic Acids Res.* 15:6273–92

18. Caddle MS, Lussier RH, Heintz NH. 1990. Intramolecular DNA triplexes, bent DNA and DNA unwinding elements in the initiation region of an amplified dihydrofolate reductase replicon. *J. Mol. Biol.* 213:19–33

19. Cantor CR., Efstratiadis A. 1984. Possible structures of homopurine-homopyrimidine S1-hypersensitive sites. *Nucleic Acids Res.* 12:8059–72

20. Christophe D, Cabrer B, Bacolla A, Targovnik H, Pohl V, Vassart G. 1985. An unusually long poly(purine)-poly(pyrimidine) sequence is located upstream from the human thyroglobulin gene. *Nucleic Acids Res.* 13:5127–44

21. Clark SP, Lewis CD, Felsenfeld G. 1990. Properties of BGP1, a poly(dG)-binding protein from chicken erythrocytes. *Nucleic Acids Res.* 18:5119–26

22. Coll M, Frederick CA, Wang AH, Rich A. 1987. A bifurcated hydrogen-bonded conformation in the $d(A \cdot T)$ base pairs of the DNA dodecamer d(CGCAAATTTGCG) and its complex with distamycin. *Proc. Natl. Acad. Sci. USA* 84:8385–89

23. Collier DA, Wells RD. 1990. Effect of length, supercoiling, and pH on intramolecular triplex formation. Multiple conformers at pur·pyr mirror repeats. *J. Biol. Chem.* 265:10652–58

24. Davis TL, Firulli AB, Kinniburgh A. 1989. Ribonucleoprotein and protein factors bind to an H-DNA-forming c-*myc* DNA element: Possible regulators of the c-*myc* gene. *Proc. Natl. Acad. Sci. USA* 86:9682–86

25. Dayn A, Malkhosyan S, Mirkin SM. 1992. Transcriptionally driven cruciform formation *in vivo*. *Nucleic Acids Res.* 20:5991–97

26. Dayn A, Malkhosyan SR, Duzhii DI, Lyamichev VI, Panchenko YA, Mirkin SM. 1991. Formation of $(dA-dT)_n$ cruciforms in *Escherichia coli* cells under different environmental conditions. *J. Bacteriol.* 173:2658–64

27. Dayn A, Samadashwily GM, Mirkin SM. 1992. Intramolecular DNA triplexes: unusual sequence requirements and influence on DNA polymerization. *Proc. Natl. Acad. Sci. USA* 89:11406–10

28. Felsenfeld G, Davies DR, Rich A. 1957. Formation of a three-stranded polynucleotide molecule. *J. Am. Chem. Soc.* 79:2023–24

29. Firulli AB, Maibenko DC, Kinniburgh AJ. 1992. The identification of a tandem H-DNA structure in the c-*myc* nuclease sensitive promoter element. *Biochem. Biophys. Res. Commun.* 185:264–70

30. Fox KR. 1990. Long $(dA)_n \cdot (dT)_n$ tracts can form intramolecular triplexes under superhelical stress. *Nucleic Acids Res.* 18:5387–91

31. Frank-Kamenetskii MD, Vologodskii AV. 1984. Thermodynamics of the B-Z transition in superhelical DNA. *Nature* 307:481–82

32. Frank-Kamenetskii MD. 1990. DNA supercoiling and unusual structures. In *DNA Topology and Its Biological Effects,* ed. NR Cozzarelli and J Wang, pp. 185-215. Cold Spring Harbor Lab. Press

33. Frank-Kamenetskii MD. 1992. Protonated DNA structures. *Methods Enzymol.* 211:180–91

34. Gilmour DS, Thomas GH, Elgin SCR. 1989. *Drosophila* nuclear proteins bind to regions of alternating C and T residues in gene promoters. *Science* 245:1487–90

35. Glaser RL, Thomas GH, Siegfried E, Elgin SCR, Lis JT. 1990. Optimal heat-induced expression of the *Drosophila* hsp26 gene requires a promoter sequence containing $(CT)_n \cdot (GA)_n$ repeats. *J. Mol. Biol.* 211:751–61

36. Griffin LC, Dervan PB. 1989. Recognition of thymine adenine base pairs by guanine in a pyrimidine triple helix motif. *Science* 245:967–71

37. Hampel KJ, Burkholder GD, Lee JS. 1993. Plasmid dimerization mediated by triplex formation between polypyrimidine-polypurine repeats. *Biochemistry* 32:1072–77

38. Hampel KJ, Crosson P, Lee JS. 1991. Polyamines favor DNA triplex formation at neutral pH. *Biochemistry* 30:4455–59

39. Hanvey JC, Klysik J, Wells RD. 1988.

Influence of DNA sequence on the formation of non-B right-handed helices in oligopurine-oligopyrimidine inserts in plasmids. *J. Biol. Chem.* 263:7386–96

40. Hanvey JC, Shimizu M, Wells RD. 1988. Intramolecular DNA triplexes in supercoiled plasmids. *Proc. Natl. Acad. Sci. USA* 85:6292–96

41. Hentchel CC. 1982. Homopolymer sequences in the spacer of a sea urchin histone gene repeat are sensitive to S1 nuclease. *Nature* 295:714–16

42. Hoffman EK, Trusko SP, Murphy M, George DL. 1990. An S1 nuclease-sensitive homopurine homopyrimidine domain in the c-Ki-*ras* promoter interacts with a nuclear factor. *Proc. Natl. Acad. Sci. USA* 87:2705–9

43. Hoogsteen K. 1963. The crystal and molecular structure of a hydrogen-bonded complex between 1 methylthymine and 9 methyladenine. *Acta Crystallogr.* 16:907–16

44. Htun H, Dahlberg JE. 1988. Single strands, triple strands and kinks in H-DNA. *Science* 241:1791–96

45. Htun H, Dahlberg JE. 1989. Topology and formation of triple-stranded H-DNA. *Science* 243:1571–76

46. Johnson AC, Jinno Y, Merlino GT. 1988. Modulation of epidermal growth factor receptor proto-oncogene transcription by a promoter site sensitive to S1 nuclease. *Mol. Cell. Biol.* 8:4174–84

47. Johnson D, Morgan AR. 1978. Unique structures formed by pyrimidine-purine DNAs which may be four-stranded. *Proc. Natl. Acad. Sci. USA* 75:1637–41

48. Johnston BH. 1988. The S1-sensitive form of d(C-T)$_n$·d(A-G)$_n$: chemical evidence form a three-stranded structure in plasmids. *Science* 241:1800–4

49. Kang S, Wells RD. 1992. Central non-pur·pyr sequences in oligo (dG·dC) tracts and metal ions influence the formation of intramolecular DNA triplex isomers. *J. Biol. Chem.* 267:20887–91

50. Kang S, Wohlrab F, Wells RD. 1992. Metal ions cause the isomerization of certain intramolecular triplexes. *J. Biol. Chem.* 267:1259–64

51. Karlovsky P, Pecinka P, Vojtiskova M, Makaturova E, Palecek E. 1990. Protonated triplex DNA in *E. coli* cells as detected by chemical probing. *FEBS Lett.* 274:39–42

52. Kato M, Shimizu N. 1992. Effect of potential triplex DNA region on the in vivo expression of bacterial β-lacta-mase gene in superhelical recombinant plasmids. *J. Biochem.* 112:492–94

53. Kennedy GC, Rattner JB. 1992. Pur-1, a zinc-finger protein that binds to purine-rich sequences, transactivates an insulin promoter in heterologous cells. *Proc. Natl. Acad. Sci. USA* 89:11498–11502

54. Kinniburgh AJ. 1989. A cis-acting transcription element of the c-*myc* gene can assume an H-DNA conformation. *Nucleic Acids Res.* 17:7771–78

55. Kiyama R, Camerini-Otero D. 1991. A triplex DNA-binding protein from human cells: purification and characterization. *Proc. Natl. Acad. Sci. USA* 88:10450–54

56. Klysik J, Rippe K, Jovin TM. 1991. Parallel-stranded DNA under topological stress: rearrangement of (dA)$_{15}$·(dT)$_{15}$ to a d(A·A·T)n triplex. *Nucleic Acids Res.* 19:7145–54

57. Kohwi Y, Kohwi-Shigematsu T. 1988. Magnesium ion-dependent, novel triple-helix structure formed by homopurine-homopyrimidine sequences in supercoiled DNA. *Proc. Natl. Acad. Sci. USA* 85:3781–88

58. Kohwi Y, Kohwi-Shigematsu T. 1991. Altered gene expression correlates with DNA structure. *Genes Dev.* 5:2547–54

59. Kohwi Y, Kohwi-Shigematsu T. 1993. Structural polymorphism of homopurine-homopyrimidine sequences at neutral pH. *J. Mol. Biol.* 231:1090-1101

60. Kohwi Y, Malkhosyan SR, Kohwi-Shigematsu T. 1992. Intramolecular dG·dG·dC triplex detected in *Escherichia coli* cells. *J. Mol. Biol.* 223:817–22

61. Kohwi Y, Panchenko Y. 1993. Transcription-dependent recombination induced by triple helix formation. *Genes Dev.* 7:1766–78

62. Kohwi Y. 1989. Cationic metal-specific structures adopted by the poly(dG) region and the direct repeats in the chicken adult b^A globin gene promoter. *Nucleic Acids Res.* 17:4493–4502

63. Kohwi-Shigematsu T, Kohwi Y. 1991. Detection of triple-helix related structures adopted by poly(dG)-poly(dC) sequences in supercoiled plasmid DNA. *Nucleic Acids Res.* 19:4267–71

64. Kolluri R, Torrey TA, Kinniburgh AJ. 1992. A CT promoter element binding protein: definition of a double-strand and a novel single-strand DNA binding motif. *Nucleic Acids Res.* 20:111–16

65. Kornberg A, Baker TA 1992. *DNA*

Replication. New York: W. H. Freeman. 2nd ed.
66. Kunkel GR, Martinson HG. 1981. Nucleosomes will not form on double-stranded RNA or over poly(dA)·poly(dT) tracts in recombinant DNA. *Nucleic Acids Res.* 9:6859–88
67. Lapidot A, Baran N, Manor H. 1989. (dT-dC)$_n$ and (dG-dA)$_n$ tracts arrest single stranded DNA replication *in vitro. Nucleic Acids Res.* 17:883–900
68. Larsen A, Weintraub H. 1982. An altered conformation detected by S1 nuclease occurs at specific region in active chick globin chromatin. *Cell* 29:609–22
69. Lee JS, Johnson DA, Morgan AR. 1979. Complexes formed by (pyrimidine)$_n$· (purine)$_n$ DNAs on lowering the pH are three-stranded. *Nucleic Acids Res.* 6:3073–91
70. Lee JS, Latimer LJ, Haug BL, Pulleyblank DE, Skinner DM, Burkholder GD. 1989. Triplex DNA in plasmids and chromosomes. *Gene* 82:191–99
71. Lilley, DMJ. 1980. The inverted repeat as a recognizable structural feature in supercoiled DNA molecules. *Proc. Natl. Acad. Sci. USA* 77:6468–72
72. Lilley DMJ. 1992. Probes of DNA structure. *Methods Enzymol.* 212:133–39
73. Liu LF, Wang JC. 1987. Supercoiling of the DNA template during transcription. *Proc. Natl. Acad. Sci. USA* 84:7024–27
74. Lyamichev VI, Mirkin SM, Danylevskaya ON, Voloshin ON, Balatskaya SV, et al. 1989. An unusual DNA structure detected in a telomeric sequence under superhelical stress and at low pH. *Nature* 339:634–37
75. Lyamichev VI, Mirkin SM, Frank-Kamenetskii MD. 1985. Structure of homopurine-homopyrimidine tract in superhelical DNA. *J. Biomol. Struct. Dynam.* 3:327–38
76. Lyamichev VI, Mirkin SM, Frank-Kamenetskii MD. 1986. Structures of homopurine-homopyrimidine tract in superhelical DNA. *J. Biomol. Struct. Dynam.* 3:667–69
77. Lyamichev VI, Mirkin SM, Frank-Kamenetskii MD. 1987. Structure of (dG)$_n$·(dC)$_n$ under superhelical stress and acid pH. *J. Biomol. Struct. Dynam.* 5:275–82
78. Lyamichev VI, Mirkin SM, Kumarev VP, Baranova LV, Vologodskii AV, Frank-Kamenetskii MD. 1989. Energetics of the B-H transition in super-

coiled DNA carrying d(CT)$_x$·d(AG)$_x$ and d(C)n·d(G)n inserts. *Nucleic Acids Res.* 17:9417–23
79. Macaya RF, Gilber DE, Malek S, Sinsheimer JS, Feigon J. 1991. Structure and stability of X·G·C mismatches in the third strand of intramolecular triplexes. *Science* 254:270–74
80. Mace HAF, Pelham HRB, Travers A. 1983. Association of an S1 nuclease-sensitive structure with short direct repeats 5' of *Drosophila* heat shock gene. *Nature* 304:555–57
81. Malkov VA, Soyfer VN, Frank-Kamenetskii MD. 1992. Effect of intermolecular triplex formation on the yield of cyclobutane photodimers in DNA. *Nucleic Acids Res.* 20:4889–95
82. Malkov VA, Voloshin ON, Veselkov AG, Rostapshov VM, Jansen I, et al. 1993. Protonated pyrimidine-purine-purine triplex. *Nucleic Acids Res.* 21:105–11
83. Manor H, Sridhara Rao B, Martin RG. 1988. Abundance and degree of dispersion of genomic d(GA)$_n$·d(TC)$_n$ sequences. *J. Mol. Evol.* 27:96–101
84. Margot JB, Hardison RC. 1985. DNase I and nuclease S1 sensitivity of the rabbit β1 globin gene in nuclei and in supercoiled plasmids. *J. Mol. Biol.* 184:195–210
85. Martinez-Balbas A, Azorin F. 1993. The effect of zinc on the secondary structure of d(GA·TC) DNA sequences of different length: a model for the formation *H-DNA. *Nucleic Acids Res.* 21:2557–62
86. Mavrothalassitis GL, Watson DK, Papas TS. 1990. Molecular and functional characterization of the promoter of ETS2, the human c-*ets*-2 gene. *Proc. Natl. Acad. Sci. USA* 87:1047–51
87. McKeon C, Schmidt A, de Crombrugghe BA. 1984. A sequence conserved in both the chicken and mouse α2(I) collagen promoter contains sites sensitive to S1 nuclease. *J. Biol. Chem.* 259:6636–40
88. Mendelsohn E, Baran N, Neer A, Manor H. 1982. Integration site of polyoma virus DNA in the inducible LPT line of polyoma-transformed rat cells. *J. Virol.* 41:192–209
89. Mergny JL, Sun JS, Rougee M, Montenay-Garestier T, Barcelo F, et al. 1991. Sequence specificity in triple-helix formation: experimental and theoretical studies of the effect of mismatches on triplex stability. *Biochemistry* 30:9791–98
90. Milbrandt JD, Heintz NH, White WC,

Rothman SM, Hamlin JL. 1981. Methotrexate-resistant Chinese hamster ovary cells have amplified a 135-kilobase-pair region that includes the dihydrofolate reductase gene. *Proc. Natl. Acad. Sci. USA* 78:6043–47

91. Mirkin SM, Lyamichev VI, Drushlyak KN, Dobrynin VN, Filippov SA, Frank-Kamenetskii MD. 1987. DNA H form requires a homopurine-homopyrimidine mirror repeat. *Nature* 330: 495–97

92. Morgan AR, Wells RD. 1968. Specificity of the three-stranded complex formation between double-stranded DNA and single-stranded RNA containing repeating nucleotide sequences. *J. Mol. Biol.* 37:63–80

93. Moser HE, Dervan PB. 1987. Sequence-specific cleavage of double helical DNA by triple helix formation. *Science* 238:645–50

94. Muraiso T, Nomoto S, Yamazaki H, Mishima Y, Kominari R. 1992. A single-stranded DNA binding protein from mouse tumor cells specifically recognizes the C-rich strand of the (AGG:CCT)n repeats that can alter DNA conformation. *Nucleic Acids Res.* 20:6631–35

95. Nelson HCM, Finch JT, Bonaventura FL, Klug A. 1987. The structure of an oligo(dA)·oligo(dT) tract and its biological implications. *Nature* 330:221–26

96. Palecek E. 1991. Local supercoil-stabilized DNA structures. *Crit. Rev. Biochem. Mol. Biol.* 26:151–226

97. Panayotatos N, Wells RD. 1981. Cruciform structures in supercoiled DNA. *Nature* 289:466–70

98. Panyutin IG, Kovalsky OI, Budowsky EI. 1989. Magnesium-dependent supercoiling-induced transition in $(dG)_n \cdot (dC)_n$ stretches and formation of a new G-structure by $(dG)_n$ strand. *Nucleic Acids Res.* 17:8257–71

99. Panyutin IG, Wells RD. 1992. Nodule DNA in the $(GA)_{37} \cdot (CT)_{37}$ insert in superhelical plasmids. *J. Biol. Chem.* 267:5495–5501

100. Parniewski P, Kwinkowski M, Wilk A, Klysik J. 1990. Dam methyltransferase sites located within the loop region of the oligopurine-oligopyrimidine sequences capable of forming H-DNA are undermethylated *in vivo*. *Nucleic Acids Res.* 18:605–10

101. Peleg M, Manor H. 1993. DNA triplex formation inhibits DNA unwinding by the SV40 large T-antigen helicase. *J. Biomol. Struct. Dynam.* 10:a149

102. Pestov DG, Dayn A, Siyanova EYu, George DL, Mirkin SM. 1991. H-DNA and Z-DNA in the mouse c-Ki-*ras* promoter. *Nucleic Acids Res.* 19:6527–32

103. Postel EH, Berberich SJ, Flint SJ, Ferrone CA. 1993. Human c-*myc* transcription factor PuF identified as nm23-H2 nucleoside diphosphate kinase, a candidate supressor of tumor metastasis. *Science* 261:478–83

104. Postel EH, Mango SE, Flint SJ. 1989. A nuclease-hypersensitive element of the human c-*myc* promoter interacts with a transcription initiation factor. *Mol. Cell. Biol.* 9:5123–33

105. Pulleyblank DE, Haniford DB, Morgan AR. 1985. A structural basis for S1 nuclease sensitivity of double-stranded DNA. *Cell* 42:271–80

106. Rahmouni AR, Wells RD. 1992. Direct evidence for the effect of transcription on local DNA supercoiling *in vivo*. *J. Mol. Biol.* 223:131–44

107. Rao S, Manor H, Martin RG. 1988. Pausing in simian virus 40 DNA replication by a sequence containing $(dG\text{-}dA)_{27} \cdot (dT\text{-}dC)_{27}$. *Nucleic Acids Res.* 16:8077–94

108. Reaban ME, Griffin JA. 1990. Induction of RNA-stabilized DNA conformers by transcription of an immunoglobulin switch region. *Nature* 348:342–44

109. Rippe K, Kuryavy VV, Westhof E, Jovin TM. 1992. Polymorphism and possible biological functions of parallel-stranded DNA. In *Structural Tools for the Analysis of Protein-Nucleic Acids Complexes. Advances in Life Sciences*, ed. DMJ Lilley, H Heumann, D Suck, pp. 81-107. Basel: Birkhauser

110. Samadashwily GM, Dayn A, Mirkin SM. 1993. Suicidal nucleotide sequences for DNA polymerase. *EMBO J.* 12:4975–83

111. Sarkar PS, Brahmachari SK. 1992. Intramolecular triplex potential sequence within a gene down regulates its expression *in vivo*. *Nucleic Acids Res.* 20:5713–18

112. Shen C-K. 1983. Superhelicity induces hypersensitivity of a human polypyrimidine·polypurine DNA sequence in the human a2-a1 globin intergenic region to S1 nuclease digestion. *Nucleic Acids Res.* 11:7899–10

113. Shimizu M, Hanvey JC, Wells RD. 1990. Multiple non-B-DNA conformations of polypurine-polypyrimidine sequences in plasmids. *Biochemistry* 29:4704–13

114. Shimizu M, Kubo K, Matsumoto U,

Shindo H. 1993. The loop sequence plays crucial roles for isomerization of intramolecular DNA triplexes in supercoiled plasmids. *J. Mol. Biol.* 235: 185–97

115. Sinden RR, Kochel TJ. 1987. Reduced 4,5,8-trimethylpsoralene cross-linking of left-handed Z-DNA stabilized by DNA supercoiling. *Biochemistry* 26: 1343–50

116. Singleton CK, Klysik J, Stirdivant SM, Wells RD. 1982. Left-handed Z-DNA is induced by supercoiling in physiological ionic conditions. *Nature* 299: 312–16

117. Stavnezer J, Reaban ME, Griffin JA. 1991. Triple-helix stabilization? *Nature* 351:447–48

118. Tabor CW, Tabor H. 1984. Polyamines. *Annu. Rev. Biochem.* 53:749–91

119. Usery DW, Sinden RR. 1993. Environmental influences on the *in vivo* level of intramolecular triplex DNA in *Escherichia coli*. *Biochemistry* 32: 6206–13

120. Vojtiskova M, Mirkin S, Lyamichev V, Voloshin O, Frank-Kamenetskii M, Palecek E. 1988. Chemical probing of the homopurine-homopyrimidine tract in supercoiled DNA at single-nucleotide resolution. *FEBS Lett.* 234:295–99

121. Voloshin ON, Mirkin SM, Lyamichev VI, Belotserkovskii BP, Frank-Kamenetskii MD. 1988. Chemical probing of homopurine-homopyrimidine mirror repeats in supercoiled DNA. *Nature* 333:475–76

122. Voloshin ON, Veselkov AG, Belotserkovskii BP, Danilevskaya ON, Pavlova MN, et al. 1992. An eclectic DNA structure adopted by human telomeric

sequence under superhelical stress and low pH. *J. Biomol. Struct. Dynam.* 9: 643–52

123. Wang AH, Quigley GJ, Kolpak FJ, Crawford JL, van Boom JH, et al. 1979. Molecular structure of a left-handed double helical DNA fragment at atomic resolution. *Nature* 282:680–86

124. Wang E, Malek S, Feigon J. 1992. Structure of a G·T·A triplet in an intramolecular DNA triplex. *Biochemistry* 31:4838–46

125. Wang JC, Peck LJ, Becherer K. 1983. DNA supercoiling and its effects on DNA structure and function. *Cold Spring Harbor Symp. Quant. Biol.* 47: 85–91

126. Wang JC. 1985. DNA topoisomerases. *Annu. Rev. Biochem.* 54:665–97

127. Weintraub H. 1983. A dominant role for DNA secondary structure in forming hypersensitive structures in chromatin. *Cell* 32:1191–03

128. Wells RD, Collier DA, Hanvey JC, Shimizu M, Wohlrab F. 1988. The chemistry and biology of unusual DNA structures adopted by oligopurine/oligopyrimidine sequences. *FASEB J.* 2: 2939–49

128a. Williamson JR. 1994. G-quartet structures in telomeric DNA. *Annu. Rev. Biophys. Biomol. Struct.* 23:703–30

129. Yagil G. 1991. Paranemic structures of DNA and their role in DNA unwinding. *Crit. Rev. Biochem. Mol. Biol.* 26: 475–559

130. Zakian VA. 1989. Structure and function of telomeres. *Annu. Rev. Genet.* 23:579–604

Annu. Rev. Biophys. Biomol. Struct. 1994. 23:577–607
Copyright © 1994 by Annual Reviews Inc. All rights reserved

CYCLIC NUCLEOTIDE-GATED ION CHANNELS AND SENSORY TRANSDUCTION IN OLFACTORY RECEPTOR NEURONS

F. Zufall, S. Firestein,[1] and G. M. Shepherd

Section of Neurobiology, Yale University School of Medicine, New Haven, Connecticut, 06510

KEY WORDS: olfactory transduction, vertebrates, second messenger kinetics, odor response

CONTENTS

[1] Present address: Department of Biology, Columbia University, New York, New York 10027.

577

PERSPECTIVES AND OVERVIEW

Sensory receptor cells of vertebrate visual and olfactory systems have emerged as model cells for examining the function and role of G-protein–mediated second-messenger signaling pathways in neuronal signal transduction. Two features are mainly responsible for this development: (a) The physiological input of sensory neurons can be relatively easily controlled during an experimental manipulation, as compared with the typical neuron in the central nervous system, and (b) the output of the second messenger cascade is coupled to an ion channel directly gated by cyclic nucleotides [the cyclic nucleotide–gated (CNG) channel], without an intermediate protein kinase, so that one can obtain detailed information about the different steps in the second-messenger cascade by recording the electrical activity of the last step, activation of the ion channel.

In this review we focus on the properties of the olfactory CNG channels. Because these channels play a critical role in the olfactory signal-transduction cascade, recent recordings from them have led to a better understanding of the mechanisms leading from the detection of external odor stimuli to the generation of an electrical signal in the receptor neurons. Our specific interest here is to relate the biophysical and physiological properties of the olfactory CNG channel to this functional role. A review of the olfactory CNG channel is timely because significant experimental results are accumulating and only a few brief reviews dealing with this specific subject are available (see 43, 123). Broader aspects of the investigations on mechanisms of olfactory transduction have been documented in several excellent reviews (4, 16, 30, 41, 75, 100, 109, 113).

There is another reason for studying CNG channels besides their role in olfactory transduction. Evidence gathered over the past few years has shown that CNG channels form a distinct gene family whose members are expressed in a wide variety of neuronal and nonneuronal cells (see 1). Many of their properties, as we review below, make CNG channels ideal candidates to act as modulators of synaptic efficacy in many regions of the central nervous system. Therefore, an understanding of CNG channels in a model neuron such as the vertebrate olfactory receptor cell may eventually lead to greater understanding of physiological processes in other cell types.

FUNCTIONAL ARCHITECTURE OF OLFACTORY RECEPTOR NEURONS

As in most other sensory neurons a fundamental principle of olfactory receptor neurons (ORNs) is compartmentalization—division of the cell into several morphological compartments, each specific for a different functional role (110). ORNs are bipolar neurons consisting of olfactory cilia (outer segment), a dendrite with a dendritic knob (inner segment), a cell soma, an axon, and axon terminals. The cilia facing the external environment are the site of primary transduction and generation of the receptor-potential response of the cell. Ultrastructural cytochemical characterization has provided direct evidence that two main components of the transduction pathway, a G-protein (G_{olf}) and a specific adenylyl cyclase, are primarily localized in distal segments of the cilia (88). The soma and dendrite contain all the necessary components for energy production and protein synthesis. Moreover, they set the resting potential, further shape and modulate the receptor potential generated by the sensory current, and transform it into an action-potential discharge, which is then transmitted through the output element, the axons forming the olfactory nerve, to the axon terminals at the first relay synapse in the olfactory bulb.

This functional specialization of the different compartments is associated with different ion channel compositions. Experiments using micropulse odor stimulation first provided strong evidence that the initial sensory transduction occurs mainly in the cilia. Stimuli directed at the cilia give the largest membrane inward currents, whereas stimuli directed at the soma give very small and delayed responses (33, 69). ORNs that have lost their cilia during the isolation procedure never show odor-induced responses; conversely, all isolated cells showing odor responses bear cilia (33). Detailed analysis of the cilia localization by microstimulation has been carried out (79).

The ion channel distribution of the soma and dendrite compartments has been described in reports from different species (34, 84, 85, 87, 90, 97, 98, 106, 115, 117, 118). These studies have demonstrated a rich repertoire of different ion channels. Among them are voltage-gated Na^+ and Ca^{2+} channels, several different K^+ channel types such as delayed rectifier, A-type and Ca^{2+}-activated K^+ channels, as well as inward rectifying Na^+-K^+ channels. These ion channels are well suited for shaping the receptor potential and transforming it into an impulse discharge. Thus, compartmentalization in ORNs is analogous to other sensory neurons such as photoreceptors (120, 121), auditory hair cells (56), and insect sex-pheromone detecting olfactory neurons (124), in which sensory transduction occurs in modified cilia or cilia-like microvilli.

Little is known, thus far, about the mechanisms of ion homeostasis in ORNs. An important goal in future studies is to develop detailed schemes regarding the mechanisms of ionic flow, sources of ion influx, intracellular sites of action of specific ions, and extrusion by pumps and ion exchangers. This knowledge should be especially important for Ca^{2+} ions that enter the cell through the CNG channels and have numerous functions in cellular adaptation (see below). Similar schemes have been provided for phototransduction (62, 74, 114).

SECOND MESSENGER CASCADE OF OLFACTORY SIGNALING

We briefly summarize the main results that have led to the present understanding of the biochemical cascade mediating olfactory transduction. Figure 1 schematically displays the key ionic and enzymatic events. Several laboratories have provided fundamental evidence for an odor-dependent, cAMP-mediated second-messenger cascade in ORNs in recent years. These pioneering investigations showed that cell-free preparations of olfactory cilia contain an adenylyl cyclase with high activity that is specifically enhanced by the application of odor molecules (92). This early result provided a vigorous stimulus for subsequent studies, and it is now clear that the components of this cascade producing cAMP (17) include odor receptors (20, 99), a specific GTP-binding protein denoted G_{olf} (58), an adenylyl cyclase (7, 92, 112), and

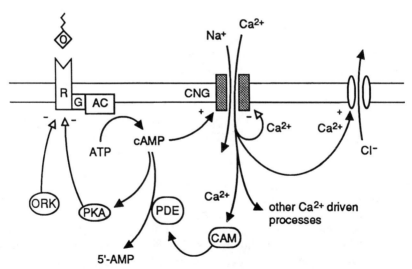

Figure 1   A schematic representation of the cyclic nucleotide pathway mediating olfactory transduction and its regulation via various feedback mechanisms. R, odor receptor; G, G-protein G_{olf}; AC, adenylyl cyclase; CNG, cyclic nucleotide–gated channel; PDE, phosphodiesterase; CAM, Ca^{2+}-calmodulin; PKA, protein kinase A; ORK, olfactory receptor kinase (see 24, 107); cAMP, adenosine 3'-5'-cyclic monophosphate.

a phosphodiesterase (5, 13). CNG channels were identified as the main target for the odor-induced cAMP. Moreover, the cAMP pathway is involved in olfactory transduction of a wide variety of odor substances (81). Thus, the cAMP pathway is the most widely studied and best understood pathway for odor transduction to date.

In addition to this pathway, other second-messenger pathways and ionic conductances may be involved in odor transduction. The most controversial example is the role of inositol-1,4,5-trisphosphate (IP_3) as a second messenger in ORNs. Although IP_3 is apparently produced by certain odors (11, 17, 103), whether and how the IP_3 pathway is related to the cAMP pathway and how IP_3 production is linked to a conductance change remains to be shown. One possibility could be the direct activation of a plasma membrane channel by IP_3 as described in the catfish (101) and in crustaceans (29). In salamander, however, no evidence has been found for an IP_3-gated conductance (31, 80), whereas CNG channels are found in virtually every olfactory cell. Other conductances involved in the electrical response to odors include Ca^{2+}-activated chloride channels (64, 73) and possibly also Ca^{2+}-gated K^+ channels (6, 27). Although the functional roles of these multiple second-messenger pathways remain unclear, certain classes of odor ligands probably differentially activate or modulate these conductances (11, 103). Therefore, a multipathway system theoretically could serve the purpose of odor discrimination and olfactory coding at the receptor cell level.

FUNCTIONAL PROPERTIES OF OLFACTORY CNG CHANNELS AND THEIR SIGNIFICANCE FOR SIGNAL PROCESSING

Molecular Identification of CNG Channels

A complete understanding of the functioning of CNG channels requires detailed knowledge about their molecular identification and structure. Clearly, CNG channels form their own multifunctional gene family, whose members share a number of distinctive features. Several reviews are available that deal with this subject (8, 60, 61).

Initial studies directed at molecular characterization of the channel were carried out in rod photoreceptors. A 63-kDa protein was purified from bovine rod outer segments (23) and, when reconstituted into planar lipid membranes, cGMP-dependent single-channel currents could be recorded that showed a number of properties of the native rod channel. In their pioneering work (63), Kaupp et al screened a bovine retinal cDNA library using probes from the purified protein. Subsequently, a clone containing 690 amino acids was isolated and sequenced, and expression of the full-length chain in *Xenopus laevis* oocytes confirmed that it was a functional cGMP-gated channel. Using this sequence as a basis, other CNG channels have been cloned from both rod and cone photoreceptors (12, 25, 94), and the olfactory epithelium of rat, bovine, and catfish (26, 46, 82); partial sequences have recently been obtained from retinal ganglion cells (1). All these studies have revealed a common structural motif as well as a strong homology in the amino acid sequences of the different CNG channel types.

Hydropathy plots of the channel sequence led to the proposal of a hypothetical model of the secondary structure of the channel (12, 63). This model (Figure 2A) contains six putative α-helical membrane-span-

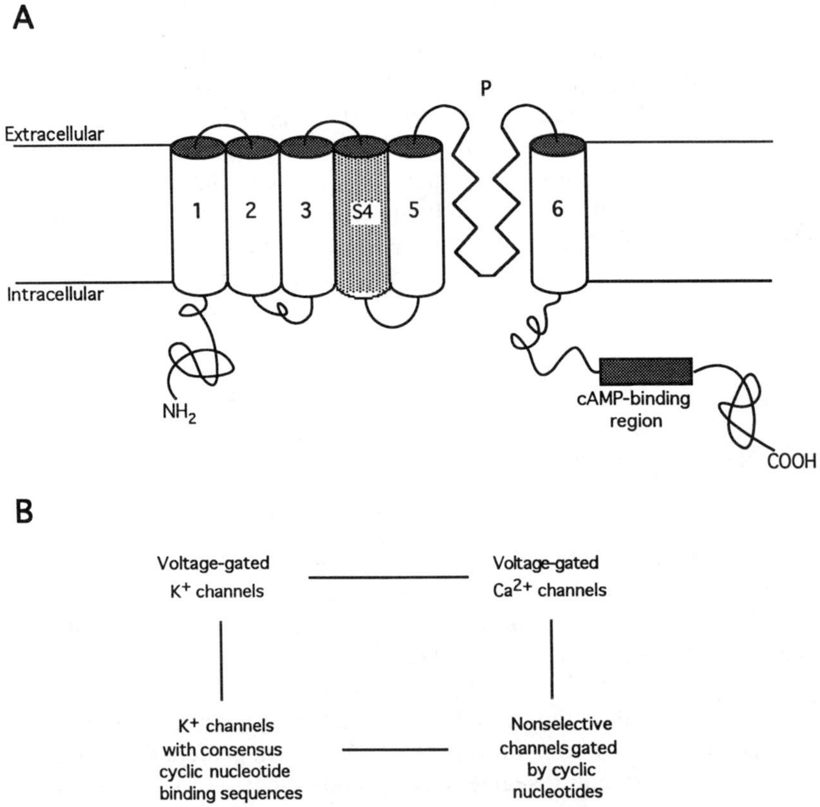

A

B

Figure 2 (A) Hypothetical model of the two-dimensional architecture of CNG channels (modified after 12). (B) Possible evolutionary connectivity between several members of the S4 ion channel superfamily (from 50).

ning regions each comprising approximately 20 amino acid residues. A seventh hydrophobic region located on the C-terminal side of domain 6 shows significant sequence similarity with other cyclic nucleotide binding sites, particularly the cGMP-dependent protein kinase and the catabolic gene activator protein (CAP) from *Escherichia coli* (63). Site-directed mutagenesis of a threonine residue in this region clearly changed the sensitivity of the channel for cyclic nucleotides (3). Data from the crystal structure of CAP was used to hypothesize a molecular model for the cyclic nucleotide-binding site (67). Because the cGMP-binding site is cytoplasmic, both N and C termini should be on the cytoplasmic side of the membrane. Interestingly, CNG channels also contain sequence motifs and structural elements reminiscent of voltage-gated channels, in particular K^+ and Ca^{2+} channels (46, 48, 50, 57, 63). Maximum homology is observed in the S4 transmembrane domain, a region that has been proposed to serve as a voltage sensor in voltage-gated channels. The low voltage sensitivity of CNG channels (see below) makes the functional significance of this motif unclear. Another structural element homologue to voltage-gated channels is a pore-forming hairpin-like β sheet (called H5, P-region, or SS1-SS2). Experiments using chimeric retinal-olfactory CNG channels have recently confirmed the role of the H5 domain in controlling ion permeation (47).

Still unsettled is the subunit composition of CNG channels. Initially, CNG channels were thought to form homooligomeric complexes, possibly as tetramers (60). Recently, a new subunit of the retinal rod CNG channel was isolated (22) that by itself cannot form functional channels. However, when coexpressed with the rod channel protein it introduces characteristic rapid flickers of single-channel currents, suggesting that the native channel is a heterooligomer. Future studies on this issue will shed light on this relationship between different functional classes of ion channels and may help to unravel a possible ancient common origin of voltage-gated and CNG channels (50) (see Figure 2B), an idea also supported by the recent cloning of a plant K^+ transport system with sequence homology to animal K^+ channels and CNG channels (108).

Odor Stimuli and Cyclic Nucleotides Activate a Common Channel

Vertebrate olfactory receptor neurons respond to odor stimuli by generating a net inward current (35, 68, 118). Some of the most characteristic properties of the odor-induced generator current are listed below:

1. The odor current increases in amplitude with increasing odor concentration. The dose-response relation can be fitted with the Hill equation using a Hill coefficient of between 2 and 4. Thus the dose-response relation is steep and the dynamic operating range of the cell typically spans approximately an order-of-magnitude change in stimulus concentration (32).
2. The current activates after a relatively long concentration-dependent latency that can range from 180 to 550 ms. However, brief pulses of odor much shorter than the latency can still elicit a response. These features are consistent with a second-messenger cascade intervening between odor binding and channel activation (33, 35).
3. A particularly interesting feature of the odor-activated current is that its peak amplitude depends not only on stimulus concentration but also on the duration of the stimulus. For stimulus pulses up to 1 s, the peak current increases with pulse duration while holding the stimulus concentration constant. Apparently olfactory neurons integrate stimulus information over a period of at least 1 s (33). The locus of the integrator is likely to be within the second-messenger system, and indeed some intriguing evidence, discussed below, suggests that the integrator is the CNG channel.
4. The time course of the odor-induced current in response to a maintained stimulus is transient, decaying back toward baseline in 3–8 s (33, 130). The mechanism underlying this adaptation is likely to be complex and may include regulation at all levels of the second-messenger cascade.

Over the past seven years evidence from different laboratories has accumulated to indicate that the initial large and rapid response to natural odor ligands is mediated by the activation of CNG channels. The first step toward this consensus was taken by Nakamura & Gold (91), who showed that excised patches from toad olfactory cilia contain a conductance that is directly activated by cAMP and cGMP. The next step was to activate this conductance with odors. Macroscopic odor-induced currents were compared with responses induced either by dialysis of ORNs with cyclic nucleotides (31, 69, 115) or with pharmacological agents causing an increase in cyclic nucleotide concentration (31, 39). These studies clearly supported the idea that cyclic nucleotides mediate olfactory transduction, but a direct demonstration of this identity at the single-channel level was still necessary. However, the high channel density of CNG channels, together with the unfavorable recording conditions in the small cilia (diameter about 0.2 μm), prevented isolation of single-channel events. An alternative was offered by the finding that CNG channels also occur at low density in the membrane of the olfactory knob, dendrites, and somata of salamander ORNs, where recordings can be obtained more easily and reliably (36, 70, 116, 126). Therefore, the strategy was to make recordings from membrane patches in which the channel density was sufficiently low to allow quantitative analysis of single-channel currents.

Single-channel events activated by a pulse of an odor mixture were recorded in the cell-attached configuration (Figure 3A). The inwardly directed single-channel currents depended on stimulus duration; a longer odor pulse elicited more single-channel activity and decreased the latency to the first opening (36). If the odor-sensitive channels recorded were the same as those underlying the previously identified CNG conductance of olfactory cilia, treatments that increase the intracellular cAMP concentration should also induce channel opening. Figure 3B shows that exogenously applied isobutyl-methyl-xanthine (IBMX), a phosphodiesterase inhibitor, induced continuous single-channel openings that resembled the odor-induced ion channel activity.

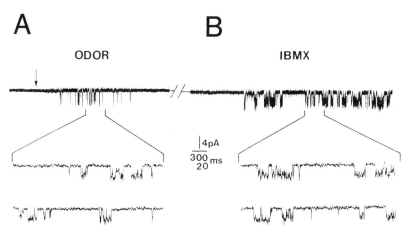

Figure 3 Odor and cyclic nucleotide-induced single-channel currents in the same membrane patch (cell-attached) taken from freshly isolated salamander ORNs. (A) A 150-ms pulse of the odor stimulus (amyl acetate, acetophenone, and cineole at 1 mM in Ringer), its delivery marked by the arrow, elicited some single-channel currents. Membrane depolarization after odor receptor activation was prevented by bathing the cells in a choline-solution [olfactory CNG channels are not permeable to choline (68)]. However, the patch of membrane sealed within the electrode remained in high Na^+ and low Ca^{2+} solution, so that channels would still conduct current when opened by intracellular factors. (B) Perfusion of the cell with 100 μM IBMX elicited very similar activity in the same patch of membrane. Pipette potential, 40 mV (from 36).

In fact, analysis of channel kinetic parameters showed no significant differences between those currents activated by odors or by IBMX. The same result was obtained by bath application of membrane-permeable cyclic nucleotides such as 8-bromo-cGMP (36).

These experiments showed conclusively that the channels activated during the odor response are also gated by intracellular cyclic AMP. These results have been supported in a recent study using flash photolysis of caged cyclic nucleotides (80). Thus, a direct link between the odor-induced production of cyclic AMP and the odor-sensitive current has been established.

Channel Density

The density of channels in the membrane is an important parameter for any model of olfactory transduction. One can estimate channel density in two ways. A combination of single-channel recordings and noise measurements from ciliary and extraciliary regions of toad ORNs has been used to estimate a channel density of 2400 channels/μm^2 in the cilia and 6 channels/μm^2 in extraciliary regions (70). In a later publication (71) these authors estimate the total number of channels per ORN to be about 250,000, with about 99% of these located in the cilia. A different approach used simultaneous whole-cell and suction electrode current recordings and estimated the ratio of extraciliary/ciliary channels to be 3.6×10^{-3} in salamander ORNs (80). The latter method probably provides a better value of this ratio because it does not have to take into account some uncertainties such as membrane patch area and local channel distribution. Nevertheless, all these data clearly show that the CNG channel is highly enriched in the olfactory cilia and that subcellular distribution of an essential component of the transduction pathway such as the CNG channel is one important feature for olfactory signal processing.

Single-Channel Properties

CHANNEL CONDUCTANCE AND LIGAND SELECTIVITY   Subsequent characterization of olfactory CNG channels has been performed in the inside-out recording mode. Figure 4 illustrates some of these single-channel currents that were activated by the direct application of a low concentration of cAMP. The properties of CNG channels at the single-channel level can only be examined in the absence of divalent cations because of a profound voltage-dependent block induced by divalents, as discussed below, that reduces the apparent open channel conductance in the salamander CNG channel to ~1.5 pS (at resting potential with 1 mM external Ca^{2+}), a value that is at the resolution limit (125).

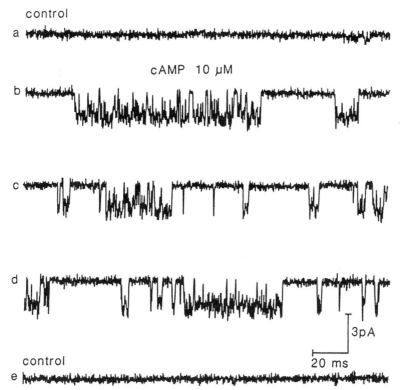

Figure 4 Activity of the salamander olfactory CNG channel in an inside-out patch. Control recording before (*a*) and after (*e*) application of agonist. Examples of single-channel currents (*b–d*) evoked by the continuous application of 10 µM cAMP. Channel openings can be classified into three kinetic classes—short single openings, bursts of channel openings, and clusters of bursts. Holding potential, −60 mV, divalent cation-free solutions (from 126).

In the absence of divalent cations, the single-channel conductance increases to 45 pS (126). This value is significantly higher than that from most other preparations reported thus far, providing a significant experimental advantage of the salamander preparation (as summarized in Table 1).

For many questions, membrane patches must contain only one CNG channel. One can consistently ensure this by taking patches from non-ciliary regions of salamander ORNs, such as the olfactory knob and dendrite. The extraciliary channels appear to have the same properties as those from the cilia (36, 71, 126). One of the most striking features of CNG channels investigated so far, and shared by the olfactory chan-

Table 1 Comparison of CNG channel properties from different olfactory preparations

Species	Source	Conductance (pS)	K_m (μM) cAMP	K_m (μM) cGMP	Hill coefficient (n)	Reference
Toad	Native	—	3.4	1.5	1.5	91
Frog	Native	12–15	4.0	1.5	1.6	40
Salamander	Native	45	20	4	2.1	126
Newt	Native	30	19	16	1.5	71
Catfish	Native	—	3.4	2.5	1.4	46
Catfish	Cloned	55	42	40	1.3	46
Rat	Native	12–15	2.5	1.0	1.3–1.8	40
Rat	Cloned	—	68	2.4	2.0	26
Bovine	Cloned	—	64	1.5	2.2–2.9	3

ncl, is the absence of desensitization in the continued presence of saturating concentrations of agonists (40, 126). This finding facilitates the interpretation of single-channel kinetics under steady-state conditions of stimulation.

As discussed above, the S4 transmembrane segment (a putative voltage sensor element) and the pore (P) regions of voltage-gated channels are unexpectedly conserved in CNG channels. This finding is especially interesting because olfactory CNG channels show little or no voltage dependence; the current-voltage relation of single-channel currents is nearly linear under divalent cation-free conditions (126). A slight voltage dependence of the open probability was reported for a cloned CNG channel from catfish olfactory epithelium (46). This effect may account for the slight outward rectification of macroscopic CNG currents (3, 40, 65, 91) although in some cases incomplete buffering of divalent cations and a voltage-dependent proton block (46, 125) may also have contributed. Recent experiments using rapid perfusion techniques show that channel onset kinetics are voltage independent (129). In contrast, channel offset kinetics show some voltage sensitivity, being somewhat slower at positive membrane potentials (129). The latter result is in agreement with a channel-gating model in which only the rate constants for channel closing are voltage sensitive and explains the finding that K_m values for channel activation are slightly lower at positive membrane potentials (40). All of these studies clearly indicate that, from a functional point of view, olfactory CNG channels should be regarded primarily as ligand-gated ion channels.

The ligand selectivity of olfactory CNG channels has aroused considerable interest because the channel is sensitive to both cAMP and cGMP. Affinities for these ligands in some preparations are very similar; in others, cGMP is even more effective in channel activation than cAMP (data summarized in Table 1). The functional significance of this result is still unclear, because it is cAMP that mediates the fast initial responses to odor stimulation (17, 76). Channel activation seems to be a cooperative process, as suggested by the high Hill coefficient that ranges from $n = 1.4$ to 2.9, as obtained from steady-state dose-response curves (Table 1). Thus the high cooperativity of the odor-induced current may result entirely from the cooperativity of the CNG channel. This idea is consistent with the absence of cooperativity in biochemical measurements in odor-induced cAMP formation (11).

NITRIC OXIDE-CYCLIC GMP PATHWAY   The high sensitivity of the olfactory channel for cGMP has given rise to the suggestion that nitric oxide (NO), the endogenous activator of the soluble form of guanylate cyclase, may play a role as an intercellular messenger in the olfactory epithelium (19). This view has been supported by the recent finding that odor-induced cGMP responses are abolished by the selective inhibitor of NO formation, L-N^G-nitroarginine (18). Further support has come from the finding that application of the NO-donor sodium nitroprusside to ORNs activates a cation conductance with properties similar to that activated by odor (78). Other studies have indicated that carbon monoxide (CO), rather than NO, may activate guanylate cyclase in ORNs (119). This interesting question remains unsettled, and a final assessment requires more information.

SINGLE-CHANNEL GATING KINETICS   The isolated salamander ORN preparation is ideal for studying the kinetic components of native CNG channels because stable patches containing only a single channel can be regularly obtained, and the single-channel conductance is high enough to resolve even very fast components of the single-channel kinetics. Detailed knowledge about the duration of the various open and closed states and their concentration dependence is important for understanding mechanisms of gating in this class of ion channels.

One of the characteristic features of CNG channels is the flickery appearance of open channel currents. Whereas investigators initially believed that flickering resulted entirely from the effects of divalent cations, it has become clear that some portion of the open channel noise occurs even in the complete absence of divalent cations (125). A so-called proton block caused by external protons seems to be the source of this Ca^{2+}-independent flickering (see below, 125). Short openings (with an average duration of 1–2 ms) resulting from this flickering comprise the largest portion of the open time distribution (126).

In the visual channel, amplitude histograms of single-channel openings indicate more than one conducting state, and these states may correspond to openings of partially and fully liganded channels (61, 121). For the salamander olfactory CNG channel, this explanation seems unlikely because the amplitude distribution does not show significant differences whether it was obtained at low or at high cyclic nucleotide concentrations (F Zufall, unpublished observation).

An interesting feature of CNG channels is the fact that the open probability does not closely approach 1 even when the channel is fully liganded (126). The presence of a long-lasting closed state is responsible for this observation. Sojourns into this state reduce the maximal open probability at saturating cyclic nucleotide concentrations to 0.6–0.7 (126). Long-lasting closed states have usually been related to mechanisms of desensitization (105); however, desensitization is completely absent in CNG channels (40, 126). A recent analysis of the concentration dependence of channel closed states determined that the duration of the long-lasting closed-time component depends on the cyclic nucleotide concentration, with an average duration of 140 ms at 6 μM cAMP and only 10 ms at 1 mM cAMP (127). Two other closed-time components, one that defines the length of single openings (average length 200 μs) and one that defines bursts of openings (about 2 ms), are not concentration dependent. This result is significant for several reasons:

1. Single-channel openings are grouped in bursts, and the bursts of openings are clustered. Because of its concentration dependence, the duration of a single cluster defines the time during which at least one agonist molecule stays bound.
2. The cluster duration can be surprisingly long, more than 100 ms at 1 mM cAMP. Therefore, single activations of the channel are much longer than previously thought.
3. Consequently, cyclic nucleotide molecules do not seem to be loosely bound to the olfactory CNG channel, as suggested for the visual system (121). A cluster duration of >100 ms predicts slow dissociation of cyclic nucleotides from the channel.

All these features are critically important for understanding the olfactory second-messenger cascade. Later sections present other measurements of the kinetic behavior of olfactory CNG channels and their relation to a model for olfactory transduction.

Blockade by Divalent Cations: Induction of Voltage Dependence

ODOR RESPONSE CURRENT–VOLTAGE RELATION   In contrast to the linear behavior of the CNG channel in divalent-free solutions, the macroscopic, odor-induced currents, under physiological ionic conditions, often show strong nonlinear characteristics as a function of the membrane potential. These include outward rectification and even a negative conductance region at negative membrane potentials (32, 68). Figure 5A shows that this effect can be so strong that essentially no odor responses are detectable at the resting potential, whereas a membrane depolarization of 10–20 mV uncovers large odor-induced inward currents. Removal of external Ca^{2+} appears to remove nonlinearities of the odor-activated conductance (68). These properties of the I-V relation have the following functional consequence for ORNs: the sensory generator current in these neurons simultaneously depends on the presence of the second messenger and on the membrane potential. In other words, these cells can potentially act as a coincidence detector (14). However, strong rectifying properties only occur in a subset of cells. ORNs from the same preparation can also display a linear I-V relation (35, 80). Thus, not all ORNs in a given preparation have the same physiological properties, and a major task in the future will be to identify cellular subtypes and their corresponding molecular substrates.

CHANNEL BLOCKAGE BY DIVALENT CATIONS   The voltage dependence of the sensory response may be largely the result of a fast, voltage-dependent block of the CNG channel pore by external divalent cations such as Ca^{2+} and Mg^{2+} (125). Early recordings had shown that the CNG conductance in excised ciliary patches is markedly enhanced in low Ca^{2+} medium (91). Recently, investigators have accounted quantitatively for this effect by using single-channel recording and subsequent biophysical analysis (125). When external divalent cations enter the open channel, they induce a so-called flicker block (see Figure 5B). The apparent channel conductance is reduced with increasing Ca^{2+} concentrations, and at 1 mM Ca^{2+} the amplitude of single-channel currents is just above the resolution level (at -100 mV). The voltage dependence of this effect creates outward rectification of the current-voltage relation. Outward rectification and flicker block are removed in divalent-free conditions (125).

The voltage dependence of this effect is consistent with a model in

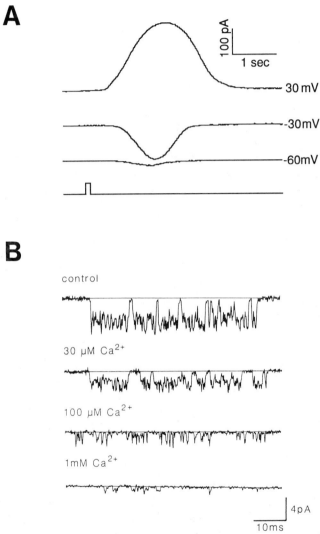

Figure 5 (A) Voltage dependence of the odor-induced generator current recorded in intact receptor neurons activated by a pulse of odor. The strong inward rectification and the negative slope conductance region between -60 and -30 mV are indicative of a channel block by divalent cations. Thus, the generator current depends on both the presence of cAMP and the membrane potential. (B) Block of CNG channels by extracellular Ca^{2+}. Records were obtained from inside-out patches at a membrane potential of -100 mV exposed to 100 μM cAMP. At increasing external Ca^{2+} concentrations, the flickering behavior of the channel increases and the apparent open channel amplitude decreases. The control solution contained less than 10 nM free Ca^{2+} and Mg^{2+} (from 125).

which divalent cations bind to a site within the pore. The resulting prolonged dwell times for the divalent cations would lower their flux rates. The rather small voltage dependence of the block, with an e-fold increase per 128 mV of depolarization, indicates that the blocking site is probably near the extracellular mouth of the pore and senses about 10% of the electric field (125). Table 2 summarizes the characteristic properties of the divalent cation-blocking site responsible for fast channel block. It remains unclear whether those ORNs that do not show a rectifying odor response have expressed a CNG channel with different molecular properties (22), or whether these channels are in a different state of modulation. For example, the very similar Mg^{2+} block of NMDA receptor channels can be reduced by modulation of protein kinase C (21).

The functional implications of the divalent cation block for generation of the odor response are interesting. With a Ca^{2+} concentration of 2–5 mM in the mucus (59) and a typical membrane resting potential of -50 to -60 mV (97, 118), the CNG channels would be in a mostly blocked condition. Although the blockage of thousands of channels may at first seem uncharacteristically wasteful, such a system might be valuable in a sensory receptor for several reasons. One possible advantage, as has been pointed out by Yau & Baylor (121) in photoreceptors, is an increase in the signal-to-noise ratio. In an electrotonically compact cell such as the olfactory neuron, a current of just a few picoamps would be sufficient to depolarize the membrane to the

Table 2 Comparison of properties of the two different Ca^{2+} binding sites at the salamander CNG channel

	Site A	Site B
Effect	Reduction of channel open time	Stabilization of a closed state without
	Reduction of channel conductance	reduction of channel conductance
Proposed mechanism	Fast open-channel block	Allosteric effect
Affinity	$Ca^{2+} > Mg^{2+}$	$K_D (Ca^{2+}) = 0.9 \ \mu M$
	$K_D(Ca^{2+}) = 10 \ \mu M$	Mg^{2+} ineffective
	$K_D(Mg^{2+}) = 300 \ \mu M$	
Location at the channel	Sensing 10% of electric field from the outside	Near the inside
Physiological significance	Enhancement of signal-to-noise ratio	Mediates fast desensitization

threshold for action-potential generation (34, 49, 83, 95). A single channel of conductance 45 pS could pass this much current with a driving force of 60 mV. Even a small basal level of cAMP would result in a finite probability of a channel opening. If the channel has a larger conductance, it will result in a larger depolarization, so that the cell will occasionally fire action potentials in the absence of a stimulus. Although more of the blocked channels must be activated to get a similar sized depolarization, the signal is far more reliable.

Because olfactory neurons generate action potentials, the divalent ion block may also act to shape the stimulus-induced signal by providing a regenerative mechanism. Activation of a sufficient number of channels to depolarize the membrane slightly would lead to a voltage-dependent relief of the block and an increase in the current flux, causing faster depolarization towards firing threshold. An indication of this can be seen from the region of so-called negative resistance between -60 and -30 mV in the I-V relation for the odor-induced current (Figure 5A). The action potential itself would further relieve the block and the sudden increase in membrane conductance could serve to sharpen the decay of the signal.

CHANNEL PERMEATION   Besides its role in depolarizing the cell membrane, the olfactory CNG channel also provides a pathway for Ca^{2+} to enter the cell. This is functionally significant because most proteins in the signaling cascade, including the CNG channel itself (see below), are regulated or modulated by Ca^{2+}. From measurements of the reversal potential of the odor response, a permeability ratio P_{Ca}/P_{Na} of 6.5 has been calculated (72). The shape of I-V curves for single-channel currents in the presence of divalent cations indicate that the channel is permeable to Ca^{2+}, while Mg^{2+} permeates the channel only to a small extent if at all (125). Recently, Ca^{2+} influx during the odor response was shown in measurements using the Ca^{2+} indicator fura-2 (102).

That the molecular structure of CNG channels, especially in the pore region, bears striking similarities to voltage-gated channels led to the suggestion that permeation is similar in CNG and voltage-gated channels. Recent experiments using chimeric retinal-olfactory channels (47) have provided direct evidence for this view, showing that ion permeation through CNG channels is largely determined by the H5 domain, similar to voltage-gated channels. However, in contrast to voltage-gated channels, especially Ca^{2+} channels, where specific ion binding is important, these experiments showed that permeation in CNG channels appears to be determined primarily by mechanisms of molecular sieving. The apparent pore diameter for the olfactory channel (catfish) has been estimated to be 6.3–6.4 Å (47).

Experiments analyzing the flicker block induced by divalent cations have presented a somewhat different view (125). The flicker block by divalents strongly argues for a channel-binding site controlling channel block and permeation, at least for divalent cations. The block is similar to that described in Ca^{2+} channels (51), e.g. the affinity of the blocking site for different divalent cations is very similar to L-type Ca^{2+} channels, with $Cd^{2+} > Ca^{2+} > Mg^{2+}$. However, a critical property of Ca^{2+} channels—anomalous mole-fraction behavior—a phenomenon interpreted as indicating several binding sites for ion movement in a single-file pore (2, 52), seems to be absent in olfactory CNG channels (40, 125). Therefore unlike the Ca^{2+} channel, a single binding site may control ionic permeation and block of CNG channels. Similar conclusions have recently been drawn for the visual CNG channels (89, 122).

The permeability sequence for monovalent ions [in native rat CNG channel (40)]:

$$Na^+ \ (1): K^+ \ (0.81): Li^+ \ (0.74): Rb^+ \ (0.60): Cs^+ \ (0.52),$$

indicates that the well of the olfactory CNG channel has a high-field-strength site (40), i.e. one with a negative charge density. Consistent with the data for channel blockade by divalents, such a site would have a higher affinity for divalent cations than for monovalent ones.

Olfactory Adaptation: Regulation of Channel Affinity by Intracellular Calcium

As noted above, a remarkable and characteristic property of isolated CNG channels measured under divalent-free conditions is the absence of desensitization, even at millimolar agonist concentrations. The response to steady application of odors, on the other hand, is transient (33, 72, 130) as is the cAMP-activated current elicited by perfusion of the whole cell with cAMP (31, 69). In the absence of extracellular Ca^{2+} both the odor response and the cAMP-elicited whole-cell current are sustained (69, 72, 130), indicating a critical role of Ca^{2+} influx for olfactory sensory adaptation and ORN gain control. The CNG channel itself seems to be a target of a Ca^{2+}-mediated negative feedback loop, because those effects also occur in the presence of the phosphodiesterase inhibitor IBMX (40, 130), when hydrolysis of internal cAMP is blocked.

The hypothesis that Ca^{2+} influx contributes to olfactory adaptation by modulating a cytoplasmic binding site at the CNG channel has been confirmed using excised membrane patches (66, 130). Micromolar in-

596   ZUFALL, FIRESTEIN & SHEPHERD

tracellular Ca^{2+} concentrations strongly reduce the channel open probability (Figure 6), an effect very different from the open channel block by divalents as described above (see Table 2). Based on single-channel analysis of this effect, an allosteric mechanism suggesting a reduced affinity of the channel for cyclic nucleotides in the presence of elevated intracellular Ca^{2+} has been proposed (130). This idea was later confirmed by measuring full dose-response curves of this effect (66).

Whether Ca^{2+}-mediated affinity regulation is a direct mechanism or involves the action of intermediate proteins remains unclear. The de-

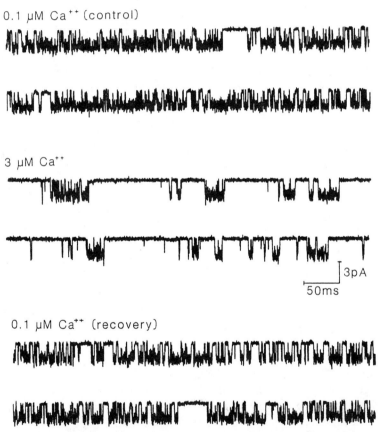

0.1 µM Ca⁺⁺ (control)

3 µM Ca⁺⁺

3pA
50ms

0.1 µM Ca⁺⁺ (recovery)

Figure 6 Activity regulation of the CNG channel by intracellular Ca^{2+}. In the presence of 3 µM intracellular Ca^{2+}, the probability of channel opening is strongly decreased, an effect very different from channel block by external divalent cations. Note that the amplitude and kinetics of channel openings are unaffected, but the record contains longer intercluster intervals. Single-channel currents were elicited by continuous application of 100 µM cAMP, membrane potential −60 mV (from 130).

scribed washout of this effect (66) strongly argues for the latter idea. Interestingly, photoreceptor CNG channels seem to use a very similar mechanism for affinity regulation (55). In this case the Ca^{2+} effect is promoted through the action of the ubiquitous Ca^{2+}-binding protein calmodulin. It remains unclear if calmodulin or some other Ca^{2+}-binding protein is responsible for these effects in olfactory neurons.

Other mechanisms probably contribute to olfactory adaptation and signal termination. Among them appears to be desensitization of odor receptors by phosphorylation of protein kinases (9, 10).

MODULATION   Although Ca^{2+} clearly has important modulatory activity at the olfactory channel, relatively little is known about the modulatory action of other physiological substances. Several reports have proposed a cross-talk between different second-messenger systems in ORNs (5, 37). Several components of alternate pathways, such as diacylglycerol, protein kinase C, Ca^{2+}-dependent protein kinases, and protein phosphatases, likely modulate CNG channel activity. As a first hint, such effects have been described in CNG channels from other preparations. For example, an insect olfactory dendrite contains a cGMP-activated channel that is also sensitive to protein kinase C activators (128). For visual rod CNG channels, evidence suggests that two different binding sites regulate channel affinity as measured by the effects of protein phosphatases (44). Furthermore, diacylglycerol analogues appear to suppress CNG-channel activity in the same preparation (45).

Pharmacology

CALCIUM-CHANNEL BLOCKERS   The pharmacology of CNG channels has not been extensively studied so far despite the critical need for selective channel blockers. Because of the possible structural relation of the CNG channel pore to Ca^{2+} channels, we predicted that some Ca^{2+}-channel blockers might also block the CNG channel. Among these blockers are divalent cations, of which Cd^{2+} appears to have the strongest blocking effect (31). Recent findings showed that nifedipine, a specific blocker of L-type Ca^{2+} channels, blocks the salamander CNG channel at 50 μM, whereas verapamil had no effect (125). Several reports describe derivatives of amiloride such as l-*cis*-diltiazem as voltage-dependent blockers of the CNG conductance and of the odor response (38, 40, 65).

PROTON CONCENTRATION   Even in the complete absence of divalent cations, CNG channels display some prominent noise associated with the single open-channel current (125). These divalent cation-independent fluctuations of the channel current seem to result from the phenomenon of proton block (see above), a mechanism that has been studied in detail for voltage-gated Ca^{2+} channels (93, 96). A change in the extracellular pH from 7.6 to 8.5 as well as a membrane depolarization (46, 125) drastically reduces the proton block of the CNG channel. This is another instance of the similarity between the open-channel conductance properties of Ca^{2+} channels and CNG channels. A somewhat different, voltage-independent inhibition of CNG channels by cytosolic acidification has also been described (40).

CYCLIC AMP DERIVATIVES   Some novel and interesting stereoisomeric thioate derivatives of cAMP (Sp-cAMPS and Rp-cAMPS) are now available; both of these are poorly hydrolyzable by cyclic nucleotide phosphodiesterases. Rp-cAMPS, an inhibitor of the cAMP-dependent protein kinase A (104), has been described as a weak, partial agonist of the olfactory CNG channel, whereas Sp-cAMP was a full agonist in the same preparation (66).

Odor Detection and Channel Kinetics: Mechanisms of Activation and Deactivation

One of the unique properties of individual ORNs is their ability to detect and discriminate between numerous odor molecules (111). What is the molecular mechanism underlying this distinctive phenomenon? One specific adaptation for this function may be the expression of odor receptors that have broad ligand specificities combined with low binding affinities (32, 75). This possibility has immediate implications for the G-protein second-messenger cascade coupled to the odor receptors. According to the equation

$$O + R \underset{k_{-1}}{\overset{k_1}{\rightleftharpoons}} OR, \qquad\qquad 1.$$

where O is an odor molecule (ligand), R a receptor molecule, and OR the odor ligand–receptor complex, low-affinity binding of odor ligands to their receptors can only be accomplished by a relatively high dissociation rate constant from the receptors (e.g. 86). With $K_D = k_{-1}/k_1$, and assuming that K_D is 1–10 μM (32) and k_1 is at the diffusion-controlled limit (10^8 $M^{-1}s^{-1}$), receptors will bind odor ligands only for brief periods of time, in the range of a few milliseconds. Such a brief activation of odor receptors requires that the G-proteins coupled to the receptor possess very rapid kinetics. Fortunately this is precisely what has been observed in biochemical studies utilizing subsecond kinetic measurements. Production of cAMP peaks within 40–75 ms after odor exposure (17), giving olfactory neurons the speed record for any G-protein–coupled system (54). Not only is the production of cAMP rapid, but it is also transient, falling rapidly back to zero within 100–500 ms of its peak amplitude (11, 17). Thus, the activation of the olfactory G-protein cascade and the subsequent production of cAMP appears to be transient rather than cumulative. This activation is also nearly an order of magnitude faster than the kinetics measured for the odor-elicited current.

This observation has important consequences for the odor response. Such a high-speed second-messenger system could result in a critical loss of sensitivity, which would be counterproductive to the high amplification factor gained in the olfactory second-messenger cascade. One possible way to gain back the sensitivity, and to reconcile the kinetics of cAMP production with that of the electrical response, is to introduce a slow step in the second-messenger cascade that would act as an integrator. The integrator would act as a summing point for rapid but transient pulses of second messenger. Indeed, such an integrator in the second-messenger cascade is to be expected from the finding that odor-elicited currents are both concentration and time dependent (33), as described above.

Recent experiments have tested the hypothesis that the CNG channel itself, at the end of the olfactory second-messenger cascade, could provide the needed integrating step. The kinetic behavior of native salamander and recombinant rat CNG channels was examined using a rapid perfusion technique (see Figure 7A) (129). Remarkably, both the activation and the deactivation kinetics of CNG channels were rather slow. Measurements of the rate of rise of cyclic nucleotide–activated currents as a function of cyclic nucleotide concentration indicate that the binding reaction of cyclic nucleotides is the rate-limiting step for channel activation even at concentrations as high as 1 mM cAMP. The rate constants for channel activation are probably in the low end of the range (10^6–10^8 $M^{-1}s^{-1}$) for binding of substrates to enzymes that have a substrate specificity (28). Slow activation kinetics have also been described by Lowe & Gold (80) using flash photolysis of caged cyclic nucleotides. A fundamental consequence of these results is that channel-activation kinetics appear to be the main determinant of the onset kinetics of the odor response.

Channel offset kinetics likewise are very slow and can outlast short second-messenger pulses for several hundred milliseconds (Figure 7B). Because of this persistent activity the population of CNG channels could act as an integrator for second-messenger pulses. Each brief

A   **B**

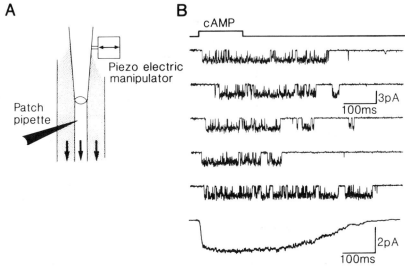

Figure 7 CNG channel activity persists after removal of agonist. (*A*) A piezo-driven rapid perfusion system was used to apply short pulses of second messenger to isolated membrane patches. Patches containing a salamander olfactory CNG channel were moved to a microchamber that was constantly perfused with intracellular control solution. Agonist-containing test solution was delivered through a polyethylene tube drawn out to a 30-μm diameter and fixed to a piezo electric crystal. Applied voltage pulses caused the tube and the filament of solution flowing from it to shift by 30 μm and thus moved the interface of the two solutions across the tip of the patch pipette. (*B*) Five consecutive records of channel activity induced by a 120-ms pulse of 100 μM cAMP. Only one channel is present in the patch. The bottom trace is the ensemble average from 92 single applications. Holding potential, -60 mV (from 129).

pulse would activate a few channels for a period of time outlasting the pulse itself by several hundred milliseconds. During that time activation of other channels by other cAMP pulses could sum together and the result would be a macroscopic current with kinetics quite different from the individual pulses of cAMP underlying its activation. In principle this is conceptually similar to what occurs at a postsynaptic membrane where the transient quanta of transmitter are transformed into a smooth postsynaptic current.

In order to understand the molecular mechanisms underlying this distinctive phenomenon, we have to consider the kinetics of single CNG channels. The burst length of single-channel currents is usually assumed to provide a measure of the time during which at least one agonist molecule is bound; in other words, a burst is terminated by the unbinding of all agonist molecules. Because the burst duration in olfactory CNG channels is rather brief (3–5 ms) (127) this assumption would indicate loose binding similar to the visual CNG channel (121). However, a fuller analysis of olfactory single-channel kinetics shows that channel openings occur in clusters of bursts, and that the intercluster closed-time depends on the agonist concentration. Single activations of an olfactory CNG channel therefore can last hundreds of milliseconds (127). Rapid perfusion experiments are consistent with this idea in showing that second-messenger dissociation from the channel is slow and that this property is responsible for the long cluster activations (129).

One advantage of a mechanism involving pulsatile rather than steadily accumulating second-messenger products would be to preserve the amplification (and concomitant sensitivity) provided by the second-messenger cascade without driving the concentration of cyclic nucleotide into a saturating range for the channel. Such an adaptive mechanism might be particularly important in the extremely fine olfactory cilia, which possess internal volumes on the order of 5×10^{-17} liters/μm of length. A saturating concentration of cAMP (1 mM) could be attained with the accumulation of only about 30,000 molecules in a 1-μm-length cilium. The calculated channel density suggests that this much cAMP would more than saturate the response capabilities of the cell.

In summary, the described mechanism could be a general principle for second-messenger cascades, especially those occurring within small cellular compartments similar to the fine cilia of olfactory neurons, such as dendritic spines. Similar ideas of transient rather than cumulative activation were proposed recently in other G-protein-mediated systems (see 15 for an interesting review and perspective). Also, central synapses equipped with NMDA-receptor channels appear to use an analogous signaling principle (42, 53, 77).

CONCLUDING REMARKS

This review has covered a variety of studies that have provided an initial description of the basic operational properties of the CNG ion channel in olfactory receptor neurons.

The olfactory CNG channel should serve as a rewarding subject for future molecular and biophysical studies of ion-channel properties. In the analysis of the effects of site-directed mutagenesis of specific residues, a comparison of the results with similar studies of other members of the superfamily of ionic channels will be particularly interesting. The fact that the olfactory receptor neuron continues to turn over during adult life, an ability unique among mammalian neurons, means that the synthesis, maturation, insertion, and degradation of this channel is available for analysis from early stages of development through the adult period. Furthermore, the analysis of channel properties in the near future will accompany an increase in information about the other components of the second-messenger pathway leading to channel activation. The fact that the channel can be activated rapidly by closely controlled stimulation of odor receptors should be a distinct advantage in developing a quantitative model of the entire pathway.

Finally, the CNG channel appears to be present in a variety of other types of neurons. The key questions that will arise will be the exact properties of those channels and how they are adapted for the specific physiological functions of those cells. The accessibility of the olfactory channel, and the ability to analyze in detail its role in a single clearly specified function, olfactory sensory transduction, should provide a valuable model for answering those questions.

ACKNOWLEDGMENTS

This work was supported by grants from the Office of Naval Research, the National Institutes of Health—National Institute on Deafness and Other Communicative Disorders, and the Deutsche Forschungsgemeinschaft. We are grateful to Dr. T Leinders-Zufall for help with the preparation of Figure 1.

Literature Cited

1. Ahmad I, Leinders-Zufall T, Kocsis JD, Shepherd GM, Zufall F, Barnstable CJ. 1994. Retinal ganglion cells express a cGMP-gated cation conductance activatable by nitric oxide donors. *Neuron* 12:155–65
2. Almers W, McCleskey EW. 1984. Non-selective conductance in calcium channels of frog muscle: calcium selectivity in a single-file pore. *J. Physiol.* 353:585–608
3. Altenhofen W, Ludwig J, Eismann E, Kraus W, Bönigk W, Kaupp UB. 1991. Control of ligand specificity in cyclic nucleotide-gated channels from rod photoreceptors and olfactory epithelium. *Proc. Natl. Acad. Sci. USA* 88:9868–72

4. Anholt RRH. 1993. Molecular neurobiology of olfaction. *Crit. Rev. Neurobiol.* 7:1–22
5. Anholt RRH, Rivers AM. 1990. Olfactory transduction: cross-talk between second-messenger systems. *Biochemistry* 29:4049–54
6. Bacigalupo J, Morales B, Ugarte G, Delgado R, Jorquera O, Labarca P. 1993. Electrophysiological studies in toad olfactory receptor neurons. *Annu. Meeting of the Assoc. Chemoreception Sci., 15th,* p. 222 (Abstr.)
7. Bakalyar HA, Reed RR. 1990. Identification of a specialized adenylyl cyclase that may mediate odorant detection. *Science* 250:1403–6
8. Barnstable CJ. 1993. Cyclic nucleo-

tide-gated nonselective cation channels: a multifunctional gene family. See Ref. 111a, pp. 121–33

9. Boekhoff I, Breer H. 1992. Termination of second messenger signaling in olfaction. *Proc. Natl. Acad. Sci. USA* 89:471–74

10. Boekhoff I, Schleicher S, Strotmann J, Breer H. 1992. Odor-induced phosphorylation of olfactory cilia proteins. *Proc. Natl. Acad. Sci. USA* 89:11983–87

11. Boekhoff I, Tareilus E, Strotmann J, Breer H. 1990. Rapid activation of alternative second messenger pathways in olfactory cilia from rats by different odorants. *EMBO J.* 9:2453–58

12. Bönigk W, Altenhofen W, Muller F, Dose A, Illing M, et al. 1993. Rod and cone photoreceptor cells express distinct genes for cGMP-gated channels. *Neuron* 10:865–77

13. Borisy FF, Ronnett GV, Cunningham AM, Julifs D, Beavo J, Snyder SH. 1992. Calcium/calmodulin-activated phosphodiesterase expressed in olfactory receptor neurons. *J. Neurosci.* 12:915–23

14. Bourne HR, Nicoll R. 1993. Molecular machines integrate coincident synaptic signals. *Neuron* 10:65–75

15. Bourne HR, Stryer L. 1992. The target sets the tempo. *Nature* 358:541–43

16. Breer H, Boekhoff I. 1992. Second messenger signalling in olfaction. *Curr. Opin. Neurobiol.* 2:439–43

17. Breer H, Boekhoff I, Tareilus E. 1990. Rapid kinetics of second messenger formation in olfactory transduction. *Nature* 345:65–68

18. Breer H, Klemm T, Boekhoff I. 1992. Nitric oxide mediated formation of cyclic GMP. *NeuroReport* 3:1030–32

19. Breer H, Shepherd GM. 1993. Implications of the NO/cGMP system for olfaction. *Trends Neurosci.* 16:5–9

20. Buck L, Axel R. 1991. A novel multigene family may encode odorant receptors: a molecular basis for odor recognition. *Cell* 65:175–87

21. Chen L, Huang L-YM. 1992. Protein kinase C reduces Mg^{2+} block of NMDA-receptor channels as a mechanism of modulation. *Nature* 356:521–23

22. Chen T-Y, Peng Y-W, Dhallan RS, Ahamed B, Reed RR, Yau K-W. 1993. A new subunit of the cyclic nucleotide-gated cation channel in retinal rods. *Nature* 362:764–67

23. Cook NJ, Hanke W, Kaupp UB. 1987. Identification, purification and functional reconstitution of the cyclic GMP-dependent channel from rod photoreceptors. *Proc. Natl. Acad. Sci. USA* 84:585–89

23a. Corey DP, Roper SD, eds. 1992. *Sensory Transduction,* Vol. 47. New York: Rockefeller Univ. Press

24. Dawson TM, Arriza JL, Jaworsky DE, Borisy FF, Attramadal H, et al. 1993. β-adrenergic receptor kinase-2 and β-arrestin-2 as mediators of odorant-induced desensitization. *Science* 259:825–29

25. Dhallan RS, Macke JP, Eddy RL, Shows TB, Reed RR, et al. 1992. Human rod photoreceptor cGMP-gated channel: amino acid sequence, gene structure, and functional expression. *J. Neurosci.* 12:3248–56

26. Dhallan RS, Yau K, Schrader KA, Reed RR. 1990. Primary structure and functional expression of a cyclic nucleotide-activated channel from olfactory neurons. *Nature* 347:184–87

27. Dubin AE, Dionne V. 1993. Modulation of Cl^-, K^+ and nonselective cation conductances by taurine in olfactory receptor neurons of the mudpuppy *Necturus maculosus. J. Gen. Physiol.* 101:496–85

28. Eigen M, Hammes GG. 1963. Elementary steps in enzyme reactions. *Adv. Enzymol.* 25:1–38

29. Fadool DA, Ache BW. 1992. Plasma membrane inositol 1,4,5-trisphosphate-activated channels mediate signal transduction in lobster olfactory receptor neurons. *Neuron* 9:907–18

30. Firestein S. 1992. Physiology of transduction in the single olfactory sensory neuron. See Ref. 23a, pp. 61–71

31. Firestein S, Darrow B, Shepherd GM. 1991. Activation of the sensory current in salamander olfactory receptor neurons depends on a G-protein mediated cAMP second messenger system. *Neuron* 6:825–35

32. Firestein S, Picco C, Menini A. 1993. The relation between stimulus and response in olfactory receptor cells of the tiger salamander. *J. Physiol.* 468:1–10

33. Firestein S, Shepherd GM, Werblin FS. 1990. Time course of the membrane current underlying sensory transduction in salamander olfactory receptor neurones. *J. Physiol.* 430:135–58

34. Firestein S, Werblin F. 1987. Gated currents in isolated olfactory receptor neurons of the larval tiger salamander. *Proc. Natl. Acad. Sci. USA* 84:6292–96

35. Firestein S, Werblin F. 1989. Odor-induced membrane currents in vertebrate olfactory receptor neurons. *Science* 244:79–82

36. Firestein S, Zufall F, Shepherd GM. 1991. Single odor sensitive channels in olfactory receptor neurons are also gated by cyclic nucleotides. *J. Neurosci.* 11:3565–72

37. Frings S. 1993. Protein kinase C sensitizes olfactory adenylate cyclase. *J. Gen. Physiol.* 101:183–205

38. Frings S, Lindemann B. 1988. Odorant response of isolated olfactory receptor cells is blocked by amiloride. *J. Membr. Biol.* 105:233–43

39. Frings S, Lindemann B. 1991. Current recording from sensory cilia of olfactory receptor cells in situ. I. The neuronal response to cyclic nucleotides. *J. Gen. Physiol.* 97:1–16

40. Frings S, Lynch JW, Lindemann B. 1992. Properties of cyclic nucleotide-gated channels mediating olfactory transduction. *J. Gen. Physiol.* 100:45–67

41. Getchell TV. 1986. Functional properties of vertebrate olfactory receptor neurons. *Physiol. Rev.* 66:772–818

42. Gibb AJ, Colquhoun D. 1991. Glutamate activation of a single NMDA receptor-channel produces a cluster of channel openings. *Proc. R. Soc. London Ser. B* 243:39–43

43. Gold GH, Nakamura T. 1987. Cyclic nucleotide-gated conductances: a new class of ion channels mediates visual and olfactory transduction. *Trends Pharmacol.* 8:312–16

44. Gordon SE, Brautigan DL, Zimmerman AL. 1992. Protein phosphatases modulate the apparent agonist affinity of the light-regulated ion channel in retinal rods. *Neuron* 9:739–48

45. Gordon SE, Zimmerman AL. 1993. Diacylglycerol analogs suppress cyclic GMP-activated conductance in rod outer segment patches in the absence of ATP. *Biophys. J.* 64:217 (Abstr.)

46. Goulding EH, Ngai J, Kramer RH, Colicos S, Axel R, et al. 1992. Molecular cloning and single-channel properties of the cyclic nucleotide-gated channel from catfish olfactory neurons. *Neuron* 8:45–58

47. Goulding EH, Tibbs GR, Liu D, Siegelbaum SA. 1993. Role of H5 domain in determining pore diameter and ion permeation through cyclic nucleotide-gated channels. *Nature* 364:61–64

48. Guy HR, Durell SR, Warmke J, Drysdale R, Ganetzky B. 1991. Similarities in amino acid sequences of *Drosophila eag* and cyclic nucleotide-gated channels. *Science* 254:730

49. Hedlund B, Masukawa LM, Shepherd GM. 1987. Excitable properties of olfactory receptor neurons. *J. Neurosci.* 7:2338–43

50. Heginbotham L, Abramson T, MacKinnon R. 1992. A functional connection between the pores of distantly related ion channels as revealed by mutant K$^+$ channels. *Science* 258:1152–55

51. Hess P, Lansman JB, Tsien RW. 1986. Calcium channel selectivity for divalent and monovalent cations. *J. Gen. Physiol.* 88:293–319

52. Hess P, Tsien RW. 1984. Mechanism of ion permeation through calcium channels. *Nature* 309:453–56

53. Hestrin S, Sah P, Nicoll RA. 1990. Mechanisms generating the time course of dual component excitatory synaptic currents recorded in hippocampal slices. *Neuron* 5:247–53

54. Hille B. 1992. G protein-coupled mechanisms and nervous signaling. *Neuron* 9:187–95

55. Hsu Y-T, Molday RS. 1993. Modulation of the cGMP-gated channel of rod photoreceptor cells by calmodulin. *Nature* 361:76–79

56. Hudspeth AJ. 1982. Extracellular current flow and the site of transduction by vertebrate hair cells. *J. Neurosci.* 2:1–10

57. Jan LY, Jan YN. 1990. A superfamily of ion channels. *Nature* 345:672

58. Jones DT, Reed RR. 1989. G$_{olf}$ An olfactory neuron specific-G protein involved in odorant signal transduction. *Science* 244:790–95

59. Joshi H, Getchell ML, Zielinski B, Getchell TV. 1987. Spectrophotometric determination of cation concentrations in olfactory mucus. *Neurosci. Lett.* 82:321–26

60. Kaupp UB. 1991. The cyclic nucleotide-gated channels of vertebrate photoreceptors and olfactory epithelium. *Trends Neurosci.* 14:150–57

61. Kaupp UB, Altenhofen W. 1992. Cyclic nucleotide-gated channels of vertebrate photoreceptor cells and olfactory epithelium. See Ref. 23a, pp. 133–50

62. Kaupp UB, Koch KW. 1992. Role of cGMP and Ca^{2+} in vertebrate photoreceptor excitation and adaption. *Annu. Rev. Physiol.* 54:153–75

63. Kaupp UB, Niidome T, Tanabe T, Ter-

ada S, Bönigk W, et al. 1989. Primary structure and functional expression from complementary DNA of the rod photoreceptor cyclic GMP-gated channel. *Nature* 342:762–66

64. Kleene SJ, Gesteland RC. 1991. Calcium-activated chloride conductance in frog olfactory cilia. *J. Neurosci.* 11: 3624–29

65. Kolesnikov SS, Zhainazarov AB, Kosolapov AV. 1990. Cyclic nucleotide-activated channels in the frog olfactory receptor plasma membrane. *FEBS Lett.* 266:96–98

66. Kramer RH, Siegelbaum SA. 1992. Intracellular Ca^{2+} regulates the sensitivity of cyclic nucleotide-gated channels in olfactory receptor neurons. *Neuron* 9:897–906

67. Kumar VD, Weber IT. 1992. Molecular model of the cyclic GMP-binding domain of the cyclic GMP-gated ion channel. *Biochemistry* 31:4643–49

68. Kurahashi T. 1989. Activation by odorants of cation-selective conductance in the olfactory receptor cell isolated from the newt. *J. Physiol.* 419:177–92

69. Kurahashi T. 1990. The response induced by intracellular cyclic AMP in isolated olfactory receptor cells of the newt. *J. Physiol.* 430:355–71

70. Kurahashi T, Kaneko A. 1991. High density cAMP-gated channels at the ciliary membrane in the olfactory receptor cell. *NeuroReport* 2:5–8

71. Kurahashi T, Kaneko A. 1993. Gating properties of the cAMP-gated channel in toad olfactory receptor cells. *J. Physiol.* 466:287–302

72. Kurahashi T, Shibuya T. 1990. Ca^{2+}-dependent adaptive properties in the solitary olfactory receptor cells of the newt. *Brain Res.* 515:261–68

73. Kurahashi T, Yau K-W. 1993. Co-existence of cationic and chloride components in odorant-induced current of vertebrate olfactory receptor cells. *Nature* 363:71–74

74. Lagnado L, Baylor D. 1992. Signal flow in visual transduction. *Neuron* 8: 995–1002

75. Lancet D. 1986. Vertebrate olfactory reception. *Annu. Rev. Neurosci.* 9: 329–55

76. Lancet D, Pace U. 1987. The molecular basis of odor recognition. *Trends Biochem.* 12:63–66

77. Lester RAJ, Clements JD, Westbrook GL, Jahr CE. 1990. Channel kinetics determine the time course of NMDA receptor-mediated synaptic currents. *Nature* 346:565–67

78. Lischka FW, Schild D. 1993. Effects of nitric oxide upon olfactory receptor neurones in *Xenopus laevis*. *Neuro Report* 4:582–84

79. Lowe G, Gold GH. 1991. The spatial distributions of odorant sensitivity and odorant-induced currents in salamander olfactory receptor cells. *J. Physiol.* 442:147–68

80. Lowe G, Gold GH. 1993. Contribution of the ciliary cyclic nucleotide-gated conductance to olfactory transduction in the salamander. *J. Physiol.* 462:175–96

81. Lowe G, Nakamura T, Gold GH. 1989. Adenylate cyclase mediates olfactory transduction for a wide variety of odorants. *Proc. Natl. Acad. Sci. USA* 86: 5641–45

82. Ludwig J, Margalit T, Eismann E, Lancet D, Kaupp UB. 1990. Primary structure of cAMP-gated channel from bovine olfactory epithelium. *FEBS Lett.* 270:24–29

83. Lynch JW, Barry PH. 1989. Action potentials initiated by single channels opening in a small neuron (rat olfactory receptor). *Biophys. J.* 55:755–68

84. Lynch JW, Barry PH. 1991. Properties of transient K^+ currents and underlying single K^+ channels in rat olfactory receptor neurons. *J. Gen. Physiol.* 97:1043–1072

85. Lynch JW, Barry PH. 1991. Slowly activating K^+ channels in rat olfactory receptor neurons. *Proc. R. Soc. London Ser. B* 244:219–25

86. Mason JR, Morton TH. 1984. Fast and loose covalent binding of ketones as a molecular mechanism in vertebrate olfactory receptors; chemical production of selective anosmia. *Tetrahedron* 40: 483–92

87. Maue RA, Dionne VE. 1987. Patch-clamp studies of isolated mouse olfactory receptor neurons. *J. Gen. Physiol.* 90:95–125

88. Menco BPM, Bruch RC, Dau B, Danho W. 1992. Ultrastructrural localization of olfactory transduction components: the G protein subunit $G_{olf}\alpha$ and type III adenylyl cyclase. *Neuron* 8:441–53

89. Menini A. 1990. Currents carried by monovalent cations through cyclic GMP-activated channels in exised patches from salamander rods. *J. Physiol.* 424:167–85

90. Miyamoto T, Restrepo D, Teeter JH. 1992. Voltage-dependent and odorant-regulated currents in isolated olfactory

receptor neurons of the channel catfish. *J. Gen. Physiol.* 99:505–29

91. Nakamura T, Gold GH. 1987. A cyclic-
nucleotide gated conductance in olfactory receptor cilia. *Nature* 325:442–44

92. Pace U, Hanski E, Salomon Y, Lancet
D. 1985. Odorant-sensitive adenylate
cyclase may mediate olfactory reception. *Nature* 316:255–58

93. Pietrobon D, Prod'hom B, Hess P.
1989. Interactions of protons with single open L-type calcium channels. pH
dependence of proton-induced current
fluctuations with Cs^+, K^+, and Na^+
as permeant ions. *J. Gen. Physiol.* 94:
1–21

94. Pittler SJ, Lee AK, Altherr MR, Howard TA, Seldin MF, et al. 1992. Primary structure and chromosomal localization of human and mouse rod
photoreceptor cGMP-gated cation
channel. *J. Biol. Chem.* 267:6257–62

95. Pongracz F, Firestein S, Shepherd
GM. 1991. Electrotonic structure of olfactory sensory neurons analyzed by
intracellular and whole cell patch techniques. *J. Neurophysiol.* 65:747–57

96. Prod'hom B, Pietrobon D, Hess P.
1989. Interactions of protons with single open L-type calcium channels. Location of protonation site and dependence of proton-induced current
fluctuations on concentration and species of permeant ion. *J. Gen. Physiol.*
94:23–42

97. Pun RYK, Gesteland RC. 1991. So-
matic sodium channels of frog olfactory receptor neurones are inactivated
at rest. *Pflügers Arch.* 418:504–11

98. Rajendra S, Lynch JW, Barry PH.
1992. An analysis of Na^+ currents in
rat olfactory receptor neurons. *Pflügers Arch.* 420:342–46

99. Raming K, Krieger J, Strotmann J,
Boekhoff I, Kubick S, et al. 1993.
Cloning and expression of odorant re-
ceptors. *Nature* 361:353–56

100. Reed RR. 1992. Signalling pathways in
odorant detection. *Neuron* 8:205–9

101. Restrepo D, Miyamoto T, Bryant BP,
Teeter JH. 1990. Odor stimuli trigger
influx of calcium into olfactory neurons of the channel catfish. *Science*
249:1166–68

102. Restrepo D, Okada Y, Teeter JH,
Lowry LD, Cowart B, Brand JG. 1993.
Human olfactory neurons respond to
odor stimuli with an increase in cytoplasmic Ca^{2+}. *Biophys. J.* 64:1961–66

103. Ronnett GV, Cho H, Hester LD,
Wood SF, Snyder SH. 1993. Odorants
differentially enhance phosphoinosi-

tide turnover and adenylyl cyclase in
olfactory receptor neuronal cultures. *J.
Neurosci.* 13:1751–58

104. Rothermel JD, Botelho LHP. 1988. A
mechanistic and kinetic analysis of the
interactions of diastereoisomers of
adenosine 3′,5′-(cyclic) phosphoro-
thioate. *Biochem. J.* 251:757–62

105. Sakmann B, Patlak J, Neher E. 1980.
Single acetylcholine-activated channels show burst-kinetics in presence of
desensitizing concentrations of agonist. *Nature* 286:71–73

106. Schild D. 1989. Whole-cell currents in
olfactory receptor cells of *Xenopus
laevis*. *Exp. Brain Res.* 78:223–32

107. Schleicher S, Boekhoff I, Arriza J, Lefkowitz RJ, Breer H. 1993. A β-adre-
nergic receptor-like enzyme is involved in olfactory signal termination.
Proc. Natl. Acad. Sci. USA 90:1420–
24

108. Sentenac H, Bonneaud N, Minet M,
Lacroute F, Salmon J-M, et al. 1992.
Cloning and expression in yeast of a
plant potassium ion transport system.
Science 256:663–65

109. Shepherd GM. 1991. Sensory transduction: entering the mainstream of
membrane signaling. *Cell* 67:845–51

110. Shepherd GM. 1988. Studies of development and plasticity in the olfactory
sensory neuron. *J. Physiol. Paris* 83:
240–45

111. Sicard G, Holley A. 1984. Receptor
cell responses to odorants: similarities
and differences among odorants. *Brain
Res.* 292:283–96

111a. Siemen D, Hescheler JK-J, eds. 1993.
*Nonselective Cation Channels: Phar-
maoclogy, Physiology and Biophysics.*
Basel, Switzerland: Birkhäuser

112. Sklar PB, Anholt RRH, Snyder SH.
1986. The odorant sensitive adenylate
cyclase of olfactory receptor cells: differential stimulation by distinct classes
of odorants. *J. Biol. Chem.* 261:15538–
43

113. Snyder SH, Sklar PB, Hwang PM,
Pevsner J. 1989. Molecular mechanisms of olfaction. *Trends Neurosci.*
12:35–38

114. Stryer L. 1987. Visual transduction:
design and recurring motifs. *Chem.
Scr. B* 27:161–71

115. Suzuki N. 1989. Voltage- and cyclic
nucleotide–gated currents in isolated
olfactory receptor cells. *In Chemical
Senses*, ed. JG Brand, JH Teeter, RH
Cagan, MR Kare, 1:469–94. New
York: Dekker

116. Suzuki N. 1990. Single cyclic nucleo-

tide-activated ion channel activity in olfactory receptor cell soma membrane. *Neurosci. Res.* 12(Suppl.): S113–26

117. Trombley PQ, Westbrook GL. 1991. Voltage-gated currents in identified rat olfactory receptor neurons. *J. Neurosci.* 11:435–44

118. Trotier D. 1986. A patch-clamp analysis of membrane currents in salamander olfactory receptor cells. *Pflügers Arch.* 407:589–95

119. Verma A, Hirsch DJ, Glatt CE, Ronnett GV, Snyder SH. 1993. Carbon monoxide: a putative neural messenger. *Science* 259:381–84

120. Watanabe SI, Matthews G. 1988. Regional distribution of cGMP-activated ion channels in the plasma membrane of the rod photoreceptor. *J. Neurosci.* 8:2334–37

121. Yau KW, Baylor D. 1989. Cyclic GMP-activated conductance of retinal photoreceptor cells. *Annu. Rev. Neurosci.* 12:289–327

122. Zimmerman AL, Baylor DA. 1992. Cation interactions within the cyclic GMP-activated channel of retinal rods from the tiger salamander. *J. Physiol.* 449:759–83

123. Zufall F. 1993. Cyclic AMP-gated cation channels of olfactory receptor neurons. See Ref. 111a, pp. 135–45

124. Zufall F. 1993. Sex-pheromone-sensitive ion channels of insect olfactory receptor neurons. In *Sensory Systems of Arthropods,* ed. K Wiese, FG Gribakin, AV Popov, S Kapitskii, G Renninger, pp. 544–54. Basel, Switzerland: Birkhäuser

125. Zufall F, Firestein S. 1993. Divalent cations block the cyclic nucleotide-gated channel of olfactory receptor neurons. *J. Neurophysiol.* 69:1758–68

126. Zufall F, Firestein S, Shepherd GM. 1991. Analysis of single cyclic nucleotide gated channels in olfactory receptor cells. *J. Neurosci.* 11:3573–80

127. Zufall F, Firestein S, Shepherd GM. 1993. Activation of a single cyclic AMP-gated channel produces a cluster of channel openings. *Soc. Neurosci. Abstr.* 19:279

128. Zufall F, Hatt H. 1991. Dual activation of a sex pheromone-dependent ion channel from insect olfactory dendrites by protein kinase C activators and cyclic GMP. *Proc. Natl. Acad. Sci. USA* 88:8520–24

129. Zufall F, Hatt H, Firestein S. 1993. Rapid application and removal of second messengers to cyclic nucleotide-gated channels from olfactory epithelium. *Proc. Natl. Acad. Sci. USA* 90: 9335–39

130. Zufall F, Shepherd GM, Firestein S. 1991. Inhibition of the olfactory cyclic nucleotide gated ion channel by intracellular calcium. *Proc. R. Soc. London Ser. B* 246:225–30

Annu. Rev. Biophys. Biomol. Struct. 1994. 23:609–43

CONFORMATIONAL AND THERMODYNAMIC PROPERTIES OF SUPERCOILED DNA

Alexander V. Vologodskii and Nicholas R. Cozzarelli

Department of Molecular and Cell Biology, University of California, Berkeley, California 94720

KEY WORDS: DNA superhelix, DNA topology, writhe, electron microscopy, sedimentation, light scattering, computer simulation of DNA structure

CONTENTS

INTRODUCTION

The study of topologically closed duplex DNA began in 1963 with the discovery by Dulbecco & Vogt that polyoma virus DNA has a closed circular form (37). The distinctive feature of closed circular molecules is that its topological state cannot be altered by any conformational rearrangement short of breaking the strands. This topological constraint is the basis for the characteristic properties of closed circular

1056-8700/94/0610-0609$05.00

DNA that have fascinated biologists, physicists, and mathematicians for the past 30 years.

Vinograd's laboratory initiated the study of the physical properties of circular DNA in 1963 (116), and by 1965, had demonstrated that circular DNA extracted from cells is negatively supercoiled (103). The history of this discovery was described by Lebowitz (63). Largely from the contributions of J Wang, we know today that supercoiling is the primary determinant of the distinctive biological features of closed DNA (105). Several reviews have considered the widespread influence of supercoiling on biological functions (2, 34, 58, 111, 113). We instead emphasize physical rather than biological properties. Nevertheless, the successful analysis of the biological effects of DNA supercoiling requires an understanding of its physical properties.

Supercoiling can result from the binding of DNA to proteins, a topic reviewed extensively elsewhere (2, 39, 42, 73, 101, 121, 122). We are instead concerned with supercoiling that results from a topological constraint. In particular, we focus on the conformational rearrangements induced by moderate levels of negative supercoiling (such as occur in vivo) that result in elastic deformations of the DNA but leave its secondary structure essentially unchanged. We consider both how supercoiling is realized in three dimensions and how physical properties of DNA are changed by supercoiling.

Local changes of DNA secondary structure, such as unwound regions, cruciforms, Z-DNA, and H-DNA, can result from high negative supercoiling. Several recent reviews have examined this category of structural rearrangements (40, 56, 74, 105, 112, 117). Although we do not consider this area directly, we discuss superhelical free energy, which is the driving force for the local changes of secondary structure under superhelical stress.

Many fundamental features of superhelical conformations are now understood despite the limitations of most available experimental methods. Supercoiling requires that the DNA be long and circular, which precludes the use of high-resolution methods such as X-ray crystallography and nuclear magnetic resonance. Most of the biological consequences of supercoiling derive from its dynamic structure, but this very plasticity means that analytical methods often perturb the structure they probe. Successful analysis of supercoiling has required a confluence of experimental methods, computer simulations, and theory. We discuss the strengths and weaknesses of each of these approaches and the extent of agreement of the results. We also analyze the dramatic effect of salt concentration on supercoiling conformations.

PRIMARY TOPOLOGICAL CONSIDERATIONS

Because the topological properties of supercoiling are well known, we describe only the basic concepts. More detailed analyses may be found in other articles (2, 30, 105, 119).

Linking-Number Difference

The two strands of the double helix in closed circular DNA are linked in the sense that the strands cannot be separated without breaking them. In topological terms, the linkage between the strands of the double helix belongs to the torus class. The quantitative description of such links is called the linking number (Lk), which may be determined as follows. One of the strands defines the edge of an imaginary surface (any such surface gives the same result). The Lk is the algebraic (i.e. sign-dependent) number of intersections between the other strand and this spanning surface. By convention, the Lk of a closed circular DNA formed by a right-handed double helix is positive. Lk depends only on the topological state of the strands and hence is maintained through all conformational changes that occur in the absence of strand breakage. Its value is always integral. The distinctive conformational properties of closed circular DNA are a consequence of its invariance.

After the supercoiling of a circular DNA has been removed by nicking and religation, it has a distribution of Lk values whose average is called Lk_o. $Lk_o = N/\gamma$, where N is the number of base pairs in the molecule and γ is the mean number of base pairs per turn of the double helix under a given set of conditions. For naturally occurring DNA, Lk is less than Lk_o. The difference between these two values is called the Lk difference, ΔLk.

$$\Delta Lk = Lk - Lk_o = Lk - N/\gamma. \qquad 1.$$

Because Lk_o depends on the solution conditions that determine γ, it follows from Equation 1 that the value of ΔLk is neither a topological invariant nor necessarily integral, even though Lk has both of these properties. Molecules that have the same chemical structure and differ only with respect to Lk are called topoisomers.

Often a more convenient way of describing DNA supercoiling is the superhelix density, σ, which is the ΔLk normalized for DNA length. This parameter is defined by the equations

$$\sigma = \Delta Lk/Lk_o = \gamma \Delta Lk/N. \qquad 2.$$

When $\Delta Lk \neq 0$, the DNA is under a stress that deforms the double

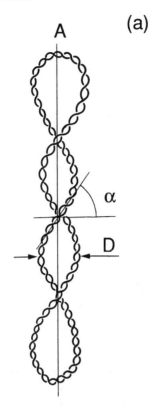

(a)

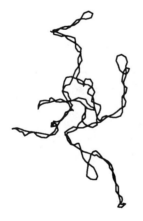

(b)

helix axis into a helix of a higher order (Figure 1). This helix-axis deformation gave rise to the terms superhelicity and supercoiling. These terms are also commonly used to describe DNA that has a non-zero σ value irrespective of axis geometry. The two different definitions of supercoiling and superhelicity are usually clear from the context and in this review are interchangeable because we only consider supercoiling arising from an Lk deficit. The form of supercoiling shown in Figure 1 is called plectonemic or interwound, because it consists of two helices wound around each other. Circular DNA extracted from cells has a σ between -0.03 and -0.09, but the value is typically near the middle of this range (5).

Twist and Writhe

Early in the study of supercoiling, Vinograd and coworkers tried to find a quantitative relationship between the deformation of the DNA axis and the number of turns of the double helix (3, 102). Advancing these efforts, Glaubiger & Hearst introduced the concept of Lk for the description of supercoiled DNA (44). At almost the same time, mathematicians independently developed an analysis of the problem. The first mathematical treatment was presented in 1961 by Calugareanu, who found the basic relationship between the geometrical and topological properties of a closed ribbon (21). However, the concept of what is now called twist was not present in a straightforward way and the treatment had some restrictions. The theorem in its current biologically relevant form was first proved by White in 1969 and is thus often called White's theorem (118). Two years later, Fuller specifically suggested how the theorem can be applied to the analysis of circular

←——————————————————————————————————

Figure 1 Negatively supercoiled DNA. (*a*) In this diagram of an unbranched supercoiled DNA, the lines correspond to the strands of the DNA double helix. The superhelix winding angle (α), diameter (D), and axis (A) are shown. It is often useful to express data in terms of a regular superhelix model in which α and D are constant and the ends are either ignored or assumed to have the same radius as that of the rest of the superhelix (17). The model shown has three superhelical turns, n, and, in this plane projection, an equal number of superhelical crossings (nodes). For the regular model, only two structural parameters of the superhelix need to be stated and the rest can be obtained from the following equations: $Wr = -n\sin\alpha$; $l = (L/2)\sin\alpha$; and $D = (L\cos\alpha)/(\pi n)$, where Wr is the superhelix writhe, l is the superhelix axis length, and L is the DNA length. Because ΔLk is usually also known, ΔTw can easily be obtained. (*b*) Stereo drawing of simulated supercoiled DNA (107). The line represents the DNA double helix. A typical conformation is presented for a 10-kb circular DNA, $\sigma = -0.06$, and 1 M monovalent ion concentration.

DNA (43). Crick in 1975 pointed out important features of this application (31). The history of the mathematical developments is discussed in more detail in several articles (76, 99, 118).

According to White's theorem, the Lk of the edges of the ribbon is the sum of two values. One is the twist of the ribbon (Tw), then a well known concept, and the second, a new concept, writhe (Wr). Thus,

$$Lk = Tw + Wr. \qquad \qquad 3.$$

Tw is a measure of the number of times one of the edges of the ribbon spins about its axis. The Tw of the entire ribbon is the sum of the Tw of its parts. The value of Wr is defined by the spatial course of the ribbon axis; i.e. it is a characteristic of a single closed curve, unlike Lk and Tw, which are properties of a closed ribbon. Wr is equal to the Gauss integral along the axis of the ribbon. Alternatively, Wr can be calculated as follows: In any projection, a curve may be seen to cross itself. Wr is the algebraic sum of such crossings of the ribbon axis averaged over all possible projections. Wr can be thought of as a measure of a curve's net right-handed or left-handed asymmetry, i.e. its chirality, and is therefore zero for a planar curve. Equation 3 states that a topological invariant, Lk, is the sum of two continuously variable geometrical properties. Thus Lk can be represented as a sum of two values that characterize the available degrees of freedom: the twist around the ribbon axis and the deformation of this axis.

To apply the theorem to circular DNA, the two strands of the double helix are considered as edges of a ribbon. In relaxed DNA, Tw equals $Lk_0 N/\gamma$ because the average writhe of relaxed DNA is zero. Because the axis of supercoiled DNA is nonplanar, the DNA has a net Wr, and Lk does not equal Tw.

From the definition of Lk_0 and the fact that the average Wr of relaxed DNA equals 0, Equation 3 can be represented in the form

$$\Delta Lk = \Delta Tw + Wr. \qquad \qquad 4.$$

Equation 4 expresses the ΔLk of a closed circular DNA as a sum of the change of twist from its equilibrium value in relaxed DNA and the introduction of writhe.

In a recently developed mathematical analysis of DNA supercoiling based on surface topology (120), Lk is decomposed into a winding number and a surface-linking number. The utility of the surface topology treatment is that for DNA lying on a surface both of these terms can be measured (121).

CONFORMATIONAL PROPERTIES

Basic Questions

Equation 4 expresses quantitatively that supercoiling can cause both torsional and bending deformations. This allows us to formulate basic questions about the conformations of supercoiled DNA. (*a*) What is the distribution of Wr and ΔTw in supercoiled DNA? (*b*) What are the typical DNA conformations for a particular value of σ? (*c*) How do the properties of supercoiled DNA depend on solution conditions?

The only value in Equation 4 that can be easily and reliably measured is ΔLk. The methods by which ΔLk can be determined have been analyzed (5, 105) and we do not consider them here. Determining the ΔTw or Wr of supercoiled DNA is much more difficult because of the conformational flexibility of long DNA molecules. We must consider an equilibrium distribution of conformations and average values of Wr and ΔTw rather than a particular conformation with a minimum elastic energy. Nevertheless, remarkable progress was made recently in the study of supercoiled DNA. We next summarize the results of these investigations.

Experimental Investigations

ELECTRON MICROSCOPY   Electron microscopy (EM) is the most straightforward way to study supercoiled DNA and gives detailed information about its conformations. This method has been used extensively since the discovery of DNA supercoiling by Vinograd and coworkers in 1965 (103). They found that supercoiled DNA has a compact, slightly interwound form. In 1968 Rhoades & Thomas obtained micrographs in which the plectonemic form of supercoiled DNA was much more clearly defined (78). Further improvements allowed Griffith and coworkers in 1984 to count the number of crossings (nodes) per DNA molecule, revealing a linear increase in node number with ΔLk (91).

Boles et al (17) performed the most extensive study of DNA supercoiling with EM, in which the properties of 3.5- and 7.0-kb supercoiled DNA molecules were examined quantitatively as a function of σ. Figure 2 shows typical micrographs of supercoiled DNA molecules. Relying on EM and a topological method described below, the authors calculated the basic parameters of superhelices in terms of a regular plectonemic model (see Figure 1*a*, legend) with uniform diameter and pitch. They found that: (*a*) The ratio $Wr/\Delta Lk$ does not depend on σ and equals 0.72; (*b*) the superhelix winding angle is about 54° and also does not

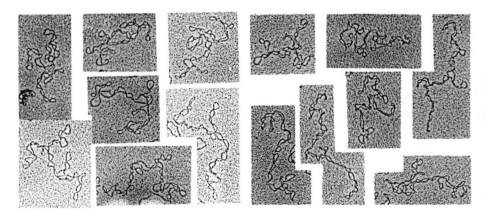

Figure 2 Electron micrographs of a 7-kb supercoiled DNA with σ equal -0.03 (*left*) and -0.06 (*right*) (from 17). The superhelices are fairly uniform, very long and thin, and often branched.

depend on σ; (*c*) the superhelix diameter is independent of DNA length but varies inversely with σ and equals only 11 nm for $\sigma = -0.06$; (*d*) the number of supercoils is proportional to σ and equals $0.9|\Delta Lk|$.

Although EM gives only a two-dimensional view of a three-dimensional solution structure, the superhelix parameters just cited are close to those found for DNA in solution with near-physiological monovalent ion concentrations (see below). However, the most labile features of conformations may change during sample preparation for EM. An example may be the branching frequency in superhelical DNA. The fraction of branched molecules differs greatly in different experimental studies (17, 62). One explanation for these different outcomes follows from the results of Monte Carlo simulations of supercoiling that show that branching is a sensitive function of DNA length, σ, and ionic conditions (107). The EM studies of Laundon & Griffith demonstrated that branching is also affected by specific nucleotide sequences and by temperature (62). Given the very different sample preparation procedures and DNA molecules used in the EM studies, the variation in branching frequency is perhaps not surprising. A serious problem for interpreting EM results is that the ionic conditions on the grid are not specified. The DNA is exposed to several different solutions and dried before being viewed, and the point at which the DNA becomes fixed in the procedure is unknown. The best recourse available is to estimate the effective monovalent ion concentration by comparison with Monte Carlo calculations summarized below.

Cryoelectron microscopy (cryo-EM) is free from some of the disadvantages of more conventional EM (35). With this technique, DNA is held inside a thin layer (50–100 nm) of vitrified water obtained by means of rapid cooling to below -140 C. Stereo viewing can supply a three-dimensional reconstruction (38). The resulting picture is superior to that from conventional EM in which the relative overlay of crossing DNA segments can be determined only after coating with a protein that distorts double helix geometry (114). Cryo-EM also requires no coverage of DNA to enhance contrast.

Although the technique is too difficult to be used routinely, Dubochet and coworkers have utilized it to perform two significant studies of DNA supercoiling. Although the ionic conditions were not well specified as a result of evaporation during sample preparation, the results they obtained at low salt concentration fit well with the conventional EM data given above. They estimated that Wr is about 2/3 of ΔLk for a molecule with a physiological level of supercoiling and that the superhelix winding angle is about 55° (1). A new result is that the superhelix collapses in the presence of either Mg^{2+} (1) or high Na^+ concentrations (9). This collapsed form allows no space between the DNA strands twining around the superhelix axis so that superhelix diameter reaches 4 nm. The collapsed region covered only part of a more weakly supercoiled molecule (9).

It is not known whether the collapse reflects the solution conformations of DNA at room temperature, as the cooling of the water layer may not be rapid enough to exclude conformational rearrangements. The average helix winding angle increases as temperature decreases (33, 36), resulting in a change in σ of -0.003 per 10°. If we extrapolate this relationship below 0°C, we conclude that the torsional stress increases greatly during the cooling for cryo-EM. As a result, nonequilibrium conformations may be observed. Alternative methods for studying superhelix structure will help establish whether or not superhelix collapse is of physiological significance.

Recently, scanning-force microscopy has confirmed the interwound structure of supercoiled DNA and proved its chirality (80). An advantage of this method is that DNA is viewed in solution without shadowing or staining. However, DNA that is not fixed to a supporting surface moves in response to the scanning tip, diminishing resolution. Future technical advances will be required to make scanning-force microscopy superior to other types of microscopy for the study of supercoiled DNA.

Some DNA sequences induce an equilibrium curvature of the DNA axis (see 32, 48a, 97 for reviews). EM showed that such intrinsically curved DNA segments are preferentially localized at the apices of a superhelix (62). Dynamic light-scattering experiments also showed a notable influence of curved segments on the conformational properties of supercoiled DNA (26, 60a). These experimental results have been supported by computer simulations of an equilibrium conformational distribution of DNA containing curved segments (60a).

INDIRECT METHODS   The hydrodynamic and optical methods do not give direct, model-independent information about the three-dimensional structure of supercoiled DNA. As a result, the frequency of their use has declined recently. These methods do, however, measure structure-dependent features of supercoiled DNA in well-defined solutions while perturbing conformation only minimally. Therefore, in combination with the other techniques that give more direct structural information, these methods can be very useful.

TRANSPORT PROPERTIES   Sedimentation analysis constituted the first physical probe of supercoiled DNA structure. It established that DNA molecules isolated from cells were $(-)$ supercoiled to about a σ of -0.06. The analyses also showed that the sedimentation coefficient, s, increases with σ, reaches a maximum, and then decreases to a local minimum (100, 109, 110) (Figure 3). The maximum value of s is greater than that of relaxed DNA by 30–60%, depending on DNA length. The initial increase in s with σ corresponds to the onset of Wr. The nonmonotonic nature of the dependence initially led to the suggestion that the superhelix conformation changes from toroidal to plectonemic near $\sigma = -0.04$. We now know that this interpretation is incorrect.

Computer simulations allow a quantitative analysis of sedimentation data. We can simulate the equilibrium set of superhelix conformations for a given value of DNA length and σ, compute the average hydrodynamic characteristics of this set, and visually examine the conformational features. Hagerman & Zimm developed this approach in 1981 for the study of linear DNA molecules (47, 49). The comparison of measured and computed values of hydrodynamic properties such as s is a good test of our understanding of supercoiled DNA structure.

Using the Kirkwood-Riseman approximation (16), we calculated the s of PM2 DNA as a function of σ from simulated supercoiled conformations (AV Vologodskii & NR Cozzarelli, unpublished data) and obtained a similar nonmonotonic dependence of s on σ (Figure 3). Although some differences between the experimental and computed results require further investigation, the shape of the s vs σ curve can now be interpreted. Only irregular and plectonemic conformations

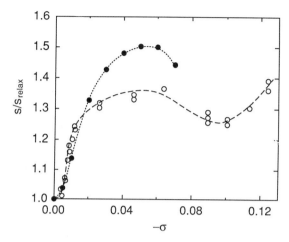

Figure 3 Dependence of sedimentation coefficient of supercoiled DNA on σ. The relative sedimentation coefficient of PM2 DNA (10 kb) is plotted as a function of σ. The experimental data (*open circles*) (from 110) are shown together with computer simulation results (*solid circles*). Sedimentation rate was measured in 3 M CsCl. Computed values were obtained from Monte Carlo simulations of equilibrium sets of superhelix conformations (AR Vologodskii & NR Cozzarelli, unpublished data). The chain was divided into beads 3.18 nm in diameter (27) and the average mobility for the conformational sets was calculated using the Kirkwood equation (16).

were obtained by simulation; toroidal forms were absent. Figure 1*b* shows a stereo drawing of a typical conformation. As the more compact plectonemic form predominates over more irregular ones, s increases rapidly with σ. The most compact branched plectonemic conformations are present at a σ of -0.05 (107). Branch frequency decreases with higher supercoiling, and thereby s for these more extended conformations also decreases. The simulation procedure has diminished applicability to DNA with $\sigma < -0.07$ because of resultant secondary structure changes. However, local structural transitions may account for the increase of s at $\sigma < -0.08$ (7). Junctions between B-form DNA and noncanonical structures decrease DNA stiffness and thereby increase compactness. The number of local transitions increases significantly as the monovalent ion concentration is lowered (for review see 105). Similarly, the increase in s for highly supercoiled DNA when the Na^+ concentration was lowered below 0.1 M (104) could result from this enhancement of local transitions.

The mobility of supercoiled DNA molecules in solution can also be measured by dynamic light scattering. Langowski and colleagues are currently using this technique to examine the diffusion coefficient of a 2.7-kb supercoiled DNA molecule and have compared their results with computed values of diffusion coefficients from simulated equilibrium sets (see reference 61 for preliminary results). Interestingly, both measured (see also 29) and computed mobility increases monotonically for this small DNA as a function of σ, probably because branching is unlikely for this short DNA at any σ (see below).

In summary, we can explain the basic features of the transport properties of supercoiled DNA in terms of the transition from irregular conformations to branched interwound superhelices. We also conclude that the measurement of transport properties in combination with computer calculations is an efficient way to study the conformational properties of supercoiled DNA.

LIGHT SCATTERING   Static light scattering results provide the average radius of gyration, R_g, of molecules in solution. This method was applied to supercoiled DNA by Campbell and coworkers (23, 24, 57). The investigators analyzed their data in terms of regular interwound or toroidal superhelices and concluded that if the superhelix is interwound it must also be branched. A more sophisticated analysis of the experimental results is now possible using computer simulation of the equilibrium conformational set. Figure 4 shows the measured R_g for SV40 DNA together with our computed values (AV Vologodskii & NR Cozzarelli, unpublished data). The initial decrease of the computed R_g with σ is correlated with interwound superhelix formation. The minimum

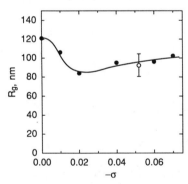

Figure 4 Variation of the radius of gyration, R_g, of supercoiled DNA with σ. The R_g of SV40 DNA (5.2 kb) is plotted as a function of σ. The experimental result (*open circle*) calculated from light scattering in 0.2 M NaCl (23) is shown together with computer simulation data for the same salt conditions (*solid circles*). The measured and calculated R_g for supercoiled DNA is one half that predicted for a straight superhelix with the same average diameter and length. The sinuous course of the superhelix and branching are responsible for the more compact conformations.

value in R_g corresponds to initial superhelix formation, in which the conformations are very irregular but have many short branches. The diminution of branching with increased supercoiling is responsible for the further changes in R_g.

Our conclusion about the utility of static light scattering parallels that for transport properties. The combination of light scattering with computer simulation provides useful information about supercoiled DNA properties. The limited data currently available show a reasonable agreement between computed and measured R_g for SV40 DNA (Figure 4), but a systematic study is necessary before firm conclusions can be drawn.

CIRCULAR DICHROISM   The circular dichroic (CD) spectrum of supercoiled DNA has long been known to be different from that of linear or nicked molecules, particularly in the 260- to 280-nm range (70). However, drawing quantitative conclusions about the structure of supercoiled DNA from this lone result was difficult. Brahms et al (18) changed this situation by performing a systematic study with improved spectral measurements. These workers found for a 4.4-kb DNA in 40 mM KF and for wavelengths between 175 and 320 nm, that the difference in CD intensity between supercoiled and relaxed forms [$\Delta(\Delta\epsilon)$] is proportional to σ, for $-0.07 \leq \sigma \leq 0.07$.

Figure 5 shows that $\Delta(\Delta\epsilon)$ is very nearly equal and opposite for ($+$)

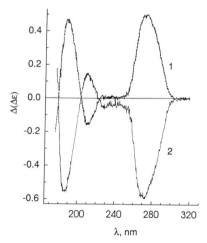

Figure 5   Effect of supercoiling on the circular dichroism of DNA. $\Delta(\Delta\epsilon)$ is the difference between the circular dichroic spectrum of supercoiled and relaxed circular DNA. The difference spectra for negatively, $\sigma = -0.07$ (*curve 1*) and positively, $\sigma = 0.07$ (*curve 2*) supercoiled pBR322 DNA (4.3 kb) were measured in 40 mM KF (replotted from 18).

and ($-$) supercoiled DNA over the whole spectral range. Because the local structural changes produced by supercoiling are small, the optical consequences can be described by the first term of a Taylor series expansion in a linear combination of increments of the angles that specify the structure of the double helix. This is a reasonable interpretation because the changes in the angles are quite minimal. For example, the change that supercoiling induces in the average helical rotation angle, $\Delta\phi$, is less than 0.5°. (This estimate follows from the relationships $\Delta\phi = 360\Delta Tw/N$ and $|\Delta Tw| < 0.5 |\Delta Lk|$.) The proportionality of $\Delta(\Delta\epsilon)$ to σ means that $\Delta\phi$ is also proportional to σ. Therefore we conclude that for $|\sigma| \leq 0.07$,

$$\Delta Tw = A\Delta Lk, \qquad\qquad 5.$$

where A is a constant. This important result implies that $Wr/\Delta Lk$ is independent of σ. Moreover, if the value of A is known, then CD provides a simple, direct measure of ΔTw. We know of no other direct measure. The proportionality between the CD spectral changes and supercoiling is lost at $\sigma < -0.07$. This is the limit for elastic deformations of DNA under the ionic conditions used; higher negative supercoiling causes local structural transitions. Brahms and coworkers proved using difference CD spectra that the major transition in their case was the formation of Z-DNA (18).

TOPOLOGICAL METHODS   Although supercoiling can be caused by a topological constraint, it is itself a geometric property. Supercoiling can thus easily change during the isolation or analysis of a DNA molecule. Two methods for studying supercoil structure are based on the conversion of supercoiling into a topological change.

One approach uses site-specific recombination by the bacteriophage λ Int system. A portion of the supercoil nodes present in a plasmid substrate are converted into knot or catenane nodes by the Int recombinase (72). In 1985, Spengler et al concluded from the topology of catenanes made by Int in vitro that supercoiled DNA must have a plectonemic conformation as opposed to a toroidal one (90). A subsequent quantitative analysis of the Int reaction revealed that the number of supercoils is equal to $0.9|\Delta Lk|$ (17), in good agreement with EM and computer simulation data. The Int method has also been used to show that about half of the ΔLk of a plasmid in *Escherichia coli* cells is in the form of plectonemic supercoils (15), the same fraction of ΔLk that results in superhelical stress in vivo (105).

The second topological approach involves the knotting of supercoiled DNA by type 2 DNA topoisomerases (69). Strand passage by these enzymes traps a portion of the supercoil nodes as knot nodes. The topology of the knotted products demonstrated that the substrate superhelix is plectonemic and probably branched (115).

The two methods just discussed are indirect. The number of catenane or knot nodes in the products can be measured accurately, but the number of substrate supercoils can only be calculated using a theoretical model. The model invokes the approximation of a regular supercoil structure and other simplifying assumptions. The final result depends not only on supercoil number but also on branching frequency. Despite these complications, the results obtained with the topological assays agree well with other data. Also, the topological methods have the advantages of ease, accuracy, and defined ionic conditions.

Theoretical Analyses

Theoretical analyses have helped to obtain a general understanding of DNA supercoiling and to analyze experimental data. They are efficient ways to study supercoiled DNA and yield information that is difficult to obtain otherwise. We separate these approaches into two categories according to the use of mechanical or statistical mechanical analysis.

ENERGY MINIMIZATION OF AN ELASTIC ROD MODEL   In the first stage of the theoretical analysis of DNA supercoiling, a thin isotropic elastic rod of infinite length is used to model double helical DNA. In this mechanical model, the elastic energy of the rod increases with the square of its curvature. Fuller, in 1971, was the first to find which conformation of the rod has the minimum elastic energy (43). He considered two possible solutions, simple and interwound helices (Figure 6). By neglecting the ends of the helices, he concluded that the Wr of a simple right-handed helix (Figure 6a) is given by

$$Wr = n(1 - \sin\alpha), \qquad \qquad 6a.$$

and that the Wr of an interwound right-handed helix (Figure 6b) has the form

$$Wr = -n\sin\alpha, \qquad \qquad 6b.$$

where n is the number of helical turns and α is the winding angle. As either helix is extended, the value of α increases, thereby decreasing the curvature of the rod and its bending energy. It follows from Equations 6a,b that as α increases, the $|Wr|$ of a simple helix diminishes, whereas that of an interwound helix increases. The torsional deformation will be less, then, for the interwound form. Therefore, the in-

(a)   (b)

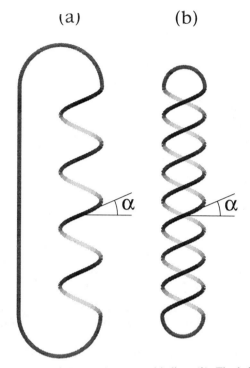

Figure 6 Diagram of simple (*a*) and interwound helices (*b*). The helix winding angles (α) are shown. The number of superhelical turns equals 4 (*a*) and 8 (*b*).

terwound superhelix should be favored over a simple one from an energetic point of view, and the value of α is expected to be large.

Because Fuller's analysis neglects entropy, excluded volume, branching, and superhelix ends, it is more qualitative than quantitative. In 1978, Camerini-Otero & Felsenfeld were the first to attempt to use measured parameters of DNA in the analysis of interwound superhelices (22). Because the DNA torsional rigidity was not known then, they tried to deduce superhelix parameters from elastic energy calculations and the experimentally measured free energy of supercoiling. They also made the first attempt to predict the experimentally measured *s* of supercoiled DNA. In addition, they provided limits for the values of superhelix parameters that have held up well considering the scarcity of available experimental data at the time.

Recently, Hunt & Hearst produced a more complete analysis of the same regular helices (55) by taking into account the experimental values of bending and torsional rigidities and excluded volume effects. They concluded that the interwound superhelix is energetically favored over the toroidal superhelix for realistic values of σ and of excluded volume.

The next step was to replace infinite helices with a closed, finite-length elastic rod with specified values of bending and torsional rigidities. The task is to find the minimum elastic energy conformation as a function of ΔLk, a problem first formulated by Benham (10). The many attempts to solve the problem analytically produced some interesting results (12–14, 66, 95, 98). One was the finding that a flat circular molecule should flip to a figure-8 conformation at some critical ΔLk value (64, 66). This transition depends on the ratio of torsional to bending rigidity for the rod; for DNA the critical ΔLk is about 1.5. This result applies only to very short DNA (< 300 bp), where the equilibrium distribution of conformations is near that of minimum elastic energy. Recently, the abrupt change in Wr of a very small DNA circle was observed experimentally (9).

For arbitrary values of ΔLk, the minimum elastic energy conformation has been obtained only numerically. This was first accomplished by Hao & Olson, who developed a simple way to describe a space curve by using the control points of B-splines (50). They also introduced Equation 4 to specify ΔTw for any conformation with a particular ΔLk and a computed value of Wr. The latter advance is important because it permits the use of a simple closed curve in calculations instead of a rod with a directly specified twist. Olson & Schlick devised an effective algorithm to find the minimum energy conformations numerically (83, 84) and identified the interwound superhelix as the minimum energy form. They found, in addition to the abrupt transition from a flat circle to a figure-8 conformation, other sudden conformational transitions at higher levels of supercoiling, implying discontinuous changes of Wr with ΔLk.

The spatial position and orientation of each base pair was specified directly in the DNA model developed by Tan & Harvey (93, 94). As a result, Tw can be calculated directly and locally. The model is highly suitable for the study of nucleotide sequence effects, such as intrinsic DNA curvature and local conformational transitions, on DNA supercoiling. They obtained the plectonemic superhelix as the minimum energy conformation for highly supercoiled DNA.

Recently, finite element analysis was used to find the minimum energy conformation for the elastic rod model (8, 123). This method also permits direct calculation of both Wr and ΔTw and allows specific nucleotide sequence effects to be taken into account. Bauer et al applied finite element analysis to supercoiled DNA with intrinsic bends (8) and showed that these bends promote writhing as $|\Delta Lk|$ increases. They found that the presence of two or more bends promotes regions with distinct linear densities of ΔTw. Theoretical analysis of the intrinsically curved elastic rod model also led to this conclusion (96).

All of the studies discussed thus far analyzed only one conformation of supercoiled DNA, that with minimum elastic energy. Although such analyses are useful as a first approximation and enhance physical insight, their quantitative application to real DNA is restricted. DNA adopts many different conformations in solution that are far from the one with minimum energy. As with other conformational properties of long polymer chains, DNA supercoiling should be considered in terms of statistical mechanics.

The complexity of a statistical mechanical analysis has limited the number of analytical treatments. Shimada & Yamakawa calculated the equilibrium variance of the Wr of short nicked chains, about one Kuhn statistical length (87). Hearst & Hunt have considered long polymer chains, although in a more qualitative fashion (52), and concluded that plectonemic supercoiling dramatically reduces conformational entropy.

Substantial advances have been made in computer simulations of the statistical mechanical properties of supercoiled DNA. In the 1970s and 1980s, investigators performed many simulations of the equilibrium distribution of Wr for nicked DNA (11, 25, 41, 60, 65, 68, 88, 108). The increasing availability of inexpensive computer power combined with the development of efficient algorithms has recently allowed for simulation of highly supercoiled DNA (59, 107). Now simulation is a powerful tool for the study of the conformations of topologically constrained DNAs. We next describe this approach and the results obtained.

COMPUTER SIMULATION OF EQUILIBRIUM DISTRIBUTION OF DNA CONFORMATIONS   The basic features of the Monte Carlo approach can be reduced to the following. One chooses a DNA model and constructs for it a random set of conformations that should correspond to its equilibrium distribution. The algorithm for the preparation of the set is usually the Metropolis procedure (71). One then uses the constructed set to determine the mean and distribution of superhelix parameters such as Wr and branch number. This computer approach is analogous to EM, which can also be considered a Monte-Carlo method, because conclusions are drawn from a limited statistical sample. Of course, a much larger set can be generated computationally.

The efficiency of the Monte Carlo method originates from the simple model that can be used for the quantitative description of DNA (59,

107). A closed DNA molecule of n Kuhn statistical lengths is modeled as a closed chain of kn rigid cylinders of equal length and diameter (d). Typically, DNA molecules up to 10 kb in length are modeled. The elastic energy of the chain is computed as the sum of the bending and torsional elastic energies. The bending rigidity constant between adjacent cylinders is chosen so that the Kuhn statistical length corresponds to k rigid segments. The simulation results do not depend on the value of k if $k \geq 10$ for DNA more than 1500 bp in length (107). The torsional energy is a quadratic function of the displacement of the chain twist from equilibrium. Because twist is not directly specified in the model, Equation 4 is used to compute it for a particular chain conformation. To do so, the desired ΔLk is assigned to the DNA, and ΔTw is obtained by subtracting the calculated Wr of each conformation.

The connection between the model chain and an actual DNA molecule is specified by three parameters. One is the Kuhn statistical length for DNA, which is twice the persistence length. It is equal to 100 nm and is independent of ionic conditions above a concentration of about 10 mM monovalent cations (M^+) or 1 mM magnesium ions (reviewed in 48). The second parameter, the torsional rigidity constant, is less well characterized, but changing the parameter in the range of uncertainty does not change the simulation results substantially (107). We have used a value of 3×10^{-19} erg·cm (48). The third parameter, the DNA effective diameter (d), specifies the electrostatic interaction between DNA segments; d is the diameter of an uncharged polymer chain that mimics the conformational properties of actual electrically charged DNA. Its value depends strongly on ionic conditions, and its dependence on [Na$^+$] is known with accuracy. Three different experimental determinations of this dependence involving knotting probability (79, 86) or equilibrium sedimentation (20) and a prior theoretical calculation (92) agree extremely well (Figure 7). The value of d can be several times greater than the geometric DNA diameter.

Because the simulation results are sensitive to the value of d, the question arises as to whether the impenetrable cylinder model is a good approximation. Although in statistical physics a hard sphere potential is commonly used instead of the actual one, the approximation may not be adequate for the very tight conformations of supercoiled DNA. To test the validity of this approximation, we performed simulations with a model that featured more realistic charged-segment interactions (AV Vologodskii & NR Cozzarelli, unpublished data). Using a Poisson-Boltzmann treatment as approximated by a Debye-Huckel potential with effective linear charge density (92), we computed the average writhe of the chains. We obtained results close to those arrived at with

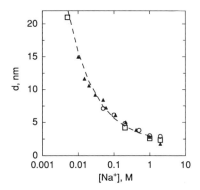

Figure 7 DNA effective diameter, *d,* as a function of solution NaCl concentration. Experimental results were taken from the equilibrium sedimentation of DNA fragments (*squares*) (20) and the probability of DNA knotting [*triangles* (from 79) and *circles* (from 86)]. The dashed line corresponds to the theoretical calculation by Stigter (92).

the hard cylinder model, even for conditions of high σ and low salt concentration (0.01 M), in which the electrostatic interaction is very strong (Figure 8). Thus for most purposes one can use the uncharged cylinder model to save computer time.

Figure 9 shows typical simulated conformations of 3.5-kb supercoiled DNA molecules for two σ values (-0.03 and -0.06) and 0.2 M and

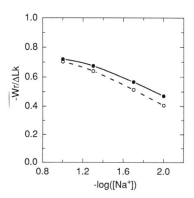

Figure 8 Monte Carlo simulations of DNA supercoiling using two different methods for incorporating electrostatic repulsion. The dependence of the average $Wr/\Delta Lk$ of supercoiled DNA on the solution ion concentration for 3.5-kb DNA with $\sigma = -0.06$ is shown. The values of Wr were computed as described (107). The electrostatic interaction of the segments of the double helix was accounted for in two ways. One procedure used a model with a Debye-Huckel potential for the segment interaction (92) (*solid circles*), and the other a model of impenetrable cylinders with corresponding effective diameter (79) (*open circles*).

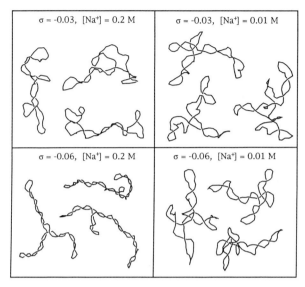

Figure 9 Typical simulated conformations of supercoiled DNA. The Monte Carlo calculations (32) were of 3.5-kb DNA molecules with a σ of -0.03 or -0.06. The DNA effective diameter corresponded to that in a solution containing the indicated concentrations of Na$^+$ or other M$^+$.

0.01 M [M$^+$]. The conformations at $\sigma = -0.03$ are not very ordered but correspond more to a plectonemic superhelix than to a toroidal one. At $\sigma = -0.06$, the regular interwound conformations are clear. Ion concentration has a dramatic effect on conformation at the higher σ. At 0.01 M M$^+$, the superhelix radius and the irregularity of the superhelix are much greater than they are at 0.2 M. The marked dependence of the average $Wr/\Delta Lk$ of a superhelix on ionic condition appears in Figure 8. This dependence reflects the ionic shielding of the electrostatic repulsion between DNA segments.

The data in Figure 8 are valid for DNA $\geq$ 2.5 kb in length. In this range, most of the conformational and energetic properties of supercoiled DNA are directly proportional to DNA length. For shorter DNA molecules, the effect of superhelix ends becomes more critical, and conformational properties depend in a more complex way on total length. Figure 10 shows the dependence of $Wr/\Delta Lk$ on σ for molecules of different length (AV Vologodskii & NR Cozzarelli, unpublished data). The ratio is practically independent of σ for long molecules, in agreement with the experimental data. For very short DNA, ΔLk is absorbed mainly by ΔTw until a transition from a nearly flat circle to

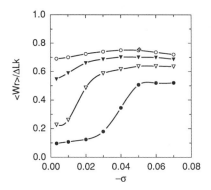

Figure 10 Effect of DNA chain length on the partitioning of ΔLk between writhe and twist. The computed values of $Wr/\Delta Lk$ are plotted as a function of σ for DNA that is 300 (*solid circles*), 600 (*open triangles*), 1200 (*solid triangles*), 3500 (*open circles*), and 7000 bp (*diamond*) in length. The data are from Monte Carlo simulations of DNA for a solution containing 0.2 M M^+.

a figure-8 conformation is reached in accordance with the energy-minimization data.

According to simulation results, branching frequency is the aspect of supercoiled DNA conformations that is most sensitive to ionic conditions and DNA characteristics (107). Branching is favored by increased conformational entropy but is opposed by the free energy of bending at the branch point and particularly at the apices of the superhelix. As a result, branching strongly diminishes with increased salt

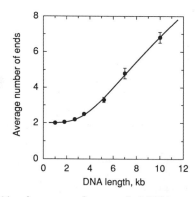

Figure 11 The branching frequency of supercoiled DNA as a function of molecular length. The average number of superhelix ends was computed with Monte Carlo simulations for a σ of -0.05 and for a solution containing 0.2 M monovalent ion. The error bars represent the standard deviations and where not shown are less than the diameter of the data symbol.

concentration and σ, conditions that increase the curvature of the apical bends. The marked increase of branching with DNA length shown in Figure 11 is attributable to the increased number of possible chain conformations. Reliable experimental measurements of branch number as a function of chain length would be a sensitive test of the accuracy of the model used in the simulations.

Supercoiling dramatically affects the spatial relationship of sites within a DNA molecule. These effects are especially important for biological processes that involve two or more DNA sites separated from each other along the chain contour. Supercoiling increases the probability of site juxtaposition (107), defined as bringing two points on the DNA within a small distance. The simulation showed that the probability of site juxtaposition is about 100-fold higher in supercoiled DNA than in relaxed circular molecules, basically because only a one-dimensional search is required for juxtaposition in a plectonemic superhelix instead of the three-dimensional search required with relaxed DNA (107).

Another important effect of supercoiling is the alteration of the angular distribution of juxtaposed sites (AV Vologodskii & NR Cozzarelli, unpublished data). In these simulations, the sites are considered tangent vectors rather than points. The angular distribution of two sites is nearly symmetric for relaxed DNA, but strongly asymmetric for supercoiled DNA (Figure 12). The maximum of the angular distribution

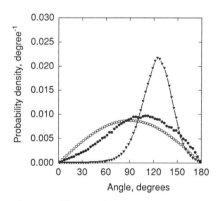

Figure 12 The effect of supercoiling on the angular distribution between juxtaposed segments of circular DNA. The vector angle between all segments within 10 nm of each other was calculated from equilibrium distributions obtained from a Monte Carlo simulation (107). The data were computed for 3.5-kb DNA that was either supercoiled ($\sigma = -0.06$) (*triangles*) or relaxed (*solid circles*). The DNA effective diameter corresponded to that in a 0.2 M monovalent salt solution. For comparison, the distribution for random vectors (*open circles*) is also shown.

depends on salt concentration and approaches 120° in 0.2 M M⁺. This corresponds to a superhelix winding angle of 60°, which is in good agreement with the EM data. One consequence of this angular bias is that the probability of site configurations suitable for specific complexes with proteins should depend strongly on the connectivity (direct or inverse) of the sites. This positioning effect of supercoiling is important in establishing the specificity of recombination reactions (58).

Computer simulation of supercoiled DNA is an efficient way to study many features of the molecule. However, the simulations are based on a highly simplified DNA model. A primary question, then, is how well the model describes the properties of true DNA. To date, there is good qualitative and quantitative agreement between most of the experimental data and the simulation results.

Three sets of experimental data agree very well with simulations of DNA at a low σ: (a) the DNA length dependence of the variance in the equilibrium topoisomer distribution centered about a ΔLk of zero (60); (b) the Na^+-concentration dependence of the probability of forming a knot during random cyclization of a linear DNA molecule (79, 86); and (c) the supercoiling induced by the catenation of two DNA rings (106). Thus, the model describes very well the basic conformational features of relaxed or weakly supercoiled DNA.

The simulation results and the experimental data for highly supercoiled DNA are also in generally good agreement: (a) The average simulation values (107) of Wr, ΔTw, the number of supercoils, and the length and diameter of the superhelix fit well with the experimental data obtained with EM and with the Int topological method (17). Figure 13 compares the computed number of supercoils as a function of ΔLk with that measured using the Int recombinase under well-defined ionic conditions. The agreement is excellent. The only apparent inconsistency with the EM results is the superhelix branching frequency, but (as discussed above) this has not been measured experimentally in a systematic fashion. (b) The ratio of ΔTw to ΔLk obtained by simulation does not depend on σ for long DNA, in agreement with the CD data. (c) The effect of supercoiling on the s and R_g values agrees reasonably well with the simulation results (Figures 3 and 4). Nevertheless, we believe that more quantitative data, especially regarding the effect of ionic conditions, on highly supercoiled DNA molecules should be gathered.

Overall, the model appears to correctly account for the basic elastic and electrostatic properties of the double helix. We know of no property of the double helix whose inclusion would substantially change the simulation results, except perhaps sequence-specific effects, which

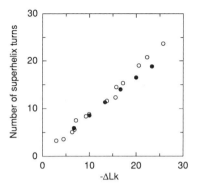

Figure 13 Comparison of computed and experimental values for the number of super-helix turns as a function of ΔLk. The average number of superhelical turns, n, is for a 3.5-kb circular DNA and near-physiological ionic conditions. The computed values, from a Monte Carlo simulation (*solid circles*), were obtained using the equation for a regular superhelix, $n = Wr/\sin\alpha$, where α is the superhelix winding angle (see Figure 1a legend). The values of α were taken from the maxima in the distribution of the angles between juxtaposed segments of a superhelix. The d value was 5 nm and corresponded to a solution of 0.2 M monovalent ion concentration. The experimental data (*open circles*) were obtained from Int recombination assays in a solution of 20 mM TrisHCl (pH 7.5), 50 mM NaCl, and 10 mM MgCl$_2$ (17).

have been outside the scope of our analyses. Of course, such properties may be found in the future. For example, we know little about the potential attraction of DNA segments promoted by di- and polyvalent cations (see 46, 86). We cannot exclude the possibility that such an interaction could change the simulation data by causing an internal collapse of the plectonemic superhelix, as discussed above. In the current model, thermal fluctuations prevent collapse.

Little is known about the dynamic properties of supercoiled DNA. Schlick & Olson (81–83) developed the first simulation of dynamic behavior, combining an elastic energy minimization with a molecular dynamics algorithm. They investigated the pathways from relaxed to supercoiled conformations under torsional stress and found that inter-wound superhelices arose from flat circles. An approach based on Brownian dynamics was developed by Chirico & Langowski (28), who found that formation of an interwound superhelix from a planar 1.1-kb circle took about 3–6 ms. They also concluded that the sliding of superhelix segments past each other requires much more time. The only experimental data concerning the kinetics of superhelix conformational changes is the elegant work of Parker & Halford (75), who found that the time of juxtaposition of two specific sites distant along chain contour is less than 0.5 s in a supercoiled DNA that is 4 kb in length.

THERMODYNAMICS OF SUPERCOILING

Free Energy of Supercoiling

An evaluation of supercoiling free energy is of critical importance for understanding the structure and physiological role of supercoiling. Many consider this an issue that was settled in 1975 by the elegant studies by the Wang and Vinograd groups (33, 77). Subsequently, the free-energy expression derived by these groups was often used in the analysis of local structural transitions favored by supercoiled DNA (reviewed in 40, 105). We believe, however, that although substantial progress has been made, further investigation is warranted.

The first estimation of the free energy of supercoiling, ΔG, was made by Bauer & Vinograd in 1970 (4), using a method based on the difference in ethidium bromide binding to supercoiled and nicked DNA. In 1975, Hsieh & Wang used the same method to discover that ΔG varies directly with the first power of DNA length and the second power of σ (54). Two other studies in 1975 by the Vinograd and Wang groups obtained supercoiling free energy from the equilibrium topoisomer distribution. The simple, but powerful, conception of these studies can be explained as follows. Consider the conversion of a nicked circular DNA to the closed form by ligation of the nick. The fluctuations of Wr and Tw in the nicked circular molecules cause a distribution of topoisomers after ligation that can be measured accurately by gel electrophoresis. According to statistical thermodynamics, the probability distribution of ΔLk, designated P, is given by

$$P \propto \exp(-\Delta G/RT), \qquad\qquad 8.$$

where R is the gas constant and T is the absolute temperature. The experimental distributions were described by the simple empirical relationship

$$P \propto \exp(-K\Delta Lk^2), \qquad\qquad 9.$$

where K is a DNA length–dependent constant (i.e. the experimental distributions were Gaussian). Comparing these two relationships, one concludes that

$$\Delta G = KRT\Delta Lk^2, \qquad\qquad 10a.$$

or, from the definition of σ,

$$\Delta G = (K/\gamma^2)RTN^2\sigma^2. \qquad\qquad 10b.$$

Both groups obtained the result that K equals $1100/N$ for N between 3 and 10 kb. Later, Shore & Baldwin (89) and Horowitz & Wang (53) obtained topoisomer distribution data for shorter DNAs. For short DNA the relative contribution of Wr to DNA supercoiling decreases, and K increases to $4000/N$ for 300-bp DNA.

The topoisomer distributions give the ΔG dependence for $|\sigma| < 0.01$ only, and their use for the higher physiological levels of supercoiling requires a long-range extrapolation. This extrapolation has been justified, in part, by the similar free-energy dependence obtained by Bauer & Vinograd (4) from ethidium bromide binding to highly supercoiled DNA. The validity of this comparison is questionable, however, because the dye titrations were carried out at very high [CsCl], and the results would not necessarily be consistent with those based on topoisomer distributions generated under physiological ionic conditions. Moreover, the free energy found by Hsieh & Wang from dye titration at high [CsCl] is about one half of that found by Bauer & Vinograd. All the experimental data reduced to a DNA length of 5.2 kb appear in Figure 14.

Figure 14 also displays the effect of salt concentration on the σ dependency of ΔG calculated from the simulation data using the method of Klenin et al (59). The computed ΔG corresponding to 0.2 M M$^+$ agrees with the commonly accepted relationship in Equation 10, which

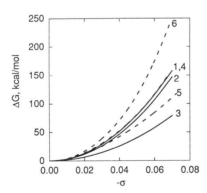

Figure 14   Experimental and theoretical estimates of the free energy of supercoiling. The ΔG values are plotted as a function of σ for a 5.2-kb DNA (the length of SV40 DNA). The experimental curves (*solid lines*) are based on empirical equations derived from topoisomer distributions [*curve 1* (from 33, 77)] and ethidium bromide titration of supercoils [*curve 2* (from 4) and *curve 3* (from 54)]. Also shown are computed results (*dashed lines*) from Monte Carlo calculations in solutions of 0.2 M Na$^+$ (*curve 4*), 1 M Na$^+$ (*curve 5*), and TBE (89 mM tris-borate and 2.5 mM EDTA) buffer (*curve 6*). The effective DNA diameter in TBE is 11 nm (VV Rybenkov, NR Cozzarelli & AV Vologodskii, unpublished data).

is based on topoisomer distributions. The computed ΔG corresponding to a 1 M M^+ is significantly lower, but still higher than that obtained by Hsieh & Wang using 3 M CsCl (54). We also calculated ΔG for Tris-borate-EDTA buffer, a low salt concentration buffer often used in studies of local structural transitions in supercoiled DNA (Figure 14). The ΔG in this case is much higher than any of the other curves. We note that the computed ΔG is close to a quadratic function of ΔLk only for the 0.2 M M^+ curve.

Although the computations of supercoiling free energy require independent experimental verification, ΔG seems to depend on ionic conditions. This conclusion is supported by a theoretical analysis of a regular model for supercoiling (55) and by the observation that local secondary structure transitions in supercoiled DNA require a lower $|\sigma|$ at lower ion concentrations (105).

Enthalpic and Entropic Contributions to Supercoiling Free Energy

The partitioning of ΔG into $T\Delta S$ and ΔH has not been studied intensively for supercoiling, but the results thus far are interesting and unexpected. A priori, the ordering of DNA into a supercoil should be accompanied by a diminished entropy, so that $\Delta S < 0$. The ΔH is expected to be positive, because supercoiling deforms the double helix. Simulation results conformed to these expectations. We calculated conformational entropy by subtracting the elastic energy of supercoiling from ΔG (107). For the introduction of a σ of -0.06 in a 5.2-kb DNA in 0.2 M M^+, the conformational entropy change ($T\Delta S$) is -40 kcal/mol and ΔG is 115 kcal/mol. The theoretical analysis of Hearst & Hunt also gave a large negative entropy of supercoiling (52).

The experimental data, however, give a very different picture of the enthalpy and entropy of supercoiling. Microcalorimetric measurements of ΔH by Seidl & Hinz (85) indicated that both ΔH and $T\Delta S$ have large positive values. Normalizing their values to a DNA 5.2 kb in length and with $\sigma = -0.06$, ΔH equals 280 kcal/mol, which is more than twice the free energy of supercoiling under physiological salt conditions (115 kcal/mol). The value of ΔG for the lower salt concentrations in the calorimetry experiments is unknown, but if we assume it is close to ΔG in physiological conditions, $T\Delta S$ is about 150 kcal/mol. Three other less direct estimations of ΔH and ΔS are based on (a) the temperature dependence of the unwinding of closed circular DNA by organic solvents (67), (b) the temperature dependence of the constant K in Equation 10, as calculated by Bauer & Benham (6) from the data obtained by Duguet (36), and (c) the analysis of early melting of supercoiled

DNA (6). Although the results differ quantitatively, they all yield even larger positive values of ΔH and $T\Delta S$ than the calorimetry.

Thus, we conclude that conformational entropy is a minor contribution to the entropy of supercoiling. Conformational entropy would be the only contribution to total entropy if the bending and torsional deformations had a purely enthalpic origin. Two attempts have been made to measure the entropic and enthalpic contributions to DNA bending directly (45, 51), but further investigation is needed. The positive entropy of supercoiling indicates a large positive entropy contribution to DNA bending and/or to torsional deformation. DNA supercoiling is entropically favorable perhaps because bending and/or twisting is accompanied by a release of bound ions or water molecules. Large positive enthalpy and entropy terms are frequently observed when conformational changes are accompanied by significant changes in hydration (19).

It is important to realize that these interesting thermodynamic results do not alter any of the conclusions presented above. This is because the conformational properties of supercoiled DNA and free energy of supercoiling depend only on the bending and torsional free energy and not on the partitioning into entropy and enthalpy.

SUMMARY AND CONCLUSIONS

Work in the 1990s has substantially increased our understanding of supercoiling conformations and energetics. We now know many of the basic properties of supercoiled DNA as a result of the synergy between experimental and theoretical analyses. We conclude by summarizing the results.

1. All available data indicate a plectonemic structure for supercoiled DNA. First, three types of EM (conventional, cryo, and scanning force) show the plectonemic form. Second, the topology of the catenanes and knots generated from supercoiled DNA by the Int recombinase demands that the substrate supercoils are plectonemic, as does the topology of knotting by type-2 topoisomerases. Third, all the theoretical and computer analyses indicate that the superhelix has the interwound form.

2. The superhelix conformations are often branched, as observed using EM and Monte Carlo simulation. Moreover, branching is required to explain the distribution of knots and catenanes produced by Int or topoisomerases as well as the dependence of s and R_g on σ. Branching frequency is very sensitive to σ, DNA length, ionic con-

ditions, DNA bends, and temperature. Despite the qualitative agreement, the quantitative differences between experimental and computational data point out the need for further studies of branching.

3. The results of Monte Carlo simulations, theoretical analyses, and cryo-EM show that the conformational and thermodynamic properties of supercoiled DNA depend strongly on ionic conditions. The reason for such a dependence is clear. Counterions shield DNA negative charges and decrease the repulsion of DNA segments in the tight interwound structure. The effective double-helix diameter increases from 3 to 15 nm as the salt concentration is reduced from 1.00 to 0.01 M. Experimental investigations of the dependence on ionic conditions of supercoiled DNA properties are just beginning.

The following conclusions refer to conditions of moderate to high monovalent or divalent ion concentrations (≥ 0.1 M [Na$^+$] or ≥ 0.01 M [Mg^{2+}], respectively).

1. Wr takes up about 3/4 of the ΔLk, and $Wr/\Delta Tw$ is independent of σ for DNA ≥ 2.5 kb in length. A constant ratio is implied by the CD data, and $Wr/\Delta Tw$ has been determined with conventional EM, cryo-EM, the Int topological method, and Monte Carlo simulation.
2. The average number of supercoils is (0.8 to 0.9) $\times$ ΔLk and is independent of DNA length. These results were obtained with EM, the Int topological method, and computer simulation.
3. The average superhelix winding angle is about 60° and does not depend on σ. Therefore the length of the superhelix is always at about 40% of the DNA length, but superhelix diameter decreases rapidly with σ. At physiological levels of σ, the superhelix is extremely long and narrow: for an 8-kb molecule, the axial ratio is about 100.
4. Monte Carlo analyses indicate that a σ of -0.06 results in about a 100-fold increase in the probability of site juxtaposition and an average angle between sites of about 120°.
5. The free energy of supercoiling is equal to $10RTN\sigma^2$ at near physiological ionic conditions. This equation follows from topoisomer distribution analyses and Monte Carlo calculations. The ΔG should depend on ionic conditions.
6. Although the conformational entropy of supercoiling is negative, the total $T\Delta S$ and ΔH have large positive values.

The methods we analyzed—EM, sedimentation, light scattering, CD, topological analyses, and computer simulation—have complementary strengths and weaknesses. Therefore, the combination of different experimental techniques with computer simulations of equilibrium distributions provides new opportunities for the study of the properties of supercoiled DNA.

ACKNOWLEDGMENTS

We are indebted to P Abola, W Bauer, C Benham, K Benjamin, D Camerini-Otero, N Crisona, J Dubochet, B Fuller, S Harvey, E Hildebrandt, J Langowski, W Olson, T Schlick, A Stasiak, J White, and L Zechiedrich for communicating results prior to publication or providing comments on the manuscript. The work in the laboratory of NRC is supported by NIH grants GM31655 and GM31657, NSF grant DMS-8820208, and NIEHSC grant ESO1896.

Literature Cited

1. Adrian M, ten Heggeler-Bordier B, Wahli W, Stasiak AZ, Stasiak A, Dubochet J. 1990. Direct visualization of supercoiled DNA molecules in solution. *EMBO J.* 9:4551–54
2. Bates AD, Maxwell A. 1993. *DNA Topology*, ed. D Rickwood. New York: Oxford Univ. Press. 114 pp.
3. Bauer W, Vinograd J. 1968. The interaction of closed circular DNA with intercalative dyes. I. The superhelix density of SV40 DNA in the presence and absence of dye. *J. Mol. Biol.* 33:141–71
4. Bauer W, Vinograd J. 1970. The interaction of closed circular DNA with intercalative dyes. II. The free energy of superhelix formation in SV40 DNA. *J. Mol. Biol.* 47:419–35
5. Bauer WR. 1978. Structure and reactions of closed duplex DNA. *Annu. Rev. Biophys. Bioeng.* 7:287–313
6. Bauer WR, Benham CJ. 1993. The free energy, enthalpy and entropy of native and of partially denatured closed circular DNA. *J. Mol. Biol.* In press
7. Bauer WR, Gallo R. 1989. Physical and topological properties of closed circular DNA. *Chromosomes: Eucariotic, Procariotic, and Viral*, ed. KW Adolph, 1:87–126. Boca Raton: CRC Press
8. Bauer WR, Lund RA, White JH. 1993.

Twist and writhe of a DNA loop containing intrinsic bends. *Proc. Natl. Acad. Sci. USA* 90:833–37
9. Bednar J, Furrer P, Stasiak A, Dubochet J, Egelman EH, Bates AD. 1993. The twist, writhe and overall shape of supercoiled DNA change during counterion-induced transition from loosely to tightly interwound superhelix. *J. Mol. Biol.* In press
10. Benham CJ. 1977. Elastic model of supercoiling. *Proc. Natl. Acad. Sci. USA* 74:2397–401
11. Benham CJ. 1978. The statistics of superhelicity. *J. Mol. Biol.* 123:361–70
12. Benham CJ. 1979. An elastic model of the large-scale structure of duplex DNA. *Biopolymers* 18:609–23
13. Benham CJ. 1983. Geometry and mechanics of DNA superhelicity. *Biopolymers* 22:2477–95
14. Benham CJ. 1987. The role of the stress resultant in determining mechanical equilibria of superhelical DNA. *Biopolymers* 26:9–15
15. Bliska JB, Cozzarelli NR. 1987. Use of site-specific recombination as a probe of DNA structure and metabolism *in vivo*. *J. Mol. Biol.* 194:205–18
16. Bloomfield VA, Crothers DM, Tinoco I. 1974. *Physical Chemistry of Nucleic Acids*. New York: Harper & Row
17. Boles TC, White JH, Cozzarelli NR.

1990. Structure of plectonemically supercoiled DNA. *J. Mol. Biol.* 213:931–51

18. Brahms S, Nakasu S, Kikuchi A, Brams JG. 1989. Structural changes in positively and negatively supercoiled DNA. *Eur. J. Biochem.* 184:297–303

19. Breslauer KJ. 1991. A thermodynamic perspective of DNA bending. *Curr. Opin. Struct. Biol.* 1:416–22

20. Brian AA, Frisch HL, Lerman LS. 1981. Thermodynamics and equilibrium sedimentation analysis of the close approach of DNA molecules and a molecular ordering transition. *Biopolymers* 20:1305–28

21. Calugareanu G. 1961. Sur las classes disotopie des noeuds tridimensionnels et leurs invariants. *Czech. Math. J.* 11:588–625

22. Camerini-Otero RD, Felsenfeld G. 1978. A simple model of DNA super helices in solution. *Proc. Natl. Acad. Sci. USA* 75:1708–12

23. Campbell A, Eason R. 1975. Effects of DNA primary structure on tertiary structure. *FEBS Lett.* 212:212–15

24. Campbell AM. 1978. Conformational variation in superhelical deoxyribonucleic acid. *Biochem. J.* 171:281–83

25. Chen Y. 1981. Monte Carlo study of freely jointed ring polymers. II. The writhing number. *J. Chem. Phys.* 75:2447–53

26. Chirico G, Beretta S, Baldini G. 1992. Light scattering of DNA plasmids containing repeated curved insertions: anomalous compaction. *Biophys. Chem.* 45:101–8

27. Chirico G, Langowski J. 1992. Calculating hydrodynamic properties of DNA through a second-order Brownian dynamics algorithm. *Macromolecules* 25:769–75

28. Chirico G, Langowski J. 1993. Kinetics of DNA supercoiling studied by Brownian dynamic simulation. *J. Mol. Biol.* In press

29. Clark DJ, Ghirlando R, Felsenfeld G, Eisenberg H. 1993. Effect of positive supercoiling on DNA compaction by nucleosome cores. *J. Mol. Biol.* In press

30. Cozzarelli NR, Boles TC, White JH. 1990. Primer on the topology and geometry of DNA supercoiling. See Ref. 30a, pp. 139–84

30a. Cozzarelli NR, Wang JC, eds. 1990. *DNA Topology and its Biological Effects*. Cold Spring Harbor, NY: Cold Spring Harbor Lab. Press

31. Crick FHC. 1976. Linking numbers and nucleosomes. *Proc. Natl. Acad. Sci. USA* 73:2639–43

32. Crothers DM, Haran TE, Nadeau JG. 1990. Intrinsically bent DNA. *J. Biol. Chem.* 265:7093–96

33. Depew RE, Wang JC. 1975. Conformational fluctuations of DNA helix. *Proc. Natl. Acad. Sci. USA* 72:4275–79

34. Drlica K. 1992. Control of bacterial DNA supercoiling. *Mol. Microbiol.* 6:425–33

35. Dubochet J, Adrian M, Dustin I, Furrer P, Stasiak A. 1992. Cryoelectron microscopy of DNA molecules in solution. *Methods Enzymol.* 211:507–18

36. Duguet M. 1993. The helical repeat of DNA at high temperature. *Nucleic Acids Res.* 21:463–68

37. Dulbecco R, Vogt M. 1963. Evidence for a ring structure of polyoma virus DNA. *Proc. Natl. Acad. Sci. USA* 50:236–43

38. Dustin I, Furrer P, Stasiak A, Dubochet J, Langowski J, Egelman E. 1991. Spatial visualization of DNA in solution. *J. Struct. Biol.* 107:15–21

39. Evans T, Felsenfeld G, Reitman M. 1990. Control of globin gene transcription. *Annu. Rev. Cell Biol.* 6:95–124

40. Frank-Kamenetskii MD. 1990. DNA supercoiling and unusual structures. See Ref. 30a, pp. 185–216

41. Frank-Kamenetskii MD, Lukashin AV, Anshelevich VV, Vologodskii AV. 1985. Torsional and bending rigidity of the double helix from data on small DNA rings. *J. Biomol. Struct. Dyn.* 2:1005–12

42. Freeman LA, Garrard WT. 1992. DNA supercoiling in chromatin structure and gene expression. *Crit. Rev. Eukariot. Gene Expr.* 2:165–209

43. Fuller FB. 1971. The writhing number of a space curve. *Proc. Natl. Acad. Sci. USA* 68:815–19

44. Glaubiger D, Hearst JE. 1967. Effect of superhelical structure on the secondary structure of DNA rings. *Biopolymers* 5:691–96

45. Gray HBJ, Hearst JE. 1968. Flexibility of native DNA from the sedimentation behavior as a function of molecular weight and temperature. *J. Mol. Biol.* 35:111–29

46. Guldbrand L, Jönsson B, Wennerström H, Linse P. 1984. Electrical double layer forces. A Monte Carlo study. *J. Chem. Phys.* 80:2221–28

47. Hagerman PJ. 1981. Investigation of the flexibility of DNA using transient

electric birefringence. *Biopolymers* 20: 1503–35

48. Hagerman PJ. 1988. Flexibility of DNA. *Annu. Rev. Biophys. Biophys. Chem.* 17:265–86

48a. Hagerman PJ. 1990. Sequence-directed curvature of DNA. *Annu. Rev. Biochem.* 59:755–81

49. Hagerman PJ, Zimm BH. 1981. Monte Carlo approach to the analysis of the rotational diffusion of wormlike chains. *Biopolymers* 20:1481–502

50. Hao M-H, Olson WK. 1989. Global equilibrium configurations of supercoiled DNA. *Macromolecules* 22: 3292–3303

51. Harrington RE. 1977. DNA chain flexibility and the structure of chromatin nu-bodies. *Nucleic Acids Res.* 4:3511–35

52. Hearst JE, Hunt NG. 1991. Statistical mechanical theory for the plectonemic DNA supercoil. *J. Chem. Phys.* 95: 9322–28

53. Horowitz DS, Wang JC. 1984. Torsional rigidity of DNA and length dependence of the free energy of DNA supercoiling. *J. Mol. Biol.* 173:75–91

54. Hsieh TS, Wang JC. 1975. Thermodynamic properties of superhelical DNAs. *Biochemistry* 14:527–35

55. Hunt NG, Hearst JE. 1991. Elastic model of DNA supercoiling in the infinite-length limit. *J. Chem. Phys.* 95: 9329–36

56. Johnston BH. 1992. Generation and detection of Z-DNA. *Methods Enzymol.* 211:127–58

57. Jolly DJ, Campbell AM. 1972. Three-dimensional structure of supercoiled deoxyribonucleic acid in solution. *Biochem. J.* 128:569–78

58. Kanaar R, Cozzarelli NR. 1992. Roles of supercoiled DNA structure in DNA transactions. *Curr. Opin. Struct. Biol.* 2:369–79

59. Klenin KV, Vologodskii AV, Anshelevich VV, Dykhne AM, Frank-Kamenetskii MD. 1991. Computer simulation of DNA supercoiling. *J. Mol. Biol.* 217:413–19

60. Klenin KV, Vologodskii AV, Anshelevich VV, Klisko VY, Dykhne AM, Frank-Kamenetskii MD. 1989. Variance of writhe for wormlike DNA rings with excluded volume. *J. Biomol. Struct. Dyn.* 6:707–14

60a. Kremer W, Klenin K, Diekman S, Langowski J. 1993. DNA curvature influences the internal motions of supercoiled DNA. *EMBO J.* 12:4407–12

61. Langowski J, Kremer W, Kapp U.

1992. Dynamic light scattering for study of solution conformation and dynamics of superhelical DNA. *Methods Enzymol.* 211:430–48

62. Laundon CH, Griffith JD. 1988. Curved helix segments can uniquely orient the topology of supertwisted DNA. *Cell* 52:545–49

63. Lebowitz J. 1990. Through the looking glass: the discovery of supercoiled DNA. *Trends Biochem. Sci.* 15:202–7

64. Le Bret M. 1979. Catastrophic variation of twist and writhing of circular DNAs with constraint? *Biopolymers* 18:1709–25

65. Le Bret M. 1980. Monte Carlo computation of supercoiling energy, the sedimentation constant, and the radius of gyration of unknotted and circular DNA. *Biopolymers* 19:619–37

66. Le Bret M. 1984. Twist and writing of short circular DNAs according to the first-order elasticity. *Biopolymers* 23: 1835–67

67. Lee CH, Mizusawa H, Kakefuda T. 1981. Unwinding of double-stranded DNA helix by dehydration. *Proc. Natl. Acad. Sci. USA* 78:2838–42

68. Levene SD, Crothers DM. 1986. Topological distributions and the torsional rigidity of DNA. A Monte Carlo study of DNA circles. *J. Mol. Biol.* 189:73–83

69. Liu LF, Liu C-C, Alberts BM. 1980. Type II DNA topoisomerases: enzymes that can unknot a topologically knotted DNA molecule via a reversible double-strand break. *Cell* 19:697–707

70. Maestre MF, Wang JC. 1971. Circular dichroism of superhelical DNA. *Biopolymers* 10:1021–30

71. Metropolis N, Rosenbluth AW, Rosenbluth MN, Teller AH, Teller E. 1953. Equation of state calculations by fast computing machines. *J. Chem. Phys.* 21:1087–92

72. Mizuuchi K, Gellert M, Weisberg RA, Nash HA. 1980. Catenation and supercoiling in the products of bacteriophage lambda integrative recombination in vitro. *J. Mol. Biol.* 141:485–94

73. Morse RH. 1992. Transcribed chromatin. *Trends Biochem. Sci.* 17:23–26

74. Murchie AIH, Lilley DMJ. 1992. Supercoiled DNA and cruciform structures. *Methods Enzymol.* 211:158–80

75. Parker CN, Halford SE. 1991. Dynamics of long-range interactions on DNA: the speed of synapsis during site-specific recombination by resolvase. *Cell* 66:781–91

76. Pohl WF. 1980. DNA and differential geometry. *Math. Intell.* 3:20–27
77. Pulleybank DE, Shure M, Tang D, Vinograd J, Vosberg HP. 1975. Action of nicking-closing enzyme on supercoiled and nonsupercoiled closed circular DNA: formation of a Boltzmann distribution of topological isomers. *Proc. Natl. Acad. Sci. USA* 72:4280–84
78. Rhoades M, Thomas CA Jr. 1968. The P22 bacteriophage DNA molecule. II. Circular intracellular forms. *J. Mol. Biol.* 37:41–61
79. Rybenkov VV, Cozzarelli NR, Vologodskii AV. 1993. Probability of DNA knotting and the effective diameter of the DNA double helix. *Proc. Natl. Acad. Sci. USA* 90:5307–11
80. Samori B, Siligardi G, Quagliariello C, Weisenhorn AL, Vesenka J, Bustamante CJ. 1993. Chirality of DNA supercoiling assigned by scanning force microscopy. *Proc. Natl. Acad. Sci. USA* 90:3598–601
81. Schlick T, Li B, Hao M-H. 1993. Calibration of the timestep for the dynamics of supercoiled DNA modeled by B-splines. *Eighth Conversation in Biomolecular Stereodynamics, Albany, NY*
82. Schlick T, Olson W. 1992. Trefoil knotting revealed by molecular dynamics simulations of supercoiled DNA. *Science* 257:1110–15
83. Schlick T, Olson WK. 1992. Supercoiled DNA energetics and dynamics by computer simulation. *J. Mol. Biol.* 223:1089–119
84. Schlick T, Olson WK, Westcott T, Greenberg JP. 1993. On higher buckling transitions in supercoiled DNA. *Biopolymers.* In press
85. Seidl A, Hinz H-J. 1984. The free energy of DNA supercoiling is enthalpy-determined. *Proc. Natl. Acad. Sci. USA* 81:1312–16
86. Shaw SY, Wang JC. 1993. Knotting of a DNA chain during ring closure. *Science* 260:533–36
87. Shimada J, Yamakawa H. 1985. Statistical mechanics of DNA topoisomers: the helical worm-like chain. *J. Mol. Biol.* 184:319–29
88. Shimada J, Yamakawa H. 1988. Moments for DNA topoisomers: the helical wormlike chain. *Biopolymers* 27:657–73
89. Shore D, Baldwin RL. 1983. Energetics of DNA twisting. II. Topoisomer analysis. *J. Mol. Biol.* 170:983–1007
90. Spengler SJ, Stasiak A, Cozzarelli NR. 1985. The stereostructure of knots and catenanes produced by phage λ integrative recombination: implications for mechanism and DNA structure. *Cell* 42:325–34
91. Sperrazza JM, Register JC III, Griffith J. 1984. Electron microscopy can be used to measure DNA supertwisting. *Gene* 31:17–22
92. Stigter D. 1977. Interactions of highly charged colloidal cylinders with applications to double-stranded DNA. *Biopolymers* 16:1435–48
93. Tan RKZ, Harvey SC. 1989. Molecular mechanics model of supercoiled DNA. *J. Mol. Biol.* 205:573–91
94. Tan RKZ, Harvey SC. 1990. Succinct macromolecular models: application to supercoiled DNA. In *Theoretical Biochemistry and Molecular Biophysics*, ed. DL Beveridge, R Lavery, 1:125–37. Guilderland, NY: Adenine
95. Tanaka F, Takahashi H. 1985. Elastic theory of supercoiled DNA. *J. Chem. Phys.* 83:6017–26
96. Tobias I, Olson WK. 1993. The effect of intrinsic curvature on supercoiling: predictions of elasticity theory. *Biopolymers* 33:639–49
97. Trifonov EN. 1985. Curved DNA. *CRC Crit. Rev. Biochem.* 19(2):89–106
98. Trusu H, Wadati M. 1986. Elastic model of highly supercoiled DNA. *Biopolymers* 25:2083–96
99. Tyson JJ, Strogatz SH. 1991. The differential geometry of scroll waves. *Int. J. Bifurcation Chaos* 1:723–44
100. Upholt WB, Gray HB Jr, Vinograd J. 1971. Sedimentation velocity behavior of closed circular SV40 DNA as a function of superhelix density, ionic strength, counterion and temperature. *J. Mol. Biol.* 62:21–38
101. van Holde KE, Lohr DE, Robert C. 1992. What happens to nucleosomes during transcription? *J. Biol. Chem.* 267:2837–40
102. Vinograd J, Lebowitz J. 1966. Physical and topological properties of circular DNA. *J. Gen. Physiol.* 49:103–25
103. Vinograd J, Lebowitz J, Radloff R, Watson R, Laipis P. 1965. The twisted circular form of polyoma viral DNA. *Proc. Natl. Acad. Sci. USA* 53:1104–11
104. Vollenweider HJ, Koller T, Parello J, Sogo JM. 1976. Superstructure of linear duplex DNA. *Proc. Natl. Acad. Sci. USA* 73:4125–29
105. Vologodskii AV. 1992. *Topology and Physics of Circular DNA.* Boca Raton, FL: CRC Press. 179 pp.
106. Vologodskii AV, Cozzarelli NR. 1993.

Monte Carlo analysis of the conformation of DNA catenanes. *J. Mol. Biol.* 232:1130–40

107. Vologodskii AV, Levene SD, Klenin KV, Frank-Kamenetskii MD, Cozzarelli NR. 1992. Conformational and thermodynamic properties of supercoiled DNA. *J. Mol. Biol.* 227:1224–43

108. Vologodskii AV, Lukashin AV, Anshelevich VV, Frank-Kamenetskii MD. 1979. Fluctuations in superhelical DNA. *Nucleic Acids Res.* 6:967–82

109. Wang JC. 1969. Variation of the average rotation angle of the DNA helix and the superhelical turns of covalently closed cyclic lambda DNA. *J. Mol. Biol.* 43:25–39

110. Wang JC. 1974. Interactions between twisted DNAs and enzymes: the effects of superhelical turns. *J. Mol. Biol.* 87:797–816

111. Wang JC. 1985. DNA topoisomerases. *Annu. Rev. Biochem.* 54:665–97

112. Wang JC. 1986. Circular DNA. *Cyclic Polymers*, ed. JA Semlyen, pp. 225–60. Essex, England: Elsevier Appl. Sci.

113. Wang JC. 1992. Template topology and transcription. In *Transcriptional Regulation*, ed. JC Wang, pp. 1253–69. Cold Spring Harbor, NY: Cold Spring Harbor Lab. Press

114. Wasserman SA, Cozzarelli NR. 1986. Biochemical topology: applications to DNA recombination and replication. *Science* 232:951–60

115. Wasserman SA, Cozzarelli NR. 1991. Supercoiled DNA-directed knotting by T4 topoisomerase. *J. Biol. Chem.* 266:20567–73

116. Weil R, Vinograd J. 1963. The cyclic helix and cyclic coil forms of polyoma viral DNA. *Proc. Natl. Acad. Sci. USA* 50:730–39

117. Wells RD. 1988. Unusual DNA structures. *J. Biol. Chem.* 263:1095–98

118. White JH. 1969. Self-linking and the Gauss integral in higher dimensions. *Am. J. Math.* 91:693–728

119. White JH. 1989. An introduction to the geometry and topology of DNA structure. In *Mathematical Methods for DNA Sequences*, ed. MS Waterman, pp. 225–53. Boca Raton, FL: CRC Press

120. White JH, Cozzarelli NR, Bauer WR. 1988. Helical repeat and linking number of surface-wrapped DNA. *Science* 241:323–27

121. White JH, Gallo RM, Bauer WR. 1992. Closed circular DNA as a probe for protein-induced structural changes. *Trends Biochem. Sci.* 17:7–12

122. Wolffe A. 1992. *Chromatin. Structure and Function.* San Diego, CA: Academic. 213 pp.

123. Yang Y, Tobias I, Olson WK. 1993. Finite element analysis of DNA supercoiling. *J. Chem. Phys.* 98:1673–86

Annu. Rev. Biophys. Biomol. Struct. 1994. 23:645–69

POLYPEPTIDE INTERACTIONS WITH MOLECULAR CHAPERONES AND THEIR RELATIONSHIP TO IN VIVO PROTEIN FOLDING

Samuel J. Landry

Department of Biochemistry, Tulane University School of Medicine, New Orleans, Louisiana 70112

Lila M. Gierasch

Department of Pharmacology, University of Texas Southwestern Medical Center, Dallas, Texas 75235-9041

KEY WORDS: heat shock proteins, GroEL, GroES, Hsp70, cooperativity, molecular recognition

CONTENTS

1056–8700/94/0610–0645$05.00

PERSPECTIVES AND OVERVIEW

The emergence of a nascent polypeptide chain from a ribosome signals the beginning of a complex process that leads to a correctly folded, localized, processed, and in some cases assembled protein product. While the amino acid sequence of a protein specifies its eventual three-dimensional structure, the cell uses additional sequence information to guide the polypeptide to its proper destination, to modulate its folding (both temporally and spatially), and to direct its rate of degradation. The expression of this information, which is critical to the in vivo protein folding process, relies on the intrinsic properties of sequences that may serve as targeting or folding mediators and on the ability of these sequences to be recognized by cellular components.

The past few years have witnessed the development of a major new view of protein folding in vivo, i.e. that proteins fold in the cell with the assistance of a family of proteins collectively termed molecular chaperones (29). These proteins are believed to play roles in the modulation and delay of folding to optimize cellular processes such as protein localization, protection of nascent chains and unfolded proteins from aggregation or proteolysis, as well as regulation of assembly and disassembly of protein complexes.

Several recent comprehensive reviews provide biochemical and physiological descriptions of molecular chaperones (21, 31, 42, 43, 51, 54, 76, 89, 125). Most molecular chaperones are heat shock proteins (Hsp); chaperone functions have been ascribed to Hsp60s (29), Hsp70s (29), Hsp15-30s (61), Hsp90s (121), and Hsp100s (110). Within classes of heat-shock proteins, members are highly homologous, but members from different classes do not appear to be related. Other proteins often included in classifications of chaperones are those that modulate specific folding, targeting, and assembly reactions, such as SecB and PapD. Because much more is known about the roles of the Hsp70 and Hsp60 families in folding, this review focuses on these classes. Both Hsp70 and Hsp60 chaperones require ATP for full expression of their functions and have ATPase activity. Most Hsp70s can exist in several oligomeric states, but they are believed to function as monomers. By contrast, Hsp60 family members are tetradecameric in their functional state, and their 60-kDa subunits are organized into two seven-subunit rings (a double doughnut). The Hsp60 class of chaperones (also known as the chaperonins or Cpn60s) works in concert with a 10-kDa co-chaperonin, termed Cpn10, which itself is an oligomer of seven subunits organized in a single ring. The *Escherichia coli* representative of the

Hsp70 class is DnaK, and its representatives of the Hsp60/Hsp10 class are GroEL and GroES.

Evidence in support of chaperone activity includes association with nascent chains or unfolded proteins (7, 10, 85), genetic lesions in the chaperone that cause defects in folding and assembly (19, 76, 125), as well as the genetically and biochemically demonstrated requirement for chaperones in the translocation of proteins across membranes (20, 24, 63, 94, 104, 122), enhancement of the activity of defective or heterologous proteins simultaneously expressed with chaperones in *E. coli* (1, 17, 28, 33, 35, 45, 64, 66, 74, 117, 123), facilitation of in vitro folding and assembly reactions (3, 14–16, 36, 40, 44, 49, 52, 56, 68, 71, 79, 82, 84, 106, 111, 118, 126), and protection from aggregation (15, 58, 61, 71, 109, 121) including from heat denaturation (57, 58, 109).

Molecular chaperones may have several physiological functions. Some of these may be specialized and may as yet be unknown. Only for the Hsp60 family members do we have compelling combined in vitro and in vivo data indicating a principal role as protein-folding assistants. Several groups have convincingly demonstrated a role for Hsp70 family members as modulators of folding in organellar import (24, 63, 91) or in secretory pathways (20, 43, and references therein), but in only two cases has an Hsp70 family member been found to facilitate a refolding reaction (107, 109). Furthermore, recent evidence from a biochemical reconstitution experiment (71) demonstrates that Hsp70 and Hsp60 chaperones may work in concert, as suggested by studies of proteins imported into the mitochondrion (51, 63, 88, 90).

Why another review of molecular chaperones? Many questions remain regarding the mechanisms of these proteins. For example, how do chaperones recognize and bind to their substrates? Is the folding pathway of an isolated protein altered by chaperone interactions? Do different classes of chaperone function analogously? How do molecular chaperones facilitate folding? What is the role of nucleoside triphosphates in chaperone action? Recent data provide partial answers for some of these questions; hence, another review is timely. Furthermore, we should consider our current understanding of chaperone action in light of the intensive ongoing study of protein folding in the test tube.

PROTEIN FOLDING IN THE TEST TUBE

The consensus view of protein folding in vitro (Figure 1) is that under conditions favoring folding of a particular protein, the ensemble of unfolded states rapidly collapses (in 10–50 ms) to a compact-inter-a

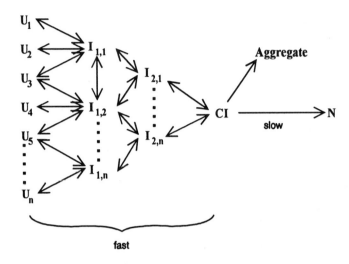

b

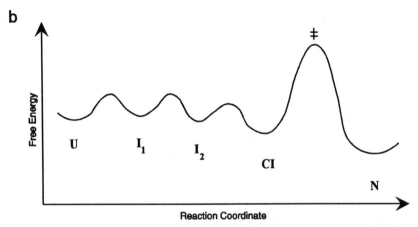

Figure 1 Schematic representations of the in vitro pathway of protein folding, illustrating (*a*) the multitude of interconversions possible among unfolded (U) and partially folded intermediates (I). All of these eventually fold to a compact intermediate (CI), which may also be an ensemble of states, before passing through a high energy state (*b*, ‡) to the native conformation (N). An off-pathway, competing aggregation step is indicated.

mediate, molten globule–like state (see below), perhaps briefly visiting other intermediate states en route (22), but with very low concentrations of any pre-molten globule forms at any given point in time. The highest energy barrier in the folding pathway occurs at the ultimate step, i.e. from the compact-intermediate to the native state, and hence this step determines the overall rate of folding, which varies from 100 ms to minutes in various examples studied to date (105). The transition state (at the top of the energy barrier approaching the native state) is likely to be characterized by a completely native-like arrangement of chain segments but without the surface-to-surface fits that provide van der Waals energy of stabilization. Native states of proteins are well packed, with an optimal reduction in solvent-exposed hydrophobic surface area. In addition, all hydrogen-bonding groups are partnered either with other protein groups or with the solvent, and nearly all interior side chains are fixed into unique rotamer conformations (97). Passage from the compact intermediate to the native state requires the fixing of all of these interacting groups into the requisite geometries at once, at a consequent high entropic cost, as well as desolvation of all interior surfaces.

The ensemble of unfolded states created under denaturing conditions represents a dynamically varying, interconverting, sequence-allowed distribution. Protein fragments, which behave much like denatured-state proteins, have conformational preferences (26, 27), and direct study of denatured states reveals the presence of significant structure (12, 34, 87, 108). Although folding is a highly cooperative process in which most molecules are in either the unfolded or the native states, considerable evidence has accumulated showing intermediate states along the pathway (indicated in Figure 1 as I_i), which are not highly populated (25). To date, detailed studies using rapid kinetics have shown native-like secondary structure in folding intermediates concurrent with a lack of tertiary interactions until late in the pathway (posttransition state) (5).

No clear evidence has been obtained for nonnative secondary or tertiary structure in protein-folding intermediates. The kinetic intermediate occurring immediately before the transition state is believed to adopt much of the secondary structure of the native protein, to be very compact with respect to the unfolded state though not packed as well as the native protein, to lack most tertiary interactions, and to have more mobile side chains than the native protein. Thus the intermediate resembles the equilibrium nonnative state termed the molten globule (5, 65, 96). The molten globule intermediate may well comprise an ensemble of compact states and certainly can interconvert rapidly with fully unfolded chains. All incompletely folded states, including the most fully unfolded, the pre-molten-globule and the molten-globule forms, expose hydrophobic surface area and would be expected to have a strong tendency to aggregate or to interact with hydrophobic surfaces in general.

These observations offer a clear explanation for the difficulty of achieving high yields of refolded protein in a test tube. Folding must compete with the tendency of the unfolded states to aggregate. Logically, lowering concentration or temperature should enhance the yield of refolded product. Also, many investigators have found that additives such as detergents or other proteins, e.g. bovine serum albumin (BSA) (62, 127) can also enhance the yield of refolded product. These additives slow the overall rate of folding, which is consistent with a mechanism of yield enhancement that relies on binding to hydrophobic surfaces exposed in intermediate states.

IN VIVO PROTEIN FOLDING: WHAT DO WE KNOW?

Although the state of a polypeptide chain during biosynthesis has not been directly studied, in vitro folding experiments offer a lesson that must be applied to the in vivo process: The rate of spontaneous folding is faster than the rate of protein synthesis (89). Therefore, chains will tend to fold during synthesis unless they are prevented from doing so. Attainment of the final native state of a protein must rely, however, on the complete synthesis of the protein (or domain for a large, multidomain protein) because of the cooperativity of folding. Incompletely folded chains are prone to aggregation (50). Studies in *E. coli* demonstrate that incompletely folded species are proteolytically labile (93). On the other hand, proteins destined to traverse a membrane must remain incompletely folded until they are translocated. In addition, some proteins that are part of oligomeric complexes must fold in concert with another subunit. Furthermore, all of these folding events must take place at the normal cellular temperature and in the presence of a high concentration of cellular components, conditions that generally disfavor effective refolding in vitro.

Thus, we can expect optimal folding under in vivo constraints only if:

1. The nascent chain is restrained from premature folding or intermolecular interaction until the entire chain is synthesized.
2. Intermediates along the folding pathway of a given protein are pro-

tected from proteolysis and are sequestered from interactions that compete with folding.

3. The folding of nascent chains destined for organellar import or secretory pathways is delayed.
4. The folding of subunits destined to assemble into oligomeric complexes is modulated for complex formation.

These are the functions that must be mediated by molecular chaperones. Despite early suggestions to the contrary (38, 99), folding in vivo should not require catalysis. The complete polypeptide chain is capable of unassisted folding. In fact, measurements of in vivo folding rates show clearly that these rates are far slower than rates observed in the test tube. Instead, the need in vivo is to protect the vulnerable species that must exist in a normal sequence-driven protein-folding reaction. Because the unfolded species and the subsequent intermediates up to and including the compact intermediate all interconvert rapidly, binding to any of these could modulate folding and protect the chain.

HOW DO MOLECULAR CHAPERONES RECOGNIZE THEIR SUBSTRATES?

Molecular chaperones bind to substrate proteins that are incompletely folded (29). Beyond this prerequisite, they show little preference for primary structures, as many substrates can bind the same chaperone (119). The facile interconversion among incompletely folded states implies that chaperone binding could rely on the characteristics of any nonnative state. The properties shared by all of these states are exposure of hydrophobic surface, incomplete packing of side chains, presence of some secondary structure, and greater side-chain dynamics than in the native state. The degree of compactness and the quantity of secondary structure in various unfolded states vary substantially. Chaperones may take advantage of the plasticity of the unfolded states to mold polypeptides into conformations that are compatible with the chaperones' binding sites.

Although molecular chaperones can discriminate between the native and incompletely folded states of proteins, they show little preference for one substrate over another, if all are unfolded. This selectivity-promiscuity paradox suggests that chaperone binding depends on features that characterize unfolded states and does not depend on a particular sequence. Still, we are left with questions. What is the nature of the chaperone/substrate complex? How do chaperones bind to unfolded states, and do different classes rely on different binding modes?

Results of several approaches have converged on a model of Hsp70 binding in which the substrate is bound in an extended conformation. Flynn et al demonstrated that peptides of 8–25 residues could bind to both the cytoplasmic Hsp70 family member, Hsc70, and the endoplasmic reticulum Hsp70 homologue, BiP, and could stimulate the ATPase activities of these chaperones (38). Because peptide fragments of fewer than 30 amino acids do not fold stably, they mimic the unfolded state without the complications that arise from using unfolded polypeptides in folding conditions, in which case an ongoing folding reaction takes place during the binding study. Subsequently, in a very ingenious use of synthetic peptides, these workers examined the specificity of BiP binding (39). They performed a simultaneous synthesis of a randomized collection of peptides of defined length. Monitoring ATPase activity of the chaperones upon addition of the peptides, they found that peptides of seven residues gave maximal stimulation. Furthermore, they attempted to determine the composition and positional preferences of the BiP-bound peptides. They found a general preference for aliphatic residues but concluded that their method could not yield positional information. The BiP binding preference was for sequences that would normally be on the inside of a native protein, which would thus enable discrimination of folded from unfolded. Moreover, many different sequences would retain significant capacity to bind, thus explaining the ability of the Hsp70 family to interact with many substrates.

BiP binding preferences were also recently explored using affinity panning of peptide libraries expressed on the surface of bacteriophage fd particles (8). Comparison of binding preferences among libraries of octapeptides or dodecapeptides revealed a statistically significant heptameric consensus motif, with strong biases toward aliphatic residues at alternating positions in the sequence. This motif is compatible with the Flynn et al (38) peptide substrate preferences.

Results obtained from nuclear magnetic resonance (NMR) experiments using transferred nuclear Overhauser effects (trNOEs), which reveal distance relationships in the chaperone-bound state of model substrate peptides, show that peptides bind to the *E. coli* Hsp70 homologue, DnaK, in an extended conformation (70). This binding mode is consistent with the results of Flynn et al (38) and Blond-Elguindi et al (8), and approximately the same number of residues appears to be involved in binding as in their studies. Patterns of peptide immobilization by DnaK, evident in the NMR data, suggest that binding is mediated in part by hydrogen bonds to the peptide backbone, as well as by side-chain interactions. This mode of binding is similar to that described for peptides in the antigen-presenting site of major histocompatibility complex (MHC) proteins (13, 77); coincidently, two groups have independently modeled the fold of the peptide-binding domain of Hsp70 family members after the structure of the MHC peptide-binding domain (37, 98). As suggested for the peptide MHC class II complex (13), backbone hydrogen bonding may provide a strong sequence-independent contribution to the binding interaction, which would be a useful property of the promiscuous Hsp70 binding site. The recent crystal structure determination of the bacterial chaperone, PapD, complexed with a bound peptide (64a) exemplifies a mode of recognition that would also be consistent with the available Hsp70-binding data: The peptide is extended, binds with several hydrogen bonds to the chaperone, and has alternate side chains in hydrophobic interactions with the chaperone-binding site, which itself is composed of a β strand.

In contrast to the extended mode of polypeptide binding exhibited by DnaK, polypeptides appear to be partially folded in association with GroEL. Langer et al (71) examined substrate preferences of DnaK, DnaJ, and GroEL using proteins with different properties. Reduced, carboxymethylated bovine α-lactalbumin, which occurs in a predominantly extended conformation, bound preferentially to DnaK, but not to GroEL. By contrast, urea-denatured rhodanese, which exists in a partially structured, molten globule–like state under the conditions of the assay, bound preferentially to GroEL and very poorly to DnaK. Similarly, casein, which displays hydrophobic surface somewhat analogously to a compact intermediate, also bound better to GroEL. Interestingly, DnaJ, whose chaperone properties are not well understood, behaved like GroEL in binding both to the partially folded state of rhodanese and to casein, but not to reduced, carboxymethylated α-lactalbumin.

TrNOE studies demonstrate that some peptides bind to GroEL as α-helices (69, 70). This feature is probably exploited by chaperonins because these peptides present hydrophobic surfaces when folded as helices. Indeed, recent studies in our laboratory of numerous peptides, including some that are very unlikely to form an α-helix (e.g. an alternating L,D sequence), have shown that other peptide conformations can be bound to GroEL (T Scott, J Maxwell, Z Wang, S Landry & L Gierasch, unpublished results). The unifying property of all the peptides that bind with relatively high affinity to GroEL is a high tendency to bind to a hydrophobic surface. In support of this conclusion, GroEL binding affinity parallels retention of the peptides in reversed phase high pressure chromatography (T Scott, J Maxwell & L Gierasch, unpublished results).

Schmidt & Buchner (106) demonstrated that GroEL could function-
ally interact with an unfolded state of an all-β protein, an F_{ab} fragment
of a monoclonal antibody. They argued that binding relied on characteristics of the early folding intermediate, such as hydrophobicity,
and likely did not require an α-helical conformation. This conclusion
was based on the assumption that the incompletely folded F_{ab} fragment
contains only native-like secondary structure when bound to the chaperone.

Thus, the Hsp70 and Hsp60 families recognize nonnative, variable
sequence polypeptide segments in different and possibly complementary ways. Distinct modes of binding could ensure that the cell is prepared for the variety of structured and unstructured proteins arising
during biosynthesis or as a result of stress. On the other hand, the low
barriers to interconversion of the incompletely folded states of proteins
argue that any of these states could be utilized by chaperones as substrates to delay folding and to disfavor aggregation.

WHAT WE KNOW ABOUT MOLECULAR
CHAPERONES FROM IN VITRO STUDIES

The seminal work of Lorimer and colleagues (44, 45) on facilitation of
refolding of bacterial ribulose-bisphosphate carboxlylase (Rubisco) by
GroEL/GroES demonstrated clearly that the chaperonin system could
enhance the yield of refolded product in an in vitro reaction. Similar
results were subsequently obtained by others (e.g. 15, 79, 82, 128). In
these and many later studies, direct evidence has been obtained for
complex formation between GroEL and the substrate protein. In cases
of proteins that fold efficiently without chaperone, ATP alone can release substrate from these complexes (3, 49, 56, 68, 79, 84, 118). Proteins that fold inefficiently in unassisted folding reactions require the
cochaperone and nucleotide to produce folded product in the GroEL-
assisted reaction.

Hsp70s have blocked folding in vitro in several experiments, but an
Hsp70 alone has facilitated the yield of refolded product in only two
cases. First, heat-denatured RNA polymerase was reactivated at very
high yield ($\sim$100%) using a DnaK/ATP system (109). A large excess
(60-fold) of DnaK was required for reactivation. However, a recent
study showed that addition of DnaJ and GrpE reduces the amount of
DnaK required for reactivation (129). Similarly, these three E. coli
proteins work in a concerted fashion in bacteriophage λ DNA replication (130). Second, Bukau and coworkers (107) have found that firefly
luciferase activity could be regenerated in vitro from heat-denatured

enzyme in good yield using a combined DnaK/DnaJ/GrpE/ATP system. Interestingly, DnaJ suppressed aggregation and enhanced the yield of folded product in both studies (107). The picture emerges that DnaJ targets DnaK to its substrate (71, 129) and that both DnaJ and GrpE enhance the effectiveness of DnaK action by stimulating its ATPase activity (75). Recent reports suggest that coupling of Hsp70s with other chaperones will provide folding assistance. For example, Langer et al developed a coupled in vitro refolding system with DnaK, DnaJ, GrpE, and GroEL/GroES/ATP (71).

To date, the mechanism by which the Hsp60-type chaperonin systems enhance folding remains unclear. As outlined in the above discussion of protein folding in vitro, the major obstacle to high yields of refolded product is aggregation. The tendency towards aggregation will increase when folding is slow (a high energy barrier to the native state), which can lead to an accumulation of incompletely folded intermediates, and when the susceptibility of the intermediate species to aggregation is great. Chaperonins could therefore act either by reducing the energy barrier (increasing the rate of folding) or decreasing the susceptibility of the intermediate species to aggregation. Considerable evidence has accumulated arguing against any enhancement of the folding rate by chaperones, i.e. they do not act as true catalysts (15, 68, 82, 83, 118).

How could a chaperone protect the incompletely folded chain from aggregation? Simply by binding to the folding intermediate a chaperone could provide some protection against aggregation and thus facilitate folding. Indeed, the early work of Tandon & Horowitz clearly demonstrated the effectiveness of detergents in the promotion of rhodanese refolding (113). BSA also promotes folding of rhodanese (62) and citrate synthase (127). Refolding of citrate synthase in the presence of Hsp90 or low-molecular-weight Hsps does not require ATP (121) and could be mechanistically identical to refolding with BSA or the detergent system. As expected, excess detergent (113), BSA (62), or Hsp (121) reduces yield because binding becomes more favored at the expense of folding.

If binding alone facilitates folding, why is the action of most chaperones ATP dependent? Regulation of the timing of binding and release by ATP hydrolysis enables a chaperone to mete out the unfolded protein at or near the rate of the slow step in folding, thus lowering the steady-state concentration of unfolded protein (15). This additional sophistication in the chaperone mechanism ensures a flux of substrate through the folding pathway regardless of the concentrations of chaperone and substrate and the relative affinities of different substrates for the chaperone.

If binding and ATP-mediated release were sufficient, why do Hsp70s not facilitate folding in vitro? Possibly the binding of substrate via an extended short segment of chain does not adequately protect the rest of the chain from competing interactions. Alternatively, multiple Hsp70s may bind a substrate polypeptide and not release it in a concerted fashion, thus impeding cooperative folding of the chain. Accurate data on binding stoichiometries of Hsp70s are scarce; one report suggests that only one Hsp70 binds per chain (92).

Binding and ATP-mediated release are clearly only part of the mechanism of Hsp60s. Their oligomeric structure and partnership with cochaperonins provide additional mechanistic advantages. Elegant recent results support the notion that the substrate is sequestered within the 60-nm cavity of the tetradecameric Hsp60 chaperone (11, 72). These findings support the so-called cage models of Hsp60 action (2, 23, 30), which propose that substrates are held within the chaperone cavity until folding is complete, and that GroES acts as gatekeeper to prevent premature dissociation. Inside the protected environment of the cage, where the substrate is isolated from other unfolded proteins, it purportedly cycles through binding and release steps until folding is complete. The principal question in these models is how the chaperone recognizes that the protein is fully folded (i.e. how the gatekeeper knows to open the gate). It is difficult to envision a mechanism that assesses the substrate's degree of foldedness without incorporating a binding interaction, which would be expected to compete with folding.

Jackson et al (60) suggested that folding yields are enhanced by chaperonin-facilitated denaturation of misfolded proteins, as well as by sequestering folding intermediates. However, little evidence suggests that proteins become kinetically trapped in misfolded states. Rather, incompletely folded states can apparently rapidly interconvert.

A MODEL FOR FACILITATION OF FOLDING IN VITRO BY GroEL/GroES

In Figure 2, we present schematic models for the mechanism of in vitro GroEL-facilitated protein folding, with and without GroES, incorporating the results of several investigators. In the absence of bound nucleotide, GroEL has high affinity for incompletely folded substrate and low affinity for GroES. Substrates bind to the nucleotide-free form of GroEL with probable stoichiometries of one substrate per tetradecamer (9, 79, 118). In the absence of GroES (Figure 2a), GroEL subunits bind nucleotide with low cooperativity and presumably undergo a conformational change that sequesters the hydrophobic bind-

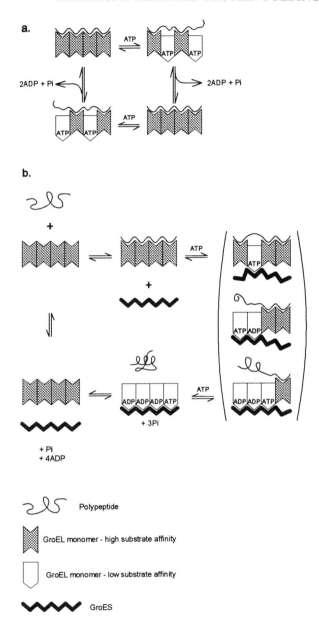

Figure 2 Schematic representations of the mechanism of action of GroEL (*a*) in the absence of GroES and (*b*) in the presence of GroES. Note that in *a*, the conformational change of GroEL subunits from high substrate affinity to low substrate affinity is not cooperative, and in *b*, species in parentheses are present in low quantities, because the binding of ATP and GroES to GroEL is highly cooperative.

ing site (6, 60). Either ATP or ADP may bind, but affinity for ADP is reported to be lower (9, 60, 114). In the absence of GroES, no more than four nucleotides have been found to bind GroEL (114). Without GroES, the conformational change in GroEL upon nucleotide binding, and hence, substrate release, would be nearly uncooperative (9, 48, 114). This lack of a cooperative release is consistent with the finding that proteins that are not aggregation-prone refold upon release by nucleotide, even in the absence of GroES (3, 49, 56, 68, 79, 84, 118), whereas proteins whose incompletely folded states have a high tendency to aggregate do not achieve a higher yield of refolding upon release by nucleotide (15, 40, 71, 79, 126). The latter class of proteins must require concerted release to fold cooperatively. Also, without GroES, all subunits of GroEL may not adopt the low-affinity conformation at once. Proteins that can be released productively under these conditions are probably those with lower-affinity binding to GroEL (smaller, less hydrophobic).

In the presence of GroES (Figure 2b), nucleotide binding, and therefore the conformational change of GroEL to a low-affinity state, is rendered considerably more cooperative (9, 60, 114). The cooperative conformational shift is probably a consequence of simultaneous high-affinity binding of a GroES seven-mer to seven sites on ATP-bound GroEL. GroES contains a highly mobile polypeptide loop that is immobilized and sequestered upon ATP-dependent formation of a GroEL/GroES complex (70a). The loop is likely to be a GroEL interactive region on GroES, and its flexibility may enable simultaneous binding to seven subunits in the structurally plastic GroEL oligomer. Whether GroES binding is favored by a nucleotide-induced subunit conformational change, a nucleotide-driven rearrangement of the quaternary structure of GroEL, or possibly the creation of a binding site on GroEL that includes nucleotide is not known at present. Electron micrographs show that ATP causes large subunit rearrangements in GroEL (102a). Also, a recent cross-linking study suggests that GroES itself may bind ATP (77a). Todd et al (114) found seven tightly held nucleotides in the GroEL/GroES complex, and electron micrographs show a substantial rearrangement in the quaternary structure of GroEL upon GroES binding (59, 72, 102). How tertiary, subunit conformational changes upon nucleotide binding are translated into quaternary structural changes is not known. GroES also reportedly inhibits the steady-state ATPase activity of GroEL (18, 120), as well as enhances its cooperativity (9, 60, 114), but this role may be achieved by inhibition of ADP release. Lorimer and coworkers noted that GroES inhibition of GroEL ATPase requires several minutes to develop; during this time, already bound

ATP molecules could be hydrolyzed (120). Similarly, recent work shows that the single-turnover rate of ATP hydrolysis by GroEL/ GroES is the same as that of GroEL alone (60, 114, 120). The role of ATP hydrolysis in facilitating the change of GroEL from high affinity to low affinity is somewhat unclear: Proteins reported to require GroES also require hydrolysis of nucleotide for productive release (15, 40, 71, 79, 126). Hydrolysis is not always necessary for productive release of proteins that do not require GroES (3, 49, 56, 68, 79, 84, 118), and ADP is sufficient in one case (84). Because ADP appears to bind GroEL less well than ATP, recycling of the chaperone back to its high-affinity state may depend on hydrolysis of all GroEL-bound nucleotides to ADP. Although the chaperonin resting state is likely to be the GroEL/ GroES complex, the cooperative association of substrate elements with GroEL subunits leads to rapid dissociation of GroES and ADP (79a).

Important issues that remain to be resolved are the number of ATP molecules required for a folding reaction and whether cycles of GroEL/ GroES association and dissociation are required for a folding reaction. An estimated 130 ATP molecules are consumed during refolding of one molecule of rhodanese (79). Recent studies suggest that multiple rounds of substrate and GroES binding occur before a protein completes its folding reaction, and this could account for the high ATP cost (79a). Although cycles of binding and release may occur in these in vitro reactions, it is not clear that cycling is obligatory for folding assistance. If the substrate fails to fold, its cooperative rebinding to GroEL will lead to dissociation of GroES and ADP, setting up a new round of the reaction.

What is the state of the substrate bound to GroEL? The stoichiometry of substrate binding to GroEL suggests that the substrate contacts more than one GroEL subunit (9, 32, 79, 118). In addition, substrate binding induces reassembly of GroEL tetradecamers from subunits dissociated by low urea concentrations (80a), suggesting that substrate stabilizes the GroEL quaternary structure, perhaps by tethering subunits together. Two groups have argued that GroEL binds to a molten-globule state of the substrate protein (79, 80). The data supporting these conclusions consisted of the development of molten globule–like fluorescence, ANS binding properties, and acquisition of proteolytic resistance in GroEL-bound proteins in the course of ATP-dependent folding assistance. However, these parameters are expected to change with an increasingly intimate association with GroEL. In the absence of ATP, proteins should be pulled in the direction of unfolding by favorable hydrophobic interactions between the unfolded form of the protein and GroEL. Indeed, labile proteins such as pre-β-lactamase (destabilized by the signal sequence) (67) and dihydrofolate reductase (118) undergo net unfolding in the presence of GroEL. Of two nonnative forms of lactate dehydrogenase (LDH), the more unfolded form associates with GroEL, and the form that more closely fits the molten globule description does not (3). One should also remember that unfolded states should interconvert easily because of the low energy barriers between them. Binding to any unfolded form of a protein should be largely equivalent in its effect on the free population of unfolded substrate.

What then is the role of the chaperone in folding if the protein is released in the same state in which it was bound? As described above, formation of a substrate-chaperone complex reduces the concentration of aggregation-prone folding intermediates, and the rate of nucleotide hydrolysis governs the rate at which these species are released into the bulk medium. Substrates that do not make it over the barrier to the native conformation before encountering another chaperone in a high-affinity state could rebind. Furthermore, a gatekeeping mechanism (as suggested in the cage models described above) may be present that favors continued association of any incompletely folded substrate with GroEL, even in its low-affinity conformation. If the binding sites in this state were of low but not negligible affinity (relative to the intramolecular interactions that lead to substrate folding), then substrates would be unlikely to diffuse from the cavity until folded. Alternatively, the compactness and consequent size of the substrate may enable it to escape the cavity only when folded. An examination of these questions must await the availability of structural data on GroEL or a homologue. Nevertheless, we argue that the most important aspect of GroEL folding assistance in vitro is the modulation of the steady-state level of folding intermediates.

ROLES OF MOLECULAR CHAPERONES IN FOLDING IN THE CELL

Molecular chaperones are essential for life. Their induction by heat-shock and other stresses places them in a key position as rescuers of proteins that have been damaged by these stressful conditions. However, this role is clearly not the only one they play—a far more central one is intimated by the in vitro studies reviewed in the previous sections. We conclude that molecular chaperones could fill all of the needs anticipated in in vivo folding: They could guide proteins that have not yet folded through the risky parts of their folding pathways; modulate the rates of folding of nascent chains to meet the needs of the cell, such as organellar import; and assist in oligomeric assembly by stabilizing incompletely folded monomers.

Folding Modulation

Hsp70s emerge as the likely modulators of folding in cases where the polypeptide chain is tethered (e.g. to the ribosome) and/or is handed off to another interaction (e.g. with a membrane-translocation apparatus or another chaperone). Supporting this idea is the capacity of Hsp70s to bind short segments of polypeptide chain in an extended conformation, which delays folding. At the same time, Hsp70s generally do not facilitate folding upon nucleotide-induced release. Many results are consistent with a direct interaction of Hsp70s with nascent chains. For example, antibodies to Hsp70s coprecipitate nascent polypeptides in cell extracts (7), and exogenously added Hsp70s bind to nascent proteins in reconstituted translation systems (101). Also, genetic lesions in Hsp70s cause altered polysome structure (86). In vitro reconstituted systems also show direct binding of the *E. coli* Hsp70 homologue, DnaK, to nascent chains (55, 71). Furthermore, data from both in vivo (24, 122) and reconstituted systems (20) support a central role for Hsp70s in folding modulation of precursors destined for organellar import or secretion, where the polypeptide chain must be passed on to the translocation apparatus. In mitochondria, genetic data show that Hsp70s are required both on the cytoplasmic side of the membrane to maintain the precursor in an unfolded state and on the matrix side to insure directionality and to hand-off the newly translocated protein to an Hsp60 (63). In both the in vitro studies of Hartl and coworkers and the mitochondrial genetic data, Hsp70s worked as part of multichaperone complexes. Clearly, the release of a polypeptide chain from an Hsp70 may not facilitate its folding unless another chaperone, like an Hsp60, can bind to the released chain.

Protection from Nonproductive Interactions

Hsp60s are the best candidates for protection of folding intermediates from nonproductive intermolecular interactions and from proteolysis. The in vitro data summarized above indicate that the GroEL type of chaperone can sequester a nonnative polypeptide and release it in such a way as to enhance its chances of folding into a native conformation. These chaperones thus can enable chains to fold in an otherwise nonoptimal setting. As chaperone abundance is regulated, they also serve as a holding tank for incompletely folded proteins or monomers of oligomeric proteins, thus preventing their aggregation or proteolytic breakdown. All but one protein whose folding yield is enhanced by GroEL in vitro are oligomeric; rhodanese, the one exception, has a large hydrophobic interface between its two structurally homologous domains. In vitro evidence argues that GroEL enhances oligomer assembly by facilitating correct folding of native monomers (116). In a strain of *E. coli* with reduced expression of both DnaK and GroEL, substantial protein aggregation occurs in vivo (46). Aggregation is partly mitigated by overexpression of either DnaK/DnaJ or GroEL/GroES (47).

In addition to these roles, Hsp60s clearly can work as part of a multiple-chaperone cascade, accepting the substrates released from Hsp70s. Because of their oligomeric structure, the ability of Hsp60s to bind substrate at multiple sites should confer on them a higher affinity for unfolded substrates than that of Hsp70s (32). This higher relative affinity would enable Hsp60s to compete successfully in stripping chaperones off nascent chains, as directly demonstrated in vitro (47). The genetic evidence that folding of imported mitochondrial proteins requires both Hsp70 and Hsp60 in the matrix implies the same pathway. The most important function of Hsp60 in vivo may be cooperative release of the newly synthesized (and/or translocated) complete polypeptide. Hsp70 can bind to the nascent chain during synthesis or translocation, but transfer of the complete chain to Hsp60 sets the stage for a productive folding reaction.

Protection from Stress Damage

Hsp70 and Hsp60 chaperones also play a critical role in protecting proteins from heat and other stresses and in rescuing stress-damaged proteins. This role of chaperones is surely not unanticipated, as the characterization of these molecules has been largely based on their status as heat-shock proteins. Indeed, many studies, both in vitro and in vivo, have recently provided evidence for this role. Hsp70, together with DnaJ and GrpE, binds and prevents aggregation of heat-denatured *E. coli* RNA polymerase (109, 129) and firefly luciferase (107). Furthermore, in a clever experiment relying on the sensitive assay of luciferase activity, Schroder et al showed that Hsp mutations in *E. coli* expressing firefly luciferase prevented reactivation of luciferase following heat shock in vivo. Hsp60 also prevents aggregation of heat-denatured proteins in vitro (53, 57, 78, 81, 112, 129).

Chaperones probably play many more in vivo roles than are envisioned at present. We expect that in addition to their roles in folding, they will be central intersections in the balancing of protein biosynthetic and degradative pathways. The Hsp70 class of chaperones provides a clue about the potential complexity of chaperone action in vivo.

Their reported functions include roles in DNA replication (4), nuclear localization (73), steroid receptor regulation (103), and clathrin uncoating from endocytic vesicles (100), among others. In all likelihood, all these processes exploit the capacity of the Hsp70s to bind extended segments of chain and to release them in an ATP-dependent manner, but the details are lacking.

FUTURE ASPECTS

As stated above, we anticipate that the list of cellular roles of molecular chaperones will expand, and that the evidence describing their functions in vitro and in vivo will be increasingly plentiful. Many new chaperones, particularly in the Hsp60 family, have been identified in new cellular contexts (40, 41, 124) and organisms (95, 115). As discussed in this review, we now have some understanding of the substrates preferred by different classes of chaperone and of the biochemical aspects of chaperone action. But the need for structural understanding of chaperones is extremely pressing. A major contribution in this research area is imminent: The crystal structure of GroEL has been solved in two forms, uncomplexed and bound to ATPγS, to high resolution (2.6 Å) (D Boisvert, K Braig, R Hegde, Z Otwinowski, P Sigler & A Horwich, unpublished data). We eagerly await the opportunity to relate the structure and function of this molecular machine. Intense effort is also underway in the quest for structural data on Hsp70 peptide-binding domains. We trust that the next review of these chaperones will include a structural description of their modes of action.

We also anticipate that the importance of molecular chaperones in the molecular basis of disease will be a burgeoning area. Many mutations associated with diseases express themselves as folding defects. The ability either to use chaperones in therapeutic treatments or to modulate the seriousness of the genetic defect by regulating chaperone action may emerge as medically significant advances.

ACKNOWLEDGMENTS

We are grateful to our many colleagues who communicated results prior to publication. We thank Patricia Clark, Josep Rizo, Teddy Scott, Zhulun Wang, and Muppalla Sukumar for critical reading of the manuscript. This work was supported by grants from the National Institutes of Health (GM27616) and from the Robert A Welch Foundation.

Literature Cited

1. Adar YY, Simaan M, Ulitzur S. 1992. Formation of the LuxR protein in the *Vibrio fischeri*–Lux system is controlled by HtpR through the GroESL proteins. *J. Bacteriol.* 174:7138–43
2. Agard DA. 1993. To fold or not to fold. *Science* 260:1903–4
3. Badcoe IG, Smith CJ, Wood S, Halsall DJ, Holbrook JJ, et al. 1991. Binding of a chaperonin to the folding intermediates of lactate dehydrogenase. *Biochemistry* 30:9195–9200
4. Baker TA, Wickner SH. 1992. Genetics and enzymology of DNA replication in *Escherichia coli*. *Annu. Rev. Genet.* 26:447–77
5. Baldwin RL. 1993. Pulsed H/D-exchange studies of folding intermediates. *Curr. Opin. Struct. Biol.* 3:84–91
6. Baneyx F, Gatenby AA. 1992. A mutation in GroEL interferes with protein folding by reducing the rate of discharge of sequestered polypeptides. *J. Biol. Chem.* 267:11637–44
7. Beckmann RP, Mizzen LA, Welch WJ. 1990. Interaction of Hsp70 with newly synthesized proteins: implications for protein folding and assembly. *Science* 248:850–54
8. Blond-Elguindi S, Cwirla SE, Dower WJ, Lipshutz RJ, Sprang SR, et al. 1993. Affinity panning of a library of peptides displayed on bacteriophages reveals the binding specificity of BiP. *Cell* 75:717–28
9. Bochkareva ES, Lissin NM, Flynn GC, Rothman JE, Girshovich AS. 1992. Positive cooperativity in the functioning of molecular chaperone GroEL. *J. Biol. Chem.* 267:6796–6800
10. Bole DG, Hendershot LM, Kearney JF. 1986. Posttranslational association of immunoglobulin heavy chain binding protein with nascent heavy chains in nonsecreting and secreting hybridomas. *J. Cell Biol.* 102:1558–66
11. Braig K, Simon M, Furuya F, Hainfeld JF, Horwich AL. 1993. A polypeptide bound by the chaperonin GroEL is localized within a central cavity. *Proc. Natl. Acad. Sci. USA* 90:3978–82
12. Broadhurst RW, Dobson CM, Hore PJ, Radford SE, Rees ML. 1991. A photochemically induced dynamic nuclear polarization study of denatured states of lysozyme. *Biochemistry* 30:405–12
13. Brown JH, Jardetzky TS, Gorga JC, Stern LJ, Urban RG, et al. 1993. 3-Dimensional structure of the human class-II histocompatibility antigen HLA-DR1. *Nature* 364:33–39
14. Brown KL, Wood S, Buttner MJ. 1992. Isolation and characterization of the major vegetative RNA polymerase of *Streptomyces coelicolor* A3(2): renaturation of a sigma subunit using GroEL. *Mol. Microbiol.* 6:1133–39
15. Buchner J, Schmidt M, Fuchs M, Jaenicke R, Rudolph R, et al. 1991. GroE facilitates refolding of citrate synthase by suppressing aggregation. *Biochemistry* 30:1586–91
16. Cannon S, Wang P, Roy H. 1986. Inhibition of ribulose bisphosphate carboxylase assembly by antibody to a binding protein. *J. Cell Biol.* 103:1327–35
17. Carrillo N, Ceccarelli EA, Krapp AR, Boggio S, Ferreyra RG, Viale AM. 1992. Assembly of plant ferredoxin-NADP$^+$ oxidoreductase in *Escherichia coli* requires GroE molecular chaperones. *J. Biol. Chem.* 267:15537–41
18. Chandrasekhar GN, Tilly K, Woolford C, Hendrix R, Georgopoulos C. 1986. Purification and properties of the GroES morphogenetic protein of *Escherichia coli*. *J. Biol. Chem.* 261:12414–19
19. Cheng MY, Hartl F-U, Martin J, Pollock RA, Kalousek F, et al. 1989. Mitochondrial heat-shock protein Hsp60 is essential for assembly of proteins imported into yeast mitochondria. *Nature* 337:620–25
20. Chirico WJ, Waters MG, Blobel G. 1988. 70K heat shock related proteins stimulate protein translocation into microsomes. *Nature* 332:805–10
21. Craig EA, Gambill BD, Nelson RJ. 1993. Heat shock proteins—molecular chaperones of protein biogenesis. *Microbiol. Rev.* 57:402–14
22. Creighton TE. 1990. Protein folding. *Biochem. J.* 270:1–16
23. Creighton TE. 1991. Molecular chaperones—unfolding protein folding. *Nature* 352:17–18
23a. Creighton TE, ed. 1992. *Protein Folding*. New York: Freeman
24. Deshaies RJ, Koch BD, Werner-Washburne M, Craig EA, Schekman R. 1988. A subfamily of stress proteins facilitates translocation of secretory and mitochondrial precursor polypeptides. *Nature* 332:800–5
25. Dobson CM. 1991. Characterization of protein folding intermediates. *Curr. Opin. Struct. Biol.* 1:22–27

26. Dyson HJ, Merutka G, Waltho JP, Lerner RA, Wright PE. 1992. Folding of peptide fragments comprising the complete sequence of proteins—models for initiation of protein folding. I. Myohemerythrin. *J. Mol. Biol.* 226: 795–817

27. Dyson HJ, Sayre JR, Merutka G, Shin HC, Lerner RA, Wright PE. 1992. Folding of peptide fragments comprising the complete sequence of proteins—models for initiation of protein folding. II. Plastocyanin. *J. Mol. Biol.* 226:819–35

28. Edgerton MD, Santos MO, Jones AM. 1993. In vivo suppression of phytochrome aggregation by the GroE chaperonins in *Escherichia coli. Plant Mol. Biol.* 21:1191–94

29. Ellis J. 1987. Proteins as molecular chaperones. *Nature* 328:378–79

30. Ellis RJ. 1993. The general concept of molecular chaperones. *Philos. Trans. R. Soc. London Ser. B Biol. Sci.* 339: 257–61

31. Ellis RJ, van der Vies SM. 1991. Molecular chaperones. *Annu. Rev. Biochem.* 60:321–47

32. Endo T. 1991. Co-operative binding of hsp60 may promote transfer hsp70 and correct folding of imported proteins in mitochondria. *FEBS Lett.* 293:1–3

33. Escher A, Szalay AA. 1993. GroE-mediated folding of bacterial luciferases in vivo. *Mol. Gen. Genet.* 238:65–73

34. Evans PA, Topping KD, Woolfson DN, Dobson CM. 1991. Hydrophobic clustering in nonnative states of a protein—interpretation of chemical shifts in nmr spectra of denatured states of lysozyme. *Proteins Struct. Funct. Genet.* 9:248–66

35. Fayet O, Louarn J-M, Georgopoulos C. 1986. Suppression of the *Escherichia coli dnaA46* mutation by amplification of the *groES* and *groEL* genes. *Mol. Gen. Genet.* 202:435–45

36. Fisher MT. 1992. Promotion of the in vitro renaturation of dodecameric glutamine synthetase from *Escherichia coli* in the presence of GroEL (chaperonin-60) and ATP. *Biochemistry* 31: 3955–63

37. Flajnik MF, Camilo C, Kramer J, Kasahara M. 1991. Which came first, MHC class I or class II?. *Immunogenetics* 33:295–300

38. Flynn GC, Chappell TG, Rothman JE. 1989. Peptide binding and release by proteins implicated as catalysts of protein assembly. *Science* 245:385–90

39. Flynn GC, Pohl J, Flocco MT, Rothman JE. 1991. Peptide-binding specificity of the molecular chaperone BiP. *Nature* 353:726–30

40. Frydman J, Nimmesgern E, Erdjumentbromage H, Wall JS, Tempst P, Hartl FU. 1992. Function in protein folding of TRiC, a cytosolic ring complex containing TCP-1 and structurally related subunits. *EMBO J.* 11:4767–78

41. Gao YJ, Thomas JO, Chow RL, Lee GH, Cowan NJ. 1992. A cytoplasmic chaperonin that catalyzes beta-actin folding. *Cell* 69:1043–50

42. Georgopoulos C. 1992. The emergence of the chaperone machines. *Trends Biochem. Sci.* 17:295–99

43. Gething MJ, Sambrook J. 1992. Protein folding in the cell. *Nature* 355:33–45

44. Goloubinoff P, Christeller JT, Gatenby AA, Lorimer GH. 1989. Reconstitution of active dimeric ribulose bisphosphate carboxylase from an unfolded state depends on two chaperonin proteins and Mg-ATP. *Nature* 342:884–89

45. Goloubinoff P, Gatenby AA, Lorimer GH. 1989. GroE heat-shock proteins promote assembly of foreign prokaryotic ribulose bisphosphate carboxylase oligomers in *Escherichia coli. Nature* 337:44–47

46. Gragerov AI, Martin ES, Krupenko MA, Kashlev MV, Nikiforov VG. 1991. Protein aggregation and inclusion body formation in Escherichia coli *rpoH* mutant defective in heat shock protein induction. *FEBS Lett.* 291: 222–24

47. Gragerov A, Nudler E, Komissarova N, Gaitanaris GA. 1992. Cooperation of GroEL/GroES and DnaK/DnaJ heat shock proteins in preventing protein misfolding in *Escherichia coli. Proc. Natl. Acad. Sci. USA* 89:10341–44

48. Gray TE, Fersht AR. 1991. Cooperativity in ATP hydrolysis by GroEL is increased by GroES. *FEBS Lett.* 292: 254–58

49. Grimm R, Donaldson GK, Vandervies SM, Schafer E, Gatenby AA. 1993. Chaperonin-mediated reconstitution of the phytochrome photoreceptor. *J. Biol. Chem.* 268:5220–26

50. Haase-Pettingell CA, King J. 1988. Formation of aggregates from a thermolabile in vivo folding intermediate in P22 tailspike maturation: a model for inclusion body formation. *J. Biol. Chem.* 263:4977–83

51. Hartl FU, Martin J, Neupert W. 1992. Protein folding in the cell—the role of molecular chaperones Hsp70 and Hsp60. *Annu. Rev. Biophys. Biomol. Struct.* 21:293–22

52. Hartman DJ, Hoogenraad NJ, Condron R, Hoj PB. 1992. Identification of a mammalian 10-kDa heat shock protein, a mitochondrial chaperonin-10 homologue essential for assisted folding of trimeric ornithine transcarbamolyase in vitro. *Proc. Natl. Acad. Sci. USA* 89:3394-98

53. Hartman DJ, Surin BP, Dixon NE, Hoogenraad NJ, Hoj PB. 1993. Substoichiometric amounts of the molecular chaperones GroEL and GroES prevent thermal denaturation and aggregation of mammalian mitochondrial malate dehydrogenase in vitro. *Proc. Natl. Acad. Sci. USA* 90:2276-80

54. Hendrick JP, Hartl FU. 1993. Molecular chaperone functions of heat-shock proteins. *Annu. Rev. Biochem.* 62: 349-84

55. Hendrick JP, Langer T, Davis TA, Hartl FU, Wiedmann M. 1993. Control of folding and membrane translocation by binding of the chaperone DnaJ to nascent polypeptides. *Proc. Natl. Acad. Sci. USA* 90:10216-20

56. Hoell-Neugebauer B, Rudolph R, Schmidt M, Buchner J. 1991. Reconstitution of a heat shock effect in vitro: influence of GroE on the thermal aggregation of α-glucosidase from yeast. *Biochemistry* 30:11609-14

57. Holl-Neugebauer B, Rudolph R, Schmidt M, Buchner J. 1991. Reconstitution of a heat shock effect in vitro—influence of GroE on the thermal aggregation of α-glucosidase from yeast. *Biochemistry* 30:11609-14

58. Horwitz J. 1992. α-Crystallin can function as a molecular chaperone. *Proc. Natl. Acad. Sci. USA* 89:10449-53

59. Ishii N, Taguchi H, Sumi M, Yoshida M. 1992. Structure of holo-chaperonin studied with electron microscopy—oligomeric cpn10 on top of two layers of cpn60 rings with two stripes each. *FEBS Lett.* 299:169-74

60. Jackson GS, Staniforth RA, Halsall DJ, Atkinson T, Holbrook JJ, et al. 1993. Binding and hydrolysis of nucleotides in the chaperonin catalytic cycle—implications for the mechanism of assisted protein folding. *Biochemistry* 32:2554-63

61. Jakob U, Gaestel M, Engel K, Buchner J. 1993. Small heat shock proteins are molecular chaperones. *J. Biol. Chem.* 268:1517-20

62. Jarabak R, Westley J, Dungan JM, Horowitz P. 1993. A chaperone-mimetic effect of serum albumin on rhodanese. *J. Biochem. Toxicol.* 8:41-48

63. Kang PJ, Ostermann J, Shilling J, Neupert W, Craig EA, Pfanner N. 1990. Requirement for hsp70 in the mitochondrial matrix for translocation and folding of precursor proteins. *Nature* 348:137-43

64. Kim HB, Kang C. 1991. Activity of chloramphenicol acetyltransferase overproduced in *E. coli* with wild-type and mutant GroEL. *Biochem. Int.* 25: 381-86

64a. Kuehn MJ, Ogg DJ, Kihlberg J, Slonim LN, Flemmer K, Bergfors T, Hultgren SJ. 1993. Structural basis of pilus subunit recognition by the PapD chaperone. *Science* 262:1234-41

65. Kuwajima K. 1989. The molten globule state as a clue for understanding the folding and cooperativity of globular-protein structure. *Proteins* 6:87-103

66. Laine PS, Meyer RR. 1992. Interaction of the heat shock protein GroEL of *Escherichia coli* with single-stranded DNA-binding protein—suppression of *ssb-113* by *groEL46*. *J. Bacteriol.* 174: 3204-11

67. Laminet AA, Kumamoto CA, Pluckthun A. 1991. Folding in vitro and transport in vivo of pre-beta-lactamase are SecB independent. *Mol. Microbiol.* 5:117-22

68. Laminet AA, Ziegelhoffer T, Georgopoulos C, Pluckthun A. 1990. The *Escherichia coli* heat shock proteins GroEL and GroES modulate the folding of the β-lactamase precursor. *EMBO J.* 9:2315-19

69. Landry SJ, Gierasch LM. 1991. The chaperonin GroEL binds a polypeptide in an α-helical conformation. *Biochemistry* 30:7359-62

70. Landry SJ, Jordan R, McMacken R, Gierasch LM. 1992. Different conformations for the same polypeptide bound to chaperones DnaK and GroEL. *Nature* 355:455-57

70a. Landry SJ, Zeilstra-Ryalls J, Fayet O, Georgopoulos C, Gierasch LM. 1993. Characterization of a functionally important mobile domain of GroES. *Nature* 364:255-58

71. Langer T, Lu C, Echols H, Flanagan J, Hayer MK, Hartl FU. 1992. Successive action of DnaK, DnaJ and GroEL along the pathway of chaperone-mediated protein folding. *Nature* 356:683-89

72. Langer T, Pfeifer G, Martin J, Baumeister W, Hartl FU. 1992. Chaperonin-mediated protein folding—GroES binds to one end of the GroEL cylinder, which accommodates the

protein substrate within its central cavity. *EMBO J.* 11:4757–65

73. Laskey RA, Mills AD, Philpott A, Leno GH, Dilworth SM, Dingwall C. 1993. The role of nucleoplasmin in chromatin assembly and disassembly. *Philos. Trans. R. Soc. London Ser. B Biol. Sci.* 339:263–69

74. Lee SC, Olins PO. 1992. Effect of overproduction of heat shock chaperones GroESL and DnaK on human procollagenase production in *Escherichia coli. J. Biol. Chem.* 267:2849–52

75. Liberek K, Marszalek J, Ang D, Georgopoulos C, Zylicz M. 1991. *Escherichia coli* DnaJ and GrpE heat shock proteins jointly stimulate ATPase activity of DnaK. *Proc. Natl. Acad. Sci. USA* 88:2874–78

76. Lindquist S, Craig EA. 1988. The heatshock proteins. *Annu. Rev. Genet.* 22:631–77

77. Madden DR, Gorga JC, Strominger JL, Wiley DC. 1991. The structure of HLA-B27 reveals nonamer self-peptides bound in an extended conformation. *Nature* 353:321–25

77a. Martin J, Geromanos S, Tempest P, Hartl FU. 1993. Identification of nucleotide-binding regions in the chaperonin proteins GroEL and GroES. *Nature* 366:279–82

78. Martin J, Horwich AL, Hartl FU. 1992. Prevention of protein denaturation under heat stress by the chaperonin Hsp60. *Science* 258:995–98

79. Martin J, Langer T, Boteva R, Schramel A, Horwich AL, Hartl FU. 1991. Chaperonin-mediated protein folding at the surface of GroEL through a molten globule-like intermediate. *Nature* 352:36–42

79a. Martin J, Mayhew M, Langer T, Hartl FU. 1993. The reaction cycle of GroEL and GroES in chaperonin-assisted protein folding. *Nature* 366:228–33

80. Mendoza JA, Butler MC, Horowitz PM. 1992. Characterization of a stable, reactivatable complex between chaperonin 60 and mitochondrial rhodanese. *J. Biol. Chem.* 267:24648–54

80a. Mendoza JA, Demeler B, Horowitz PM. 1993. Alteration of the quaternary structure of Cpn60 modulates chaperonin assisted folding: implications for the mechanism of chaperonin action. *J. Biol. Chem.* In press

81. Mendoza JA, Lorimer GH, Horowitz PM. 1992. Chaperonin cpn60 from *Escherichia coli* protects the mitochondrial enzyme rhodanese against heat inactivation and supports folding at elevated temperatures. *J. Biol. Chem.* 267:17631–34

82. Mendoza JA, Rogers E, Lorimer GH, Horowitz PM. 1991. Chaperonins facilitate the in vitro folding of monomeric mitochondrial rhodanese. *J. Biol. Chem.* 266:13044–49

83. Miller AD, Maghlaoui K, Albanese G, Kleinjan DA, Smith C. 1993. Escherichia coli chaperonins Cpn60 (GroEL) and Cpn10 (GroES) do not catalyse the refolding of mitochondrial malate dehydrogenase. *Biochem. J.* 291:139–44

84. Mizobata T, Akiyama Y, Ito K, Yumoto N, Kawata Y. 1992. Effects of the chaperonin GroE on the refolding of tryptophanase from *Escherichia coli*—refolding is enhanced in the presence of ADP. *J. Biol. Chem.* 267:17773–79

85. Munro S, Pelham HRB. 1986. An Hsp70-like protein in the ER: identity with the 78 kd glucose-regulated protein and immunoglobulin heavy chain binding protein. *Cell* 46:291–300

86. Nelson RJ, Ziegelhoffer T, Nicolet C, Werner-Washburne M, Craig EA. 1992. The translation machinery and 70 kd heat shock protein cooperate in protein synthesis. *Cell* 71:97–105

87. Neri D, Billeter M, Wider G, Wuthrich K. 1992. NMR determination of residual structure in a urea-denatured protein, the 434-repressor. *Science* 257:1559–63

88. Neupert W, Pfanner N. 1993. Roles of molecular chaperones in protein targeting to mitochondria. *Philos. Trans. R. Soc. London Ser. B Biol. Sci.* 339:355–62

89. Nilsson B, Anderson S. 1991. Proper and improper folding of proteins in the cellular environment. *Annu. Rev. Microbiol.* 45:607–35

90. Ostermann J, Horwich AL, Neupert W, Hartl F-U. 1989. Protein folding in mitochondria requires complex formation with hsp60 and ATP hydrolysis. *Nature* 341:125–30

91. Ostermann J, Voos W, Kang PJ, Craig EA, Neupert W, Pfanner N. 1990. Precursor proteins in transit through mitochondrial contact sites interact with hsp70 in the matrix. *FEBS Lett.* 277:281–84

92. Palleros DR, Welch WJ, Fink AL. 1991. Interaction of hsp70 with unfolded proteins—effects of temperature and nucleotides on the kinetics of binding. *Proc. Natl. Acad. Sci. USA* 88:5719–23

93. Parsell DA, Sauer RT. 1989. The structural stability of a protein is an important determinant of its proteolytic susceptibility in *Escherichia coli*. *J. Biol. Chem.* 264:7590–95

94. Phillips GJ, Silhavy TJ. 1990. Heat-shock proteins DnaK and GroEL facilitate export of LacZ hybrid proteins in *E. coli*. *Nature* 344:882–84

95. Phipps BM, Typke D, Hegerl R, Volker S, Hoffmann A, et al. 1993. Structure of a molecular chaperone from a thermophilic archaebacterium. *Nature* 361:475–77

96. Ptitsyn OB. 1987. Protein folding: hypotheses and experiments. *J. Protein Chem.* 6:273–93

97. Richards F. 1992. Folded and unfolded proteins: an introduction. See Ref. 23a, pp. 1–58

98. Rippman F, Taylor WR, Rothbard JB, Green NM. 1991. A hypothetical model for the peptide binding domain of Hsp70 based on the peptide binding domain of HLA. *EMBO J.* 10:1053–59

99. Rothman JE. 1989. Polypeptide chain binding proteins: catalysis of protein folding and related processes in cells. *Cell* 59:591–601

100. Rothman JE, Schmid SL. 1986. Enzymatic recycling of clathrin from coated vesicles. *Cell* 46:5–9

101. Ryan C, Stevens TH, Schlesinger MJ. 1992. Inhibitory effects of HSP70 chaperones on nascent polypeptides. *Protein Sci.* 1:980–85

102. Saibil H, Dong Z, Wood S, Mauer AAD. 1991. Binding of chaperonins. *Nature* 353:25–26

102a. Saibil HR, Zheng D, Roseman AM, Hunter AS, Watson GMF, et al. 1993. ATP induces large quaternary rearrangements in a cage-like chaperonin structure. *Curr. Biol.* 3:265–73

103. Sanchez ER, Hirst M, Scherrer LC, Tang HY, Welsh MJ, et al. 1990. Hormone-free mouse glucocorticoid receptors overexpressed in chinese hamster ovary cells are localized to the nucleus and are associated with both hsp70 and hsp90. *J. Biol. Chem.* 265:20123–30

104. Sanders SL, Whitfield KM, Vogel JP, Rose MD, Schekman RW. 1992. Sec61p and BiP directly facilitate polypeptide translocation into the ER. *Cell* 69:353–65

105. Schmid F. 1992. Kinetics of unfolding of single domain proteins. See Ref. 23a, pp. 197–241

106. Schmidt M, Buchner J. 1992. Interaction of GroE with an all-β-protein. *J. Biol. Chem.* 267:16829–33

107. Schroder H, Langer T, Hartl F-U, Bukau B. 1993. DnaK, DnaJ, and GrpE form a cellular chaperone machine capable of repairing heat-induced protein damage. *EMBO J.* 12:4137–44

108. Shortle D. 1993. Denatured states of proteins and their role in folding and stability. *Curr. Opin. Struct. Biol.* 3:66–74

109. Skowyra D, Georgopoulos C, Zylicz M. 1990. The E. coli DnaK gene product, the Hsp70 homolog, can reactivate heat-inactivated RNA polymerase in an ATP hydrolysis-dependent manner. *Cell* 62:939–44

110. Squires C, Squires CL. 1992. The Clp proteins—proteolysis regulators or molecular chaperones? *J. Bacteriol.* 174:1081–85

111. Taguchi H, Konishi J, Ishii N, Yoshida M. 1991. A chaperonin from a thermophilic bacterium, thermus-thermophilus, that controls refoldings of several thermophilic enzymes. *J. Biol. Chem.* 266:22411–18

112. Taguchi H, Yoshida M. 1993. Chaperonin from thermus-thermophilus can protect several enzymes from irreversible heat denaturation by capturing denaturation intermediate. *J. Biol. Chem.* 268:5371–75

113. Tandon S, Horowitz PM. 1987. Detergent-assisted refolding of guanidinium chloride-denatured rhodanese. *J. Biol. Chem.* 262:4486–91

114. Todd MJ, Viitanen PV, Lorimer GH. 1993. The hydrolysis of ATP by *Escherichia coli* GroEL: the effects of GroES and K^+. *Biochemistry* 32:8560–67

115. Trent JD, Nimmesgern E, Wall JS, Hartl FU, Horwich AL. 1991. A molecular chaperone from a thermophilic archaebacterium is related to the eukaryotic protein T-complex polypeptide-1. *Nature* 354:490–93

116. van der Vies SM, Viitanen PV, Gatenby AA, Lorimer GH, Jaenicke R. 1992. Conformational states of ribulosebisphosphate carboxylase and their interaction with chaperonin 60. *Biochemistry* 31:3635–44

117. Van Dyk TK, Gatenby AA, LaRossa RA. 1989. Demonstration by genetic suppression of interaction of GroE products with many proteins. *Nature* 342:451–53

118. Viitanen PV, Donaldson GK, Lorimer

GH, Lubben TH, Gatenby AA. 1991. Complex interactions between the chaperonin-60 molecular chaperone and dihydrofolate reductase. *Biochemistry* 30:9716–23

119. Viitanen PV, Gatenby AA, Lorimer GH. 1992. Purified chaperonin 60 (GroEL) interacts with the nonnative states of a multitude of *Escherichia coli* proteins. *Protein Sci.* 1:363–69

120. Viitanen PV, Lubben TH, Reed J, Goloubinoff P, O'Keefe DP, Lorimer GH. 1990. Chaperonin-facilitated refolding of ribulosebisphosphate carboxylase and ATP hydrolysis by chaperonin 60 (GroEL) are K^+ dependent. *Biochemistry* 29:5665–71

121. Wiech H, Buchner J, Zimmermann R, Jakob U. 1992. Hsp90 chaperones protein folding in vitro. *Nature* 358:169–70

122. Wild J, Altman E, Yura T, Gross CA. 1992. DnaK and DnaJ heat shock proteins participate in protein export in *Escherichia coli*. *Genes Dev.* 6:1165–72

123. Wynn RM, Davie JR, Cox RP, Chuang DT. 1992. Chaperonins GroEL and GroES promote assembly of heterotetramers ($\alpha 2\beta 2$) of mammalian mitochondrial branched-chain α-keto acid decarboxylase in *Escherichia coli*. *J. Biol. Chem.* 267:12400–3

124. Yaffe MB, Farr GW, Miklos D, Horwich AL, Sternlicht ML, Sternlicht H.

1992. TCP1 complex is a molecular chaperone in tubulin biogenesis. *Nature* 358:245–48

125. Zeilstra-Ryalls J, Fayet O, Georgopoulos C. 1991. The universally conserved GroE (Hsp60) chaperonins. *Annu. Rev. Microbiol.* 45:301–25

126. Zheng XX, Rosenberg LE, Kalousek F, Fenton WA. 1993. GroEL, GroES, and ATP-dependent folding and spontaneous assembly of ornithine transcarbamylase. *J. Biol. Chem.* 268:7489–93

127. Zhi W, Landry SJ, Gierasch LM, Srere PA. 1992. Renaturation of citrate synthase: influence of denaturant and folding assistants. *Protein Sci.* 1:522–29

128. Zhi W, Srere PA, Evans CT. 1991. Conformational stability of pig citrate synthase and some active-site mutants. *Biochemistry* 30:9281–86

129. Ziemienowicz A, Skowyra D, Zeilstra-Ryalls J, Fayet O, Georgopoulos C, Zylicz M. 1993. Both the *Escherichia coli* chaperone systems, GroEL/ES and DnaK/DnaJ/GrpE, can reactivate heat-treated RNA polymerase; different mechanisms for the same activity. *J. Biol. Chem.* 268:25425–31

130. Zylicz M, Ang D, Liberek K, Georgopoulos C. 1989. Initiation of λ DNA replication with purified host- and bacteriophage-encoded proteins: the role of the DnaK, DnaJ and GrpE heat shock proteins. *EMBO J.* 8:1601–8

Annu. Rev. Biophys. Biomol. Struct. 1994. 23:671–701

THE β-RIBBON DNA RECOGNITION MOTIF

Simon E. V. Phillips

Department of Biochemistry and Molecular Biology, University of Leeds, Leeds LS2 9JT, United Kingdom

KEY WORDS: protein-nucleic acid interactions, β-sheet, DNA-binding proteins, repressor, RNA-binding proteins

CONTENTS

PERSPECTIVES AND OVERVIEW

Before 1980 we knew little of the three-dimensional structures of proteins that interact with DNA and RNA. Since then, several structural studies of protein-nucleic acid complexes have been carried out using X-ray crystallography and NMR spectroscopy, and an understanding of the principles of recognition has begun to emerge. Particular interest has centered on sequence-specific binding, via both direct contacts

1056–8700/94/0610–0671$05.00

between amino acid side chains and the bases, and sequence-dependent conformational properties of the nucleic acids (see 21, 25, 45, 69, 77 for reviews).

The protein-DNA contacts found in the structures of specific complexes may be divided into two classes, those contacting the base pairs and those contacting the sugar-phosphate backbone. In describing the crystal structure of the *Escherichia coli trp* repressor-operator complex, Otwinowski et al (44) coined the convenient terms *direct readout* to describe sequence specificity arising from base contacts and *indirect readout* for specificity derived from DNA conformation that may be sensed through sugar-phosphate backbone contacts. In the known structures of protein-DNA complexes, many of these backbone contacts are to nonesterified phosphate oxygens, donated by peptide backbone NH groups or side chains. The observation of peptide NH contacts is interesting because the secondary-structure motif most commonly observed mediating specific protein-DNA interactions is the α-helix, for instance in the helix-turn-helix (HTH) motif. In a helix, the peptide NH groups cannot participate in such interactions except at the N-terminus (27). In the other major type of protein secondary structure, the β-sheet, the peptide backbone NH groups are available for interaction with DNA (or RNA). Recently, the structural information available for proteins that use β-sheet motifs to recognize DNA and RNA has expanded greatly.

Structural Complementarity Between β-Strands and Nucleic Acid Duplexes

In an early model-building study of the structure of nucleoprotamine (18), Feughelman et al proposed that an extended polyarginine chain could be wrapped helically around a B-DNA duplex in such a way that regularly arranged arginine side chains could interact with the phosphate groups, since the repeat distance of side chains in an extended polypeptide is related to that of the nucleotides. Table 1 shows some currently accepted values for repeat distances in polypeptides and nucleic acids; the distance between alternate residues in extended polypeptides (7.3 Å) or β-strands (6.9 Å) is very similar to the spacing of adjacent phosphates in B-DNA (6.7 Å).

In 1974 Carter & Kraut (9), and later Church et al (10), noted that the inherent right-handed twist observed for β-sheets in protein structures results in structural complementarity with nucleic acid double helices. In particular, a pair of antiparallel β-strands with their characteristic twist (a β-ribbon), if infinitely repeated, forms a right-handed polypeptide double helix with a pitch and radius roughly in the range

Table 1   Selected repeat distances in regular secondary structures of polypeptides and nucleic acids

Structure	Distance (Å)
Polypeptides	
Fully extended $\phi = \psi = 180°$	$C\alpha_i\text{-}C\alpha_{i+1} = 3.8$
	$N_i\text{-}N_{i+2} = 7.3$
Antiparallel β-sheet $\phi = -135°$ $\psi = 135°$	$N_i\text{-}N_{i+2} = 6.9$
Nucleic acids	
B-DNA (10-fold)	$P_i\text{-}P_{i+1} = 6.7$
	$OM_i\text{-}OM_{i+1} = 6.7^a$
	$Om_i\text{-}Om_{i+1} = 7.3^a$
	$O3'_i\text{-}O3'_{i+1} = 6.0$
	$O5'_i\text{-}O5'_{i+1} = 6.5$
A-DNA (11-fold)	$P_i\text{-}P_{i+1} = 5.5$
	$OM_i\text{-}OM_{i+1} = 4.9^a$
	$Om_i\text{-}Om_{i+1} = 5.9^a$
	$O3'_i\text{-}O3'_{i+1} = 5.9$
	$O5'_i\text{-}O5'_{i+1} = 5.4$
	$C2'_i\text{-}C2'_{i+1} = 5.6$

[a] OM and Om are nonesterified phosphate oxygens on major- and minor-groove sides, respectively.

observed for nucleic acid duplexes. Figure 1a shows a continuous antiparallel β-ribbon as modeled by Church et al (10). Furthermore, the local symmetry properties are also the same. In a nucleic acid duplex, pseudo two-fold axes perpendicular to the helix axis pass alternately between and through base pairs. Two-fold axes between base pairs can be exact if the base sequences on either side form an inverted repeat. Similar symmetry holds for the helical antiparallel β-ribbon, which has two types of two-fold axes alternating along its length such that their arrangement in space is similar to that of the nucleic acid two-fold axes. The polypeptide two-fold axes relate the main-chain atoms and may be exact if the amino acid side chains are equivalent on opposite strands. The conservation of symmetry in macromolecular assemblies is a fundamental principle that immediately suggests a series of models in which the nucleic acid and β-ribbon symmetry axes coincide. The β-ribbon might bind in the major or minor groove in parallel or antiparallel orientations, as shown in Figure 1. The possibility that a short section of β-ribbon might approach the DNA, presenting its convex rather than its concave face, and just dip into the groove over a short distance rather than run along it, was not considered in the modeling study, but this arrangement has been observed for *Met* repressor (see below).

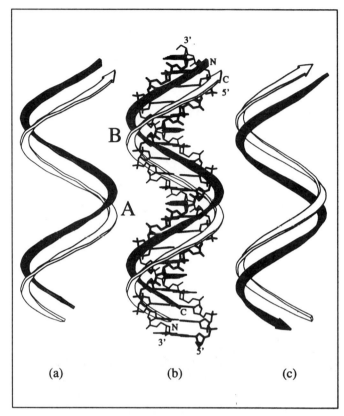

Figure 1   Antiparallel polypeptide β-ribbons shown alongside B-form duplex DNA. (*a*) β-Ribbon double helix as modeled by Church et al (10) arranged with N-C chain polarity opposite to that of DNA (5'-3'). (*b*) The β-ribbon from *a* docked to the minor groove of B-form DNA (10). Note the antiparallel arrangement of adjacent polypeptide and polynucleotide chains. (*c*) Antiparallel β-ribbon with reversed chain polarity with respect to *a*. If docked to DNA, the adjacent polypeptide and polynucleotide chains would be parallel. [Drawn with the program MOLSCRIPT (37), as are other molecular ribbon diagrams in this review.]

Carter & Kraut (9) were specifically concerned with RNA in A or A' forms, in which the β-ribbon was proposed to bind in the minor groove, because they believed the major groove was too narrow for such binding. They built a stereochemically reasonable model in parallel orientation in which the alternate peptide NH groups were exposed at the edges of the β-ribbon forming hydrogen bonds to successive 2' hydroxyl groups on the ribose rings. They suggested that binding to B-DNA would be different because, in that form, the minor groove is

too narrow, and the 2′ hydroxyl groups are not present. Church et al
(10) concentrated on B-DNA and built both parallel and antiparallel
models with the β-ribbon lying in the minor groove and in which the
exposed peptide NH groups interacted with the esterified phosphate
oxygens O3′.

The models are attractive in their symmetry conservation, structural
complementarity, and the use of the polypeptide backbone to recognize
the nucleic acid backbone in a non-sequence-specific way, leaving
amino acid side chains and bases to form sequence-specific interactions. In the β-ribbon, every other side chain on each strand points in
towards the bases in the minor groove, and the hydrogen-bonding interactions between them could mediate sequence-specific recognition.
Structural studies have revealed that two nucleic acid–binding proteins, *Bacillus stearothermophilus* HU and *E. coli* MetJ (*met* repressor), recognize duplex DNA by using β-ribbon motifs, as well as several
other proteins that contain β structure.

THE MetJ PROTEIN FAMILY

MetJ (⟨M⟩met⟨D⟩ Repressor)

Biosynthesis of methionine in *E. coli* (reviewed in 43, 53) is regulated
by the *met* repressor, as originally postulated by Cohen & Jacob (12).
The active *met* repressor is a complex of the *metJ* gene product with
S-adenosylmethionine (SAM), rather than with methionine itself. An
E. coli cell contains about 600 *met* repressor molecules, and these can
bind to at least 6 independent operators associated with the various
met biosynthetic genes spread throughout the chromosome. The *metJ*
gene was cloned and sequenced by Saint-Girons et al (52) and the
protein subsequently overexpressed and purified (51). It is a stable
dimer (M_r 23,988) of identical 104 amino acid subunits. The *apo* repressor, i.e. the *metJ* product without bound SAM, has relatively low
affinity for DNA, but binds two molecules of SAM noncooperatively
to form the high-affinity active repressor.

THREE-DIMENSIONAL STRUCTURE OF *met* REPRESSOR   The crystal structure of the repressor has been solved in several forms, in the presence
and absence of SAM, and as a complex with a synthetic operator fragment (48, 49, 66). Figure 2 shows the structure of the repressor, which
is unlike any other known protein structure, with the exception of Arc
repressor from bacteriophage P22 (6) (see below). In each subunit of
the symmetrical dimer, an extended N-terminal region leads to a flex-

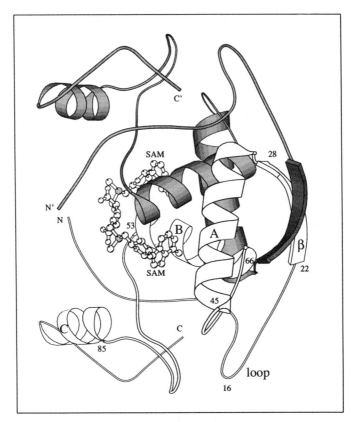

Figure 2   Overall structure of the active *met* repressor, viewed from the side with the
molecular dyad horizontal and in the plane of the page. α-Helices are shown as coiled
ribbons and β-strands as flat arrows. The SAM molecules are shown as balls and sticks,
with the sulfur atoms shaded. One subunit is shaded, and the other has the major elements
of secondary structure labeled (β, A, B, C), together with some residue numbers. Chain
termini are marked N and C for the light subunit, and N′ and C′ for the shaded one. The
symmetry-related pair of β-strands on the right forms an antiparallel β-ribbon that binds
in the major groove of DNA. This ribbon should be compared with the segment of β-
ribbon marked A in Figure 1. Except where otherwise noted, all the protein-structure
diagrams in this review are oriented in this way, with dyad (or pseudo dyad) axes horizontal, and the DNA-binding site on the right. [Drawn from coordinates available from
the Brookhaven Protein Data Bank (PDB) as entry 1cmc.]

ible β-hairpin (residues 12–20) labeled "loop" in Figure 2, followed by
a single β-strand (residues 22–28). This strand pairs with the symmetry-
related strand of the other subunit to form a two-stranded antiparallel
β-ribbon, lying on one face of the molecule centered on the dyad axis.
A short link from the end of the strand leads to the long α-helix A

(residues 30–45), lying on the outside of the dimer, followed by a longer loop and helix B (residues 52–66). An extended loop leads to the C helix (residues 86–94), a turn, and the short C-terminal region. The loop (residues 12–20) is flexible, adopting different conformations in different crystal environments and changes dramatically in response to DNA binding. The corepressor, SAM, binds at two independent symmetry-related sites on the opposite face of the repressor to that containing the β-ribbon. The purine ring is inserted into a pocket beside the B helix otherwise occupied by the side chain of Phe65 in the *apo* repressor, and the positively charged methylated sulfur is positioned at the C-terminal end of the B helix. SAM binding dramatically raises the operator affinity, but it induces little change in the repressor structure.

THE *met* OPERATORS   The known *met* operator sequences for both *E. coli* and *Salmonella typhimurium* vary in length from 16 to 40 base pairs (bp) as defined by sequence homology. They consist of two to five tandem repeats of eight bp sequences homologous to a palindromic consensus sequence AGACGTCT, known as the met box (2). The consensus sequence is highly symmetrical, with centers of inverted repeats (local dyad axes for a DNA duplex in three dimensions) at the center of each met box, as well as the junctions between adjacent boxes. Although met box sequences are quite variable, base A_3 (where bases within each met box are numbered 1–8 from the 5' end) is highly conserved, as is T_6, which is related to it by the central dyad symmetry axis.

Detailed studies, using both natural and synthetic operators, of repressor-operator affinity in vitro and repression efficiency in vivo (14, 26, 47, 48) allowed an analysis of sequence specificity and the effect of corepressor binding. Half-maximal binding of repressor to target DNA fragments containing at least two tandem met boxes is observed at approximately nanomolar repressor concentration in the presence of saturating levels of SAM, but falls to the micromolar range in its absence. DNA targets containing only single met boxes, however, are not strongly bound at the lower end of this concentration range, even in the presence of SAM, indicating that the shortest viable operator should contain at least two met boxes, the length of the natural *metC* operator. The affinity studies also showed that operator binding is cooperative with respect to repressor concentration. This cooperativity results from the binding of arrays of repressors to the extended operator regions. Each one binds to one met box with its dimer two-fold axis coincident with the central dyad of the box. In three dimensions, the array corresponds to a left-handed superhelix of repressors wound around duplex B-DNA, with a relative rise and rotation between adjacent protein molecules of 8 bp (~27 Å) and 90° respectively, and in which protein-protein contacts mediate the cooperativity.

STRUCTURE OF THE *met* REPRESSOR–OPERATOR COMPLEX   In the crystal structure (66) of a complex between the repressor and a self-complementary 19-mer oligonucleotide operator fragment (see Figure 3 for sequence), two repressor molecules bind to a single oligonucleotide duplex, each one lying with its intramolecular dyad coincident with the central dyad of a met box, i.e. between bases 4–5 and 12–13 (Figure 4). In each case the two-stranded β-ribbon is inserted into the DNA major groove, but only dips into it over a short range because the

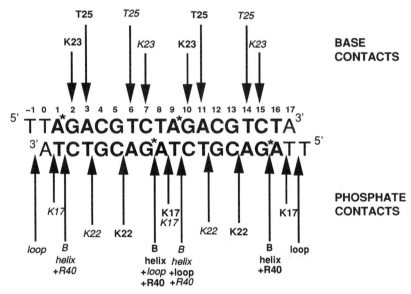

Figure 3   Base sequence and numbering for the synthetic oligonucleotide used in crystallization of the repressor-operator complex (66). The lower strand is related to the upper one by dyad symmetry and is exactly equivalent in the structure. Base pairs 1–8 and 9–16 correspond to consensus met boxes and are boldfaced. Asterisks mark phosphate groups showing strong ethylation interference (47). Contacts to the repressor are shown schematically, with direct base contacts above the sequence, and contacts to phosphates below. Labels in italics indicate contacts to the opposite strand, i.e. to the bottom strand for base contacts and the top strand for phosphate contacts, while non-italicized labels indicate base contacts to the top strand and phosphate contacts to the bottom strand. Major contacts to the phosphodiester backbone are made by the B helix and the 12–20 loop. (Reproduced from Ref. 48 with permission.)

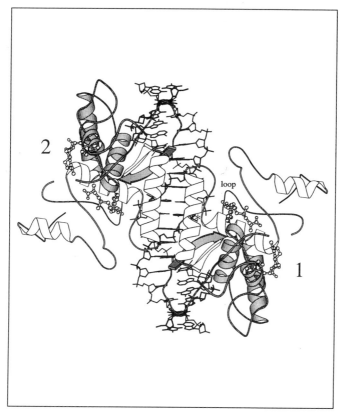

Figure 4   The crystal structure of the repressor-operator complex, with repressors drawn as for Figure 2. Two repressors, 1 and 2, bind to the DNA fragment, at the lower right and upper left, respectively. These are related by an exact crystallographic dyad axis through the center of the complex between met boxes. This axis also relates the two equivalent DNA strands. The local intramolecular dyads of the repressors coincide with local dyads in the met box centers. The two repressors correspond to two units of a superhelical array. Repressor β-ribbons occupy the DNA major groove at lower right and upper left, while their A helices form a long, antiparallel protein-protein contact above the minor groove in the center of the diagram. The phosphate 5′ to G_{10} lies at the end of one of the B helices of repressor 1 and is marked with an asterisk. The four SAM molecules lie on the outer surface of the complex, remote from the DNA. (Redrawn from Ref. 48 using coordinates from PDB entry 1cma.)

curvatures of the DNA and polypeptide backbones are opposite. In Figure 1 this corresponds to the β-ribbon segment at A being translated into the adjacent major groove and rotated by approximately 90° about the two-fold axis at that point, instead of being wrapped around the minor groove. A cutaway view of the protein-DNA interface (Figure

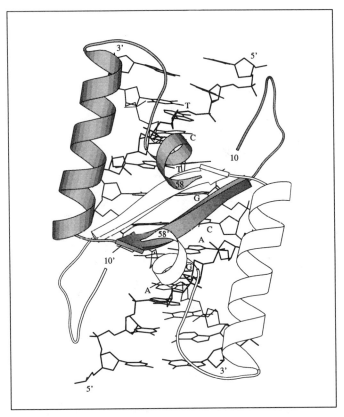

Figure 5 Cutaway view of the DNA-binding motif of one repressor in the complex, oriented along the molecular dyad, with residues 1–9 and 59–104, as well as the SAM molecules, removed for clarity. The central region of the DNA shown is one met box, with the bases labeled on one strand. The β-ribbon lies in the major groove, with minor grooves to the upper left and lower right. (Redrawn from Ref. 48 using coordinates from PDB entry 1cma.)

5) shows the three regions of the repressor that make major contributions to protein-DNA interactions, namely the loop, β-ribbon, and B helix. A detailed view of the β-ribbon-DNA contacts appears in Figure 6.

The only direct contacts to the base pairs are made by two side chains from each strand of the β-ribbon. Thr25 Oγ1 donates a hydrogen bond to N_7 of A_3, and Lys23 Nξ donates an H-bond to O_6 (and possibly N_7) of the G paired to C_7, i.e. G_{10} of the bottom strand. Therefore, when all the symmetry-related interactions are accounted for, the complex has eight direct hydrogen bonds to bases (Figure 3). A_3 is the most

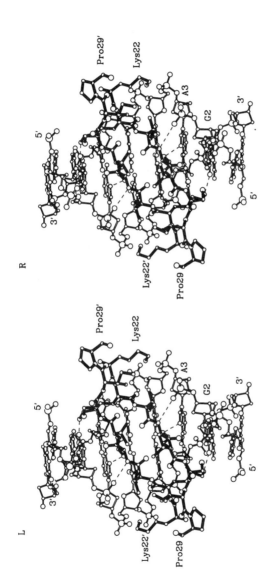

Figure 6 Stereo diagram of the β-ribbon-DNA interface, in the same orientation as in Figure 5. Residues 22–29 of each repressor are shown as balls and sticks with filled bonds. The DNA has open bonds. Dotted lines depict hydrogen bonds between amino acid side chains and bases, and the weak interaction between the NH group of Thr25 and a phosphate.

conserved base in the natural operator sequences and causes the largest drop in repressor-operator affinity observed in a systematic mutation experiment (48). Its contact to Thr25 is an example of direct readout. The β-ribbon fits loosely in the major groove as judged by the van der Waals surfaces, leaving room for several solvent molecules to intrude. Only four of these are sufficiently well ordered to be visible in electron density maps at 2.8-Å resolution, and some of them mediate further contacts between Lys23 and adjacent bases. No strong hydrogen bonds connect main-chain amide NH groups on the β-ribbon to the DNA backbone, but one weak interaction occurs between the NH of Thr25 and a nonesterified phosphate oxygen (O_M type in Table 1). This interaction is weak because the major groove is too wide, although it is about 2 Å narrower than in regular B-DNA. The minor groove opposite is correspondingly wider, and the DNA is consequently bent by about 25° towards the repressor at this point.

The repressor makes numerous contacts to backbone phosphate groups (Figure 3), partly via basic side chains, but particularly through main-chain amide NH groups in the loop and B helix. The N terminus of the B helix points at the phosphate group 5′ to G_{10} on the bottom strand, and at its symmetry equivalents (Figures 4, 5), hydrogen bonding to it through both main-chain amide NH groups and the side chains of Asn53 and Ser54. This phosphate is displaced from its expected position in a regular B-DNA duplex, probably as a result of overwinding of the adjacent T_8A_9 dinucleotide step. Although the repressor and the bases themselves have no contacts at positions 8 and 9, binding assays show reduced affinities when these bases are replaced with any others (48). Hence, this structure appears to be an example of indirect readout, in which the repressor senses the base sequence from the conformational properties of the DNA.

The extensive protein-protein contact between the antiparallel A helices of adjacent repressors is mostly hydrophobic, and accounts for much, if not all, of the cooperativity of repressor binding. Disruption of this contact by site-directed mutagenesis greatly reduces observed binding affinities and repression efficiency (26), indicating that the formation of the cooperative arrays is essential to repressor function. The basic DNA-binding motif is the dimeric unit shown in Figure 5, with the antiparallel β-ribbon inserted into the DNA major groove such that its side chains contact the bases, the outer A helices forming essential cooperative protein-protein contacts to adjacent repressors in the array, and the inner B helices locking the motif down onto the phosphate backbone via their amino termini.

Arc and Mnt Repressors

The other structure known for a protein in the MetJ family, Arc repressor of *Salmonella* bacteriophage P22, is smaller than *met* repressor, being a homodimer of 53 amino acid subunits. Its structure was determined using NMR spectroscopy (6). Arc and Mnt, another repressor, are encoded in the *immunity I* region of the phage, and each is autoregulatory (see 33 for review). Mnt is a homotetramer and shares 40% sequence homology with Arc (Figure 7). Both repressors bind to DNA as tetramers (7), almost certainly in an arrangement related to that observed in the *met* repressor–operator complex, which could be best described as a dimer of dimers. Whereas Mnt remains tetrameric in solution, Arc dissociates into dimers at moderate concentrations and monomers at concentrations below the point where half-maximal operator binding occurs (10^{-9} M) (3). Figure 8 shows the operator sequences.

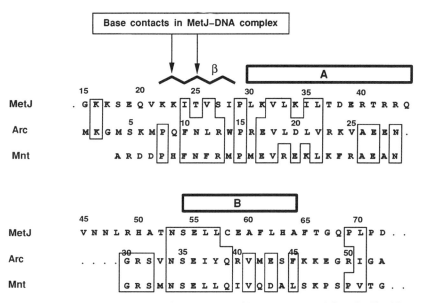

Figure 7 Amino acid sequences of Met, Arc, and Mnt repressors (after 6). The Met repressor alignment is based partly on sequence and partly on secondary structure. The Arc sequence is complete, but only those parts of the Met and Mnt sequences corresponding to that of Arc are shown. Amino acid similarities are boxed. The locations of secondary structural elements are shown above as bars for α-helices and a pleated line for the β-strand. Arrows indicate the two side chains making base contacts in the *met* repressor–operator complex.

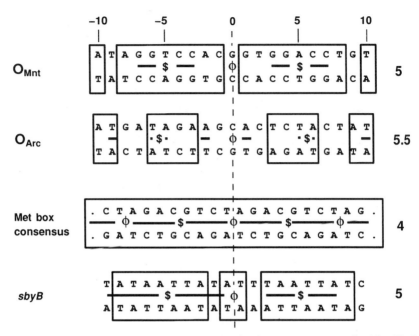

Figure 8 Summary of sequences and symmetries for operators recognized by MetJ family proteins (redrawn from 46). The positions of the central and related dyad axes are marked by φ, and alternative dyads by $. Boxed regions indicate inverted repeat symmetry about φ axes, and solid lines between the strands show symmetry about $ axes. The number at the right of each operator is the spacing of the dyad axes. The met box sequence is a consensus and therefore perfectly symmetrical. The Mnt operator is highly symmetrical, with outer dyads five base pairs from the center. Arc is less symmetrical, but ethylation data and weak sequence symmetry suggest dyads spaced 5.5 base pairs from center. *SbyB* is also highly symmetrical, but the AT-rich sequence could imply unusual conformation

Figure 9 illustrates the structure of Arc repressor in a similar orientation to that of *met* repressor in Figure 2. The similarity is immediately obvious, and Arc seems to correspond to the minimal DNA-binding motif of *met* repressor, containing only the β-ribbon and helices A and B. Unlike *met* repressor, however, Arc does not bind a corepressor. With the sequence alignment in Figure 7, the rms difference in polypeptide backbone atom positions between residues 8–28 and 32–45 of Arc and 22–42 and 51–64 of Met is 2.2 Å. If residues 52–65 of Met are used instead, the rms difference falls to 1.2 Å, corresponding to a rotation of about 100° in the B helix. In the Met complex, the N-terminus of helix B binds to a phosphate, so the difference in sequence register may indicate a slightly different location of the β-ribbon motif in the major groove. The side chain of Ser54 in *met* repressor also contacts the phosphate, and this residue is conserved in Arc and Mnt. In fact, of only five residues conserved in all three repressors, three lie at the N terminus of the B helix.

Of course, the operators also differ (Figure 8). The length of *arc* and *mnt* operators is limited to 21 bp, so that arrays of more than two repressors would not be expected, and the symmetry is less pronounced than for *met* operators. Additionally, the central two-fold axes in *arc* and *mnt* operators pass through rather than between base-pairs, and the outer two-fold axes lie 5.5 and 5.0 bases from the centers, respectively. This arrangement would place adjacent repressors at least

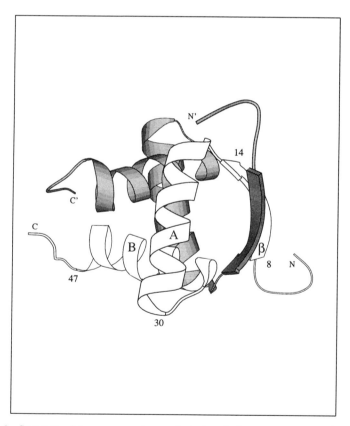

Figure 9 Structure of Arc repressor in an orientation similar to *met* repressor in Figure 2. The N-terminal arms are flexible, and poorly determined by the NMR constraints, hence their asymmetry in the model. (Drawn from coordinates supplied by R Kaptein.)

two bases farther apart than in the *met* repressor complex, with a further 70° rotation, so they would lie on the same face of the DNA. Thus, the interaction between repressors must be somewhat different. The two Arc repressors do interact, however, and operator binding is highly cooperative (8), apparently proceeding from free monomers in solution, through DNA-bound dimers to the tetramer. In contrast to this, *met* repressor remains a dimer in solution.

The sequence specificity of Arc and Mnt resides chiefly in the N-terminal region, as evidenced by the observation that replacement of residues 1–6 of Mnt with 1–9 of Arc produces a mutant Mnt repressor that binds to *arc* operators (35) (in contrast to the wild-type, which does not). The TAGA sequences in the Arc operator (Figure 8) are related by the central dyad but are not symmetrically disposed around the outer dyads. Nevertheless, they have been shown to be particularly important to sequence recognition in experiments using operator mutants (82). Operator binding studies, using methylation and hydroxyl radical protection (34), on wild-type and mutant Mnt repressors show patterns very similar to those obtained for *met* repressor, with symmetry about the outer dyad axes. Residues Arg2, His6, Asn8, Phe9, and Arg10 are particularly important for operator binding, consistent with the *met* complex arrangement in which the base-contacting residues Lys23 and Thr25 align with His6 and Asn8 (Figure 7). The apparent difference between the spacings of the dyad axes in Arc and Mnt operators is surprising, but recent results with Mnt mutants suggest a model in which the repressor is centered 5.5 bp from the central dyad (36).

Other Proteins in the MetJ Family

The only other protein found in the sequence database that may belong to the MetJ family is TraY from the F episome. This protein bears some sequence similarity to Arc and Mnt (4), but the fit to MetJ is poor. In particular, the conserved Ser54 would be replaced by Phe, Ile, or Asn in TraY variants. TraY has at least three binding sites, one in the *oriT* region (*sbyA*), and two others in its own promoter (*sbyB* and *sbyC*) (30). Figure 8 shows the sequence of *sbyB*, which has alternating dyad symmetry with axes spaced at five-bp intervals. DNase protection studies show that TraY binding protects 36 bp of DNA at *sbyA*, suggesting an extended array similar to that in *met* repressor–operator complexes in which protection can extend up to 40 bp. The two other sites show protection over 24 bp.

THE HU PROTEIN FAMILY

HU

The HU protein (sometimes called NS or DNA-binding protein II) is found in prokaryotes where it binds nonspecifically to DNA and forms nucleoprotein structures resembling eukaryotic nucleosomes (16). It is a small, basic protein that normally occurs as a homodimer ($M_r \approx$ 19,000), except in *E. coli* where it is a heterodimer of α and β subunits. Given the high sequence homology between HU proteins from different organisms, the crystal structure of the homodimeric DNA-binding protein II (HU) from *B. stearothermophilus* (76, 83, 84) is probably a good model for the whole family. Two other homologous proteins, *E. coli* integration host factor (IHF) and *Bacillus subtilis* phage SPO1 transcription factor 1 (TF1) almost certainly have very similar structures.

Figure 10 shows the structure of the HU dimer. The monomer has 90 residues and forms two distinct regions. The N-terminal region (residues 1–37) consists of two α-helices (α1 and α2), and the C-terminal region is mainly a three-stranded antiparallel β-sheet (β1–3) followed by a short helix (α3). The base of the dimer (on the left in Figure 10) is V-shaped, and two arms formed by strands β2 and β3 from each subunit extend away from it. Residues 60–67 are not visible in the electron density maps and must be flexible and disordered in the crystal structure. The arms formed by the two β2β3 ribbons are ideally placed to bind to a DNA groove, and the view of them in Figure 10 should be compared with the modeled β-ribbon at point B in Figure 1. Chemical protection studies with the homologous IHF (89) show protection in the minor groove, suggesting that the β ribbons lie along it. Models of the HU-DNA complex (76, 83, 84) conserve symmetry by aligning the protein dyad with one of the DNA pseudodyads, as if the globular base lay at B in Figure 1, with the β ribbons extending up the minor groove to either side. No crystal structure has been reported for an HU-DNA complex, but NMR data have begun to emerge (62).

A major function of HU is formation of nucleosome-like particles in which the DNA is bent and negatively supercoiled, and HU often acts as an accessory factor in other protein-DNA interactions, such as replication, inversion, transposition, and homologous recombination (15). Bending the DNA around the protein in the model improves the structural complementarity, in particular allowing contacts to the conserved Lys83 at the N terminus of the C-terminal helix α3. The minor groove probably expands to accommodate the β-ribbon, unlike in the *met* repressor complex in which the major groove is compressed around the

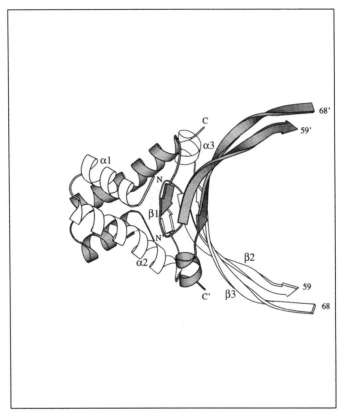

Figure 10 Structure of HU (DNA binding protein II) from *B. stearothermophilus*, with one subunit of the dimer shaded. The DNA-binding site is on the right hand side, and the disposition of the two antiparallel β-ribbon arms should be compared to the arrangement of the β-ribbons at point B in Figure 1. The elements of secondary structure are labeled for the light subunit. (Drawn with coordinates supplied by K Wilson.)

ribbon. In fact, the β-ribbon motif is a little wider than the available space in the minor groove, but narrower than the major groove, so that inserting it in either would result in DNA bending towards the major groove side. In the model, adjacent wedge-shaped HU dimers bind to the DNA and pack into a circular nucleosome-like particle through protein-protein interactions, with 8–10 dimers and 80–100 bp per turn of DNA supercoil. Bending therefore results from both protein-DNA interactions and contacts between proteins as they pack into a compact array.

TF1

Two members of the family, IHF and TF1, differ from HU in that they bind DNA with a degree of specificity. Another member of the family may be encoded by a gene found in African swine fever virus (41). TF1 is a homodimer of 99 amino acid subunits and preferentially binds DNA containing hydroxymethyluracil (reviewed in 23). Binding of one TF1 dimer bends the DNA sharply and protects 30–40 bp from DNase I attack (56). To generate the DNA bending, and the long nuclease footprint, the DNA probably wraps around the body of the protein in addition to passing through its arms (57). Three basic residues in HU, at positions 53, 61, and 83, are replaced by valine, phenylalanine, and glutamic acid residues, respectively, in TF1, suggesting reduced affinity for normal DNA (83) and possibly contributing to the specificity of binding. The substitution at position 61 is striking, because arginine is found there in all members of the HU family except TF1. Therefore, this residue plays a specific role in DNA recognition, and mutagenesis experiments have led to the proposal that it interacts directly with the bases, possibly even intercalating between them (54).

IHF

IHF (see 22 for review) is a heterodimer comprising IHFα (M_r 10,500) and IHFβ (M_r 9500) subunits. It does not have an essential function in *E. coli* but participates in DNA transactions, such as recombination, replication, and partitioning, of genetic free agents (e.g. phages, transposons, plasmids). IHF can also regulate expression of some host genes by binding to their promoters (11, 24, 39, 78, 79, 80, 85). Experiments introducing phased IHF sites in DNA fragments derived from the *attP* integration site show that the DNA is bent by more than 140° when IHF is bound (64, 65).

A model built for the IHF-DNA complex based on the HU crystal structure was derived from footprinting, interference, and stoichiometry measurements (89). One bound IHF protects at least 25 base pairs of DNA, with weaker effects in the flanking regions, implying tight bending of the DNA around it. Protection and interference occur almost exclusively in the minor groove, which is interesting for a sequence-specific DNA-binding protein because the base pairs are less accessible in the minor than in the major groove, and the pattern of functional groups available to discriminate between different sequences is not as variable (60). In the model IHF-DNA complex, the antiparallel β-ribbon arms run along the minor groove, and the DNA is bent by 140° around the protein to lie along the sides of the α-helical base region near helices $\alpha 3$. White et al (83) have independently proposed a similar model of the complex.

THE TATA-BOX BINDING PROTEIN

The TATA-box binding protein (TBP) was first identified as a central component of the general class II eukaryotic initiation factor TFIID, which is required for transcription of genes by RNA polymerase II, but TBP is now known to be required for transcription by all three nuclear RNA polymerases (see 61 for review). Comparison of TBP sequences from different species shows that the molecule has a highly conserved C-terminal region of about 180 residues and an N-terminal region that varies greatly in length (19–174 residues) and sequence between species (reviewed in 13, 59). The C-terminal region comprises two 40% conserved repeats of 66–67 amino acids linked by a highly basic segment known as the basic repeat. This part of the molecule is responsible for high-affinity sequence-specific binding to DNA at the TATA box [consensus sequence TATAa/tAa/t, where a/t indicates either A or T (50, 88)]. It interacts with the minor groove (38, 67), bends the DNA (29), and causes some underwinding (74).

The crystal structure has been determined for TBP from *Arabidopsis thaliana* (Figure 11), which has only 19 residues in the N-terminal region (42). The structure consists of a 10-stranded antiparallel β-sheet twisted into the shape of a saddle about 60 Å across, with four α-helices lying on its upper surface (note that the saddle is shown on its side in Figure 11). One can immediately see that the molecule has approximate two-fold symmetry about an axis passing through the center of the saddle. Each half consists of 88–89 residues, with equivalent sets of β-strands (S1–S5 and S1′–S5′) and α-helices (H1, H2 and H1′, H2′). The halves are linked by a short segment of chain between H2 and S1′ and together form a single domain. The two halves correspond to the conserved sequence repeat, but the close structural similarity between them encompasses almost the whole domain, extending beyond the 66- to 67-residue limit of sequence similarity. The molecule can be regarded as an intramolecular pseudodimer.

Hanging down on either side of the saddle are two stirrups, formed by antiparallel pairs of β-strands S2–S3 and S2′–S3′, where the strands in each pair are joined by short loops. The disposition of these loops resembles that of the arms of HU (Figure 10) and, indeed, part of the β-ribbons at point B in Figure 1. In fact, the overall shape of the molecule is complementary to the structure of DNA and could sit quite snugly astride it rather like a saddle on a horse. This arrangement could also bring the pseudodyad axis of TBP into coincidence with one of the DNA pseudodyads. Although the details of the protein-DNA interaction, and the origin of the DNA bending, will only be known when the structure of a complex has been determined, biochemical and genetic data are consistent with this overall view. All point mutations affecting DNA binding map to the underside or edges of the molecular saddle, while those on the upper surface affect the interaction of TBP with other factors (50, 70, 88). TBP interacts with the minor groove (38, 67) and protects about 15 bp from DNaseI digestion in the complex (28).

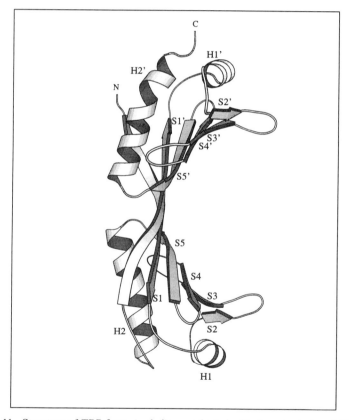

Figure 11   Structure of TBP from *A. thaliana,* oriented with the pseudo two-fold axis horizontal and in the plane of the page. The two pairs of β-strands S2–S3 and S2'–S3', together with the loops linking them, protrude from the molecule in an arrangement reminiscent of the arms of HU (Figure 10). Again, it is interesting to compare these with the β-ribbon at point B in Figure 1. (Drawn using coordinates supplied by S Burley.)

TBP and its DNA-binding site have only approximate two-fold symmetry. In TBP the side chains differ in the two halves of the DNA-binding surface, and the TATA box sequences do not form perfect inverted repeats. This asymmetry is necessary as TBP must bind in the correct orientation relative to the RNA polymerase site in order to initiate transcription in the correct direction. This is a case in which departures from strict symmetry conservation seem to play an important role.

OTHER CASES

In a few other cases, β structure interacts with nucleic acids in a variety of ways, not necessarily as β-ribbons. Some examples are given below.

⟨M⟩Eco⟨D⟩RV

EcoRV is a type II restriction endonuclease with some interesting DNA sequence–recognition properties (81). It is a symmetric dimer of identical subunits with M_r of $2 \times 29,000$. Its crystal structure was determined in the absence of DNA and as both specific and nonspecific protein-DNA complexes (86). In the specific complex (Figure 12), the protein engulfs the DNA and induces a sharp bend of almost 90° towards the major groove. In Figure 12b, the major groove lies in the center of the complex facing the reader. Inserted into the groove from the upper right and lower left are two hairpin loops, residues 182–186, between antiparallel pairs of β-strands. These loops are termed the recognition loops and provide side chains for sequence-specific contacts to central bases in the recognition sequence. This view of the complex can be compared with that of the met repressor binding motif in the major groove shown in Figure 5, where the arrangement is similar. If the two hairpin loops in EcoRV were cut, and the strands continued across the major groove to join up to their counterparts in the other subunit, then the resulting structure would be a β-ribbon much as in the met repressor complex.

Gene-V DNA-Binding Protein

The gene-V protein of filamentous phage forms a complex with the single-stranded circular viral DNA to form a regular helical assembly (32). It can also bind to RNA and act as a translational repressor. The crystal structure of the gene-V DNA-binding protein from bacteriophage fd (5) is a symmetric dimer with 87 amino acid–residue subunits and is composed entirely of β structure (Figure 13). A more recently determined NMR structure of the protein (20) differs in the sequence

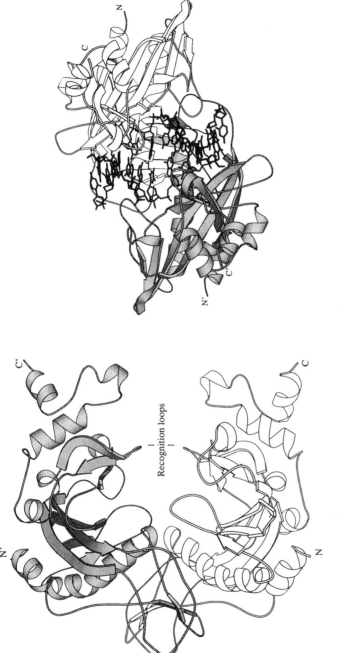

Figure 12 Structure of the restriction enzyme *Eco*RV in its specific complex with an oligonucleotide fragment corresponding to the restriction site. (*Left*) The protein structure with the DNA omitted from its binding site in the central cavity. The molecular dyad axis is horizontal, and one subunit of the dimer is shaded. The two recognition loops (residues 182–186) are labeled and protrude to lie in the DNA major groove. (*Right*) View along the dyad axis with the DNA included. The loops lie in the major groove facing the reader to the upper right and lower left of the center. (Drawn using coordinates from PDB entry 4rve.)

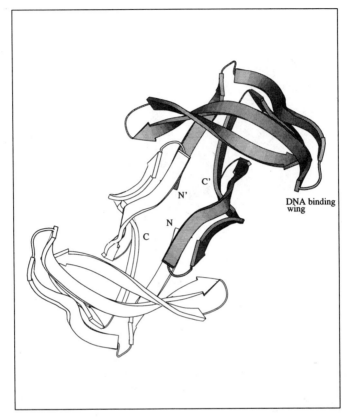

Figure 13   Structure of the gene-V DNA-binding protein from bacteriophage fd viewed along the dimer two-fold axis. One subunit is shaded, and the chain termini are labeled. The DNA-binding wings are the outer β-sheet structures lying to the upper right and lower left. (Drawn using coordinates from PDB entry 2gn5.)

alignment in some secondary structure elements, but the overall architecture is the same. Its function is to bind to single rather than double-stranded DNA, but the exact mode of interaction is not known. It probably binds to the faces of the β-sheet structures at the outer ends of the dimer, referred to as DNA-binding wings, as indicated by NMR (19) and fluorescence (68) studies showing that residues in this region are involved in contacts to the DNA.

U1

Figure 14 shows the crystal structure of a 95-residue fragment corresponding to the RNA-binding domain (RNP domain) of human U1 small nuclear RNA-binding protein (40). It is composed of two α-helices, A and B, and a four-stranded antiparallel β-sheet, with the latter containing two sequence motifs, RNP1 and RNP2, on strands β3 and β1, respectively. These motifs are found in many RNA-binding proteins and are therefore likely to interact with the RNA. Although no experimental structure is available for the complex with its target stem loop from the U1 RNA molecule, a model has been built by using a predicted structure for the RNA and docking the protein to it, incorporating a body of data from protection and mutagenesis studies (17). In the model, the surface of the β-sheet lies in the major groove of the RNA stem-loop near its tip, where the twist of the groove surface

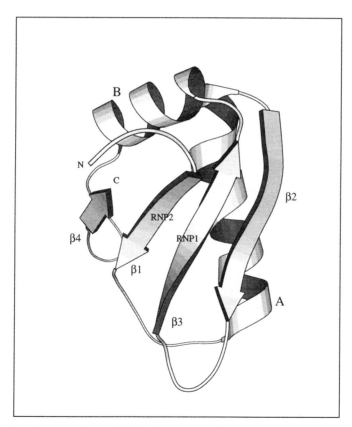

Figure 14   Structure of the RNA-binding domain of human U1. The RNP1 and RNP2 sequence motifs are labeled. In the model of the complex, the RNA stem loop would lie on top of the β-sheet facing the reader. (Drawn using coordinates supplied by P Evans and K Nagai.)

matches that of the β-sheet. The main-chain amide NH groups of strand β2 interact with the phosphates along the RNA backbone, and the RNP1 and RNP2 motifs face the bases in the groove.

CspB

The major cold-shock response protein in *B. subtilis*, CspB, contains an example of the cold-shock domain (CSD), which is conserved from bacteria to humans (87). It also contains the RNP1 motif and its structure was recently determined (55, 58). It is a small protein of only 67 residues and consists entirely of an antiparallel β-sheet formed into a five-stranded β-barrel. The dimer found in two different crystal forms bears a remarkable resemblance to the gene-V protein, and it binds preferentially to single-stranded DNA. The RNP1 sequence motif forms part of the structure analogous to the DNA-binding wing of gene-V protein.

Arms, Tails, and Peptides

In several cases, N- or C-terminal arms of DNA-binding proteins form extended strands or hairpins and interact with the DNA, often in the minor groove. For instance, in the crystal structure of the 434 repressor–operator complex (1), the C-terminal arm is extended and lies along the minor groove with its peptide NH groups interacting with the phosphates. A related sequence in Hin recombinase (63) is also used to bind to the minor groove and is probably similar in structure. The SPKK sequence motifs, found in the DNA-binding arms of histones H1 and H2B, may form β-turns and bind in the minor groove, especially at A/T rich sites (71–73). A cationic peptide from horseshoe crab, Tachyplesin I, also binds to DNA (90). It has 17 amino acid residues, with two disulfide bridges, and a single chain forms a β-ribbon structure in solution with a type II β-turn at residues 8–11 (31). It binds as a ribbon to the minor groove but is not sequence specific. A related synthetic peptide T22 (75) has the same structure and has been shown to be active against HIV.

CONCLUSION

β-Ribbons are particularly well suited to nucleic acid recognition by virtue of their inherent structural complementarity. β-Sheets and extended strands can also take advantage of the equivalent spacings of functional groups, but without the elegant symmetry properties shown by the ribbons. Despite this, the number of known examples of such interactions is small compared with those between DNA and α-helices, possibly because the helix is a self-contained folding unit comprising a single stretch of polypeptide chain, which can often be observed in solution for short peptides of appropriate sequence in suitable solvents. To form a β-ribbon, two peptides have to come together, or a longer one has to form an extended hairpin loop, which would be less stable in the absence of a folded protein structure to support it. Nevertheless, several examples of protein-DNA complexes using β-ribbons have been found, and the motif seems to be useful in DNA bending. Insertion into the minor groove causes it to widen, while binding in the major groove results in narrowing. No doubt further examples of the use of this motif will come to light in the future.

NOTE ADDED IN PROOF

Two independent crystal-structure determinations of complexes of TBP with a TATA-box oligonucleotide have recently been reported (31a, 31b). They show that, while TBP does bind to the minor groove, the DNA is dramatically bent and the complex differs from the simple prediction. The minor groove is opened very wide and makes contact with the entire under-surface of the TBP saddle.

ACKNOWLEDGMENTS

I thank K Wilson, S Burley, R Kaptein, P Evans, and K Nagai for supplying coordinates for some of the diagrams. I am grateful to S Halford for pointing out to me the similarity between *Eco*RV and MetJ, and to my colleagues at Leeds for continuing valuable discussions. I am a Senior Fellow of the Science and Engineering Research Council and International Research Scholar of the Howard Hughes Medical Institute, to whom I owe my thanks for financial support.

Literature Cited

1. Aggarwal AK, Rodgers DW, Drottar M, Ptashne M, Harrison SC. 1988. Recognition of a DNA operator by the repressor of phage 434—a view at high resolution. *Science* 242:899
2. Belfaiza J, Parsot C, Martel A, Bouthier de la Tour C, Margarita D, et al. 1986. Evolution in biosynthetic pathways—two enzymes catalyzing consecutive steps in methionine biosynthesis originate from a common ancestor and pos-

ses a similar regulatory region. *Proc. Natl. Acad. Sci. USA* 83:867
3. Bowie JU, Sauer RT. 1989. Equilibrium dissociation and unfolding of the Arc repressor dimer. *Biochemistry* 28:7139
4. Bowie JU, Sauer RT. 1990. TraY proteins of F and related episomes are members of the Arc and Mnt repressor family. *J. Mol. Biol.* 211:5
5. Brayer GD, McPherson A. 1983. Refined structure of the gene-5 DNA-bind-

ing protein from Bacteriophage Fd. *J. Mol. Biol.* 169:565

6. Breg JN, van Opheusden JHJ, Burgering MJM, Boelens R, Kaptein R. 1990. Structure of Arc repressor in solution—evidence for a family of β-sheet DNA-binding proteins. *Nature* 346:586

7. Brown BM, Bowie JU, Sauer RT. 1990. Arc repressor is tetrameric when bound to operator DNA. *Biochemistry* 28:11189

8. Brown BM, Sauer RT. 1993. Assembly of the Arc repressor-operator complex—cooperative interactions between DNA-bound dimers. *Biochemistry* 32:1354

9. Carter CW Jr, Kraut J. 1974. A proposed model for the interaction of polypeptides with RNA. *Proc. Natl. Acad. Sci. USA* 71:283

10. Church GM, Sussman JL, Kim S-H. 1977. Secondary structural complementarity between DNA and proteins. *Proc. Natl. Acad. Sci. USA* 74:1458

11. Claverie-Martin F, Magasanik B. 1991. Role of integration host factor in the regulation of the *GlnHP2* promoter of *Escherichia coli. Proc. Natl. Acad. Sci. USA* 88:1631

12. Cohen GN, Jacob F. 1959. Sur la répression de la synthèse des enzymes intervenant dans la formation du tryptophane chez *E. coli. CR Acad. Sci. Paris* 248:3490

13. Cormack BP, Struhl K. 1992. The TATA-binding protein is required for transcription by all three nuclear RNA polymerases in yeast cells. *Cell* 69:685

14. Davidson BE, Saint-Girons I. 1989. The *Escherichia coli* regulatory protein MetJ binds to a tandemly repeated 8bp palindrome. *Mol. Microbiol.* 3:1639

15. Dri AM, Moreau PL, Rouviere-Yaniv J. 1992. Role of the histone-like proteins Osmz and HU in homologous recombination. *Gene* 120:11

16. Drlica K, Rouviere-Yaniv J. 1987. Histone-like proteins of bacteria. *Microbiol. Rev.* 51:301

17. Evans PR, Oubridge C, Jessen T-H, Li J, Teo CH, et al. 1993. Model of the interaction between the UI small nuclear ribonucleoprotein and U1 small nuclear RNA stem/loop II. *Biochem. Soc. Trans.* 21:605

18. Feughelman M, Langridge R, Seeds WE, Stokes AR, Wilson HR, et al. 1955. Molecular structure of deoxyribose nucleic acid and nucleoprotein. *Nature* 175:834

19. Folkers PJM, Stassen APM, VanDuynhoven JPM, Harmsen BJM, Kanings RNH, Hilbers CW. 1991. Characterization of wild-type and mutant MI3 Gene-V proteins by means of H^1-NMR. *Eur. J. Biochem.* 200:139

20. Folkers PJM, VanDuynhoven JPM, Jonker AJ, Harmsen BJM, Kanings RNH, Hilbers CW. 1991. Sequence-specific H^1-NMR assignment and secondary structure of the Tyr4l→His mutant of the single-stranded DNA-binding protein, Gene-V protein, encoded by the filamentous bacteriophage M13. *Eur. J. Biochem.* 202:349

21. Freemont PS, Lane AN, Sanderson MR. 1991. Structural aspects of protein-DNA recognition. *Biochem. J.* 278:1

22. Friedman DI. 1988. Integration host factor—a protein for all reasons. *Cell* 55:545

23. Geiduschek EP, Schneider GJ, Sayre MH. 1990. TF1, a bacteriophage-specific DNA-binding and DNA-bending protein. *J. Struct. Biol.* 104:84

24. Giladi H, Gottesman M, Oppenheim AB. 1990. Integration host factor stimulates the phage λ *Pl* promoter. *J. Mol. Biol.* 213:109.

25. Harrison SC, Aggarawal AK. 1990. DNA recognition by proteins with the Helix-turn-helix motif. *Annu. Rev. Biochem.* 59:933

26. He Y-Y, McNally T, Manfield I, Navratil O, Old IG, et al. 1992. Probing met repressor-operator recognition in solution. *Nature* 359:431

27. Hol WGJ. 1985. The role of the α-helix dipole in protein structure and function. *Prog. Biophys. Mol. Biol.* 45:149

28. Horikoshi M, Bertuccioli C, Takada R, Wang J, Yamamoto T, Roeder RG. 1992. Transcription factor TFIID induces DNA bending upon binding to the TATA element. *Proc. Natl. Acad. Sci. USA* 89:1060

29. Horikoshi M, Wang CK, Fuji H, Cromlish JA, Weil PA, Roeder RG. 1989. Purification of a yeast TATA box binding protein that exhibits human transcription factor TFIID activity. *Proc. Natl. Acad. Sci. USA* 86:4843

30. Inamoto I, Ohtsubo E. 1990. Specific binding of the TraY protein to *OriT* and the promoter region for the *TraY* gene of plasmid R100. *J. Biol. Chem.* 265:6461

31. Kawano K, Yoneya T, Miyata T, Yoshikawa K, Tokunaga F, et al. 1990. Antimicrobial peptide, Tachyplesin-I, isolated from hemocytes of the horseshoe crab (*Tachypleus tridentatus*)—NMR determination of the β-sheet structure. *J. Biol. Chem.* 265:15365

31a. Kim JL, Nikolov DB, Burley SK. 1993. Co-crystal structure of TBP recognizing the minor groove of a TATA element. *Nature* 365:520

31b. Kim K, Geiger JH, Hahn S, Sigler PB. 1993. Crystal structure of a yeast TBP/TATA-box complex. *Nature* 365:512

32. Kneale GG, Freeman R, Marvin DA. 1982. Pfl bacteriophage replication-assembly complex—X-ray fiber diffraction and scanning-transmission electron microscopy. *J. Mol. Biol.* 156:279

33. Knight KL, Bowie JU, Vershon AK, Kelley RD, Sauer RT. 1989. The Arc and Mnt repressors—a new class of sequence-specific DNA-binding protein. *J. Biol Chem.* 264:3639

34. Knight KL, Sauer RT. 1989. Identification of functionally important residues in the DNA-binding region of Mnt repressor. *J. Biol. Chem.* 264:13706

35. Knight KL, Sauer RT. 1989. DNA-binding specificity of the Arc and Mnt repressors is determined by a short region of N-terminal residues. *Proc. Natl. Acad. Sci. USA* 86:797

36. Knight KL, Sauer RT. 1992. Biochemical and genetic analysis of operator contacts made by residues within the β-sheet DNA-binding motif of Mnt repressor. *EMBO J.* 11:215

37. Kraulis PJ. 1991. MOLSCRIPT—a program to produce both detailed and schematic plots of protein structures. *J. Appl. Cryst.* 24:946

38. Lee DK, Horikoshi M, Roeder RG. 1991. Interaction of TFIID in the minor groove of the TATA element. *Cell* 67:1241

39. Mohr CD, Deretic V. 1992. *In vitro* interactions of the histone-like protein IHF with the *AlgD* promoter, a critical site for control of mucoidy in *Pseudomonas aeruginosa*. *Biochem. Biophys. Res. Commun.* 189:837

40. Nagai K, Oubridge CJ, Jessen TH, Li J, Evans PR. 1990. Crystal structure of the RNA-binding domain of the U1 small nuclear ribonucleoprotein-A. *Nature* 348:515

41. Neilan JG, Lu Z, Kutish GF, Sussman MD, Roberts PC, et al. 1993. An African swine fever virus gene with similarity to bacterial DNA-binding proteins, bacterial integration host factors, and the *Bacillus* phage SPO1 transcription factor, TF1. *Nucleic Acids Res.* 21:1496

42. Nikolov DB, Hu S-H, Lin J, Gasch A, Hoffmann A, et al. 1992. Crystal structure of TFIID TATA-box binding protein. *Nature* 360:40

43. Old IG, Phillips SEV, Stockley PG,

Saint-Girons I. 1991. Regulation of methionine biosynthesis in the enterobacteriaceae. *Prog. Biophys. Mol. Biol.* 56:145

44. Otwinowski Z, Schevitz RW, Zhang R-G, Lawson CL, Joachimiak A, et al. 1988. Crystal structure of *Trp* repressor-operator complex at atomic resolution. *Nature* 335:321

45. Pabo CO, Sauer RT. 1992. Transcription factors—structural families and principles of DNA recognition. *Annu. Rev. Biochem.* 61:1053

46. Phillips SEV. 1991. Specific β-sheet interactions. *Curr. Opin. Struct. Biol.* 1:89

47. Phillips SEV, Boys CWG, He Y-Y, Manfield I, McNally T, et al. 1993. *E. coli met* repressor: DNA recognition by β-strands. *Nucleic Acids and Molecular Biology*, ed. F Eckstein, DMJ Lilley, 7:28. Berlin: Springer-Verlag

48. Phillips SEV, Manfield I, Parsons I, Davidson BE, Rafferty JB, et al. 1989. Cooperative tandem binding of *Met* repressor of *Escherichia coli*. *Nature* 341:711

49. Rafferty JB, Somers WS, Saint-Girons I, Phillips SEV. 1989. Three-dimensional crystal structures of *Esherichia coli Met* repressor with and without corepressor. *Nature* 342:705

50. Reddy P, Hahn S. 1991. Dominant negative mutations in yeast TFIID define a bipartite DNA-binding region. *Cell* 65:349

51. Saint-Girons I, Belfaiza J, Guillou Y, Peffin D, Guiso N, et al. 1986. Interactions of the *E. coli* methionine repressor with the *MetF* operator and with its corepressor, S-adenosylmethionine. *J. Biol. Chem.* 261:10936

52. Saint-Girons I, Duchange N, Cohen GN, Zakin MM. 1984. Structure and autoregulation of the *MetJ* regulatory gene in *E. coli*. *J. Biol. Chem.* 259:14282

53. Saint-Girons I, Parsot C, Zakin MM, Bârzu O, Cohen GN. 1988. Methionine biosynthesis in enterobacteriaceae—biochemical, regulatory and evolutionary aspects. *CRC Crit. Rev. Biochem.* 23:Sl

54. Sayre MH, Geiduschek EP. 1990. Effects of mutations at amino-acid 61 in the arm of TFI on its DNA-binding properties. *J. Mol. Biol.* 216:819

55. Schindelin H, Marahiel MA, Heinemann U. 1993. Universal nucleic acid-binding domain revealed by crystal structure of the *Bacillus subtilis* major cold-shock protein. *Nature* 364:164

56. Schneider GJ, Geiduschek EP. 1990.

Stoichiometry of DNA binding by the bacteriophage Spo1 encoded DNA-binding protein TF1. *J. Biol. Chem.* 265: 10198

57. Schneider GJ, Sayre MH, Geiduschek EP. 1991. DNA-bending properties of TF1. *J. Mol. Biol.* 221:777

58. Schnuchel A, Wiltscheck R, Czisch M, Herrler M, Willimsky G, et al. 1993. Structure in solution of the major cold-shock protein from *Bacillus subtilis*. *Nature* 364:169

59. Schultz MC, Reeder RH, Hahn S. 1992. Variants of the TATA-binding protein can distinguish subsets of RNA polymerase-I, polymerase-II and polymerase-III promoters. *Cell* 69:697

60. Seeman NC, Rosenberg JM, Rich A. 1976. Sequence-specific recognition of double helical nucleic acids by proteins. *Proc. Natl. Acad. Sci. USA* 73:804

61. Sharp PA. 1992. TATA-binding protein is a classless factor. *Cell* 68:819

62. Shindo H, Kurumizaka H, Furubayashi A, Sakuma C, Matsumoto U, et al. 1993. Proton NMR study on a histone-like protein, HU-α, from *Escherichia coli* and its complex with oligo DNAs. *Biol. Pharm. Bull.* 16:437

63. Sluka JP, Horvath SJ, Glasgow AC, Simon NE, Dervan PB. 1990. Importance of minor groove contacts for recognition of DNA by the binding domain of Hin recombinase. *Biochemistry* 29: 6551

64. Snyder UK, Thompson JF, Landy A. 1989. Phasing of protein-induced DNA bends in a recombination complex. *Nature* 341:255

65. Snyder UK, Thompson JF, Landy A. 1989. Phasing of protein-induced DNA bends in a recombination complex. (correction). *Nature* 342:206

66. Somers WS, Phillips SEV. 1992. Crystal structure of the *met* repressor-operator complex at 2.8Å resolution reveals DNA recognition by β-strands. *Nature* 359:387

67. Starr DB, Hawley DK. 1991. TFIID binds in the minor groove of the TATA box. *Cell* 67:1231

68. Stassen APM, Harmsen BJM, Schoenmakers JGC, Hilbers CW, Konings RNH. 1992. Fluorescence studies of the binding of bacteriophage M13 Gene-V mutant proteins to polynucleotides. *Eur. J. Biochem.* 206:605

69. Steitz TA. 1990. Structural studies of protein-nucleic acid interaction: the sources of sequence-specific binding. *Q. Rev. Biophys.* 23:205

70. Strubin M, Struhl K. 1992. Yeast and human TFIID with altered DNA-binding specificity for TATA elements. *Cell* 68:721

71. Suzuki M. 1989. SPKK, a new nucleic acid binding unit of protein found in histone. *EMBO J.* 8:797

72. Suzuki M. 1989. SPKK motifs prefer to bind to DNA at A/T-rich sites. *EMBO J.* 8:4189

73. Suzuki M. 1990. The heptad repeat in the largest subunit of RNA polymerase-II binds by intercalating into DNA. *Nature* 344:562

74. Tabuchi H, Handa H, Hirose S. 1993. Underwinding of DNA on binding of yeast TFIID to the TATA element. *Biochem. Biophys. Res. Commun.* 192: 1432

75. Tamamura H, Kuroda M, Masuda M, Otaka A, Funakoshi S, et al. 1993. A comparative study of the solution structures of tachyplesin-I and a novel anti-HIV synthetic peptide, T22 ([Tyr(5,12),Lys(7)] - polyphemusin - II), determined by nuclear magnetic resonance. *Biochim. Biophys. Acta* 1163:209

76. Tanaka I, Appelt K, Dijk J, White SW, Wilson KS. 1984. 3Å structure of a protein with histone-like properties in prokaryotes. *Nature* 310:376

77. Travers AA. 1989. DNA conformation and protein binding. *Annu. Rev. Biochem.* 58:427

78. Tsui P, Freundlich M. 1988. Integration host factor binds specifically to sites in the *IlvGMEDA* operon in *Escherichia coli*. *J. Mol. Biol.* 203:817

79. Tsui P, Huang L, Freundlich M. 1991. Integration host factor binds specifically to multiple sites in the *OmpB* promoter of *Escherichia coli* and inhibits transcription. *J. Bacteriol.* 173:5800

80. Vanrijn PA, Vandeputte P, Goosen N. 1991. Analysis of the IHF binding site in the regulatory region of bacteriophage Mu. *Nucleic Acids Res.* 19:2825

81. Vermote CLM, Vipond IB, Halford SE. 1992. EcoRV restriction endonuclease—communication between DNA recognition and catalysis. *Biochemistry* 31:6089

82. Vershon AK, Kelley RD, Sauer RT. 1989. Sequence-specific binding of Arc repressor to DNA—effects of operator mutations and modifications. *J. Biol. Chem.* 264:3267

83. White SW, Appelt K, Wilson KS, Tanaka I. 1989. A protein structural motif that bends DNA. *Proteins: Struct. Funct. Genet.* 5:281

84. Wilson KS, Tanaka I, Appelt K, White S. 1989. Double-stranded DNA binding protein HU. *Basic Life Sci.* 51:133

85. Winkelman JW, Hatfield GW. 1990. Characterization of the integration host factor binding site in the *IlvPGl* promoter region of the *IlvGMEDA* operon of *Escherichia coli. J. Biol. Chem.* 265: 10055

86. Winkler FK, Banner DW, Oefner C, Tsernoglou D, Brown RS, et al. 1993. The crystal structure of EcoRV endonuclease and of its complexes with cognate and non-cognate DNA fragments. *EMBO J.* 12:1781

87. Wolffe AP, Tafuri S, Ranjan M, Familari M. 1992. The Y-box factors—a family of nucleic acid binding proteins conserved from *Escherichia coli* to man. *New Biol.* 4:290

88. Yamamoto T, Horikoshi M, Wang J, Hasegawa S, Weil PA, Roeder RG. 1992. A bipartite DNA-binding domain composed of direct repeats in the TATA-box binding factor TFIID. *Proc. Natl. Acad. Sci. USA* 89:2844

89. Yang C-C, Nash HA. 1989. The interaction of *E. coli* IHF protein with its specific binding sites. *Cell* 57:869

90. Yonezawa A, Kuwahara J, Fujii N, Sugiura Y. 1992. Binding of Tachyplesin-I to DNA revealed by footprinting analysis—significant contribution of secondary structure to DNA binding and implication for biological action. *Biochemistry* 31:2998

Annu. Rev. Biophys. Biomol. Struct. 1994. 23:703–30

G-QUARTET STRUCTURES IN TELOMERIC DNA

James R. Williamson

Department of Chemistry, Massachusetts Institute of Technology, 77 Massachusetts Avenue, Cambridge, Massachusetts 02139

KEY WORDS: NMR, monovalent ions, polymorphism, replication, quadruplex

CONTENTS

PERSPECTIVES AND OVERVIEW

Telomeres are the structures at the termini of linear eukaryotic chromosomes, consisting of particular DNA sequences and associated pro-

1056–8700/94/0610–0703$05.00

teins. Telomeres stabilize the ends of chromosomes, and are involved in replication of the ends as well as the organization of chromosomes within the nucleus. In many organisms, the telomere contains tens to hundreds of thousands of base pairs. This review focuses on the structures formed in vitro by the repeated G-rich DNA sequences found at the extreme termini of most eukaryotic chromosomes.

Telomere and Telomeric DNA Reviews

Several general reviews are available on telomeres. Of these, an early review of telomere and centromere structure serves as a good introduction to the biology of telomeres (9). More recent reviews thoroughly discuss the function of telomeres with particular attention to mechanisms for telomere replication (6, 7, 93). Guschlbauer et al (33) have written a historical perspective that summarizes the earlier work on gel formation by guanine nucleosides and nucleotides. The structures of G-rich telomeric DNAs have also been recently reviewed (72, 78, 89). This review concentrates on newer studies in the past year, and on generalizations of results from a variety of methods.

BACKGROUND

Telomeric DNA Sequences

The telomeric DNA sequences known from a diverse set of organisms generally consist of many tandem repeats of G-rich sequences. The sequences $d(TTTTGGGG)_n$, $d(TTGGGG)_n$, and $d(TTAGGG)_n$ correspond to the telomeric sequences from *Oxytricha*, *Tetrahymena*, and humans, respectively. The sequences that have a regular short repeat fit into the general consensus $d[T_{1-3}-(T/A)-G_{3-4}]_n$ (9, 90). More extensive lists of sequences can be obtained in other reviews (9, 78, 93). Although some telomeric sequences are not G-rich, and some chromosomal termini do not bear telomeric DNA sequences (5), most eukaryotic telomeres are characterized by repetitive G-rich sequences.

In several cases, the nature of the extreme 3' end of the telomeric DNA is known with certainty. *Oxytricha* macronuclear DNA has a 16-nucleotide 3' single-stranded overhang of d(TTTTGGGGTTTTGGGG), and *Euplotes* macronuclear DNA has a 14-nucleotide overhang of d(TTTTGGGGTTTTGG) (45, 62). *Tetrahymena* and *Didymium* have a 12- to 16-nucleotide 3' extension as judged by sensitivity to single-stranded chemical probes (38). Thus, the 3' terminal extension of the G-rich strand seems to be a conserved feature of telomeric DNAs from a number of organisms.

The number of tandem repeats of telomeric DNAs can vary greatly, both from organism to organism, and sometimes from telomere to telomere. The length of the macronuclear telomeres from the holotrichous ciliated protozoans (*Oxytricha, Euplotes, Stylonychia*) are uniform in length, each chromosome bearing four to four and a half repeats of telomeric DNA (9, 93). Most other organisms exhibit much longer telomeres, up to several kilobases, that are variable in length (9, 93). The nearly universal conservation of G-rich sequences suggests that the structures that can be formed by these sequences may play an important role in telomere function. Consequently, much attention has recently focused on characterization of G-rich telomeric DNA structures in vitro, using a variety of biophysical techniques.

G-Quartets, Guanosine, and Poly-G Structures

The main structural motif for telomeric DNAs is the G-quartet, also known as the guanine tetrad or simply G-DNA. The G-quartet consists of four guanine bases in a square planar array arranged in a cyclic hydrogen-bonding pattern, where each guanine is both the donor and acceptor of two hydrogen bonds, as shown in Figure 1*a*. The unique feature of the G-quartet as a structural motif is a pocket at the center lined by electronegative carbonyl oxygens that is thought to be the site of interaction with a cation. This cation-interaction site distinguishes telomeric DNA structures from other DNA structures based primarily on hydrogen-bonding interactions.

The first proposal of the G-quartet structure was offered as an explanation of the curious property of gel formation by guanine nucleotides (24). A wide variety of guanine nucleotides will form gels, and a great many of the properties now observed for telomeric DNAs were observed in the gel-formation studies, in particular the cation dependence of the structure formation (33). Rich (67) first proposed a cyclic hydrogen bond array as a model for poly-I structure based on fiber diffraction data (67). Interestingly, the three-stranded structure proposed at that time was preferred over the now-accepted four-stranded structure, because of the presence of a sizeable hole at the center of the structure. The cation dependence, which would have provided a plug for the hole, was not well established until a later time.

The stability of most nucleic acid helices is relatively insensitive to the identity of the counterions present. Duplex B-DNA structures exhibit a two-fold preference in binding for the monovalent ion series: $Cs^+ > K^+ > Li^+ > Na^+$ (10). In contrast, guanine nucleotide gels, poly-G helices, and telomeric DNAs all exhibit a strong dependence of the melting temperature on the monovalent ion present.

a)

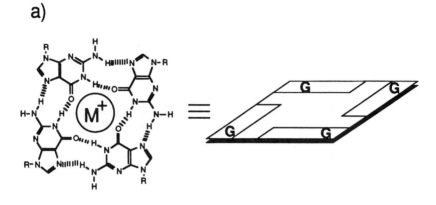

b)

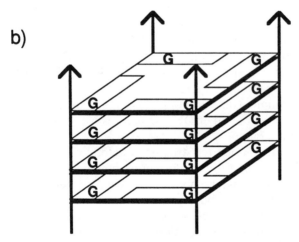

Figure 1 (*a*) The G-quartet is a cyclic array of four guanine bases, each of which is the acceptor and donor of two hydrogen bonds. At the center of the G-quartet is a pocket that is the site of interaction with monovalent cations. (*b*) Schematic diagram of how stacks of G-quartets form quadruple helical structures.

Fiber diffraction studies on poly-G helices suggested a quadruple helix structure with a 3.4-Å rise per step, and a 30° right-handed helical twist (95). The structure of poly-G may be thought of as stacks of G-quartets arranged in a helical manner, as illustrated schematically in Figure 1*b*. In the poly-G structure, all of the glycosidic torsion angles were in the *anti* conformation, and all of the phosphodiester backbones were arranged in a parallel 5'-to-3' manner. In this respect, telomeric

DNAs often differ, as they contain both *syn* and *anti* glycosidic conformations, and the backbone on adjacent strands may sometimes be antiparallel.

Models for Telomeric DNA Structures

The first indication that telomeric DNA sequences adopt unusual structures was the observation of compact folded structures adopted by G-rich telomeric DNAs on nondenaturing polyacrylamide gels (37). NMR studies also indicated the presence the unusual *syn* glycosidic torsions for some dG residues, and the presence of G-G hydrogen bonds was inferred from the imino proton spectrum of d(TTGGGG)₄ (37). Subsequent studies showed that the formation of these structures depended on the monovalent cations present in the sample (80, 90).

Model structures were proposed for telomeric DNAs based on the G-quartet as a structural unit. A unifying model of telomeric DNA structure could be based on stacks of G-quartets capped by loops of T or A residues. The conserved sequence element, the G-strings, takes the place of the core structural element, while the variable sequences (T/A) are placed in variable loops. The attractive feature of these models is that the structure can accommodate most known telomeric DNA sequences.

Related Structures

Sequences other than telomeric DNAs also form structures based on the G-quartet. The first of these identified was a G-rich sequence from the immunoglobulin switch region (70). Sequences from the retinoblastoma susceptibility genes can form G-quartet structures in vitro (56), as do sequences from the tRNA *supF* gene (3). Any sequence that has runs of tandem G residues can indeed form these structures and given the opportunity will most likely do so. Single-stranded DNAs with one string of Gs frequently form quadruplex structures by association of four strands into a tetrameric complex. Although these sequences may not be functionally related to telomeric DNAs, their fundamental structure is similar.

Motivation for Study of Telomeric DNA Structure

Although the biological role of G-quartet structures is still unresolved, an understanding of their biophysical chemistry is still important. The G-rich sequences at the ends of chromosomes are ubiquitous, and therefore structures that can be formed by these sequences under physiological conditions are necessarily of interest. Only by a thorough understanding of the structures of telomeric DNA, and the thermodynamics and kinetics of these systems, can we have a complete understanding of their potential biological roles.

In addition to the biological aspects of telomeric sequences, several very basic and interesting biophysical questions can be addressed. G-quartet structures exhibit a variety of behaviors that are unique or unusual for nucleic acids. First, they can readily discriminate between different monovalent cations. Second, they are very polymorphic. Telomeric DNAs can form various similar, yet distinct, structures, and understanding why one structure forms in preference to another requires understanding the details of how molecular forces shape nucleic acid structure. Third, the folding and unfolding transitions for telomeric DNAs can be extremely slow. Thus, telomeric DNA structures are both thermodynamically and kinetically stable, a fact that must have implications for the possible biological roles of telomeric DNAs.

STRUCTURAL CHARACTERIZATION OF TELOMERIC DNA

Chemical Probes

Chemical probes are useful tools for the study of telomeric DNAs. The guanine base in a G-quartet is nearly saturated with hydrogen bonds, and therefore the G-quartet structure is particularly sensitive to these types of perturbations. In the absence of detailed NMR or crystallographic data, chemical probing methods offer the best diagnostic evidence for G-quartet formation.

NUCLEASE SENSITIVITY   G-quartet structures are resistant to probing by single-stranded nuclease. Dimer forms of *Oxytricha* macronuclear DNA are resistant to both endo- and exonucleases (58). Telomeric DNA sequences in closed circular plasmid DNA have been probed with S1 nuclease, and under superhelical stress the G-strand is protected from nuclease action (12, 82). Telomeric oligonucleotides and G-quartets structures from retinoblastoma susceptibility gene sequences are protected from attack by nuclease S1 (2, 56). Proximity to a tight G-quartet core must render even the loosely structured adjacent T-residues resistant to nuclease attack.

UV CROSSLINKING   A variety of telomeric DNAs form ultraviolet light (UV)–induced covalent crosslinks characteristic of the folded G-quartet form. Thymidine residues from different repeats can be brought into proximity by structure formation, and this proximity may be detected by formation of a crosslink. UV-induced crosslinks have been observed in telomeric oligonucleotides from *Oxytricha* and *Tetrahymena* (90), in the quadruplex formed by d(TTTTGGGG) (49), as well as in several other model telomeric sequences (29). No crosslinks were observed in the *Chlamydomonas* telomeric oligonucleotide d(TTTTAGGG)$_4$ (61). The presence of a crosslink is useful for demonstrating proximity of nonadjacent sequences. However, the absence of a crosslink is not necessarily significant, as efficient crosslinking requires precise alignment of the two bases involved in the crosslink.

CHEMICAL PROTECTION   A variety of chemical probes have been used in the study of telomeric DNAs. The most characteristic signature of G-quartet formation is the strong protection conferred by the structure to methylation of the guanine N7 by dimethyl sulfate (DMS). Frequently in telomeric DNAs, most or all of the guanine N7s are resistant to methylation by DMS. This protection is conferred by the involvement of the N7s in hydrogen bonds with neighboring bases. DMS has been used to probe quadruplex structures in a variety of nontelomeric G-rich DNA sequences (3, 56, 59, 70), and in telomeric sequences in plasmids under superhelical stress (51, 82). Numerous studies have used DMS modification to probe telomeric DNA sequences from a variety of organisms (2, 29, 30, 39, 49, 58, 61, 71, 73, 80, 81, 90). The N7 of guanines in a G-quartet is also resistant to modification by diethyl pyrocarbonate (DEPC) (80).

Potassium permanganate and osmium tetroxide are bulky reagents that will react with exposed thymidine residues. Attack of these reagents requires that the 5–6 double bond in T be accessible from above or below the plane. A variety of G-quartet structures have been probed with one of these reagents (2, 4, 51, 56, 81). In general the thymines in telomeric sequences are less accessible than in single strands, but more accessible than in duplex DNA.

Nuclear Magnetic Resonance

Nuclear magnetic resonance (NMR) is an invaluable tool for the study of nucleic acid structures, and many NMR studies have been carried out on G-quartet structures. However, the repetitive nature of the sequences hampers the NMR study of telomeric structures. The assignment of NMR spectra relies heavily on good chemical shift dispersion due to nearest-neighbor effects. In a sequence such as d(TTTTGGGG)$_4$, the NMR spectrum is very crowded, and difficult at best to assign. These problems have been ameliorated by studying structures that are two-fold or four-fold symmetric, which effectively reduces the complexity of the spectrum.

The first NMR studies of telomeric DNA sequences did not immediately provide detailed structural information but did indicate that telomeric structures were unusual. NMR studies of d(TTGGGG)$_4$ revealed that nonstandard G-G base pairs must be present, and that some of the guanines existed in the unusual *syn* conformation (37). The *syn* conformation, also found in the G residues in Z-DNA, is readily observed owing to the short distance between the guanine H8 proton and the H1' deoxyribose proton, which results in an unusually strong nuclear Overhauser effect (NOE) between these protons.

The first detailed NMR study of a G-quartet structure was done on the oligomer d(GGTTTTGG), shown to form a tetramolecular complex by calorimetric analysis (41, 86). The first significant finding of these studies was that the glycosidic torsion angle alternated *syn-anti* for each adjacent pair of Gs along the strand. The alternation of glycosidic torsion angles was also observed in the similar sequence d(GGTTTTCGG) (85). Although the alternation of glycosidic conformation had been predicted on the basis of molecular models for Gs within the same G-quartet, no prediction of glycosidic conformation alternation along the strand had been made. Early models of telomeric DNA structure (80, 90) made the assumption, based largely on model structures from fiber diffraction studies, that the glycosidic conformation would not vary along the strand. The second significant result from the d(GGTTTTTGG) studies was that multiple conformers were present in the NMR samples, and that these conformations were in slow exchange on the NMR timescale.

Qualitative NMR studies also revealed that the structures formed by telomeric DNAs differed according to the presence of Na$^+$ vs K$^+$ as the counterion and that the stability of the structures also depended on the monovalent cation present (35). Both d(TTGGGG)$_4$ and d(TTAGGG)$_4$ were studied with NMR in Na$^+$-phosphate or K$^+$-phosphate buffers. The complexity of the imino proton spectrum for these molecules indicates that multiple species are present at the high concentrations required for these studies. The imino proton spectrum in Na$^+$ vs K$^+$ was markedly different for both oligomers. Temperature-dependent imino proton spectra revealed that the K$^+$ forms were more stable than the Na$^+$ forms. In addition, imino protons were still observable for the K$^+$ form of d(TTGGGG)$_4$, even at 90°C.

TETRAPLEX STRUCTURES   Several NMR studies have been performed on short G-rich sequences that form parallel four-stranded complexes.

A tetraplex is formed by the oligoribonucleotide r(UGGGGU) (16). In this case, all of the G residues are in the *anti* conformation. In addition, slowly exchanging G imino protons are observed, and four U residues on one end of the G-quartet core also form a cyclic U-quartet. Because of the small size of this oligomer, an unusually large number of NOE restraints were obtained, and the resulting structure, schematically shown in Figure 2*a*, is very well defined. Similar conformations have been defined for d(TGGGGT) (1), d(GGGGGTTTTT) (68), d(TTAGGG) and d(TTGGGG) (87), and d(TTTTGGGG) (32). In addition, ^{15}N NMR has been applied to the study of the quadruplex formed by d(TGGGT) (23, 42).

INTRAMOLECULAR TETRAPLEX STRUCTURES   In vitro selection experiments have identified a telomere-like DNA sequence that binds to and inhibits thrombin (11). The sequence, d(GGTTGGTGTGGTTGG), forms and intramolecular quadruplex composed of two G-quartets (52, 84), as determined by NMR. As was observed for d(GGTTTTTGG), the glycosidic conformation alternates *syn-anti* for each adjacent pair of guanine residues. Figure 2*b* schematically illustrates this structure.

HAIRPIN DIMER STRUCTURES   An imino proton NMR study of d(GGGTTTGGG) revealed that a dimeric G-quartet structure was formed by dimerization of two hairpins (69). However, the spectra revealed that the dimer was asymmetric and that the geometry of the two strands was distinct. In addition, two different spectra are observed in sodium versus potassium solution.

The most detailed NMR study of a telomeric DNA has been performed on d(GGGGTTTTGGGG) (76, 77). In the presence of 50 mM NaCl, this oligomer forms a single predominant species even at 4 mM strand concentration. Eight imino protons are observed, one for each of the guanines, indicating that each guanine is involved in hydrogen bonding. As was observed for d(GGTTTTTGG), the glycosidic torsion angles alternate *syn-anti-syn-anti* along the strand.

Detailed NOE studies revealed a surprising geometry for the thymidine loops of this structure. The loops were found to cross the G-quartet core diagonally at opposite ends of the core, rather than spanning adjacent strands as predicted in earlier models, as illustrated schematically in Figure 2*c*. This diagonal loop crossing was also reported for d(G$_4$T$_4$G$_4$T$_4$G$_4$T$_4$G$_4$). This loop geometry has two important implications. First, there are now three different grooves in the G-quartet core, and adjacent strands are parallel on two sides and antiparallel on the other two sides. Second, the folding mechanism for this type of

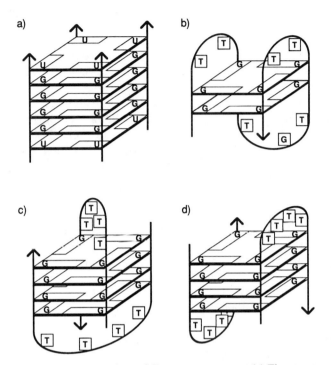

Figure 2   Schematic representations of G-quartet structures. (*a*) The structure formed by ribo(UGGGGU)₄. (*b*) The structure of the thrombin-binding DNA aptamer d(GGTTGGTGTGGTTGG). (*c*) The structure of d(GGGGTTTTGGGG) in Na⁺ solution as determined with NMR spectroscopy. (*d*) The structure of d(GGGGTTTTGGGG) in K⁺ solution as determined with X-ray crystallography.

structure might be complex. Usually, dimer formation is thought to occur by dimerization of two foldback Hoogsteen base-paired structures. In this case, both the hydrogen bond donors and acceptors for any G residue are on a different molecule. During folding, intermolecular hydrogen bonding must compete with intramolecular hydrogen bonding.

X-Ray Crystallography

In addition to NMR analyses (76, 77), X-ray crystallographic analysis has been performed on d(GGGGTTTTGGGG) (43) and supports the general model features for the G-quartet core structure. The glycosidic torsion angles alternate *syn-anti-syn-anti* along the strand and around any given G-quartet. The thymidine loops are located on opposite ends of the G-quartet core in head-to-tail fashion, and unlike the structure obtained by NMR, join adjacent strands, as shown in Figure 2*d*.

The crystal structure reveals detailed structural features that are difficult to observe with NMR. Examination of the G-quartets from different levels in the core reveals that the base geometry is often distorted from the ideal square planar arrangement of guanines. In addition, the guanines are somewhat buckled out of the plane of the G-quartet. Also, the central channel has electron density that probably results from a bound potassium ion. The ion is located between the second and third G-quartets at the center of the core structure.

POLYMORPHISM

The contrast between the structures derived from X-ray crystallography and NMR spectroscopy for the same oligomer nicely illustrates an emerging theme: Telomeric DNAs are polymorphic. As we shall see, numerous structures are possible for telomeric DNAs, and it is difficult to determine a priori which of these structures should form under a given set of conditions. The intriguing aspect of telomeric DNA structures is that the same bases can be assembled in many different ways with the same basic hydrogen-bonding structure.

Classes of Polymorphism

PARALLEL VS ANTIPARALLEL STRANDS One fundamental source of structural variation is the possibility of forming G-quartets where the strands have different polarities. Four strands can come together in a tetrameric complex in at least three different ways, shown in Figure 3*a*. All four strands can be parallel, and there are two permutations of two parallel and two antiparallel strands. In principle, three parallel strands and one antiparallel strand could form a tetraplex, but this type of structure has not yet been observed.

STRAND STOICHIOMETRY The same oligomer can form different types of structures by association of one or more molecules. For example, a telomeric DNA sequence containing four repeats can form an intramolecular quadruplex, a dimer, or a true quadruplex, as shown in Figure 3*b*. This type of polymorphism depends on the concentration of the DNA. Representative members for each of these three classes have been characterized structurally and are illustrated in Figure 2.

GLYCOSIDIC CONFORMATION Guanines in G-quartets are observed in both the *syn* and *anti* conformation. A string of four G residues can in

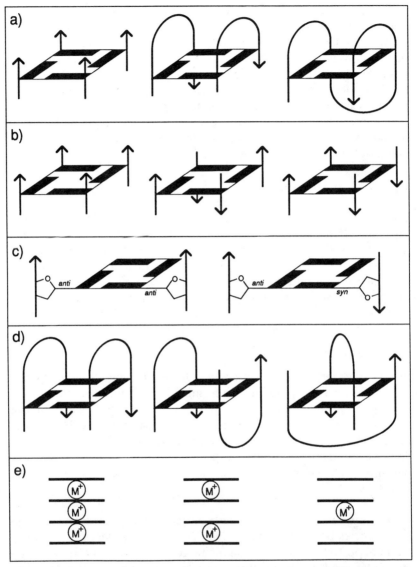

Figure 3 Different types of polymorphism exhibited by G-quartet structures. (*a*) Structures can be formed by the association of four, two, or one strand. (*b*) The relative arrangement of adjacent backbones can be all parallel, alternating antiparallel, or adjacent antiparallel. (*c*) Adjacent Gs in the same G-quartet can have the same or the opposite glycosidic torsion angle. (*d*) The loops connecting different strings of G residues can adopt either a head-to-head, head-to-tail, or diagonal arrangement. (*e*) Ions can bind with different stoichiometry by occupying different combinations of G-quartet sites.

principle adopt a variety of combinations of glycosidic conformations. The only observed patterns thus far are all-*anti* and alternating *syn-anti*. Bases involved in the same G-quartet that are on parallel strands must have the same glycosidic torsion, while bases on antiparallel strands must have opposite glycosidic torsions, as illustrated in Figure 3*c*. The glycosidic conformation changes the relative orientations of the bases on adjacent G-quartets, and so can affect the stacking energy between G-quartets.

LOOP GEOMETRY   When the G-quartet formation is unimolecular or bi-molecular, a variety of combinations of loop crossings can connect different G-strings. For example, in dimeric species, loops can join adjacent or diagonal strands, and the two loops can be oriented in a head-to-tail or head-to-head manner. Figure 3*d* illustrates these types of polymorphism.

ION-BINDING GEOMETRY   Different ions may interact with the G-quartet structures in different ways and can bind with different stoichiometries. The ion binding geometry is known with certainty only for d(GGGGTTTTGGGG) in the potassium form, for which there is a crystal structure (43). The electron density for the K^+ ion is found in between the second and third G-quartet levels. Other ion stoichiometries are possible, and ions might bind to every G-quartet, or to every other G-quartet, as shown in Figure 3*e*.

Not all of the factors that contribute to the polymorphism of telomeric DNAs can vary independently. In particular, requirements for hydrogen bonding in the G-quartet restrict the possible combinations of glycosidic torsion angles with strand direction or with loop geometry (55). The guanine bases in a G-quartet are related by a simple 90° rotation about the helix axis in the plane of the G-quartet. If guanines are on adjacent antiparallel strands in a G-quartet structure, they cannot hydrogen bond properly unless one of them is *syn,* and one of them is *anti*. Thus fixing the loop geometry fixes the relative strand orientation, which in turn places restriction on the relative glycosidic torsion angles within a G-quartet level.

Despite these restrictions on the structures that can be formed, a considerable number of different structures are still possible. The major factor contributing to the stability of telomeric DNA structures is the G-quartet core. This core structure can be assembled in many energetically very similar ways. Understanding why only a few of the myriad possible structures are observed will be a challenging problem.

Nondenaturing Electrophoresis

Nondenaturing, or native, gel electrophoresis has proven to be a simple yet powerful method for the analysis of structures formed by telomeric DNAs. Electrophoretic mobility is determined by the size, shape, and charge of the molecule as it passes through the gel medium. In denaturing gels, DNA fragments exist primarily as single strands that migrate in order of molecular weight. In nondenaturing gels, DNA fragments that adopt particular structures migrate differently from single-stranded DNAs of the same length. This technique is therefore useful for detecting structure formation by oligonucleotides.

Native gels are particularly useful for obtaining the following types of information on telomeric DNA oligonucleotides: (*a*) structure formation, (*b*) multiple or oligomeric structures, (*c*) strand stoichiometry, (*d*) ion dependence of structures, and (*e*) temperature dependence of structures. Many studies have used native gel electrophoresis to obtain this type of data on a variety of telomeric oligonucleotides. The method is powerful because it is simple, rapid, and many samples can be run in parallel.

ASSAY FOR STRUCTURE FORMATION   The first observation of unusual gel mobility of telomeric DNA was the coherence of macronuclear DNA from *Oxytricha* (58). Macronuclear chromosomes are 2–10 kb in length, and have 3′ single-stranded extensions of d(TTTTGGGGTTTTGGGG) at both ends. Multimerization of these chromosomes occurred by interaction of the terminal fragments, and the stability of the oligomers formed depended strongly on whether Na^+ or K^+ was present.

A variety of telomeric oligonucleotides assume compact high mobility forms on native gels (37). Oligonucleotides composed of telomeric G-strand repeats from *Tetrahymena, Oxytricha, Dictyostelium,* trypanosomes, and yeast, all assumed high mobility forms at 5°C. In contrast, oligonucleotides from telomeric C-strands, or oligonucleotides without G-strings, did not form high mobility species. This simple assay has become routinely used to check for structure formation in a variety of telomeric DNA sequences (2, 3, 29, 30, 35, 39, 50, 56, 61, 80, 90, 92).

ASSAY FOR MULTIPLE OR OLIGOMERIC STRUCTURES   Native gels are particularly useful for detection of multiple species in an oligonucleotide, due to alternate conformers or higher-order structures. Telomeric DNAs are polymorphic in that they form both multiple conformers and oligomeric species. Alternate conformers typically have similar, yet distinct, mobilities, while dimers and other structures exhibit quite different mobilities. Many telomeric oligonucleotides can form alternate conformers (15, 61, 90, 92). G-quartet structures, frequently detected as thermodynamic mixtures of forms by native gel electrophoresis (15, 61, 73, 90, 92), can be formed by dimerization or tetramerization of oligonucleotides. Also, higher-order structures formed by the end-to-end association of quadruplexes has been studied using native gels (73, 81).

STRAND STOICHIOMETRY   A simple and elegant method for determining the stoichiometry of a complex involves mixing oligonucleotides that have tails of different lengths. Usually, extra nucleotides can be added to either end of a G-string oligonucleotide without perturbing the ability to form G-quartet structures. If equimolar amounts of an oligonucleotide A are mixed with oligonucleotide B, then the stoichiometry of a given complex can be determined from the number of mixed species that are produced. For example, dimer formation would result in three different complexes resolved on a native gel, the AA, AB, and BB complexes. Tetramer formation would result in a pattern with five complexes: AAAA, AAAB, AABB, ABBB, and BBBB. This simple technique has been used to demonstrate dimer formation by telomeric oligonucleotides (2, 30, 71, 80) and tetramer formation in nontelomeric and telomeric oligonucleotides (44, 56, 70, 74).

ION-DEPENDENT STRUCTURE FORMATION   Telomeric DNAs exhibit a strong preference for binding certain cations. Consequently, the counterion used in a native gel experiment can change the stability of structured forms. Dimerization of macronuclear DNA from *Oxytricha* is preferentially stabilized by K^+ in native gels (58). *Oxytricha* telomeric oligonucleotides do not form a structure in the absence of added counterions or in the presence of Li^+ but readily form a structure in the presence of Na^+ or K^+ added to the gel running buffer (2, 58, 90). K^+ stabilized the quadruplex formed by r(UGGGGU) better than Na^+ (44), and Sr^{2+} also stabilizes quadruplex formation (15).

TEMPERATURE-DEPENDENT STRUCTURE FORMATION   Because the dissociation of G-quartet structures is often slow, native gels can be used to monitor the temperature dependence of structure formation. *Oxytricha* telomeric DNA dimers are stable in K^+ up to 70°C (2). Gels run at different temperatures have been used to compare the relative stabilities of a set of related sequences (4) or simply to monitor structure formation (49).

THERMODYNAMICS AND KINETICS

Thermal Denaturation by Ultraviolet and Circular Dichroism Spectroscopy

UV SPECTRA   The UV spectra of telomeric DNAs typically exhibit two overlapping peaks in the 260- to 280-nm range. Characteristic absorption changes are observed upon folding of telomeric DNAs. The absorbance at 275 nm typically decreases by ~10%, and the absorbance at 295 nm increases by 100% (92). Consequently, these wavelengths can be used to monitor folding or unfolding processes.

CD SPECTRA   The circular dichroism (CD) spectra of telomeric DNAs are very dependent on the conformation. Of the two basic CD spectra usually observed for telomeric DNAs (4), one form exhibits a positive CD band at ~265 nm and a negative band at ~240 nm (type I), while the other form exhibits a positive band at ~295 nm and a negative band at ~260 nm (type II).

These two CD spectra appear to be strongly correlated to the conformation of the G-quartet core (4). CD spectra recorded for similar sequences constrained to form parallel or antiparallel quadruplexes bear out this observation. The parallel quadruplex structure formed by d(3'-GGGGTT-5'-5'TTGGGG) exhibits a type I CD spectrum, while the antiparallel quadruplex formed by d(GGGGTTTTGGGG) exhibits a type II CD spectrum (50).

The CD spectrum has been recorded in the cases where NMR has revealed structural evidence for the conformation. The parallel quadruplex where all guanines are in the *anti* conformation is strongly correlated with the Type I CD spectrum (23, 42), while the antiparallel quadruplex where the guanines alternate *syn-anti* is strongly correlated with the Type II CD spectrum (31, 76).

CD spectra are extremely sensitive to base stacking geometry; hence, these two conformations should, and do, exhibit different CD spectra. Although the conformation of telomeric DNAs and the CD spectrum appear strongly correlated, it is dangerous to use the CD spectrum alone to assign a particular conformation. Many reported CD spectra appear different from the prototypical type I or II CD spectra (4, 15, 29–31, 35, 36). In many of these cases, multiple conformations may be present that are a mixture of parallel and antiparallel quadruplexes.

THERMAL DENATURATION   Several studies have used thermal denaturation as monitored by changes in UV or CD to obtain thermodynamic information on telomeric DNAs (4, 30, 35, 36, 61). In general, telomeric sequences are very stable, and their stability depends strongly on the identity of the monovalent cation present (15, 29, 42, 49, 69, 92). Drawing clear general conclusions from the data presented in the literature thus far is difficult. First, many different sequences are under study, and second, many different salts, salt concentrations, and DNA concentrations are used. In addition, evidence is rarely presented that the thermal denaturation studies were carried out at equilibrium. Telomeric DNA sequences are notorious for undergoing slow folding and unfolding kinetics (vide infra), and this presents experimental difficulties when determining thermodynamic parameters.

The parallel quadruplexes formed by d(TTTTGGG) in K^+ solution are extremely stable, with a $\Delta G°$ of -47 kcal/mol at 25°C (29). In contrast, the quadruplex formed by d(TGGGT) in K^+ exhibits a $\Delta G°$ of -7 kcal/mol (42). The main difference between these two sequences is the presence of a $3'$ terminal T residue that apparently can greatly affect the stability of the quadruplex structure.

The difference in stability of a parallel and antiparallel hairpin dimer structure adopted by the same sequences has been determined using thermal denaturation (50). The antiparallel structure formed by d(GGGGTTTGGGG) is ~ 5 kcal/mol less stable than the parallel structure adopted by d($3'$GGGGTT-$5'$-$5'$-TTGGGG-$3'$). This difference presumably represents the net change between forcing glycosidic torsion angles to the *syn* conformation and the different stacking and ionic interaction energies in the two structures.

Calorimetry

Although few calorimetric studies have been performed on telomeric DNAs, those done have been very illuminating. The calorimetric enthalpy should be the same as that determined from the concentration dependence of the T_m, which serves as a check for a two-state transition. Alternatively, given a calorimetrically determined ΔH, one can determine the strand stoichiometry by using thermal denaturation to examine the concentration dependence of melting (41). In the case of quadruplex formation, this method yielded the expected molecularity of four (41). The combination of calorimetric data and thermal denaturation data have also been used to compare parallel and antiparallel quadruplexes (42, 50). The thermodynamics of G-quartet structures can be compared on a per-G-quartet basis, since the enthalpy of G-quartet formation in several different structures is between -21 and -26 kcal/

mol per G-quartet (42). However, in these structures different types of ions are bound, and specifically bound monovalent ions may be present in varying numbers. The stacking interactions between G-quartets and the ionic interactions may be quite different in the structures surveyed, but give a comparable net effect. Calorimetric studies offer a powerful tool to study the complex thermodynamic forces that shape G-quartet structures.

Ion Binding

One of the most intriguing aspects of telomeric DNAs is their specific interaction with monovalent cations. In general, the order of preference is $K^+ > Na^+ > Cs^+ > Li^+$ (2, 90). Studies on guanosine gels, poly-G, and telomeric DNAs are all consistent with this general order (33). The main difference between these similar monovalent ions is the ionic radius, and there appears to be an optimal size of ion that will interact with the G-quartet structures. The ion-binding site is thought to be a pocket between two G-quartets that is lined by eight carbonyl oxygen atoms, and indeed the X-ray crystal structure of d(GGGGTTTTGGGG) has electron density attributable to a monovalent cation (43).

The simplest model for ion binding would be that a certain ion of an optimal size fits within the central cavity of the G-quartet. Consideration of the thermodynamics of ion binding suggests that the decision as to which ion is best will not be straightforward. The hydration energies of monovalent ions are inversely proportional to their ionic radii. A simple electrostatic picture of ion hydration implies that the closer the solvent water molecules can be to the ion, the larger the hydration energy. The hydration energies for the monovalent cations are very large, ranging from 70–120 kcal/mol (13). The G-quartet binding site must provide a stronger coordination energy than does water, and therefore the net affinity of the G-quartet structure for different ions is dictated by the small difference between the large coordination energies in water and in the G-quartet.

Several types of data support the simple electrostatic picture of the ionic contribution. Divalent ions also stabilize G-quartet structures, sometimes to a greater extent than monovalents (15, 81). In addition, the relative order of stabilities of the ions in G-quartet structures in the monovalent and divalent series depends on the ionic radius. The two optimal ions, K^+ and Sr^{2+}, are similar in ionic radius, but the divalent ion interacts more strongly with the G-quartet than does the monovalent (15, 81), which would be expected on electrostatic grounds because of the increase in charge. In principle, trivalent ions should interact with G-quartet structures even more strongly. A recent report suggests that Tb^{3+} does in fact interact with telomeric DNAs (57).

Slow Folding and Unfolding Kinetics

Another characteristic of telomeric DNA structures is that they often exhibit extremely slow kinetic properties. Slow kinetics of conformational transitions have been observed using a variety of techniques. Binding experiments with the *Oxytricha* telomere-binding protein indicated that the unfolding rate of d(TTTTGGGG)$_4$ in K$^+$ solution was 10^{-5} s^{-1}, while the folding rate was 0.02 s^{-1} (65). Unfolding of a tetraplex structure has been estimated at 0.01 s^{-1} for d(TTGGGGTT) in Na$^+$ solution (74). Dimerization of two hairpins to form a quadruplex structure is not rapid, with second-order rate constants of 5 M^{-1} s^{-1} reported for dimerization of d(TTTTGGGGTTTTGGGG) (30).

Several NMR studies have revealed slowly exchanging imino protons in G-quartet structures. Samples that are dried from H_2O, then redissolved in D_2O, still exhibit imino proton resonances for days to weeks (16, 32, 76, 87). The fact that these normally labile protons do not exchange is unprecedented in the field of nucleic acids. Thus, the telomeric DNAs exhibit extraordinary kinetic stability.

The slow kinetic transitions of G-quartet structures have some important consequences for the biophysical community. A researcher must be sure to allow adequate time for sample equilibration. This time constraint can be a big problem, particularly for thermal-denaturation experiments. Typically, the temperature is varied at 1°C/min; however, the half-time for unfolding of d(TTTTGGGG)$_4$ at 45°C in 50 mM NaCl is ~20 minutes (JR Williamson & E Dias, unpublished results). A useful check for the existence of this problem is to perform the thermal denaturation by increasing the temperature, then reversing the temperature change to perform a renaturation experiment. We have observed a difference in T_m of 15°C in the two directions when 1°C/min changes were used (JR Williamson & E Dias, unpublished results). One must take the slow folding kinetics into account when measuring thermodynamic parameters.

Equilibria Between Forms

Many telomeric DNA sequences can form several different types of structures. The relative amounts of each structure can depend upon experimental variables, such as temperature, DNA concentration, salt concentration, and in particular, on the nature of the counterions. For example, an oligonucleotide composed of four tandem repeats of sequence can fold up into a monomeric intramolecular quadruplex, or form a quadruplex by dimerization of two hairpins, or form a tetraplex by association of four molecules (see Figure 3b). Low temperature, high DNA concentration, and high ion concentrations will favor the tetrameric structures. In this example, the three types of structures exist in a sequential equilibrium, and the position of the equilibrium can be affected by the conditions. Addition of potassium is likely to stabilize all possible forms, relative to sodium and, under a given set of conditions, possibly cause a shift from monomeric to dimeric forms. This observation does not necessarily imply that potassium preferentially stabilizes the dimeric form. Potassium may also stabilize all of the forms equally, and the observed shift to the dimer form may simply be caused by the resulting shift in the sequential equilibria.

G-QUARTETS AND BIOLOGY

Proteins That Recognize Telomeric DNA

Various proteins have been found that interact with telomeric DNAs. Some bind to double-stranded telomeric DNA and are probably not G-quartet binding proteins. A terminal telomere-binding protein found in several organisms binds to the 3' single-stranded extension in the telosome complex. Finally, several other proteins have been found that bind to G-quartet structures, but whether or not these complexes with G-quartet structures serve any biological roles is not clear.

TELOMERE BINDING PROTEINS   In all of the cases known, a terminal telomere-binding protein is bound to the end of the telomeric DNA. The telomere-binding protein from *Oxytricha* was identified (25) and subsequently reconstituted into a nucleoprotein complex in vitro (64, 66). The protein consists of a 56- and 41-kDa subunit, and both subunits have been cloned and overexpressed (26, 40). Telomere-binding proteins have also been identified in species of *Euplotes* (63), *Stylonychia* (21), and *Physarum* (19, 20). These proteins bind to telomeric oligonucleotides and usually bind to either single-stranded G-rich oligonucleotides or to duplex DNA with the 3' terminal G-rich extension. Vertebrate proteins that bind to single-stranded telomeric repeats were also identified recently (14, 54). An avian telomere-binding protein has been found that requires G-G base-pair formation, but not G-quartet formation, for binding to single-stranded telomeric oligonucleotides (28).

TELOMERASE   Telomere terminal transferase, or telomerase, is a ribonucleoprotein that catalyzes the de novo addition of telomeric DNA sequences using telomeric DNAs as substrates (8). Telomerase contains an essential RNA component that acts as an internal template for DNA synthesis (27, 75). Telomerase is clearly an important enzyme required for maintenance of telomere and for telomere replication, but no evidence indicates that telomerase recognizes G-quartet structures. In fact, formation of G-quartet structures inhibits the use of oligonucleotides as primers for telomerase (92). This is presumably because G-quartet formation interferes with the direct base-pairing interaction with the internal RNA template of telomerase.

OTHER TELOMERIC PROTEINS   A telomeric DNA–specific DNA primase activity has been identified in *Oxytricha*. This activity synthesizes ribonucleotide primers using telomeric DNA as a substrate, which may be involved in priming DNA synthesis during replication of the telomere (91). Various proteins bind to double-stranded telomeric DNA, including the RAP1 protein, which binds to the subtelomeric region in yeast (18, 48), and two other proteins, TBFα and TBFβ, which bind to double-stranded yeast telomeric DNA (47). A mammalian protein that binds to double-stranded d(TTAGGG) repeats was also recently identified (94).

MISCELLANEOUS PROTEIN BINDING TO G-QUARTETS   A variety of apparently unrelated proteins have been identified that bind specifically to the G-quartet structure. The transcription factor MyoD binds to G-quartet DNA (83), and chromatin assembled in vitro from the insulin gene-linked polymorphic region forms a G-quartet structure (34). Topoisomerase II was found to cleave parallel-stranded G-quartet structures (17), and macrophage scavenger receptors bind to G-quartet structures (60). The biological reasons for these interactions are in no case clear. The G-quartet structures may present an array of phosphates that is favorable for binding basic proteins.

G-QUARTETS IN RNA   Recent experiments showed that sequences from the dimer linkage structure of the human immunodeficiency virus (HIV) form G-quartet structures (53, 79). HIV genomic RNA is packaged into the virion as a dimer, facilitated by the association of gag proteins. The dimerization of two like strands is not possible without inverted repeat sequences if Watson-Crick base pairing is maintained. However, by using G-quartets, two like strands can be dimerized. A similar dimerization might be used to promote telomere-telomere associations via G-quartet structures.

Biological Roles for Telomeric DNA Structures

As yet a role for G-quartet structures in the biology of telomeres has not been proven. These structures are not substrates for telomerase (92) and are not bound by the telomere-binding protein (65). Many variations on mechanisms for telomere replication have been proposed (7, 91, 93). At present, there are no data that suggest G-quartet formation is required at any time during telomere replication. However, results from three recent studies offer tantalizing possibilities that may connect G-quartets to telomere biology.

SINGLE-STRANDED G-TAILS   Yeast telomeres acquire 3′ single-stranded extensions of TG_{1-3} during S phase (88). The length of the single-stranded tails increases and then decreases in a cell-cycle dependent manner. The increase in the length of the 3′ terminal single-stranded regions could result from either the action of telomerase adding new single-stranded nucleotides, or from exposure of single-stranded nucleotides by degradation of the complementary C-strand by an exonuclease. In addition, circular forms of linear plasmids were observed that arose from telomere-telomere associations. Although not rigorously demonstrated in this study, this telomere-telomere association may result from G-quartet formation by the long single-stranded G-tails acquired during replication.

A CATALYST FOR G-QUARTET FORMATION   The β subunit of the *Oxytricha* telomere-binding protein catalyzes G-quartet formation (22). The only known function of the telomere-binding protein is involvement in the telosome complex, in which the telomeric DNA does not adopt a G-quartet structure (65). However, the mechanism of telosome-complex formation is not known, and other roles for the telomere-binding protein subunits prior to association with the telosome are not precluded. The acceleration of DNA dimerization might be a nonspecific effect resulting from the presence of a highly basic protein. However, point mutants in the β subunit, as well as other basic proteins, were much less efficient at promoting G-quartet formation (22). These results suggest that the β subunit might act as a catalyst to increase the rate of G-quartet formation at some point during the telomere-replication process.

A G-QUARTET NUCLEASE   There is a preliminary characterization of a nuclease activity in yeast extracts that uses G-quartet structures as substrates (46). The G-quartet–specific nuclease cleaved 15–20 nucleotides 5' to the G-quartet structure. The activity appears to be structure specific and not sequence specific. Although no definitive role for this activity has been demonstrated in vivo, it provides new mechanistic possibilities that can be considered in the process of telomere replication.

The fact that G-quartet folding and unfolding is extremely slow in vitro has always been problematic in discussing the potential roles of this structure in biology. However, recent findings have suggested ways in which the cell might deal with these slow kinetics. Slow folding kinetics might be accelerated by the telomere-binding protein itself (22), while the extremely slow unfolding of K^+ G-quartet structures might be circumvented by direct removal by a G-quartet–specific nuclease (46).

CONCLUSIONS AND REMAINING QUESTIONS

Despite the increasing number of studies on telomeric DNA structures and G-quartet structures, several fundamental biophysical questions remain to be answered:

1. What is the role of the monovalent ion in stabilizing the structure? Monovalent ion binding appears to be the dominant energetic driving force for G-quartet formation. We need to understand the electrostatic basis for this unusual stabilization.

2. How do the *syn* guanines affect the stability of the G-quartet structures? The presence of two different glycosidic torsion angles permits many different base-stacking arrangements. We need to understand the energetics of these stacking geometries, and how the monovalent ion–binding site is affected by glycosidic torsion.

3. What is the ion-binding stoichiometry? Different types of structures may bind different numbers of ions, and the stoichiometry may also vary with ion type.

4. Why are the G-quartet structures so kinetically stable? Hydrogen-bonding interactions in nucleic acids typically breathe, as evidenced by the exchange of base-pairing protons. We need to understand the physical basis for the slow imino proton exchange rate observed in telomeric DNAs.

5. What is the folding mechanism for telomeric DNA structures? In particular for the dimeric and tetrameric species, little is known about how the thermodynamically favored structure is formed.

And of course,

6. What is the biological role for G-quartet structures in telomeric DNA?

G-quartet formation in vitro requires single-stranded telomeric DNA and K^+ ions. Both of these requirements are met in vivo during telomere replication. This fact suggests that G-rich telomeric DNA sequences are nearly universally conserved because the G-quartet structure is intimately involved in telomere replication. What remains is to find conclusive evidence linking G-quartet formation to telomere replication in vivo.

The past several years have seen a tremendous gain in our insight into this novel class of DNA structures. On a purely biophysical basis, G-quartets offer a great opportunity to study the complex interplay of molecular forces that govern nucleic acid structure. This opportunity is enhanced by the hope that understanding these structures may ultimately contribute to our understanding of telomere function.

ACKNOWLEDGMENTS

I thank Eric Henderson for a critical reading of this manuscript. This work was supported by a grant from the NIH (GM46314).

Literature Cited

1. Aboul-Ela F, Murchie AIH, Lilley DMJ. 1992. NMR study of parallel-stranded tetraplex formation by the hexadeoxynucleotide d(TG₄T). *Nature* 360: 280–82
2. Acevedo OL, Dickinson LA, Macke TJ, Thomas CAJ. 1991. The coherence of synthetic telomeres. *Nucleic Acids Res.* 19:3409–19
3. Akman SA, Lingeman RG, Doroshow JH, Smith SS. 1991. Quadruplex DNA formation in a region of the tRNA gene *supF* associated with hydrogen peroxide mediated mutations. *Biochemistry* 30:8648–53
4. Balagurumoorthy P, Brahmachari SK, Mohanty D, Bansal M, Sasisekharan V. 1992. Hairpin and parallel quartet structures for telomeric sequences. *Nucleic Acids Res.* 20:4061–67
5. Biessmann H, Carter SB, Mason JM.

1990. Chromosome ends in *Drosophila* without telomeric DNA sequences. *Proc. Natl. Acad. Sci. USA* 87:1758–61
6. Biessmann H, Mason JM. 1992. Genetics and Molecular Biology of Telomeres. *Adv. Genet.* 30:185–49
7. Blackburn EH. 1991. Structure and function of telomeres. *Nature* 350:569–73
8. Blackburn EH. 1992. Telomerases. *Annu. Rev. Biochem.* 61:113–29
9. Blackburn EH, Szostak JW. 1984. The Molecular Structure of Centromeres and Telomeres. *Annu. Rev. Biochem.* 53:164–94
10. Bleam ML, Anderson CF, Record MT Jr. 1980. Relative binding affinities of monovalent cations for double-stranded DNA. *Proc. Natl. Acad. Sci. USA* 77:3085–89
11. Bock LC, Griffin LC, Latham JA, Ver-

maas EH, Toole JJ. 1992. Selection of single-stranded DNA molecules that bind and inhibit human thrombin. *Nature* 355:564–66
12. Budarf M, Blackburn E. 1987. S1 nuclease sensitivity of a double-stranded telomeric DNA sequence. *Nucleic Acids Res.* 15:6273–92
13. Burgess J. 1978. *Metal Ions in Solution.* Chichester: Ellis-Horwood
14. Cardenas ME, Bianchi A, de Lange T. 1993. A *Xenopus* egg factor with DNA-binding properties characteristic of terminus-specific telomeric proteins. *Genes Dev.* In press
15. Chen FM. 1992. Strontium(2⁺) facilitates intermolecular G-quadruplex formation of telomeric sequences. *Biochemistry* 31:3769–76
16. Cheong C, Moore PB. 1992. Solution structure of an unusually stable RNA tetraplex containing G- and U-quartet structures. *Biochemistry* 31:8406–14
17. Chung IK, Mehta VB, Spitzner JR, Muller MT. 1992. Eukaryotic topoisomerase II cleavage of parallel stranded DNA tetraplexes. *Nucleic Acids Res.* 20:1973–77
18. Conrad MN, Wright JH, Wolf AJ, Zakian VA. 1990. RAP1 Protein interacts with yeast telomeres in vivo: overproduction alters telomere structure and decreases chromosome stability. *Cell* 63:739–50
19. Coren JS, Epstein EM, Vogt VM. 1991. Characterization of a telomere-binding protein from *Physarum polycephalum*. *Mol. Cell. Biol.* 11:2282–90
20. Coren JS, Vogt VM. 1992. Purification of a telomere-binding protein from *Physarum polycephalum*. *Biochim. Biophys. Acta* 1171:162–66
21. Fang G, Cech TR. 1991. Molecular cloning of telomere-binding protein genes from *Stylonychia mytilis*. *Nucleic Acids Res.* 19:5515–18
22. Fang G, Cech TR. 1993. The β Subunit of oxytricha telomere-binding protein promotes G-quartet formation by telomeric DNA. *Cell.* In press
23. Gaffney BL, Wang C, Jones RA. 1992. Nitrogen-15-labeled oligodeoxynucleotides. 4. Tetraplex formation of d[G(¹⁵N7)GTTTTGG and d[T(¹⁵N7)-GGGT] monitored by proton detected nitrogen-15 NMR. *J. Am. Chem. Soc.* 114:4047–50
24. Gellert M, Lipsett MN, Davies DR. 1962. Helix formation by guanylic acid. *Proc. Natl. Acad. Sci. USA* 48:2013–18
25. Gottschling DE, Zakian VA. 1986. Telomere proteins: specific recognition and

protection of the natural terminii of Oxytricha macronuclear DNA. *Cell* 47:195–205
26. Gray JT, Celander DW, Price CM, Cech TR. 1991. Cloning and expression of genes for the Oxytricha telomere binding protein: specific subunit interactions in the telomeric complex. *Cell* 67:807–14
27. Greider CW, Blackburn EH. 1987. The telomere terminal transferase of Tetrahymena is a ribonucleoprotein enzyme with two kinds of primer specificity. *Cell* 51:887–98
28. Gualberto A, Patrick RM, Walsh K. 1992. Nucleic acid specificity of a vertebrate telomere-binding protein: evidence for G-G base pair recognition at the core-binding site. *Genes Dev.* 6:815–24
29. Guo Q, Lu M, Kallenbach NR. 1992. Adenine affects the structure and stability of telomeric sequences. *J. Biol. Chem.* 267:15293–15300
30. Guo Q, Lu M, Kallenbach NR. 1993. Effect of thymine tract length on the structure and stability of model telomeric sequences. *Biochemistry* 32:3596–3603
31. Guo Q, Lu M, Marky LA, Kallenbach NR. 1992. Interaction of the dye ethidium bromide with DNA containing guanine repeats. *Biochemistry* 31:2451–55
32. Gupta G, Garcia A, Guo Q, Lu M, Kallenbach NR. 1993. Structure of a parallel-stranded tetramer of the Oxytricha telomeric DNA sequence dT₄G₄. *Biochemistry* 32:7098–7103
33. Guschlbauer W, Chantot JF, Thiele D. 1990. Four-stranded nucleic acid structures 25 years later: from guanosine gels to telomer DNA. *J. Biomol. Struct. Dyn.* 8:491–511
34. Hammond-Kosack MCU, Kilpatrick MW, Docherty K. 1993. The human insulin gene-linked polymorphic region adopts a G-quartet structure in chromatin assembled in vitro. *J. Mol. Endocrinol.* 10:121–26
35. Hardin CC, Henderson E, Watson T, Prosser JK. 1991. Monovalent cation induced structural transitions in telomeric DNAs: G-DNA folding intermediates. *Biochemistry* 30:4460–72
36. Hardin CC, Watson T, Corregan M, Bailey C. 1992. Cation-dependent transition between the quadruplex and Watson-Crick hairpin forms of d(CGCG₃GCG). *Biochemistry* 31:833–41
37. Henderson E, Hardin CC, Walk SK,

Tinoco I Jr, Blackburn EH. 1987. Telomeric DNA oligonucleotides form novel intramolecular structures containing guanine-guanine base pairs. *Cell* 51: 899–908

38. Henderson ER, Blackburn EH. 1989. An overhanging 3′ terminus is a conserved feature of telomeres. *Mol. Cell. Biol.* 9:345–48

39. Henderson ER, Moore M, Malcolm BA. 1990. Telomere G-strand structure and function analyzed by chemical protection, base analogue substitution, and utilization by telomerase in vitro. *Biochemistry* 29:732–37

40. Hicke BJ, Celander DW, MacDonald GH, Price CM, Cech TR. 1990. Two versions of the gene encoding the 41-kilodalton subunit of the telomere binding protein of *Oxytricha nova*. *Proc. Natl. Acad. Sci. USA* 87:1481–85

41. Jin R, Breslauer KJ, Jones RA, Gaffney BL. 1990. Tetraplex formation of a guanine-containing nonameric DNA fragment. *Science* 250:543–46

42. Jin R, Gaffney BL, Wang C, Jones RA, Breslauer KJ. 1992. Thermodynamics and structure of a DNA tetraplex: a spectroscopy and calorimetric study of the tetramolecular complexes of d(TG$_3$T) and d(TG$_3$T$_2$G$_3$T). *Proc. Natl. Acad. Sci. USA* 89:8832–36

43. Kang CH, Zhang X, Ratliff R, Moyzis R, Rich A. 1992. Crystal structure of four-stranded *Oxytricha* telomeric DNA. *Nature* 356:126–31

44. Kim J, Cheong C, Moore PB. 1991. Tetramerization of an RNA oligonucleotide containing a GGGG sequence. *Nature* 351:331–32

45. Klobutcher LA, Swanton MT, Donini P, Prescott DM. 1981. All gene-sized DNA molecules in four species of hypotrichs have the same terminal sequence and an unusual 3′ terminus. *Proc. Natl. Acad. Sci USA* 78:3015–19

46. Liu Z, Frantz JD, Gilbert W, Tye B-K. 1993. Identification and characterization of a nuclease activity specific for G4 tetrastranded DNA. *Proc. Natl. Acad. Sci. USA* 90:3157–61

47. Liu Z, Tye BK. 1991. A yeast protein that binds to vertebrate telomeres and conserved yeast telomeric junctions. *Genes Dev.* 5:49–59

48. Longtine MS, Wilson NM, Petracek ME, Berman J. 1989. A yeast telomere binding activity binds to two related telomere sequence motifs and is indistinguishable from RAP1. *Curr. Genet.* 16: 225–39

49. Lu M, Guo Q, Kallenbach NR. 1992. Structure and stability of sodium and potassium complexes of dT$_4$G$_4$ and dT$_4$G$_4$T. *Biochemistry* 31:2455–59

50. Lu M, Guo Q, Kallenbach NR. 1993. Thermodynamics of G-tetraplex formation by telomeric DNAs. *Biochemistry* 32:598–601

51. Lyamichev VI, Mirkin SM, Danilevskaya ON, Voloshin ON, Balatskaya SV, et al. 1989. An unusual DNA structure detected in a telomeric sequence under superhelical stress and at low pH. *Nature* 339:634–37

52. Macaya RF, Schultze P, Smith FW, Roe JA, Feigon J. 1993. Thrombin-binding DNA aptamer forms a unimolecular quadruplex structure in solution. *Proc. Natl. Acad. Sci. USA* 90:3745–49

53. Marquet R, Baudin F, Gabus C, Darlix J-L, Mougel M, et al. 1991. Dimerization of human immunodeficiency virus (type 1) RNA: stimulation by cations and possible mechanism. *Nucleic Acids Res.* 19:2349–57

54. McKay SJ, Cooke H. 1992. A protein which specifically binds to single stranded TTAGGG$_n$ repeats. *Nucleic Acids Res.* 20:1387–91

55. Mohanty D, Bansal M. 1993. Conformational polymorphism in G-tetraplex structures: strand reversal by base flipover or sugar flipover. *Nucleic Acids Res.* 21:1767–74

56. Murchie AIH, Lilley DMJ. 1992. Retinoblastoma susceptibility genes contain 5′ sequences with a high propensity to form guanine-tetrad structures. *Nucleic Acids Res.* 20:49–53

57. Nagesh N, Bhargava P, Chatterji D. 1992. Terbium(III)-induced fluorescence of four-stranded G4-DNA. *Biopolymers* 32:1421–44

58. Oka Y, Thomas CA Jr. 1987. The cohering telomeres of *Oxytricha*. *Nucleic Acids Res.* 15:8877–98

59. Panyutin IG, Koval'skii OI, Budovskii EI, Dickerson RE, Rikhirev ME, Lipanov AA. 1990. G-DNA: a twice-folded DNA structure adopted by single-stranded oligo(dG) and its implications for telomeres. *Proc. Natl. Acad. Sci. USA* 87:867–70

60. Pearson AM, Rich A, Krieger M. 1993. Polynucleotide binding to macrophage scavenger receptors depends on the formation of base-quartet-stabilized four-stranded helices. *J. Biol. Chem.* 268: 3546–54

61. Petracek ME, Berman J. 1992. *Chlamydomonas reinhardtii* telomere re-

peats form unstable structures involving guanine-guanine base pairs. *Nucleic Acids Res.* 20:89–95

62. Pluta AF, Kaine BP, Spear BB. 1982. The terminal organization of macronuclear DNA in *Oxytricha fallax*. *Nucleic Acids Res.* 10:8145–54

63. Price CM. 1990. Telomere structure in *Euplotes crassus:* characterization of DNA-protein interactions and isolation of a telomere-binding protein. *Mol. Cell. Biol.* 10:3421–31

64. Raghuraman MK, Cech TR. 1989. Assembly and self-association of Oxytricha telomeric nucleoprotein complexes. *Cell* 59:719–28

65. Raghuraman MK, Cech TR. 1990. Effect of monovalent cation-induced telomeric DNA structure on the binding of *Oxytricha* telomeric protein. *Nucleic Acids Res.* 18:4543–52

66. Raghuraman MK, Dunn CJ, Hicke BJ, Cech TR. 1989. *Oxytricha* telomeric nucleoprotein complexes reconstituted with synthetic DNA. *Nucleic Acids Res.* 17:4235–53

67. Rich A. 1958. The molecular structure of polyinosinic acid. *Biochem. Biophys. Acta* 29:502

68. Sarma MH, Luo J, Umemoto K, Yuan RD, Sarma RH. 1992. Tetraplex formation of d(GGGGGTTTTT): proton NMR study in solution. *J. Biomol. Struct. Dyn.* 9:1131–53

69. Scaria PC, Shire SJ, Shafer RH. 1992. Quadruplex structure of d($G_3T_4G_3$) stabilized by potassium or sodium is an asymmetric hairpin dimer. *Proc. Natl. Acad. Sci. USA* 89:10336–40

70. Sen D, Gilbert W. 1988. Formation of parallel four-stranded complexes by guanine-rich motifs for meiosis. *Nature* 334:364–66

71. Sen D, Gilbert W. 1990. A sodium-potassium switch in the formation of four-stranded G4-DNA. *Nature* 344:410–14

72. Sen D, Gilbert W. 1991. The structure of telomeric DNA:DNA quadriplex formation. *Curr. Opin. Struct. Biol.* 1:435–38

73. Sen D, Gilbert W. 1992. Novel DNA superstructures formed by telomere-like oligomers. *Biochemistry* 31:65–70

74. Shida T, Yokoyama K, Tamai S, Sekiguchi J. 1991. Self-association of telomeric short oligodeoxyribonucleotides containing a dG cluster. *Chem. Pharm. Bull.* 39:2207–11

75. Shippen-Lentz D, Blackburn EH. 1990. Functional evidence for an RNA template in telomerase. *Science* 247:546–52

76. Smith FW, Feigon J. 1992. Quadruplex structure of *Oxytricha* telomeric DNA oligonucleotides. *Nature* 356:164–68

77. Smith FW, Feigon J. 1993. Strand orientation in the DNA quadruplex formed from the Oxytricha telomere repeat oligonucleotide d($G_4T_4G_4$) in solution. *Biochemistry* 32:8682

78. Sundquist WI. 1991. The structures of telomeric DNA. *Nucleic Acids Mol. Biol.* 5:1–24

79. Sundquist WI, Heaphy S. 1993. Evidence for interstrand quadruplex formation in the dimerization of human immunodeficiency virus 1 genomic RNA. *Proc. Natl. Acad. Sci. USA* 90:3393–97

80. Sundquist WI, Klug A. 1989. Telomeric DNA dimerizes by formation of guanine tetrads between hairpin loops. *Nature* 342:825–29

81. Venczel EA, Sen D. 1993. Parallel and antiparallel G-DNA structures from a complex telomeric sequence. *Biochemistry* 32:6220–28

82. Voloshin ON, Veselkov AG, Belotserkovskii BP, Danilevskaya ON, Pavlova MN, et al. 1992. An eclectic DNA structure adopted by human telomeric sequence under superhelical stress and low pH. *J. Biomol. Stereodyn.* 9:643–52

83. Walsh K, Gualberto A. 1992. MyoD binds to the guanine tetrad nucleic acid structure. *J. Biol. Chem.* 267:13714–18

84. Wang KY, McCurdy S, Shea RG, Swaminathan S, Bolton PH. 1993. A DNA aptamer which binds to and inhibits thrombin exhibits a new structural motif for DNA. *Biochemistry* 32:1899–1904

85. Wang Y, de los Santos C, Gao X, Greene K, Live D, Patel DJ. 1991. Multinuclear nuclear magnetic resonance studies of Na cation-stabilized complex formed by d(GGTTTTCGG) in solution. *J. Mol. Biol.* 222:819–32

86. Wang Y, Jin R, Gaffney B, Jones RA, Breslauer KJ. 1991. Characterization by ^{1}H NMR of glycosidic conformations in the tetramolecular complex formed by d(GGTTTTTGG). *Nucleic Acids Res.* 19:4619–22

87. Wang Y, Patel DJ. 1992. Guanine residues in d(T_2AG_3) and d(T_2G_4) form parallel-stranded potassium cation stabilized G-quadruplexes with antiglycosidic torsion angles in solution. *Biochemistry* 31:8112–19

88. Wellinger RJ, Wolf AJ, Zakian VA. 1993. Saccharomyces telomeres acquire single-strand TG_{1-3} tails late in S phase. *Cell* 72:51–60

89. Williamson JR. 1993. Guanine quartets. *Curr. Opin. Struct. Biol.* 3:357–62
90. Williamson JR, Raghuraman MK, Cech TR. 1989. Monovalent cation-induced structure of telomeric DNA: the G-quartet model. *Cell* 59:871–80
91. Zahler AM, Prescott DM. 1989. DNA primase and the replication of the telomeres in *Oxytricha nova*. *Nucleic Acids Res.* 17:6299–6317
92. Zahler AM, Williamson JR, Cech TR, Prescott DM. 1991. Inhibition of telomerase by G-quartet DNA structures. *Nature* 350:718–20
93. Zakian VA. 1989. Structure and function of telomeres. *Annu. Rev. Genet.* 23: 579–604
94. Zhong Z, Shiue L, Kaplan S, De Lange T. 1992. A mammalian factor that binds telomeric TTAGGG repeats in vitro. *Mol. Cell. Biol.* 12:4834–43
95. Zimmerman SB, Cohen GH, Davies DR. 1975. X-ray fiber diffraction and model-building study of polyguanylic acid and polyinosinic acid. *J. Mol. Biol.* 92:181–92

Annu. Rev. Biophys. Biomol. Struct. 1994. 23:731–61

MOLECULAR DYNAMICS SIMULATIONS OF THE GRAMICIDIN CHANNEL

Benoît Roux

Department of Physics, Université de Montréal, C.P. 6128, succ. A, Canada
H3C 3J7

Martin Karplus

Department of Chemistry, Harvard University, 12 Oxford St., Cambridge,
Massachusetts 02138

KEY WORDS: ion, membrane, transport, ion diffusion, free energy
            profile

CONTENTS

1056–8700/94/0610–0731$05.00

PERSPECTIVE AND OVERVIEW

The ion channel formed by a dimer of the gramicidin A molecule is
the model system for studying, experimentally as well as theoretically,
the microscopic processes underlying ion movements across lipid
membranes. Gramicidin A is a simple linear antibiotic pentadecapep-
tide produced by *Bacillus brevis* consisting of alternating L– and D–
amino acids: HCO-L-Val1-Gly2-L-Ala3-D-Leu4-L-Ala5-D-Val6-L-Val7-
D-Val8-L-Trp9-D-Leu10-L-Trp11-D-Leu12-L-Trp13-D-Leu14-L-Trp15-
NHCH$_2$CH$_2$OH. The ion conducting conformation of the gramicidin
A channel in a membrane is well established (4, 66, 89, 105). Two-
dimensional ^{1}H NMR in SDS micelles (4) and solid-state ^{15}N (66) and
^{13}C (88) NMR in oriented DMPC bilayers show that the channel is an
N-terminal–to–N-terminal (head-to-head) dimer formed by two single-
stranded right-handed $\beta^{6.3}$-helices. The dimer is stabilized by the formation of 20 intramonomer and 6 intermonomer $-$NH$\cdots$O$-$ backbone
hydrogen bonds to form a pore about 26 Å long and 4 Å in diameter.
The hydrogen-bonded carbonyls line the pore, and the amino acid side
chains, most of them hydrophobic, extend out into the membrane lipid.
The structure of the channel is such that the permeation process must
involve the single-file translocation of a partially dehydrated ion and
water through the interior of a narrow pore.

The channel is permeable to water molecules and to monovalent
cations with the selectivity sequence Li$^+$ < Na$^+$ < K$^+$ < Rb$^+$ < Cs$^+$,
which corresponds to their mobility in bulk water; it is impermeable
to anions and blocked by divalent cations. Cation binding sites are
located at the C terminus of the monomers, near D-Leu10 (67, 88, 97).
Monovalent cations partition spontaneously into the channel, but the
equilibrium binding constant of the monovalent cations is relatively
weak, suggesting that the free energy in the binding site is similar to
the chemical potential in bulk water (35). The effective diffusion constants of a water molecule and of a Na$^+$ in the interior of the pore have
a similar order of magnitude and are both much smaller than in bulk
solution (see 79). The channel can be occupied by two permeating ions
at sufficiently high concentration, and double occupancy is relatively
more likely for the larger cations. Chemical modifications of the side
chains can influence ion permeation (2, 7) and the stability of the dimer
channel in the lipid bilayer (6).

The gramicidin channel provides a tool for studying the fundamental
principles governing the properties of ion channels. Comprehending
how any ion channel functions from a microscopic point of view, even
the one formed by the relatively simple gramicidin molecule, represents

a challenge. Although modern molecular dynamics techniques have been shown to be powerful methods for the study of biological systems of ever-increasing complexity (12), theoretical investigations of ion transport are faced with particularly difficult problems. First, a very accurate model for the interactions involved is necessary. The large solvation-free energies of ions (e.g. around -100 kcal/mol for Na^+) contrast with the activation energies for transport through the channel, deduced from experimentally observed ion-fluxes; they generally do not exceed 10 k_BT (1, 22). This implies that the energetics of ion transport results from a delicate balance of very large interactions. Second, the time-scales involved are long relative to possible simulation times. The passage of one ion across a channel takes place on a microsecond time scale (1, 22, 37), while realistic simulations of biological systems typically do not exceed a few nanoseconds (12). A variety of special computational techniques are necessary to extract information about these slower and more complex processes (12).

Because these difficulties imply that straightforward simulations can supply only limited information about the properties of the gramicidin channel, vastly different theoretical models have been proposed to study the permeation process. The goal of this review is to provide an overview of the theoretical approaches based on atomic models that have been used to study the gramicidin channel and to present our current level of understanding of the channel. Other channel-forming and ion-transport molecules, as well as phenomenological descriptions based on continuum electrostatics (40, 68), barrier hopping models (53), or the Nernst-Planck continuum diffusion equation (57), are not included. The conducting channel properties, such as selectivity, flux, double occupancy, water permeability, competition, and blocking have been reviewed previously (1, 22, 37).

SHORT HISTORY

Theoretical studies of the gramicidin channel at the atomic level started in 1973 with the simplified dipole model of Läuger (53), which was concerned with the basic problem of the rate of ion transport. Since then there has been an evolution in computer power, potential energy functions, ab initio calculations, molecular dynamics simulations, activated dynamics, and free-energy simulation techniques (12). Also, the potential of mean force (PMF), which was introduced by Kirkwood in 1935 (51) for the structure of fluids, has become a central concept in the treatment of transition rates and reaction dynamics in liquids (14), in general, and of ion transport, in particular, and special simulation techniques were developed for its evaluation (for a review, see 12). Similarly, experimental knowledge of the structure of membrane peptides and proteins has progressed significantly. Several of the early theoretical studies were done at a time when there remained some confusion about the microscopic significance of rate theories (for example, see 68a, p. 275) and the validity of the left- or right-handedness of the dimer channel conformation (see 105 for a review).

The oldest and simplest model is the stylized periodic helix, which was introduced in 1981 by Fischer, Brickmann & Läuger (FBL) (30); it dates back to the simple periodic array of dipoles used by Läuger in 1973 (53). In the same period, several realistic models with atomic details were developed independently by Pullman & Etchebest (PE) (74), Fornili, Vercauteren & Clementi (FVC) (31), and Mackay, Berens, Wilson & Hagler (MBWH) (58). The MBWH model, which made use of the recent development of molecular dynamics simulations of proteins (62), had a profound influence on subsequent studies of the gramicidin channel; even though the full paper describing the work never appeared in print, it seems to have had a wider circulation and readership than many published papers. Prior to this model, the channel was represented as a rigid structure fixed in space (PE and FVC; FBL allowed some restricted librational motions). Subsequent to MBWH, the theoretical models developed by Lee & Jordan (LJ) (56), Chiu, Subramaniam, Jakobsson & McCammon (CSJM) (19), Åqvist & Warshel (AW) (3), and Roux & Karplus (RK) (79) all accounted, to varying degrees, for the flexibility of the channel.

Simulations of the full atomic model of the gramicidin dimer in the presence of water and a simplified treatment of the membrane have been used recently for a detailed study of the mechanism of ion transport (81). The next stage in theoretical models of the gramicidin channel includes the phospholipid membrane environment surrounding the channel. Several such studies are in progress (101, 102, 106–108).

MICROSCOPIC MODELS AND COMPUTATIONAL APPROACHES

This section briefly reviews the conformational models used for the gramicidin channel. Acronyms referring to a model are based on the names of the authors of the initial paper (see above). Particular attention is given to the nature of the approximations involved in each model; i.e. the structure used for the channel, the treatment of hydration, the potential functions used, and the computational techniques employed. An attempt is made to describe results obtained from the various models and to evaluate their validity in light of our present knowledge.

Structural Models

The head-to-head left-handed helical dimer first proposed by Urry in 1971 (96; see also 99), which is now known to be correct in general though of the wrong handedness, was refined by Ventakachalam & Urry (98) using energy minimization techniques with helix symmetry constraints. The flexibility of the structure and the energetics of the peptide libration were examined in another study (100). The potential function used for these studies was based on the ECEPP force field (63) in which the ϕ,ψ dihedral angles are allowed to vary; other internal coordinates (i.e. bond length and angles) are kept fixed. Based on standard peptide geometry, Koeppe & Kimura constructed families of β-helices and proposed a left-handed helical dimer structure (52). No potential energy function was used by Koeppe & Kimura in their work, i.e. the conformation was constructed as a perfect helix from geometrical considerations (above).

Infinite periodic poly (L,D)-alanine β-helices were studied by Roux & Karplus (79), Naik & Krimm (65) and by Monoi (64). Refined left- and right-handed models of the helical dimer were obtained using full geometry optimization with energy minimization techniques. The left-handed RK dimer was obtained from the Ventakachalam-Urry conformation using the CHARMM program (78); the Koeppe-Kimura conformation was refined using GROMOS (CSJM) (19). The CSJM (17) and RK (81) models of the right-handed dimer were obtained by use of experimental NMR data from Arseniev et al (4).

The experimental determination of the structure of the ion-conducting conformation of the gramicidin A channel in a membrane also made use of molecular modeling. The conformation of the right-handed dimer incorporated in SDS micelles was obtained by Arseniev et al (4) from the experimentally determined proton-proton nuclear Overhauser effects (NOEs) observed by two-dimensional NMR, which were used as distance constraints in a geometry optimization (4). The conformation of the backbone and tryptophan side chains of the right-handed dimer in a dimyristoyl phosphatidylcholine (DMPC) bilayer was determined (TA Cross, personal communication) using geometrical constraints based on the chemical shifts and dipolar couplings observed by solid-state NMR of isotopically labeled gramicidin channels aligned parallel to the magnetic field direction (66); the complete determination of the conformation of the other side chains is in progress.

The FBL Model

Fischer, Brickmann & Läuger (FBL) (30) proposed a simplified gram-icidin-like model. In this model, the channel is represented by a rigid periodic helical arrangement of dipolar carbonyl groups consisting of two point charges, one for the carbon and one for the oxygen atoms. There are six carbonyl groups per helix turn pointing in alternating directions and located on the surface of a cylinder of radius 3.2 Å. The flexibility due to the carbonyl librational motions is incorporated by allowing limited displacements of the oxygens that result in small varia-tions of the tilt angle of the dipolar group relative to the helix axis.

The simplicity of the FBL helix made it an attractive computational model for illustrating formal theoretical developments. For example, Läuger used it in 1982 (54) to calculate the PMF of an ion constrained on the axis of the FBL helix model by means an explicit numerical integration of the partition function. Most of the early molecular dy-namics simulations of the FBL helix were reviewed by Polymeropoulos & Brickmann (72). In the later studies by Skerra & Brickmann, mo-lecular dynamics simulations of Li^+, Na^+, and K^+ were performed in the FBL helix in the presence of explicit water molecules to inves-tigate the structure and dynamics of one-dimensional ionic solutions (86) and the effect of voltage on ion diffusion (87; see also 84). The interaction of the ions with the helix atoms were represented in terms of partial-charge electrostatics and Lennard-Jones potentials. The TIP4P water-water potential was used for the explicit water molecules (45). The total number of waters included varied from six to nine. The ion mobility was extracted from the average drift in the presence of an external potential (87).

The PE Model

Pullman & Etchebest (PE) (74) developed a model in which the channel is represented in detail by a rigid polyglycine analogue of the left-handed helical dimer. The side chains were omitted except in one study (23). Solvent was considered but no membrane environment was in-cluded.

Because the channel is rigidly fixed in space, the potential energy concerns only the nonbonded ion-water, ion-peptide, water-water, and water-peptide interactions. One notable feature of the PE model is the nature of the molecular mechanism's potential function; it is based entirely on ab initio calculations. The interactions are described as a sum of terms including an electrostatic multipole expansion, van der

Waals dispersion effects, overlap repulsion, charge transfer and first-order induced polarization (33).

Several studies were done using an approach that relied mostly on the analysis of optimized configurations obtained from energy minimization techniques. In particular, adiabatic energy profiles were calculated by fixing the ion at various position along the channel axis and optimizing the configuration of the channel system. Because it is extracted from energy minimized configurations, an adiabatic energy profile does not account for thermal fluctuations and, thus, corresponds to a zero-Kelvin approximation to the PMF.

The approach based on the calculation of adiabatic energy profiles was used to investigate the energetics of Na^+ in the singly and doubly occupied channel without (74) and with (24, 25, 75) water, the influence of the flexibility of the ethanolamine tail (28), the influence of side chains (23, 34), the influence of handedness, the binding of Ca^{2+} (29), and the energy profile of Cs^+ with water (27; for a review, see 73).

In all the studies [except the one concerned with the handedness of the channel (26)] the structure of the channel was rigidly fixed in the left-handed Urry dimer conformation (99). The optimization of only a limited number of degrees of freedom was considered in each, such as the influence of the isomerization of the ethanolamine tail. A few water molecules (16 to 24) were included in the single-file region and at the channel entrance to study the effect of dehydration (24, 25, 75).

The FVC Model

In the model developed by Fornili, Vercauteren & Clementi (FVC) (31), the channel is represented as a rigid left-handed structure including all the backbone and side-chain atoms. Because the channel is rigidly fixed in space (as in the PE model), the potential energy concerns only the nonbonded ion-water, ion-peptide, water-water, and water-peptide interactions. All nonbonded interactions were described in terms of Lennard-Jones and partial charge electrostatics with 6-12-1 radial functions; the parameters were obtained by fitting ab initio calculations. The hydration was taken into account explicitly by including 80 water molecules inside a cylindrical volume. During the simulations, the waters were constrained to stay within the cylindrical volume, and a translational symmetry constraint was imposed along the channel axis (periodic boundary conditions) (50). The MCY potentials were used for the water-water interactions (60). The membrane environment was ignored.

The model was used in Metropolis Monte Carlo simulations of the waters and cation at 300 K in the presence of the fixed channel structure. Average potential energy profiles were calculated and analyzed in terms of the various contributions for fixed positions of the cations along the channel axis. The water structure (31) and the energetics and hydration shell structure of Li^+, Na^+, and K^+ inside the channel were examined (49, 50). A related study of the effect of voltage on Na^+ and K^+ was made by Kim using the FVC model (48); a voltage difference of 500 mV was applied over a distance of 32 Å. The reorientation of the water molecule due to the applied voltage was analyzed, and the average potential energy was calculated for different ion locations along the channel axis.

The MBWH Model

In the model developed by Mackay, Berens, Wilson & Hagler (MBWH) (58), the channel is represented as a fully flexible left-handed Urry-like structure that includes all the atoms of the backbone and of the side chains (552 atoms). The potential function consisted of terms for bonds, angles, and dihedral angles; nonbonded interactions were described with a Lennard-Jones term and a term for the Coulombic interactions (details in 58).

The MBWH model was the first to include the full flexibility of a realistic representation of the gramicidin molecule based on a molecular dynamics simulation. The simulations were used to study the structure and dynamics of water and cations (Li^+, Na^+, K^+, and Cs^+) inside the channel (58, 59). Thirteen waters were included to provide the primary hydration in the single-file region; the SPC water model was used (8). One water was replaced by a cation for the one monomer-centered and dimer-centered ion position. The monovalent cations Li^+, Na^+, K^+, and Cs^+ were studied. The simulations were relatively short, 5 ps in the initial study of the cation systems (58) and 30 ps for the water-filled channel (59). Qualitative observations were made concerning the structure and dynamics of a flexible gramicidin channel, the single-file structure of the internal waters, and the deformation of the backbone in the presence of a cation.

In an ambitious investigation, never published but reported by Jordan (41), Mackay, Edelsten & Wilson calculated the free energy of materialization of a Cs^+ ion at five different locations along the channel axis by using free-energy simulation techniques. The model system included 1 gramicidin dimer channel, 8–10 waters filling the channel interior, and 90 waters at the pore's openings, representing the bulk-water interface. A translational symmetry constraint was imposed along the channel axis (periodic boundary conditions). The membrane environment was ignored.

The RK Models

THE RK-HELIX   Roux & Karplus developed a periodic poly (L,D)-alanine β-helix gramicidin-like model to investigate the translocation mechanism in the interior of the gramicidin A channel (79, 80); the side chains of gramicidin were neglected to simplify the system and introduce periodicity. The approach is reminiscent of the FBL helix, although the atomic representation of the structure is more realistic. The microscopic interactions and the potential functions were based on a polar-hydrogen representation of the system, in which all heavy atoms and all polar hydrogens (those able to form hydrogen bonds) are included; the aliphatic hydrogens are treated as part of the carbon to which they are attached. The model used TIP3P water (45), and peptide-peptide and water-peptide potential functions from the CHARMM (11). Special care was given to the parametrization of the interaction of the ion with the channel and water. The potential was developed from ab initio calculations of the interactions of sodium with water and of sodium with acetamide and N-methylacetamide; the latter were chosen as models of the carbonyl group of the peptide backbone (79). First-order polarization induced by the ion on the peptide was included. All degrees of freedom were allowed to vary except the bonds involving the polar hydrogens, which were constrained to a fixed length.

The PMF of Na^+ and K^+ along the axis of the periodic helix were determined with the free-energy perturbation difference technique (79). An integrated mean force decomposition was used to analyze the important contributions to the PMF (79). Based on this formulation, the mean force is decomposed linearly to obtain the various contributions to the PMF along the reaction path. The transport properties of water, Na^+, and K^+ in the periodic β-helix were investigated with methods appropriate for each of these species. For water, the mean-square displacement was determined from a simulation; for Na^+, an activated dynamics approach was used; and for K^+, the response to an external field was analyzed (80). The transmission coefficient and the deviation from transition state theory were estimated from the Na^+-activated dynamics trajectories. A cross-coupling friction decomposition method was used to analyze the factors contributing to the total friction acting on ions. The instantaneous deviation of the force is decomposed into a sum of contributions to obtain information about the underlying factors giving rise to the friction coefficient, as is done in the integrated mean force decomposition method.

THE RK DIMER   Roux & Karplus (78) developed a model of the helical dimer embedded in a model membrane, including all the side chain atoms. To produce a hydrocarbon-like membrane environment and to prevent waters from reaching the lateral side of the dimer, a model membrane made up of Lennard-Jones spheres corresponding to the size of a CH_3 group was included. The entrance of the channel was fully solvated by 190 water molecules. Periodic boundary conditions were applied along the channel axis. A cylindrical confining potential was applied in the radial direction on the water oxygens to maintain the proper density in the bulk-like regions of the system. The system consists of 314 peptide atoms for the gramicidin dimer, 190 water molecules and 85 "membrane" spheres. The model also employed the same polar hydrogen representation and potential function as used for the periodic helix.

In a first study, a system was constructed with the left-handed helical dimer conformation embedded in the model membrane to study the dynamics of water in the interior of the channel (B Roux & M Karplus, unpublished calculations; see also 76). In a second study, the PMF of Na^+ along the dimer axis was calculated using a free-energy perturbation difference technique (81); the method is the same as that used for the periodic helix model. The reaction coordinate was defined as the projection of the ion position onto the vector joining the centers of mass of the gramicidin monomers. The channel was constructed as a right-handed head-to-head helical dimer from the coordinates of the Arseniev structure (4). Three regions were investigated in detail: the monomer-monomer junction, the beginning of the single file, and the dehydration step at the entrance. The main results are shown in Figure 1 (below). The position of the binding site was determined (see Table 1, below). The solvation properties of the single-file region, the dehydration process at the entrance of the channel, and the translocation barrier at the monomer-monomer junction were analyzed. These results were combined with those from the periodic helix to obtain an estimate of the potential of mean force acting on the ion throughout the entire channel.

Organic Ion Models

The extended atom RK dimer model, based on the CHARMM force field (11) was used by Busath et al (13), and by Turano et al (95), to study the permeation of large organic ions. The adiabatic energy profiles of guanidinium, acetamidinium, and formamidinium were calculated, i.e. the configuration of the channel and of the ion was optimized using energy minimization techniques for restricted position of the ion along the channel axis. The organic cation structures and parameters were derived from the standard CHARMM arginine side chain. No water molecules were included.

The CSJM Model

Chiu, Subramaniam, Jakobsson & McCammon (CSJM) (19) developed a model of the helical dimer including all the side-chain atoms in an extended atom representation using the standard GROMOS force field and dynamics program (100a). In most studies, the channel was constructed as a right-handed helical dimer (15, 16, 18); a left-handed structure was used initially (19). An artificial nonelastic time relaxation restraint was applied directly to the helix atoms to mimic the influence of the surrounding lipids and to maintain the helical dimer in the neighborhood of the Koeppe-Kimura model-built structure (52).

To introduce the solvent in the single-file region in the interior of the channel, approximately 23 waters were included in the first simulation (19); the SPC water model was used (8). The number was increased to 109 in later simulations to provide a bulk-like region at the mouth of the channel; the bulk waters were maintained as hemispherical caps with a cube-shaped boundary potential (15, 16, 18).

The CSJM model was used in several molecular dynamics simulations to study the correlated motions of water molecules in the channel (16, 19), to compare the average structure with that deduced from solid state NMR data (17), to study the side-chain conformations in vacuum (15), and to examine the displacement of a Na^+ in the interior of the channel (18). The motions of water and ion were analyzed in terms of time-correlation functions. The translocation barrier of Na^+ in the interior of the channel was estimated by interpreting the mean-square-displacement of the center of mass of the ion-water complex in terms of a Langevin equation (18).

The LJ Model

The model developed by Lee & Jordan (LJ) (56) represents the channel as a polyglycine analogue of the Urry left-handed helical dimer. The formyl and ethanolamine end groups are included and the side chains are neglected.

The potential function used differs significantly from the more common biomolecular force fields such as used in MBWH, RK, and CSJM. The influence of polarization is treated explicitly and the polarization is calculated self-consistently by an iterative method (56; see also 44).

The basic peptide dynamical units are uncharged dipolar polarizable groups (CO and NH), rather than individual atoms with partial charges (C, O, N, and H). It is possible that the parametrization of the potential is not optimal for protein simulations (44); the hydrogen bonds of the dimer were not stable and it was necessary to add a peptide group localization energy term (an artificial harmonic restraint) to maintain the helical structure.

The LJ model was used in a series of studies to investigate cation motions (56), valence selectivity (91, 92), the properties of different channel conformations (93, 94), and the permeation process of Cs^+ (41–44). Few waters were included in the initial investigations (56), and the polarizable electropole water model of Finney and coworkers was used (5). In the most recent investigations (43, 44), the PMF of Cs^+ was calculated using umbrella sampling (70). The channel was embedded in a model membrane of 589 hydrocarbon-like CH_2 spheres. In the calculations, bulk water was approximated by hemispherical regions with an 18-Å radius at each end of the channel; 419 water molecules were included (44). Thus, the overall system is constructed similarly to that of RK, although very different potential functions are used.

The AW Model

The model developed by Åqvist & Warshel (AW) (3) was used in a single study of the PMF of Na^+ along the channel axis. The channel is represented as a polyglycine analogue of the left-handed helical dimer including the formyl and ethanolamine end groups; the side chains were neglected. The peptide-peptide potential function was taken from Warshel & Levitt (103). Special care was given to the treatment of the long-range electrostatic interactions with the hydrocarbon membrane region. The channel was embedded in a model hydrocarbon membrane environment represented by a cylindrical region containing a polarizable cubic lattice with a dielectric constant of 2. The Lennard-Jones parameters for the Na^+ ion were fitted empirically to reproduce the experimental free energy of solvation of Na^+ in water.

The free energy of the alchemical transformation of a Na^+ ion into a water molecule was calculated explicitly for two ion locations along the channel axis with the free-energy perturbation molecular dynamics simulation technique. Twenty waters were included. To obtain the free energy relative to that of bulk water, the transformation was made both in the channel and in a bulk water environment. The methodology to determine the other points of the PMF along the channel axis was based on the protein dipole Langevin dipole (PDLD) approach, in which explicit waters are replaced by dipoles located on a cubic grid, and only two waters were treated explicitly. The remaining waters of the single-file region, as well as the bulk water, were represented by the PDLD approach. Problems may occur with the approximation near the entrance of the channel, as the Na^+ and the two single-file waters leave the interior of the channel and enter the bulk water region described by the lattice (see Figure 2 in Ref. 3). In constructing the grid, the PDLD dipoles overlapping with the ion core are excluded (those within a distance of 2.4 Å). The exclusion distance has a role similar to the ionic radius in the Born model of solvation (10). The PDLD approach is similar in spirit to approximate solvation models based on continuum electrostatics, such as the Poisson-Boltzmann equation (32), although the dielectric medium here is represented by discrete dipoles on a grid. Thus, the AW calculation uses a mixed method involving both atomistic and phenomenological representations of matter.

MAIN RESULTS

Channel Conformation

Distorsion of the ideal β-helical symmetry, which was excluded in the Ventakachalam-Urry (98) and Koeppe-Kimura (52) models, has been observed in models accounting for the full flexibility of the structure (17, 44, 78). The mouth of the channel is deformed and slightly constricted in the CHARMM-based (11) RK-dimer model (13, 76, 78, 95), while it is closer to an ideal helix in the GROMOS-based (100a) CSJM model (17). The deformations at the channel ends were attributed to a break in the hydrogen-bond network of the helix due to the inward bending of the carbonyl oxygens of Trp13 and Trp15 (13, 76, 78, 95) or to side-chain steric interferences (17).

The CSJM (17) and RK (81) models of the right-handed helical dimer conformation were compared to the structure determined by solid-state NMR (T Cross, personal communication; see also 17). It is found that the overall structure of both models is in very good agreement with the experimental data. However, careful analysis of the NMR results suggests that finer details of the backbone conformation, in particular small deviations from planarity of the peptide linkage near the channel mouth, may not be correctly reproduced.

Structure and Dynamics of Single-File Water

Several studies of the structure and dynamics of the single-file waters have been made because they represent a very interesting feature of this channel and might be of significance for extended water chains in the interior of some proteins (e.g. the existence of water chains in the interior of bacteriorhodopsin has been proposed). Analyses have been made by CSJM (19, 16), PE (24, 25, 75), FVC (31), LJ (44), MBWH (58, 59) and RK (76, 80). Given the considerable variations in the theoretical approaches, the calculated properties of the water structure inside the channel are remarkably consistent. Most simulations resulted in 8–10 water molecules in the single-file region, in qualitative agreement with experiments (1). In the channel interior, the water molecules always form essentially linear hydrogen-bonded chains with the water hydrogens interacting preferentially with the oxygens of L-carbonyl groups and the ethanolamine end in the PE model (in the left-handed helical dimer) (24, 25, 75). There are, however, some differences among the theoretical results. This indicates that certain aspects of the hydrogen-bonded water chain are sensitive to the details of the microscopic models, including the choice of the potential function. The FVC (31), PE (24, 25, 75), MBWH (58, 59), RK-helix (79, 80), and CSJM (19, 17) models resulted in configurations in which the water molecules in the interior of the channel point in the same direction along the channel axis. In contrast, the single-file water chain does not show persistent orientational correlations propagating through the whole length of the channel in the more realistic RK-dimer model (76) and in the LJ (44) models. Gaps and defects, breaking the continuous hydrogen-bonded water chains, have been found, and it is possible that the perfect single file of water molecules is interrupted over significant time intervals. In fact, a closer examination of the results reported for CSJM (19) and FVC (31) reveals that noncorrelated linear structures, in which all water molecules do not point in the same direction, occurred in the simulations, though they were infrequent. The dynamics and mobility of the water molecules along the axis of the dimer channel also differ. The calculated diffusion constants, 6×10^{-6} cm^2/s (17) and 2.5×10^{-7} cm^2/s (76), do not differ significantly from that estimated from the experimental water permeability: 4.4×10^{-7} cm^2/s (see 79). The diffusion constant of water molecules inside the channel is reduced relative to its value in bulk water both in the simulations and from experiment; i.e. in bulk water, the experimental value is 2.1×10^{-5} cm^2/s, and molecular dynamics yields 3.2×10^{-5} and 3.7×10^{-5} cm^2/s for TIP3P and SPC, respectively (17, 79).

The dynamical properties of the single-file water chain were found to be affected by the strength of artificial restraints on the backbone conformation (17); i.e. the translational mobility of the single-file waters is facilitated by peptide motions and is dramatically reduced by holding the channel rigid. The tendency of the oxygen of the water molecules in each monomer to point towards the bulk solution at the N-terminus has been related to an increase in the water-carbonyl interactions at the mouth of the channel that result from the helical distortion and pore constriction at the termini (76); the constriction makes the carbonyl at the termini more accessible for hydrogen bonding with the single-file water molecules. The orientation of the waters at the termini, in the absence of an ion, has been attributed to the interactions with the carbonyl groups in the channel mouth (44).

The properties of the single-file water configuration are very sensitive to the water-water and water-peptide potential energy functions (58); decreasing the water-backbone hydrogen-bonding interactions by 5% altered the single-file structure significantly; it caused some of the waters to leave the pore. Generally, the water models used, i.e. the MCY water model (60) used in FVC, the SPC water model (8) used in MBWH and CSJM, the TIP3P water model (45) used in RK, and the TIP4P water model (45) used in FBL (86, 87), are all based on pairwise effective nonpolarizable, Lennard-Jones partial charge electrostatic, 6-12-1 potential functions. The SIBFA waters (33) used in PE, and the polarizable electropole water model (5) used in LJ are significantly different. The SPC, TIP3P, and TIP4P models were parametrized to reproduce the properties of bulk water; the SIBFA and MCY waters were developed from ab initio potentials; the polarizable electropole water model was adjusted to reproduce several properties of small water clusters (5). Incorporation of polarizability markedly affects the properties of the single-file water (44); the average induced dipole of the single-file waters (2.31 Debye) is smaller than in bulk water (2.47 Debye). In comparison, the nonpolarizable TIP3P waters have a fixed dipole of 2.35 Debye (45). Thus, whether the most widely employed water models realistically describe the energetics of the single-file water molecules in the confined environment of a pore is uncertain.

Energy Profiles

Several studies were concerned with the mapping of the adiabatic energy profile along the permeation pathway (see all the PE studies). Others have considered the thermally averaged potential energy profile of ions and water inside the channel (e.g. see all FVC references) (56). These quantities, although of considerable interest, do not provide a direct link with the modern statistical mechanical theories of dynamical rate processes in liquids (9, 14). Furthermore, the rigid channel structure used in the PE and FVC studies introduce artifacts because the flexibility of the backbone is important (58, 78, 79, 81). Thus, except for some structural features, such as the position of the stable energy wells (see below), these early results are not truly comparable to the PMF calculations performed subsequently.

Four calculations of the PMF of ions along the axis of the gramicidin channel have been reported: (*a*) DH Mackay, PM Edelsten & KR Wilson calculated the PMF for Cs^+ along the axis of a left-handed dimer (MBWH model) (unpublished calculation reported in 41); (*b*) Åqvist & Warshel calculated the PMF of Na^+ along the axis of a polyglycine left-handed dimer using an alchemical transformation technique (AW model) (3); (*c*) Jordan calculated the PMF of Cs^+ along the axis of a polyglycine left-handed dimer using umbrella sampling (LJ model) (44); (*d*) Roux & Karplus calculated the PMF of Na^+ along the axis of a right-handed dimer channel embedded in a model membrane using a free-energy difference perturbation technique (RK dimer) (81). The last investigation (*d*) was the only one that used the known experimental right-handed dimer channel conformation, and at present it is the PMF calculation that is based on the most realistic gramicidin model. Other studies provide closely related information about the translocation barriers in the interior of the channel. Roux & Karplus calculated the PMF of Na^+ and K^+ along the axis of a periodic helix (RK helix) using a free-energy difference perturbation technique (79). A study by Chiu et al (18) provided information related to the PMF of Na^+ (CSJM model). The translocation free-energy barrier was estimated from the mean-square-displacement time correlation function. Skerra & Brickmann studied the translocation rate of ions along the axis of a periodic helix (FBL) (86, 87).

Although the results are qualitatively reasonable, there are quantitative problems. Most calculated activation free-energy barriers are too large compared with experimental estimates (44, 81; see also DH Mackay, PM Edelsten & KR Wilson, unpublished calculation reported in 41); e.g. the largest barriers for Na^+ found by RK are in the range of 8–12 kcal/mol, while experiments suggest an upper bound on the order of 5–10 kcal/mol (1, 22). In several calculations, the ion was more stable in bulk solution than inside the pore (3, 44). Imbalances of the large ion-water and ion-peptide interaction energy are probably responsible for the overestimated activation barriers. An important test of the potential functions is provided by calculations on small model systems which can be compared directly with experimental data. For example, in the gas phase the ion-water interaction is 34, 24, and 18 kcal/mol for Li^+, Na^+, and K^+, respectively (46); the corresponding interaction with dimethylformamide, taken as a model of the carbonyl peptide group, is 51 kcal/mol for Li^+ (90), 38 for Na^+ from ab initio calculations (see 79), and 31 kcal/mol for K^+ (47). Standard biomolecular force fields, such as those used in several models (FBL, FVC, MBWH, CSJM, AW, and TPB), can lead to a significantly underestimated ion-peptide interaction; e.g. an affinity of 32 kcal/mol for Na^+ and dimethylformamide is found instead of the correct value of 38 kcal/mol (B Roux & M Karplus, unpublished results). Polarization and nonadditive effects may also be important (77, 82). Nevertheless, the results share some interesting features that are described below.

On a methodological note, simulation techniques based on small local free-energy differences in the neighborhood of a sequence of reference ion positions, such as umbrella sampling (43, 44), free-energy difference perturbation, or integrated mean force (79, 81), appear to be most appropriate for calculating the PMF. An important problem with the materialization (41) or alchemical transformation (3) techniques is that the PMF along the axis of the channel is extracted from small variations of a large number. For example, the absolute free energy of a Na^+ at any position x along the channel axis is approximately 100 kcal/mol, whereas the PMF is expected to have variations smaller than 5 kcal/mol. The advantages of the approach used by Chiu et al (18), which was based on an interpretation of the mean-square displacement in terms of a Langevin equation, over more standard techniques are unclear because time correlation functions have a larger statistical error than equilibrium averages (55). With all the free-energy techniques, it is necessary to perform long simulations to avoid hysteresis effects (79, 81). Such sampling bias, caused by a lack of equilibration, has also been observed in free-energy calculations in bulk water (61).

ION BINDING SITES   The free-energy profile of Na^+ along the axis of the right-handed dimer channel calculated by Roux & Karplus is shown in Figure 1 (below). The main binding site was found 9.3 Å from the center of the channel, where the Na^+ is bound to D-Val8, D-Leu10, L-Trp13, and L-Trp15, in good agreement with experimental observations (67, 88, 97). The binding sites are located in the single-file region, where the ion is in close contact with four carbonyl oxygens and two water molecules.

Jordan has found a stable position for a Cs^+ around 9.0 Å in a left-handed dimer, although this position did not correspond to a global free-energy minimum (44); the most stable position was found around 13.5 Å, where the ion maintains most of its hydration. The most stable position found by Åqvist & Warshel was around 14.0 Å, outside the single-file region of the channel. However, because their calculation was based on the approximate PDLD method and includes only two waters explicitly, the significance of the free-energy profile at the entrance of the channel, where the Na^+ is only partly dehydrated, is not clear (see the section on the AW model, above); Na^+ is still directly coordinated by three to four waters at 14.0 Å in the right-handed helix (81).

The PE adiabatic energy profile and the FVC average potential energy, which were based on energy calculations with rigid structures, have their deepest minimum for Na^+ at 4.5 Å, inside the single-file region, and at 15 Å, outside the channel. However, rigid structures do not give a valid representation of the inward deflection of the $C=O$ carbonyl in the presence of an ion (58). Ion-carbonyl interactions and the local flexibility of the backbone are essential factors giving rise to the binding site around 9.3 Å (81).

ELEMENTARY TRANSLOCATION BARRIER IN THE INTERIOR OF THE CHANNEL   Based on the calculations of Roux & Karplus (81), a sequence of small free-energy barriers oppose the movements of the permeating cation in the interior of the channel, where a hydrated complex must translocate in single file. The principal energy barrier is at the entrance of the channel, at the beginning of the single-file region. The small barriers, superimposed on the more global features of the PMF (see below), are due to the association of the ions with individual carbonyls along the channel axis. In the single-file region, the Na^+ is coordinated by four carbonyls and two water molecules. The magnitude of the translocation barrier is 4–5 kcal/mol, with a slightly smaller barrier at the monomer-monomer junction. Other estimates for the elementary Na^+ translocation barrier inside the pore are 3.5 kcal/mol (56), 4–5 kcal/mol (3), and 3.2 kcal/mol (18). The effect of handedness is expected to be small in the channel interior. Consequently, it is possible to compare results obtained for left- and right-handed helices for the translocation mechanism inside the pore, away from the ends and the monomer-monomer junction (79) (see also the section on channel conformation, above).

The structural and energetic aspects of the elementary translocation steps of Na^+ in the interior of the pore were investigated in more detail with the periodic RK-helix (79). Two residues form the basic building block and the system is expected to have a periodicity of 1.55 Å. It follows that the PMF along the axis of the RK-helix is made up of a sequence of well-defined binding sites and energy barriers separated by 1.55 Å; there is one such local well for every (L,D) pair of carbonyl oxygens. These results for the periodic helix can be compared with the relative minima in the PMF for Na^+ obtained for the full dimer channel model. Minima (81) are observed at 6.20, 7.75, 9.30, and 10.85 Å in the entrance region and at 0.0 and 1.65 Å in the dimer contact region. Thus, the positions of these minima corresponds approximately to integer multiples of 1.55 Å (n = 0, 1, 4, 5, 6, 7), i.e. the length of the helical unit in the periodic RK-helix. For Na^+, the right-handed dimer channel has 15 such local free-energy minima (see Table 1, below). The pattern of ion-carbonyl contacts in the local minima is an attribute of the β-helix structure. A Na^+ is in close contact with carbonyls i, $i+2$, $i+5$, and $i+7$, where i corresponds to the number of and L-amino acid for a left-handed helix and to the number of a D-amino acid for a right-handed helix. For example, Åqvist & Warshel reported local energy minima with carbonyls 3, 5, 8, and 10, and 7, 9, 12, and 14 from calculations of a Na^+ in a left-handed helix, which is entirely consistent with this analysis.

The magnitude of the free-energy barrier for the elementary translocation is a decreasing function of the ion radius. Roux & Karplus compared Na^+ and K^+ and found a reduction of the activation free energy from 4.5 for Na^+ to 1.0 kcal/mol for K^+ in the interior of the pore (79). Using the free-energy perturbation method, it was shown that for a fictitious ion with a radius intermediate between Na^+ and K^+ the barrier is between 2 and 3 kcal/mol. This is in accord with the results of Jordan, who found that the free-energy profile of a Cs^+ is completely uniform in the interior of the channel (44). Similar observations were also made from studies based on the rigid channel models (FVC and PE). Several investigations led to the conclusion that the stronger association of smaller cations with the carbonyl oxygens is an important factor in the larger elementary translocation barrier (28, 56, 58, 79). In the interior of the channel, Li^+ and Na^+ tend to be significantly off-axis at the minima, while the larger ions are closer to the center (58). Also, larger ions produce less distortion of the β-helix hydrogen bonding network, which contributes to the reduction of the free-energy barrier (79). Such results are qualitatively consistent with the selectivity sequence of the gramicidin channel and the greater ionic conductance for the large cations (1, 22).

In contrast with the results of most calculations, Skerra & Brickmann reported that the translocation barrier for Na^+ was much smaller than for Li^+ and K^+ in the FBL helix (87). As a result, the mobility of cations did not increase with the ion size and the correct selectivity sequence was recovered by adjusting the number of water molecules in the channel.

The integrated mean force decomposition method was used to show that the water and the channel make approximately equal contributions to the activation free energy of Na^+, but that only water contributes to the activation free energy of K^+ (see Figure 2, below) (79). Also, it was found that there is an increase in entropy at the transition state, which is associated with the larger fluctuations of the more loosely bound ion. The free-energy profile of ions is not controlled by the large interaction energies involving the ion (i.e. ion-water and ion-peptide), but rather by the weaker water-water, water-peptide, and peptide-peptide hydrogen bond interactions. This conclusion is fundamentally different from that of previous approaches to the study of ion selectivity in channels, in which the channel structure was essentially rigid, and the ion-channel interaction energy was thought to be the controlling factor in ion selectivity (e.g. in the PE and FVC models).

LIMITATIONS OF THE CONTINUUM MODEL   Early applications of continuum electrostatic approximations to membrane transport (40, 68) were inspired by the success of the Born model of ion solvation (10). It was argued that the main cause of the free-energy barrier for crossing the channel arises from from the fact that the membrane region (low dielectric constant) provides a less favorable environment than bulk water (high dielectric constant) (40, 68). This interpretation has been given the name the *image-charge* energy barrier, from the mathematical technique that is used to solve the continuum electrostatic problem for the channel and membrane (see 40).

The importance of such image-charge contributions to the highest free-energy activation barrier observed for Na^+ at $x = 7$ Å along the axis of the right-handed dimer channel was investigated with the integrated mean force decomposition (81). It was found that the long-range electrostatic interactions of the continuum-like farthest bulk and channel water molecules, i.e. those that are not in direct contact with the ion (eight water molecules are in the channel and the others are in the bulk region), have the opposite effect of that expected from the continuum electrostatic models. As expected, the average force arising from the bulk region tends to attract the ion outside the channel. However, this effect is more than compensated by the significant attractive forces arising from the electrostatic interactions with the eight water molecules pointing toward the ion inside the channel. Because the orientational freedom of the water molecules inside the channel differs from bulk water (i.e. they are all oriented in one direction), a continuum electrostatic approximation based an isotropic dielectric constant does not account for the directionality induced by the pore environment. Interpretations based on continuum electrostatics do not account for the discrete nature of the water molecules inside the single-file region (69) and the increased solvation capacity of a linear solvent structure

(58). The increased understanding of ion solvation obtained from detailed simulations has clarified the significance of molecular effects and the limitations of continuum approximations for this system (36, 39, 71, 83).

DEHYDRATION STEP   Because of the narrowness of the pore, a permeating ion must exchange the first hydration shell waters for backbone carbonyls in entering the channel. Roux & Karplus (81) observed that the transformation from bulk to single-file solvation of Na^+ is progressive and takes place over a distance of approximately 5 Å between 15 to 10 Å from the center of the dimer; Jordan (44) noted that the number of waters in the first coordination shell of Cs^+ decreased from five to two between 13.7 and 9.5 Å from the center of the dimer. The dehydration of Na^+ and Cs^+ proceeds similarly in the energy minimization calculations of Etchebest & Pullman (26, 73). Association of Na^+ (28, 81) and Cs^+ (44) with the ethanolamine tail was also observed in these calculations.

However, although the structural features of the dehydration process are similar, the calculated PMF differ markedly. Roux & Karplus (81) found no sharp free-energy barrier at the entrance of the channel; the magnitude of the ion-channel interactions is sufficient to compensate for the loss of favorable interactions of the Na^+ with the bulk water molecules. In contrast, dehydration results in a large entrance barrier of almost 20 kcal/mol in the calculation by Jordan (44). The large entrance barrier may be due to an imbalance of the ion-water and ion-peptide interactions of the potential energy function based on groups rather than individual atoms; estimated corrections for the differential effects caused by the cut-off errors and the polarization of the hydrocarbon membrane region could not reduce the entrance barrier by more than 5 kcal/mol.

Other Ions

The permeation of ions other than the five common monovalent cations has been addressed in some studies. Etchebest & Pullman (29) examined the potential energy profile for the entry of a divalent cation, Ca^{2+}. The very low permeability and the blocking effect of this divalent cation was attributed to a deep and narrow potential energy minimum at 10.5 Å. Sung & Jordan (41) studied the potential energy profile of an anion, Cl^-. The experimental observation that this anion neither permeates nor blocks the channel was attributed to a large barrier found at the entrance of the channel (41). Turano et al (95) examined the applicability of the size-exclusion concept for the selectivity of the gramicidin channel. They studied the permeation of large organic cations such as guanidinium, acetaminidium, and formamidinium. Using full energy minimization of the cation-channel system, they showed that the channel can accommodate the passage of formamidinium with a small energy barrier, but that a significant residual barrier remains for guanadinium and acetaminidium. The residual barrier results primarily from the disruption of the hydrogen-bonding network of the channel and could provide an explanation for the measured selectivity of gramicidin for formamidinium over guanadinium.

Dynamical Factors

Using activated dynamics trajectories, Roux & Karplus (80) estimated that the translocation rate for Na^+ is 2.3×10^8 s^{-1}, which corresponds to an effective diffusion constant of 0.55×10^{-7} cm^2/s. From the mean displacement in the presence of an applied voltage, Skerra & Brickmann (87) estimated the mobility of Li^+, Na^+, and K^+ and found that the calculated mobilities varied with the number of waters present in the FBL helix; a value of 0.58×10^{-5} cm^2/s was found for Na^+ with seven waters. Chiu et al estimated the translocation rate of the sodium-water chain complex to be 6.25×10^9 s^{-1}, which corresponds to an effective diffusion constant of 0.94×10^{-6} cm^2/s. Based on the measured saturated maximum sodium conductance (14.6 pmho), the effective diffusion constant in the interior of the pore is approximately 0.94×10^{-7} cm^2/s (see 80), in reasonable agreement with the result of the RK simulation.

Roux & Karplus (80) analyzed the dynamical factors controlling the movements of Na^+ and K^+ in the interior of the channel. By use of the cross-coupling friction decomposition method, it was shown that water-water, channel-channel, and water-channel cross-coupling contribute equally to the total static friction acting on Na^+ in the interior of the channel. In contrast, the friction acting on K^+ in the interior of the channel is controlled by rapidly fluctuating water forces. The importance of the water-channel cross-coupling contribution in the case of Na^+ suggests that the ion-ligand complex is more tightly structured than in the case of K^+. The motion of Na^+ at the transition state is controlled by local interactions arising from collisions with the neighboring carbonyls and the two nearest water molecules. The motion of K^+, in contrast, is controlled by the diffusion of water. Both Na^+ and K^+ suffer many rapid collisions; their dynamics are overdamped and noninertial. Consequently, the selectivity of ions in the β-helix is not influenced strongly by their mass. This contradicts the mass-dependent transition state theory of Schroeder et al (85).

As described above, the PMF of Na^+ is composed of a sequence of small free-energy barriers and the the translocation proceeds in terms of an activated hopping process between discrete states, as in classical transition-state models. However, classical transition-state theory does not provide an adequate picture of the dynamics of ions in the interior of the channel and overestimates the exact rate by one order of magnitude (80). The calculated transition state–theory rate for Na^+ in the RK-helix was $2.1 \times 10^9 \text{ s}^{-1}$. To account for the collisional recrossings and dynamical dissipative processes taking place at the transition state (9), the transition state–theory rate must be multiplied by the transmission coefficient. The transmission coefficient, calculated using activated dynamics techniques is 0.11 (80). A high friction approximation for the transmission coefficient of Na^+ gives 0.08. The latter value is in close agreement with the transmission coefficient obtained by Chiu et al (18) from their molecular dynamics trajectory based on an analysis in terms of an approximate Langevin equation. The transmission coefficient is not as small as predicted by the high friction approximation because of inertial non-Markovian dynamical factors (80). Since the dynamics at the barrier top is controlled primarily by high-frequency fluctuations, the transmission coefficient of Na^+ is insensitive to the full static friction assumed in the high friction approximation. However, the high friction approximation provides a better estimate than classical transition-state theory. In the case of K^+, the PMF does not have a large activation barrier and the translocation proceeds in terms of continuous diffusion, as in the Nernst-Planck diffusion approximation. Here the high-friction limit is appropriate.

CONCLUSION AND CRITICAL DISCUSSION

The results of the molecular dynamics calculations with the right-handed dimer channel (81) and with the periodic β-helix (79, 80) provide an understanding of ion transport through the gramicidin channel. The PMF of Na^+ along the axis of the dimer channel consists of a sequence of 15 small free-energy wells, one for every (L,D) pair (see Figure 1 and Table 1). The deepest minimum along the PMF corresponding to the cation-binding sites are at the extremities of the channel, in agreement with experiment (67, 88, 97). No large free-energy barrier appears to be associated with the dehydration process at the entrance of the pore. In the interior of the pore (see Figure 2), the (L,D) elementary free-energy barriers are on the order of 4.5 kcal/mol for Na^+. Almost half of each barrier is caused by the two neighboring single-file waters and results from a loss of water-peptide hydrogen bonds. The translocation

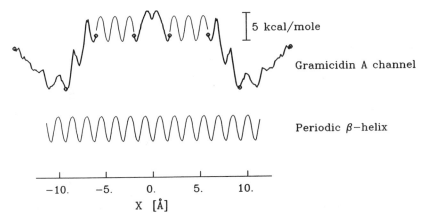

Figure 1   PMF along the gramicidin RK dimer obtained by assembling the three regions considered explicitly in the free-energy calculations (*bold line*) and a connector going from 6.02 to 1.65 Å (*thin line*) constructed from the PMF inside the periodic RK helix (shown at the bottom, see also Figure 2). The position of the connector was adjusted vertically by adding a constant energy term to the periodic PMF to match the values at $x = 6.02$ Å. Its amplitude was not scaled, and the horizontal position was neither adjusted nor scaled. Thus, the distance between the well of the periodic connector is 1.55 Å and the energy barriers are 4.5 kcal/mol as calculated in the periodic β-helix. The vertical position of the intermonomer segment was adjusted so that the energy in the first wells located at ±1.55 Å is equal to the energy in the fourth wells located at ±6.02 Å. The lowest energy minima are located at ±9.30 and ±11.05 Å corresponding to the Na$^+$ binding sites. The largest energy barrier is about 8 kcal/mol in the entrance region between wells 5 and 4 located at ±6.97 Å (taken from Ref. 81 with permission).

Table 1   Position of the free energy minima in the RK-dimer channel

Minima	Residues[a]				Position x (Å)
0	L-Val1'	L-Ala3	L-Ala3'	L-Val1	0.00
1	Formyl	L-Ala5	L-Val1'	L-Ala3	1.65
2[b]	Gly2	L-Ala7	Formyl	L-Ala5	3.10
3[b]	D-Leu4	L-Trp9	Gly2	L-Ala7	4.65
4	D-Val6	L-Trp11	D-Leu4	L-Trp9	6.17
5	D-Val8	L-Trp13	D-Val6	L-Trp11	7.75
6[c]	D-Leu10	L-Trp15	D-Val8	L-Trp13	9.30
7[c]	D-Leu12	Ethanol	D-Leu10	L-Trp15	11.05

[a] Primed residue numbers belong to the second monomer.
[b] Predicted from the periodic RK β-helix.
[c] Lowest free energy minima and probably the major Na$^+$ binding sites.

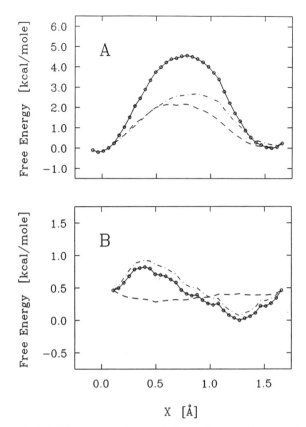

Figure 2 PMF of Na$^+$ (*A*) and K$^+$ (*B*) ions in the periodic RK-helix as obtained from the free-energy difference perturbation technique. A hysteresis of 0.8 and 1.0 kcal/mol was corrected for Na$^+$ and K$^+$, respectively. Water (*dot-dashed line*) and channel (*dashed line*) contributions to the PMF of Na$^+$ (*A*) and K$^+$ (*B*) ions from the mean force decomposition are shown. The PMF in the periodic helix is an approximation to the elementary translocation free-energy barrier for one (L,D) unit in the interior of the dimer channel (taken from Ref. 79, with permission).

proceeds from random hopping transitions, occurring at a rate of about $2.3 \times 10^8 \text{ s}^{-1}$, between distinct energy wells. For K$^+$, the very small (L,D) elementary free-energy barriers, on the order of 1.0 kcal/mol, are due entirely to the waters; the translocation proceeds as a continuous chaotic diffusive motion controlled by the dissipative forces acting on the single-file movements of water.

Although the absolute binding constant for a cation depends on the large ion-water and ion-channel interactions, the elementary translocation barriers in the interior of the pore are not controlled by the large interaction energy involving the ion. Instead they arise from the weaker water-water, water-peptide, and peptide-peptide hydrogen bond interactions. The water molecules make a significant contribution to the free energy of activation (see Figure 2) and to the dissipative forces acting on the ions. Classical transition state theory does not provide an adequate description of the dynamics of ions in the interior of the channel; both Na^+ and K^+ suffer many dissipative damping collisions and their dynamics are chaotic.

It is likely that several of the present conclusions provide a general microscopic picture of the permeation process through narrow single-file molecular pores and are not limited to the gramicidin channel. However, the motion of ions through ATP-driven pumps or pores and larger channels may be governed by other microscopic mechanisms due to differences in the molecular arrangements, water structures, and other pore-specific factors.

The nature of the gramicidin results demonstrates the importance of having information on the structure of the channel prior to investing the time (human and computer) for such simulations. Furthermore, despite the sophistication of modern computational methods, it is important to realize that the simulations have limitations, particularly in studying complex biological systems. Experimentally measured differences in ion permeabilities can often be accounted for by changes of only a few kilocalories per mole in the activation energies. Such small differences are within the uncertainty of present computational methods. The errors of the Born-Openheimer energy surface obtained directly from ab initio quantum chemistry methods, or approximated through a potential energy function, make it very difficult to achieve the accuracy needed for predicting the selectivity of ion channels. Thus, in a theoretical study of ion permeation based on a detailed atomic model, the analysis of the microscopic factors not directly accessible to experimental measurements is of greater interest than the absolute rate.

In a near future, the growing body of experimental data on the properties of modified gramicidin channels will be exploited. Experiments involving amino acid substitutions and chemical modifications will allow the investigation of the influence of particular molecular groups on the permeation process (2, 6, 7) and on the stability of monomer-monomer association in the lipid membrane (6). The gramicidin molecule is particularly well suited for such studies in view of of its structural and functional simplicity. Currently, investigations are underway of the gramicidin channel incorporated in a realistic membrane environment, including the bulk water and the surrounding phospholipids (101, 102, 106–108), the thermodynamic factors governing double-ion occupancy (82), and the flickering kinetics of a dioxalone-linked channel (21).

This review demonstrates that modern computational methods, such as molecular dynamics simulations, provide powerful tools for the study of ion transport in complex biological systems. As the three-dimensional structures of biologically relevant channels become available, the theoretical methods outlined in this review should provide a roadmap for studies of the function of such systems. As an example, simulations on the dynamics of porins (20, 104), large pores that have been shown to be β-barrel trimers, are in progress (M Watanabe, J Rosenbusch, T Schirmer & M Karplus, in preparation).

ACKNOWLEDGMENTS

This review was supported in part by a grant from the National Science Foundation to MK. We thank David Busath for supplying a file containing over 700 references.

Literature Cited

1. Andersen OS. 1984. Gramicidin channels. *Annu. Rev. Physiol.* 46:531–48
2. Andersen OS, Koeppe RE II, Durkin JT, Mazet JL. 1987. Structure-function on linear gramicidins: site specific modifications in a membrane channel. See Ref. 109, pp. 295–314
3. Åqvist J, Warshel A. 1989. Energetics of ion permeation through membrane channels. *Biophys. J.* 56:171–82
4. Arseniev AS, Bystrov VF, Ivanov TV, Ovchinnikov YA. 1985. ^{1}H-NMR study of gramicidin-A transmembrane ion channel. Head-to-head right-handed single stranded helices. *FEBS Lett.* 186:168–74
5. Barnes P, Finney JL, Nicholas JD, Quinn JE. 1979. Cooperative effects in simulated water. *Nature* 282:459–64
6. Becker MD, Greathouse DV, Koeppe RE II, Andersen OS. 1991. Amino acid sequence modulation of gramicidin channel function: effects of tryptophane-to-phenylalanine substitutions on the single-channel conductance and duration. *Biochemistry* 30:8830–39
7. Becker MD, Koeppe RE II, Andersen OS. 1992. Amino acid substitution and ion channel function. *Biophys. J.* 62: 25–27
8. Berendsen HJC, Postma JPM, van Gunsteren WF, Hermans J. 1981. Interaction models for water in relation to proteins hydration. In *Intermolecular Forces*, ed. B Pullman, pp. 331–42. Dordrecht: Reidel
9. Berne BJ, Borkovec M, Straub JE. 1988. Classical and modern methods in reaction rate theory. *J. Phys. Chem.* 92:3711–25
10. Born M. 1920. Volumen und hydratationswarme der ionen. *Z. Phys.* 1:45
11. Brooks BR, Bruccoleri RE, Olafson BD, States DJ, Swaminathan S, Karplus M. 1983. CHARMM: a program for macromolecular energy minimization and dynamics calculations. *J.Comput. Chem.* 4:187–217
12. Brooks CL III, Karplus M, Pettitt BM. 1988. Proteins. A theoretical perspective of dynamics, structure and thermodynamics. *Adv. Chem. Phys.* Vol. 71
13. Busath D, Hemsley G, Bridal T, Pear

M, Gaffney K, Karplus M. 1988. Guanidnium as a probe of the gramicidin channel interior. See Ref. 75a, pp. 187–201

14. Chandler D. 1978. Statistical mechanics of isomerization dynamics in liquids and the transition state approximation. *J. Chem. Phys.* 68:2959–70

15. Chiu SW, Gulukota K, Jakobsson E. 1992. Computational approaches to understanding the ion channel-lipid system. In *Proteins: Structures, Interactions, and Models,* ed. A Pullman, B Pullman, J Gortner, pp. 315–38. Dordrect: Kluwer Academic

16. Chiu SW, Jakobsson E, Subramaniam S, McCammon JA. 1991. Time-correlation analysis of simulated water motion in flexible and rigid gramicidin channels. *Biophys. J.* 60:273–85

17. Chiu SW, Nicholson LK, Brenneman MT, Subramaniam S, Teng Q, et al. 1991. Molecular dynamics computations and solid state state NMR of the gramicidin cation channel. *Biophys. J.* 60:974–78

18. Chiu SW, Novotny JA, Jakobsson E. 1993. The nature of ion and water barrier crossings in a simulated ion channel. *Biophys. J.* 64:98–108.

19. Chiu SW, Subramaniam S, Jakobsson E, McCammon JA. 1989. Water and polypeptide conformations in the gramicidin channel. *Biophys. J.* 56:253–61

20. Cowan SW, Schirmer T, Rummel G, Steiert M, Ghosh R, et al. 1992. Crystal structures explain functional properties of two *E. coli* porins. *Nature* 358:727

21. Crouzy S, Woolf T, Roux B. 1992. Molecular dynamics exploration of gating in dioxolae ring linked gramicidin. *Biophys. J.* 61:A525

22. Eisenman G, Horn R. 1983. Ionic selectivity revisited: the role of kinetic and equilibrium processes in ion permeation through channels. *J. Membr. Biol.* 76:197–225

23. Etchebest C, Pullman A. 1985. The effect of the amino-acid side chains on the energy profiles for ion transport in the gramicidin A channel. *J. Biomol. Struct. Dyn.* 2:859–70

24. Etchebest C, Pullman A. 1986. The gramicidin A channel: energetics and structural characteristics of the progression of a sodium ion in the presence of water. *J. Biomol. Struct. Dyn.* 3:805–25

25. Etchebest C, Pullman A. 1986. The gramicidin-A channel—the energy profile calculated for Na$^+$ in the presence of water with inclusion of the flexibility of the ethanolamine tail. *FEBS Lett.* 204:261–65

26. Etchebest C, Pullman A. 1988. The gramicidin A channel: left versus right-handed helix. See Ref. 75a, pp. 167–85

27. Etchebest C, Pullman A. 1988. Energy profile of Cs$^+$ in gramicidin A in the presence of water. Problem of the ion selectivity of the channel. *J. Biomol. Struct. Dyn.* 5:1111–25

28. Etchebest C, Pullman A, Ranganathan S. 1984. The gramicidin A channel: comparison of the energy profiles of Na$^+$, K$^+$ and Cs$^+$. Influence of the flexibility of the ethanolamine end chain on the profiles. *FEBS Lett.* 173:301–6

29. Etchebest C, Pullman A, Ranganathan S. 1985. The gramicidin A channel: theoretical energy profile computed for single occupancy by a divalent cation Ca^{2+}. *Biochim. Biophys. Acta* 818:23–30

30. Fischer W, Brickmann J, Läuger P. 1981. Molecular dynamics study of ion transport in transmembrane protein channels. *Biophys. Chem.* 13:105–16

31. Fornili SL, Vercauteren DP, Clementi E. 1984. Water structure in the gramicidin A transmembrane channel. *Biochim. Biophys. Acta* 771:151–64

32. Gilson MK, Honig B. 1988. Calculation of the total electrostatic energy of a macromolecular system. *Protein* 4:7–18

33. Gresh N, Claverie P, Pullman A. 1979. Intermolecular interactions: reproduction of the results of *ab initio* supermolecule computations by an additive procedure. *Int. J. Quant. Chem.* 13:243–53

34. Heitz F, Daumas P, Van Mau N, Lazaro R, Trudelle Y, Etchebest C, Pullman A. 1988. Linear gramicidins: influence of the nature of the aromatic side chains on the channel conductance. See Ref. 75a, pp. 167–85

35. Hinton JF, Fernandez JQ, Shungu DC, Whaley WL, Koeppe RE II, Millett FS. 1988. Tl-205 nuclear magnetic resonance determination of the thermodynamic parameters for the binding of monovalent cations to Gramicidin A and C. *Biophys. J.* 54:527–33

36. Hirata F, Redfern P, Levy RM. 1988. Viewing the born model for ion hydration through a microscope. *Int. J. Quant. Chem. Quant. Biol. Symp.* 15:179–90

37. Hladky SB, Haydon DA. 1984. Ion movements in gramicidin channels. *Curr. Top. Membr. Transp.* 21:327–72
38. Deleted in proof
39. Jayaram B, Fine R, Sharp K, Honig B. 1989. Free energy calculations of ion hydration: an analysis of the born model in terms of microscopic simulations. *J. Phys. Chem.* 93:4320–27
40. Jordan PC. 1984. The total electrostatic potential in a gramicidin channel. *J. Membr. Biol.* 78:91–102
41. Jordan PC. 1987. Microscopic approach to ion transport through transmembrane channels. The model system gramicidin. *J. Phys. Chem.* 91:6582–91
42. Jordan PC. 1988. Ion transport through transmembrane channels: ab initio perspectives. *Curr. Top. Membr. Transp.* 33:91–111
43. Jordan PC. 1988. A molecular dynamics study of cesium ion motion in a gramicidin-like channel. See Ref. 75a, pp. 237–51
44. Jordan PC. 1990. Ion-water and ion-polypeptide correlations in a gramicidin-like channel. A molecular dynamics study. *Biophys. J.* 58:1133–56
45. Jorgensen WL, Chandrasekhar J, Madura JD, Impey RW, Klein ML. 1983. Comparison of simple potential functions for simulating liquid water. *J. Chem. Phys.* 79:926–35
46. Kebarle P. 1977. Ion thermochemistry and solvation from gas phase ion equilibria. *Annu. Rev. Phys. Chem.* 28:445–76
47. Kebarle P, Caldwell C, Magnera T, Sunner J. 1985. Ion-gas phases and solution-dipolar aprotic solvents. *Pure Appl. Chem.* 57:339–46
48. Kim KS. 1985. Microscopic effect of an applied voltage on the solvated gramicidin A transmembrane channel in the presence of Na^+ and K^+ cations. *J. Comp. Chem.* 6:256–63
49. Kim KS, Clementi E. 1985. Energetics and hydration structure of a solvated gramicidin A channel for K^+ and Na^+ cations. *J. Am. Chem. Soc.* 107:5504–13
50. Kim KS, Vercauteren DP, Welti M, Chin S, Clementi E. 1985. Interaction of K^+ ion with the solvated gramicidin A transmembrane channel. *Biophys. J.* 47:327–35
51. Kirkwood JG. 1935. Statistical mechanics of fluid mixtures. *J. Chem. Phys.* 3:300
52. Koeppe RE II, Kimura M. 1984. Computer building of β-helical polypeptide models. *Biopolymers* 23:23–38
53. Läuger P. 1973. Ion transport through pores: a rate theory analysis. *Biochim. Biophys. Acta* 311:423–41
54. Läuger P. 1982. Microscopic calculation of ion-transport rates in membrane channels. *Biophys. Chem.* 15:89–100
55. Lee S, Karplus M. 1984. Brownian dynamics simulation: statistical error of correlation functions. *J. Chem. Phys.* 81:6106–18
56. Lee WK, Jordan PC. 1984. Molecular dynamics simulation of cation motion in water-filled gramicidin-like pores. *Biophys. J.* 46:805–19
57. Levitt DG. 1986. Interpretation of biological channel flux data—reaction-rate theory versus continuum theory. *Annu. Rev. Biophys. Biophys. Chem.* 15:29–57
58. Mackay DH, Berens PH, Wilson KR, Hagler AT. 1984. Structure and dynamics of ion transport through gramicidin A. *Biophys. J.* 46:229–48
59. Mackay DH, Wilson KR. 1986. Possible allosteric significance of water structures in proteins. *J. Biomol. Struct. Dyn.* 4:491–500
60. Matsuoka O, Clementi E, Yoshimine M. 1976. CI study of the water dimer potential surface. *J. Chem. Phys.* 64:1351–61
61. Mazor M, Pettitt MB. 1991. Convergence of the chemical potential in aqueous simulations. *Mol. Simul.* 6:1
62. McCammon JA, Gelin BR, Karplus M. 1977. Dynamics of folded proteins. *Nature* 267:585–90
63. Momany FA, McGuire RF, Burgess AW, Scheraga HA. 1975. Energy parameters in polypeptides vii. *J. Chem. Phys.* 79:2361–81
64. Monoi H. 1993. Energy-minimized conformation of gramicidin-like channels. I. Infinitely long poly (L,D)-alanine $β^{6.3}$-helix. *Biophys. J.* 64:36–43
65. Naik VM, Krimm S. 1986. Vibrational analysis of the structure of gramicidin A. 1. Normal mode analysis. *Biophys. J.* 49:1131–45
66. Nicholson LK, Cross TA. 1989. The gramicidin cation channel: an experimental determination of the right-handed helix sense and verification of β-type hydrogen bonding. *Biochemistry* 28:9379–85
67. Olah GA, Huang HW, Liu W, Wu Y. 1991. Location of ion-binding sites in the gramicidin channel by X-ray diffraction. *J. Mol. Biol.* 218:847–58
68. Parsegian A. 1969. Energy of an ion

crossing a low dielectric membrane: solution to four relevant electrostatic problems. *Nature* 221:844–46

68a. Parsegian VA, ed. 1984. *Ionic Channels in Membranes. Biophysical Discussions.* New York: Rockefeller Univ. Press

69. Partenskii MB, Jordan PC. 1992. Nonlinear dielectric behavior of water in transmembrane ion channels: ion energy barriers and the channel dielectric constant. *J. Phys. Chem.* 96:3906–10

70. Patey GN, Valeau JP. 1975. A Monte Carlo method for obtaining the interionic potential of mean force in ionic solution. *J. Chem. Phys.* 63:2334–39

71. Pettitt BM, Rossky PJ. 1986. Alkali halides in water: ion-solvent and ion-ion potential of mean force at infinite dilution. *J. Chem. Phys.* 84:5836–44

72. Polymeropoulos EE, Brickmann J. 1985. Molecular dynamics of ion transport through transmembrane model channels. *Annu. Rev. Biophys. Biophys. Chem.* 14:315–30

73. Pullman A. 1987. Energy profiles in the gramicidin A channel. *Q. Rev. Biophys.* 20:173–200

74. Pullman A, Etchebest C. 1983. The gramicidin A channel: the energy profile for single and double occupancy in a head-to-head beta(6.3 3,3)-helical dimer backbone. *FEBS Lett.* 163:199–202

75. Pullman A, Etchebest C. 1987. The effect of molecular structure and of water on the energy profiles in the gramicidin A channel. See Ref. 109, pp. 277–93

75a. Pullman A, Gortner J, Pullman B, eds. 1988. *Transport Through Membranes: Carriers Channels and Pumps.* Boston: Kluwer Academic

76. Roux B. 1993. Theory of transport in ion channels: from molecular dynamics simulations to experiments. In *Computer Simulation in Molecular Biology,* ed. J Goodefellow. Weinheim: VCH. In press

77. Roux B. 1993. Nonadditivity in cation-peptide interactions: a molecular dynamics and ab initio study of Na^+ in the gramicidin channel. *Chem. Phys. Lett.* 212:231–40

78. Roux B, Karplus M. 1988. The normal modes of the Gramicidin A dimer channel. *Biophys. J.* 53:297–309

79. Roux B, Karplus M. 1991. Ion transport in a gramicidin-like channel: structure and thermodynamics. *Biophys. J.* 59:961–81

80. Roux B, Karplus M. 1991. Ion transport in a gramicidin-like channel: dynamics and mobility. *J. Phys. Chem.* 95:4856–68

81. Roux B, Karplus M. 1993. Ion transport in the gramicidin channel: free energy of the solvated right-handed dimer in a model membrane. *J. Am. Chem. Soc.* 115:3250–60

82. Roux B, Karplus M. 1993. Double ion occupancy in the gramicidin channel: a molecular dynamics study. *Biophys. J.* 64:A354

83. Roux B, Yu HA, Karplus M. 1990. Molecular basis for the born model of ion solvation. *J. Phys. Chem.* 94:4683–88

84. Schlenkrich M, Bopp Ph, Skerra A, Brickmann J. 1988. Structure and dynamics of water on membrane surfaces and in narrow transmembrane channels—molecular dynamics simulations. See Ref. 75a, pp. 219–235

85. Schroeder H, Brickmann J, Fischer W. 1983. Cation transport through biological transmembrane channels. Theoretical study of mass dependent anomalies in the diffusion constant. *Mol. Phys.* 49:973–79

86. Skerra A, Brickmann J. 1987. Structure and dynamics of one-dimensional ionic solutions in biological transmembrane channels. *Biophys. J.* 51:969–76

87. Skerra A, Brickmann J. 1987. Simulation of voltage-driven hydrated cation transport through narrow transmembrane channels. *Biophys. J.* 51:977–83

88. Smith R, Thomas DE, Atkins AR, Separovic F, Cornell BA. 1990. Solid-state ^{13}C-NMR studies of the effects of sodium ions on the gramicidin A ion channel. *Biochim. Biophys. Acta* 1026:161–66

89. Smith R, Thomas DE, Separovic F, Atkins AR, Cornell BA. 1989. Determination of the structure of a membrane-incorporated ion channel. *Biophys. J.* 56:307–14

90. Stanley RH, Beauchamp JL. 1975. Intrinsic acid-base properties of molecules. Binding of Li^+ to π- and n-donor bases. *J. Am. Chem. Soc.* 97:5920–21

91. Sung SS, Jordan PC. 1987. The interaction of Cl^- with a gramicidin-like channel. *Biophys. Chem.* 27:1–6

92. Sung SS, Jordan PC. 1987. Why is gramicidin valence selective? A theoretical study. *Biophys. J.* 51:661–72

93. Sung SS, Jordan PC. 1988. Theoretical study of the antiparallel double-

stranded helical dimer of gramicidin as an ion channel. *Biophys. J.* 54:510–26

94. Sung SS, Jordan PC. 1989. The channel properties of possible gramicidin dimers. *J. Theor. Biol.* 140:369–80

95. Turano B, Pear M, Busath D. 1992. Gramicidin channel selectivity. Molecular mechanics for formamidinium, guanidinium and acetamididium. *Biophys. J.* 63:152–61

96. Urry DW. 1971. The gramicidin A transmembrane channel: a proposed π_{LD} helix. *Proc. Natl. Acad. Sci. USA* 68:672–76

97. Urry DW, Trapane TL, Prasad KU. 1983. Is the gramicidin A transmembrane channel single-stranded or double stranded helix? A simple unequivocal determination. *Science* 221:1064–67

98. Urry DW, Venkatachalam CM. 1983. Theoretical conformation analysis of the gramicidin A transmembrane channel. I. Helix sense and the energetics of head-to-head dimerization. *J. Comp. Chem.* 4:461–69

99. Urry DW, Venkatachalam CM, Prasad KU, Bradley RJ, Parenti-Castelli G, Lenaz G. 1981. Conduction process of the gramicidin channel. *Int. J. Quant. Chem. Quant. Biol. Symp.* 8:385–99

100. Urry DW, Venkatachalam CM. 1984. Theoretical conformation analysis of the gramicidin A transmembrane channel. II. Energetics of helical states of the channel. *J. Comp. Chem.* 5:64–71

100a. van Gunsteren WF, Berendsen HJC. 1987. Biomos. *Nijenborgh* Vol. 16

101. Wang J, Pullman A. 1990. The intrinsic molecular potential of glyceryl monooleate layers and its effect on the conformation and orientation of an inserted molecule: example of gramicidin A. *Biochim. Biophys. Acta* 1024:10–18

102. Wang J, Pullman A. 1991. Interactions and packing of lipids around a helical hydrophobic polypeptide—the system gramicidin-A glycerylmonooleate. *Chem. Phys. Lipids* 57:1–16

103. Warshel A, Levitt M. 1976. Theoretical studies of enzymatic reactions: dielectric, electrostatic and steric stabilization of the cabonium ion in the reaction of lysozyme. *J. Mol. Biol.* 103:2218–24

104. Weiss MS, Abele U, Weckesser J, Welte W, Schiltz E, Schulz GE. 1991. Molecular architecture and electrostatic properties of a bacterial porin. *Science* 254:1627

105. Wooley GA, Wallace BA. 1992. Model ion channels: gramicidin and alamethecin. *J. Membr. Biol.* 129:109–36

106. Woolf TB, Roux B. 1993. Molecular dynamics of proteins in lipid membranes: the first steps. *Biophys. J.* 64:A354

107. Xing J, Scott HL. 1989. Monte Carlo studies of lipid chains and gramicidin A in a model membrane. *Biophys. Biochem. Res. Commun.* 165:1–6

108. Xing J, Scott HL. 1992. Monte Carlo studies of a model for lipid-gramicidin A bilayers. *Biochim. Biophys. Acta* 1106:227–32

109. Yagi K, Pullman B, eds. 1987. *Ion Transport Through Membranes*. Boston: Kluwer Academic

Annu. Rev. Biophys. Biomol. Struct. 1994. 23:763–85

MASS SPECTROMETRY OF MACROMOLECULES: Has Its Time Now Come?

M. W. Senko and F. W. McLafferty

Department of Chemistry, Cornell University, Ithaca, New York 14853-1301

KEY WORDS: electrospray, FTMS, MALDI, MS/MS, protein

CONTENTS

PERSPECTIVES AND OVERVIEW

Mass spectrometry has been known for many years as the most accurate and sensitive method of obtaining molecular weight information for small molecules (<1 kDa). Entry-level instruments such as quadrupoles can routinely maintain mass-measuring errors near 0.1% with a mass resolving power of 1000 and sample consumption of only nanograms—capabilities orders of magnitude better than those of gel electrophoresis or size-exclusion chromatography (SEC). However, revolutionary developments in ionization techniques and instrumentation have recently suggested that these capabilities can be extended to molecules much larger than 10 kDa. For such a purpose, matrix-assisted laser desorption/ionization (MALDI) (33) and electrospray ionization

763

1056–8700/94/0610–0763$05.00

(ESI) (22, 60) coupled with time-of-flight (TOF) (17) and Fourier-transform mass spectrometry (FTMS) (7, 54) appear particularly promising.

The accurate mass-measuring capabilities of mass spectrometry give it unique advantages not only for molecular weight determination but also for stable isotope measurement and structure determination from dissociation products of the ionized molecule. Linear molecules such as peptides, nucleotides, and carbohydrates are especially amenable to this approach. For example, the amino acid sequence of the molecule (fragment masses, Daltons, in parentheses) $H_2N(16)$-*gly*(57)-*ala*(71)-*ser*(87)-OH(17) would be indicated by masses 233 (molecular ion), 73 (H_2N-*gly*), 104 (*ser*-OH), 144 (H_2N-*gly-ala*), and 175 (*ala-ser*-OH); ^{13}C-labeling on *ser* would yield masses 234, 73, 105, 144, and 176.

Tandem mass spectrometry (MS/MS) (8, 57) combines these attributes. "Soft" ionization of a mixture containing this oligopeptide with many others would give all their molecular ions, from which this mass-234 ion could be separated by MS-I. Its dissociation could then give the fragment ions shown for separation by MS-II. Repeating this process for the separated molecular ions could then provide sequence information on each of these other components.

The Sample Vaporization Problem

Because mass spectrometry is based on the mass-dependent motion of isolated charged particles in electric and magnetic fields, it is restricted to the analysis of gas-phase ionized species. For condensed-phase samples, this restriction necessitates both vaporization and ionization, which were separate processes in early mass spectrometry. The sample was normally heated until a significant vapor pressure was achieved; ionization of the neutral gas phase analyte was then effected by energetic (e.g. 70 eV) electrons (EI). Unfortunately, most biological molecules undergo thermal decomposition long before a significant vapor pressure is obtained using thermal heating.

The initial solution thermal instability was to modify the analyte chemically to increase its vapor pressure. For example, converting a carboxylic acid to its corresponding methyl ester eliminates many of the hydrogen bonds that reduce the vapor pressure. For the later "energy sudden" method, less volatile samples heated at a high rate can be converted to the gas phase faster than they thermally decompose. However, these methods were not effective for many 1-kDa molecules.

The first technological breakthrough widely applicable to the mass spectrometry of molecules of low vapor pressure came with the introduction of fast-atom bombardment (FAB) (3). Bombarding a sample in a nonvolatile liquid matrix with high-energy (keV) neutrals or ions could persuade the analyte into the gas phase; it could then be ionized and mass analyzed with minimal decomposition. FAB combined with the use of sector instruments permitted the analysis of molecules in the low kilodalton range, with resolution greater than unity and mass errors <0.01%. The use of FAB for MS/MS in combination with collisional activation on sector instruments can solve many interesting biological mixture problems for relatively small molecules (25, 56).

Unfortunately, the ionization and fragmentation methods impose a ceiling of a few kilodaltons. Analysis of larger molecules requires these first to be chemically or enzymatically reduced in size; the original molecule must then later be reconstructed from the mass spectral data of the smaller sections. Here we consider a sample that is not amenable to analysis using FAB as a large molecule.

One method capable of ionizing large biomolecules is plasma desorption (PD) (64). The first report of its use for biomolecules (51) in 1976 actually predates FAB, but it has never gained equal popularity owing to some significant disadvantages. Both FAB and PD use high-energy particles to desorb an analyte from a surface. However, where FAB uses keV particles from an ion gun, PD uses ~100-MeV particles from the spontaneous fission of a ^{252}Cf source placed near the sample. Although PD can create intact molecular ions of species as large as 45 kDa (38), the typical ^{252}Cf source produces only 5000 fission events per second, which provides an extremely low ion current. For this reason, PD couples poorly with scanning instruments like quadrupoles and sectors. PD needs an instrument that can measure all masses at once, like the time-of-flight (TOF) mass spectrometer (17); and most applications have used this. For higher performance, PD has also been used with the Fourier-transform mass spectrometer (FTMS) (65, 72). PDMS methods are now used only in special applications, although their pioneering results stimulated the research that has produced the present promising ionization methods.

NEW IONIZATION METHODS

The introduction of two ionization methods in the later 1980s, matrix-assisted laser desorption/ionization (MALDI) (33, 39) and electrospray ionization (ESI) (13, 22, 60), and the coupling in the 1990s of these ionization sources to high-performance analyzers, such as (FTMS) (7, 54), have allowed mass spectrometrists to break through the 3-kDa ceiling and obtain molecular weight, structural, and even conformational information for significantly larger molecules.

Matrix Assisted Laser Desorption/Ionization (MALDI)

A sample can be heated rapidly with the use of a laser. A sample irradiated at a wavelength it absorbs will heat quickly, vaporize, and ionize before it can decompose. By means of this method molecules as massive as 3 kDa can be analyzed with minimal fragmentation. Because the energy goes directly into the analyte, however, significant dissociation occurs in larger molecules. Because laser desorption is inherently a pulsed technique, its sensitivity benefits greatly when an analyzer is used that can measure all masses simultaneously from a single ionization event. The simplest analyzer with this capability is the time-of-flight (TOF) mass spectrometer, to which almost all laser desorption sources are connected.

The major advance in laser desorption was the introduction of matrices (MALDI) by Hillenkamp (39). In the first study reported, melittin, a linear polypeptide of 26 amino acids (2843 Da), was mixed with an excess of nicotinic acid and irradiated with a pulsed frequency-quadrupled Nd-YAG laser at 266 nm. The mass spectrum, recorded using TOF, showed a predominant pseudo-molecular ion $(M + H^+)$ at m/z (mass divided by charge) 2844 and matrix ion peaks below m/z 600. The complete absence of molecular fragmentation was attributed to irradiation at a wavelength strongly absorbed by the matrix, not by the analyte. The matrix was able to transfer energy more gently to the analyte, and gas phase ions were formed with significantly less internal energy than those formed by laser desorption in the absence of a matrix. A major benefit of producing only molecular ions is that the technique can easily be applied to direct analysis of mixtures, which is made more complicated if each species produces multiple signals. MALDI has been utilized for compounds in excess of 100 kDa, as demonstrated by the spectrum of an immunoglobulin (148 kDa) in Figure 1.

A slightly different matrix method was introduced a short time later by Tanaka (66). In this case the matrix was a mix of ultra-fine cobalt powder (300 Å diameter) and glycerol. Molecules as large as chymotrypsinogen (25,717 Da), and a 7-mer of lysozyme (100,000 Da) were ionized and detected with no significant fragmentation. However, peak widths were substantially broader than that expected from isotopic distributions, in most cases >1000 Da.

This announcement of the success of MALDI led many groups to test various compounds in an attempt to find a universal matrix. Other compounds that have proven advantageous in specific cases include 2,5-dihydroxybenzoic acid and sinapinic acid for almost all wavelengths, and succinic acid, glycerol, and urea for IR desorption, using

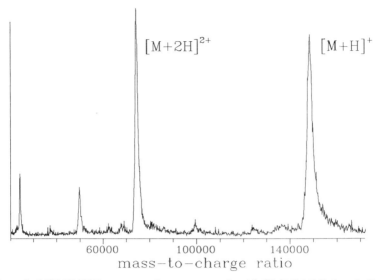

Figure 1   MALDI-TOF spectrum of mouse monoclonal IgG1 (148,140 Daltons). Courtesy of RC Beavis and BT Chait, Rockefeller University.

matrix:analyte ratios between 100:1 and 50,000:1 (33). The general consensus is there is no universal matrix. Different compounds may require different matrices and different wavelengths.

A novel approach capitalizing on the basic idea of MALDI is the use of derivatized probe surfaces in place of the matrix, a technique termed surface-enhanced neat desorption (SEND) (36). As an initial example, α-cyano-4- hydroxycinnamic acid was bound to agarose beads (75–300 μm diameter), placed on an inert probe, and 2 pmol of horse-heart myoglobin were added. In normal MALDI, the matrix typically forms photo-adducts with the analyte, causing peak broadening; and matrix peaks tend to dominate the low-mass (m/z <1000) range. The SEND-TOF spectra of myoglobin in Figure 2 shows no evidence of peak broadening due to photo-adducts, and only a few matrix peaks, all below m/z 100. Another benefit of SEND, and a major motivating factor in its development, is that molecules maintain their biological activity on the probe in the absence of a matrix. This allows biochemical reactions to be performed on the probe, minimizing sample consumption.

An interesting application of MALDI is in the amino acid sequencing of peptides and proteins (12). Edman degradation was performed on the analyte in the presence of a terminating agent (5% phenylisocyanate). The terminating agent stops the Edman chemistry for a small

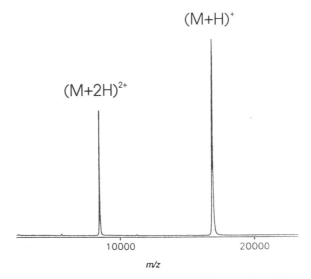

Figure 2   SEND-TOF spectrum of horse myoglobin. Reprinted from Ref. 20.

fraction of molecules at each step. This leaves a mixture of peptides, each shorter by one amino acid. Using MALDI's ability to analyze complex mixtures, a spectrum was taken that contained a ladder of peaks, each separated by the mass of the corresponding amino acid. That this method can be applied to larger peptides is demonstrated by performing the MALDI analysis on a synthetic mixture of peptides from the solid-phase synthesis of the HIV-1 protease monomer, as shown in Figure 3. The sequence is easily determined for this mixture of peptides from 3.4–7.5 kDa. If "peptide ladders" can be constructed efficiently for these larger peptides, then this method could rival typical Edman techniques.

MALDI combined with TOF instruments presents a simple yet powerful technique for the analysis of large biological samples, although photo-adducts on the molecular ion tend to cause systematic errors in mass determination. The high resolution available with FTMS provides the ability to eliminate this systematic error. The first measurement of large biomolecules using MALDI/FTMS was reported by Wilkins (10). Melittin (2845 Da) was measured with a resolving power of 3300, and larger molecules like trypsinogen (24 kDa) were successfully trapped and detected, although with much lower resolutions.

The cause of this poor resolution was reported to be metastable decay of the molecular ion. Although no decay is observed using similar conditions for short (few microseconds) TOF experiments, the time scale

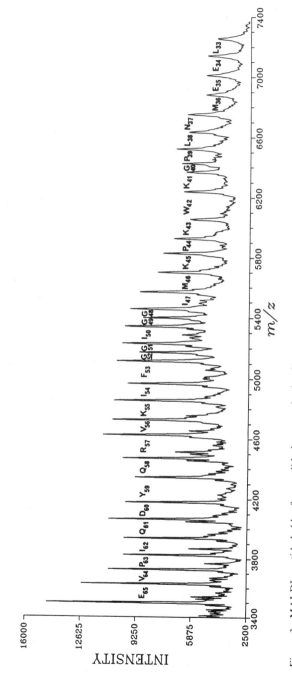

Figure 3 MALDI peptide ladder from solid phase synthesis of HIV-1 protease. Courtesy of BT Chait, R Wang, and SBH Kent, Rockefeller University.

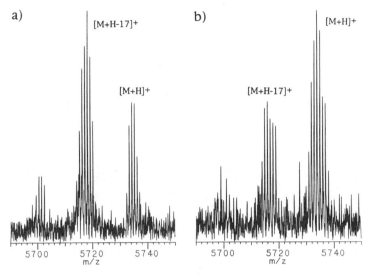

Figure 4 MALDI-FTMS spectrum of bovine insulin. Resolving power: 30,000. Reprinted from Ref. 24.

of the FTMS experiment (10^{-2} to 10^1 s) allows for significant fragmentation. Metastable decay was minimized with the addition of sugar (sucrose or fructose) in an equal molar ratio with the matrix, 2,5-dihydroxybenzoic acid (11, 40). This method produced a spectrum of bovine insulin with a resolving power (RP) of 30,000 (Figure 4) and greater than unit resolving power for cytochrome c (RP > 12,000). The reduction of metastable decay is attributed to a temporary increase in pressure (H_2O and CO_2) created by the decomposition of sugar during the desorption process, which collisionally cools the analyte. Ion cloud location and shape in the ion trap have become a concern, and ion manipulation routines like quadrupolar cooling (27, 28) have been shown to increase resolving power dramatically for MALDI-generated ions in an FTMS, as demonstrated by a resolution of 1.8×10^6 for leucine enkephalin (594 Da); but quadrupolar cooling has yet to be applied to larger species.

Electrospray Ionization (ESI)

The other major advancement for the analysis of large biomolecules by mass spectrometry was the application of electrospray ionization (ESI) to biopolymers (69). This soft ionization technique forms stable, multiply charged ions of large molecules by evaporation of solvent from small electrostatically charged droplets at atmospheric pressure. The number of charges in the gas phase reflects the number of charges the analyte carries in the solution phase. The ions remaining after the evaporation of the solvent are transported into the high vacuum of the mass spectrometer through several stages of pumping. The greatest benefit of multiply charged ions is that they extend the mass range of the analyzer. A 100-kDa molecule carrying 100 charges can be analyzed on a quadrupole with an upper m/z limit of only 1000. Multiply charged ions are also much more easily dissociated, such as by collision, with extensive MS/MS data reported for albumin, 67 kDa (46).

Electrospray spectra are characterized by an envelope of different charge states; compare the MALDI and ESI spectra of immunoglobulins (Figures 1 and 5). Because the mass spectrometer measures m/z, z must be determined to obtain mass (m) information. This can be done using the spacing between adjacent charge states of the same mass value (53); however, this becomes difficult for mixtures of even a few components, as the ions have multiple values of m as well as z. Deconvolution algorithms have been employed with some success to resolve this difficulty (41, 59).

Electrospray has proven successful for the molecular weight determination of 200-kDa molecular ions (20), with a quadrupole instrument limited to m/z 2400. Typical mass errors using a quadrupole are 0.01%– 0.1%, equal to that obtained with MALDI-TOF. One problem with ESI is that it tends to produce molecular ions that carry adducts from impurities in the solution. These adducts can be minimized by the application of collisional activation in the high-pressure ion transfer region of the mass spectrometer, but they are rarely eliminated. These adducts are typically of Na^+, K^+, or other metal cations; they cause

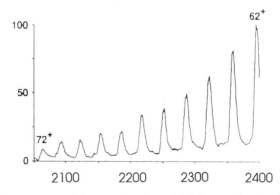

Figure 5   ESI spectrum anti-(human α1-antitrypsin) IgG monoclonal antibody (148,484 Daltons). Adapted from Ref. 32.

a systematic error when determining molecular weight when they cannot be resolved from the molecular ion, especially when working in negative mode (48) for the analysis of acidic proteins or oligonucleotides. To resolve adducts, electrospray ionization has been coupled successfully to sector instruments, most recently producing a resolving power of 20,000 and a mass measuring error of 1 ppm for horse-heart myoglobin using peak matching. Since sensitivity is dramatically reduced at high resolving powers with sector instruments, a large amount of sample was consumed (200 pmol) while only a small mass range was observed (6 m/z at m/z 1300) (19).

The FTMS may be the ideal mass analyzer for studying large molecules. The greatest obstacle for coupling ESI to FTMS was the vast pressure difference between ion formation (760 torr) and ion measurement ($<10^{-8}$ torr). The first coupling was reported in 1989 (32), using a 7-T magnet and four stages of pumping. Although a base pressure of

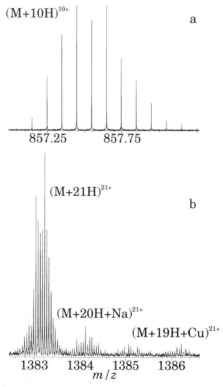

Figure 6   High-resolution ESI-FTMS spectra of (*a*) 10 + charge state of bovine ubiquitin, resolving power 2 × 10^6; (*b*) 21 + charge state of bovine carbonic anhydrase, resolving power 5 × 10^5. Adapted from Ref. 39.

only 10^{-7} torr was achieved, this was sufficient to obtain a resolving power of 5000 for gramicidin S (1040 Da), and a mass error of only 17 ppm for bovine insulin (5734 Da). Use of a 3-T instrument, but with 5 stages of differential pumping, allowed an operating pressure of 3×10^{-9} torr, and a resolving power >75,000 for cytochrome c (12 kDa) while consuming only 3 fmol of sample (31).

This instrument was later modified by increasing the magnetic field to 6.2 T and improving the pumping and data system. The molecular weight of myoglobin was determined with an error of <1 ppm (4), providing direct confirmation of a correction reported earlier for the published sequence (76). The resolving power was increased to 2×10^6 for bovine ubiquitin (8.6 kDa) and 5×10^5 for carbonic anhydrase (29 kDa), as shown in Figure 6 (5). This resolving power is more than sufficient to resolve cation adducts that would adversely affect mass-measurement accuracy. The largest molecule for which unit resolution has been obtainable is porcine serum albumin (67 kDa), which shows microheterogeneity to be a major contributor to peak widths in low-resolution spectra.

Ganem & Henion first demonstrated the utility of ESI for analyzing noncovalent complexes by showing that FK506 and rapamycin, new immunosuppressive drugs, remain bound to the cytoplasmic receptor FKBP (11.8 kDa) (23) (Figure 7). Specificity was demonstrated by the

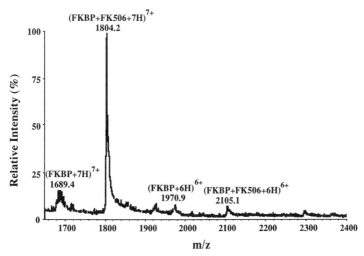

Figure 7   ESI spectrum of noncovalent complex of FKBP and FK506. Courtesy of B Ganem and JD Henion, Cornell University.

absence of complex under denaturing conditions. An equal molar mixture of the two ligands showed the rapamycin-FKBP complex to be twice as abundant as the FK506-FKBP complex, in agreement with experimental binding constants. Noncovalent interactions have also been studied for enzyme-substrate (24), HIV protease (2), oligonucleotide (45), and leucine zipper peptide (43) complexes.

Although ESI may seem a quick and powerful method for assessing biological binding, there is insufficient experimental evidence to suggest that the results are more than qualitative, and that binding forces in the gas phase are the same as those in solution. Most studies have been performed on quadrupole instruments, where experimental time scales (ms) may kinetically limit observed dissociation. As an example, the leucine zipper peptides form dimers in solution owing to hydrophobic interactions. The quadrupole results were confirmed using FTMS (43), where the dimer was observed to be completely stable in vacuum on the time scale of minutes, although solvent (and therefore hydrophobic interactions) was absent.

In order to gain further insight into the role of solvent in protein conformer stabilization, the structural and dynamic properties of protein ions in vacuo have been probed by hydrogen-deuterium exchange in a FTMS (63). For cytochrome c ions, the existence of at least three distinct gaseous conformers is indicated by the substantially different values—52, 113, and 74—of reactive H atoms. The compactness in vacuo corresponds directly to that of known solution conformers.

NEW INSTRUMENTAL METHODS

The success of high-molecular-weight mass spectrometry is also heavily dependent on the development of new instrumental capabilities, especially the TOF and FT mass spectrometers, tandem MS (MS/MS, MS^n), and chromatographic/MS combinations. Details of the principles and advantages of these methods should help illustrate their promise for problems involving large molecules.

Time-of Flight (TOF)

The theory of operation for TOF analyzers is based on the equation for kinetic energy

$$E = 1/2 \ mv^2 \qquad\qquad 1.$$

After ions are created, they are accelerated to the same kinetic energy, and directed down a flight tube (usually 1 m long) to a detector. With all ions having equal kinetic energy, heavier ions will travel slower and take longer to reach the detector. Mass values can be obtained from Equation 1, the flight-tube length, and acceleration voltage. Besides TOF's ability to analyze all masses from a single ionization event, it has a virtually unlimited mass range, another benefit in its application to large molecules.

The TOF instruments are highly sensitive, as essentially all ions should reach the detector. After striking the detector surface, secondary electrons are emitted, with this signal enhanced 10^6–10^7 in an electron multiplier. However, the yield of secondary electrons drops dramatically as the ion velocity goes below approximately 10^6 cm s^{-1}; with use of a constant accelerating potential, the ion velocity decreases as its mass decreases. Thus the ions are often accelerated by a large (>20 kV) potential just before striking the detector.

Resolving power for TOF instruments is based on many factors (17), including the spatial and temporal distribution of ion formation, initial kinetic energy distributions, and flight-tube length. The initial kinetic energy distribution due to desorption from the surface is usually the limiting factor. Spatial distribution in MALDI is not a problem, because all ions are formed from a surface and the temporal distribution is minimized by using short laser pulses. As a result of the initial kinetic energy spread, the resolving power for linear TOF instruments rarely exceeds 500, but this weakness can be corrected somewhat with the use of an ion-mirror or reflectron (52). Ions are accelerated towards an ion mirror and are then reflected towards a detector. The ion mirror is held at a slightly higher potential than the acceleration potential. Ions with higher kinetic energies will penetrate further into the ion mirror, producing a longer path length, thus allowing all ions of the same m/z to arrive at the detector simultaneously. By working in reflectron mode, resolving powers can be more than doubled. Unfortunately, the resolving power is still not high enough to separate molecular ion peaks from adduct peaks. To permit such separation, a higher-performance instrument must be used.

Fourier-Transform Mass Spectrometry (FTMS)

This instrumentation is ideally suited for measurements on large molecules using both MALDI and ESI. Ultra-high resolving power, as high as 2×10^8 for He (1), combined with high mass accuracy make the FTMS far more powerful even than sector instruments. FTMS was introduced in 1974 by Comisarow & Marshall (15) and is based on the principle of ion-cyclotron resonance, where charged particles orbit in the presence of a magnetic field. The cyclotron frequency (f) is related to the mass to charge ratio (m/z) and magnetic field (B) by the following equation:

$$f = B/(m/z) \hspace{6cm} 2.$$

Ion bundles are excited to cyclotron radii of a centimeter or so by an appropriate RF signal applied to a pair of opposed plates perpendicular to the cyclotron motion. The ion bundles then induce an image current on a second set of opposed plates, which is digitized and stored. This time-domain signal is then Fourier-transformed to retrieve the component frequencies, which are converted to the corresponding masses using Equation 2.

If they are to be measured using FTMS, ions must be trapped and held in a confined region for times between 10^{-2} and 10^1 s. The magnetic field contains the ions in the x and y directions owing to cyclotron motion, but electrostatic trapping is necessary to contain the ions in the z direction. A pair of plates in the x-y plane, separated by a few centimeters, are held at a few volts positive to trap positive ions between them, and a few volts negative for negative ions. In the absence of electrostatic trapping plates, the m/z range of FTMS is virtually unlimited. The electrostatic field created to contain the ions in the z-direction tends to force ions out in the x and y directions and places an upper m/z limit of 40,000 for thermal ions using a 3-T magnet (55). Because MALDI ions are initially of greater than thermal energy, this limit is significantly lower using static trapping potentials (74), unless the ions are translationally cooled prior to trapping.

In the successful application of FTMS to MALDI by Wilkins, the laser probe was placed outside the cell; at the time of the laser pulse, the front trap plate was at 0 V and the back trap plate was at 9 V (10). Shortly after the laser was fired, both trap plates were brought down to 3 V for excitation and detection. This "pulsed-trapping" method allows deceleration of high-velocity ions without the adverse effects of high-static trap potentials, which would normally reduce the m/z range.

A key factor in obtaining high resolution using an external ESI source on a FTMS was found to be translational cooling of the trapped ions after their introduction from the external ESI source (31). Pulsed N_2 creates a transient pressure increase in the cell ($>10^{-5}$ torr) for improved trapping efficiency and cooling of axial motion, but it allows a normal base pressure ($<10^{-8}$ torr) for optimal spectrometer performance. Winger et al constructed similar instrumentation (73) but added a unique cryopumping system and shutters in the ion source to reduce effects due to neutral beam penetration of the trapped ion cell. High resolution was shown to be beneficial in the analysis of RNase B (14.9

kDa): The differently glycosolated forms were easily distinguished. Although transients in excess of 1 min were recorded, frequency shifts limited resolution to 7×10^5 for bovine insulin. A method for correcting for this frequency shift by postacquisition modulation of the data acquisition rate has been shown to increase resolution to $> 2 \times 10^6$ (6).

Another benefit of the FTMS is its nondestructive ion measurement, which makes possible their subsequent dissociation for MS/MS or remeasurement for enhanced sensitivity (70). When orbiting large ions strike small background molecules, the former undergo negligible deflection; but the multiple collisions tend to relax the ions back to the center of the cell. They can then be remeasured to improve signal-to-noise (S/N) ratios. Although long delays between scans were necessary, remeasurement efficiencies of 98% were shown for gramicidin D (1.9 kDa), producing a fourfold increase in signal-to-noise with 25 remeasurements. A later report by Laude (29) showed that larger ions (up to 133 kDa) relax more efficiently back to the center of the cell, and on a shorter time scale. A single scan for bovine albumin dimer gave a S/N of only 3:1, but this was increased to 25:1 by 50 remeasurements. Remeasurements of >98% efficiency have been achieved in our laboratory recently for large (12 kDa) ions at high (>50,000) resolving power. Although it is mass selective, the use of quadrupolar axialization of ions (62) enhanced remeasurement dramatically by improving efficiencies over a broad range of experimental conditions.

Tandem Mass Spectrometry (MS/MS)

The combination of MALDI or ESI with high performance mass analyzers provides the ability to observe even small (1 Da) changes in the molecular weight of large molecules. Tandem mass spectrometry (MS/MS) techniques can provide information about not only whether a change has occurred in a molecule, but also where the change has occurred.

The implementation of MS/MS capabilities with TOF instrumentation faces several difficulties. Selecting ions of a specific m/z for dissociation during flight, and depositing sufficient energy for their dissociation at the exact time and place required, are challenging problems. However, several experimental TOF MS/MS configurations appear promising (16, 37). Singly charged ions show extremely low dissociation efficiencies above 3 kDa; MS/MS experiments on large molecules have therefore been performed almost exclusively on ions generated by ESI, where 150-kDa antibodies have been successfully dissociated (21).

If the analyte is relatively pure, initial mass separation is unneccessary, and fragmentation can be induced by multiple low-energy collisions in the high-pressure (1 torr) region of the electrospray source by increasing the voltage bias between initial electrostatic elements. This type of dissociation was termed "nozzle/skimmer dissociation" in its first experimental demonstration (50). The advantage of performing dissociation in the source is that only one mass analyzer is required for recording a product ion spectrum. This method was recently applied to distinguish forms of hemoglobin that differed by single amino acid substitutions (44). The lack of mass selectivity is a weakness of this method, in that only pure samples can be analyzed and that, owing to their multiple fragments and charge states, spectra for molecules >15 kDa are extremely complex.

One way to simplify the product ion spectra is to select a single charge state before dissociation, thus minimizing the number of possible charge states for product ions. Tandem techniques usually involve separating the stages of mass spectrometry in space, where the analyte is first selected, then the dissociation products are mass analyzed. The first implementation of such a tandem technique was with the addition of more sectors to the back of a double-focusing instrument. This procedure allowed high collision energies for large molecules. For quadrupole instruments, tandem techniques involve the use of three quadrupoles; the first is for precursor ion selection, the second contains ions radially during the collision process, and the third mass analyzes the dissociation products. Such an instrument is termed a triple quadrupole (75), for obvious reasons, and is commercially available from a number of companies. Triple quadrupoles have been the primary instrument for tandem mass spectrometry studies of large ions (47). In Smith's MS/MS study of hemoglobins (44), the $(M + 19H)^{19+}$ ion of Hb β^A-chain hemoglobin yielded 13 peaks whose m/z values corresponded to the known sequence. Only one fragment could be identified by multiple z values, making the normal method of mass and charge assignment impossible (53).

In the cases where a mass shows only one charge state, the best solution is to resolve the isotopic peaks (30). Isotopic peaks normally separated by 1 Dalton will appear closer by a factor of the charge, unambiguously providing charge state information. Dissociation of bovine ubiquitin produced a set of peaks at 726.5 m/z separated by 0.11 m/z each (49), establishing a mass of 6527.44 Daltons, which corresponds well with the y_{58} fragment (6527.49 Daltons).

The advantages of the Cornell ESI-FTMS instrument have been extended to the analysis of carbonic anhydrase (29 kDa), a molecule whose nozzle/skimmer dissociation spectrum of ~100 peaks from quadrupole instruments is otherwise too complicated to analyze. Charge states could be assigned to over 100 isotopic clusters, which corresponded to over 20 different fragments, as shown in the box diagram of Figure 8. Dissociation produced many complimentary ion pairs (whose mass sum equals that of the molecular ion) and dissociation patterns that allow for the assignment of fragments to either the N or C terminus.

Although nozzle/skimmer dissociation has demonstrated its utility in many studies, it is limited by being a nonmass-selective method that cannot be repeated for MS^n studies. The FTMS is uniquely suited to MS^n applications, because its implementation requires no additional instrumentation. FTMS can be performed in the trapped ion cell by exciting selected ions to high cyclotron energies and then pulsing in a high-pressure background gas for collisional activation (9, 14). The high background gas pressures necessary ($>10^{-6}$ torr) and the formation of fragments away from the center of the cell cause problems when applying this method to high-resolution MS^n studies of large molecules.

Photodissociation may be the ideal answer to these problems, because in this method the addition of gas to the cell is unnecessary and fragment ions are created on the center axis of the cell. The use of 193-nm radiation from an excimer laser has effectively provided sequence information for peptides (26), but has proven less effective for larger molecules (5). One option effective for larger molecules is to use

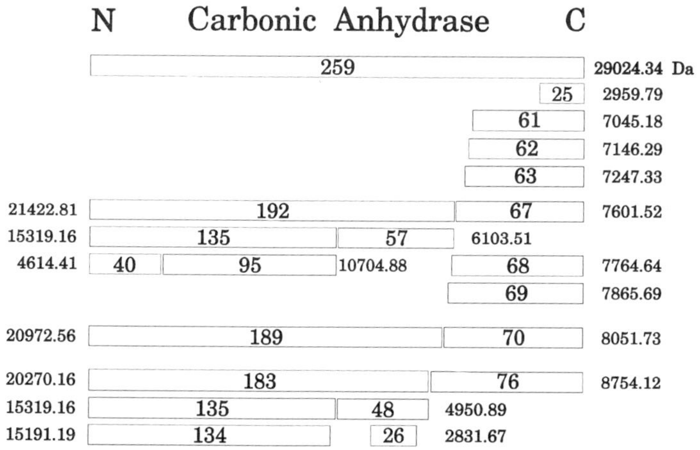

N   Carbonic Anhydrase   C

N (mass)	box	box	C (mass)
	259		29024.34 Da
		25	2959.79
		61	7045.18
		62	7146.29
		63	7247.33
21422.81	192	67	7601.52
15319.16	135	57	6103.51
4614.41	40 · 95	10704.88 · 68	7764.64
		69	7865.69
20972.56	189	70	8051.73
20270.16	183	76	8754.12
15319.16	135	48	4950.89
15191.19	134	26	2831.67

Figure 8 Box diagram of nozzle-skimmer dissociation fragments of bovine carbonic anhydrase. Numbers inside boxes indicate the number of amino acids for the fragment, and the numbers outside indicate the molecular weight.

infrared multiphoton dissociation (IRMPD) (67), which slowly adds energy to the molecule in a manner similar to the nozzle/skimmer activation process. Preliminary studies on bovine ubiquitin using a 25-watt CW-IR laser on the Cornell ESI-FTMS instrument demonstrated that IRMPD is highly efficient (60%) for large molecules and provides selective dissociation.

Chromatographic/MS Coupling

The complexity of many biological samples necessitates a chromatographic step for the simplification of mass spectral analysis. The coupling of methods like high-performance liquid chromatography (HPLC) and capillary electrophoresis (CE) to ESI, and to a lesser extent to MALDI, has been the pursuit of many research groups.

HPLC has been a great challenge, because the high flow rate (typically 1 ml min^{-1}) is incompatible with the optimal ESI flow rate ($<$ 10 μl min^{-1}). Splitting of the LC effluent before the electrospray source is an obvious solution but is complicated by solvent gradients, which can dynamically alter split-ratios. By pneumatically assisting the electrospray process (dubbed Ion Spray), Henion increased the acceptable flow rate to 200 μl min^{-1} (18). This increase was further extended to 2 ml min^{-1} by the addition of a "liquid shield" before the vacuum interface to prevent the entrance of larger droplets (35). A commercial alternative recently introduced is the use of ultrasonic instead of pneumatic nebulization to assist the electrospray process, which is applicable at flow rates up to 1 ml min^{-1} (68).

Capillary electrophoresis/MS has been more successful at vaporizing ionic species than other methods used to date owing to compatible flow rates (61). The most impressive results have been obtained with the coupling of CE to a high-performance ESI-FTMS instrument (34). A synthetic mixture of six proteins was separated using CE, and greater than unit resolution ESI spectra were obtained for molecules as large as carbonic anhydrase (29 kDa) (Figure 9). Fewer than 10 fmol of each component were injected, while acceptable S/N ($>$ 40:1) was maintained. The major weakness of CE is the slow scan speed (6 s per scan), which limits the duty cycle of the mass spectrometer to less than 10%. Improvements in data acquisition and storage should be able to increase scan speeds significantly.

The coupling of MALDI to chromatographic sources has been more problematic owing to the incompatibilities between the continuous flow of sample and a pulsed ionization method. An interface using a continuous flow of sample and a liquid matrix (3-nitrobenzylalcohol) onto the laser probe has been developed, but it is limited to low flow rates

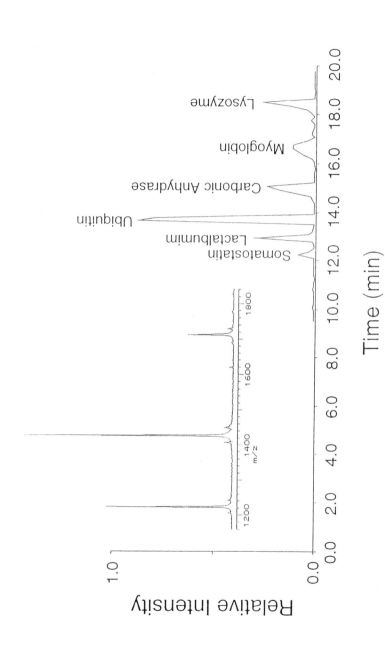

Figure 9 CE-ESI-FTMS ion electropherogram from 6 fmol/component. Inset is mass spectrum obtained for bovine ubiquitin. Reprinted from Ref. 34.

(<5 μl min^{-1}) and has not achieved high resolution (42). An alternative method is direct liquid introduction followed by MALDI on the ice extruded from the end of the capillary (71). Using pneumatic nebulization, Russell has recently demonstrated that MALDI can be performed on aerosol particles (58). Although the initial report showed poor sensitivity due to the low duty cycle of the laser, the technique has demonstrated the ability to function at much higher flow rates (0.5 ml min^{-1}) than the former methods.

CONCLUSION

The introduction of ESI and MALDI has enabled the intact ionization of large biomolecules for mass spectral analysis. Commercial ESI/quadrupole and MALDI/TOF instruments are now used routinely for many applications. The coupling of these ionization sources to high-performance analyzers like FTMS can provide high mass accuracy and resolution as well as MS^n for structural characterization. Instruments with similar performance, now becoming available commercially, should become standard analytical tools in the biochemical laboratory.

ACKNOWLEDGMENT

The authors thank SC Beu, DP Little, PB O'Connor, JP Speir, and TD Wood for assistance with the manuscript. Figures were generously provided by BT Chait, R Feng, and B Ganem. This manuscript was prepared with generous financial support from the National Institutes of Health (GM16609) and the Society of Analytical Chemists of Pittsburgh (summer fellowship for MWS).

Literature Cited

1. Alber GM, Marshall AG, Hill NC, Schweikhard L, Ricca TL. 1993. Ultra-high-resolution Fourier transform ion cyclotron resonance mass spectrometer. *Rev. Sci. Instrum.* 64:1845–52
2. Baca M, Kent SBH. 1992. Direct observation of a ternary complex between the dimeric enzyme HIV-1 protease and a substrate-based inhibitor. *J. Am. Chem. Soc.* 114:3992–93
3. Barber M, Bordoli RS, Sedgwick RD, Tyler AN. 1981. Fast atom bombard-

ment of solids (F.A.B.): a new ion source for mass spectrometry. *J. Chem. Soc. Chem. Commun.* pp. 325–27
4. Beu SC, Senko MW, Quinn JP, McLafferty FW. 1993. Improved Fourier-transform ion-cyclotron-resonance mass spectrometry of large biomolecules. *J. Am. Soc. Mass Spectrom.* 4:190–92
5. Beu SC, Senko MW, Quinn JP, Wampler FM III, McLafferty FW. 1993. Fourier-transform electrospray instru-

mentation for tandem high-resolution mass spectrometry of large molecules. *J. Am. Soc. Mass Spectrom.* 4:557–65

6. Bruce JE, Anderson GA, Hofstadler SA, Winger BE, Smith RD. 1993. Timebase modulation for the correction of cyclotron frequency shifts observed in long-lived transients from Fourier-transform ion-cyclotron-resonance mass spectrometry of electrosprayed biopolymers. *Rapid Commun. Mass Spectrom.* 7:700–3

7. Buchanan MV, Hettich RL. 1993. Fourier transform mass spectrometry of high-mass biomolecules. *Anal. Chem.* 65:A245–59

8. Busch KL, Glish GL, McLuckey SA. 1988. *Mass Spectrometry/Mass Spectrometry.* New York: VCH. 333 pp.

9. Carlin TJ, Freiser BS. 1983. Pulsed valve addition of collision and reagent gases in Fourier transform mass spectrometry. *Anal. Chem.* 55:571–74

10. Castoro JA, Köster C, Wilkins CL. 1992. Matrix-assisted laser desorption/ionization of high-mass molecules by Fourier-transform mass spectrometry *Rapid Commun. Mass Spectrom.* 6:239–41

11. Castoro JA, Wilkins CL. 1993. Ultrahigh resolution matrix-assisted laser desorption/ionization of small proteins by Fourier transform mass spectrometry. *Anal. Chem.* 65:2621–27

12. Chait BT, Wang R, Beavis RC, Kent SBH. 1993. Protein ladder sequencing *Science* 262:89–92

13. Clegg GA, Dole M. 1971. Molecular beams of macroions. III. Zein and polyvinylpyrrolidone. *Biopolymers* 10:821–26

14. Cody RB, Amster IJ, McLafferty FW. 1985. Peptide mixture sequencing by Tandem Fourier-transform mass spectrometry. *Proc. Natl. Acad. Sci. USA* 82:6367–70

15. Comisarow MB, Marshall AG. 1974. Fourier transform ion cyclotron resonance spectroscopy. *Chem. Phys. Lett.* 25:282–83

16. Cornish TJ, Cotter RJ. 1993. Tandem time-of-flight mass spectrometer. *Anal. Chem.* 65:1043–47

17. Cotter RJ. 1992. Time-of-flight mass spectrometry for the structural analysis of biological molecules. *Anal. Chem.* 65:A1027–39

18. Covey TR, Bonner RF, Shushan BI, Henion J. 1988. The determination of protein, oligonucleotide and peptide molecular weights by ion-spray mass

spectrometry. *Rapid Commun. Mass Spectrom.* 2:249–56

19. Dobberstein P, Schroeder E. 1993. Accurate mass determination of a high molecular weight protein using electrospray ionization with a magnetic sector instrument. *Rapid Commun. Mass Spectrom.* 7:861–64

20. Feng R, Konishi Y. 1992. Analysis of antibodies and other large glycoproteins in the mass range of 150,000–200,000 Da by electrospray ionization mass spectrometry. *Anal. Chem.* 64:2090–95

21. Feng R, Konishi Y. 1993. Collisionally-activated dissociation of multiply charged 150-kDa antibody ions. *Anal. Chem.* 65:645–49

22. Fenn JB, Mann M, Meng CK, Wong SF, Whitehouse CM. 1990. Electrospray ionization-principles and practice. *Mass Spectrom. Rev.* 9:37–70

23. Ganem B, Li Y-T, Henion JD. 1991. Detection of noncovalent receptor-ligand complexes by mass spectrometry. *J. Am. Chem. Soc.* 113:6294–96

24. Ganem B, Li Y-T, Henion JD. 1991. Observation of noncovalent enzyme-substrate and enzyme-product complexes by ion-spray mass spectrometry. *J. Am. Chem. Soc.* 113:7818–19

25. Gaskell SJ, ed. 1986. *Mass Spectrometry in Biomedical Research.* Chichester: Wiley. 492 pp.

26. Griffin PR, Kumar S, Shabanowitz J, Charbonneau H, Namkung PC, et al. 1989. The amino acid sequence of the sex steroid–binding protein of rabbit serum. *J. Biol. Chem.* 264:19066–75

27. Guan S, Marshall AG. 1993. Multiply pulsed collision gas for ion axialization in Fourier-transform ion cyclotron resonance mass spectrometry. *Rapid Commun. Mass Spectrom.* 7:857–60

28. Guan S, Wahl MC, Wood TD, Marshall AG. 1993. Enhanced mass resolving power, sensitivity, and selectivity in laser desorption Fourier transform ion cyclotron resonance mass spectrometry by ion axialization and cooling. *Anal. Chem.* 65:1753–57

29. Guan Z, Hofstadler SA, Laude DA. 1993. Remeasurement of electrosprayed proteins in the trapped ion cell of a Fourier transform ion cyclotron resonance mass spectrometer. *Anal. Chem.* 65:1588–93

30. Henry KD, McLafferty FW. 1990. Electrospray ionization with Fourier-transform mass spectrometry. Charge state assignment for resolved isotopic peaks. *Org. Mass Spectrom.* 25:490–92

784   SENKO & McLAFFERTY

31. Henry KD, Quinn JP, McLafferty FW. 1991. High-resolution electrospray mass spectra of large molecules. *J. Am. Chem. Soc.* 113:5447–49
32. Henry KD, Williams ER, Wang BH, McLafferty FW, Shabanowitz J, Hunt DF. 1989. Fourier-transform mass spectrometry of large molecules by electrospray ionization. *Proc. Natl. Acad. Sci. USA* 85:9075–78
33. Hillenkamp F, Karas M, Beavis RC, Chait BT. 1991. Matrix-assisted laser desorption/ionization mass spectrometry of biopolymers. *Anal. Chem.* 63: A1193–203
34. Hofstadler SA, Wahl JH, Bruce JE, Smith RD. 1993. On-line capillary electrophoresis with Fourier transform ion cyclotron resonance mass spectrometry. *J. Am. Chem. Soc.* 115:6983–84
35. Hopfgartner G, Wachs T, Bean K, Henion J. 1993. High-flow ion spray liquid chromatography/mass spectrometry. *Anal. Chem.* 65:439–46
36. Hutchens TW, Yi T-T. 1993. New desorption strategies for the mass spectrometric analysis of macromolecules. *Rapid Commun. Mass Spectrom.* 7: 576–80
37. Jardine DR, Morgan J, Alderdice DS, Derrick PJ. 1992. A tandem time-of-flight mass spectrometer. *Org. Mass Spectrom.* 27:1077–83
38. Jonsson G, Hedin A, Hakansson P, Sundqvist BUR, Bennich H, Roepstorff P. 1989. Compensation for non-normal ejection of large molecular ions in plasma-desorption mass spectrometry. *Rapid Commun. Mass Spectrom.* 3: 190–91
39. Karas M, Bachmann D, Bahr U, Hillenkamp F. 1987. Matrix-assisted ultraviolet laser desorption of non-volatile compounds. *Int. J. Mass Spectrom. Ion Proc.* 78:53–68
40. Köster C, Castoro JA, Wilkins CL. 1992. High-resolution matrix-assisted laser desorption/ionization of biomolecules by Fourier transform mass spectrometry. *J. Am. Chem. Soc.* 114:7572–74
41. Labowsky M, Whitehouse C, Fenn JB. 1993. Three-dimensional deconvolution of multiply charged spectra. *Rapid Commun. Mass Spectrom.* 7:71–84
42. Li L, Wang APL, Coulson LD. 1993. Continuous-flow matrix-assisted laser desorption ionization mass spectrometry. *Anal. Chem.* 65:493–95
43. Li Y-T, Hsieh Y-L, Henion JD, Senko MW, McLafferty FW, Ganem B. 1993. Mass spectrometric studies on noncovalent dimers of leucine zipper peptides. *J. Am. Chem. Soc.* 115:8409–13
44. Light-Wahl KJ, Loo JA, Edmonds CG, Smith RD, Witkowska HE, et al. 1993. Collisionally activated dissociation and tandem mass spectrometry of intact hemoglobin β-chain variant proteins with electrospray ionization. *Biol. Mass Spectrom.* 22:112–20
45. Light-Wahl KJ, Springer DL, Winger BE, Edmonds CG, Camp DG, et al. 1993. Observation of a small oligonucleotide duplex by electrospray ionization mass spectrometry. *J. Am. Chem. Soc.* 115:803–4
46. Loo JA, Edmonds CG, Smith RD. 1991. Tandem mass spectrometry of very large molecules: serum albumin sequence information from multiply charged ions formed by electrospray ionization. *Anal. Chem.* 63:2488–99
47. Loo JA, Edmonds CG, Smith RD. 1993. Tandem mass spectrometry of very large molecules. 2. Dissociation of multiply charged proline-containing proteins from electrospray ionization. *Anal. Chem.* 65:425–38
48. Loo JA, Loo RRO, Light KJ, Edmonds CG, Smith RD. 1992. Multiply charged negative ions by electrospray ionization of polypeptides and proteins. *Anal. Chem.* 64:81–88
49. Loo JA, Quinn JP, Ryu SI, Henry KD, Senko MW, McLafferty FW. 1992. High-resolution tandem mass spectrometry of large biomolecules. *Proc. Natl. Acad. Sci. USA* 89:286–89
50. Loo JA, Udseth HR, Smith RD. 1988. Collisional effects on the charge distribution of ions from large molecules, formed by electrospray-ionization mass spectrometry. *Rapid Commun. Mass Spectrom.* 2:207–10
51. Macfarlane RD, Torgerson DF. 1976. Californium-252 plasma desorption mass spectrometry. *Science* 191:920–25
52. Mamyrin BA, Karatajev VI, Shmikk DV, Zagulin VA. 1973. The Mass-reflectron, a new nonmagnetic time-of-flight mass spectrometer with high resolution. *Soviet Phys. JETP* 37:45–48
53. Mann M, Meng CK, Fenn JB. 1989. Interpreting mass spectra of multiply charged ions. *Anal. Chem.* 61:1702–8
54. Marshall AG, Grosshans PB. 1991. Fourier transform ion cyclotron resonance mass spectrometry: the teenage years. *Anal. Chem.* 63:A215–29
55. Marshall AG, Verdun FR. 1990. *Fourier Transforms in NMR, Optical, and Mass*

Spectrometry. Amsterdam: Elsevier 450 pp.

56. McEwen CN, Larsen BS, eds. 1990. *Mass Spectrometry of Biological Materials.* New York: Dekker. 515 pp.

57. McLafferty FW, ed. 1983. *Tandem Mass Spectrometry.* New York: Wiley. 506 pp.

58. Murray KK, Russell DH. 1993. Liquid sample introduction for matrix-assisted laser desorption ionization. *Anal. Chem.* 65:2534–37

59. Reinhold BB, Reinhold VN. 1992. Electrospray ionization mass spectrometry: deconvolution by an entropy-based algorithm. *J. Am. Soc. Mass Spectrom.* 3:207–15

60. Smith RD, Loo JA, Loo RRO, Busman M, Udseth HR. 1991. Principles and practice of electrospray ionization—mass spectrometry for large polypeptides and proteins. *Mass Spectrom. Rev.* 10:359–451

61. Smith RD, Wahl JH, Godlett DR, Hofstadler SA. 1993. Capillary electrophoresis/mass spectrometry. *Anal. Chem.* 65:A574–84

62. Spier JP, Gorman GS, Pitsenberger CC, Turner CA, Wang PP, Amster IJ. 1993. Remeasurement of ions using quadrupolar excitation Fourier transform ion cyclotron resonance spectrometry. *Anal. Chem.* 65:1746–52

63. Suckau D, Shi Y, Beu SC, Senko MW, Quinn JP, et al. 1993. Coexisting stable conformations of gaseous protein ions. *Proc. Natl. Acad. Sci. USA* 90:790–93

64. Sundqvist B, Macfarlane RD. 1985. ^{252}Cf-plasma desorption mass spectrometry. *Mass Spectrom. Rev.* 4:421–60

65. Tabet JC, Rapin J, Poretti M, Gaumann T. 1986. ^{252}Cf plasma desorption-ionization with a Fourier transform mass spectrometer: analysis of thermolabile and non-volatile biomolecules. *Chimia* 40:169–71

66. Tanaka K, Hiroaki W, Ido Y, Akita S, Yoshida Y, Yoshida T. 1988. Protein and polymer analyses up to m/z 100,000 by laser ionization time-of-flight mass spectrometry. *Rapid Commun. Mass Spectrom.* 2:151–53

67. Watson CH, Baykut G, Eyler JR. 1987. Laser photodissociation of gaseous ions formed by laser desorption. *Anal. Chem.* 59:1133–38

68. Whitehouse CM, Andrien B, Banks F, Quinn J, Shen S. 1993 *Performance improvements of an ultrasonic nebulizer assisted electrospray ion source.* Presented at 41st ASMS Conf. Mass Spectrom. Allied Top., San Francisco

69. Whitehouse CM, Dreyer RN, Yamashita M, Fenn JB. 1985. Electrospray interface for liquid chromatographs and mass spectrometers. *Anal. Chem.* 57: 675–79

70. William ER, Henry KD, McLafferty FW. 1990. Multiple remeasurement of ions in Fourier-transform mass spectrometry. *J. Am. Chem. Soc.* 112:6157–62

71. William ER, Jones GC, Fang L, Zare RN. 1992. Laser-desorption tandem time-of-flight mass spectrometry with continuous liquid introduction. In *Applied Spectroscopy in Material Science II,* ed. WE Golden, 2:172–81. Bellingham, WA: SPIE. 230 pp.

72. Williams ER, McLafferty FW. 1990. High resolution and tandem Fourier-transform mass spectrometry with californium-252 plasma desorption. *J. Am. Soc. Mass Spectrom.* 1:427–30

73. Winger BE, Hofstadler SA, Bruce JE, Udseth HR, Smith RD. 1993. High-resolution accurate mass measurements of biomolecules using a new electrospray ionization ion cyclotron resonance mass spectrometer. *J. Am. Soc. Mass Spectrom.* 4:566–77

74. Wood TD, Schweikhard L, Marshall AG. 1992. Mass-to-charge ratio upper limits for matrix-assisted laser desorption Fourier transform ion cyclotron resonance mass spectrometry. *Anal. Chem.* 64:1461–69

75. Yost RA, Enke CG. 1983. See Ref. 57, pp. 175–95

76. Zaia J, Annan RS, Biemann K. 1992. The correct molecular weight of myoglobin, a common calibrant for mass spectometry. *Rapid Commun. Mass Spectrom.* 6:32–36

Annu. Rev. Biophys. Biomol. Struct. 1994. 23:787–818

MECHANICAL PROPERTIES OF THE RED CELL MEMBRANE IN RELATION TO MOLECULAR STRUCTURE AND GENETIC DEFECTS

Narla Mohandas

Life Sciences Division, Lawrence Berkeley Laboratory, University of California, Berkeley, California 94720

Evan Evans

Departments of Pathology and Physics, University of British Columbia, Vancouver, Canada

KEY WORDS: membrane rigidity, erythrocyte, skeletal protein, integral protein, hemoglobin

CONTENTS

787

1056–8700/94/0610–0787$05.00

INTRODUCTION

Over the past 20 years or so, extensive biochemical and biophysical evidence has been accumulated that yields a complex picture of membrane composition, microstructure, and cell deformability. Although detailed, the picture at present remains essentially a phenomenological "sketch" with some confusing (even conflicting) elements. However, encouraging developments have begun to bridge the gap between what we know about membrane biochemistry and our knowledge of in situ physical properties. Our intent here is to provide a contemporary view of the relation between red cell membrane molecular architecture and material (mechanical) properties, emphasizing new developments and unexpected features to underscore the subtleties of all "ultrasoft" cell interfaces. We do not present a thorough historical review of research in this area because several excellent reviews are available.

UNIVERSAL MATERIAL DESIGN FOR EUKARYOTIC CELL INTERFACES

A common material design (28) has evolved for the capsular shell of eukaryotic organisms: i.e. a lamellar composite with a lipid bilayer core, supported by a cortical scaffolding of peripheral proteins, and studded with a superficial forest of peptidoglycans (see schematic Figure 1a). The complete cortex structure is usually thin in comparison to cell dimensions but topographically rough on the submicroscopic scale. The mechanical stiffness of the membrane capsule is embodied in a set of independent rigidities that represent local opposition of the composite interface to deformation by surface expansion (dilation), shear (rectangular extension without expansion), and bending (35). Though much is known about the deformability of the red cell, the essential question is how to relate the deformation properties of the whole cell to the molecular composition and architecture of the membrane. In addressing this question, we begin with a brief overview of the structural organization and biochemical composition of the red cell membrane and note the insights gained from studies of red cell mem-

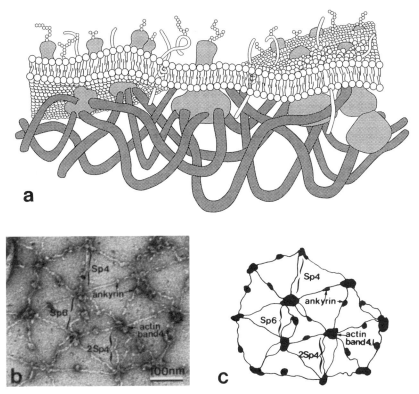

Figure 1 (*a*) Artistic perspective of red cell membrane architecture on the nanoscale. The sketch emphasizes the dimensional proportionality of the thick cytoskeletal structure to the undulating bilayer topography. (*b, c*) Spread red cell membrane skeleton examined by negative staining electron microscopy: (*b*) High magnification of the spread meshwork reveals the hexagonal lattice of junctional complexes; (*c*) putative location of the structural elements is shown schematically (panels *b* and *c* kindly proved by Dr. Shih-Chun Liu).

brane pathologies. Then, in the context of these molecular features, we examine the current working model for the structural basis of membrane elastic properties.

BIOCHEMICAL AND STRUCTURAL ORGANIZATION OF THE RED CELL MEMBRANE

The red cell membrane has been well characterized biochemically and the structural organization of the various lipid and protein components well delineated (3, 4, 37, 47, 75, 76, 79). About 52% of the membrane mass is protein, 40% is lipid, and 8% is carbohydrate. The major lipid components are unesterified cholesterol and phospholipids, which are present in nearly equimolar quantities, while free fatty acid and glycolipids are present in small amounts. The phospholipid composition of the membrane is as follows: phosphatidylcholine (PC), 30%; sphingomyelin (SM), 25%; phosphatidylethanolamine (PE), 28%; and phosphatidylserine (PS), 14%, with phospholipids such as phosphatidic acid, phosphatidylinositol 4-phosphate, and phosphatidylinositol 4, 5-diphosphate constituting about 2–3% of the total. These phospholipids are asymmetrically distributed in the membrane, with more that 75% of the choline-containing neutral phospholipids PC and SM found in the outer monolayer of lipid bilayer, while 80% of PE and all PS, the negatively charged phospholipids, are localized in the inner monolayer.

Analysis of proteins of the red cell membrane by sodium dodecyl sulfate-polyacrylamide gel electrophoresis (SDS-PAGE) in one dimension reveals about a dozen distinct species, most of which have been characterized (37). By contrast, two-dimensional separation employing isoelectric focusing and SDS-PAGE shows the membrane to be composed of more than 100 different proteins, many of which are yet to be characterized. The proteins of the membrane are divided into two general groups: integral and peripheral proteins. The integral proteins are tightly bound to the membrane through hydrophobic interactions with the lipids in the bilayer. Band 3 and glycophorins belong to this class; these proteins span the membrane and have distinct structural and functional domains, both within the bilayer and on either side of the membrane. The peripheral membrane proteins are located on the cytoplasmic surface of the lipid bilayer and can be readily released from the membrane by simple manipulation of ionic strength of the milieu or various other protein perturbants. The peripheral proteins, which include spectrin, actin, and protein 4.1, constitute the membrane skeleton.

The most abundant and best-studied integral proteins of the red cell membrane are band 3 and a family of sialoglycoproteins called glycophorins (1, 12, 71). Band 3 is the major integral protein, constituting about 15–20% of total membrane protein. Recent cloning studies (48, 72) have demonstrated that this protein is the product of a gene that encodes a 911-amino acid protein (101,791 M_r). There are approximately 1×10^6 copies of band 3 in each red cell. This protein is composed of three dissimilar and functionally distinct domains (48, 72). The hydrophilic, cytoplasmic domain (residues 1 to 403) interacts in vitro with a variety of peripheral membrane and cytoplasmic proteins, including ankyrin, protein 4.1, protein 4.2, hemoglobin, and a variety of glycolytic enzymes. The hydrophobic transmembrane domain (residues 404 to 882) contains multiple membrane-spanning domains that form the anion transporter. The function of the acidic C-terminal domain (residues 883 to 911) is unknown. Both the N and C termini of band 3 are on the cytoplasmic side of the membrane. Band 3 contains a single N-glycosidically linked oligosaccharide that can express the blood group antigen activities I and i. The two established functions of band 3 in the membrane are: (*a*) its ability to transport anions (which results in the one-for-one exchange of HCO_3^- or Cl^- across the membrane) and (*b*) its apparent role in physically linking the lipid bilayer to the underlying membrane skeleton, putatively through its interaction with ankyrin and secondarily through binding to protein 4.1 or protein 4.2 (46).

The four sialic acid–rich glycoproteins (glycophorins A, B, C, and D) belong to a class of integral proteins termed glycophorins, constituting approximately 2% of the total red cell membrane proteins (1, 12, 43, 52). Glycophorins A, B, and C are distinctly different polypeptides containing 131, 72, and 128 residues, respectively. These proteins are made up of three domains: The cytoplasmic domain contains a cluster of basic residues positioned near the plasma membrane; the hydrophobic domain forms a single α-helix spanning the bilayer; and the extracellular domain is heavily glycosylated. The glycophorin A molecule carries the MN blood group specificity, glycophorin B the Ss specificity, and glycophorin C the Gerbich blood group specificity. The presence of sialic acid residues imparts a strong net negative charge to the cell surface; this charge is functionally important in reducing the interaction of red cells with one another as well as of red cells with other cells, including vascular endothelium (12). Glycophorin C appears to interact with protein 4.1 and, through this association, regulate the membrane content of protein 4.1 (61). In addition to these sialoglycoproteins, a number of integral proteins are present in the red cell membrane that carry blood group–specific determinants, such Rh, Duffy, and Kell. It is thought that some of these integral proteins have both a membrane skeleton–linking function as well as a transport function in the red cell.

The filamentous network of peripheral proteins seems to be anchored to the bilayer by a number of integral proteins. The network, generally referred to as the membrane skeleton, is composed of three principal components: spectrin, actin, and protein 4.1 (3, 4). Spectrin is a flexible, rodlike molecule present in red cells at approximately 2×10^5 copies per cell (constituting 20–25% of the mass of membrane proteins). Spectrin is composed of two nonidentical subunits of 260,000 Daltons

(α-subunit) and 246,000 Daltons (β-subunit) intertwined side by side to form a heterodimer with a contour length of approximately 100 nm (40). Each polypeptide is organized into a number of independently folded domains, each containing 106 residues (67). These subunits are linked by flexible regions analogous to beads on a string. Spectrin heterodimers associate head to head to form ($\alpha\beta$)$_2$ tetramers, which have a contour length of approximately 200 nm. Tetrameric species of spectrin appear to predominate in the membrane skeleton. Oligomers larger than the tetramers are also observed that appear to be formed by spectrin dimers joined by head-to-head linkages at a central ring (58). The tail ends of spectrin tetramers are associated with short oligomers of actin composed of 12 monomers. Red cell actin is unusual in being organized into short, highly uniform filaments approximately 35 nm long. Actin constitutes approximately 5% of the mass of membrane proteins. The strict control of actin filament length may be modulated by the proteins tropomyosin and tropomodulin (39). On average, six spectrin ends complex with each actin oligomer to create an irregular network with an approximately hexagonal lattice. Each spectrin-actin junction is stabilized by the formation of a ternary complex with protein 4.1. Protein 4.1 is composed of 622 amino acids; approximately 2 $\times$ 10^5 copies of this molecule, constituting approximately 5% of the mass of membrane proteins, are present in each red cell. Independent spectrin-actin interactions are weak but become greatly stabilized by protein 4.1 (17). This stabilization occurs through direct interaction of protein 4.1 with spectrin at sites on the molecule close to the region in which spectrin interacts with actin oligomers. Adducin is yet another skeletal protein that may stabilize the interaction of spectrin with actin (4, 41). However, adducin is much less abundant than protein 4.1 in the red cell, with only 3 $\times$ 10^4 molecules present in each cell. Thus, the red cell membrane skeleton is envisioned as an irregular network in which the basic unit is a hexagonal lattice composed of six spectrin molecules (9, 45). This structural model for organization of the membrane skeleton is supported by high-resolution electron micrographs of isolated membranes (Figure 1b). The micrographs show a highly periodic and remarkably regular organization of the spectrin-actin-protein 4.1 complexes in which each complex is linked to adjacent complexes by multiple spectrin tetramers.

The physical linkage of membrane skeleton to the lipid bilayer is provided by ankyrin (band 2.1), which appears to interact with spectrin in the skeleton and with band 3 localized in the bilayer. Ankyrin, a polypeptide of 1879 amino acids, demonstrates distinct binding sites in vitro for both β-spectrin and band 3 and is present in the red cell at

1×10^5 copies per cell, constituting approximately 5% of the mass of membrane proteins (49). The ankyrin-binding site on β-spectrin is located approximately 20 nm from the C terminus. It has been suggested that interaction of the integral protein glycophorin C with the skeletal component protein 4.1 may also provide additional linkage between the skeleton and the bilayer. However, experimental evidence to support this thesis is not strong. Ankyrin appears to be the primary determinant of mechanical coupling of the lipid bilayer to the membrane skeleton. The composite structure of network and bilayer is responsible for the unique properties of the red cell membrane.

For the membrane to deform normally, the skeletal network must be able to undergo a conformational rearrangement in which spectrin molecules fold and unfold (11). If intermolecular or intramolecular associations of spectrin are increased, conformational changes will be hindered and deformability decreased. The proximity of the network to the bilayer also plays a role in determining the ability of the red cell membrane to deform. For example, a large increase in the number of linkages between the bilayer and the membrane skeleton will bring a large portion of the skeletal network close to the bilayer and again inhibit the ability of the spectrin molecules to undergo the necessary structural rearrangements. This mechanism implies that increased association of the cytoplasmic domains of integral proteins with the skeletal network could markedly hinder the ability of the membrane to undergo deformation. Also, intercalated components such as auxiliary structural proteins and bound hemoglobin molecules could act as network expanders and restrict conformations of the network or increase viscous retardation and thereby alter the response of the membrane to dynamic deformation. Finally, membrane failure following hyperextension occurs at the weakest of the protein–protein linkages (spectrin–spectrin junction or spectrin–actin–protein 4.1 junction). Thus, the durability and deformability of the membrane depend critically on structural features of the membrane governed by skeletal network topology, the linkages between the network and the bilayer, and even cytoplasmic components that act as network expanders.

INSIGHTS GAINED FROM STUDIES OF RED CELL MEMBRANE PATHOLOGIES

Altered membrane function has long been recognized as a distinguishing feature of red cells in a number of congenital and hereditary hemolytic anemias. Recent biochemical and molecular-biological analyses have indeed defined a number of specific protein defects in various red cell phenotypes, while biophysical characterization of these red cells has defined corresponding membrane alterations (54, 55). The combination of these approaches is beginning to provide a clearer understanding both of the molecular basis for red cell abnormalities and of the functional consequences of these abnormalities. Here we limit our discussion to outlining how information obtained from characterization of the various pathologic cells can be used to assess various hypotheses about the structural basis for red cell membrane mechanical properties.

Effect of Lateral Skeletal Protein Linkages on Membrane Cohesion

Membrane failure due to weakening of the lateral protein–protein linkages (spectrin–spectrin junction, spectrin–actin–protein 4.1 junction) leads to generation of fragmented red cells and other shape abnormalities as seen in the congenital red cell disorders, hereditary elliptocytosis (HE) and hereditary pyropoikilocytosis (HPP) (54). In HE, elliptocytic shape is the dominant morphologic feature of red cells, whereas more striking shape abnormalities (including fragmented cells and microspherocytes) characterize red cells in HPP. A number of different membrane protein defects have been shown to result in elliptocytosis. Qualitative defects in α-spectrin, β-spectrin, and protein 4.1 and a quantitative deficiency of protein 4.1 have been identified in HE (17, 20). A common feature of the red cell in these disorders, irrespective of the underlying molecular defect, is that membrane mechanical stability is decreased (54). Correlation of decreased membrane mechanical stability of red cells with qualitative and quantitative defects in protein 4.1 is well documented (50, 73). Partial deficiency of protein 4.1 (50% decrease) results in elliptocytic morphology and some reduction in membrane stability but does not lead to cell fragmentation in vivo. By comparison, complete deficiency of protein 4.1 results in marked elliptocytosis and pronounced cell fragmentation in vivo. Likewise, membrane stability is greatly reduced in vitro. Normal mechanical stability can be restored to these unstable membranes by reconstitution of the purified protein 4.1 into deficient membranes (70). Red cells from a heterozygous individual show a qualitative defect in protein 4.1 that results from deletion of 80 amino acids that encode the spectrin binding domain (protein $4.1_{68/65}$). These cells also exhibit decreased mechanical stability and elliptocytic morphology (50). These data firmly establish an important functional role for protein 4.1 in regulating membrane cohesion. They also lend support to the general concept that weakening of spectrin-actin-protein 4.1 association will lead to decreased membrane cohension. In other studies of elliptocytic red cells that possess decreased spectrin self-association (decreased spectrin tetramer and increased dimer content of the membrane) due to mutations in α- and β-spectrin, reductions in membrane mechanical stability have also been documented (42). Again, the degree of mechanical instability appears directly related to the extent of decrease in spectrin self-association—i.e. the greater the decrease in membrane spectrin tetramer content the greater is the decrease in membrane mechanical stability (42, 44). Together, these studies of elliptocytes confirm the prediction that disruption of either of the two identified lateral protein associations in the membrane skeleton will damage membrane mechanical integrity and cohesion.

Effect of Bilayer–Skeletal Protein Network Linkages on Membrane Cohesion

The other form of membrane failure involves a separation of the lipid bilayer from the underlying membrane skeleton—a separation that reflects a decreased cohesion between the bilayer and the membrane skeleton. This type of failure is demonstrated by red cells in hereditary spherocytosis (HS), which is considered to be a prototypical red cell disorder involving membrane dysfunction (2, 15, 19). Recent biochemical evidence suggests that the HS disorder is heterogeneous in terms of molecular defects. Decreased membrane spectrin content, as well as quantitative deficiencies of band 3, ankyrin, and protein 4.2, have been reported in association with the HS phenotype (15, 40, 62, 63). A common feature of these red cells, irrespective of the underlying molecular defect, is that they all exhibit loss of surface area. The loss of surface area is the result of dissociation of the bilayer from the skeleton. The spherocytosis caused by spectrin deficiency indicates a requirement for normal spectrin density to ensure proper cohesion between the bilayer and the membrane skeleton, whereas spherocytoses due to band 3, protein 4.2, and ankyrin deficiencies point to the requirement for linkages between the bilayer and the membrane skeleton to ensure membrane cohesion (15, 62, 63). Clearly, reduction either in skeletal density or in number of linkages between the bilayer and the skeleton can lead to loss of membrane cohesion. There are, however, significant gaps in our understanding of the coupling between the bilayer and the membrane skeleton and of the forces necessary to disrupt this linkage.

Effect of Bilayer–Skeletal Protein Network Linkages on Membrane Deformation

Physical association of the network to the bilayer is an important determinant in the elastic resilience of the red cell membrane shape. Clearly, a minimum number of linkages between the bilayer and the membrane skeleton are needed for membrane cohesion, but a large increase in the number of linkages will draw major portions of the skeletal network close to the bilayer and thereby hinder the ability of the spectrin molecules to undergo the conformation rearrangements necessary for deformation. The marked decrease in the ability of hereditary ovalocytic red cells to undergo membrane deformation appears to be an example of the importance of this mechanism in regulating membrane deformation. Measurement of membrane deformability (using the ektacytometer and elastic shear modulus by micropipette method) showed that ovalocytic membranes are 10–20 times more rigid than normal membranes (56, 57). However, in contrast to elliptocytes, ovalocytes are mechanically stable. Recent studies have shown that a mutation in band 3 involving the deletion of amino acids 400–408 at the boundary between the cytoplasmic and the first transmembrane domain is responsible for the ovalocytic phenotype (57, 65). Based on the structural consequences of this mutation, it has been proposed that the mutation in band 3 induces a conformational change in the cytoplasmic domain that leads to increased interaction and entanglement with the skeletal network. The network could be pulled closer to the bilayer where normal unwinding and stretching of the spectrin tetramers would be hindered and membrane rigidity thus increased.

Further support for a role of the cytoplasmic domains of integral proteins in regulating membrane rigidity is provided by studies on ligand-induced changes in properties of normal red cell membranes. Binding of monoclonal antibodies specific for the exoplasmic domain of glycophorin A to red cell membranes led to phenomenal increases in membrane rigidity (13, 14). Because Fab fragments also induced membrane rigidity, it appeared that formation of an external lattice of cross-linked glycophorin A molecules was not responsible for the stiffening, and that the process was likely to involve a transmembrane communication through the cytoplasmic domain of glycophorin A. The importance of the cytoplasmic domain was underscored by the finding that binding of antibodies to a variant glycophorin A with truncated cytoplasmic domain (Miltenberger V) did not induce increased membrane rigidity. On the basis of these findings, Chasis et al proposed that (a) ligand binding to glycophorin A induces a conformational change in the cytoplasmic domain that results in its increased association with the skeletal network and (b) this increased association is responsible for changes in membrane rigidity. Recent lateral mobility studies on glycophorin A have confirmed the increased association of the cytoplasmic domain with the membrane skeleton following ligand binding (16).

Effect of Network Expanders on Membrane Deformation

Auxiliary structural proteins and membrane-associated hemoglobin molecules act to impede changes in the conformation of spectrin. For example, measurements of the extensional rigidity and elastic recovery after extension of oxygenated sickle red cells have shown that both membrane shear modulus and viscous retardation increased with increasing cell hemoglobin concentration, whereas these properties were independent of hemoglobin concentration in normal red cells (31). That the increased rigidity of sickle cells was improved by hydrating the cells and decreasing cell hemoglobin concentration implied that increased association of sickle hemoglobin with the membrane could be responsible for the observed membrane behavior. This implication was borne out by the observations that extensional rigidity of normal membranes resealed with sickle hemoglobin was higher than those of either normal membranes reloaded with normal hemoglobin or native normal red cells (32). These data lend strong support to the concept that increased concentration of mutant hemoglobins can affect membrane material behavior by acting as network expanders.

   Most of the pathologic red cells just discussed are examples of cells in which genetically inherited defects involving different membrane proteins lead to defective assembly of the membrane with altered material properties. These defects in membrane assembly appear to be responsible for the varying expression of increased membrane extensional rigidity, decreased cohesion between the bilayer the membrane skeleton, or increased membrane mechanical instability. Studies on pathologic red cells are thus beginning to elucidate the effects of various membrane components, and that of cytoplasmic proteins such as hemoglobin, on the mechanical behavior of the red cell membrane.

STRUCTURAL DETERMINANTS OF RED CELL MEMBRANE ELASTIC PROPERTIES

Over the past 20 years the working model for the red cell membrane has been a simple superposition. The bilayer core has been treated as a tightly condensed surface liquid and the protein scaffolding as a loose elastic network (30). The superficial carbohydrate and peptide moieties have been considered part of the bilayer component because they are anchored to integral membrane proteins and lipids embedded in the fluid region. Although this model remains viable, many subtle features and important refinements have come to light in recent years. Here we examine the structural determinants of the elastic rigidities as exposed by mechanical experiments carried out over the past 20 years.

Membrane Area (Dilational Elasticity)

The material model for the red cell membrane was introduced originally to rationalize an apparent anomaly: Osmotically swollen red cell spheres seem to be undeformable (and rupture under small expansions) whereas unswollen red cells are extremely flaccid, and easily extend without rupture (23, 24, 66). Initially recognized intuitively (30) and subsequently proven (23, 24, 66), the origin of the cell area restriction is the lipid bilayer component of the membrane, which creates an envelope of nearly fixed area with little mechanical opposition to shape change unless it is completely filled to a sphere. The tight area restrictions of both a lipid bilayer vesicle and a red cell are readily demonstrated by mechanical aspiration into a suction pipette (Figure 2a). The suction pressure P rises sharply when the aspiration length L is sufficient to sphere the exterior portion of these capsules. Indeed, as shown in Figure 2b, the pressure increases (when scaled by the outer radius R_o) are nearly identical if the phospholipid:cholesterol ratio is the same for both red cell and lipid bilayer vesicle. Pressurization of the spherical form must increase the total area of the capsule because the interior volume remains essentially constant (held by the strong osmotic activity of impermeable solutes). Thus, the slopes of the linear elastic responses exhibited in Figure 2b yield comparable elastic constants ($K_M \approx K_{Bl}$) for area expansion of the whole red cell and vesicle as given approximately by,

$$K \approx \frac{R_o^2}{(1 - R_p/R_o)^2} \left(\frac{dP}{dL}\right) \qquad \sim 500 \text{ dyn cm}^{-1} @ 20°C \qquad 1.$$

where R_p is the pipette radius. [The modulus K relates the proportionality between membrane tensions $\bar{\tau}$ (reduction in surface pressure) and the fractional increase α in area of the surface.]

The lipid bilayer component also dominates the cohesive strength of the red cell as quantitated by the tension at lysis (6, 33, 59). Both red cells and lipid bilayer vesicles rupture at about the same area expansion (~ 2–3%). There is no indication that the peripheral protein scaffolding

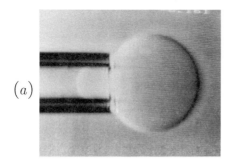
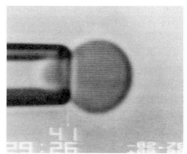

(a)

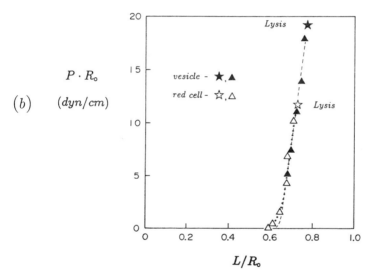

(b) $P \cdot R_o$ (dyn/cm)

Figure 2 (*a*) Videomicrographs of a giant phospholipid bilayer vesicle (left-diameter ~20 μm) and an osmotically preswollen red cell (right-diameter 6 μm) drawn into suction micropipets. The lipid composition of the bilayer was a 1:1 mixture of phosphatidyl-choline:cholesterol. (*b*) Relation between suction pressure P (scaled by outer spherical radius R_o) and projection length L (normalized by radius R_o). The increase in projection length is proportional to dilation of total membrane area and the slope yields the elastic modulus.

adds to the area dilation resistance for the whole red cell or to its cohesion. Recent studies have shown that elastic dilation properties of red cells are dominated by the cholesterol content of the membrane (6, 33, 59). High concentrations of cholesterol (nearly 1:1 with phospholipids) greatly strengthen the bilayer; the lysis tension is increased several fold over that of pure phospholipid bilayers. It is interesting that red cells lyse at tension levels ($\sim$10 dyn cm^{-1}) somewhat lower than values for bilayer vesicles ($\sim$20 dyn cm^{-1}) of the same phospholipid:cholesterol ratio (33, 36, 60, 77). Perhaps integral proteins act to weaken the bilayer? Although the overall cell area is held fixed by the cohesive lipid bilayer, large local expansions or condensations of the subsurface protein (spectrin) network are permitted by linkage of the network to the fluid bilayer (see below).

Membrane Bending Elasticity

In the hierarchy of mechanical rigidities for deformation of the red cell, the lipid bilayer dominates both the largest stiffness—the restriction to area dilation—and the smallest stiffness—the opposition to bending (35). Over the years, red cell deformation and shape transformation have been predicted by several analyses based on the concept that bending elasticity fully regulates the shape of flaccid unswollen cells (10, 21, 25). Even though such a fluid model is inadequate for the red cell membrane, bending rigidity remains the essential elastic property that smoothes the surface when deformed. For example, when tension is applied to the membrane by suction of a cell into a pipette, the bending stiffness k_c regulates the sharpness of the membrane bend at the entrance (27); the square of the local curvature $\hat{c}_m^2$ is proportional to the ratio τ_m/k_c. Since the bend at the entrance to the pipette in Figure 2 is too sharp to be detected optically even when the tension is as low as $\sim$0.01 dyn cm^{-1}, i.e. $>4 \times 10^4$ cm^{-1}, the curvature elastic modulus must be well below 10^{-11} erg. A similar bound is found from the threshold suction P_c required to bend the membrane into a hemispherical cap inside the micropipet of radius R_p, i.e.

$$P_c \approx c \cdot k_c / R_p^3 \qquad\qquad 2.$$

where the prefactor c is of order 4–6. This threshold suction is only a few microatmospheres (10^{-6} atm $\approx$ 0.01 mm H$_2$O).

Several types of experiments have been employed to evaluate the bending stiffness of the red cell membrane (7, 26, 80). Because of experimental limitations, the results vary by an order of magnitude from 10^{-13} to 10^{-12} erg. However, the values are consistent with bending rigidities measured for lipid bilayers of various compositions—in the range from 0.4–3 $\times$ 10^{-12} erg (34, 38, 64). Bending rigidity is related to the elastic coefficients for area dilation of membrane lamelli scaled by the square of the mechanical leverage (i.e. separation h) between layers—i.e. for two layered materials, $k_c \sim Kh^2/c$ (where the constant

c is of order 10). This relation correlates well with properties measured for lipid bilayer membranes (i.e. $k_c \sim 10^{-12}$ erg). Hence, for the red cell membrane, the contribution to bending stiffness from the subsurface protein scaffolding should be of order $k_c \sim K_N h_N^2/c$, where K_N is the elastic coefficient for dilation of the protein network and h_N is the network thickness. Since the bending rigidity of the red cell appears comparable to that of the lipid bilayer membrane, the contribution of the protein network to membrane stiffness must be small. This observation leads to an upper bound for the area compressibility modulus of the protein network: i.e. $K_N h_N^2 \ll 10^{-12}$ erg implies that $K_N < 1$ dyn cm^{-1}. The network is much more compliant than the lipid bilayer. As we discuss next, recent evidence indicates that the network is indeed soft, with an even smaller dilation modulus on the order of 10^{-2} dyn cm^{-1}.

Extensional Elasticity of the Red Cell Membrane

The lipid bilayer dominates the total area compliance and bending stiffness of the red cell. Hence the surface-area:volume ratio for the cell is the major determinant of extrinsic deformabilities of the red cell (e.g. osmotic fragility, minimum capillary dimension for transit, etc). However, the bilayer is a surface liquid and contributes negligibly to the extensional rigidity of unswollen cells. This feature becomes immediately apparent when a flaccid discocyte is aspirated into a small suction pipette. As seen in Figure 3a, there is little change in the shape of the red cell; thus the cell interior remains unpressurized. On the other hand, the suction pressure applied to the red cell must be increased progressively to advance the projection (Figure 3b). Furthermore, these suctions (1–10 mm H$_2$O) are 10–100 times greater than the minuscule threshold pressure required to overcome the bending rigidity of the membrane. This augmented suction exposes the solid-like extensional rigidity of the red cell membrane. The slope of suction pressure versus aspiration length yields an elastic coefficient for extensional rigidity of the red cell, i.e.

$$\bar{\mu} \approx \frac{R_p^2}{2}\left(\frac{P}{dL}\right) \qquad \sim 6 \times 10^{-3} \text{ dyn cm}^{-1} @ 23^\circ C \qquad 3.$$

Recognized many years ago (23, 24, 30, 66), extensional elasticity of the red cell membrane represents the major restoring force of recovery after large cell deformations and emanates totally from protein scaffolding underneath the bilayer.

From the viewpoint of mechanics, the subsurface scaffolding introduces a special elastic property to the membrane—shear rigidity—that

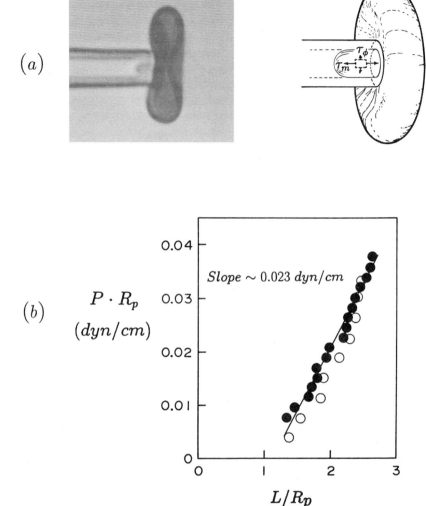

Figure 3 (*a*) Videomicrograph (*left*) of aspiration of a red cell discocyte (diameter ~8 μm) in isotonic buffer. Schematic (*right*) of the tension components (τ_m and $\tau\phi$) produced along the meridian and around the azimuth, respectively, by the symmetric deformation. (*b*) Relation between suction pressure P (scaled by pipette radius R_p) and projection length L (normalized by radius R_p). The increase in projection length is proportional to suction pressure, and the slope yields the extensional rigidity of the red cell membrane.

opposes surface extension even in the absence of area dilation (35). More subtly (as illustrated in Figure 3a), aspiration of a red cell into a small pipette produces separate tension components that involve both shear and dilational deformations. Thus, the stiffness derived from suction pressure versus aspiration embodies two elastic properties of the network: the area dilation modulus K_N and the shear modulus μ_N. Following the paradigm of ideal (Hookean) materials, surface extensional rigidity is like a "Young's modulus"—proportional to serial coupling of the intrinsic elastic properties, i.e.

$$\bar{\mu} \sim \mu_N K_N / (\mu_N + K_N).$$ 4.

For uniaxial stretch of the ideal material, tension would be given by $\tau_m = 4\bar{\mu} \, (\Delta L / L_0)$ in terms of the fractional change in length of a material element. This idealized expression serves to illustrate that the measured extensional rigidity lies somewhere between the elastic coefficients for network area dilation K_N and shear μ_N. However, when a red cell is aspirated into a small pipette, membrane tensions are not purely uniaxial; elements of the material surface are subjected to biaxial forces (as shown in Figure 3a) that vary with position. Unless the ratio μ_N / K_N is known a priori, measurements of extensional rigidity in red cell aspiration tests are not sufficient to define the separate elastic coefficients.

In early analyses of red cell membrane elasticity, an ad hoc assumption was made that the elastic area compliance of the network was negligible (23, 24, 35, 66). This assumption was motivated by the observation that red cell area was difficult to expand through osmotic pressurization and by the expectation that integral protein linkages for the network would be crowded on the bilayer surface. As such, the extentional rigidity $\bar{\mu} \rightarrow \mu_N$ and deformations of the membrane network were treated as constant density "maps." Researchers subsequently determined that the constant density assumption is overly restrictive and that the network may dilate or condense relative to the constant density bilayer envelope (68). Only the total area of the network must remain constant. Most important, knowledge of both area and shear elastic compliances provides complementary insights into the material structure (see below).

Energetics of Membrane Cytoskeletal Elasticity

Red cells are capable of large elastic extensions without rupture of their network scaffolding. Twenty years ago, this hyperelastic behavior and the ultralow coefficient of extensional rigidity led investigators to posit that the extensional elasticity was derived from the configurational entropy of flexible spectrin polymers (24, 35). Simple arithmetic exposes the intuition behind the concept: i.e. the extensional rigidity $\bar{\mu} \approx 6 \times 10^{-3}$ erg cm^{-2} divided by the surface density of spectrin chains $\rho_N \sim (10^5/\text{cell})/(10^{-6} \text{ cm}^2/\text{cell}) \approx 10^{11}/\text{cm}^2$ is on the order of thermal energy $kT \sim 4 \times 10^{-14}$ erg. Subsequently, the entropic concept was questioned because tests of the temperature dependence of extensional rigidity seemed to conflict with the behavior expected for a network of ideal Gaussian chains. Extensional rigidity was observed to decrease with temperature rather than increase (78). Stokke et al extended the initial concept of an entropic network to include electrostatic interactions (an ionic gel) and pointed out that added enthalpic contributions could lead to a reduction in density of the network with temperature (68), presumably as chains expand away from the bilayer. If large enough, such effects would cause a decrease in the extensional rigidity with temperature, even though the network elasticity at fixed temperature is driven mainly by entropy. More generally, both electrostatic and steric interactions within the network are expected to promote expansion with temperature. At low ionic strengths (<10 mM salt), electrostatics should dominate—an expectation supported by the behavior of solubilized spectrin in vitro and by disruption of the red cell network it situ (69, 75). On the other hand, at high ionic strengths (>100 mM salt), steric actions should dominate because the decay of electrostatic interactions falls below 10 Å. Consequently, the large proteins intercalated into the network may be principal contributors to expansion in physiological buffers (e.g. ankyrin, junctional complexes of actin protofilaments with band 4.1, cytoplasmic tails of band 3, etc). In addition to expanding the network, steric restrictions may alter the elastic compliance of the tethered spectrin array by hindering or blocking changes in conformation of the flexible filaments.

It is clear from observations of large extensions of intact red cells (30, 35, 78) and large expansions of detergent-extracted cytoskeletons (69, 75) that the spectrin network is hyperelastic. Energetically, a hyperelastic membrane network can be represented by an elastic energy per reference area of material (erg cm^{-2}) given by the following relation (35):

$$\bar{E} \approx \mu_N(\lambda_1^2 + \lambda_2^2)/2 \qquad\qquad 5.$$

where λ_1 and λ_2 are principal stretch (extension) ratios for surface deformation of a material element. (Starting with a square element $L_o \times L_o$, $\lambda_1 = L_1/L_o$ and $\lambda_2 = L_2/L_o$ when the element is stretched into a rectangle $L_1 \times L_2$.) The elastic coefficient μ_N is only weakly dependent on extension until the chains approach their fully stretched length represented by $\hat{\lambda}$ (74). What remain obscure at present are the area expansional characteristics of the network including effects of the intercalated constituents and steric interference to configurational transitions caused by proximity of the bilayer interface. Energies for excluded volume effects should decay as the area is expanded. However, with large proteins embedded in the network and the proximity of the bilayer interface, extension of network chains may become hindered well before the chains reach their fully extended length. These opposing tendencies are embodied in the following phenomenological model for the energetics of network dilation:

$$\tilde{E} \approx K_N(\tilde{A}^2 + 2/n\tilde{A}^n)/2 \qquad\qquad 6.$$

where the elastic stiffness K_N for the area expansion is dominated by network-bilayer repulsion and the exponent n represents excluded volume interactions. The area ratio $\tilde{A} = \lambda_1\lambda_2$ is the reciprocal of the relative network density field, $\tilde{A} \equiv 1/\tilde{\rho}$. Similar relations have been used successfully to model the energetics of polymer chains grafted to surfaces (53).

The combined energies of expansion and extension yield a working model for the elasticity of the cytoskeletal network that accommodates the molecular mechanisms of network chain extension, protein–protein, and network bilayer interactions. The mechanical response of the network is expressed by the following constitutive relations for tension along each principal direction of deformation:

$$\tau_1 \equiv \frac{1}{\lambda_2}\left(\frac{\partial \tilde{E}}{\partial \lambda_1}\right) = K_N(\tilde{A} - 1/\tilde{A}^{n+1}) + \mu_N(\lambda_1/\lambda_2 - 1)$$

$$\qquad\qquad\qquad\qquad\qquad\qquad\qquad\qquad 7.$$

$$\tau_2 \equiv \frac{1}{\lambda_1}\left(\frac{\partial \tilde{E}}{\partial \lambda_2}\right) = K_N(\tilde{A} - 1/\tilde{A}^{n+1}) + \mu_N(\lambda_2/\lambda_1 - 1).$$

Below, we discuss how this general model can be used to examine structural properties of the cytoskeletal network.

Mechanical Response of the Membrane Cytoskeletal Network

Many approaches have been used to probe red cell membrane elasticity, including cell extension by high-frequency electric fields (22) and hydrodynamic shear in viscometer-like devices (5), indentation by mechanical "pokers" (18), and so on. In general, the force fields and deformed cell shapes in these techniques are not axially symmetric; this fact means that the modeling of experimental results requires extremely complicated analyses involving either excessive numerical computations or coarse approximations. Even so, these techniques often provide useful methods for studying the deformability of red cell populations. Such techniques as cell filtration through microsieves are so qualitative (and dominated by irrelevant factors) that they are inappropriate to the study of red cell membrane elasticity. Among existing techniques, the micropipette approach yields the most reliable results for membrane elasticity because the displacement length L inside the pipette can be monitored accurately through videomicroscopy, and the mechanical deformation preserves the axial symmetry of the cell shape. Thus, using the working model for network elasticity we discuss how cytoskeletal structure affects membrane deformation response when cells are pulled into small tubes; we also describe a new advance in this technology that allows complete definition of elastic compliance for the cytoskeletal network in situ.

Pipette aspiration of a red cell discocyte (see Figure 3a) produces large membrane extensions along the projection inside the pipette. When the cytoskeletal network is compressible, large dilations occur near the cap of the aspirated projection and progressively condense toward the tube entrance. These regional dilations must be compensated by slight condensation of the network over the major area of the cell capsule exterior to the tube. The signature of network surface compressibility is a surface density variation along the projections inside the pipette. One can easily see this response when a loosely woven fabric is pushed into a tube. Analysis of deformation of a flat network into a small tube shows that density gradient along the tube axis depends on the ratio of elastic coefficients and projection length as embodied in the following relation between the ratio of network density at the pipette entrance ρ_e to density at the cap ρ_c:

$$\left(\frac{\mu_N}{K_N}\right) \frac{L}{R_p} \approx \frac{3}{4}\left[1 - \left(\frac{\rho_c}{\rho_e}\right)^2\right] + \left[\frac{\rho_e}{2\rho_c} + \frac{\mu_N}{K_N}\right] \ln\left(\frac{\rho_e}{\rho_c}\right). \qquad 8.$$

Computational analysis of elastic network deformation for a model red cell pulled into a tight spherical form at different cell volumes yields nearly identical results for network density ratio versus projection length (Figure 4). In addition, the phenomenological rigidity derived from analysis of aspiration of a model red cell discocyte exhibits the same serial coupling of elastic properties as the equation for an ideal Hookean elastic membrane, i.e. $\bar{\mu} \sim K_N\mu_N/(K_N+\mu_N)$. However, the phenomenological rigidity diminishes slightly as the projection length is increased beyond $L/R_p \sim 5$. Over the range of projections valid for pipette measurements ($L/R_p < 3$–4), the effect would be difficult to detect experimentally.

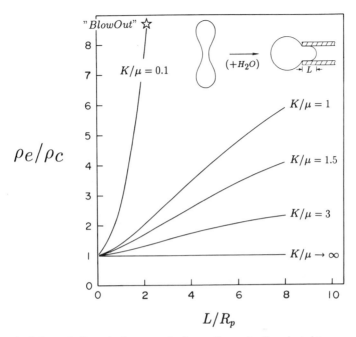

$$\rho e / \rho c$$

$$L/R_p$$

Figure 4   Schematic (*insert*) of an osmotically swollen red cell aspirated to a maximum projection length L (limited by surface area and volume) inside a micropipette. Based on the working model for cytoskeletal network tensions described in the text, analysis of the balance of network forces tangent to the tight spherical boundary and cylindrical projection leads to predictions of the ratio of network density ρ_e at the pipette entrance to the density ρ_c at the cap of the projection. Network density gradient increases with projection length and as the ratio K_N/μ_N of elastic moduli for dilation:shear is reduced. Also, the star for $K_N/\mu_N = 0.1$ denotes the "blow-out" condition where maximum dilation is reached at the cap ($\hat{A} = 7:1$).

As noted in Figure 4, aspiration of highly deformable networks into tubes could result in maximum extension of network filaments at the cap. Based on ultrastructural measurements of network dimensions, extension of spectrin chain in the membrane is limited to a ratio of $\hat{\lambda}$ ~ 3:1 for fully stretched:normal length (9, 69, 75). Indeed, Markin & Kozlov predicted (51) that aspiration of red cells into pipettes should lead to maximal dilation of the cytoskeletal network at the cap of the projection when the network elasticity is purely entropic (i.e. $K_N = 0$). Even when $K_N \geq \mu_N$, the principal extension ratio λ_1 along the membrane cylinder can reach this limit where local network elements resist further extension. [Technically, the limit to network extension is defined by $(\lambda_1^2 + \lambda_2^2)/2 \leq \hat{\lambda}^2$.] Continued displacement into the tube requires circumferential constriction of the network without filament elongation and, most likely, would cause the membrane cylinder to buckle. Numerical computations show that even for modest area rigidity ($K_N/\mu_N \approx 1$), filament extension ratios remain well below maximal stretch (e.g. at $L/R_p = 8$, the maximum stretch is only 2.3:1). Hence over the range of projection lengths where micropipette aspiration is usable, it is unlikely that network filaments become fully stretched.

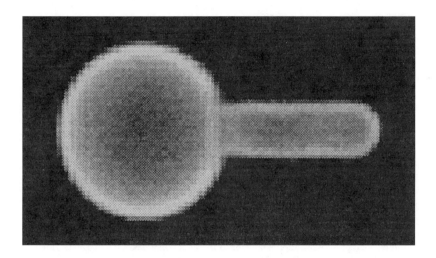

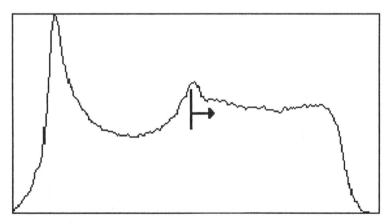

Figure 5 Fluorescence intensity maps (both a topographical contour and an axial section) observed for labeled lipids (fluorescein phosphatidyl-ethanolamine) in a red cell surface. Note the uniform density along the axis of the projection inside the pipette and around the outer spherical segment.

Recognizing that network compliance is encoded in the network density map, we have developed a new experimental method (D Discher, N Mohandas, and EA Evans, unpublished) for exposing the hidden elasticity of the membrane network in situ. The approach is to quantitate fluorescence intensity emitted from labeled proteins along the membrane projection inside a pipette. To obtain well-defined cell geometries and to avoid surface buckling, red cells are osmotically preswollen so that aspiration causes the cell to sphere outside the pipette (see Figure 2a). The volume increase regulates the projection length inside the pipette. When the lipid bilayer component is labeled by incorporation of a fluorescent lipid probe (e.g. fluorescein-PE), the fluorescence intensity appears uniform over both a fully sphered cell or a partially aspirated cell as anticipated for constant surface density (Figure 5). When band 3 proteins are labeled endogenously by EMA (eosin maleimide) or network actin filaments are labeled internal to the red cell by rhodamine phalloidin, the fluorescence intensity also appears uniform over fully sphered cells; in contrast, a strong intensity gradient appears along the projection inside the pipette for aspirated cells (Figure 6). Complete swelling of a red cell discocyte into a sphere can only produce small extensions (maximum of 15–20% given by the ratio of diameters), so the intensity appears nearly uniform over fully sphered red cells with both lipid and protein labels. The strong density gradient observed along the aspirated projection for the labeled proteins demonstrates the differential expansion of the membrane cytoskeleton relative to the lipid bilayer. [It is interesting that the intensity gradient observed for labeled band 3 does not diminish over periods of nearly an hour and immediately recovers (becomes uniform) after the cell is released from the pipette. Hence, the mobile fraction of band 3 must be trapped in network domains when the cytoskeleton is pulled towards the bilayer owing to dilation.] The measured ratios of intensity near the tube entrance ρ_e to the cap intensity ρ_c progressively increase with projection length as shown in Figure 7. Comparison of these intensity ratios with the density ratios predicted in Figure 4 shows that the dilation modulus of the network is significant and is more than double the network shear modulus (i.e. $K_N/\mu_N \approx 2$).[1]

Of major consequence, network area elasticity is sufficient to prevent mechanical instabilities that lead to "blow-out" at large extensions.

---

[1] The ratio K_N/μ_N represents the ratio of network area to shear rigidities in the large dilation regime where $\bar{A} = 1/\rho > 1.5$. In the regime of small deformations where $|\bar{A} - 1| < 1.5$ and in compression, the effective modulus for area changes in Equations 7 is much greater than K_N—i.e. $K_{eff} \sim (n + 2)K_N$.

Such effects are notorious in rubber-like materials. The instability arises when the surface dilation stress or isotropic tension $\bar{\tau} = (\tau_m + \tau\phi)/2$ approaches a plateau at large expansions. This is the situation with the Flory approximation for an elastomer in two dimensions (Equation 5) if only stabilized by excluded volume interactions. Since the experimental evidence shows that the density of the network at the cap continues to decrease with projection length, the isotropic tension in the network must continue to increase even at large extensions. Sta-

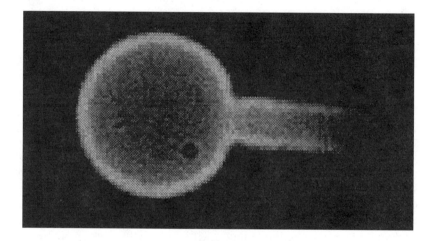

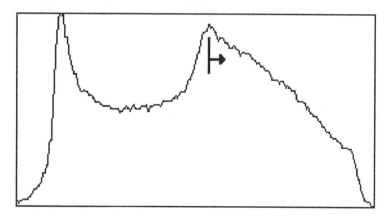

Figure 6 Fluorescence intensity maps observed for phalloidin-labeled actin proteins inside a red cell. Note the uniform density around the contour of the spherical cell and the strong gradient down the axis of the pipette for the highly extended cell. Similar profiles are seen for labeled band 3.

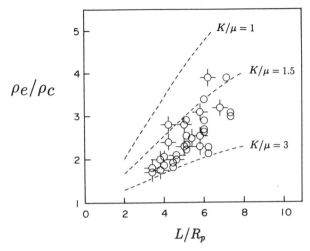

Figure 7   Measurements of intensity ratios (entrance density: cap density) for labeled actin inside red cell ghosts as a function of projection length inside pipettes. Superposed are predictions of density ratio (*dashed lines*) for dilation:shear elasticities of 1:1 and 3:1 taken from Figure 4.

bilization (resistance to area dilation) of the network probably arises from steric opposition to reduction in network thickness as the network is drawn towards the bilayer. This deduction is consistent with theoretical computations (8) and experimental estimates (our unpublished data) of red cell membrane thickness (>300Å) which show that interactions within the network push the network into the cell interior away from the bilayer surface. Even for simple random walks of flexible polymers pinned to a reflecting boundary (i.e. the bilayer), configurations are sterically repelled from the surface in order to maximize entropy (8). Such steric effects will be greatly enhanced when other large molecules decorate the polymer lattice. Consequently, the thickness of the spectrin network could reach dimensions comparable to the normal lattice spacing in red cells ($\sim$600–700 Å). Dilation properties in large deformations yield important insight into molecular interactions within the network that depend on all protein constituents as well as spectrin.

Unusual Material Features and Surprises

Elastic models relate membrane material properties to compositional structure (lipid bilayer, peripheral protein scaffolding, etc). With the refinements noted, the superposition model seems to be well supported by experimental evidence. However, the success of the model at the coarse material level leaves many unanswered questions about physical assembly of the membrane structure at the molecular level. Some features are obvious, e.g. that network scaffolding must be anchored or pinned to the fluid bilayer (we presently assume that it is anchored by integral proteins like band 3). But less obvious are the submicroscopic origins of the stable-smooth shape and the resilient (fatigue resistant) hyperelasticity. These features appear even more profound when it is recognized that the coefficient of elastic rigidity for membrane extension ($\bar{\mu} = 6 \times 10^{-3}$ dyn cm^{-1}) is ~100 times smaller than the rigidity of a soft latex rubber with an equivalent (10^{-6} cm) thickness.[2] In addition, soft latex is not resilient; it flows plastically or fails after only a few cycles of large extension. By comparison, the ultrasoft red cell traverses regions of high extension in small capillaries nearly 10^5 times over its 120-day life span—a feat that implies strong network connections.

However, the contemporary view established through in vitro biochemistry is that the network is dynamic and labile with relatively high rates of spectrin dimer-tetramer exchange. Why is such a fluid-like picture difficult to reconcile with red cell membrane material behavior? The prominent feature of a fluid membrane capsule is that the shape is extremely deformable unless swollen to a sphere. A very delicate balance is required between monolayers to keep a bilayer smooth, and the environment must be quiescent. When unpressurized, small changes in monolayer surface densities lead to enormous changes in curvature (34). If an ideal polymer network is pinned to a fluid bilayer, entropy-driven condensation will contribute a negative surface pressure on the order of the network elastic modulus μ_N to one side of the structure. If unopposed, this contraction will increase the characteristic curvature by $\sim \mu_N h_N / k_c$. Hence the interface should wrinkle and randomly protrude with a form much like that of a white blood cell. Also, roughening produced by network contraction should be increased by the tendency of an electrically charged glycocalyx to expand. The presence of charged lipids on the inside of the red cells could oppose roughening; however, the shapes of charged lipid bilayer vesicles are so easily perturbed by changes in temperature and pH that the lipid bilayer is not likely to maintain the smooth contour of the red cell membrane.

It is obvious that red cell shape may be stabilized by steric interaction among proteins embedded in the network and at the network-bilayer

---

[2] The 3D extension modulus for ideal rubber is on the order of 10^6 dyn cm^{-2} or 1 atm, which converts to a surface extension modulus of 1 dyn cm^{-1} when multiplied by a thickness of 10^{-6} cm.

interface. Steric exclusion within the protein structure could easily oppose network contraction and establish an expanded "stress-free" density state. Also, resistance to network condensation could counteract roughening driven by the electrostatic pressure in the glyocalyx. Observations of fluorescently labeled proteins over the surface of highly extended red cells (see Figure 6) show that the network greatly resists area compression and that the exponent for excluded volume interactions in Equations 7 must exceed two (i.e. $n + 1 \geq 2$). On the other hand, steric repulsion between the network and bilayer appears essential to prevent network blow-out and coagulation. Without this interaction, the entropic network would easily reach maximal dilation and relax over time by coalescence of defects (missing connections). Even without extreme dilation, the network could phase-separate (coagulate) over time and form a condensed patch at one side of the capsule, leaving a large region of unsupported bilayer. The naked bilayer region could then form an aneurysm that would easily fragment from the capsule. Such effects occur precipitously when red cells are heated from 48 to 49°C (Figure 8) and may be the origin of membrane loss in red cell pathologies like hereditary spherocytosis.

The origin of the elastic resilience and durability of the membrane network probably lies in strong-durable crosslinks and attachments to the bilayer. The evidence supporting this conclusion is that large deformations of the network do not cause the network to detach from the bilayer interface. Even more surprising is the observation that large deformations can be held for long periods (~1 hr) with little relaxation of the network. If crosslinks and bilayer attachments were labile (i.e.

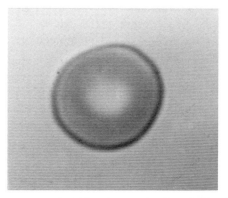 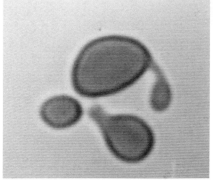

Figure 8 Videomicrographs of a smooth red cell discocyte at 48°C (*left*) and (*right*) after 1°C heating to 49°C. Disruption of the spectrin network leaves the red cell surface vulnerable to aneurism and fragmentation.

held by low binding energies with frequent dynamic dissociations), the strong chemical gradients produced by large deformations would rapidly drive the network to detach from the bilayer or rend (open up a large hole)—neither of which seems to happen experimentally. The magnitude of membrane elastic properties seems to indicate that mechanical energies in large deformations reach several kT per crosslink. However, the energy stored by a crosslink bond will be much smaller (following the analogy of soft elastic springs attached by stiff elastic glue). The important requirement is that the strength of the crosslink bond must exceed the spectrin filament tension, i.e. 10^{-6}–10^{-5} dyn. The implication is that network crosslinks must be bound together by forces as strong as hydrogen bonds but perhaps weaker than covalent bonds. Likewise, attachment of the network to the bilayer must be strong enough to resist detachment of the network as the bilayer is pushed away by the hydrostatic pressure. Assuming that attachment sites and network lattice dimensions are spaced equally ($\sim 10^{11}$ cm^{-2}), each site of attachment to the bilayer must be able to support a force of $\sim 10^{-7}$ dyn or more to prevent extraction from the bilayer near the cap of a membrane projection inside a small pipette. In this case, the force is much smaller than the strength of a hydrogen bond. Experimental evidence shows that even hydrophobic linkage of proteins in a fluid bilayer is probably sufficient to withstand a detachment force of this level (29).

With the capability to specify completely the elastic properties of the membrane cytoskeleton in situ, we expect that biochemical and ultrastructural data can be tied much more closely to physical properties in the near future. In support of this goal, studies of red cell membrane pathologies and genetic structural mutations provide exceptional opportunities to test critically hypotheses for the origins of material behavior at the molecular level. With the aid of molecular engineering and cell reconstitution methods, it should be possible not only to unravel mysteries of biomembrane design but also to create new design motifs with potential for structural improvement or remediation.

ACKNOWLEDGMENTS

Our published and unpublished work discussed in this review was supported by grants from the National Institutes of Health #HL31579 and DK26263. Mr. Dennis Discher is responsible for those fluorescence experiments described in this review that expose the membrane network density under large cell deformations.

Literature Cited

1. Anstee DJ. 1981. The blood group MNSS-active sialoglycoproteins. *Sem. Hematol.* 18:13–31
2. Becker PS, Lux SE. 1985. Hereditary spherocytosis and related disorders. *Clin. Haematol.* 14:15–43
3. Bennett V. 1985. The membrane skeleton of human erythrocytes and its implication for more complex cells. *Annu. Rev. Biochem.* 54:273–304
4. Bennett V. 1990. Spectrin-based membrane skeleton—a multipotential adapter between plasma membrane and cytoplasm. *Physiol. Rev.* 70:1029–60
5. Bessis M, Mohandas N. 1975. A diffractometric method for the measurement of cellular deformability. *Blood Cells* 1:307–13
6. Bloom M, Evans E, Mouritsen OG. 1991. Physical properties of the fluid lipid-bilayer component of cell membranes: a perspective. *Q. Rev. Biophys.* 24:293–397
7. Brochard F, Lennon JF. 1975. Frequency spectrum of the flicker phenomenon in erythroctyes. *J. Physiol.* (Paris) 36:1035–40
8. Boal DH, Seifert U, Zilker A. 1992. Dual network model for red blood cell membranes. *Phys. Rev. Lett.* 69:3405–8
9. Byers T, Branton D. 1985. Visualization of the protein association in the erythrocyte membrane skeleton. *Proc. Natl. Acad. Sci. USA* 82:6153–57
10. Canham PB. 1970. The minimum energy of bending as a possible explanation of the biconcave shape of the human red blood cell. *J. Theor. Biol.* 36:61–75
11. Chasis JA, Mohandas N. 1986. Erythrocyte membrane deformability and stability: two distinct membrane properties that are independently regulated by skeletal protein associations. *J. Cell. Biol.* 103:343–50
12. Chasis JA, Mohandas N. 1992. Red cell glycophorins. *Blood* 80:1869–79
13. Chasis JA, Mohandas N, Shohet SB. 1985. Erythrocyte membrane rigidity induced by glycophorin A–ligand interaction. *J. Clin. Invest.* 75:1919–26
14. Chasis JA, Reid ME, Jensen RH, Mo-

handas N. 1988. Signal transduction by glycophorin A: role of extracellular and cytoplasmic domains in a modulatable process. *J. Cell Biol.* 107:1351–57
15. Chasis JA, Agre P, Mohandas N. 1988. Decreased membrane mechanical stability and in vivo loss of surface area reflect spectrin deficiencies in hereditary spherocytosis. *J. Clin. Invest.* 82: 617–23
16. Chasis JA, Knowles D, Winardi R, George E, Mohandas N. 1991. Conformational changes in cytoplasmic domains of band 3 and glycophorin A affect red cell membrane properties. *Blood* 78(Suppl. 1):252a
17. Conboy J. 1993. Structure, function and molecular genetics of erythroid membrane skeletal protein 4.1 in normal and abnormal red blood cells. *Semin. Hematol.* 30:58–73
18. Daily B, Elson EL, Zahalak GI. 1984. Cell poking: determination of elastic area compressibility modulus of the erythrocyte membrane. *Biophys. J.* 45: 671–82
19. Davies KA, Lux SE. 1989. Hereditary disorders of the red cell membrane skeleton. *Trends Genet.* 5:222–27
20. Delaunay J, Dhermy D. 1993. Mutations involving the spectrin heterodimer contact site: clinical expression and alterations in specific function. *Semin. Hematol.* 30:21–33
21. Dueling HJ, Helfrich W. 1976. Red blood cell shapes as explained on the basis of curvature elasticity. *Biophys. J.* 16:861–72
22. Engelhardt H, Sackmman E. 1988. On the measurement of shear elastic moduli and viscosities of erythrocyte plasma membranes by transient deformaion in high frequency electric fields. *Biophys. J.* 54:495–505.
23. Evans EA. 1973. A new material concept for red cell membranes. *Biophys. J.* 13:926–40
24. Evans EA. 1973. New membrane concept applied to the analysis of fluid shear and micropipet deformed red blood cells. *Biophys. J.* 13:941–54
25. Evans EA. 1974. Bending resistance

and chemically induced moments in membrane bilayers. *Biophys. J.* 14:923–31

26. Evans EA. 1983. Bending elastic modulus of red blood cell membrane derived from buckling instability in micropipet aspiration tests. *Biophys. J.* 43:27–30

27. Evans EA. 1985. Detailed mechanics of membrane-membrane adhesion and separation. *Biophys. J.* 48:175–83

28. Evans EA. 1992. Physics of complex-biological membranes and cell interfaces. *Ma.t Res. Soc. Symp. Proc.* 255:31–41

29. Evans EA, Berk D, Leung A. 1991. Detachment of agglutinin-bonded red blood cells: I. Forces to rupture molecular-point attachments. *Biophys. J.* 59:838–48

30. Evans EA, Hochmuth RM. 1977. A solid-liquid composite model of the red cell membrane. *J. Membr. Biol.* 30:351–62

31. Evans EA, Mohandas N, Leung A. 1984. Static and dynamic rigidities of normal and sickle erythrocytes: major influence of cell hemoglobin concentration. *J. Clin. Invest.* 73:477–88

32. Evans EA, Mohandas N. 1987. Membrane-associated sickle hemoglobin: a major determinant of sickle erythrocyte rigidity. *Blood* 70:1443–49

33. Evans EA, Needham D. 1987. Cohesive properties of lipid bilayer membranes containing cholesterol. *J. Phys. Chem.* 91:4219–28

34. Evans EA, Ravicz W. 1990. Entropy-driven tension and bending elasticity in condensed-fluid membranes. *Phys. Rev. Lett.* 64:2094–97

35. Evans EA, Skalak R. 1980. *Mechanics and Thermodynamics of Biomembranes*, pp. 1–254. Boca Raton, Florida: CRC Press

36. Evans EA, Waugh R, Melnik L. 1976. Elastic area compressibility modulus of red cell membrane. *Biophys. J.* 16:585–95

37. Fairbanks G, Steck TL, Wallach DFH. 1971. Electrophoretic analysis of the major polypeptides of the human erythrocyte membrane. *Biochemistry* 10:2606–17

38. Faucon JF, Mitov MD, Meleard P, Bivas I, Bothorel P. 1989. Bending elasticity and thermal fluctuations of lipid membranes. Theoretical and experimental requirements. *J. Physiol.* (Paris) 50:2389–92

39. Fowler VM. 1990. A cytoskeletal protein that binds to the end of erythrocyte tropomyosin and inhibits tropomyosin biding to actin. *J. Cell Biol.* 111:471–82

40. Gallagher PG, Forget BG. 1993. Spectrin genes in health and disease. *Semin. Hematol.* 30:4–21

41. Gilligan DM, Bennet V. 1993. The junctional complex of the membrane skeleton. *Semin. Hematol.* 30:74–83

42. Lane PA, Shaw RL, Iarocci TA, Mohandas N, Hays T, Mentzer W. 1987. A unique alpha spectrin mutant in a kindred with common hereditary eilliptocytosis. *J. Clin. Invest.* 79:989–96

43. Le Van Kim C, Colin Y, Blanchard D, Dahr W, London J, Cartron JP. 1987. Biochemistry and genetics of the blood group Gerbich antigens. *Biochem. Soc. Trans.* 15:609–10

44. Liu SC, Palek J. 1980. Spectrin tetramer-dimer equilibrium and the stability of erythrocyte membrane skeletons. *Nature* 285:586–88

45. Liu SC, Derick L, Palek J. 1987. Visualization of hexagonal lattice in the erythrocyte membrane skeleton. *J. Cell Biol.* 104:527–36

46. Low PS. 1986. Structure and function of the cytoplasmic domain of band 3: center of erythrocyte membrane-peripheral protein interactions. *Biochim. Biophys. Acta* 864:145–67

47. Lutz HU, Liu SC, Palek J. 1977. Release of spectrin-free vesicles from human erythrocytes during ATP depletion. *J. Cell Biol.* 73:548–66

48. Lux SE, John KM, Kopito RR, Lodish HF. 1989. Cloning and characterization of band 3, the human erythrocyte anion-exchange protein (AE1). *Proc. Natl. Acad. Sci. USA* 86:9089–93

49. Lux SE, John KM, Bennet V. 1990. Analysis of cDNA for human erythrocyte ankyrin indicates a repeated structure with homology to tissue-differentiation. *Nature* 344:36–42

50. Marchesi S, Conboy J, Agre P, Letsinger JT, Marchesi VT, et al. 1990. Molecular analysis of insertion/deletion mutations in protein 4.1 in elliptocytosis: I. Biochemical identification of rearrangements in the spectrin/actin binding domain and functional characterizations. *J. Clin. Invest.* 86:516–23

51. Markin VS, Kozlov MM. 1988. Mechanical properties of the red cell membrane skeleton: analysis of axisymmetric deformation. *J. Theor. Biol.* 133:147–67

52. Merry AH, Hodson C, Thompson E, Mallinson G, Anstee DJ. 1986. The use of monoclonal antibodies to quantify the

levels of sialoglycoproteins α and β and variant sialoglycoproteins in human erythrocyte membrane. *Biochem. J.* 233:93–98

53. Milner ST, Witten TA, Cates ME. 1988. Theory of the grafted polymer brush. *Macromolecules* 21:2610–19
54. Mohandas N, Chasis JA. 1993. Red cell deformability, membrane material properties and shape: regulation by transmembrane, skeletal and cytosolic proteins and lipids. *Semin. Hematol.* 30: 171–92
55. Mohandas N, Chasis JA, Shohet SB. 1983. The influence of membrane skeleton on red cell deformability, membrane material properties, and shape. *Semin. Hematol.* 20:255–42
56. Mohandas N, Lie-Injo LE, Freidman M, Mak JW. 1984. Rigid membranes of Malayan ovalocytes: a likely genetic barrier against malaria. *Blood* 63:1385–92
57. Mohandas N, Winardi R, Knowles D, Leung A, Parra M, et al. 1992. Molecular basis for membrane rigidity of hereditary ovalocytosis: a novel mechanism involving the cytoplasmic domain of band 3. *J. Clin. Invest.* 89:686–92
58. Morrow JS, Marchesi, VT. 1981. Self-assembly of spectrin oligomers in vitro: a basis for a dynamic cytoskeleton. *J. Cell Biol.* 88:463–68
59. Needham D, Nunn RS. 1990. Cohesive properties of lipid bilayer membranes containing cholesterol. *Biophys. J.* 58: 997-1009
60. Rand RP. 1964. Mechanical properties of the red cell membrane. II. Viscoelastic breakdown of the membrane. *Biophys. J.* 4:303–12
61. Reid ME, Takakuwa Y, Conboy J, Tchernia G, Mohandas N. 1990. Glycophorin C content of human erythrocyte membrane is regulated by protein 4.1. *Blood.* 75:2229–34
62. Rybicki AC, Heath R, Wolfe JF, Lubin B, Schwartz RS. 1988. Deficiency of protein 4.2 in erythrocytes from a patient with Coombs negative hemolytic anemia. Evidence for a role of protein 4.2 in stabilizing ankyrin on the membrane. *J. Clin. Invest.* 81:839–46
63. Saad STO, Liu SC, Golan D, Corbett JB, Thatte HS, et al. 1991. Mechanism underlying band 3 deficiency in a subset of patients with hereditary spherocytosis. *Blood* 78 (Supp. 1):81a
64. Schneider MD, Jenkins JT, Webb WW. 1984. Thermal fluctuations of large quasi-spherical bimolecular phospho-

lipid vesicles. *J. Physiol.* (Paris) 45: 1457–62
65. Schofield AE, Tanner MJA, Pinder JC, Clough B, Bayley PM, et al. 1992. Basis of unique red cell membrane properties in hereditary ovalocytosis. *J. Mol. Biol.* 223:949–58
66. Skalak R, Tozeren A, Zarda RP, Chien S. 1973. Strain energy function of red blood cell membranes. *Biophys. J.* 13: 245–53
67. Speicher DW, Marchesi VT. 1984. Erythrocyte spectrin is composed of many homologous triple helical segments. *Nature* 311:177–80
68. Stokke BT, Mikkelsen A, Elgsaeter A. 1986. The human erythrocyte membrane skeleton may be an ionic gel. *Eur. Biophys. J.* 13:203–18
69. Svoboda K, Schmidt CF, Barton D, Block SM. 1992. Conformation and elasticity of the isolated red blood cell membrane skeleton. *Biophys. J.* 63: 784–93
70. Takakuwa Y, Tchernia G, Rossi M, Benabadji M, Mohandas N. 1986. Restoration of normal membrane stability to unstable protein 4.1 deficient membranes by incorporation of purified protein 4.1. *J. Clin. Invest.* 78:80–85
71. Tanner MJA. 1993. Molecular and cellular biology of the erythrocyte anion exchanger (AE1). *Semin. Hematol.* 30: 34–57
72. Tanner MJA, Martin PG, High S. 1988. Genetic variants of human erythrocyte membrane ialoglycoprotein β. Study of the alterations occurring in the sialoglycoprotein β gene. *Biochem. J.* 256: 703–12
73. Tchernia G, Mohandas N, Shohet SB. 1981. Deficiency of skeletal membrane protein 4.1 in homozygous hereditary elliptocytosis. *J. Clin. Invest.* 68: 454–60
74. Treloar LRG. 1946. The physics of rubber elasticity. *Trans. Faraday Soc.* 42: 77–102
75. Vertessy BG, Steck TL. 1989. Elasticity of the human red cell membrane skeleton, effects of temperature and denaturant. *Biophys. J.* 55:255–62
76. Verkleij AJ, Zwall RFA, Roelofsen B. 1973. The asymmetric distribution of phospholipid. *Biochim. Biophys. Acta* 323:178–90
77. Waugh R, Evans E 1977. Osmotic correction to elastic area compressiblility measurements on red cell membrane. *Biophys. J.* 20:307–13
78. Waugh R, Evans EA. 1979. Thermal

elasticity of red blood cell membrane. *Biophys. J.* 26:115–32

79. Ways P, Hanahan DJ. 1964. Characterization and quantification of red cell lipids in normal man. *J. Lipid Res.* 5:313–28

80. Zilker A, Ziegler M, Sackmann E. 1993. Spectral analysis of erythrocyte flickering by microinterferometry combined with fast image processing. *Phys. Rev. A.* 46:7998–8001

Annu. Rev. Biophys. Biomol. Struct. 1994. 23:819–46

VOLTAGE-DEPENDENT GATING OF IONIC CHANNELS

Francisco Bezanilla

Department of Physiology, UCLA School of Medicine, Los Angeles, California 90024

Enrico Stefani

Department of Molecular Physiology and Biophysics, Baylor College of Medicine, Houston, Texas, 77030

KEY WORDS: gating currents, inactivation of conductance, site-directed mutagenesis, expressed channels, channel activation

CONTENTS

INTRODUCTION

The conduction of ions across cell membranes is vital for the maintenance and modification of the potential difference across the membrane and to maintain cell homeostasis. As the lipid bilayer is an effective barrier for ion permeation (50), the transfer of ions occurs through two types of specialized integral membrane proteins: the channels and the carriers. The main difference between these two transporting systems is the number of ions that cross the membrane in each conducting event. Thus, while the channel may transport several millions of ions per conducting event, the carrier may translocate only a few. In this review, we discuss the operation of ion channels, but we focus only on those ion channels whose permeation event is controlled by the membrane potential.

Excitable cells, and in particular nerve cells, undergo dramatic changes in their membrane potential. These changes are used to encode and transmit information between different points of the nervous system. In axons, the action potential is a signal that propagates as a transient change in membrane potential, lasting only one or two milliseconds. The change consists of a sudden decrease in the normal resting potential with a reversal of the polarity of the voltage, and a subsequent repolarization. This action potential is concomitant with a decrease in the membrane resistance (16), and this decrease results in an exchange of ions across the cell membrane (36).

Hodgkin and coworkers, in their classic studies (28, 29), found that the conductance change was separated in two different conduction systems that operated with different kinetics, one for sodium and another for potassium. One of the most important results of this work was the discovery that the sodium and potassium conductances depend on the membrane potential. This discovery laid the foundation of our present knowledge of voltage-dependent conductances that have been identified with ionic channels.

In the first part of this review, we describe the basic principles required for the operation of voltage-dependent channels, followed by a description of a few functional aspects of Na^+, K^+, and Ca^{2+} channels. Many different types of channels have been described (see 27) and the amino acid sequence of many channels has been deduced based on the sequence of the encoding cDNA. Currently, one can study a single channel in isolation using the patch clamp technique (25), or many channels simultaneously, to record macroscopic ionic currents or gating currents in expression systems that allow control of which molecule is being studied, either in wild-type or mutated form. The second part of this review attempts to correlate structure and function on the basis of studies in normal channels and channels whose amino acid sequence has been modified by site-directed mutagenesis.

THE VOLTAGE-DEPENDENT CONDUCTANCE

Since the classic work of Hodgkin & Huxley (28), we have learned that the Na^+ and K^+ conductances are steep functions of the membrane potential. The value of sodium conductance is negligible at the resting potential (near -70 mV, inside minus outside potential), and it increases abruptly at around -40 mV and saturates at around 0 mV. If the logarithm of the conductance is plotted as a function of voltage, at negative potentials an almost linear relationship appears, from which one can calculate a slope factor. In the case of the squid axon sodium channel, the conductance changes by e-fold every 4 mV. As shown below, this result has important mechanistic consequences because it gives a lower estimate of the charge of the voltage sensor.

The advent of single-channel recording techniques (25) have enabled investigators to observe the operation of one channel as a function of voltage and time. For the most part, voltage-dependent sodium and potassium channels have only two conducting states: open and closed, although each one of these could represent many conformational states of the channel macromolecule. Recordings of the single-channel events for a large number of identical voltage pulses have demonstrated that the time course of the average open probability corresponds to the measured macroscopic current, as if the channels behaved independently. Varying the amplitude of the voltage pulse has shown that the voltage dependence of the unitary conductance of the channel is very shallow and, under certain ionic conditions, essentially independent of voltage. However, the probability (P_o) for the channel to be in the open, or conducting, state, is very voltage dependent and closely matches the voltage dependence of the conductance. This means that the voltage dependence of the macroscopic conductance is not an intrinsic property of the ion conduction of the channel, but rather it reflects the voltage dependence of the ability of the channel to become conducting. Now, we can easily separate the two processes in the ionic current: gating and conduction. Gating refers to the process of opening and closing of the channel. Thus, when the channel gate opens, conduction through the open channel occurs and continues as long as the gate remains in the open conformation. In this view, the voltage affects the operation of the gate, such that at negative potentials, the gate is closed most of the time while at positive potentials it is usually open.

This separation of the gating and conduction processes is a simple interpretation of the operation of single channels but is implicit in the original Hodgkin & Huxley formulation (28). In the case of the potassium channel, the current I is given by

$$I = \bar{g}_K n^4 (V - V_K),$$

where $V - V_K$ is the driving force and n^4 corresponds to P_o and $\bar{g}_K$ corresponds to $N\gamma$, where N is the number of channels and γ is the conductance of one open channel. The term $\bar{g}_K$ is the macroscopic conductance, and n is the probability of each activating particle being in the active state. Although this separation is convenient, one should remember that ionic effects produced by ion conduction interact with the gating machinery (65).

Voltage-Dependent Channels

Our understanding of the voltage-dependent channel consists of an analytical description of the physical process underlying the P_o and its modulation by the membrane potential. This understanding can be at the phenomenological level, i.e. kinetic equations that relate analytically the membrane potential with P_o, or at the molecular (or atomic) level, where the actual energy barriers and wells and the physical states of the channel are correlated with physical conformations of the channel macromolecule. In this chapter, we first describe progress made at the phenomenological level and later review some of the results on correlation between structure and function that have given insights to the molecular-level understanding of gating.

The basic principle, stated by Hodgkin & Huxley (28), is that the channel conformations—closed or open—are regulated by the membrane potential, which implies that a voltage sensor must link the voltage to these conformational changes. The obvious candidates are magnetic or electric charges embedded in the electric field of the membrane. Of these two, electric charges are easier to identify with the charged groups of amino acid side chains of the protein or local polarization of electronic clouds or dipoles, either permanent or induced. These charges or dipoles, called gating charge, would act as sensors, and somehow their movement, or orientation change, would ultimately modify the conformation of the molecule. The ultimate understanding of gating would be the identification of the groups and their coupling to other regions of the molecule that make the channel conducting.

VOLTAGE DEPENDENCE OF P_o Hodgkin & Huxley (28) demonstrated that to account for the steep conductance-voltage relationship (g-V curve) of Na^+ conductance, six elementary electronic charges must be moved across the whole membrane field. The derivation is based on a two-state model in which the proportion of channels in one or the other state follows a Boltzmann distribution. Almers (3) extended the formulation to a multistate model and found a similar result when the P_o is very small. In a channel with many closed states starting in state s_0 and ending in one open state s_n, the P_o can be written as

$$P_o = \frac{1}{1 + \sum_{j=0}^{n-1} G_j} \quad \text{with } G_j = \prod_{i=j}^{n-1} \mu_i,$$

where μ_i is the voltage-dependent equilibrium constant between transitions i and $i+1$ and has the general form

$$\mu_i = A_i \exp\left(\frac{-q_i V}{kT}\right),$$

where A_i is the equilibrium value in the absence of the field and q_i is the gating charge (charge times fraction of the field). Then in the limit, when $V \rightarrow -\infty$, the expression becomes

$$P_o = A \cdot \exp\left(\frac{V}{kT} \sum_{i=1}^{n} q_i\right) \quad \text{with } A = \prod_{i=0}^{i=n-1} A_i,$$

which is a simple exponential dependence on V with the sum of all the individual charges as the coefficient. Under these conditions, in a plot of $\ln(P_o)$ vs V, the slope of the line can be used to estimate the total gating charge required for this voltage dependence. This is called the *limiting slope method* and is normally used to estimate the charge of the voltage sensor (i.e. the *effective valence*) in voltage-dependent channels. However, this is only a lower estimate of the correct charge times the fraction of the field. Figure 1 is an example of a plot of P_o vs V for a five-state channel. In this case, the estimated total valence computed from the logarithmic plot in the range of $P_o > 0.001$ is 5.7e (shallow line), while the value estimated with a $P_o < 10^{-27}$ (steeper line) is 8e, equal to the real value. Clearly, the correct value of the total charge is not estimated properly unless the voltage is negative enough so that the P_o is less than 10^{-18}. Depending on the distribution of the charges in the different steps, the estimate can be better or even worse. Measurements of P_o have rarely been done below 0.005; therefore the estimates of the gating charge can be in serious error.

Gating Currents and the Activation of the Conductance

The macroscopic current and single channel fluctuations give information on the kinetics and voltage dependence of the open probability of the channel. Another type of electric expression of voltage depen-

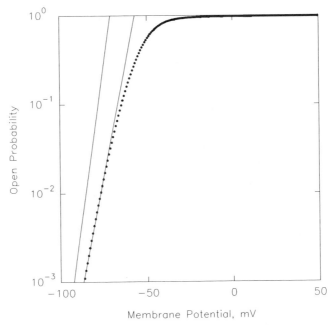

Figure 1 Estimation of the total charge from the open probability vs voltage curve. The model used had 4 closed and 1 open states. The transitions from the first closed to the open state had the following charges and equilibrium points (in electrons and millivolts, respectively): 1, -120; 3, -80; 3, -30; 1, -20; 0. The steeper straight line was fitted to curve with probabilities in the range of 10^{-28} while the shallower line was fitted between probabilities ranging from 0.0013 to 0.017.

dent–channel operation is the *gating current,* also predicted by Hodgkin & Huxley (28). The origin of this current is the movement of the voltage sensor resulting from a change in the membrane field, and it is detected as a transient current in the external circuit. Because the sensor is tethered in the membrane, there is no net continuous transport of charge across the membrane. From the electrical point of view, the gating current behaves like a capacitive current, and it corresponds to charge reorientation in the membrane field, as occurs in lossy dielectrics. Thus, for a transient current to be a gating current, in contrast to an ionic current, the charge moving during the pulse must be identical to the charge moving back at the end of the pulse. The movement of the sensor is clearly associated with the events leading to the opening of the channel; therefore the recording of gating currents should provide important information on conformational changes of the macromolecule that lead to the opening of the channel. This is particularly important in channels that have several closed states because the ionic current only shows the opening, which is quite insensitive to the details of the transitions between closed states, while gating currents show the charge movement between closed states.

STEADY-STATE ACTIVATION   The time integral of the gating current for a given voltage step (V) gives the charge moved at that potential. A plot of this charge vs V (the Q-V curve) gives the functional relation between the movement of the sensor and the membrane potential. The Q-V curve estimates two important parameters: the total amount of charge transported and the steepness of the Q vs V relation. The total amount of charge, normally recorded for a large population of channels, can be used to compute the charge per channel when the total number of channels is known. The actual value computed corresponds to the total number of electronic charges times the fraction of the electric field they traverse. This quantity is important because it can be directly compared with the charged groups or dipoles postulated from the amino acid sequence of the channel protein to be part of the voltage sensor.

Schoppa et al (56) measured gating currents in *Shaker* K$^+$ channels and, using fluctuation analysis, estimated in the same patch of membrane the number of channels. They determined that the product of total charge transferred times the fraction of the field was 12–13 electronic charges per channel.

Estimates from the steepness of the P_o vs V curve gave a much lower value for the gating charge per channel, confirming the uncertainty of the limiting slope procedure. The steepness of the Q-V curve may be estimated by fitting it to a Boltzmann distribution, but only in the two-state model is this method guaranteed to estimate correctly the product of the charge times the fraction of the field for that particular transition. For example, if the channel opens when four subunits have made a first-order transition (as in the Hodgkin & Huxley formulation of the potassium channel) the Q-V curve can be fit, by a simple Boltzmann distribution, with a valence equal to one fourth of the total charge per channel. In practice [for Na$^+$ (62) and K$^+$ (13) channels], Q-V curves do not follow simple Boltzmann distributions, but they show several components that can be operationally separated as a sum of several two-state Boltzmann distributions.

The functional expressed *Shaker,* and several other cloned K$^+$ channels, seem to consist of four identical subunits (40). The α subunit of sodium channels is sufficient for expression of functional Na$^+$ channels and consists of four homologous domains, each one similar to the K-channel subunit. A natural assumption, especially in the case of K$^+$

channels, is then that the gating process of each subunit will be reflected in the Q-V curve of the channel. If each subunit gates independently, the components of the Q-V curve can be attributed to the individual subunit, and the opening of the channel will correspond to the concerted operation of the four subunits. On the other hand, if the subunits interact, the Q-V curve will reflect the charge transitions of the multiple combinations of the subunit transitions. For example, if the Q-V curve is made of two Boltzmann distributions, one interpretation is that each subunit gates independently between three discrete states. Another explanation is that in each subunit, two charges are moving independently of each other and independently of the other subunits. Still another interpretation is that each subunit has at least two states and the transition probability of one subunit is modified by the position of the adjacent subunit.

In a general sequential scheme the total charge transfer is given by

$$Q = \sum_{i=1}^{i=n} q_i F_i$$

where q_i is the effective charge moving from state $i - 1$ and i, F_i is the change in the relative population of state $i - 1$ when the potential has been changed from minus infinity to the value V. To illustrate how the features of the Q-V curve are related to the properties of the subunits, we shall consider four identical subunits, each one undergoing a first-order transition with possibilities of interaction. This particular scheme is made of 16 states, but considering that the subunits are identical, it can be simplified to 5 states (see 76):

$$S_0 \underset{h}{\overset{4a}{\rightleftharpoons}} S_1 \underset{2g}{\overset{3b}{\rightleftharpoons}} S_2 \underset{3f}{\overset{2c}{\rightleftharpoons}} S_3 \underset{4e}{\overset{d}{\rightleftharpoons}} S_4$$

where a is the forward rate when one subunit makes the transition and the other three stay behind, b is the forward rate when one subunit makes the transition and two are left behind, etc. In the reverse direction, e is the backward rate for one subunit and the other three left behind, etc. The case of no interaction (28) corresponds to $a = b = c = d$ and $e = f = g = h$. If each subunit carries the same charge q, we can use the above equation to calculate the Q-V curve as

$$Q = q(4 - 4y_0 - 3y_1 - 2y_2 - y_3),$$

where

$$y_j = \frac{G_j}{1 + \sum_{j=0}^{n-1} G_j},$$

and, as before, $\mu_i = k_i^{-1}/k_i^1$, with k_i^{-1} and k_i^1 being the backward and forward rate respectively (i.e. in the above scheme, $k_0^1 = 4a$, $k_1^1 = 3b$, $k_3^{-1} = 4e$, etc). Figure 2 shows an example of a Q-V curve in which the q was set to 2e. Of the two cases considered, the first had independent transitions and the second case had positive cooperativity. When these Q-V curves were fitted, the independence case gave a value of $z = 2e$ as expected, but when cooperativity among subunits was present, the Q-V showed a steeper relation that could be approximately fitted by a Boltzmann distribution with a $z = 5e$, showing that the Q-V curve does not give a direct estimate of the gating charge because

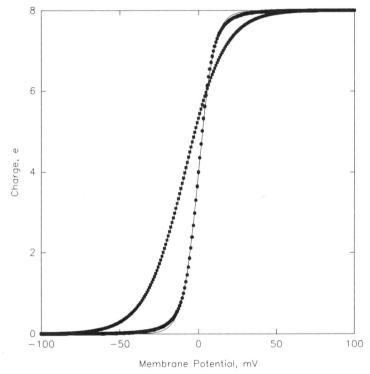

Figure 2   The effect of cooperativity in the Q-V curve. Squares designate the computed Q from a model with four independent identical subunits. The continuous line is a fitted Boltzmann distribution that gives a charge of 2e, the value used in the model. Circles indicate the computed Q-V for same model with positive cooperativity. The rates were (in s^{-1}) 10, 50, 70, and 100, for one subunit making the transition and 3 left behind, 2 making the transition and 2 left behind, etc. With this cooperativity the relation is steeper and is not properly fit by a Boltzmann distribution. The continuous line shows the best least square fit, which gives a charge of 5e.

it is model dependent. Therefore, although the features of the Q-V curve give much more information about the operation of the voltage sensor than the g-V curve, clearly they still do not give a unique interpretation of the operation of the channel subunit.

KINETICS OF GATING   The time course of the gating current contains information on the kinetics of the charge reorientation in the membrane electric field. In the simple case, where a charge moves between two discrete states, the gating current in response to a step of voltage is a simple exponential decay. In the presence of n subunits, all making identical first order transitions [Hodgkin & Huxley type (28)], the gating current will still be a simple exponential decay. The experimental situation is very different (see below) because gating currents show rising phases and multiple exponential decays. This is not surprising in view of the fact that the charge movement may occur in several steps in different parts of the molecule.

Some features of the kinetics are important in deciding details of kinetic models of activation. For example, the presence of a rising phase indicates that the initial step is slower and/or carries less charge than the subsequent steps (14). If the order of the transition rates in the kinetic scheme of the Hodgkin & Huxley model is reversed, the gating current shows a pronounced rising phase, although the time course of the ionic current remains essentially unaffected. This observation again demonstrates that gating currents, in contrast to the ionic currents, tell us much more about the transition between closed states.

The multiple exponential decay in the gating current is a direct indication of a multistep gating process. The time constants of the exponentials correspond to the reciprocals of the eigenvalues of the solution of the system and do not correspond directly to the actual rate constants of the kinetic scheme. Conformational changes in which charge is not moved (uncharged steps) can produce a rising phase if they are the initial steps in the sequence. If they are in the middle of the sequence they can produce humps in the gating current decay or they may not be noticeable at all when they are very fast.

GATING CURRENT FLUCTUATIONS   If the total charge per channel that moves is known, the next question is how does the movement occur? Is it in many small steps or a few large steps? The Q-V curve can give us some idea of the relative distribution of the charged steps with respect to the kinetic pathway, but it cannot provide a definite answer on the actual charge per transition or the number of transitions.

When the gating charge of one channel makes the transition in the electric field, it produces an electric current. If the transition is between two discrete states separated by a large energy barrier, the charge will spend most of the time in either of the two states and the jump across the barrier will occur extremely fast. The jump is analogous to the activated state of the Eyring rate theory (22). In this case, the current lasts a very short time (a current shot) and the time integral of this current represents the actual charge moved. If the transition occurs within nanoseconds, it is too fast to be recorded with present patch clamp technology. However, if a large number of channels are gating, the current recorded should fluctuate, owing to the current shots that contribute to the total gating current. The magnitude of these fluctuations (the variance of the current) will reflect the magnitude of the elementary charge involved in the transition. The first measurements of gating current fluctuations were done by Conti & Stühmer (18) on gating currents of the rat brain Na^+ channel type II expressed in *Xenopus laevis* oocytes. They found a detectable fluctuation that corresponded to about two electronic charges moving the entire membrane field. If several transitions are involved in the gating of the channel, each one will contribute to the fluctuations, but then it becomes quite difficult to separate the individual transitions unless a model is used to interpret the data, as in the case of the Q-V curve. Interestingly, if one knows the total charge per channel of the gating process, the determination of the fluctuations can aid in defining the number of steps involved, although steps that carry little charge will not be accounted for easily in the fluctuation analysis.

An analysis of macroscopic, single-channel, and specially gating currents has shown that Na^+ and K^+ channels must move through many closed states before opening (e.g. 28, 73), and in some cases so many states are required (17, 80) that investigators have questioned whether the assumption of discrete states, as opposed to a continuous process, is valid. Because the total charge is a constant, if we increase the number of states, the charge per transition becomes smaller, and the dwelling in each state will become shorter. In the limit, when the number of transitions goes to infinity, we approach the diffusional case and the fluctuations should become unmeasurable. The results of Conti & Stühmer (18) for the sodium channel, and Sigg et al (60) for the potassium channel, showing fluctuations in the gating current argue strongly against a pure diffusional process for the charge movement of the gating process, but they do not rule out the possibility of a combination of a diffusional process followed by discrete transitions.

Gating Currents and Inactivation

Hodgkin & Huxley (28) described the decrease of the Na^+ current during a maintained depolarization as the inactivation of the conductance. This process is voltage and time dependent and is also observed in some K^+ and Ca^{2+} channels. The microscopic interpretation of the current decay during inactivation is the population of another closed state or states. These inactivated states are differentiated from the normal closed states because the probability of their occupancy is increased with membrane depolarization, as opposed to the case of closed states, which are more populated at negative potentials.

The macroscopic fast inactivation of the squid sodium channel develops in few milliseconds, and its rate is voltage dependent. As such, it should have a voltage sensor and produce a gating current. In the model of Hodgkin & Huxley, inactivation was made voltage dependent and completely independent of the activation process, but later work in *Myxicola* axons suggested that the two processes were coupled (23). The recordings of Na^+-channel gating currents did not show a component associated with the inactivation process, but instead the activation gating charge was affected by the development of inactivation. When the membrane was depolarized and the gating current developed, it returned quickly at the end of a short depolarizing pulse to -120 mV. For long depolarizations, the return had two components: a fast one carrying only one-third of the charge and a very slow one carrying the rest. The development of the slow component followed the time course of the macroscopic inactivation and the time course of the slow component corresponded with the time course of the recovery from inactivation (6). When the potential was returned to -70 mV, the slow component was too slow to be detected and the charge measured was only one-third of the total. This observation gave rise to the term *charge immobilization*. These results clearly indicated that inactivation is coupled to the activation process, from which comes most of the voltage dependence of inactivation, although the inactivation step may have some voltage dependence of its own and will vary depending on the preparation (62, 77). Single channel studies have also demonstrated the coupling between activation and inactivation (2, 30, 77).

RELATIONSHIP BETWEEN STRUCTURE AND FUNCTION

Molecular cloning techniques have made possible the deduction of the amino acid sequences of many ion channels, including several voltage-dependent channels. The first sequence was obtained for the Na$^+$ channel of the eel electroplaque (47) and revealed a structure with four homologous domains, each containing six putative membrane-spanning segments based on hydrophobicity analysis. Most of the Na$^+$ channels cloned so far have a similar structure for the α subunit. A β subunit, not required for basic channel function, was also cloned recently (34). In the widely diverse voltage-dependent potassium channels [delayed-rectifier type and inactivating type (A-type)] many different families are conserved across species (35). However, within this diversity lies a basic sequence in which one can recognize six putative membrane spanning segments (S1 through S6) analogous to the six putative membrane segments of each of the four domains of the Na$^+$ channels (74).

The primary sequence has been used to postulate possible three-dimensional structures (21, 24), but little experimental evidence supports any detailed structural model of these channels. Nevertheless, predicted structures are very useful in predicting functional modifications induced by site-directed mutagenesis. In fact, at this stage, the main progress is in recognizing specific regions of the macromolecule that may be important in specific functions of the channel. One important example is the location of the amino acid sequence that seems to be important in the formation of the conduction pore (24)—a region between segments S5 and S6 in Na$^+$ and K$^+$ channels (26, 26a, 41, 81). The regions important for inactivation in Na$^+$ and K$^+$ channels have also been identified (see below). With regard to the site(s) responsible for the voltage dependence of activation, the situation is much less clear, as discussed below.

Because many results correlating the structure and function have been obtained in cloned expressed channels, we briefly mention a few examples of functional assays of mutated channels that have been useful in assessing the role of particular amino acids in the channel structure.

Properties of Gating Currents, and Channel Activation in Expressed Channels

Gating current properties have been studied in cloned and expressed Na$^+$, K$^+$, and Ca^{2+} channels. In macropatches of *Xenopus laevis* oocytes, the properties of rat brain II Na$^+$-channel gating current (18) were similar to those of gating currents previously observed in native nerve preparations (see 10), although the mechanistic interpretation was different. In Conti & Stühmer's work (18), the gating subunits were modeled identical and independent, based on the gating current noise analysis. Recently Crouzy & Sigworth (19) showed that the noise data from Conti & Stühmer (18) are also compatible with a sequential model such as the one proposed by Armstrong & Gilly (8). At present, a more extensive characterization of expressed Na^+ gating currents is lacking. On the other hand, recent studies performed on K^+ channels and Ca^{2+} channels are providing new insight into channel function. In the remainder of this section, we expand mainly on the results on the K^+ channel gating currents that have been studied in more detail than Na^+- and Ca^{2+}-channel gating currents.

MEASUREMENTS OF GATING CURRENTS   In initial experiments, gating-current measurements in expressed K^+ channels were isolated with the established procedure (11) of subtracting membrane linear capacitive and resistive components from the currents elicited by the stimulating pulse, using membrane currents elicited by small subtracting negative pulses (12). Recently, the properties of these subtracted gating currents were confirmed with the first recordings of unsubtracted gating currents from DRK1 and *Shaker* K^+ channels (53, 61, 67).

Recent experiments revealed that macropatches in the cell-attached mode could be used to record gating current that had properties identical to the gating currents recorded with the internally perfused cut open oocyte technique (COVG). However, the differences appeared as soon as the patches were excised. Upon excision, the OFF gating currents become progressively slower, until it is often difficult to separate the OFF current from the baseline noise (59, 61). Patch excision may result in some alteration of the channel properties, which produces a progressive decrease in the rate of charge return. This presumption agrees with recent observations showing a progressive slowdown of the OFF charge movement as well as movement of the inward K^+ tail currents after patch excision (59).

These observations explain why the records of Stühmer et al (63) and Schoppa et al (56), obtained in excised macropatches, show no gating current at the OFF of the pulse. Stühmer et al's study (63) also showed a lack of OFF gating current because (*a*) their experiments were done in the presence of internal tetraethylammonium (TEA) shown to induce charge immobilization in a way similar to the inactivation process (12, 53, 54), and (*b*) the chimeric K^+ channel clone used in their experiments deactivates slowly (63).

KINETIC PROPERTIES   The salient features common among DRK1 and *Shaker* K^+ clones are: (*a*) the turn-on of the gating current shows a rising phase, suggesting that the hypothetical activating subunits are not independent (see above); (*b*) the more negative position of the charge-voltage curve vs the conductance-voltage curve and the charge displacement by hyperpolarizing prepulses indicates that a large fraction of the voltage dependence occurs in the transitions between closed states; and (c) the open-to-closed transition is weakly voltage dependent, as suggested by the presence of a rising phase in the OFF gating currents. Exclusive properties to the *Shaker* K$^+$ clone are: (a) the OFF gating charge is partially immobilized for large depolarizing pulses, expected for an inactivating channel, while in mutant channels lacking inactivation the charge returns quickly at the end of the pulse, and (b) internal TEA mimics the inactivation particle inducing charge immobilization without affecting the ON charge.

DO THE SUBUNITS INTERACT DURING GATING?   As explained above, in a tetrameric channel model, in which four identical and independent gating subunits undergo a single voltage-dependent structural change for channel opening, gating currents should rise instantaneously and then decay following a single exponential. The slow rising phase found in K$^+$ channels' ON gating currents (12, 54) disproves the hypothesis that the activation process follows the movement of four identical gating subunits with two states responding to voltage in an independent manner. This model was also discarded for the Na$^+$ channel, for which the gating current tail has kinetics similar to the deactivation of the ionic currents while the model predicts that the gating current will be three times slower than the ionic current (6). These results speak in favor of cooperative interactions among the gating subunits or a multistate process for each subunit. Alternatively, they all can be explained with a sequential model in which early, less voltage-dependent transitions between very early closed states are followed by more voltage-dependent transitions (carrying more charge) between later closed states, and finally by a slightly voltage-dependent transition between the last closed state and the open state (13) (see Figure 3).

Sequential models of this type can account for many of the properties of *Shaker* K$^+$-channel single, macroscopic, and gating currents (12, 37, 53, 54, 61, 67, 75). Sequential models may be correlated with the operation of the individual subunits with or without cooperativity, as shown above for the case of first-order process of each subunit. If each subunit can undergo a higher-order process, it becomes very difficult to decide the presence of cooperativity. On the other hand, cooperativity among gating subunits has also been inferred from the voltage dependence of the K$^+$ conductance of heterotetramers made up from combinations of subunits with different gating phenotypes (32, 75). However, in view of the results on dimer constructs of McCormack

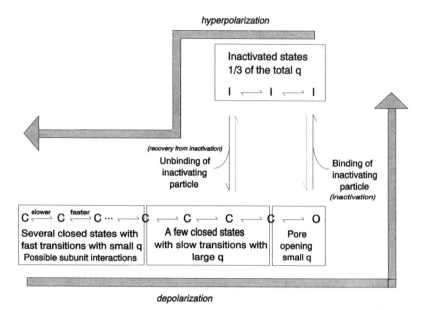

Figure 3 State diagram of a *Shaker* K channel. C represents closed states, O represents the open state, and I the inactivated states. The large gray arrows indicate the main pathway followed during depolarization and repolarization. For details, see text.

et al (42), who found that dimers did not necessarily form the expected phenotype, the results with tandem constructs must be interpreted with caution.

DO GATING CURRENTS RELATE TO CHANNEL OPENING?   The main question is to define how the voltage sensor movement and protein reorientation under the electric field is coupled to the channel opening. Several lines of evidence support the view that charge movement and pore opening are closely correlated: (*a*) the correlation in a kinetic scheme of gating and ionic current properties (61), (*b*) the correspondence in expressed channels between charge movement and ionic current amplitudes (56, 67), (*c*) the fact that modifications of initial conditions by prepulse potentials equally affect charge movement and ionic current time course (61, 73), and (*d*) the presence of mutations in the S4 region that altered simultaneously the voltage dependence of charge movement and K^+ ionic currents (54, 55).

THE COLE-MOORE SHIFT   Cole & Moore (17) reported that K^+ currents were delayed by hyperpolarizing prepulses. A similar phenomenon found for Na$^+$ currents was also correlated with an equivalent shift of the Na$^+$ gating currents (73). In experiments with *Shaker* K$^+$ channels, hyperpolarizing and depolarizing pulses preceding ionic and gating currents influenced those currents in a similar way. In addition, the charge moving in negative regions, where the K$^+$ conductance is practically zero, was found to be responsible for the time shifts recorded in the ionic current (61). The correspondence in the time shifts of ionic and gating currents strongly supported the hypothesis that most of the charge movement, including that occurring at very negative potentials and prior to channel opening, is associated with conformational changes leading to the opening of the channel. Furthermore, the presence of a more prominent rising phase with hyperpolarizing prepulses and its decrease by preceding depolarizations is in agreement with the view that initial transitions among the early closed states carry less charge (12, 13, 67).

MUTATIONS IN THE PORE REGION: GATING CURRENT IN NONCONDUCTING CHANNELS   The initial description of *Shaker* B K$^+$ channel gating currents came from a study in which K$^+$ ionic currents were eliminated by replacing the cytoplasmatic oocyte solution with K-free solution through an internal perfusion system (12). A major advance in gating current studies was the introduction (by R MacKinnon) of a nonconducting pore mutation (W434F) that had normal charge-movement properties (53). This clone allowed the direct measurement of charge movement in the presence of normal permeating ions and without channel blockers. Gating currents show that this channel still undergoes its normal voltage-sensitive conformational changes in response to membrane depolarization, including charge immobilization. In addition, the internal mouth of this mutant seems to open because TEA can immobilize the charge. These results indicate that this mutant channel must maintain the normal structure, except for a region in the pore. Whether the movement through the channel aqueous pore is obliterated or whether the last closed-to-open transitions [which may carry little charge (82)] were affected by this mutation remains unknown.

MODULATION OF THE COUPLING OF THE VOLTAGE SENSOR AND THE ION-CHANNEL OPENING   The *Shaker* B W434F mutation is an extreme case in which the charge movement is uncoupled from the pore opening. Studies on the action of regulatory subunits of Ca^{2+} ionic and gating currents may provide clues on the coupling between charge movement and pore opening. Using the COVG technique (68), Birnbaumer and coworkers (45, 52, 78) studied gating and ionic currents of the rabbit cardiac Ca^{2+} channel α_1 subunit (α_{1Ca}) and of α_1 coexpressed with β. Their main conclusion was that the β_2 subunit potentiates Ca^{2+} currents without affecting the charge movement. They suggested that this modulatory activity results from events that occur late in the activation sequence, after most of the gating charge has moved and before the actual opening of the pore.

As with K^+ channels, the Q-V curves for Ca^{2+} channels started at more negative potentials than the g-V curves, and the effective valence for the voltage dependence of the ionic conductance was approximately two times that for charge movement (1, 45). Thus, expressed Ca^{2+} channels go through multiple closed states before opening and at least two voltage-sensing elements or gates control the activation. Furthermore, in dysgenic myotubes lacking the skeletal α_1 subunit, the expression of exogenous skeletal and cardiac α_1 subunits restored dihydropyridine-sensitive Ca^{2+} currents, charge movement, and skeletal or cardiac type excitation-contraction coupling, respectively. In chimeric cardiac-skeletal α_1 subunits, the first domain was enough to convey the Ca^{2+} current activation kinetics characteristic of the channel source, either cardiac or skeletal (9, 69–72).

The Q_{on} and Q_{off} were identical in cardiac α_1 channel expressed in dysgenic myotubes and in oocytes (45, 70). Thus, Ca^{2+} channels do not undergo charge immobilization as seen with rapidly inactivating Na^+ channels (6) and in transient K^+ channels (12).

The Activation of the Conductance

TWO COMPONENTS OF THE GATING CHARGE   Recent studies on gating currents of Shaker K^+ channels have demonstrated that the Q-V curve has two components (13). The first component (q_1) carries about one-third of the charge with an equivalent charge of about 2e and a midpoint of -63 mV. The second component (q_2) carries about two-thirds of the charge with an equivalent charge of about 5e and a midpoint of -44 mV. The q_1 component has been identified with transitions between closed states and is largely responsible for the Cole-Moore shift (see above), while the q_2 component is closely associated with the opening of the channel, although the very last transition to the open state has little voltage dependence (82) (see Figure 3).

IN SEARCH OF THE VOLTAGE SENSOR   A common feature in voltage gated Na^+, Ca^{2+}, and K^+ channels is that the fourth putative transmembrane segment (S4) contains several positively charged amino acids (arginines or lysines) at every third position, generally in between hydrophobic residues. One exciting hypothesis is that the voltage sensor of voltage-dependent channels consists of these charged groups in the S4 segments (46, 47). In this view, the gating currents could originate from the reorientation of the charges in S4 segments induced by changes in the electric field. A consequence of this hypothesis is that a neutralization or reversal of the positively charged residues should reduce the voltage dependence of channel opening.

With this general rationale, the role of the S4 segment has been investigated with mutagenesis experiments by evaluating the effects of the mutations on the voltage dependence of the channel opening. Substitution or neutralization of the charged residues in the S4 segment revealed a variety of effects in expressed Na^+ and K^+ channels (49, 64). The most common phenomenon was a parallel shift in the activation voltage curve, whereas a change in the slope of the curves was restricted to fewer substitutions. For example, the R368Q mutation for *Shaker* K^+ channels (49) and K226E for Na^+ channels (64) reduced the slope of the g-V curve. The calculated change in charge is uncertain because of the limitations of the measurements: in the case of the Na^+ channel, the effects of the mutations were evaluated with reference to the Hodgkin-Huxley model (64) and in the K^+ channel it was done by fitting Boltzmann distributions to the g-V curves or calculating the charge with the limiting slope method (see above).

Liman et al (38) obtained better resolution by measuring the limiting slope of the P_o-V curve from inward tail currents at negative potentials and in high external Rb (38). Slower tails induced by Rb ions gave a more accurate measurement of ionic tail currents, allowing the estimation of P_o at more negative potentials. The P_o-V curves fit well to a model consisting of four subunits, giving origin to five closed states and a final voltage-independent step (37). These authors concluded, in agreement with previous work, that the S4 charges are involved in the voltage-dependent conformational changes occurring during channel activation (38).

In all of these experiments, the effects of individual-residue replacements were not equivalent, indicating that the orientation and position of the residues within the folded protein play a major role in the voltage-sensing properties. One main concern in these experiments was to evaluate the extent to which the mutations were specific for the voltage-sensing properties of the channel protein. The fact that other channel properties, such as the selectivity to Na^+ or K^+, and the kinetics of inactivation remained mostly unaffected favors the view of a specific action of the S4 mutations on the voltage sensor (49, 64). On the other hand, conservative substitutions of hydrophobic residues in the S4 segment of *Shaker* K^+ channels caused shifts comparable to the ones observed with substitutions of charged residues (39). As with the mutations of the S4 charged groups, other channel properties such as K^+ selectivity and fast inactivation were not altered (39). Thus, in addition to electrostatic interactions of the charged residues, hydrophobic interactions between the S4 segment and regions surrounding it seem to influence voltage-dependent activation.

A shift of the activation curve in the voltage axis to more positive potentials can be interpreted as a change in the equilibrium between the closed and the open states, favoring the closed states, while a change in the slope is a more direct indication of a change in the number of charges that are sensing the electric field (see above). However, channel opening is the final stage of channel activation, and alterations in the coupling between the voltage sensor and channel opening may modify the final ionic current recorded (45, 56). Thus, the functions of the voltage sensor are better assessed by a direct measurement of the gating currents and the resulting ionic currents (12, 55, 56, 67).

Using this approach, Schoppa et al (56) measured ionic and gating currents in *Shaker* K^+ channels with the mutation L370V (V2 mutant) (43). This residue is part of the leucine zipper motif encompassing part of the S4 segment. Hurst et al (32) created a similar mutation in an equivalent position in a rat brain K^+ channel (RBK1) in a tetrameric construct. Both mutant channels display a large positive shift in the voltage dependence of channel opening. Simultaneous measurements of charge movement and ionic currents showed that the V2 mutant had a smaller effective valence (slope) in the P_o-V curve but that the total amount of charge per channel remained equal to that of the wild-type (56).

This important finding highlights the need for a critical evaluation of the measurement of ionic currents as an indication of the function of the voltage sensor, because changes in the P_o-V curve may not result from changes in the voltage sensor, but may be caused by an alteration in the coupling between the voltage sensor and channel opening. On the other hand, the parallel shifts of the g-V curves cannot be regarded as specific for an alteration in the voltage sensor because local changes of potential, such as a modification in surface potential, may account for this result. For example, pore mutations in a chimeric delayed rectified (DRK1-NGK) channel that affect K^+-to-Rb^+ selectivity cause a parallel shift of the activation curve for ionic current and charge movement. The lack of a change in the slope in this pore mutation strongly suggests that the voltage-sensing structure remained intact (66).

Gating current measurements in *Shaker* K^+ channels (55) have uncovered major consequences of the mutation R368Q in the S4 segment on ionic currents and charge movement, while showing that the mutations R377K and R371Q were much less effective. Still other mutations in the S4 segment were not testable because the protein did not properly assemble (R377Q). The R368Q *Shaker* S4 mutant showed a wide separation of the two components (q_1 and q_2) of charge movement. The reduction in the slope of the P_o-V curve and the correlation with a reduction in the effective valence of the second component q_2 (55), thought to be directly involved in channel opening (13), strongly suggests that the transmembrane electric field is sensed by the positive charge at position 368.

Gating current measurements may provide further information on the domains of the channel protein that sense the voltage. However, the interpretation that point charge residues embedded in a hydrophobic environment are the actual voltage sensors, and that their substitution with neutral or negatively charged residues may lead to a direct subtraction of the charge involved, is an over-simplified view. Most likely, the movable parts of the assembled channel protein may respond to voltage following a series of dipole moment changes resulting from the weighted sum of each charge element. In this sum, important factors are the distances and the dielectric constant surrounding the charged elements, in addition to the local electric field, which is changed by the position of the charges and their counter charges. Thus, until the channel's three-dimensional structure becomes available, the interpretation of the mutagenesis results is very speculative. Nevertheless, this approach, critically evaluated, may yield insight into the amino acids that are important in the voltage-sensor structure and the coupling between the voltage-sensor displacement and pore opening.

THE CHANNEL GATE   Once the charges or dipoles have reoriented and regions of the molecule have moved, how does the pore become conducting? This is an area of wide speculation. In the batrachotoxin-treated Na channel, opening involves a conformational change that decreases the degrees of freedom of the channel components (18a). The gate could be an actual occlusion of the pore, as it seems to be in the case of inactivation (see below); a shutter type mechanism (a group that interposes in the middle of the channel); or an electrostatic interaction (positive charges that swing into the pore vicinity preventing conduction). The model of Durell & Guy (21) proposes that the small region that links segment S4 with S5 is a blocking segment that may move out of the way upon relocation of the S4 segment, which, by virtue of its charge, moves upon depolarization. Interestingly, the V2 mutation studied by Schoppa et al (56) is in that region and produces a significant uncoupling between the charge movement and the channel opening. In addition, part of the possible receptor for the inactivation particle seems to be located in the segment (see below) (33) that would become available as the channel opens. This hypothesis is attractive because it ties the movement of the voltage sensor (S4) with the conformational change that uncovers the pore and exposes the receptor for the inactivation particle, which thus leads to inactivation of the conductance and immobilization of the gating charge.

Inactivation and Gating-Charge Immobilization

Fast inactivation is completely eliminated by proteases such as pronase and trypsin (7, 77) or reagents cleaving peptide bonds such as n-bromo acetamide (48). Pronase also eliminated charge immobilization. The chemical modifications of inactivation clearly indicated a polypeptidic origin, which was envisioned as a plug that could stop conduction by blocking the pore and, by interacting with the gating charges, could produce charge immobilization (6).

In a landmark paper, Hoshi et al (31) demonstrated that the actual region of the *Shaker* B channel that acts as the inactivation particle resides in amino acids in the N-terminal region of the channel, by testing a series of deletion mutants in the N terminus of the channel. Deletions that encompassed the first 20 amino acids eliminated inactivation. They restored inactivation by applying a peptide corresponding to the first 20 amino acids to the cytoplasmic face of the channel previously made noninactivating by the deletion of amino acids 6–46 of the N terminus (83). In the Na^+ channel, a highly conserved region in the linker between domains three and four was necessary for inactivation (51). In this region, F1489 was necessary for fast inactivation (79).

Armstrong (4, 5) demonstrated that blocking by internal TEA occludes the pore of the potassium channel in the squid in experiments in which the block was relieved by raising the external K concentration (the knock off effect). The view that fast inactivation results from the blockade of the inner mouth of the *Shaker* channel by the inactivating peptide was further strengthened by a similar experiment demonstrating that TEA competed with inactivation and that raising K^+ in the external side speeded up recovery from fast inactivation (15, 20).

Cloned K channels have provided a direct means of testing the hypothesis that the process of fast inactivation is related to charge immobilization (12, 54). In fact, gating current measurements in noninactivating Shaker K clones (by deletion of aminoacids 6–46) have shown that the charge at the end of a long (50 ms) depolarizing pulse is rapidly and fully recovered. In contrast, in the wild-type (inactivating) clone of *Shaker* B K$^+$ channel, at the end of a 50 ms depolarizing pulse, charge movement recovery was greatly slowed down (charge immobilization). The time course and voltage dependence of the charge immobilization coincided with the time course and voltage dependence of inactivation. These results indicate that the same region of the N-terminal that blocks the channel and induces inactivation is also responsible for immobilization of the gating charge; hence, fast inactivation of the ionic current and charge immobilization are correlated. The inactivating particle immobilizes about two-thirds of the total charge. This means that, upon repolarization, one-third of the charge moves back, tracing a different set of closed states (the inactivated states; see Figure 3). The return of the other two-thirds proceeds only after the particle unbinds—the rate-limiting step, which is a transition connecting the last inactivated state with one of the closed states that allows the reaction to proceed to the closed states populated at hyperpolarized potentials (Figure 3).

The ability to induce charge immobilization is not considered to be restricted to the inactivating peptide, because a similar finding was observed with the internal application of TEA (12, 54). The W434F mutation of the *Shaker* noninactivating channel, besides having the normal kinetics of the gating charge movements, shows charge immobilization induced by internal TEA as in the normal conducting channel, thus indicating that the inner pore of this mutant channel physically opens upon membrane depolarization (53). External potassium did not remobilize the charge in the W434F channel, suggesting that the possible site that must be occupied by K for the knock off to occur is not functional in this mutant. The nature of the interaction remains to be determined, but given that internal TEA produces charge immobilization, the immobilization mechanism does not appear to depend on the intrinsic structure of the N-terminal segment. The interaction might occur because the presence of the particle in a site located in the internal mouth facilitates the coupling to the voltage sensor. This coupling may be different in DRK1 channels because, although they have a similar internal TEA sensitivity for ion conduction block, TEA does not induce charge immobilization (67).

Thus, in a schematic way one can separate this process into three main aspects: (*a*) the nature of the inactivating particle, (*b*) the particle receptor, and (*c*) the coupling between the occupancy of the particle receptor and the charge immobilization. In this respect, structure-function studies of the inactivating peptide suggest that nonpolar residues stabilize the binding through hydrophobic interactions. Also, an increase in the net positive charge near the COOH terminal increased the k_{on} (with little effect on the k_{off}), suggesting electrostatic focusing of the particle towards its binding site (44).

One important point to investigate is the relative ability of the inactivating peptide mutants to induce charge immobilization in relation to their binding constants. With respect to the peptide receptor itself, mutagenesis experiments have shown that the stretch of amino acids that connects the S4 with the S5 segment is directly involved (33). Whether these residues involved in fast inactivation also participate in the coupling between the inner mouth occupancy by the inactivating peptide and charge immobilization remains to be shown.

CONCLUSIONS

The tools of molecular biology have provided important means to advance our understanding of the correlation between amino acid sequence and the function of ion channels by recognizing segments and particular amino acids of the macromolecule as important players in specific actions of the activation and inactivation processes of the channels. We know that certain charges of the S4 segments are involved in the sensing of the voltage, but we know very little about the specific site or sites of the sensors. Fast inactivation is much better defined, and we know the sequence of the inactivating particle and part of its receptor.

Molecular biological techniques have also advanced the functional details of channels because they have allowed high levels of expression of single-type channels in native or mutated forms. These clones have been studied in detail with single-channel, macroscopic, and gating-current recordings. We now know the details of the components of gating currents and the relative charges carried in each of them (see Figure 3). The high expression of channels has allowed the recording of gating current fluctuations (18, 60), which confirms, in the case of the K channel, that a large number of transitions between closed states carry small charges and produce undetectable fluctuations (the q_1 component) followed by a transition (or transitions) that carries a significant charge (about 2 to 3e across the membrane field) that precedes channel opening (the q_2 component) (60). The transitions that make up the q_1 component are likely reorientations of the subunits that have many stable states that, once completed, lead to a large charge transfer in the whole molecule, an event that must be necessary for the final conformational change that renders the pore conductive (see Figure 3). The challenge that remains is the identification of all the charge components within the structure and the eventual description of the atomic rearrangements that produce the gating of the channel.

ACKNOWLEDGMENTS

We thank Drs. Ana M Correa, David E Patton, L Toro, and E Perozo for reading and commenting on the manuscript. Supported by USPHS GM30376 and HL37044.

Literature Cited

1. Adams BA, Tanabe T, Mikami A, Numa S, Beam KG. 1990. Intramembrane charge movement restored in dysgenic skeletal muscle by injection of dihydropyridine receptor cDNAs. *Nature* 346:569–72
2. Aldrich RW, Corey DP, Stevens CF. 1983. A reinterpretation of mammalian sodium channel gating based on single channel recording. *Nature* 306:436–41
3. Almers W. 1978. Gating currents and charge movements in excitatory membranes. *Rev. Physiol. Biochem. Pharmacol.* 82:96–190
4. Armstrong CM. 1975. Ionic pores, gates, and gating currents. *Q. Rev. Biophys.* 7:179, 210
5. Armstrong CM. 1971. Interaction of tetraethylammonium ion derivatives with the potassium channels of giant axons. *J. Gen. Physiol.* 58:413–37
6. Armstrong CM, Bezanilla F. 1977. Inactivation of the sodium channel. II. Gating current experiments. *J. Gen. Physiol.* 70:567–90
7. Armstrong CM, Bezanilla F, Rojas E. 1973. Destruction of sodium conductance inactivation in squid axons perfused with pronase. *J. Gen. Physiol.* 62:375–91
8. Armstrong CM, Gilly WF. 1979. Fast and slow steps in the activation of sodium channels. *J. Gen. Physiol.* 74:691–711
9. Beam KG, Adams BA, Niidome T, Numa S, Tanabe T. 1992. Function of a truncated dihydropyridine receptor as both voltage sensor and calcium channel. *Nature* 360:169–71
10. Bezanilla F. 1985. Gating of sodium and potassium channels. *J. Membr. Biol.* 88:97–111
11. Bezanilla F, Armstrong CM. 1977. Inactivation of the sodium channel. I. Sodium current experiments. *J. Gen. Physiol.* 70:549–66
12. Bezanilla F, Perozo E, Papazian DM, Stefani E. 1991. Molecular basis of gating charge immobilization in Shaker potassium channels. *Science* 254:679–83
13. Bezanilla F, Perozo E, Stefani E. 1994. The gating of Shaker K^+ channels. II. The components of gating currents and a model of channel activation. *Biophys. J.* In press
14. Bezanilla F, Taylor RE. 1982. Voltage-dependent gating of sodium channels. In *Abnormal Nerves and Muscles as Impulse Generators*, ed. WJ Culp, J Ochoa, pp. 62–79. New York/Oxford: Oxford Univ. Press
15. Choi KL, Aldrich RW, Yellen G. 1991. Tetraethylammonium blockade distinguishes two inactivation mechanisms in voltage-activated K^+ channels. *Proc. Natl. Acad. Sci. USA* 88:5092–95
16. Cole KS, Curtis HJ. 1939. Electrical impedance of the squid giant axon during activity. *J. Gen. Physiol.* 22:649–70
17. Cole KS, Moore JW. 1960. Potassium ion current in the squid giant axon: dynamic characteristics. *Biophys. J.* 1:161–202
18. Conti F, Stühmer, W. 1989. Quantal charge redistributions accompanying the structural transitions of sodium channels. *Eur. Biophys. J.* 17:53–59
18a. Correa AM, Bezanilla F, Latorre R. 1992. Gating kinetics of batrachotoxin-modified Na^+ channels in the squid giant axon. Voltage and temperature effects. *Biophys. J.* 61:1332–52
19. Crouzy SC, Sigworth FJ. 1993. Fluctuations in ion channel gating currents.

Analysis of nonstationary shot noise. *Biophys. J.* 64:68–76

20. Demo DD, Yellen G. 1991. The inactivation gate of the Shaker K^+ channel behaves like an open-channel blocker. *Neuron* 7:743–53

21. Durell SR, Guy HR. 1992. Atomic scale structure and functional models of voltage-gated potassium channels. *Biophys. J.* 62:238–50

22. Eyring H, Lumry R, Woodbury JW. 1949. Some applications of modern rate theroy to physiological systems. *Rec. Chem. Prog.* 10:100–14

23. Goldman L, Schauf CL. 1972. Inactivation of the sodium current in *Myxicola* giant axons. Evidence for coupling to the activation process. *J. Gen. Physiol.* 59:659–75

24. Guy HR, Seetharamulu P. 1986. Molecular model of the action potential sodium channel. *Proc. Natl. Acad. Sci. USA* 83:508–12

25. Hamill OP, Marty A, Neher E, Sakmann B, Sigworth FJ. 1981. Improved patch-clamp techniques for high-resolution current recording from cells and cell-free membrane patches. *Pflüger Arch.* 391:85–100

26. Hartmann HA, Kirsch GE, Drewe JA, Taglialatela M, Joho RH, Brown AM. 1991. Exchange of conduction pathways between two related K^+ channels. *Science* 251:942–44

26a. Heinemann SH, Terlau H, Stuhmer W, Imoto K, Numa S. 1992. Calcium channel characteristics conferred on the sodium channel by single mutations. *Nature* 356:441–43

27. Hille B. 1992. *Ionic Channels of Excitable Membranes.* Sunderland, MA: Sinauer

28. Hodgkin AL, Huxley AF. 1952. A quantitative description of membrane current and its application to conduction and excitation in nerve. *J. Physiol.* 117:500–44

29. Hodgkin AL, Huxley AF, Katz B. 1952. Measurement of current-voltage relations in the membrane of the giant axon of *Loligo*. *J. Physiol.* 116:424–48

30. Horn R, Vandenberg CA. 1984. Statistical properties of single sodium channels. *J. Gen. Physiol.* 84:505–34

31. Hoshi T, Zagotta WN, Aldrich RW. 1990. Biophysical and molecular mechanisms of Shaker potassium channel inactivation. *Science* 250:533–38

32. Hurst RS, Kavanaugh MP, Yakel J, Adelman JP, North RA. 1992. Cooperative interactions among subunits of a voltage-dependent potassium channel. Evidence from expression of concatenated cDNAs. *J. Biol. Chem.* 267:23742–45

33. Isacoff EY, Jan YN, Jan LY. 1991. Putative receptor for the cytoplasmic inactivation gate in the Shaker K^+ channel. *Nature* 353:86–90

34. Isom LL, De Jongh KS, Patton DE, Reber BF, Offord J, et al. 1992. Primary structure and functional expression of the beta 1 subunit of the rat brain sodium channel. *Science* 256:839–42

35. Jan LY, Jan YN. 1990. How might the diversity of potassium channels be generated. *Trends Neurosci.* 13:415–19

36. Keynes RD. 1951. The ionic movements during nervous activity. *J. Physiol.* 114:119–50

37. Koren G, Liman ER, Logothetis DE, Nadal Ginard B, Hess P. 1990. Gating mechanism of a cloned potassium channel expressed in frog oocytes and mammalian cells. *Neuron* 4:39–51

38. Liman ER, Hess P, Weaver F, Koren G. 1991. Voltage-sensing residues in the S4 region of a mammalian K^+ channel. *Nature* 353:752–56

39. Lopez GA, Jan YN, Jan LY. 1991. Hydrophobic substitution mutations in the S4 sequence alter voltage-dependent gating in Shaker K^+ channels. *Neuron* 7:327–36

40. MacKinnon R. 1991. Determination of the subunit stoichiometry of a voltage-activated potassium channel. *Nature* 350:232–35

41. MacKinnon R, Yellen G. 1990. Mutations affecting TEA blockade and ion permeation in voltage-activated K^+ channels. *Science* 250:276–79

42. McCormack K, Lin L, Iverson LE, Tanouye MA, Sigworth FJ. 1992. Tandem linkage of Shaker K^+ channel subunits does not ensure the stoichiometry of expressed channels. *Biophys. J.* 63:1406–11

43. McCormack K, Tanouye MA, Iverson LE, Lin J-W, Ramaswami M, et al. 1991. A role for hydrophobic residues in the voltage-dependent gating of Shaker K^+ channels. *Proc. Natl. Acad. Sci. USA* 88:2931–35

44. Murrel-Lagnado RD, Aldrich RW. 1993. Interactions of the amino terminal domains of Shaker K channels with a pore blocking site studied with synthetic peptides. *J. Gen. Physiol.* 102:949–75

45. Neely A, Wei X, Olcese R, Birnbaumer L, Stefani E. 1994. Potentiation by the β subunit of the ratio of ionic current to the charge movement in the cardiac calcium channel. *Science* 262:575–78

46. Noda M, Ikeda T, Kayano T, Suzuki H, Takeshima H, et al. 1986. Existence of

distinct sodium channel messenger RNAs in rat brain. *Nature* 320:188–92

47. Noda M, Shimizu S, Tanabe T, Takai T, Kayano T, et al. 1984. Primary structure of *Electrophorus electricus* sodium channel deduced from cDNA sequence. *Nature* 312:121–27

48. Oxford GS, Wu CH, Narahashi T. 1978. Removal of sodium channel inactivation in squid axons by N-bromoacetamide. *J. Gen. Physiol.* 71:227–47

49. Papazian DM, Timpe LC, Jan YN, Jan LY. 1991. Alteration of voltage-dependence of Shaker potassium channel by mutations in the S4 sequence. *Nature* 349:305–10

50. Parsegian A. 1969. Energy of an ion crossing a low dielectric membrane: solutions to four relevant electrostatic problems. *Nature* 221:844–46

51. Patton DE, West JW, Catterall WA, Goldin AL. 1992. Amino acid residues required for fast Na$^+$-channel inactivation: charge neutralization and deletions in the III-IV linker. *Proc. Natl. Acad. Sci. USA* 89:10905–9

52. Perez-Reyes E, Castellano A, Kim HS, Bertrand P, Baggstrom E, et al. 1992. Cloning and expression of cardiac/brain β subunit of the L-type calcium channel. *J. Biol. Chem.* 267:1792–97

53. Perozo E, MacKinnon R, Bezanilla F, Stefani E. 1993. Gating currents from a non-conducting mutant reveal open-closed conformations in Shaker K$^+$ channels. *Neuron.* In press

54. Perozo E, Papazian DM, Stefani E, Bezanilla F. 1992. Gating currents in Shaker K$^+$ channels. Implications for activation and inactivation models. *Biophys. J.* 62:160–71

55. Perozo E, Santacruz-Toloza L, Stefani E, Bezanilla F, Papazian DM. 1994. S4 mutations alter gating currents of Shaker K channels. *Biophys. J.* 66:345–54

56. Schoppa NE, McCormack K, Tanouye MA, Sigworth FJ. 1992. The size of gating charge in wild-type and mutant Shaker potassium channels. *Science* 255:1712–15

57. Schwarz TL, Tempel BL, Papazian DM, Jan YN, Jan LY. 1988. Multiple potassium-channel components are produced by alternative splicing at the Shaker locus in *Drosophila*. *Nature* 331:137–42; 1988. Erratum. *Nature* 332(6166):740

58. Deleted in proof

59. Sigg D, Bezanilla F, Stefani E. 1994. Slowing of deactivation kinetics in Shaker B as seen in macropatch recordings of gating and ionic currents. *Biophys. J.* 66:A438

60. Sigg D, Stefani E, Bezanilla F. 1994. Gating current noise produced by elementary transitions in Shaker K$^+$ channels. *Science.* In press

61. Stefani E, Toro L, Perozo E, Bezanilla F. 1994. The gating of Shaker K + channels. I. Ionic and gating currents. *Biophys. J.* In press

62. Stimers JR, Bezanilla F, Taylor RE. 1985. Sodium channel activation in the squid giant axon. Steady state properties. *J. Gen. Physiol.* 85:65–82

63. Stühmer W, Conti F, Stocker M, Pongs O, Heinemann SH. 1991. Gating currents of inactivating and non-inactivating potassium channels expressed in *Xenopus* oocytes. *Pflüger Arch.* 418:423–29

64. Stühmer W, Conti F, Suzuki H, Wang XD, Noda M, et al. 1989. Structural parts involved in activation and inactivation of the sodium channel. *Nature* 339:597–603

65. Swenson RP, Armstrong CM. 1981. K$^+$ channels close more slowly in the presence of external K$^+$ and Rb$^+$. *Nature* 291:427–29

66. Taglialatela M, Kirsch GE, VanDongen AM, Drewe JA, Hartmann HA, et al. 1992. Gating currents from a delayed rectifier K$^+$ channel with altered pore structure and function. *Biophys. J.* 62:34–36

67. Taglialatela M, Stefani E. 1993. Gating currents of the cloned delayed-rectifier K$^+$ channel DRK1. *Proc. Natl. Acad. Sci. USA* 90:4758–62

68. Taglialatela M, Toro L, Stefani E. 1992. Novel voltage clamp to record small, fast currents from ion channels expressed in *Xenopus* oocytes. *Biophys. J.* 61:78–82

69. Tanabe T, Adams BA, Numa S, Beam KG. 1991. Repeat I of the dihydropyridine receptor is critical in determining calcium channel activation kinetics. *Nature* 352:800–3

70. Tanabe T, Beam KG, Adams BA, Niidome T, Numa S. 1990. Regions of the skeletal muscle dihydropyridine receptor critical for excitation-contraction coupling. *Nature* 346:567–69

71. Tanabe T, Beam KG, Powell JA, Numa S. 1988. Restoration of excitation-contraction coupling and slow calcium current in dysgenic muscle by dihydropyridine receptor complementary DNA. *Nature* 336:134–39

72. Tanabe T, Mikami A, Numa S, Beam KG. 1990. Cardiac-type excitation-con-

traction coupling in dysgenic skeletal muscle injected with cardiac dihydropyridine receptor cDNA. *Nature* 344: 451–53

73. Taylor RE, Bezanilla F. 1983. Sodium and gating current time shifts resulting from changes in initial conditions. *J. Gen. Physiol.* 81:773–84

74. Tempel BL, Papazian DM, Schwarz TL, Jan YL, Jan LY. 1987. Sequence of a probable potassium channel component encoded at Shaker locus of *Drosophila*. *Science* 237:770–75

75. Tytgat J, Hess P. 1992. Evidence for cooperative interactions in potassium channel gating. *Nature* 359:420–23

76. Vandenberg CA, Bezanilla F. 1991. A sodium channel gating model based on single channel, macroscopic ionic, and gating currents in the squid giant axon. *Biophys. J.* 60:1511–33

77. Vandenberg CA, Horn R. 1984. Inactivation viewed through single sodium channels. *J. Gen. Physiol.* 84:535–64

78. Wei XY, Perez Reyes E, Lacerda AE, Schuster G, Brown AM, Birnbaumer L. 1991. Heterologous regulation of the cardiac Ca^{2+} channel alpha 1 subunit by skeletal muscle beta and gamma subunits. Implications for the structure of cardiac L-type Ca^{2+} channels. *J. Biol. Chem.* 266:21943–47

79. West JW, Patton DE, Scheuer T, Wang Y, Goldin AL, Catterall WA. 1992. A cluster of hydrophobic amino acid residues required for fast Na^+-channel inactivation. *Proc. Natl. Acad. Sci. USA* 89:10910–14

80. White MM, Bezanilla F. 1985. Activation of squid axon K^+ channels. *J. Gen. Physiol.* 85:539–54

81. Yellen G, Jurman ME, Abramson T, MacKinnon R. 1991. Mutations affecting internal TEA blockade identify a probable pore-forming region of a K^+ channel. *Science* 251:939–42

82. Zagotta WN, Aldrich RW. 1990. Voltage-dependent gating of Shaker A-type potassium channels in *Drosophila* muscle. *J. Gen. Physiol.* 95:29–60

83. Zagotta WN, Hoshi T, Aldrich RW. 1990. Restoration of inactivation in mutants of Shaker potassium channels by a peptide derived from ShB. *Science* 250:568–71

Annu. Rev. Biophys. Biomol. Struct. 1994. 23:847–63

MOLECULAR MECHANICS IN BIOLOGY: From Structure to Function, Taking Account of Solvation

W. F. van Gunsteren

Laboratory of Physical Chemistry, Swiss Institute of Technology Zurich, ETH Zentrum, CH-8092 Zurich, Switzerland

F. J. Luque

Department of Physical Chemistry, Faculty of Pharmacy, University of Barcelona, E-08028 Barcelona, Spain

D. Timms

Zeneca Pharmaceuticals, Alderley Park, Macclesfield, Cheshire SK10 4TG, United Kingdom

A. E. Torda

Laboratory of Physical Chemistry, Swiss Institute of Technology Zurich, ETH Zentrum, CH-8092 Zurich, Switzerland

KEY WORDS: computer simulation, molecular dynamics, solvent effects, hydration, solvation models

CONTENTS

1056–8700/94/0610–0847$05.00

847

INTRODUCTION

In molecular biology it is attempted to obtain an understanding of biological function in terms of structure, interactions, and processes at the molecular or even atomic level. Experimental techniques, such as X-ray crystallography and NMR spectroscopy, are routinely used to provide an atomic picture of the structure and mobility of biomolecules, for example proteins and DNA fragments. More flexible molecules, such as lipids and sugars, are less accessible to structure determination by these methods. Information with respect to dynamics is even more difficult to obtain; only spectroscopic measuring techniques yield such information, but only for special groups of atoms, not for all atoms in a biomolecule. Generally, energetic information cannot be measured at the atomic level. Because of the limitations of experimental measuring techniques, the characterization of a biomolecular system at the atomic level in terms of structure, mobility, dynamics, and energetics is incomplete. These four types of information are listed in the order of decreasing knowledge about them. This incomplete molecular picture makes it difficult to establish the link between molecular structure, mobility, dynamics, and interactions on the one hand, and biological function on the other.

An alternative way to study biomolecular systems at the atomic level is simulation on a computer. It involves three basic choices.

1. A biomolecular system generally has too many degrees of freedom (electronic, atomic) to be simulated. However, the ones that are essential to a proper representation of the quantity or phenomenon

one is interested in, must be explicitly present in the molecular model.

2. An interaction function for these degrees of freedom must be defined, which contains the average effect of the degrees of freedom that have been omitted in the molecular model.

3. The motion of the molecular system is governed by equations of motion. Depending on the type of degrees of freedom in the model (quantum-mechanical, classical, or stochastic), this can be Schrödinger's, Newton's or Lagrange's, or Langevin's equation of motion. The length of the simulation must be sufficiently long to allow for an adequate sampling of essential degrees of freedom.

Whether a biomolecular system can be usefully simulated depends on three factors:

1. the time scale of the quantity or process of interest,
2. the required accuracy of the simulated property or process,
3. the available computing power.

In Figure 1 it is illustrated that the three basic choices of molecular simulation depend on the three factors listed above. One should choose as few degrees of freedom and as simple an interaction as possible in order to allow for as long as possible simulation, without throwing the

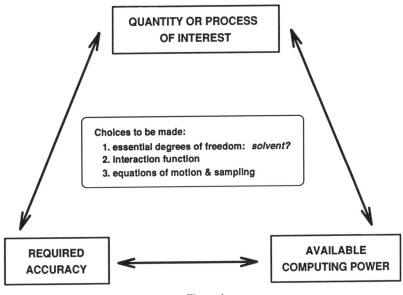

Figure 1

baby out with the bathwater: insufficient accuracy of the simulated quantity or process of interest.

An obvious way to limit the number of degrees of freedom in a biomolecular simulation is to omit all or almost all solvent degrees of freedom. Due to the abundance of solvent degrees of freedom for a biomolecule in solution, omission of these in a simulation easily reduces the required computing power by a factor of 10–50. In fact, the first protein simulations were carried out for a protein in vacuo (32). On the other hand, it is clear that the complete neglect of solvent effects will limit the accuracy of the biomolecular properties obtained from an in vacuo simulation. So, what is the role of solvent molecules in a biomolecular system? To answer this question we focus on proteins in aqueous solution, but corresponding considerations with respect to nucleic acids, sugars, lipids, or other solvents can be given.

Solvent molecules play different roles with respect to protein properties one is interested in, for example:

1. The structure and stability of a folded protein depends on the type of solvent. In aqueous solution a protein tends to minimize its apolar surface area: the hydrophobic effect.
2. Individual water molecules play a structural role in folded proteins, e.g. the four internally bound water molecules in bovine pancreatic trypsin inhibitor (BPTI).
3. Polar solvents exert a dielectric screening effect on interactions between protein charges.
4. The viscosity of the solvent will influence the dynamics of the protein atoms and may thereby influence the kinetics of processes.

In this paper we briefly review the treatment of solvent and solvent effects in biomolecular simulation. It is not meant to be a complete review of the relevant literature, only a discussion of the relevant issues, in which we draw examples mainly from our own work. Other reviews discuss specific aspects of solvent effects and treatment (1, 40, 41, 57).

STUDIES OF BIOMOLECULES USING EXPLICIT SOLVENT MOLECULES

When simulating a microscopic system of finite size, the boundary of the system should be treated such as to minimize edge effects. The standard procedure is to use periodic boundary conditions. The biomolecule and its surrounding solvent molecules are put into a periodic space-filling box, which is treated as if it is surrounded by identical translated images of itself. In this way basically an infinite periodic system is simulated. The periodic box should be taken large enough to avoid interactions between molecules and their periodic images. This condition leads to sizeable amounts of solvent molecules, typically a few thousand, to solvate a protein. In an early protein simulation of this type, the protein BPTI could only be simulated over 20 ps (53), due to limited computing resources at the time. Presently, a state-of-the-art molecular dynamics (MD) simulation of a protein in solution covers at least an order of magnitude longer period (6–8, 11, 12, 29, 31, 60).

Since BPTI is a small, well-characterized protein, it is often used to test molecular models and simulation procedures. Levitt & Sharon (29) analyzed the solvent effect on some protein properties by a comparison of MD simulations in vacuo and in water, covering about 200 ps. The hydration behavior of water molecules in a 1.4-ns MD simulation of BPTI was analyzed and compared to NMR derived data recently (7). Ahlström et al (2) studied the properties of interfacial water molecules for different proteins in solution. The effect of various degrees of hydration upon the structural and dynamical properties of myoglobin was studied by Steinbach et al (48). Solvent viscosity effects (18) and dielectric screening effects (46) have also been analyzed. Structural, dynamical, and energetic effects of high-pressure solvation have been studied for BPTI (8, 24). Other studies concern the role of water molecules in DNA operator-repressor binding (14), α-helix bending (15), or unfolding (51). The studies show that the explicit inclusion of solvent molecules in a simulation significantly improves the description of the average structural and energetic protein properties. They also illustrate the necessity of explicit solvent treatment when studying properties such as protein stability or complexation.

EXPLICIT TREATMENT OF SOLVENT IN THE SIMULATION

Roles of Solvent Molecules

Solvent molecules play different roles in a protein simulation. First, they may serve to improve the packing in the interior of the protein or in the interface of a protein complex. Surface tension effects generally reduce the likelihood of occurrence of sizeable cavities inside a protein, since they tend to minimize the free surface area. If a cavity in a protein in a simulation is not filled with solvent molecules, it is likely to collapse, thereby inducing distortions in the protein structure.

When the solvent molecules possess hydrogen-bonding capacity, they may also play a role in satisfying unmatched hydrogen bond–donor or –acceptor groups of the protein. For example, one of the four internal water molecules in BPTI makes four hydrogen bonds to the protein.

When the solvent molecules possess a sizeable dipole moment, they exert a shielding effect on the electric interaction between charges or dipoles in the protein. As a consequence, the protein structure and stability may change depending on the polarity of the solvent.

Finally, the viscosity of the solvent may influence the dynamics of protein atoms or segments near the surface. This effect may even be transmitted through the protein matrix to affect the dynamical properties of the protein interior.

The model for the solvent molecules that is used in biomolecular simulations should possess the properties that allow it to play the roles discussed here.

Types of Solvent

Solvents that are used to dissolve proteins or polypeptides are water, dimethylsulfoxide (DMSO), chloroform ($CHCl_3$), and carbontetrachloride (CCl_4), to mention the most important ones. Good-quality molecular models for these solvents are available in the literature (4, 5, 16, 22, 34, 39).

Solvent Models

An important aspect of choosing an interatomic interaction function for a biomolecular system including explicit solvent molecules is the consistency between different parts of the interaction function, for example the protein-protein, protein-solvent, and solvent-solvent terms (57). When combining a solvent model with a protein force field, the definition of the protein-solvent interaction requires special attention. In most cases this interaction is defined using so-called combination rules. In most biomolecular force fields, the r_{ij}^{-12} repulsive only r_{ij}^{-6} attractive van der Waals interaction parameters $C_{12}(i,j)$ and $C_6(i,j)$ for a pair of atoms are given in terms of one-atom parameters $C_{12}(i)$ and $C_6(i)$, from which the pair interaction parameters are obtained by the application of a combination rule such as

$$C_{12}(i,j) = \sqrt{C_{12}(i)C_{12}(j)} \qquad \text{1a.}$$

and

$$C_6(i,j) = \sqrt{C_6(i)C_6(j)} \qquad \text{1b.}$$

When the van der Waals interaction is expressed in terms of an energy ϵ_{ij} and a distance σ_{ij} with ·

$$C_{12}(i,j) = 4\epsilon_{ij}\sigma_{ij}^{12} \tag{2a.}$$

and

$$C_6(i,j) = 4\epsilon_{ij}\sigma_{ij}^6, \tag{2b.}$$

a different combination rule is sometimes used, e.g.

$$\epsilon_{ij} = \sqrt{\epsilon_i\epsilon_j} \tag{3a.}$$

and

$$\epsilon_{ij} = (\epsilon_i + \epsilon_j)/2. \tag{3b.}$$

From Equations 1–3 it is clear that combination rule 1 defines a different protein-solvent interaction than combination rule 3. If protein and solvent force fields are of different types, the application of combination rules like 1 and 3 may lead to an imbalance between protein-protein, protein-solvent, and solvent-solvent interactions.

Treatment of Boundaries

Application of periodic boundary conditions is the best way to avoid distortions due to the presence of boundaries in a finite size system. Yet, one should keep in mind that the periodicity generally is an artifact, which may affect the simulated properties, unless the periodic box is chosen sufficiently large to avoid these. Since the simulation of a protein in a periodic box containing many solvent molecules is computationally expensive, the explicit treatment of solvent molecules is often limited to the first solvation shell. Although such a treatment is more realistic than a complete omission of solvent molecules, it still suffers from surface tension distortions of the solvent layer and lack of dielectric screening due to the vacuum outside the solvation shell.

Treatment of Long-Range Electrostatic Effects

The electrostatic interaction between (partial) charges on atoms is inversely proportional to r_{ij}, the distance between atoms i and j. This distance dependence gives the electrostatic interaction a very long range. In a polar solvent, however, the full charge-charge interaction will be screened by the solvent molecules that orient themselves to reduce the total (free) energy of the system. In order to properly account for the solvent screening, the computational box should be chosen sufficiently large, and long-range electrostatic interaction should be included, at least in an approximate, average manner. A variety of methods for the treatment of long-range electrostatic interactions in molecular systems have been reviewed earlier (13, 55). Two techniques that are most useful in the simulation of solvated biomolecules using periodic boundary conditions are the so-called twin-range method (55) and the reaction field approach including ionic effects. In the twin-range method, two interaction ranges are distinguished and treated differently. The short-range interactions are exactly calculated, whereas for the longer-ranged interactions, say beyond 8–10 Å, the high-frequency components are neglected. In the second mentioned approach, the reaction field from the charges inside the cut-off sphere due to an electrostatic continuum, with given dielectric permittivity ϵ and ionic strength I outside the cut-off sphere, is calculated using the linearized Poisson-Boltzmann equation. The use of these reaction-field forces in a MD simulation avoids the concentration of ions just outside the cut-off sphere.

Although the long-ranged interactions between ions in aqueous solution can be adequately approximated in a simulation, the inclusion of ions in a simulation of a protein in aqueous solution may not yield reliable results, since the relaxation time of an ionic distribution is likely to be longer than the simulation period. This slow relaxation is caused by the slow diffusion of hydrated ions in solution. In a biomolecular simulation including water and counterions, the simulation averages may be easily based on nonequilibrated ion distributions, causing sizeable deviations from the mean effect of the ions. Therefore, the mean influence of the ionic solution might be better approximated by a simulation, which only includes solvating water molecules.

COMPARISON OF SIMULATED WITH EXPERIMENTAL DATA

The quality of the model for the solvent and the solvent-protein interaction should be assessed by a comparison of simulated with experimental data with respect to solvation properties or behavior of solvent molecules in the solvation layer. Below, we give a number of examples of such a comparison, all taken from the literature. They concern MD simulations of proteins, peptides, or sugars in which the GROMOS force field (54) is used in conjunction with the SPC (5) and SPC/E (4) water models.

X-Ray and Neutron Diffraction Data

X-ray and neutron diffraction studies of biomolecular crystals may yield information on the behavior of solvent molecules, usually in the form of occupancy factors for solvent sites in the crystal. For cyclo-dextrins, both X-ray and neutron diffraction data are available, which indicate a partially mobile network of cyclodextrin-water and water-water hydrogen bonds. A number of the hydrogen bonds show so-called flip-flop behavior, in which donor and acceptor exchange their roles (42). Such a system is ideal to test the relative strength of solute-water and water-water hydrogen-bond interactions. In a number of MD simu-lation studies, Koehler et al (25–28) found that the flip-flop phenom-enon was observed in the simulations, and that the relative occupancy of the water and hydroxyl hydrogen (deuterium) atom sites was re-produced too. Almost all experimentally observed three-center hydro-gen bonds were found in the simulations, even with respect to the asymmetry of the three-center geometry. This example shows the use-fulness of a comparison of simulated solvation behavior with experi-mentally observed data.

NMR Spectroscopic Data

Using new NMR techniques, the residence times of water molecules in the surface hydration shell of polypeptides and proteins can be stud-ied, and very rough estimates can be obtained (36). These have been compared to residence times calculated from a long MD simulation of BPTI in aqueous solution (7). The simulated results are in good agree-ment with the experimental data. The residence times of individual water molecules coming near a given BPTI atom, as obtained from the simulation, vary greatly and range between 10 and 500 ps.

Dielectric Permittivity Data

Experimental determination of the dielectric permittivity of proteins shows that the dielectric dispersion curves generally contain two dis-tinct regions (20). The dielectric response is constant up to frequencies of the order of 1 MHz, at which point the response decreases signif-icantly. The lower dielectric response is then constant within the 1–100 MHz range. At approximately 100 MHz it drops again to that of pure water. The response observed at 100 MHz has been attributed to the slower orientational relaxation of protein-bound water molecules compared with bulk water molecules (20). Smith et al (46) have ana-lyzed the dielectric response of the proteins BPTI and lysozyme using 1-ns MD simulations of these proteins in aqueous solution and found that the calculated frequency-dependent dielectric constant was con-sistent with known experimental dielectric dispersion curves for pro-teins in aqueous solution. This example shows the importance of ex-plicit inclusion of water molecules, both in the hydration shell and in the bulk, in the simulation when studying dielectric relaxation effects.

Fluorescence Decay Data

Fluorescence anisotropy decay measurements can be used to probe the interaction between tryptophan-containing peptides and the surrounding solvent molecules. Chen et al (9) have determined the orientational correlation decay times of the transition moment of the Trp side chain in a number of Trp-containing mono- and dipeptides in aqueous solution at different pH and temperature values. They found values ranging from 19 to 43 ps for the monopeptides. MD simulation of a Trp residue in water, using the GROMOS force field and SPC water, resulted in a too short decay time of about 8 ps (9). The origins of this discrepancy are not yet known. Further investigations are required to determine whether it is due to a too-weak peptide-water interaction or to technical aspects of the simulation with respect to the chosen values of the time step Δt, the application of bond-length constraints, and the coupling time constant τ_T of the coupling to the heat bath. We standardly use constraints for all bond lengths, $\Delta t = 2$ fs and $\tau_T = 0.1$ ps, (14, 25, 46, 54, 55). Chen et al (9) only constrained bonds involving hydrogen atoms and used $\Delta t = 2$ fs and $\tau_T = 0.5$ ps, which will lead to more noise in the simulation and a higher mean temperature than when the standard parameter settings are used. However, it is clear that studies such as Chen et al's (9) are very useful to evaluate protein-solvent interactions.

APPROXIMATE TREATMENT OF SOLVENT EFFECTS

Mean Force and Dynamic Effects

An alternative to the explicit treatment of solvent molecules in a biomolecular simulation is an implicit one: the influence of the solvent on the solute degrees of freedom is incorporated in the interaction function and equations of motion of the latter in an average manner. The solvent effect upon the structure and dynamics of a solute can be divided into different types.

1. The average or mean interaction between solute atoms is affected by the presence of solvent. When the solvent is omitted from the simulation, the solute force field should be changed to incorporate the mean solvent effect, that is, a potential of mean force should be used for the solute.

2. The solvent exerts a dynamical effect on the solute, which can be mimicked by the introduction of a frictional force representing sol-

vent drag, and of a randomly fluctuating force representing collisions with solvent molecules, into the equations of motion. In the
simplest case the frictional force is taken proportional to the velocity
of the solute atom to which it applies, and the random force is of
white noise character, uncorrelated between the different degrees
of freedom:

$$m_i \mathrm{d}v_i(t)/\mathrm{d}t = F_i^{\mathrm{mean}}(t) - m_i\gamma_i v_i(t) + R_i(t). \qquad 4.$$

This is the Langevin equation in which the (solute) atomic mass, friction
coefficient, and velocity are denoted by m_i, γ_i, and v_i. The mean force
is F_i^{mean} and the random force is R_i (45).

Local vs Long-Range Mean Forces

A potential of mean force that describes the average solvent effect upon
the solute degrees of freedom can be derived along different lines of
approach.

1. The mean force on the solute atoms can be determined from a full
   MD simulation including explicit solvent molecules (52). This is a
   very costly procedure.
2. Integral equation theories, such as the reference interaction site
   model (RISM), can be used to define potentials of mean force. Examples are given in (37) for ion-water mixtures, and in (30) for hydrocarbon-water systems.
3. A third possibility is to make an educated guess with respect to the
   functional form of the dependence of the potential of mean force
   on the solute atomic coordinates, and to adjust the model parameters
   such that specific experimental data, like vapor-to-water transfer
   energies, are reproduced by the model.

The latter type of mean force potential is mostly used when studying
biomolecular systems. Two different types of contribution to the mean
force of solvation are generally distinguished (3, 49).

1. The first one represents local solute-solvent interactions and is often
   assumed to be proportional to the solvent-accessible surface area
   of a solute atom, or to another measure of the local solute-solvent
   contacts. It should account for the energy of cavity formation, solute-solvent dispersion interactions, etc.
2. The second contribution represents long-range solute-solvent interactions due to dielectric screening and polarization effects.

Although this distinction is conceptually and practically useful, it bears
the danger of incorporating specific solvent effects twice, especially

when the mean force parameters are obtained by fitting to experimental data.

Accessible Surface Area Type Models

In this type of mean solvation model the local solvent contribution to the potential of mean force for solute atoms is taken proportional to the area of the solute atom or group of atoms that is accessible to solvent molecules (17, 21, 35, 43, 49, 59). Other local quantities, such as the hydration volume (23, 58) or the number of solute-solvent contacts (10, 50), can be used too. The detailed implementation of such models allows much room for variation of model features and calibration of parameters. We only mention a number of important aspects:

1. Is the solvation energy split into terms representing solute atoms or groups of atoms?
2. How is the accessible surface area or hydration volume defined, and is it calculated exactly (analytically or numerically) or using an approximate expression?
3. Which are the solute molecules and solvents that are used to calibrate the model parameters?
4. Which conformations of the solute molecules are used in the parameter calibration procedure?
5. Which experimental data are used for the calibration, e.g. vapor-to-water transfer (free) energies, or apolar solvent–to-water transfer (free) energies?
6. Which force field is used in conjunction with the accessible surface area mean force term when calibrating the mean force parameters?

Currently, it is not clear whether accessible surface area solvation models are an efficient way to account for solvent effects. The calculation of the surface area of an atom generally involves nonnegligible computational effort. When simulating larger molecules it is more efficient to incorporate a (thick) layer of solvation molecules than to evaluate the accessible surface area for all solute atoms.

Simple Pairwise Solvation-Force Models

The expression for the accessible surface area of a solute atom generally depends on the coordinates of the solute atom itself and those of its nearest-neighbor solute atoms. Thus, a mean force potential based on an accessible-area model becomes a many-body interaction. The computation of the mean force of solvation would be considerably simplified and sped up, if the mean force could be formulated as a sum of pairwise (two-body) interactions. In fact, the mean force potential in the solvent-contact or occupancy model (50) can be expressed as a sum of two-body terms, which are proportional to $\exp(-r_{ij}^2/2\sigma^2)$. We have tried a slightly different functional form (WF van Gunsteren, FJ Luque, D Timms & AE Torda, unpublished work):

$$
V^{\text{mean}}(r_{ij}) =
\begin{cases}
= V_{\text{des}}^{ij} & r_{ij} < R_1^{ij} \\[2mm]
= V_{\text{des}}^{ij} \left\{ 1 - \left[\dfrac{(r_{ij} - R_1^{ij})}{(R_2^{ij} - R_1^{ij})} \right]^2 \right\}^2 & R_1^{ij} \le r_{ij} \le R_2^{ij}, \\[4mm]
= 0 & r_{ij} > R_2^{ij}
\end{cases}
\qquad 5.
$$

in which r_{ij} is the distance between atoms i and j. The model parameters are R_1^{ij}, an inner distance at which desolvation is complete, R_2^{ij}, an outer solvent-separated distance at which solvation is complete, and V_{des}^{ij}, the energetic cost of desolvation. The distance range over which the desolvation force derived from Equation 5 is nonzero is governed by the van der Waals radii of the various types of solute atoms and the size of a solvent (water) molecule. The parameters in Equation 5 were determined from experimental aqueous second virial coefficients for small molecules.

Although a simple pairwise solvation force induces only a minor increase of the required computing effort, it remains to be investigated whether its accuracy is comparable to that of a simulation including a (thick) layer of solvent molecules.

Dielectric Screening Models

Different approximate models for treating the long-range solute-solvent interactions due to dielectric screening and polarization effects are available too (19, 33, 38, 44, 47, 49). Still et al (49) use an expression involving only one-body and two-body terms, which is based on the continuum approximation of a dielectric medium. A simpler approach is to make the relative dielectric permittivity, ϵ, distance dependent. Pickersgill (38) proposes $\epsilon = 4.5r_{ij}$ Å, based on a calculation of shifts in pK_a values in the protein papain. Mehler (33, 47) proposes to use a sigmoidal function of the distance:

$$
\epsilon(r_{ij}) = A + B/[1 + k \exp(-\lambda B r_{ij})], \qquad 6.
$$

where $B = \epsilon_0 - A$, ϵ_0 is the dielectric constant of water, and A, λ, and k are model parameters.

A much more complicated way to incorporate long-range electrostatic effects using a continuum representation of the solvent is based on solving the Poisson-Boltzmann equation on a three-dimensional grid

(19, 44). A simple two-body interaction term is proposed that accounts for charge-solvent interactions in an average way (19).

The dielectric solvation models discussed so far all assume an instantaneous dielectric response of the solvent surrounding a solute molecule. The time lag of the reaction field, corresponding to the frequency dispersion of the dielectric constant, has been neglected. For a proper mean representation of the dynamic properties of the solute, the treatment of the long-range electrostatic forces should be based on the expressions for the delayed reaction field (56) in conjunction with a randomly fluctuating electric field term representing solvent fluctuations.

Stochastic Dynamics Simulation

The influence of the solvent on the dynamics of a solute molecule can be mimicked by the inclusion of a frictional force and a random force in Newton's equations of motion (see Equation 4). The width of the Gaussian distribution of the random force $R_i(t)$ is related to the friction coefficient γ_i by the second fluctuation-dissipation theorem

$$\langle R_i(o) \cdot R_j(t) \rangle = 6m_i\gamma_i k_B T_{ref} \delta_{ij} \delta(t), \qquad 7.$$

where k_B is Boltzmann's constant and T_{ref} is the reference temperature of the solvent bath (45). The choice of appropriate atomic friction coefficients γ_i will in general depend on the type of system that is considered. It may be derived from the solvent viscosity η and the atomic radius R and mass M of a solvent molecule via Stokes' law

$$\gamma_i = (6\pi R\eta/M)w_i, \qquad 8.$$

in which the parameter w_i represents the degree of solvent exposure of solute atom i (45). A comparison of the dynamic properties of an undecapeptide, cyclosporin A, in water and in CCl_4 as obtained from a stochastic dynamics (SD) simulation with those obtained from MD simulations with explicit treatment of these solvent molecules, shows that the SD simulation technique offers a good approximation of the mean dynamic solvent effect (45).

OUTLOOK

For an accurate description of the structure, mobility, dynamics, and energetics of a biomolecule in solution, a simulation including explicit treatment of solvent molecules and periodic boundary conditions to minimize edge effects is generally necessary. When choosing an atomic interaction function, the solute-solvent terms should be balanced with respect to the solute-solute and solvent-solvent terms to ensure proper solvation behavior. For systems containing charged atoms, the long-range electrostatic interaction should be included, at least in an average manner. The inclusion of counterions in a simulation is only recommended when a well-equilibrated initial ion distribution is available and the simulation period is longer than the relaxation time of the ion distribution. Simulations including explicit solvent molecules may be made more accurate by the inclusion of polarizability into the biomolecular and solvent force fields.

The approximate treatment of solvent effects in the form of mean solvation models works well for apolar solvents but poses considerable difficulties to the definition of a simple, efficient, and yet accurate potential of mean force to be used for large biomolecules. SD simulation yields a good approximation of the mean dynamic effects of a solvent on a solute.

Finally, we note that the lack of detailed experimental data with respect to solute-solvent interactions at the atomic level is hampering both the testing of atomic force fields, which include explicit solute-solvent interaction terms, and the calibration of the parameters of the empirical mean-solvation-force models against experiment. Once the reliability of simulation models is well established, computer simulation provides a basis upon which to build the connection between biomolecular structure, dynamics, and energetics on the one hand and biomolecular function on the other.

Literature Cited

1. Abagyan RA. 1993. Towards protein folding by global energy optimization. *FEBS Lett.* 325:17–22
2. Ahlström P, Teleman O, Jönsson B. 1989. Interfacial water studied by molecular dynamics simulations. *Chem. Scr.* 29A:97–101
3. Ben-Naim A, Ting KL, Jernigan RL. 1989. Solvation thermodynamics of biopolymers. I. Separation of the volume and surface interactions with estimates for proteins. *Biopolymers* 28:1309–25
4. Berendsen HJC, Grigera JR, Straatsma TP. 1987. The missing term in effective pair potentials. *J. Phys. Chem.* 91:6269–71
5. Berendsen HJC, Postma JPM, van Gun-steren WF, Hermans J. 1981. Interaction models for water in relation to protein hydration. In *Intermolecular Forces,* ed. B Pullman, pp. 331–42. Dordrecht, The Netherlands: Reidel
6. Brooks CL III. 1992. Characterization of "native" apomyoglobin by molecular dynamics simulation. *J. Mol. Biol.* 227: 375–80
7. Brunne RM, Liepinsh E, Otting G, Wüthrich K, van Gunsteren WF. 1993. Hydration of proteins: a comparison of experimental residence times of water molecules solvating the bovine pancreatic trypsin inhibitor with theoretical model calculations. *J. Mol. Biol.* 231: 1040–48

8. Brunne RM, van Gunsteren WF. 1993. Dynamical properties of bovine pancreatic trypsin inhibitor from a molecular dynamics simulation at 5000 atm. *FEBS Lett.* 323:215–17

9. Chen LXQ, Engh RA, Fleming GR. 1988. Reorientation of tryptophan and simple peptides: onset of internal flexibility and comparison with molecular dynamics simulation. *J. Phys. Chem.* 92:4811–16

10. Colonna-Cesari F, Sander C. 1990. Excluded volume approximation to protein-solvent interaction. The solvent contact model. *Biophys. J.* 57:1103–7

11. Daggett V, Levitt M. 1991. A molecular dynamics simulation of the C-terminal fragment of the L7/L12 ribosomal protein in solution. *Chem. Phys.* 158:501–12

12. Daggett V, Levitt M. 1992. A model of the molten globule state from molecular dynamics simulations. *Proc. Natl. Acad. Sci. USA* 89:5142–46

13. Davis ME, McCammon JA. 1990. Electrostatics in biomolecular structure and dynamics. *Chem. Rev.* 90:509–21

14. De Vlieg J, Berendsen HJC, van Gunsteren WF. 1989. An NMR-based molecular dynamics simulation of the interaction of the *lac* repressor headpiece and its operator in aqueous solution. *Proteins* 6:104–27

15. DiCapua FM, Swaminathan S, Beveridge DL. 1991. Theoretical evidence for water insertion in α-helix bending: molecular dynamics of Gly$_{30}$ and Ala$_{30}$ in vacuo and in solution. *J. Am. Chem. Soc.* 113:6145–55

16. Dietz W, Heinzinger K. 1985. A molecular dynamics study of liquid chloroform. *Ber. Bunsenges. Phys. Chem.* 89: 968–77

17. Eisenberg D, McLachlan AD. 1986. Solvation energy in protein folding and binding. *Nature* 319:199–203

18. Ghosh I, McCammon JA. 1987. Solvent viscosity effects on the rate of sidechain rotational isomerization in a protein molecule. *J. Phys. Chem.* 91:4878–81

19. Gilson MK, Honig B. 1991. The inclusion of electrostatic hydration energies in molecular mechanics calculations. *J. Comput. Aided Mol. Des.* 5:5–20

20. Grant EH, Sheppard RJ, South GP. 1978. *Dielectric Behaviour of Biological Macromolecules in Solution.* Oxford: Clarendon

21. Hasel W, Hendrickson TF, Still WC. 1988. A rapid approximation to the solvent accessible surface areas of atoms. *Tetr. Comp. Method.* 1:103–16

22. Jorgensen WL, Chandrasekhar J, Madura JD, Impey RW, Klein ML. 1983. Comparison of simple potential functions for simulating liquid water. *J. Chem. Phys.* 79:926–35

23. Kang YK, Gibson KD, Némethy G, Scheraga HA. 1988. Free energies of hydration of solute molecules. 4. Revised treatment of the hydration shell model. *J. Phys. Chem.* 92:4739–42

24. Kitchen DB, Reed LH, Levy RM. 1992. Molecular dynamics simulation of solvated protein at high pressure. *Biochemistry* 31:10083–93

25. Koehler JEH, Saenger W, van Gunsteren WF. 1987. A molecular dynamics simulation of crystalline α-cyclodextrin hexahydrate. *Eur. Biophys. J.* 15:197–210

26. Koehler JEH, Saenger W, van Gunsteren WF. 1987. Molecular dynamics simulation of crystalline β-cyclodextrin dodecahydrate at 293 K and 120 K. *Eur. Biophys. J.* 15:211–24

27. Koehler JEH, Saenger W, van Gunsteren WF. 1988. The flip-flop hydrogen bonding phenomenon. Molecular dynamics simulation of crystalline β-cyclodextrin. *Eur. Biophys. J.* 16:153–68

28. Koehler JEH, Saenger W, van Gunsteren WF. 1988. On the occurrence of three-center hydrogen bonds in cyclodextrins in crystalline form and in aqueous solution: comparison of neutron diffraction and molecular dynamics results. *J. Biomol. Struct. Dyn.* 6:181–98

29. Levitt M, Sharon R. 1988. Accurate simulation of protein dynamics in solution. *Proc. Natl. Acad. Sci. USA* 85: 7557–61

30. Lue L, Blankschtein D. 1992. Liquid-state theory of hydrocarbon-water systems: application to methane, ethane, and propane. *J. Phys. Chem.* 96:8582–94

31. Mark AE, van Gunsteren WF. 1992. Simulation of the thermal denaturation of hen egg white lysozyme: trapping the molten globule state. *Biochemistry* 31: 7745–48

32. McCammon JA, Gelin BR, Karplus M. 1977. Dynamics of folded proteins. *Nature* 267:585–90

33. Mehler EL, Solmajer T. 1991. Electrostatic effects in proteins: comparison of dielectric and charge models. *Protein Eng.* 4:903–10

34. Mierke DF, Kessler H. 1991. Molecular dynamics with dimethyl sulfoxide as a solvent. Conformation of a cyclic hexapeptide. *J. Am. Chem. Soc.* 113:9466–70

35. Ooi W, Oobatake M, Némethy G, Scheraga HA. 1987. Accessible surface areas as a measure of the thermodynamic parameters of hydration of peptides. *Proc. Natl. Acad. Sci. USA* 84: 3086–90

36. Otting G, Wüthrich K. 1989. Studies of protein hydration in aqueous solution by direct NMR observation of individual protein-bound water molecules. *J. Am. Chem. Soc.* 111:1871–75

37. Perkyns JS, Pettitt BM. 1992. A dielectrically consistent interaction site theory for solvent-electrolyte mixtures. *Chem. Phys. Lett.* 190:626–30

38. Pickersgill RW. 1988. A rapid method of calculating charge-charge interaction energies in proteins. *Protein Eng.* 2: 247–48

39. Rebertus DW, Berne BJ, Chandler D. 1979. A molecular dynamics and Monte Carlo study of solvent effects on the conformational equilibrium of *n*-butane in CCl₄. *J. Chem. Phys.* 70:3395–3400

40. Richards WG, King PM, Reynolds CA. 1989. Solvation effects. *Protein Eng.* 2: 319–27

41. Saenger W. 1987. Structure and dynamics of water surrounding biomolecules. *Annu. Rev. Biophys. Biophys. Chem.* 16:93–114

42. Saenger W, Betzel Ch, Hingerty B, Brown GM. 1982. Flip-flop hydrogen bonding in a partially disordered system. *Nature* 296:581–83

43. Schiffer CA, Caldwell JW, Stroud RM, Kollman PA. 1992. Inclusion of solvation free energy with molecular mechanics energy: alanyl dipeptide as a test case. *Protein Sci.* 1:396–400

44. Sharp K. 1991. Incorporating solvent and ion screening into molecular dynamics using the finite-difference Poisson-Boltzmann method. *J. Comput. Chem.* 12:454–68

45. Shi YY, Wang L, van Gunsteren WF. 1988. On the approximation of solvent effects on the conformation and dynamics of cyclosporin A by stochastic dynamics simulation techniques. *Mol. Simul.* 1:369–83

46. Smith PE, Brunne RM, Mark AE, van Gunsteren WF. 1993. Dielectric properties of trypsin inhibitor and lysozyme calculated from molecular dynamics simulations. *J. Phys. Chem.* 97:2009–14

47. Solmajer T, Mehler EL. 1991. Electrostatic screening in molecular dynamics simulations. *Protein Eng.* 4:911–17

48. Steinbach PJ, Loncharich RJ, Brooks BR. 1991. The effects of environment and hydration on protein dynamics: a simulation study of myoglobin. *Chem. Phys.* 158:383–94

49. Still WC, Tempczyk A, Hawley RC, Hendrickson T. 1990. Semianalytical treatment of solvation for molecular mechanics and dynamics. *J. Am. Chem. Soc.* 112:6127–29

50. Stouten PFW, Frömmel C, Nakamura H, Sander C. 1993. An effective solvation term based on atomic occupancies for use in protein simulations. *Mol. Simul.* 10:97–120

51. Tirado-Rives J, Jorgensen WL. 1991. Molecular dynamics simulations of the unfolding of an α-helical analogue of ribonuclease A S-peptide in water. *Biochemistry* 30:3864–71

52. Tobias DJ, Sneddon SF, Brooks CL III. 1990. Reverse turns in blocked dipeptides are intrinsically unstable in water. *J. Mol. Biol.* 216:783–96

53. van Gunsteren WF, Berendsen HJC. 1984. Computer simulation as a tool for tracing the conformational differences between proteins in solution and in the crystalline state. *J. Mol. Biol.* 176:559–64

54. van Gunsteren WF, Berendsen HJC. 1987. *Groningen Molecular Simulation (GROMOS) Library Manual.* Groningen, The Netherlands: Biomos

55. van Gunsteren WF, Berendsen HJC. 1990. Computer simulation of molecular dynamics: methodology, applications, and perspectives in chemistry. *Angew. Chem. Int. Ed. Engl.* 29:992–1023

56. van Gunsteren WF, Berendsen HJC, Rullmann JAC. 1978. Inclusion of reaction fields in molecular dynamics: application to liquid water. *Faraday Discuss. Chem. Soc.* 66:58–70

57. van Gunsteren WF, Mark AE. 1992. On the interpretation of biochemical data by molecular dynamics computer simulation. *Eur. J. Biochem.* 204:947–61

58. Vila J, Williams RL, Vàsquez M, Scheraga HA. 1991. Empirical solvation models can be used to differentiate native from near-native conformations of bovine pancreatic trypsin inhibitor. *Proteins* 10:199–218

59. Wesson L, Eisenberg D. 1992. Atomic solvation parameters applied to molecular dynamics of proteins in solution. *Protein Sci.* 1:227–35

60. York DM, Darden TA, Pedersen LG, Anderson MW. 1993. Molecular dynamics simulation of HIV-1 protease in a crystalline environment and in solution. *Biochemistry* 32:1443–53

SUBJECT INDEX

A

Abscisic acid
  K$^+$ channels and, 462
Acanthamoeba spp.
  bacterial flagellar motor and,
    528
Accessible surface area type models
  solvation and, 858
Acetamidinium
  gramicidin channel and, 740,
    752
Acetylation
  bacterial flagellar motor and,
    522
Acetylcholine
  microphysiometry and, 106
Acidification
  light-addressable potentiometric sensor and, 97, 102–3,
    105, 107
Acquired immunodeficiency syndrome (AIDS) antivirals
  protein structure-based drug design and, 358–62
Actin
  red cell membrane and, 791–92, 794–95, 804
Adducin
  red cell membrane and, 792
Adenosine diphosphate (ADP)
  protein folding and, 657–59
Adenosine triphosphate (ATP)
  bacterial flagellar motor and,
    510, 518, 528–29, 534–35
  gramicidin channel and, 756
  K$^+$ channels and, 462
  light-addressable potentiometric sensor and, 102–3
  protein folding and, 646, 654–59, 663
S-Adenosylmethionine
  met and, 675–77, 680
Adenylyl cyclase
  olfactory receptor neurons and,
    579–80
A-DNA
  repeat distances and, 673
Aggregation
  protein folding and, 647–48,
    655, 658, 660–62
Alamethicin
  aggregation and, 154–56
  analogue activity and, 149–50
  conductance and, 146–49
  crystal structure and, 150–51

general features and sequence
    of, 145–46
  ion channel structure and, 156–57
  ion transport and, 143–45
  membrane binding and, 154–56
  multimeric state and, 161
  perspectives and overview,
    141–43
  planar bilayers and, 146–47
  single channel and, 147
  spectroscopy and, 152–53
  vesicles and, 147–49
  voltage-dependent gating, 157–60
α-helicity
  EF-hand proteins and, 478, 480
  IHF protein and, 689–90
  met repressor and, 676
  protein folding and, 653–54
  TBP protein and, 690
  U1 protein and, 695
Aluminum
  toxicity
    K$^+$ channels and, 458–59,
      464
Amiloride
  olfactory transduction and, 597
Amino acids
  global statistics of protein sequences and, 412–14, 416-19, 421–23
AMPA/kainate receptors
  overview of, 321–26
Amphiphiles
  global statistics of protein sequences and, 428
  hydration pressure and, 34–35
Amphiuma spp.
  EF-hand proteins and, 493–94
Aneurism
  red cell membrane and, 813
Ankyrin
  red cell membrane and, 792–93, 795, 804
Annexins
  calcium-binding sites and, 198–201
  ion channel proteins and, 209–10
  membrane bridging and, 206–9
  molecular structure of, 195–98
  perspectives and overview,
    193–95
  phospholipid membranes and,
    201–6
  quaternary structure and, 202–3
  self-association and, 202–3

Antibodies
  H-DNA and, 564
  light-addressable potentiometric sensor and, 98–99, 101
Anticholinesterase insecticides
  light-addressable potentiometric sensor and, 98
Antijunctions
  branched DNA and, 56, 77–78
Antiparallelism
  branched DNA and, 60
  Holliday junctions and, 63–67
Anti-preS2 antibody
  light-addressable potentiometric sensor and, 101
Antiproliferative agents
  protein structure-based drug design and, 365–68
apo repressor
  met repressor and, 675, 677
Aplysia spp.
  EF-hand proteins and, 488,
    502–3
Aqueous solubility
  molecular nanomachines and,
    398
Aquipecten spp.
  EF-hand proteins and, 479,
    489–90
Arabidopsis thaliana
  K$^+$ channels and, 444, 452–53,
    462, 464
  TBP protein and, 690–91
Arachidonic acid
  K$^+$ channels and, 463
Arbacia spp.
  EF-hand proteins and, 502–3
Arc repressor
  β-ribbon DNA and, 683–86
  pressure dissociation of, 311–12
Arms
  β-ribbon DNA and, 696
Arrhenius behavior
  diffusion and, 9, 11
  field gradient ESR and, 20
Aspergillus spp.
  EF-hand proteins and, 488, 503
Astacus spp.
  EF-hand proteins and, 491, 498
Atomic force microscope (AFM)
  biological membranes and,
    122–26
  cell surfaces and, 126–27
  chromatin and, 122
  chromosomes and, 121–22
  combination microscopes and,
    118

structural models and, 72–76
symmetric immobile junctions
and, 63
tethered junctions and, 62
thermodynamics and, 65–70,
72–76
three-arm junctions and, 72–77
DnaJ protein
protein folding and, 654–55,
662
DnaK protein
protein folding and, 647, 652–
55, 661–62
DNA polymerization
H-DNA and, 564–68
DNA primase
G-quartet structures and, 723
DNase I
TBP protein and, 691
TF1 protein and, 689
DNA topoisomerases
supercoiled DNA and, 622, 637
Docking
β-ribbon DNA and, 674
protein structure-based drug de-
sign and, 356–58
Dodecapeptides
protein folding and, 652
Domain grouping
EF-hand proteins and, 486
Double-crossover molecules
branched DNA and, 56, 81
Holliday junctions and, 63–65
Double doughnut
protein folding and, 646
Drag forces
free volume model and, 14
DRK1 channel
voltage gating and, 832, 838,
841
Drosophila melanogaster
atomic force microscope and,
121
EF-hand proteins and, 476,
488–90, 502–3
H-DNA and, 568
K⁺ channels and, 463
Dynamic imaging of diffusion
electron spin resonance
(DID- ESR)
cholesterol and, 7–10
comparison with other techniques, 10
Fourier transform ESR imaging and, 21–22
free volume model and, 13–15
mixed model membranes and,
10, 12
lateral diffusion and 7–12
lipid and, 7–10
order parameter and, 15–17
orientational order parameter
and, 10–13

overview of, 4–7
rotational diffusion and, 11–13
spectral-spatial imaging and,
17–21
thermodynamics and, 15–17

E

ECEPP force field
gramicidin channel and, 735
Echo decay
Fourier transform ESR imaging and, 21
Eclectic DNA
overview of, 559–61
EF-hand proteins
branching order and, 486
calcium and, 474, 480–81
calmodulin contradiction and,
500–2
chromosomal distributions
and, 500
classification of, 482–99
congruence and, 482–86
domain grouping and, 486
EF-hand domains and, 474,
478–79
encoding DNA and, 486–88
introns and, 499, 504
overview of, 473–74
pairs of domains and, 479–80
subfamilies of, 474–77, 488–99
Effective concentration
mechanosynthesis and, 380–82
Effective valence
voltage dependence of P $_{apO}$
$_{ap}$ and, 823
EGF-R promoter
H-DNA and, 569
Egg phosphatidylcholine (EPC)
hydration pressure and, 38–44,
46–47
Elasticity
red cell membrane and, 797–
814
Elastic linkages
bacterial flagellar motor and,
531–535
Elastic rod model
supercoiled DNA and, 623–
26
Electromagnetic theory
optical forces and, 264–67
Electron density profile
hydration pressure and, 37–38,
41
Electron-electron dipolar interactions
field gradient ESR and, 19–20,
22
Electron microscopy
supercoiled DNA and, 615–18,
637–38

Electron spin resonance (ESR)
field gradient, 1–21
Electrophorus spp.
EF-hand proteins and, 482,
494, 503
Electrospray ionization (ESI)
biomolecules and, 770–74
Electrostatic effects
bacterial flagellar motor and,
531–32
hydration pressure and, 31–32,
43, 45–46
K⁺ channels and, 449–52
light-addressable potentiometric sensor and, 94
red cell membrane and, 804,
812–13
solvation and, 853–54
supercoiled DNA and, 627–29,
632
voltage gating and, 842
Elementary translocation barrier
gramicidin channel and, 748–
50
Elliptocytosis
red cell membrane and, 794–95
Encoding DNA (eDNA)
EF-hand proteins and, 486–88
Endoplasmic reticulum
membrane proteins and, 178–
79
protein folding and, 652
Endosymbiont theory
membrane proteins and, 179
Enthalpy
red cell membrane and, 804
supercoiled DNA and, 636–37
Entropy
gramicidin channel and, 750
phospholipid bilayers and, 33–
34, 41
red cell membrane and, 804
supercoiled DNA and, 624,
630, 636–37
Environmental controls
bacterial flagellar motor and,
530–31
Enzymatic synthesis
molecular nanomachines and,
379–80
Enzyme-linked immunoassays
light-addressable potentiometric sensor and, 98–102
Escherichia coli
bacterial flagellar motor and,
510–18, 520, 523, 525–
27, 530–31
H-DNA and, 562–64
HU protein and, 687
IHF protein and, 687, 689
membrane protein assembly
and, 171, 174, 178, 181
met and, 675, 677

growing new molecules and,
357–58
HIV proteinase inhibitors and,
358–62
interactive graphics ap-
proaches and, 355
perspectives and overview,
349–51
purine nucleoside phosphorylase inhibitors and, 362–65
rhinovirus canyon binders and,
368–71
structure determination and accuracy, 352–53
Proteolysis
protein folding and, 651, 661
Proton concentration
olfactory transduction and,
597–98
Protrusion pressure
phospholipid bilayers and, 34
PuF protein
H-DNA and, 569
Pulsed field gradient NMR
diffusion and, 2–3
Purine nucleoside phosphorylase
inhibitors
protein structure-based drug design and, 362–65
Pyropoikilocytosis
red cell membrane and, 794

Q

Quadrilaterals
branched DNA and, 56
Quadruplex structures
G-quartet structures and, 707
Quasielectric neutron scattering
diffusion and, 2, 20
Q-V curve
voltage gating and, 825–29,
836

R

R368Q mutation
voltage gating and, 837, 839
Raja spp.
EF-hand proteins and, 493–94
Raman difference spectroscopy
nonresonance
covalent bonds and, 229–30
enzymatic catalysis and,
236–40
equipment and, 221–24
general considerations of,
218–28
hydrogen bonding and, 230–
35
individual residues and, 240–
42
isotope editing and, 225–27

ligand-protein interactions
and, 228–36
mutation effects and, 240–42
perspectives amd overview,
216–18
Raman spectroscopy and,
218–19
reducing systematic errors
and, 227
resonance Raman spectros-
copy and, 228
signal size and, 219–21
sources of error and, 219–21
weak electrostatic interactions and, 230–35
Rana spp.
EF-hand proteins and, 482, 494
RAP1 protein
G-quartet structures and, 723
Rattus spp.
EF-hand proteins and, 488–90,
494–95, 497, 502–3
Ray-optics theory
optical forces and, 262–64
Rb+
gramicidin channel and, 732
olfactory transduction and, 595
voltage gating and, 837
RBK1 channel
voltage gating and, 838
Recognition loops
EcoRV and, 692–93
Red cell membrane
bilayer-skeletal protein network linkages and, 795–
97
biochemical organization, 789–
93
cohesion and, 794–95
cytoskeletal network and, 805–
11
deformation and, 796–97
elasticity and, 797–814
eukaryotic cell interfaces and,
788–89
introduction to, 788
lateral skeletal protein linkages
and, 794–95
network expanders and, 797
pathologies and, 793–97
structural organization and,
789–93
universal material design and,
788–89
unusual features and, 811–14
Redox potential
light-addressable potentiometric sensor and, 93, 98–
100
Reference interaction site model
solvation and, 857
Religation
supercoiled DNA and, 611

Resolvases
branched DNA and, 72
Reticulomyxa filosa
bacterial flagellar motor and,
530
Rhinovirus canyon binders
protein structure-based drug design and, 368–71
Rhodanese
protein folding and, 653, 655,
662
Ribosomes
protein folding and, 646, 661
Ribulose-biphosphate car-
boxylase (Rubisco)
protein folding and, 654
RK models
gramicidin channel and, 739–
40
RNA
atomic force microscope and,
118–22
editing
glutamate receptors and,
330–31
G-quartet structures and, 723–
24
RNA polymerase
H-DNA and, 563–64
protein folding and, 654, 662
TBP protein and, 692
RNP domain
CspB protein and, 696
U1 protein and, 694–96
Rotamer conformations
protein folding and, 649
Rotational diffusion
orientational order parameter
and, 11–13
Rotational reorientation
free volume model and, 13
Rp-cAMPS
olfactory transduction and, 598

S

S4 ion superfamily
olfactory transduction and,
582, 588
Saccharomyces cerevisiae
EF-hand proteins and, 491, 499
K+ channels and, 452–53
Saccharopolyspora spp.
EF-hand proteins and, 477, 498
Salmonella spp.
Arc repressor and, 683
Salmonella typhimurium
bacterial flagellar motor and,
511–12, 515, 518–19,
523, 525–26
met operators and, 677
Samanea saman
K+ channels and, 444

CUMULATIVE INDEXES

CONTRIBUTING AUTHORS, VOLUMES 19–23

CHAPTER TITLES, VOLUMES 19–23

INDEXED BY KEYWORD